APPROXIMATE ATOMIC WEIGHTS
OF SOME OF THE COMMONER ELEMENTS

NAME	SYMBOL	ATOMIC NUMBER	ATOMIC WEIGHT	NAME	SYMBOL	ATOMIC NUMBER	ATOMIC WEIGHT
Aluminum	Al	13	27.0	Manganese	Mn	25	54.9
Antimony	Sb	51	121.8	Mercury	Hg	80	200.6
Arsenic	As	33	74.9	Molybdenum	Mo	42	95.9
Barium	Ba	56	137.3	Nickel	Ni	28	58.7
Beryllium	Be	4	9.0	Nitrogen	N	7	14.0
Bismuth	Bi	83	209.0	Oxygen	O	8	16.0
Boron	B	5	10.8	Phosphorus	P	15	31.0
Bromine	Br	35	79.9	Platinum	Pt	78	195.1
Cadmium	Cd	48	112.4	Potassium	K	19	39.1
Calcium	Ca	20	40.1	Radium	Ra	88	226.1
Carbon	C	6	12.0	Rubidium	Rb	37	85.5
Cesium	Cs	55	132.9	Selenium	Se	34	79.0
Chlorine	Cl	17	35.5	Silicon	Si	14	28.1
Chromium	Cr	24	52.0	Silver	Ag	47	107.9
Cobalt	Co	27	58.9	Sodium	Na	11	23.0
Copper	Cu	29	63.5	Strontium	Sr	38	87.6
Fluorine	F	9	19.0	Sulfur	S	16	32.1
Germanium	Ge	32	72.6	Tellurium	Te	52	127.6
Gold	Au	79	197.0	Tin	Sn	50	118.7
Hydrogen	H	1	1.01	Titanium	Ti	22	47.9
Iodine	I	53	126.9	Tungsten	W	74	183.9
Iron	Fe	26	55.9	Uranium	U	92	238.0
Lead	Pb	82	207.2	Vanadium	V	23	50.9
Lithium	Li	3	6.9	Zinc	Zn	30	65.4
Magnesium	Mg	12	24.3	Zirconium	Zr	40	91.2

College Chemistry

LINUS PAULING

RESEARCH PROFESSOR OF THE PHYSICAL AND BIOLOGICAL SCIENCES,
CENTER FOR THE STUDY OF DEMOCRATIC INSTITUTIONS,
SANTA BARBARA, CALIFORNIA

College Chemistry

AN INTRODUCTORY TEXTBOOK

OF GENERAL CHEMISTRY

THIRD EDITION

Illustrations by Roger Hayward

W. H. FREEMAN AND COMPANY

SAN FRANCISCO AND LONDON

To the memory of

DR. THOMAS ADDIS

who in applying science to medicine

kept always uppermost

his deep sympathy for mankind

Preface

During the last decade the science of chemistry has continued to change. Descriptive chemistry, the tabulation of the observed physical and chemical properties of substances, is still an important part of chemistry; with each passing decade, however, it becomes possible to correlate these facts in terms of theory in a more and more satisfactory manner.

The theories of greatest value in modern chemistry are the theories of atomic and molecular structure, quantum theory (quantum mechanics), and statistical mechanics. I believe that the concepts involved in these theories can be learned by the beginning student of chemistry sufficiently well for him to apply them in correlating and understanding the facts of descriptive chemistry. Moreover, the fundamental experiments upon which these theories are based can be understood by the beginning student. The theories in their detailed mathematical treatment can then be studied later.

In the third edition of this book I have introduced some aspects of modern chemistry that have not in the past been considered to be a part of introductory college chemistry. There is continued emphasis on atomic and molecular structure in relation to the properties of substances. The discussion of quantum mechanics has been expanded by the inclusion of the description of some of the fundamental experiments and by the elementary treatment of some additional aspects of quantum mechanical theory, such as the decreased heat capacity of crystalline and gaseous substances at low temperatures, the photoelectric effect, and the uncertainty principle.

No effort is made to present chemical thermodynamics in a thorough way. Instead, emphasis is placed on the thermochemical properties of substances, especially the values of the enthalpy of formation of compounds from the elements in their standard states and the use of the standard values of enthalpy of formation for calculation of the amount of heat emitted or absorbed during a chemical reaction. An effort is made to correlate the enthalpies of formation of compounds with the electronic structure of atoms, as expressed in the values of the electronegativity.

I believe that an understanding of statistical mechanics is more easily obtained by the beginning student than an understanding of chemical thermodynamics, and that statistical mechanics is more useful to him than thermodynamics in the interpretation of natural phenomena. I have accordingly introduced a discussion of the Boltzmann distribution law in Chapter 5, and have applied it to various problems in the following chapters. An example is the development of the distribution law for molecular velocities, discussed in Chapter 6 in connection with the kinetic theory of gases. There is also included in Chapter 6 a description of one of the experiments carried out to check the distribution function for molecular velocities.

A novel feature of the new edition is a chapter devoted to the chemistry of the fundamental particles. During the last few years many new particles have been discovered. These particles have been classified by physicists as leptons and antileptons, mesons and antimesons, baryons and antibaryons, and resonance particles or resonance complexes. The reactions by which they are formed and are destroyed are in many ways analogous to chemical reactions, and I believe that it is sensible to study these particles and their properties in connection with the study of general chemistry, rather than to wait for a course in advanced physics. I have attempted, in Chapter 29, to present an account of this field that will be found by the student and teacher to be interesting and useful. I trust that the reader who finds it difficult to understand this chapter will not attribute his difficulty entirely to me. The subject of the structure and properties of these particles is now in a primitive state, which may be compared with the subject of the structure of molecules as it was about a century ago. I hope that it will be possible to present a far simpler and clearer discussion of the structure of these particles in the fourth edition of this book.

This edition, like the earlier editions, is designed for use either by students who have not studied chemistry in preparatory school or by students who have had some previous acquaintance with chemistry. Some knowledge of elementary physics and mathematics has been assumed. Many of the chapters begin with a discussion of descriptive chemistry or elementary chemical theory and end with sections of somewhat more advanced theory, sometimes in fine print to indicate that these sections may be omitted. Students who have had the benefit of a good introduction to chemistry in preparatory school may find it possible to pass by the first few sections of these chapters and to devote their attention to the new concepts, fundamental experiments, and theories that are described in the later sections.

I am grateful to the many teachers of chemistry who have given advice to me during the preparation of this edition, and especially to Dr. Gustav Albrecht, Prof. L. E. Malm, Prof. Grant Smith, and Prof. P. R. O'Connor.

28 February 1963   *Linus Pauling*

Preface

In the preparation of the second edition of this book an effort has been made to increase the clarity of the presentation of the subject. The first part of the book has been largely revised in such a way that the facts, concepts, and theories of chemistry are introduced more gradually and more systematically than in the first edition. Some new, rather simple illustrative exercises are given in the text, immediately following the sections that they illustrate. The exercises at the ends of the chapters have also been considerably revised, with elimination of some of the more difficult ones. Answers are given to many of the exercises that involve calculations.

The sequence of chapters has been changed to increase the systematization of the subject. The book has been divided into six parts, and, in order that the student may be helped to keep himself oriented during the year, each part is provided with an introduction, describing the chapters contained within this part and telling why the subjects in these chapters are being taken up at that place in the course.

Part 1, which constitutes an introduction to the subject, deals with both descriptive chemistry and elementary chemical theory. Theoretical chemistry is taken up more thoroughly in Part 2, Chapters 8 to 12, and Part 4, Chapters 17 to 23. In Part 3, Chapters 13 to 16, there is given a discussion of the chemistry of a number of the non-metallic elements, as systematized by theoretical principles; and the nature of metals and alloys, metallurgy, and the chemistry of many metals are discussed in Part 5, Chapters 24 to 29. Part 6 consists of two chapters on chemical substances related to living organisms and one chapter on nuclear chemistry.

There has been a significant increase in the amount of organic chemistry in the book. In Chapter 7, on carbon and the compounds of carbon, there is a detailed discussion of the paraffin hydrocarbons, hydrocarbons containing double and triple bonds, organic isomers, the chloromethanes, alcohols, ethers, and organic acids, and a brief discussion of the chemical reactions of organic

substances. Organic substances are also discussed, together with inorganic substances, in several other chapters of the book, in connection with the theories
of chemistry. Chapter 30, Organic Chemistry, and Chapter 31, Biochemistry,
deal exclusively with organic substances.

Chapter 3, The Electron and the Nuclei of Atoms, is a new chapter, designed
to help the student to understand the electronic theory of molecular structure,
upon which modern chemistry is based. In this chapter a non-mathematical
account is given of some of the experiments carried out during the period of
twenty years commencing about 1895 which led to the discovery of the electron
and of the nuclei of atoms and the measurement of the properties of these
fundamental particles. The electronic structure of atoms is then discussed in
Chapter 5, in connection with the periodic table. Oxidation-reduction reactions
and valence are introduced in a simple way in Chapter 6, preliminary to the
more detailed discussion of these subjects and of the electronic theory of molecular structure given in Chapters 10, 11, and 12.

Many of my colleagues in the California Institute of Technology and many
other teachers of chemistry have given advice during the preparation of this
edition, and it is a pleasure for me to express my gratitude to them. I thank
especially Professor F. J. Allen, of Purdue University, and Professor Ogden
Baine, of Southern Methodist University, for their help.

23 March 1955   *Linus Pauling*

Preface

TO THE FIRST EDITION

The fundamental principles underlying the planning of the present book have been expressed in the preface of my earlier textbook, "General Chemistry, An Introduction to Descriptive Chemistry and Modern Chemical Theory," published three years ago. The first two paragraphs of the Preface of "General Chemistry" summarize these principles:

"Chemistry is a very large subject, which continues to grow, as new elements are discovered or made, new compounds are synthesized, and new principles are formulated. Nevertheless, despite its growth, the science can now be presented to the student more easily and effectively than ever before. In the past the course in general chemistry has necessarily tended to be a patch-work of descriptive chemistry and certain theoretical topics. The progress made in recent decades in the development of unifying theoretical concepts has been so great, however, that the presentation of general chemistry to the students of the present generation can be made in a more simple, straightforward, and logical way than formerly.

"For example, every boy now knows about atoms, and accepts them as part of his world—they are split in the atomic bomb and in the comic papers, they stare at him from advertisements. In this book I begin the teaching of chemistry by discussing the properties of substances in terms of atoms and molecules. The subject is then developed in as orderly a manner as has seemed possible at the present stage of chemical knowledge."

Although "General Chemistry" was written primarily for use by students planning to major in chemistry and related fields, it has been found useful also by students with primary interest in other subjects, including some who have not received instruction in chemistry in high school. Experience has shown, however, that there is need for a book based on the approach of "General Chemistry," but written in a more slowly paced, less mathematical form. The present book, "College Chemistry," provides this more gradual introduction to modern chemistry. I propose, in the near future, to revise "General Chemistry" in such a way as to make it especially suited to use by first-year college students who plan to major in chemistry and by other well-prepared students with a special interest in the subject.

The present book does not present any change in point of view from the earlier one. Some of the chapters, especially those dealing with elementary theory, have been incorporated with little change. The effort has been made to introduce all new concepts gradually, with satisfactorily thorough discussion and precise definition. The treatment of the more advanced theoretical subjects has been simplified. Use is made of no mathematics but elementary algebra, and instruction is given in the ratio method of solving problems. The treatment of the gas laws has been completely revised, and the chapter devoted to gases has been moved forward. Descriptive chemistry has been introduced more gradually, with more thorough discussion of the chemistry of the common elements, especially hydrogen, oxygen, nitrogen, and carbon. A chapter on biochemistry, a discussion of color photography, and some other new features have been introduced.

In general, new technical words and terms are defined in the text. Use has also been made of some other words with which the student may not be familiar; it may occasionally be necessary for him to find the meaning of one of these words by looking it up in the dictionary. It is my hope that every student who reads the book will benefit by an increase in his general vocabulary as well as in his scientific vocabulary and also by an increase in the precision and soundness of his thinking about non-scientific questions as well as about scientific questions.

I am indebted for assistance in various ways in the preparation of the book to Dr. Philip A. Shaffer, Jr., Prof. Norman Davidson, Prof. Ernest H. Swift, Prof. F. O. Koenig, Prof. Harper W. Frantz, Prof. Lloyd E. Malm, Mr. Linus Pauling, Jr., Mr. Peter J. Pauling, Dr. Eugene K. Maun, Miss Selina Weinbaum, and especially Mr. Roger Hayward, the illustrator. I also thank Dr. R. W. G. Wyckoff, Dr. D. S. Clark, Dr. S. Kyropoulos, Prof. C. E. Hall, Dr. J. A. Leermakers, the Malleable Founders' Society, and the Griffith Observatory for providing figures. I am further indebted to Prof. L. H. Farinholt, Prof. J. A. Timm, Prof. F. E. Blacet, Prof. J. F. Baxter, and many other teachers of chemistry who have made suggestions of ways in which my earlier book could be improved.

28 February 1950   *Linus Pauling*

Contents

CHAPTER 6. *Hydrogen and Oxygen. The Properties of Gases*

CHAPTER 7. *The Chemical Elements, the Periodic Law, and the Electronic Structure of Atoms*

3 SOME NONMETALLIC ELEMENTS AND THEIR COMPOUNDS

4 WATER, SOLUTIONS, AND CHEMICAL EQUILIBRIUM

CHAPTER 16. *Water*

CHAPTER 17. *The Properties of Solutions*

5 METALS AND ALLOYS AND THE COMPOUNDS OF METALS

6 ORGANIC CHEMISTRY, BIOCHEMISTRY, THE CHEMISTRY OF THE FUNDAMENTAL PARTICLES, AND NUCLEAR CHEMISTRY

1

An Introduction to Modern

Chemistry

Chemistry is the investigation and discussion of the properties of substances —of thousands of different substances. A part of chemistry, called *descriptive chemistry,* consists in the tabulation of the properties of substances as observed or as found by experiment. Another part, *theoretical chemistry,* consists in the formulation of principles that systematize and correlate the facts of descriptive chemistry.

Both theoretical chemistry and descriptive chemistry are presented in this book, in a sequence that has been designed to help you to understand the principles and to remember the facts of chemistry.

The book is divided into six parts. Part 1, Chapters 1 to 4, constitutes an introduction to modern chemistry. In Chapter 1 some fundamental concepts and definitions relating to kinds of substances are presented. In Chapter 2, on the atomic structure of matter, there is a discussion of the way in which substances are built out of atoms and of the relation between the properties of substances and their atomic structure. The method of determining the structure of crystals by the diffraction of x-rays is described, and the Bragg equation is derived. Atoms themselves are known to be built of electrons and atomic nuclei; the nature of the electron and of the nuclei of atoms is presented in Chapter 3, together with a discussion of several of the important experiments that led to the development of the theory of the electronic structure of atoms. The light quantum (photon) is introduced by means of the photoelectric effect, and the de Broglie equation for the wavelength of the electron is presented. The classification of substances into elements and compounds is then discussed in Chapter 4.

The background of knowledge of chemical facts provided by these chapters will then enable you to embark upon the study of some further aspects of theoretical chemistry, in Part 2, Chapters 5 to 9. Part 3, Chapters 10 to 15, presents a discussion of the chemistry of a number of elements, as systematized by theoretical principles. Part 4 consists of four chapters dealing mainly with theoretical subjects. The nature of metals and alloys and the chemistry of many metals are discussed in Part 5, Chapters 20 to 26. Two chapters on the chemical substances related to living organisms, one chapter on the chemistry of the fundamental particles, and one chapter on nuclear chemistry constitute the concluding section, Part 6.

Chemistry is not something that exists only between the covers of a textbook. It is an important part of man's effort to understand the world in which we live and to obtain a mastery of natural forces. I hope that, as you continue your study of chemistry, you will find pleasure in having a better understanding of the nature of the world and of the phenomena that take place about you, and that when you come to the end of this book and of your course in chemistry you will feel that the efforts that you have made to master the subject have been justified by the enlargement of your mental horizons.

CHAPTER ▪ 1

Chemistry and Matter

The rapid progress true Science now makes occasions my regretting sometimes that I was born so soon. It is impossible to imagine the heights to which may be carried, in a thousand years, the power of man over matter. O that moral Science were in as fair a way of improvement, that men would cease to be wolves to one another, and that human beings would at length learn what they now improperly call humanity.—

BENJAMIN FRANKLIN,
in a letter to the chemist Joseph Priestley, 8 February 1780.

Why study chemistry? An important reason is indicated in the foregoing statement by Benjamin Franklin—it is through chemistry and her sister sciences that the power of man, of mind, over matter is obtained. Nearly two hundred years ago Franklin said that science was making rapid progress. We know that the rate of progress of science has become continually greater, until now the nature of the world in which we live has been greatly changed, through scientific and technical progress, from that of Franklin's time.

Science plays such an important part in the modern world that no one can now feel that he understands the world in which he lives unless he has an understanding of science.

The science of chemistry deals with *substances*. At this point in the study of chemistry we shall not define the word substance in its scientific sense, but shall assume that you have a general idea of what the word means. Common examples of substances are water, sugar, salt, copper, iron, oxygen—you can think of many others.

A century and a half ago it was discovered by an English chemist, Sir Humphry Davy (1778–1829), that common salt can be separated, by passing electricity through it, into a soft, silvery metal, to which he gave the name sodium, and a greenish-yellow gas, which had been discovered some time earlier, and named chlorine. Chlorine is a corrosive gas, which attacks many metals, and irritates the mucous membranes of the nose and throat if it is inhaled. That the substance salt is composed of a metal (sodium) and a corrosive gas (chlorine) with properties quite different from its own properties is one of the many surprising facts about the nature of substances that chemists have discovered.

A sodium wire will burn in chlorine, producing salt. The process of combination of sodium and chlorine to form salt is called a *chemical reaction.* Ordinary fire also involves a chemical reaction, the combination of the fuel with oxygen in the air to form the products of combustion. For example, gasoline contains compounds of carbon and hydrogen, and when a mixture of gasoline and air explodes (burns rapidly) in the cylinders of an automobile a chemical reaction takes place, in which the gasoline and the oxygen of the air react to form carbon dioxide and water vapor (plus a small amount of carbon monoxide), and at the same time to release the energy that moves the automobile. Carbon dioxide and carbon monoxide are compounds of carbon and oxygen, and water is a compound of hydrogen and oxygen.

Chemists study substances, in order to learn as much as they can about their properties (their characteristic qualities) and about the reactions that change them into other substances. Knowledge obtained in this way has been found to be extremely valuable. It not only satisfies man's curiosity about himself and about the world in which he lives, but it also can be applied to make the world a better place to live in, to make people happier, by raising their standards of living, ameliorating the suffering due to ill health, and enlarging the sphere of their activities.

Let us consider some of the ways in which a knowledge of chemistry has helped man in the past and may help him in the future.

It was discovered centuries ago that preparations could be made from certain plants, such as poppies and coca, which, when taken by a human being, serve to deaden pain. From these plants chemists isolated pure substances, morphine and cocaine, which have the pain-deadening property. These substances have, however, an undesirable property, that of inducing a craving for them that sometimes leads to drug addiction. Chemists then investigated morphine and cocaine, to learn their chemical structure, and then made in the laboratory a great number of other substances, somewhat similar in structure, and tested these substances for their powers of deadening pain and of producing addiction. In this way some drugs that are far more valuable than the natural ones have been discovered; one example is procaine, a local anesthetic used in minor surgery.

A related story is that of the discovery of general anesthetics. In 1800 Humphry Davy, as a young man just beginning his scientific career, tested many gases on himself by inhaling them. (He was lucky that he did not kill himself, because one of the gases he inhaled is very poisonous.) He discovered that one gas produced a state of hysteria when inhaled, and that people under the influence of this gas, which was given the name laughing gas, seemed not to suffer pain when they fell down or bumped into an object. He suggested its use in surgery in the following words: "As nitrous oxide, in its extensive operation, seems capable of destroying physical pain, it may probably be used with advantage in surgical operations." His suggestion, however, remained unheeded for nearly half a century. Then in 1844 nitrous oxide was used for the extraction of a tooth by Dr. Horace Wells in Hartford, Conn., and two years later the first surgical operation under diethyl ether anesthesia was carried out (in Massachusetts General Hospital, Boston). Ether, chloroform, and nitrous oxide were soon brought into general use. The discovery of anesthesia was a great discovery, not only because it relieves pain, but also because it permits delicate surgical operations to be carried out that would be impossible if the patients remained conscious.

The rubber industry may be mentioned as an example of a chemical industry. This industry began when it was discovered that raw rubber, a sticky material made from the sap of the rubber tree, could be converted into vulcanized rubber, which has superior properties (greatly increased strength, freedom from stickiness), by mixing it with sulfur and heating it. During recent years artificial materials similar to rubber (called synthetic rubber) have been made, which are in many ways better than natural rubber. The synthetic rubbers are made from petroleum or natural gas.

The steel industry is another great chemical industry. Steel, which consists mainly of the metal iron, is our most important structural material. It is made from iron ore by a complex chemical process. In the United States the production of steel is carried on at the rate of about 1000 lbs per person per year.

Chemistry plays such an important part in the life of twentieth-century man that this age may properly be called the chemical age.

1-1. The Study of Chemistry

Chemistry has two main aspects: **descriptive chemistry,** *the discovery and tabulation of chemical facts;* and **theoretical chemistry,** *the formulation of theories that, upon verification, unify these facts and combine them into a system.**

It is not possible to obtain a sound knowledge of chemistry simply by learning theoretical chemistry. Even if a student were to learn all the chemical theory that is known he would not have a knowledge of the science, because a major part of chemistry (many of the special properties of individual

---

* The broad field of chemistry may also be divided in other ways. An important division of chemistry is that into the branches *organic chemistry* and *inorganic chemistry*. Organic chemistry is the chemistry of the compounds of carbon, especially those that occur in plants and animals. Inorganic chemistry is the chemistry of the compounds of elements other than carbon. Each of these branches of chemistry is in part descriptive and in part theoretical. Many other branches of chemistry, which in general are parts of organic chemistry and inorganic chemistry, have also been given names; for example, analytical chemistry, physical chemistry, biochemistry, nuclear chemistry, industrial chemistry. Their nature is indicated by their names.

substances) has not yet been well incorporated into chemical theory. It is accordingly necessary for the student to learn a number of the facts of descriptive chemistry simply by memorizing them. The number of these facts that might be memorized is enormous, and increases rapidly year by year, as new discoveries are made. In this book a selection from the more important facts is presented. *You should learn some of these facts by studying them, and by frequently referring to them and renewing your knowledge of them. You should also learn as much about chemistry as possible from your own experience in the laboratory and from your observations of chemical substances and chemical reactions in everyday life.*

A special effort has been made in this book to present the subject of chemistry in a logical and simple manner, and to correlate descriptive chemistry with the theories of chemistry. It is therefore necessary that the theoretical sections of the book be carefully studied and thoroughly understood. Read each chapter with care. Examine the arguments to be sure that you understand them.

1-2. Matter

The universe is composed of **matter** *and* **radiant energy.**

The chemist is primarily interested in matter, but he must also study radiant energy—light, x-rays, radio waves—in its interaction with substances. For example, he may be interested in the color of substances, which is produced by their absorption of light.

Matter consists of all the materials around us—gases, liquids, solids. This statement is really not a definition. The dictionary states that matter is "that of which a physical object is composed; material." Then it defines material and physical object as matter, so that we are back where we started. The best course that we can follow is to say that no one really knows how to define matter, but that we agree to start out by using the word. Often in science it is necessary to begin with some undefined words.

Mass and Weight.   All matter has *mass*. Chemists are interested in the masses of materials, because they want to know how much material they need to use to prepare a certain amount of a product.

The **mass** *of an object is the quantity that measures its resistance to change in its state of rest or motion.*

The mass of an object also determines its *weight*. The weight of an object is only a measure of the *force* with which the object is attracted by the earth. This force depends upon the mass of the object, the mass of the earth, and the position of the object on the earth's surface, especially the distance of the object from the center of the earth. Since the earth is slightly flattened at its poles, the distance of its surface at the North Pole or South Pole from its center is less than that at the equator. In consequence the weight of an object as measured by a spring balance, which measures the force, is greater at the North or South Pole than at the equator. For example, if your weight, measured by a spring balance, is 150.0 lbs at the equator, it would be 150.8 lbs at the North Pole, measured on the same spring balance—nearly a pound more. Your mass, however, is the same.

The mass of an object remains the same at the North Pole as at the equator, and it can easily be determined, at any place on the earth's surface, by comparison with a standard set of masses (standard "weights"). For small objects a *chemical balance* is used. Since the weights of two bodies of equal mass are the same at any place on the earth's surface, these bodies will balance one another when placed on the two pans of a balance with arms of equal length.

It is common practice to refer to the masses of objects as their weights. It might be thought that confusion would arise from the practice of using the word weight to refer both to the mass of an object and to the force with which the object is attracted by the earth. In general it does not, but if there is danger of confusion you should use the word mass.

The standard masses (standard weights) in the metric system are calibrated (checked) by comparison with the standard kilogram in Paris (Appendix 1).* The metric unit of mass is the *gram*. The abbreviation for gram is g, and for kilogram kg (1 kg = 1000 g).

1-3. Kinds of Matter

As we look about us we see material objects, such as a stone wall or a table, or one of the objects shown in Figure 1-1. The chemist is primarily interested not in the objects themselves, but in the kinds of matter of which they are composed. He is interested in wood as a material (a kind of matter), whether it is used for making a table or a chair. He is interested in granite, whether it is in a stone wall or in some other object. Indeed, his interest is primarily in those properties (characteristic qualities) of a material that are independent of the objects containing it.

The word **material** *is used in referring to any kind of matter, whether homogeneous or heterogeneous.*

A **homogeneous** *material is a material with the same properties throughout.*

A **heterogeneous** *material consists of parts with different properties.*

Wood, with soft and hard rings alternating, is obviously a heterogeneous material, as is also granite, in which grains of three different species of matter (the minerals† quartz, mica, and feldspar) can be seen (Figure 1-2).

Heterogeneous materials are mixtures of two or more homogeneous mate-

---

* There are many systems of weights and measures, which are ordinarily used in different countries. In order to avoid confusion, all scientists use the *metric system*, which is described in Appendix 1, in their scientific work. In general, we shall use the metric system in this book, but an occasional exercise or example may be given in the American system.

† A *mineral* is any homogeneous material occurring naturally as a product of inorganic processes (that is, not produced by a living organism).

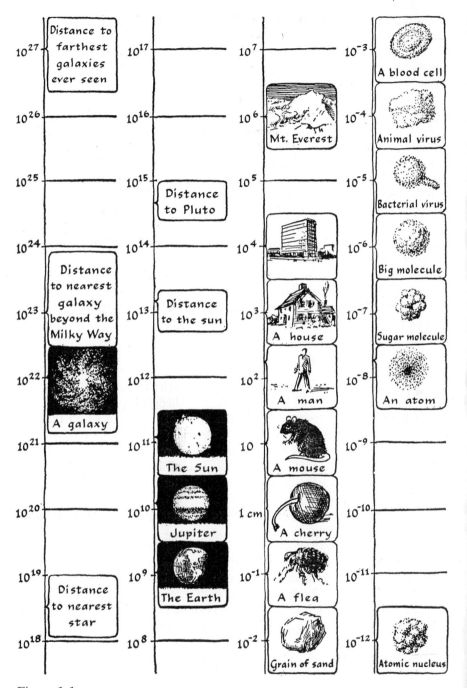

Figure 1-1

A diagram showing dimensions of objects, from 10⁻¹² cm (the nucleus of an atom) to 10²⁷ cm (the radius of the known universe).

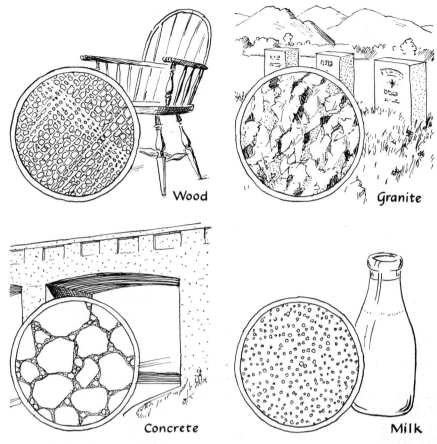

Figure **1-2**

Some heterogeneous materials.

rials. For example, each of the three minerals quartz, mica, and feldspar that constitute the rock granite is a homogeneous material (Figure 1-3).

Let us now define the words *substance* and *solution.*

A **substance** *is a homogeneous material with definite chemical composition.*

A **solution** *is a homogeneous material that does not have a definite composition.**

Pure salt, pure sugar, pure iron, pure copper, pure sulfur, pure water, pure oxygen, and pure hydrogen are representative substances. Quartz is also a substance (Figure 1-3).

On the other hand, a solution of sugar in water is not a substance according to this definition: it is, to be sure, homogeneous, but it does not satisfy the

* The word solution is commonly used for liquid solutions. Chemists also refer to gaseous solutions (mixtures of two or more pure gases) and to solid solutions (such as a gold-copper alloy).

Quartz crystals

Gasoline

Figure 1-3

Some homogeneous materials.

second part of the above definition, inasmuch as its composition is not definite, but is widely variable, being determined by the amount of sugar that happens to have been dissolved in a given amount of water. Gasoline is also not a pure substance; it is a solution of several substances.

Sometimes the word substance is used in a broader sense, essentially as equivalent to material. Chemists usually restrict the use of the word in the way given by the definition above. The chemist's usage of the word substance may be indicated by using the phrase "pure substance."

Most materials that the chemist classifies as substances (pure substances) have definite chemical composition; for example, all samples of salt contain 39.4% sodium and 60.6% chlorine. Other compounds, however, show a small range of variation of chemical composition; an example is the iron sulfide that is made by heating iron and sulfur together. This homogeneous material when made in different ways ranges in composition from 35% to 39% sulfur.

> **Kinds of Definition.** Definitions may be either precise or imprecise. The mathematician may define precisely the words that he uses; in his further discussion he then adheres rigorously to the defined meaning of each word. But the words that are used in describing nature, which is itself complex, may not be capable of precise definition. In giving a definition for such a word the effort is made to describe the accepted usage.
>
> For example, sometimes it is difficult to decide whether a material is homogeneous or heterogeneous. A specimen of granite, in which grains of three different species of matter can be seen, is obviously a mixture. An emulsion of fat in water (a suspension of small droplets of fat in the water, as in milk, Figure 1-2) is also a mixture. The heterogeneity of a piece of granite is obvious to the eye. The heterogeneity of milk can be seen if a drop of milk is examined under a microscope.

Substances are classified as *elementary substances* or *compounds.*

A substance that can be decomposed into two or more substances is a **compound.**

A substance that cannot be decomposed is an **elementary substance** (*or* **element**).*

Salt can be decomposed by an electric current into two substances, sodium and chlorine. Hence salt is a compound.

Water can be decomposed by an electric current into two substances, hydrogen and oxygen. Hence water is a compound.

Mercuric oxide can be decomposed by heat, to form mercury and oxygen. Hence mercuric oxide is a compound.

No one has ever succeeded in decomposing sodium, chlorine, hydrogen, oxygen, or mercury into other substances.† Hence these five substances are accepted as elementary substances (elements).

At the present time (1963) 103 elements are known. Several hundred thousand compounds of these elements have been found in nature or made in the laboratory.

The process of decomposing a compound into two or more simpler substances is sometimes called *analysis*. The reverse process, of forming a substance by combining two or more substances, is called *synthesis*.

The composition of a compound can be determined by analysis. For example, a *qualitative analysis* of salt might be carried out by decomposing it with an electric current and identifying the products as sodium and chlorine; the chemist could then say that the salt is a compound of the two elements sodium and chlorine. To carry out a *quantitative analysis* he would have to weigh the substances; he could then report the composition as 39.4% sodium, 60.6% chlorine.

Our classification of matter is summarized in the following chart. You may find it worth while to examine this chart carefully. Can you define all of the words? Can you give two or three examples of each of the six kinds of materials that might constitute an object? Can you think of one or two materials that are hard to classify?

Illustrative Exercises

1-1. Is ice an elementary substance or a compound?

1-2. Is maple syrup (or corn syrup) a homogeneous material or a heterogeneous material? Is it a solution or a substance (pure substance)?

1-3. The name holosiderite is given to metallic meteorites, which are alloys of iron and nickel. Many homogeneous holosiderites have been analyzed. They have been found to contain various amounts of nickel, between 6% and 10%. Is holosiderite an iron-nickel compound, or is it a solid solution?

1-4. When the substance calcite is heated it forms lime and carbon

* The discovery of radioactivity made it necessary to change these definitions slightly (see Section 4-8).

† In this discussion the word substance is considered not to include electrons and atomic nuclei. Atoms of sodium and other elements can be decomposed into fundamental particles (Chapters 3 and 29).

dioxide. Is calcite an elementary substance or a compound? Can you say from the foregoing information whether lime is an elementary substance or a compound?

1-5. When diamond is heated in a vacuum (no other material present) it is converted completely into graphite. Does this prove that diamond is a compound?

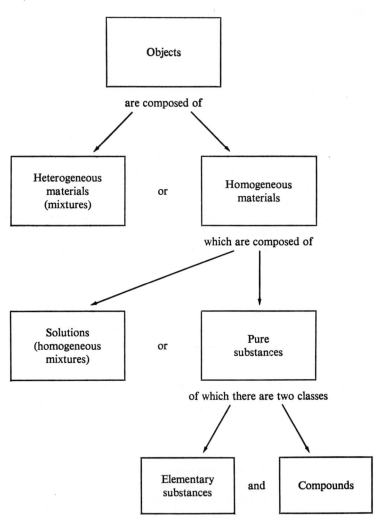

1-4. The Physical Properties of Substances

The study of the properties of substances constitutes an important part of chemistry, because their properties determine the uses to which they can be put.

The **properties** *of substances are their characteristic qualities.*

The **physical properties** *are those properties of a substance that can be observed without changing the substance into other substances.*

Let us again use sodium chloride, common salt, as an example of a substance. We have all seen this substance in what appear to be different forms—table salt, in fine grains; salt in the form of crystals a quarter of an inch in diameter, for use with ice for freezing ice cream; and natural crystals of rock salt an inch or more across. Despite their obvious difference, all of these samples of salt have the same fundamental properties. In each case the crystals, small or large, are naturally bounded by square or rectangular *crystal faces* of different sizes, but with each face always at right angles to each adjacent face. The *cleavage* of the different crystals of salt is the same: when crushed, the crystals always break (cleave) along planes parallel to the original faces, producing smaller crystals similar to the larger ones. The different samples have the same salty *taste*. Their *solubility* is the same: at room temperature 36 g of salt can be dissolved in 100 g of water. The *density* of the salt is the same, 2.16 g/cm³. The density of a substance is the mass (weight) of a unit volume (1 cubic centimeter) of the substance.

There are other properties besides density and solubility that can be measured precisely and expressed in numbers. Such another property is the *melting point*, the temperature at which a solid substance melts to form a liquid. On the other hand, there are also interesting physical properties of a substance that are not so simple in nature. One such property is the *malleability* of a substance—the ease with which a substance can be hammered out into thin sheets. A related property is the *ductility*—the ease with which the substance can be drawn into a wire. *Hardness* is a similar property: we say that one substance is less hard than the second substance when it is scratched by the second substance. The *color* of a substance is an important physical property.

It is customary to say that under the same external conditions all specimens of a particular substance have the same physical properties (density, hardness, color, melting point, crystalline form, etc.). Sometimes, however, the word substance is used in referring to a material without regard to its state. For example, ice, liquid water, and water vapor may be referred to as the same substance. Moreover, a specimen containing crystals of rock salt and crystals of table salt may be called a mixture, even though the specimen may consist entirely of one substance, sodium chloride. This lack of definiteness in usage seems to cause no confusion in practice.

The concept "pure substance" is, of course, an idealization; all actual substances are more or less impure. It is a useful concept, however, because we have learned through experiment that the properties of various specimens of an impure substance with different impurities are nearly the same if the impurities are present in only small amounts. These properties are accepted as the properties of the ideal substance.

1-5. The Chemical Properties of Substances

The **chemical properties** *of a substance are those properties that relate to its participation in chemical reactions.*

Chemical reactions *are the processes that convert substances into other substances.*

Thus sodium chloride has the property of changing into a soft metal, sodium, and a greenish-yellow gas, chlorine, when it is decomposed by passage of an electric current through it. It also has the property, when it is dissolved in water, of producing a white precipitate when a solution of silver nitrate is added to it; and it has many other chemical properties.

Iron has the property of combining readily with the oxygen in moist air, to form iron rust; whereas an alloy* of iron with chromium and nickel (stainless steel) is found to resist this process of rusting. It is evident from this example that the chemical properties of materials are important in engineering.

Many chemical reactions take place in the kitchen. When biscuits are made with use of sour milk and baking soda there is a chemical reaction between the baking soda and a substance in the sour milk, lactic acid, to produce the gas carbon dioxide, which leavens the dough by forming small bubbles in it. And, of course, a great many chemical reactions take place in the human body. Foods that we eat are digested in the stomach and intestines. Oxygen in the inhaled air combines with a substance, hemoglobin, in the red cells of the blood, and then is released in the tissues, where it takes part in many different reactions. Many biochemists and physiologists are engaged in the study of the chemical reactions that take place in the human body.

Most substances have the power to enter into many chemical reactions. The study of these reactions constitutes a large part of the study of chemistry. Chemistry may be defined as *the science of substances—their structure, their properties, and the reactions that change them into other substances.*

Illustrative Exercises

1-6. Which of the following processes would you class as chemical reactions?

(a) The boiling of water.
(b) The burning of paper.
(c) The preparation of sugar syrup by adding sugar to hot water.
(d) The formation of rust on iron.
(e) The manufacture of salt by evaporation of sea water.

1-7. A kilogram of gold (2.2 lbs) occupies the volume 51.5 cm³. What is the density of gold? (Answer: 19.4 g/cm³.)

If the gold were in the form of a cube, what would be the length of its edge? Find the answer in centimeters, and also in inches.

* An *alloy* is a metallic material containing two or more elements. It may be either homogeneous or heterogeneous (a mixture of grains of two or more kinds). If homogeneous, it may be either a pure compound or a solid solution, or even a liquid solution—many alloys of mercury and other metals are liquid.

1-8. The density of gold is 19.4 g/cm^3 and the density of copper is 9.0 g/cm^3. An alloy of gold and copper is described as x-carat gold when 24 g of the alloy contains x g of gold. Using the assumption that there is no change in volume when the pure metals are mixed (melted together) to form the alloy, calculate the density of 18-carat gold.

1-9. Archimedes (born about 287 B.C.) is said to have discovered a way of checking the possible adulteration of gold with copper in a crown made for King Hiero of Syracuse, Sicily. His method was to compare the volume of water displaced by the crown with the volumes displaced by equal weights of pure gold and pure copper. Let us suppose that the crown weighed 1000 g and displaced the volume 71.5 cm^3.

(a) What is the density of the crown?

(b) To what percentage of gold in the gold-copper alloy does this density correspond? (Make the assumption given in the preceding exercise.)

1-6. Energy and Temperature

The concept of *energy* is as difficult to define as that of matter. Energy is involved in doing work, or in heating an object. A boulder at the top of a mountain has *potential energy*. As it rolls down the mountainside, its potential energy is changed into the *kinetic energy* of its motion. If it were to fall into a lake, and be slowed down by the friction of its motion through water, part of its kinetic energy would be changed by friction into *heat*, which then would raise the temperature of the boulder and of the water. In addition, part of its kinetic energy would be transferred to the water, and would evidence itself in waves radiating from the point of impact.

Another important kind of energy is *radiant energy*. Visible light, infrared radiation, ultraviolet radiation, x-rays, and radio waves are radiant energy. They are all closely similar in nature (see Sections 3-10, 3-11, 3-12, 25-5).

When a mixture of gasoline vapor and air is exploded, energy is liberated—energy that can do the work of propelling an automobile, and that in addition causes an increase in temperature of the engine and the exhaust gases. This energy is said to have been stored up in the gasoline and air as *chemical energy*.

The Law of Conservation of Energy. It has been found that *whenever energy of one form disappears an equivalent amount of energy of other forms is produced.* This principle is called the *law of conservation of energy.**

All chemical reactions are accompanied by either the liberation of energy or the absorption of energy. Usually this energy is in the form of heat. If some

---

* This law is a special case of the more general *law of conservation of mass-energy*, which will be discussed in Sections 5-1 and 30-6.

substances when mixed together in a flask undergo a chemical reaction with liberation of heat, the contents of the flask become warmer. If, on the other hand, they undergo a chemical reaction with absorption of heat, the contents of the flask become colder. These facts can be described by saying that every substance has a certain *heat content*, and that in general the heat contents of the products of a reaction differ from the heat contents of the reactants. In accordance with the law of conservation of energy, the *heat of the reaction* is the difference in heat contents of the products and the reactants, both at standard temperature. For example, a mixture of gasoline and oxygen has a greater total heat content than the products of their reaction, which are carbon dioxide and water, at the same temperature. In consequence, some heat is liberated during the reaction, raising the temperature of the products and of other materials in contact with them.

Under some conditions chemical energy is liberated during a chemical reaction in forms other than heat. For example, the chemical energy stored up in an explosive may do work, in breaking a stone cliff into fragments. The chemical energy in the substances of an electric battery is converted into electric energy during the operation of the battery. Some of the chemical energy in a fuel may be converted into radiant energy as the fuel burns.

Temperature.   If two objects are placed in contact with one another, heat may flow from one object to the other one. *Temperature* is the quality that determines the direction in which heat flows—it flows from the object at higher temperature to the object at lower temperature.

Temperatures are ordinarily measured by means of a thermometer, such as the ordinary mercury thermometer, consisting of a quantity of mercury in a glass tube. The temperature scale used by scientists is the *centigrade scale* or *Celsius scale;* it was introduced by Anders Celsius, a Swedish professor of astronomy, in 1742. On this scale the temperature of freezing water is 0°C and the temperature of boiling water is 100°C.

On the *Fahrenheit scale*, used in everyday life in English-speaking countries, the freezing point of water is 32°F and the boiling point of water is 212°F. On this scale the freezing point and the boiling point differ by 180°, rather than the 100° of the centigrade scale.*

The relation between the centigrade scale and the Fahrenheit scale is indicated in Figure 1-4. To convert temperatures from one scale to another, you need only remember that the Fahrenheit degree is $\frac{100}{180}$ or $\frac{5}{9}$ of the centigrade degree, and that 0°C is the same temperature as 32°F. You may find it convenient to use the method described in Exercise 1-11.

---

* The Fahrenheit scale was devised by Gabriel Daniel Fahrenheit (1686–1736), a natural philosopher who was born in Danzig and settled in Holland. He invented the mercury thermometer in 1714; before then alcohol had been used as the liquid in thermometers. As the zero point on his scale he took the temperature produced by mixing equal quantities of snow and ammonium chloride. His choice of 212° for the boiling point of water was made in order that the temperature of his body should be 100°F. The normal temperature of the human body is 98.6°F; perhaps Fahrenheit had a slight fever while he was calibrating his thermometer.

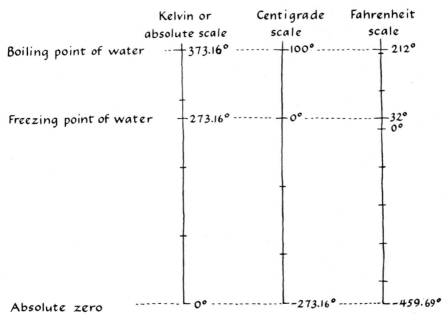

Figure 1-4

Comparison of Kelvin, Centigrade, and Fahrenheit scales of temperature.

Example 1.   A school room may be kept at 68°F. What is this temperature on the centigrade scale?

   Solution.   68°F is 36°F (that is, 68° − 32°) above the freezing point of water. This number of Fahrenheit degrees is equal to $\frac{5}{9} \times 36 = 20$°C. Since the freezing point of water is 0°C, the temperature of the room is 20°C.

The Absolute Temperature Scale.   About 175 years ago it was noticed by scientists that a sample of gas that is cooled decreases in volume in a regular way, and it was seen that if the volume were to continue to decrease in the same way it would become zero at about −273°C. The concept was developed that this temperature, −273°C (more accurately, −273.16°C), is the minimum temperature, the *absolute zero*. A new temperature scale was then devised by Lord Kelvin, a great British physicist (1824–1907). It is called either the *absolute temperature scale* (A) or the *Kelvin scale* (K). The unit on this scale is the centigrade degree.* In order to convert a temperature from the centigrade scale to the absolute scale it is only necessary to add 273.16°. Thus the freezing point of water, 0°C, is 273.16°K. The relation of the Kelvin scale to the centigrade scale and the Fahrenheit scale is also shown in Figure 1-4.

   * Another absolute scale, the *Rankine scale*, is sometimes used in engineering work in the English-speaking countries. It uses the Fahrenheit degree, and has 0°R at the absolute zero.

The Calorie. The unit of heat (energy) is the *calorie*, which is defined as 4.1840×10^7 erg. It is, to within ordinary requirements of accuracy, the amount of heat required to raise the temperature of 1 g of liquid water by 1°C, at any temperature. The abbreviation for calorie is cal. A larger unit, the *kilocalorie*, is also used; one kilocalorie (1 kcal) is equal to 1000 cal.

Illustrative Exercises

1-10.   Mercury freezes at about −40°C. What is this temperature on the Fahrenheit scale?

1-11.   A simple way to convert from the Fahrenheit to the centigrade scale or from the centigrade to the Fahrenheit scale is to add 40°, multiply by $\frac{5}{9}$ or $\frac{9}{5}$, respectively, and then subtract 40°. Verify this statement by use of the definitions of the two scales.

1-12.   Assuming that the change in potential energy in the earth's gravitational field is used completely to heat the water that flows over Niagara Falls, calculate the difference in temperature of the water below the falls and that above the falls. Remember that the potential energy of mass m at height h is mgh, with g equal to 980 cm/sec². The height of Niagara Falls is about 5000 cm (164 feet). (Answer: 0.109°C.)

1-13.   Into a flask containing 100 g of water at 18.0°C, with a small amount of hydrochloric acid dissolved in it, there was poured 100 g of water, also at 18.0°C, containing a small amount of sodium hydroxide. The temperature of the mixed solution increased to 24.5°C. Neglecting the effect of the substances dissolved in the water and the loss of heat to the flask, calculate how much heat (how many calories) was produced by the reaction of the acid and the sodium hydroxide.

1-7. Pressure

In chemical work it is often necessary to know not only the temperature at which an experiment is carried out, but also the *pressure*. For example, the large-scale industrial preparation of ammonia is carried out at high pressure, because the chemical reaction does not proceed satisfactorily at ordinary pressure.

Pressure is force per unit area.   Pressure may be measured in grams per square centimeter, or in pounds per square inch, or in other units. The atmosphere of the earth exerts a pressure on all objects at the surface of the earth. The pressure of the atmosphere is 14.7 pounds per square inch.

Another unit of pressure that is often used is the *atmosphere* (abbreviation atm). The pressure 1 atm is the average pressure at the surface of the earth (at sea level) that is due to the weight of the air.

The pressure due to the atmosphere can be measured by means of a *barometer*. A simple barometer is made by filling a long glass tube, which is closed at one end, with mercury, being careful that no air remains entrapped, and then inverting the open end of the tube under the surface of some mercury in a cup. If the tube is longer than 760 mm, the surface of the mercury at the upper end of the tube drops until the height of the mercury column, measured from the level of mercury in the cup, is just enough to balance the atmospheric pressure. This occurs when the weight of the column of mercury per unit area is equal to the pressure of the atmosphere.

Pressure is often reported as the height of the column of mercury required to balance it. For example, the pressure 1 atm is equal to 760 mm of mercury (abbreviated as mm Hg).

The units used to measure pressure are summarized in the following equation:

$$1 \text{ atm} = 760 \text{ mm Hg} = 14.7 \text{ pounds per square inch*} = 1.0133 \times 10^6 \text{ dyne cm}^{-2}$$

Illustrative Exercises

1-14. Pressure can also be reported in grams per square centimeter. The density of mercury is 13.595 g/cm³ What is 1 atm pressure in g/cm²? (Remember that 1 atm = 76 cm Hg.)

1-15. The density of water is about 1 g/cm³. At what depth would a diver have to descend under the surface of a lake in order that the pressure acting on him would be 3 atm, rather than the 1 atm that is due to the weight of the air? What is this depth in feet?

1-8. Solids, Liquids, and Gases

Materials may exist as solids, liquids, or gases. A specimen of a solid, such as a piece of ice, has a definite volume and also has rigidity. It retains its shape even when acted on by an outside force, provided that the force is not great enough to break the specimen. A liquid, such as a portion of water in a cup, has a definite volume, but adjusts its shape to the shape of the bottom part of its container. A gas, such as steam (water vapor) in the cylinder of a steam engine, has neither definite shape nor definite volume—it changes its shape and also its volume with change in the shape and volume of the container.

Ice, water, and water vapor represent the same chemical substance, water substance, in three different states. Ice is the *solid state (crystalline state)*, water the *liquid state*, and water vapor the *gaseous state*.

Scientists usually distinguish between *crystalline solids* and *noncrystalline solids*.

A **crystal** *is a homogeneous material* (either a pure substance or a solution) *that, as a result of its regular internal structure, has spontaneously assumed the shape of a figure bounded by plane faces.*

For example, when a solution of salt evaporates small cubes of solid salt form. These cubes, which are bounded by plane square faces, are crystals.

Most solid substances are crystalline in nature. Sometimes the individual

* Engineers use the abbreviation psi for pounds per square inch.

crystals, with plane faces and sharp edges and corners, are visible to the naked eye; sometimes they can be seen only under a microscope.

Some solids, such as charcoal, do not show any crystalline character even when examined with a microscope of high power; these solids are called *amorphous solids* (the word amorphous means without shape).

Certain other materials, of which sealing wax is an example, are called *supercooled liquids*. When a stick of sealing wax, which is hard and brittle at room temperature, is gradually warmed, it begins to soften and finally becomes a mobile liquid. As it is being cooled it shows a gradual change from a mobile liquid to a viscous liquid, and then to a solid. Even at room temperature it might be described as a liquid which is so viscous that it flows only extremely slowly.

1-9. The Scientific Method

During your study of chemistry you will also learn something about the *scientific method*.

Scientists do their work in many ways. A great scientific discovery is often the result of a great flight of the imagination—a brilliant new idea. If you have studied physics, you probably read that Archimedes is said to have been taking a bath when he had his brilliant idea, a "flash of genius," about the change in weight of a body immersed in a liquid (Archimedes' principle). Curiosity and an active imagination are great assets to a scientist.

No one knows the method for having brilliant new ideas, and this is not part of what is ordinarily called the scientific method. But scientists also work by applying common sense, reliable methods of reasoning, to the problems that they are attacking, and the procedure that they follow, which is called the scientific method, can be learned.

Part of the scientific method is the requirement that the investigator be willing to accept all of the facts. He must not be prejudiced; prejudice might keep him from giving proper consideration to some of the facts or to some of the logical arguments involved in applying the scientific method, and in this way keep him from getting the right answer. If you were to say "I have made up my mind—don't confuse me with a lot of facts," you would not be applying the scientific method.

The remaining part of the scientific method consists of logical argument.

The first step in applying the scientific method is to obtain some facts, by observation and experiment. The next step is to classify and correlate the facts by general statements. If a general statement is simple in form it may be called a *law of nature*. If it is more complex it is called a *theory*. Both laws of nature and theories are called *principles*.

The discussion of the scientific method will be continued in the first section of the following chapter.

1-10. How to Study Chemistry

You may feel, now that you are just beginning your formal study of chemistry, that you know nothing about this subject; *but in fact you already know a great deal*—many things that the foremost scientists did not know a century or two ago. From your general reading, from the comic papers, the advertisements, and your contact with automobiles, street signs, and other features of our modern world, you probably know not only that oxygen, hydrogen, iron, and copper are elements, but also that helium, neon, and argon are elements, and that they are gases; that copper, zinc, tin, and lead are elements, and are metals; and that sulfur, phosphorus, and bromine are elements that are nonmetals. In addition to knowing that water and sodium chloride are compounds, you know that penicillin is a compound used for the treatment of infectious diseases. You know that substances are composed of atoms, and that the atoms themselves consist of nuclei and electrons. You probably even know, from reading the newspapers, that neutrons can cause the nuclei of atoms of uranium 235 and plutonium 239 to split—to undergo fission during the detonation of an atomic bomb; this is knowledge that was possessed by nobody in the world a generation ago.

By studying chemistry you can make the understanding that you have of the nature of the universe more precise, and you can add greatly to it.

It was mentioned in Section 1-1 that part of the study of chemistry consists in memorizing some of the facts of descriptive chemistry. If you are planning to become a chemist, or a scientist or professional man or woman in a field in which chemistry is important, you should try to learn a large number of the facts of descriptive chemistry. If your reason for studying chemistry is not a professional one you may not want to learn so many of these facts, but only some of them, especially those that are significant to everyday life.

In applying a theoretical principle in the solution of a problem you should make use of the following procedure. First, decide on the applicable principle and get it clearly in mind. Then apply it in a straightforward manner. *Do not guess:* if you are not sure of the proper step, think about the matter further, until you are sure.

In working problems you must be sure that you understand the theoretical principle that you are using before you make the calculations. It is important to keep track of the physical units that are involved in the problem. One good way of doing this is to write the abbreviations for the units beside the numbers, and to cancel them when possible. For example, if you are told that 1.73 g of a substance occupies the volume 2.00 cm^3, and are asked to calculate the density, you may write 1.73 g/2.00 cm^3, and obtain immediately the answer 0.865 g/cm^3. The fact that the answer is in units g/cm^3 gives you a check on the correctness of the procedure that you have followed, inasmuch as you know that density is measured in units g/cm^3.

EXERCISES

1-16. A sphere of plutonium metal (one of the five crystalline modifications) 7.4 cm in diameter weighs 3.92 kg. What is the density of this form of plutonium?

1-17. Classify the following materials as homogeneous or heterogeneous:

pure gold	air	glass	granite
milk	ice	sugar	quartz
wood	gasoline	coffee	snow

1-18. According to the definition of mineral (first footnote, Section 1-3), is the ice in a glacier to be classified as a mineral?

1-19. Classify the following homogeneous materials as substances or solutions:

| rainwater | ocean water | oxygen | honey |
| air | salt | mercury | vodka |

1-20. What is the evidence proving that water is a compound, and not an element? What is the evidence indicating that oxygen is an element, and not a compound? Why is the word "proving" used in the first of the preceding sentences, and "indicating" in the second?

1-21. How much heat is needed to raise the temperature of 100 g of water from 10°C to 50°C? (Answer: 4000 cal.)

1-22. The melting point of pure iron is 1535°C. What is this temperature on the Fahrenheit scale?

1-23. One liter of boiling water is poured into a vessel containing three liters of water at 20°C. What is the temperature of the water after stirring? (Ignore the heat loss to the container.)

1-24. A liter of water weighs 1000 g. What is the weight in ounces (16 oz = 1 lb) of one cubic foot of water?

REFERENCES

Much useful information is tabulated in the following handbooks. It is suggested that the student majoring in chemistry obtain a copy of one of them:

Charles D. Hodgman (Editor in Chief), *Handbook of Chemistry and Physics*, Chemical Rubber Publishing Co., Cleveland, Ohio.

N. A. Lange, *Handbook of Chemistry*, Handbook Publishers, Sandusky, Ohio.

Detailed information about the elements and inorganic compounds may be found in comprehensive treatises of inorganic chemistry; the greatest of these in English is

J. W. Mellor, *A Comprehensive Treatise on Inorganic and Theoretical Chemistry*, Longmans, Green & Co., Inc., New York, 1922–1937.

Many interesting articles may be found in the *Journal of Chemical Education* and in the *Scientific American*. The chemical articles in the *Encyclopaedia Britannica* are excellent.

CHAPTER **2**

The Atomic and Molecular Structure

of Matter

The properties of any kind of matter are most easily and clearly learned and understood when they are correlated with its structure, in terms of the molecules, atoms, and still smaller particles that compose it. This subject, the atomic structure of matter, will be taken up in this chapter.

The chapter begins with a brief discussion of hypotheses, theories, and laws (Section 2-1). The next section (2-2) describes the atomic theory of matter and presents the arguments advanced by Dalton in support of the theory a century and a half ago. A brief discussion of modern methods of studying atoms and molecules follows (Section 2-3). There are then described, as examples, a crystal of copper, built of atoms in a simple regular arrangement (Section 2-4), and a crystal of iodine, built of molecules (groups of atoms, Section 2-6). Section 2-5 presents the way of describing the arrangement of atoms in a crystal, together with a brief discussion of the classification of crystals into systems. Some photographs of molecules made with the electron microscope are shown in Section 2-6. The nature of gases and liquids and the processes of evaporation and sublimation are treated in Sections 2-7 and 2-8, and the relation between temperature and the motion of molecules is discussed in Section 2-9. All of these aspects of atomic and molecular theory are important for the further study of chemistry.

The last section (Section 2-10) presents a discussion of the x-ray diffraction method of determining the structure of crystals. It begins with a description of interference and reinforcement of waves on the surface of a liquid. The Bragg equation, which gives the values of the angles at which a beam of x-rays is diffracted by a crystal, is then derived, and the way in which the structure of a crystal can be determined is briefly discussed. This subject is, it is true, often considered to be a part of physics rather than of chemistry. The results of the use of physical methods of investigating the structure of molecules and crystals have, however, become so important to the understanding of the chemical properties of substances that it is now necessary to include these methods in the chemistry course.

2-1.   Hypotheses, Theories, and Laws

When it is first found that an idea explains or correlates a number of facts, the idea is called a *hypothesis*. A hypothesis may be subjected to further tests and to experimental checking of deductions that may be made from it. If it continues to agree with the results of experiment the hypothesis is dignified by the name of *theory* or *law*.

A theory, such as the atomic theory, usually involves some idea about the nature of some part of the universe, whereas a law may represent a summarizing statement about observed experimental facts. For example, there is a law of the constancy of the angles between the faces of crystals. This law states that whenever the angles between corresponding faces of various crystals of a pure substance are measured they are found to have the same value. The law simply expresses the fact that the angles between corresponding faces on a crystal of a pure substance are found to have the same value whether the crystal is a small one or a large one; it does not in any way explain this fact. An explanation of the fact is given by the atomic theory of crystals, the theory that in crystals the atoms are arranged in a regular order (as described later in this chapter).

It may be mentioned that chemists and other scientists use the word theory in two somewhat different senses. The first meaning of the word is that described above, namely, a hypothesis that has been verified. The second use of the word theory is to represent a systematic body of knowledge, compounded of facts, laws, theories in the limited sense described above, deductive arguments, etc. Thus by the atomic theory we mean not only the idea that substances are composed of atoms, but also all the facts about substances that can be explained and interpreted in terms of atoms and the arguments that have been developed to explain the properties of substances in terms of their atomic structure.

2-2.   The Atomic Theory

The most important of all chemical theories is the atomic theory. In 1805 the English chemist and physicist John Dalton (1766–1844), of Manchester, stated the hypothesis that *all substances consist of small particles of matter, of several different kinds, corresponding to the different elements.* He called these particles atoms, from the Greek word *atomos*, meaning indivisible. This hypothesis gave a simple explanation or picture of previously observed but unsatisfactorily explained relations among the weights of substances taking part in chemical reactions with one another. As it was verified by further work in chemistry and physics, Dalton's atomic hypothesis became the atomic theory. The existence of atoms is now accepted as a fact.

The rapid progress of our science during the current century is well illustrated by the increase in our knowledge about atoms. In a popular textbook of chemistry written in the early years of the twentieth century atoms were defined as the "imaginary units of which bodies are aggregates." The article on "Atom" in the 11th edition of the *Encyclopaedia Britannica,* published in 1910, ends with the words "The atomic theory has been of priceless value to chemists, but it has more than once happened in the history of science that a hypothesis, after having been useful in the discovery and the coordination of knowledge, has been abandoned and replaced by one more in harmony with later discoveries. Some distinguished chemists have thought that this fate may be awaiting the atomic theory. . . . But modern discoveries in radioactivity are in favor of the existence of the atom, although they lead to the belief that the atom is not so eternal and unchangeable a thing as Dalton and his predecessors had imagined." Now, only half a century later, we have precise knowledge of the structure and properties of atoms and molecules. Atoms and molecules can no longer be considered "imaginary."

Dalton's Arguments in Support of the Atomic Theory.   The concept of atoms is very old. The Greek philosopher Democritus (about 460–370 B.C.), who had adopted some of his ideas from earlier philosophers, stated that the universe is composed of void (vacuum) and atoms. The atoms were considered to be everlasting and indivisible—absolutely small, so small that their size could not be diminished. He considered the atoms of different substances, such as water and iron, to be fundamentally the same, but to differ in some superficial way; atoms of water, being smooth and round, could roll over one another, whereas atoms of iron, being rough and jagged, would cling together to form a solid body.

The atomic theory of Democritus was pure speculation, and was much too general to be useful. Dalton's atomic theory, however, was a hypothesis that explained many facts in a simple and reasonable way.

In 1785 the French chemist Antoine Laurent Lavoisier (1743–1794) showed clearly that there is no change in mass during a chemical reaction—the mass of the products is equal to the mass of the reacting substances.

In 1799 another general law, the **law of constant proportions,** was enunciated by the French chemist Joseph Louis Proust (1754–1826). The law of constant proportions states that *different samples of a substance contain its elementary constituents (elements) in the same proportions.* For example, it was

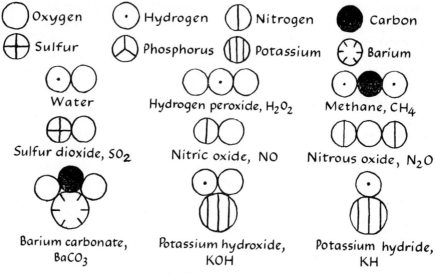

Figure 2-1

Atomic symbols and molecular formulas used by John Dalton, about 1803.

found by analysis that the two elements hydrogen and oxygen are present in any sample of water in the proportion by weight 1:8. One gram of hydrogen and 8 g of oxygen combine to form 9 g of water.

Dalton stated the hypothesis that elements consist of atoms, all of the atoms of one element being identical, and that compounds result from the combination of a certain number of atoms of one element with a certain number of atoms of another element (or, in general, from the combination of atoms of two or more elements, each in definite number). In this way he could give a simple explanation of the law of conservation of mass, and also of the law of constant proportions.

A **molecule** *is a group of atoms bonded to one another.* If a molecule of water is formed by the combination of two atoms of hydrogen with one atom of oxygen, the mass of the molecule should be the sum of the masses of two atoms of hydrogen and an atom of oxygen, in accordance with the law of conservation of mass. The definite composition of a compound is then explained by the definite ratio of atoms of different elements in the molecules of the compound.

Dalton also formulated another law, the **law of simple multiple proportions.** * This law states that *when two elements combine to form more than one compound, the weights of one element that combine with the same weight of the*

---

* The discovery of the law of simple multiple proportions was the first great success of Dalton's atomic theory. This law was not induced from experimental results, but was derived from the theory, and then tested by experiments.

other are in the ratios of small integers. It is found by experiment that, whereas water consists of hydrogen and oxygen in the weight ratio 1:8, hydrogen peroxide consists of hydrogen and oxygen in the ratio 1:16. The weights of oxygen combined with the same weight of hydrogen, 1 g, in water and hydrogen peroxide are 8 g and 16 g; that is, they are in the ratio of the small integers 1 and 2. This ratio can be explained by assuming that twice as many atoms of oxygen combine with an atom of hydrogen in hydrogen peroxide as in water. This situation is illustrated in Figure 2-1, which shows the symbols used by Dalton to represent the atoms of some elements and the molecules of compounds.

Dalton had no way of determining the correct formulas of compounds, and he arbitrarily chose formulas to be as simple as possible: for example, he assumed that the molecule of water consisted of one atom of hydrogen and one atom of oxygen, as shown in the figure, whereas in fact it consists of two atoms of hydrogen and one of oxygen.

2-3. Modern Methods of Studying Atoms and Molecules

During the second half of the nineteenth century chemists began to discuss the properties of substances in terms of assumed structures of the molecules— that is, of definite arrangements of the atoms relative to one another. Precise information about the atomic structure of molecules and crystals of many substances was finally obtained during the recent period, beginning about 1913. The physicists have developed many powerful methods of investigating the structure of matter. One of these methods is the interpretation of the *spectra* of substances (see Figure 25-1). A flame containing water vapor, for example, emits light that is characteristic of the water molecule; this is called the spectrum of water vapor. Measurements of the lines in the water spectrum have been made and interpreted, and it has been found that the two hydrogen atoms in the molecule are about 0.97 Å from the oxygen atom. Moreover, it has been shown that the two hydrogen atoms are not on opposite sides of the oxygen atom, but that the molecule is bent, the angle formed by the three atoms being 105°. The distances between atoms and the angles formed by the atoms in many simple molecules have been determined by spectroscopic methods.

Also, the structures of many substances have been determined by the methods of diffraction of electrons and diffraction of x-rays. In the following pages we shall describe many atomic structures that have been determined by these methods. The x-ray diffraction method of determining the structure of crystals is discussed in Section 2-10.

In the preceding paragraph the Ångström (symbol Å) is used as the unit of length. The Ångström has the value 1×10^{-8} cm. This very small unit of length is convenient because atoms are usually from 1 Å to 4 Å from neighboring atoms in a molecule or crystal, and it is easier to write 0.97 Å than

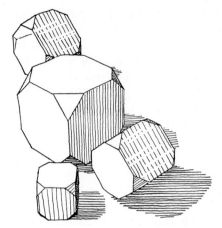

Figure **2-2** *Crystals of native copper.*

0.97×10^{-8} cm or 0.0000000097 cm. It was named in honor of a Swedish physicist, Anders Jonas Ångström (1814–1874).

2-4. The Arrangement of Atoms in a Crystal

Most solid substances are crystalline in nature. Sometimes the particles of a sample of solid substance are themselves single crystals, such as the cubic crystals of sodium chloride in table salt. Sometimes these single crystals are very large; occasionally crystals of minerals several yards in diameter are found in nature.

In our discussion we shall use *copper* as an example. Crystals of copper as large as a centimeter on edge, as shown in Figure 2-2, are found in deposits of copper ore. An ordinary piece of the metal copper does not consist of a single crystal of copper, but of an aggregate of crystals. The crystal grains of a specimen of a metal can be made clearly visible by polishing the surface of the metal, and then etching the metal lightly with an acid. Often the grains are small, and can be seen only with the aid of a microscope (Figure 2-3), but sometimes they are large, and can be easily seen with the naked eye, as in some brass doorknobs.

Figure **2-3** *A polished and etched surface of a piece of cold-drawn copper bar, showing the small crystal grains that compose the ordinary metal. Magnification 200 × (200-fold linearly). The small round spots are gas bubbles.*

It has been found by experiment (Section 2-10) that *every crystal consists of atoms arranged in a three-dimensional pattern that repeats itself regularly.* In a crystal of copper all of the atoms are alike, and they are arranged in the way shown in Figures 2-4 and 2-5. This is a way in which spheres of uniform size may be packed together to occupy the smallest volume.* This structure, called

* It is interesting that this statement, which is almost certainly true, has never been rigorously proved. There are other ways of packing spheres with the same volume per sphere as cubic closest-packing (hexagonal closest-packing Section 20-2), but none with a smaller volume has been discovered.

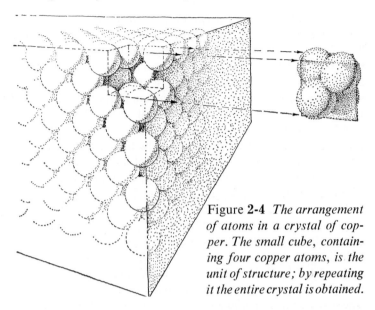

Figure **2-4** *The arrangement of atoms in a crystal of copper. The small cube, containing four copper atoms, is the unit of structure; by repeating it the entire crystal is obtained.*

the *cubic closest-packed structure*, was assigned to the copper crystal by W. L. Bragg in 1913.

You must remember while looking at Figures 2-4 and 2-5 that the atoms are shown greatly enlarged relative to the crystal. Even if the crystal were a small one, with edges only about 0.1 mm long, there would still be about 400,000 atoms in a row along each edge.

It is the **regularity of arrangement** *of the atoms in a crystal that gives to the*

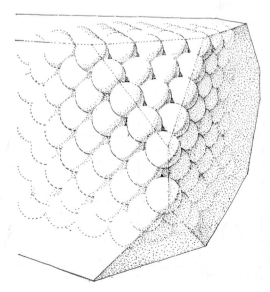

Figure **2-5** *Another atomic view of a copper crystal, showing small octahedral faces and large cube faces.*

crystal its characteristic properties, in particular the property of growing in the form of polyhedra. (A polyhedron is a solid figure bounded by plane faces.) The faces of crystals are defined by surface layers of atoms, as shown in Figures 2-4 and 2-5. These faces lie at angles to one another that have definite characteristic values, the same for all specimens of the same substance. The sizes of the faces may vary from specimen to specimen, but the angles between them are always constant. The principal surface layers shown in Figures 2-4 and 2-5 for copper correspond to the faces of a cube (*cubic faces* or *cube faces*); these faces are always at right angles with one another. The smaller surface layer, obtained by cutting off a corner of a cube, is called an *octahedral face*. Native copper, found in deposits of copper ore, often is in the form of crystals with cubic and octahedral faces (Figure 2-2).

Atoms are not hard spheres, but are soft, so that by increased force they may be pushed more closely together (be compressed). This compression occurs, for example, when a copper crystal becomes somewhat smaller in volume under increased pressure. The sizes that are assigned to atoms correspond to the distances between the center of one atom and the center of a neighboring atom of the same kind in a crystal under ordinary circumstances. The distance from a copper atom to each of its twelve nearest neighbors in a copper crystal at room temperature and atmospheric pressure is 2.55 Å; this is called the *diameter* of the copper atom in metallic copper. The radius of the copper atom is half this value.

2-5. The Description of a Crystal Structure

Chemists often make use of the observed shapes of crystals to help in the identification of substances. The description of the shapes of crystals is the subject of the science of *crystallography*. The method of studying the struc-

Figure **2-6**

Arrangement of atoms in a plane. The unit of structure is a square. Small atoms have the coordinates 0, 0 and large atoms the coordinates $\frac{1}{2}, \frac{1}{2}$.

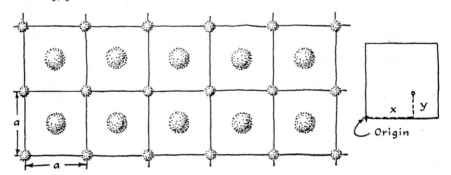

ture of crystals by the diffraction of x-rays, which was discovered by the German physicist Max von Laue (1879–1960) in 1912 and developed by the British physicists W. H. Bragg (1862–1942) and W. L. Bragg (born 1890), has become especially valuable in recent decades. Much of the information about molecular structure that is given in this book has been obtained by the x-ray diffraction technique.

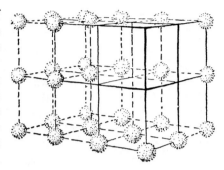

Figure **2-7** *The simple cubic arrangement of atoms. The unit of structure is a cube, with one atom per unit, its coordinates being 0, 0, 0.*

The basis of the description of the structure of a crystal is the *unit of structure*. For cubic crystals the unit of structure is a small cube, which, when repeated parallel to itself in such a way as to fill space, reproduces the entire crystal.

The way in which this is done can be seen from a two-dimensional example. In Figure 2-6 there is shown a portion of a square lattice. The unit of structure of this square lattice is a square; when this square is repeated parallel to itself in such a way as to fill the plane, we obtain a sort of two-dimensional crystal. In this case there are present a lattice of atoms of one sort, represented by small spheres at the intersections of the lattice lines, and a lattice of atoms of another sort, represented by larger spheres at the centers of the unit squares. We might describe the structure by the use of coordinates x and y, giving the positions of the atoms relative to an origin at the corner of the unit of structure, with x and y taken as fractions of the edges of the unit of structure, as indicated in the figure. The atom represented by the small sphere would then have the coordinates $x = 0$, $y = 0$, and the atom at the center of the square would have the coordinates $x = \frac{1}{2}$, $y = \frac{1}{2}$.

Figure **2-8** *The cubic unit of structure for the face-centered cubic arrangement, corresponding to cubic closest packing of spheres. There are four atoms in the unit, with coordinates 0, 0, 0; 0, $\frac{1}{2}$, $\frac{1}{2}$; $\frac{1}{2}$, 0, $\frac{1}{2}$; $\frac{1}{2}$, $\frac{1}{2}$, 0.*

Similarly, for a cubic crystal the unit of structure can be taken as a cube, which when reproduced in parallel orientation would fill space to produce a cubic lattice, as shown in Figure 2-7. The unit of structure could be described, for a cubic crystal, by giving the value of the edge of the unit, a, and the values of the coordinates x, y, and z for each atom, as fractions of the edge of the unit. Thus, for the cubic closest-packed structure, represented by metallic copper, the unit of structure is cubic, with edge $a = \sqrt{2} \times 2.55$ Å, and with four

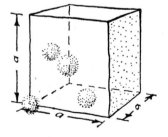

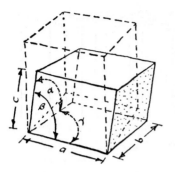

Figure **2-9** *The parallele-*
piped representing a general
unit of structure. It is deter-
mined by the lengths of its
three edges, and by the three
angles between the edges.

atoms per unit, with coordinates $x = 0$, $y = 0$, $z = 0$; $x = 0$, $y = \frac{1}{2}$, $z = \frac{1}{2}$; $x = \frac{1}{2}$, $y = 0$, $z = \frac{1}{2}$; and $x = \frac{1}{2}$, $y = \frac{1}{2}$, $z = 0$, as shown in Figure 2-8. Often these coordinates are written without giving the symbols x, y, and z; it is then said that there are four copper atoms in the unit, at 0, 0, 0; 0, $\frac{1}{2}$, $\frac{1}{2}$; $\frac{1}{2}$, 0, $\frac{1}{2}$; $\frac{1}{2}$, $\frac{1}{2}$, 0. These are called the *coordinates* of the atoms in the unit cube.

Note that in the unit cube shown in Figure 2-8 an atom is represented at only one of the eight corners. Of course, when this unit cube is surrounded by other unit cubes, atoms are placed at the seven other corners, these atoms being formally associated with the adjacent unit cubes.

The unit of structure of a crystal other than a cubic crystal is a parallelepiped. In the case of the most general sort of crystal, a triclinic crystal (see the paragraph after Example 2 below), the parallelepiped is a general one, as shown in Figure 2-9. It can be described by giving the values of a, b, and c, the lengths of the three edges, and also the values of α, β, and γ, the angles between pairs of edges.

Example 1. The metal iron is cubic, with $a = 2.86$ Å, and with two iron atoms in the unit cube, at 0, 0, 0 and $\frac{1}{2}$, $\frac{1}{2}$, $\frac{1}{2}$. How many nearest neighbors does each iron atom have, and how far away are they?

Figure **2-10** *The unit*
of structure correspond-
ing to the cubic body-
centered arrangement.
There are two atoms in
the unit, with coordinates
0, 0, 0 and $\frac{1}{2}$, $\frac{1}{2}$, $\frac{1}{2}$.

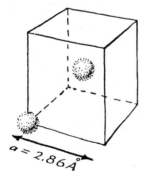

Solution. We draw a cubic unit of structure, with edge 2.86 Å, as shown in Figure 2-10, and we indicate in it the positions 0, 0, 0 and $\frac{1}{2}$, $\frac{1}{2}$, $\frac{1}{2}$. When cubes of this sort are reproduced parallel to one another, we see that we obtain the structure shown in Figure 20-2; this is called the *body-centered arrangement*. It is seen that the atom at $\frac{1}{2}$, $\frac{1}{2}$, $\frac{1}{2}$ is surrounded by eight atoms, the atom at 0, 0, 0 and seven similar atoms. Also, the atom at 0, 0, 0 is surrounded by eight atoms. In each case the surrounding atoms are at the corners of a cube. This situation is described by saying that each atom in the body-centered arrangement has *ligancy* 8 (or *coordination number* 8).

To calculate the interatomic distance, we note that, by the theorem of Pythagoras, the square of the distance is equal to $(a/2)^2 + (a/2)^2 + (a/2)^2$, and hence the distance itself is equal to $\sqrt{3}\,a/2$. Thus the distance between each iron atom and its neighbors is found to be 1.732×2.86 Å$/2 = 2.48$ Å. The metallic radius of iron is hence 1.24 Å.

Example 2. The English mathematician and astronomer Thomas Harriot (1560–1621), who was tutor to Sir Walter Raleigh and who traveled to Virginia in 1585, was interested in the atomic theory of substances. He believed that the hypothesis that substances consist of atoms was plausible, and capable of explaining some of the properties of matter. His writings contain the following propositions:

"9. The more solid bodies have Atoms touching on all Sydes.

"10. Homogeneall bodies consist of Atoms of like figure, and quantitie.

"11. The waight may increase by interposition of lesse Atoms in the vacuities betwine the greater.

"12. By the differences of regular touches (in bodies more solid), we find that the lightest are such, where euery Atom is touched with six others about it, and greatest (if not intermingled) where twelve others do touch euery Atom."

Assuming that the atoms can be represented as hard spheres in contact with one another, what difference in density would there be between the two structures described in the above proposition 12?

    Solution. The structure where every atom is in contact with six others about it that Harriot had in mind is probably the simple cubic arrangement, shown in Figure 2-11. In this arrangement of atoms the unit of structure is a cube, containing one atom, which can be assigned the coordinates 0, 0, 0. Each atom is then in contact with six other atoms, which are at the distance d from it. The volume of the unit cube is accordingly d^3. If the mass of the atom is M, the density for this arrangement is M/d^3.

    The more dense structure referred to by Harriot, where twelve atoms are in contact with each atom, is the cubic closest-packed arrangement described in the preceding section. (Harriot had apparently discovered that there is no way of packing equal hard spheres in space that gives a greater density than is given by this arrangement.) The cubic unit of structure for this arrangement contains four atoms. Its edge, a, is equal to $2^{1/2}d$, and its volume to $2^{3/2}d^3$. The mass contained in the unit cube is $4M$, and the density is accordingly $4M/2^{3/2}d^3$, or $2^{1/2}M/d^3$.

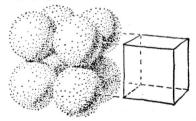

Figure **2-11** *Simple cubic packing of spheres.*

We thus have found that the dense structure described by Harriot has density $\sqrt{2} = 1.414$ times that of the less dense structure; it is accordingly 41.4% denser than the less dense structure.

The Six Crystal Systems.   Every crystal can be classified in one of the six crystal systems, called cubic (or isometric), hexagonal, tetragonal, orthorhombic, monoclinic, and triclinic. Some characteristic shapes (forms) of crystals of these six systems are shown in Figures 2-12 and 2-13.

The symmetry of the crystals representing these different systems is such that their units of structure may be chosen in special ways, except for triclinic crystals (Figure 2-9). These special ways involve restrictions on the relative values of the three edges and values of the three angles (Figure 2-9), as follows:

Cubic crystals: three equal edges, with length a, at right angles to one another.

Tetragonal crystals: two equal edges, with length a, and a third edge, with different length c, all at right angles to one another.

Hexagonal crystals: two equal edges, with length a, at 120° to one another, and a third edge, with length c, at right angles to the other two.

Figure **2-12**

Representative crystal forms of the cubic and hexagonal systems.

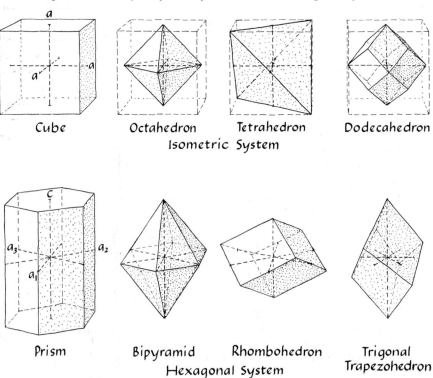

Cube   Octahedron   Tetrahedron   Dodecahedron

Isometric System

Prism   Bipyramid   Rhombohedron   Trigonal
                                            Trapezohedron

Hexagonal System

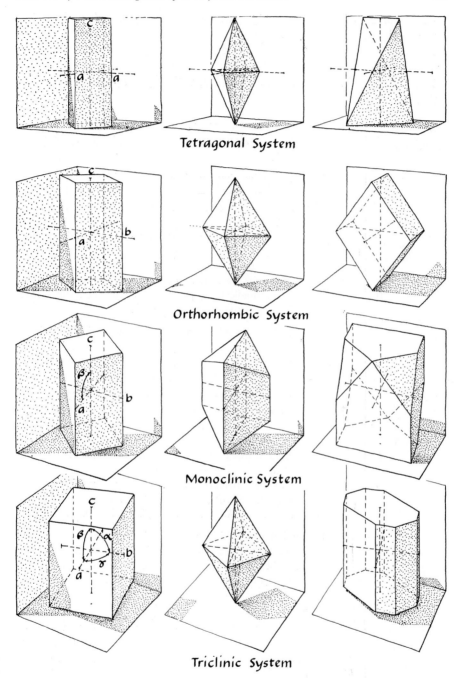

Tetragonal System

Orthorhombic System

Monoclinic System

Triclinic System

Figure 2-13

Representative crystal forms of the tetragonal, orthorhombic, monoclinic, and triclinic crystal systems.

Orthorhombic crystals: three edges, with unequal lengths a, b, and c, all at right angles to one another.

Monoclinic crystals: two edges, a and c, at the angle β with one another, and a third, b, at right angles to a and c.

Triclinic crystals: three edges, a, b, and c, with angles α, β, and γ between them.

Illustrative Exercises

2-1. The crystal cesium chloride, CsCl, is cubic. The cubic unit of structure has $a = 4.11$ Å. The atomic positions are Cs at 0, 0, 0 and Cl at $\frac{1}{2}, \frac{1}{2}, \frac{1}{2}$.

(a) Make a drawing showing the atomic positions.

(b) What is the smallest Cs—Cl distance? (Answer: 3.56 Å.)

(c) How many chlorine atoms are at this distance from each cesium atom?

(d) How many cesium atoms are at this distance from each chlorine atom?

(e) What is the smallest distance between cesium atoms? How many cesium atoms are at this distance from each cesium atom?

(f) What is the smallest distance between chlorine atoms? How many chlorine atoms are at this distance?

2-2. The metal tin containing a small amount of impurity is reported to form hexagonal crystals with $a = b = 3.20$ Å and $c = 2.98$ Å, and with one atom of tin per unit cell. The coordinates of this atom can be taken to be $x = 0$, $y = 0$, $z = 0$.

(a) Make a drawing showing the axes a and b, at 120° to one another, in the plane $z = 0$. Outline the rhomb that is the base of one unit cell and locate the tin atom assigned to this cell.

(b) Outline the eight rhombs touching the first one. How many near neighbors in this plane does each tin atom have?

(c) At what distances are these neighbors?

(d) How many near neighbors does a tin atom have in the direction of the c axis (positive and negative)? At what distance? [Answer: (b) Six; (c) All at 3.20 Å; (d) Two, both at 2.98 Å.]

2-3. Magnesium crystallizes with the hexagonal closest-packed arrangement of atoms, described in Section 20-2 and illustrated in Figure 20-1. Its hexagonal unit of structure has $a = b = 3.19$ Å and $c = 5.20$ Å, and contains two magnesium atoms, one with coordinates $x = 0$, $y = 0$, $z = 0$, and the other with coordinates $x = \frac{1}{3}$, $y = \frac{2}{3}, z = \frac{1}{2}$.

(a) Make a drawing showing the magnesium atoms in one plane, with $x = 0$. How many nearest neighbors in this plane does each magnesium atom have? (Compare Exercise 2-2.) At what distance are they?

(b) Make a drawing of the plane $z = \frac{1}{2}$, showing the sections (rhombs) of the unit cells, and locate the magnesium atoms with coordinates $x = \frac{1}{2}$, $y = \frac{2}{3}$, $z = \frac{1}{2}$. How many of these atoms are at the minimum distance from an atom in the plane with $z = 0$?

(c) Calculate the distance from $x = 0$, $y = 0$, $z = 0$, to $x = \frac{1}{3}$, $y = \frac{2}{3}$, $z = 0$, and the distance from $x = \frac{1}{3}$, $y = \frac{2}{3}$, $z = 0$ to $x = \frac{1}{3}$, $y = \frac{2}{3}$, $z = \frac{1}{2}$. From these values calculate the distance between an atom in the plane $z = 0$ and the nearest atoms in the adjacent plane $z = \frac{1}{2}$.

(d) How many nearest neighbors does a magnesium atom have in the metal?

[Answer: (a) 6, at 3.19 Å; (b) 3; (c) 1.84 Å, 2.60 Å, 3.19 Å; (d) 12.]

2-6. The Molecular Structure of Matter

Molecular Crystals. The crystal of copper, which we have discussed as an example of a kind of matter, is built up of *atoms* arranged in a regular pattern. We shall now discuss crystals that contain *discrete groups of atoms* (distinct groups), which are called *molecules*. These crystals are called *molecular crystals*.

An example of a molecular crystal is shown in the upper left part of Figure 2-14, which is a drawing representing the structure of a crystal of the blackish-gray solid substance *iodine*. It is seen that the iodine atoms are grouped together in pairs, to form molecules containing two atoms each. Iodine is used as an example in this section and the following ones because its molecules are simple (containing only two atoms), and because it has been thoroughly studied by scientists.

The distance between the two atoms of iodine in the same molecule of this molecular crystal is less than the distances between atoms in different molecules. The two iodine atoms in each molecule are only 2.70 Å apart, whereas the smallest distance between iodine atoms in different molecules is 3.54 Å.

The forces acting between atoms within a molecule are very strong, and those acting between molecules are weak. As a result of this, it is hard to cause the molecule to change its shape, whereas it is comparatively easy to roll the molecules around relative to one another. For example, under pressure a crystal of iodine decreases in size: the molecules can be pushed together until the distances between iodine atoms in different molecules have decreased by several percent; but the molecules themselves retain their original size, with no appreciable change in interatomic distance within the molecule. When a crystal of iodine at low temperature is heated it expands, so that each of the molecules occupies a larger space in the crystal; but the distance between the two iodine atoms in one molecule stays very close to the normal 2.70 Å.

The molecules of different chemical substances contain varying numbers of atoms, bonded tightly together. An example of a more complicated molecule is shown in Figure 2-15, which represents a portion of a crystal of *naphthalene*. The molecule of naphthalene contains ten carbon atoms, arranged in two

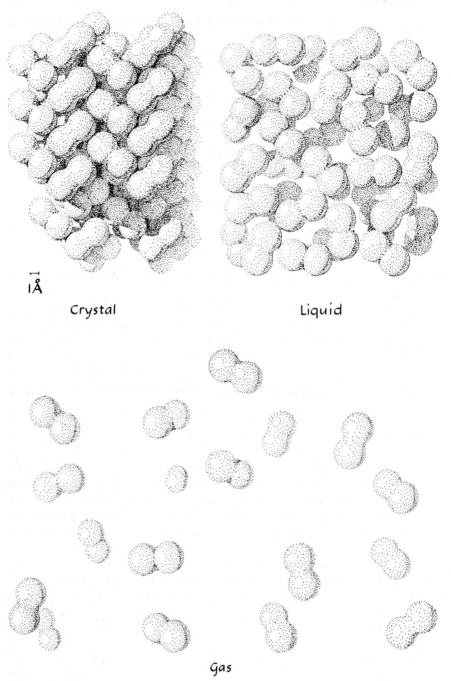

Figure 2-14

Crystal, liquid, and gaseous iodine, showing diatomic molecules I₂.

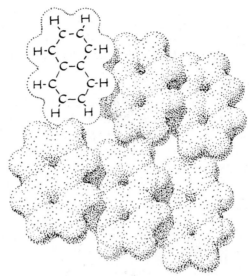

Figure **2-15**

A portion of a crystal of naphthalene, showing molecules $C_{10}H_8$.

hexagonal rings that have one edge in common, and eight hydrogen atoms. Naphthalene is a rather volatile substance, with a characteristic odor. In the form of moth balls, it is used as a moth repellent. The properties of naphthalene are determined by the structure of its molecules.

Illustrative Exercise

2-4. At $-80°C$ the substance silicon tetrafluoride, SiF_4, forms cubic crystals. The value of a for the unit cube is 5.46 Å. There are two molecules SiF_4 in the unit, one at the origin (one corner) and the other at the center of the cube. For the molecule at the origin the atomic coordinates x, y, z are 0, 0, 0 for the silicon atom; the coordinates are x, x, x; $x, \bar{x}, \bar{x}$; $\bar{x}, x, \bar{x}$; $\bar{x}, \bar{x}, x$ for the four fluorine atoms, with $x = 0.165$. (Note that $\bar{x}$ is used by crystallographers to mean $-x$.)

(a) Make a perspective drawing showing the silicon atom and the four fluorine atoms. How are the fluorine atoms arranged?
(b) How far are the fluorine atoms from the silicon atom? From each other?
[Answer: (a) Tetrahedrally; (b) 1.56 Å, 2.55 Å.]

Photographs of Molecules Made with the Electron Microscope. In the last few years it has finally become possible to see and to photograph molecules. They are too small to be seen with a microscope using ordinary visible light, which cannot permit objects much smaller in diameter than the wavelength of light, about 5000 Å, to be seen. A wonderful new instrument, the *electron micro-*

scope, has now been developed, which permits objects a hundred times smaller in diameter to be seen. The electron microscope uses beams of electrons in place of beams of light. Its linear magnifying power is about 500,000, as compared with about 1000 for the ordinary microscope. It is accordingly possible to see objects as small as 10 Å in diameter with the electron microscope.

Figure 2-16

Electron micrograph of a single layer of tomato bushy stunt virus molecules. The photograph was made to show added contrast by depositing a very thin layer of gold on the specimen at a small angle, giving the impression of shadows cast by the molecules. Linear magnification 55,000. [From Price, Williams, and Wyckoff, Arch. Biochem., 7, 175 (1946).]

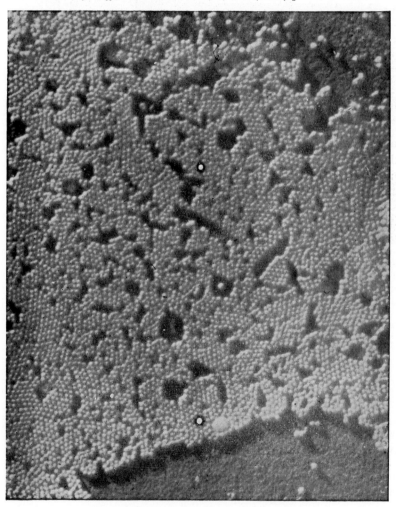

Figure **2-17**

Electron micrograph of crystals of necrosis virus protein, showing individual molecules in ordered arrangement. Linear magnification 65,000. [From R. W. G. Wyckoff.]

Two photographs made with the electron microscope are reproduced here, as Figures 2-16 and 2-17. They show molecules of viruses that cause disease in tomato plants.* Each "bushy stunt" virus molecule is about 230 Å in diameter. It is made of about 750,000 atoms. The "necrosis" virus molecules are somewhat smaller, about 195 Å in diameter. In each photograph the individual molecules can be clearly seen, and in the photograph of necrosis-virus-protein molecules the regular way in which the molecules arrange themselves in the crystals is evident.

The magnifying power of the electron microscope is not yet great enough to permit ordinary molecules, such as those of naphthalene, to be seen and photographed, but scientists are working on methods of improving the instrument, and perhaps an electron micrograph of naphthalene will be available for inclusion in the fourth edition of this book. Moreover, some powerful new method of determining the structure of molecules may become available—there are still great opportunities for making scientific discoveries.

* A brief discussion of viruses is given in Chapter 28.

2-7. Evaporation of Crystals. The Nature of a Gas

At a very low temperature the molecules in a crystal of iodine lie rather quietly in their places in the crystal (Figure 2-14). As the temperature increases the molecules become more and more agitated; each one bounds back and forth more and more vigorously in the little space left for it by its neighbors, and each one strikes its neighbors more and more strongly as it rebounds from them.

A molecule on the surface of the crystal is held to the crystal by the forces of attraction that its neighboring molecules exert on it. Attractive forces of this kind, which are operative between all molecules when they are close together, are called *van der Waals attractive forces;* this name is used because it was the Dutch physicist J. D. van der Waals (1837–1923) who first gave a thorough discussion of intermolecular forces in relation to the nature of gases and liquids.

These attractive forces are quite weak, much weaker than the forces between the atoms in one molecule. Hence occasionally a certain molecule may become so agitated as to break loose from its neighbors, and to fly off into the surrounding space. If the crystal is in a vessel, there will soon be present in the space within the vessel through this process of evaporation a large number of these free molecules, each moving in a straight-line path, and occasionally colliding with another molecule or with the walls of the vessel to change the direction of its motion. These free molecules constitute *iodine vapor* or *iodine gas* (Figure 2-14). The gas molecules are very much like the molecules in the crystal, their interatomic distance being practically the same; but the distances between molecules are much larger in a gas than in a crystal.

It may seem surprising that molecules on the surface of a crystal should evaporate directly into a gas, instead of going first through the stage of being in a liquid layer; but in fact the process of slow evaporation of a crystalline substance is not uncommon. Solid pieces of camphor or of naphthalene (as used in moth balls, for example) left out in the air slowly decrease in size, because of the evaporation of molecules from the surface of the solid. Snow may disappear from the ground without melting, by evaporation of the ice crystals at a temperature below that of their melting point. Evaporation is accelerated if a wind is blowing, to take the water vapor away from the immediate neighborhood of the snow crystals, and to prevent the vapor from condensing again on the crystals.

The characteristic feature of a gas is that *its molecules are not held together, but are moving about freely, in a volume rather large compared with the volume of the molecules themselves.* The attractive forces between the molecules still operate whenever two molecules come close together, but usually these forces are negligibly small because the molecules are far apart.

Because of the freedom of motion of its molecules a specimen of gas does not have either definite shape or definite size. *A gas shapes itself to its container.*

Gases at ordinary pressure are very dilute—the molecules themselves constitute only about one one-thousandth of the total volume of the gas, the rest being empty space. Thus 1 g of solid iodine has a volume of about 0.2 cm³ (its density* is 4.93 g/cm³), whereas 1 g of iodine gas at 1 atm pressure and at the temperature 184°C (its boiling point) has a volume of 148 cm³, over 700 times greater. The volume of all of the molecules in a gas is accordingly very small compared with the volume of the gas itself at ordinary pressure. On the other hand, the diameter of a gas molecule is not extremely small compared with the distance between molecules; in a gas at room temperature and 1 atm pressure the average distance from a molecule to its nearest neighbors is about ten times its molecular diameter, as indicated in the drawing of gaseous iodine, Figure 2-14.†

The Vapor Pressure of a Crystal. A crystal of iodine in an evacuated vessel will gradually change into iodine gas by the evaporation of molecules from its surface. Occasionally one of these free gas molecules will again strike the surface of the crystal, and it may stick to the surface, held by the van der Waals attraction of the other crystal molecules. This is called *condensation* of the gas molecules.

The rate at which molecules evaporate from a crystal surface is proportional to the area of the surface, but is essentially independent of the pressure of the surrounding gas, whereas the rate at which gas molecules strike the crystal surface is proportional to the area of the surface and also proportional to the concentration of molecules in the gas (the number of gas molecules in unit volume).

If some iodine crystals are put into a flask, which is then stoppered and allowed to stand at room temperature, it will soon be seen that the gas in the flask has become violet in color, showing that a quantity of iodine has evaporated. After a while it will be evident that the process of evaporation has apparently ceased, because the intensity of coloration of the gas will no longer increase, but will remain constant. This steady state is reached when the concentration of gas molecules becomes so great that the rate at which gas molecules strike the crystal surface and stay there is just equal to the rate at which molecules leave the crystal surface. *The corresponding gas pressure is called the* **vapor pressure** *of the crystal.*

A steady state of such a sort is an example of *equilibrium.* It must be recognized that equilibrium does not represent a situation in which nothing is happening, but rather a situation in which opposing reactions are taking place at the same rate, so as to result in no over-all change. This is indicated in Figure 2-18.

---

* It was mentioned in Section 1-4 that the density of a substance is the mass (weight) of a unit volume of the substance; in the metric system, grams per cubic centimeter.

† You will remember that a cube 1 inch on edge has a diameter one tenth as great as that of a cube 10 inches on edge, an area one one-hundredth as great, and a volume one one-thousandth as great.

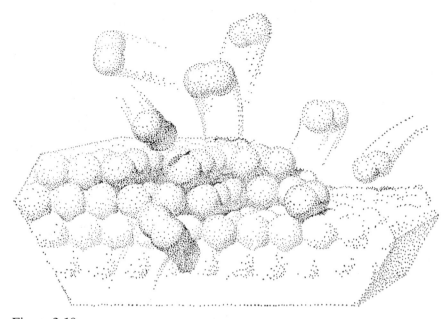

Figure **2-18**

Equilibrium between molecules evaporating from an iodine crystal and gas molecules depositing on the crystal.

2-8.   The Nature of a Liquid

When iodine crystals are heated to 114°C they melt, forming liquid iodine. The temperature at which the crystals and the liquid are in equilibrium—that is, at which there is no tendency for the crystals to melt or for the liquid to freeze—is called the *melting point* of the crystals, and the *freezing point* of the liquid. This temperature is 114°C for iodine.

Liquid iodine differs from the solid (crystals) mainly in its *fluidity*. It is like the gas in being able to adjust itself to the shape of its container. However, like the solid, and unlike the gas, it has a definite volume, 1 g occupying about 0.2 cm³.

From the molecular viewpoint the process of melting can be described in the following way. As a crystal is heated its molecules become increasingly agitated, and move about more and more vigorously; but this thermal agitation does not carry any one molecule a significant distance away from the position fixed for it by the arrangement of its neighbors in the crystal. At the melting point the agitation finally becomes so great as to cause the molecules to slip by one another and to change somewhat their location relative to one another. They continue to stay close together, but do not continue to retain a regular fixed arrangement; instead, the grouping of molecules around a given molecule changes continually, sometimes being much like the close packing of the crystal, in which each iodine molecule has twelve near neighbors, and sometimes considerably different, the molecule having only ten or nine or eight near neighbors, as shown in Figure 2-14. Thus in a liquid, as in a crystal, the molecules are piled rather closely together; but whereas a crystal is characterized by regularity of atomic or molecular arrangement, a liquid is characterized by randomness of structure. The randomness of structure usually causes the density of a liquid to be somewhat less than that of the corresponding crystal; that is, the volume occupied by the liquid is usually somewhat greater than that occupied by the crystal.

The Vapor Pressure and Boiling Point of a Liquid.   A liquid, like a crystal, is, at any temperature, in equilibrium with its own vapor when the vapor molecules are present in a certain concentration. The pressure corresponding to this concentration of gas molecules is called the *vapor pressure of the liquid* at the given temperature.

The vapor pressure of every liquid increases with increasing temperature. *The temperature at which the vapor pressure reaches a standard value (usually 1 atm) is called the* **boiling point** *of the liquid.* At this temperature it is possible for bubbles of the vapor to appear in the liquid and to escape to the surface.

The vapor pressure of liquid iodine reaches 1 atm at 184°C. Hence 184°C is the boiling point of iodine.

Other substances undergo similar changes when they are heated. When copper melts, at 1083°C, it forms liquid copper, in which the arrangement of the copper atoms shows the same sort of randomness as that of the molecules of liquid iodine. Under 1 atm pressure copper boils at 2310°C to form copper gas; the gas molecules are single copper atoms.

Note that it is customary to refer to the particles that move about in a gas as molecules even though each one may be only a single atom, as in the case of copper.

The Dependence of Vapor Pressure on Temperature.   It has been found by experiment that the vapor pressure of crystals and liquids increases as the temperature is raised. Curves showing the vapor pressure of iodine crystals and liquid iodine are shown in Figure 2-19.

2-9. The Meaning of Temperature

In the preceding discussion the assumption has been made that molecules move more rapidly and violently at any given temperature than at a lower one. This assumption is correct—the temperature of a system is a measure of the vigor of motion of all the atoms and molecules in the system.

With increase in temperature there occurs increase in violence of molecular motion of all kinds. Gas molecules rotate more rapidly, and the atoms within a molecule oscillate more rapidly relative to one another. The atoms and

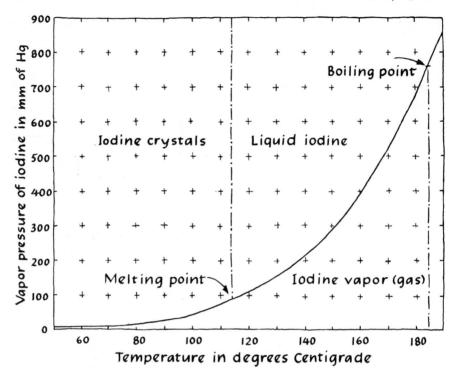

Figure 2-19

A graph showing the vapor-pressure curve of iodine crystal and the vapor-pressure curve of liquid iodine. The melting point of the crystal is the temperature at which the crystal and the liquid have the same vapor pressure, and the boiling point of the liquid (at 1 atm pressure) is the temperature at which the vapor pressure of the liquid equals 1 atm.

molecules in liquids and solids carry out more vigorous vibrational motions. This vigorous motion at high temperatures may result in chemical reaction, especially decomposition of substances. Thus when iodine gas is heated to about 1200°C at 1 atm pressure about one-half of the molecules dissociate (split) into separate iodine atoms (Figure 2-20).

You can get a better understanding of many of the phenomena of chemistry by remembering that the absolute temperature is a measure of the vigor of the motion of atoms and molecules.

2-10. The X-Ray Diffraction Method of Determining the Structure of Crystals. The Bragg Equation

Much of our present information about the structure of crystals, such as that presented earlier in this chapter, has been obtained by a method involving the

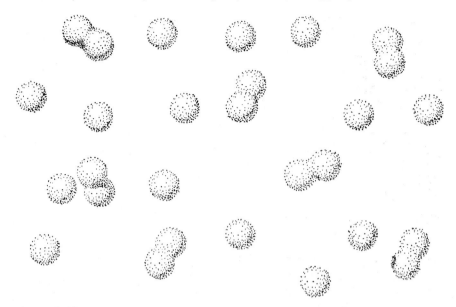

Figure **2-20**

Iodine vapor at elevated temperature; this vapor contains both diatomic molecules (I_2) and monatomic molecules (I) of iodine.

diffraction of x-rays. X-rays were discovered in 1895 (see Section 3-8). The question of their nature remained unanswered until 1912, when Max von Laue, at the University of Munich, suggested an experiment, the diffraction of x-rays by crystals, which was successfully carried out, and which showed immediately that x-rays are similar in nature to ordinary light, but have a far smaller wavelength than ordinary light. The diffraction of x-rays by crystals has been of great importance to chemistry, not only through the determination of the wavelengths of x-rays characteristic of different elements (which will be discussed in Section 4-9), but also because it has permitted the determination of the atomic arrangement in crystals, and in this way has contributed to the development of modern structural chemistry.

Waves and Their Interference.   During the nineteenth century it was recognized that light can be produced by moving an electric charge back and forth in an oscillatory manner. The motion of the electric charge produces an oscillatory change in the electric field surrounding the charge, and this change is transmitted through space with the velocity of light, 3.00×10^{10} cm/sec.

Figure **2-21**   *Diagram representing wave motion.*

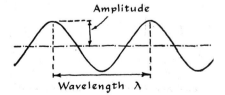

The nature of the wave motion is

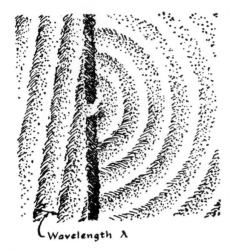

Figure **2-22** *Diagram representing waves on the surface of water, from the left, striking a pier; waves propagated through the opening in the pier then spread out in circles.*

represented by the sine curve shown in Figure 2-21. This curve might represent, for example, the instantaneous contour of waves on the surface of the ocean. The distance between one crest and an adjacent crest is called the *wavelength*, usually represented by the symbol λ (Greek letter lambda). The *amplitude* of the wave is the height of the crest, which is also the depth of the trough, with reference to the average level. If the waves are moving with the velocity c cm/sec, the frequency of the waves, represented by the symbol ν (Greek letter nu), is equal to c/λ; that is, it is the number of waves that pass by a fixed point in unit time (1 sec). The dimensions of the wavelength are those of length. The dimensions of frequency, number of waves per second, are [time^{-1}]. We see that the product of wavelength and frequency has the dimensions [length] [time^{-1}]—that is, the dimensions of velocity. The equation connecting wavelength λ, frequency ν, and velocity c is

$$\lambda\nu = c \tag{1}$$

For a light wave the sine curve shown in Figure 2-21 is considered to represent the magnitude of the electric field in space. The electric field of a light wave is perpendicular to the direction of motion of the beam of light.

Figure **2-23** *The interference and reinforcement of two sets of circular waves, from two openings.*

The phenomenon of *interference of waves* is used to determine the wavelength of light waves and x-rays. This phenomenon can be illustrated by Figures 2-22 and 2-23. In Figure 2-22 there is shown a set of water waves approaching a jetty in which there is a small opening. The waves that strike the jetty dissipate their energy among the rocks of the jetty, but the part of the waves that strikes the opening causes a disturbance on the other side of the jetty. This disturbance is in the form of a set of circular waves that spread out from the opening of the jetty. The wavelength of these circular waves is the same as the wavelength of the incident water waves. When light or x-rays strike atoms,

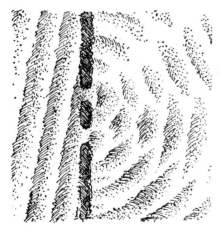

part of the energy of the incident light is scattered by the atoms. Each atom scatters a set of circular waves. If two atoms that are excited by the same incident waves scatter light, as illustrated in Figure 2-23, there are certain directions in which the circular waves (spherical waves for atoms in three-dimensional space) from the two scattering centers reinforce one another, producing waves with twice the amplitude of either set, and other directions in which the trough of one set of waves coincides with the crest of the other set, and interference occurs. The directions of reinforcement and interference for two sets of circular waves are shown in the figure.

It is easy to calculate the angles at which reinforcement and interference would occur, in terms of the distance between the two

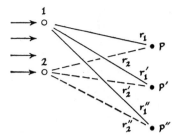

Figure **2-24** *Diagram illustrating the conditions for interference and reinforcement of circular waves from two points, 1 and 2. The incident waves are moving toward the right, as shown by the arrows.*

scattering centers and the wavelength of the waves. The way in which the calculation is made is shown in Figure 2-24. Here r_1 is the distance from the first scattering center, and r_2 the distance from the second scattering center. At all points in the median plane these two distances are equal. Accordingly, a crest of a wave of the first set will reach a distant point P at the same time as a crest of a wave of the second set, and there will be reinforcement at this point. The point P'' lies at such distances r_1'' and r_2'' that $r_1'' - r_2''$ is just equal to one wavelength of the waves. Accordingly, the crest of a wave from the first scattering center will reach P'' at the same time as the crest of the preceding wave from the second scattering center, and again there will be reinforcement. At the intermediate point P', however, the difference $r_1' - r_2'$ is just one-half of a wavelength. The crest of a wave from one scattering center will coincide with the trough of a wave from another scattering center, and there will be interference.

The Bragg Equation for the Diffraction of X-rays by Crystals. It was shown during the decade after the discovery of x-rays that if these rays were similar to ordinary light their wavelength must be of the order of magnitude of 1 Å—that is, about 1/5000 of the wavelength of visible light. Then Max von Laue had the idea that crystals, in which atoms are arranged in a regular lattice with interatomic distances of a few Ångströms, might serve to produce diffraction effects with x-rays. The experiment was immediately carried out by two experimental physicists, Friedrich and Knipping, with use of a crystal of copper sulfate pentahydrate. A narrow beam of x-rays from an x-ray tube was passed through the crystal, and photographic plates were placed around the crystal. It was found that on the photographic plate behind the crystal there was a blackened spot representing the position where the direct beam of x-rays had struck the plate, and also several other spots, showing the preferential scattering of the beam of x-rays in certain directions, corresponding to diffraction maxima. This experiment showed at once that x-rays are similar to light, in having a wave nature,

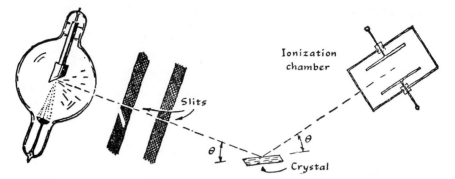

Figure **2-25**

The Bragg ionization-chamber technique of investigating the diffrac-
tion of x-rays by crystals.

and that the wavelength of the x-rays produced by the x-ray tube that was used
was of the order of 1 Å.

W. H. Bragg and W. L. Bragg then succeeded in determining the structure of
many crystals by the use of the phenomenon of x-ray diffraction, and also in
determining the wavelengths of the x-rays produced by different x-ray tubes.
Their experimental method is shown in Figure 2-25. A beam of x-rays is defined
by a slit system, usually slits in a piece of lead. The beam impinges on the face of
a crystal, such as the cleavage face of a salt crystal. An instrument for detecting
x-rays (in the original experiments by the Braggs an *ionization chamber*, but in
modern work a *Geiger counter* may be used) was then placed as shown in the
figure. W. L. Bragg had developed a simple theory of diffraction of x-rays by
crystals. This theory is illustrated in Figures 2-26 and 2-27. He pointed out that
if the beam of rays incident on a plane of atoms and the scattered beam are in
the same vertical plane and at the same angle with the plane, as shown in Figure 2-26, the conditions for reinforcement are satisfied. This sort of scattering is
called *specular reflection;* it is similar to
reflection from a mirror. He then formulated the conditions for reinforcement of
the beam specularly reflected from one
plane of atoms and the beam specularly
reflected from another plane of atoms
separated from it by the *interplanar distance d.* This situation is illustrated in Figure 2-27. We see that the difference in path
is equal to $2d \sin \theta$, in which θ is the
Bragg angle (the angle between the incident
beam and the plane of atoms). In order to
have reinforcement this difference in path
$2d \sin \theta$ must be equal to the wavelength λ
or an integral multiple of this wavelength—
that is, to $n\lambda$, in which n is an integer. We

Figure **2-26**   *Diagram showing the*
equality of path lengths when the
conditions for specular reflection
from a layer are satisfied.

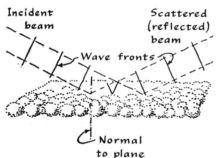

thus obtain the *Bragg equation* for the diffraction of x-rays:

$$n\lambda = 2d \sin \theta \qquad (2)$$

The way in which the structure of crystals was then determined is illustrated in Figure 2-28. Here we show a simple cubic arrangement of atoms, as seen along one of the cube faces. It is evident that there are layers of atoms, shown by their traces in the plane of the paper, with spacings d_1, d_2, d_3, etc., which are in the ratios $1:2^{-1/2}:5^{-1/2}$, etc. Since the relative values of the spacings d_1, d_2, d_3, etc. could be determined without knowledge of the wavelengths of x-rays, but simply

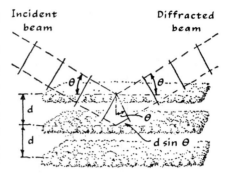

Figure **2-27** *Diagram illustrating the derivation of the Bragg equation for the diffraction of x-rays by crystals.*

as inversely proportional to their values of $\sin \theta$, the nature of the atomic arrangement could be discovered by the Bragg experiments.

A reproduction of some of the first experimental measurements made by the Braggs is shown as Figure 2-29. It is seen that there occurs a pattern of reflections that is repeated at values of $\sin \theta$ representing the values 1, 2, and 3 for the integer n, which is called the *order of the reflection*. The pattern that is repeated consists of a weak scattered beam, at the smaller angle, and a stronger scattered beam, at the larger angle. This shows that there were present in the beam of x-rays produced by the x-ray tube a shorter wavelength and a longer wavelength, with greater intensity of the x-rays of longer wavelength than of shorter wavelength.

Within a few months (1913) the Braggs had succeeded in determining the wavelengths of x-rays (to within about 1%) and also in determining the structures of about twenty different crystals. We had discussed one of the first structures to be determined, that of the metal copper, in Section 2-4.

Example 3. The Braggs calculated from the density of salt and Millikan's value of the charge of the electron, by a method which we shall discuss later (Section 8-7, Exercise 8-45), that the spacing d_1 for the cube face of the sodium chloride crystal has the value 2.81 Å. Using the experimental data given in Figure 2-29, find the wavelengths of the two kinds of radiation produced by the x-ray tube that they used.

Figure **2-28** *Spacings between different rows of atoms in a two-dimensional crystal.*

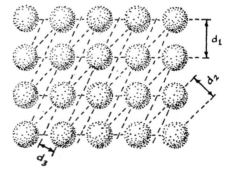

Solution. Let us first calculate the wavelength of the x-rays with shorter wavelength. This is called the $K\beta$ line. The Bragg

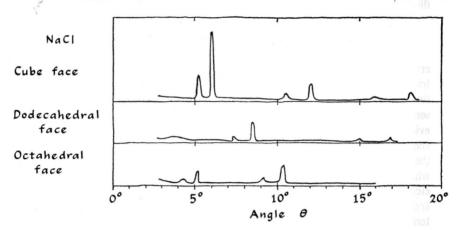

Figure 2-29

Experimental data obtained by the Braggs for the diffraction of x-rays by the sodium chloride crystal.

angle θ for this line in the first order is seen from the figure to be 5°18′. The value of $\sin \theta$ is accordingly 0.0924. The Bragg equation for $n = 1$ is

$$\lambda = 2d \sin \theta$$

We insert the value 2.81 Å for d and 0.0924 for $\sin \theta$ and obtain

$$\lambda = 2 \times 2.81 \times 0.0924 = \mathbf{0.519 \; Å}$$

This is the value of the wavelength for the $K\beta$ line. In the same way we calculate for the other line, using the observed value of θ of 6°0′, the value

$$\lambda = \mathbf{0.587 \; Å}$$

This is the wavelength of the $K\alpha$ line. These two wavelengths correspond to the metal palladium, which was the target (the anode) of the x-ray tube used by the Braggs in this experiment. The two lines are part of the *characteristic x-radiation* of the element palladium.

EXERCISES

2-5. Give an example of a solid material that is crystalline and of one that is not crystalline.

2-6. Classify the following statements as hypotheses, theories, laws, or facts:

(a) The moon is made of granite.
(b) With a few exceptions, substances increase in volume on melting.
(c) The core of the earth is composed of a metallic form of hydrogen, which has

not yet been prepared in the laboratory.

(d) Hydrogen, oxygen, nitrogen, and neon are all gases under ordinary conditions.

(e) All crystals are composed of atoms arranged in a regular way.

2-7. Spectroscopic study of moonlight and sunlight has shown that the reflectivity of the moon (its power of reflecting light of different colors) is not the same as that of granite. Does this single observed fact eliminate the hypothesis that the moon is composed of granite? Would you change the classification from hypothesis to theory if it had been found that the reflectivity of the moon was (to within experimental error) the same as that of granite?

2-8. It is stated in the text that copper atoms are 2.55 Å in diameter.

(a) How many Ångströms are there in 1 inch?

(b) How many copper atoms side by side in contact would make a line 1 inch long?

(c) How many atoms of the same size in a simple square array would cover 1 square inch of surface?

(d) How many atoms of the same size in a simple cubic array would occupy 1 cubic inch?

2-9. There are about 0.5×10^{24} molecules of water in 1 cubic inch of water. If 1 cubic inch of water were poured into the ocean and thoroughly stirred, and 1 cubic inch of ocean water were then removed, about how many molecules from the original cubic inch would be found in it? Assume the volume of the ocean to correspond to an average depth of 1 mile over the entire surface of the earth.

2-10. If the molecules in a glass of water (say 10 cubic inches) were to be increased in diameter a millionfold, making each molecule the size of a small grain of sand, to what depth could the surface of the earth be covered uniformly with the enlarged molecules?

2-11. Carbon dioxide (dry ice) consists of CO_2 molecules. These molecules are linear, with the carbon atom in the center. Make three drawings, representing your concepts

of carbon dioxide gas, carbon dioxide liquid, and carbon dioxide crystal.

2-12. Define vapor pressure of a crystal, and also vapor pressure of a liquid. Can you think of an argument showing that these two vapor pressures of a substance must be equal at the melting point?

2-13. The vapor pressure of solid carbon dioxide at its melting point, $-56.5°C$, is 5 atm. How do you explain the fact that solid carbon dioxide when used for packing ice cream does not melt to form liquid carbon dioxide? If you wanted to make some liquid carbon dioxide, what would you have to do?

2-14. Arrange marbles, steel balls, or other spheres of the same size in a close-packed layer, such that each sphere is surrounded by six spheres in contact with it. Pack a similar layer on top of the first one, so that each sphere in the second layer is in the pocket formed by three spheres in the lower layer. Note that a third layer could then be put directly above the first layer, or in another position; the second of these alternatives, repeated, leads to the structure of the copper crystal. Repeat this process to build a triangular pyramid, which is a regular tetrahedron.

2-15. Describe qualitatively the structure of a crystal of iodine, the structure of liquid iodine, of gaseous iodine at low temperature, and of gaseous iodine at high temperature.

2-16. What is the effect of increase in pressure on the boiling point of a liquid? Estimate the boiling point of liquid iodine at a pressure of $\frac{1}{2}$ atm (see Figure 2-21).

2-17. The crystal sodium chloride has a cubic unit of structure, with $a = 5.628$ Å. There are four sodium atoms in the unit of structure, with coordinates 0, 0, 0; 0, $\frac{1}{2}$, $\frac{1}{2}$; $\frac{1}{2}$, 0, $\frac{1}{2}$; $\frac{1}{2}$, $\frac{1}{2}$, 0; and also four chlorine atoms, with coordinates $\frac{1}{2}$, $\frac{1}{2}$, $\frac{1}{2}$; $\frac{1}{2}$, 0, 0; 0, $\frac{1}{2}$, 0; 0, 0, $\frac{1}{2}$. Make a drawing showing the cubic unit of structure and the positions of the atoms. How many nearest neighbors does each atom have, what is the interatomic distance for these neighbors, and what polyhedron is formed by them? (This arrangement of atoms, called the sodium chloride arrangement, is a common one for salts.)

2-18. The mineral fluorite, CaF_2, has a cubic unit of structure, with $a = 5.45$ Å. The unit cube contains four calcium atoms, with coordinates $\frac{1}{4}, \frac{1}{4}, \frac{1}{4}; \frac{1}{4}, \frac{3}{4}, \frac{3}{4}; \frac{3}{4}, \frac{1}{4}, \frac{3}{4}$; and $\frac{3}{4}, \frac{3}{4}, \frac{1}{4}$. There are eight fluorine atoms, with coordinates $0, 0, 0; 0, \frac{1}{2}, \frac{1}{2}; \frac{1}{2}, 0, \frac{1}{2}; \frac{1}{2}, \frac{1}{2}, 0$; $\frac{1}{2}, 0, 0; 0, \frac{1}{2}, 0; 0, 0, \frac{1}{2}$; and $\frac{1}{2}, \frac{1}{2}, \frac{1}{2}$. Make a drawing showing the positions of the atoms. How many nearest neighbors does each calcium atom have? each fluorine atom? What is the Ca—F distance? (Answer: 8, 4, 2.36 A.)

2-19. It has been found that hemoglobin molecules spread on the surface of a solution of ammonium sulfate form a unimolecular layer of hemoglobin, 36 Å thick. Assuming that the density of the hemoglobin in this layer is 1.35 g/cm³, calculate what surface area would be covered by 1 mg of hemoglobin, spread into a unimolecular layer. (Answer: 2060 cm².)

2-20. The metal indium forms tetragonal crystals. The unit of structure is a rectangular parallelepiped, with edges $a = 3.24$ Å, $b = 3.24$ Å, and $c = 4.94$ Å. There are two atoms in the unit of structure, with coordinates $0, 0, 0$ and $\frac{1}{2}, \frac{1}{2}, \frac{1}{2}$. Calculate distances from each atom to its twelve nearest neighbors; note that four are at one distance, and eight at another distance. (Answer: 3.24 Å, 3.37 Å.)

3

The Electron and the Nuclei of Atoms

In the preceding chapter we have discussed the atomic theory and have seen that some of the properties of substances can be explained by this theory. The two substances copper and iodine, which were used as the principal examples in the discussion, have different properties because their atoms are different.

Chemists of the nineteenth century asked whether it might be possible to understand the differences between atoms of different elements, such as copper and iodine, but they were not able to answer the question. About fifty years ago, however, it was discovered that atoms themselves are composed of still smaller particles. The discovery of the components of atoms and the investigation of the structure of atoms—the ways in which atoms of different kinds are built of the smaller particles—constitute one of the most interesting stories in the history of science. Moreover, knowledge about the structure of atoms has during recent years permitted the facts of chemistry to be systematized in a striking way, making the subject easier to understand and to remember. The student of chemistry can be helped greatly in mastering his subject by first obtaining a good understanding of atomic structure.

The particles that constitute atoms are *electrons* and *atomic nuclei*. Electrons and atomic nuclei carry electric charges, and these electric charges are in large part responsible for the properties of the particles and for the structure of atoms. We shall accordingly begin this chapter with a discussion of the nature of electricity.

3-1. The Nature of Electricity

The ancient Greeks knew that when a piece of amber is rubbed with wool or fur it achieves the power of attracting light objects, such as feathers or bits of straw. This phenomenon was studied by William Gilbert (1540–1603), Queen Elizabeth I's physician, who invented the adjective *electric* to describe the force of attraction, after the Greek word *elektron*, meaning amber. Gilbert and many other scientists, including Benjamin Franklin, investigated electric phenomena, and during the nineteenth century many discoveries about the nature of electricity and of magnetism (which is closely related to electricity) were made.

It was found that if a rod of sealing wax, which behaves in the same way as amber, is rubbed with a woolen cloth, and a rod of glass is rubbed with a silken cloth, an electric spark will pass between the sealing-wax rod and the glass rod when they are brought near one another. Moreover, it was found that a force of attraction operates between them. If the sealing-wax rod that has been electrically charged by rubbing with a woolen cloth is suspended from a thread, as shown in Figure 3-1, and the charged glass rod is brought near one end of it, this end will turn toward the glass rod. An electrified sealing-wax rod is repelled, however, by a similar sealing-wax rod, and also an electrified glass rod is repelled by a similar glass rod (Figure 3-1).

Through the experimental study of such phenomena the ideas were developed that there are two kinds of electricity, which were called resinous electricity (that which is picked up by the sealing-wax rod) and vitreous electricity (that which is picked up by the glass rod), and that the two kinds of electricity attract one another, whereas each kind repels itself. Franklin simplified this picture of electricity somewhat, by assuming that only one kind of electricity can flow from an object to another object. He assumed that when a glass rod is rubbed with a silken cloth this electric "fluid" is transferred from the cloth to the glass rod, and he described the glass rod as *positively charged*, meaning that it had an excess of the electric fluid. He described the cloth as having a deficiency of the electric fluid, and being *negatively charged*. He pointed out that he did not really know whether the electric fluid had been transferred from the silken cloth to the glass rod or from the glass rod to the silken cloth, and that accordingly the decision to describe vitreous electricity as positive (involving an excess of electric fluid) was an arbitrary one. We

Figure **3-1**

Experiments showing the attraction of unlike charges of electricity and the repulsion of like charges.

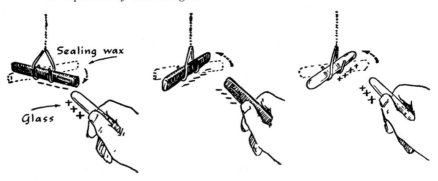

now know, in fact, that when the glass rod is rubbed with a silken cloth negatively charged particles, the electrons, are transferred from the glass rod to the silken cloth, and that Franklin thus made the wrong decision in his assumption.

Units of Electric Charge.   The unit of electric charge in the metric system is called the *statcoulomb*. (The definition of this unit is given in textbooks of physics.) In practical work there is need for a larger unit of electric charge. The larger unit that has been adopted is the *coulomb*, which is closely equal to 3×10^9 statcoulombs:

$$\textbf{1 coulomb} = \textbf{3} \times \textbf{10}^9 \textbf{ statcoulombs}$$

3-2.   The Discovery of the Electron

The idea that there are electric particles in substances was proposed, as a hypothesis, by G. Johnstone Stoney, an English scientist. Stoney knew that substances can be decomposed by an electric current—for example, water can be decomposed into hydrogen and oxygen in this way. He also knew that Michael Faraday had found that a definite amount of electricity is needed to liberate a certain amount of an element from one of its compounds. (The experiment carried out by Faraday will be discussed in Chapter 8 of our book.) In 1874, after thinking about these facts, Stoney stated that they indicate that *electricity exists in discrete units*, and that these units are associated with atoms. In 1891 he suggested the name *electron* for his postulated unit of electricity. The discovery of the electron by experiment was made in 1897 by Sir Joseph John Thomson (1856–1940), in Cambridge University, England.*

The Properties of the Electron.   The electron is a particle with a negative electric charge of magnitude -4.802×10^{-10} statcoulombs, or -1.601×10^{-19} coulombs.

The mass of the electron is 9.107×10^{-28} g, which is 1/1837 of the mass of the hydrogen atom.

The electron is very small. The radius of the electron has not been determined exactly, but it is known to be less than 1×10^{-13} cm.

In 1925 it was discovered that the electron spins about an axis and that it has a magnetic moment. The spin and magnetic moment are discussed in Sections 7-5 and 7-7.

3-3.   The Flow of Electricity in a Metal

Knowledge of the existence of electrons permits us to discuss some of the properties of electricity in a simple way.

In a metal or similar conductor of electricity there are electrons which have

* The experiments that led to the discovery of the electron are described in Section 3-7.

considerable freedom of motion, and which move along between the atoms of the metal when an electric potential difference is applied. A direct current of electricity passing along a copper wire is a *flow of electrons* along the wire.

Let us call to mind the analogy between the flow of electricity along a wire and the flow of water in a pipe. *Quantity* of water is measured in liters or cubic feet; quantity of electricity is usually measured either in *coulombs* or in *statcoulombs*. *Rate of flow*, or *current*, of water, the quantity passing a given point of the pipe in unit time, is measured in liters per second, or cubic feet per second; current of electricity is measured in *amperes* (coulombs per second). The rate of flow of water in a pipe depends on the *difference in the pressures* at the two ends of the pipe, with atmospheres or pounds per square inch as units. The current of electricity in a wire depends on the *electric potential difference* or *voltage drop* between its ends, which is usually measured in *volts*. The definitions of the unit of quantity of electricity (the coulomb) and the unit of electric potential (the volt) have been made by international agreement.

An electric generator is essentially an electron pump, which pumps electrons out of one wire and into another. A generator of direct current pumps electrons continually in the same direction, and one of alternating current reverses its pumping direction regularly, thus building up electron pressure first in one direction and then in the other. A 60-cycle generator reverses its pumping direction 120 times per second.

Illustrative Exercises	**3-1.** An ordinary electric light bulb is operated under conditions such that one ampere of current (one coulomb per second) is passing through the filament. How many electrons pass through the filament each second? (Remember that the charge of the electron is -1.60×10^{-19} coulombs.)

3-2. If a golf ball could be magnified 250,000,000 times, making it as big as the earth, each atom (3 or 4 Å in diameter) would become 3 or 4 inches in diameter. Would the electrons then look like peas, or birdshot, or fine grains of sand, or particles of dust?

3-4. The Nuclei of Atoms

In 1911 the British physicist Ernest Rutherford carried out some experiments* which showed that every atom contains, in addition to one or more electrons, another particle, called the *nucleus* of the atom. Every nucleus has a positive electric charge. It is very small, being only about 10^{-12} cm in diameter, and it is very heavy—the lightest nucleus is 1836 times as heavy as an electron.

There are many different kinds of nuclei; those of the atoms of one element are different from those of every other element. The nucleus of the hydrogen atom has the same electric charge as the electron, but with opposite sign, positive instead of negative. The nuclei of other atoms have positive charges that are multiples of this fundamental charge.

* These experiments are described in later sections of this chapter.

3-5. The Proton and the Neutron

The *proton* is the simplest atomic nucleus. It is the nucleus of the most abundant kind of hydrogen atom, which is the lightest of all atoms.

The proton has an electric charge 4.802×10^{-10} statcoulomb or 1.601×10^{-19} coulomb. This charge is exactly the same as that of the electron, except that it is positive, whereas the charge of the electron is negative.

The mass of the proton is 1.672×10^{-24} g. This is 1836 times the mass of the electron.

The *neutron* was discovered by the English physicist James Chadwick in 1932. The mass of the neutron is 1.675×10^{-24} g, which is 1839 times the mass of the electron. The neutron has no electric charge.

It is customary for chemists to use an *atomic mass unit*, which is approximately the mass of the proton. Both the proton and the neutron have masses that are approximately one atomic mass unit.

3-6. The Structure of Atomic Nuclei

Several hundred different kinds of atomic nuclei are known to exist. Together with the electrons that surround them, they make up the atoms of the different chemical elements. At the present time physicists all over the world are working on the problem of the structure of atomic nuclei. They have not yet solved this problem, although they have learned a great deal about the properties of the nuclei and the ways in which they can be made from other particles or converted into other particles. This phase of chemistry, which we call *nuclear chemistry*, is discussed in Chapter 30 of our book.

Although the detailed structures of nuclei are not known, physicists seem to be agreed in accepting the idea that they can all be described as being built up of protons and neutrons.

Let us first discuss, as an example, the *deuteron*. This is the nucleus of the *heavy hydrogen atom*, or *deuterium atom*. The deuteron has the same electric charge as the proton, but has about twice the mass of the proton. It is thought that the deuteron is

Figure **3-2** *Hypothetical structures of some atomic nuclei. We do not yet know just how these nuclei are constructed out of elementary particles, but it is known that nuclei are approximately 10^{-12} cm in diameter, and are, accordingly, very small even compared with atoms.*

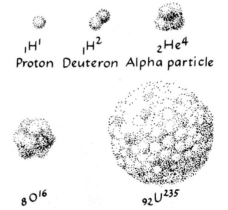

$_1H^1$ $_1H^2$ $_2He^4$
Proton   Deuteron   Alpha particle

$_8O^{16}$ $_{92}U^{235}$

made of one proton and one neutron, as indicated in Figure 3-2.

The nucleus of the helium atom, which is also called the *alpha particle*, has electric charge twice as great as that of the proton, and mass about four times as great as that of the proton. It is thought that the alpha particle is composed of two protons and two neutrons.

In Figure 3-2 there is also shown a drawing representing the nucleus of an oxygen atom, composed of eight protons and eight neutrons. The electric charge of this nucleus is eight times the electric charge of the proton. This electric charge would accordingly be neutralized by the negative charges of eight electrons. The mass of this oxygen nucleus is about 16 mass units.

There is also shown in the figure a hypothetical drawing of the nucleus of a uranium atom. This nucleus is composed of 92 protons and 143 neutrons. The electric charge of this nucleus is 92 times that of the proton; it would be neutralized by the negative charges of 92 electrons. The mass of this nucleus is about 235 times the mass of the proton.

In thinking about atoms and atomic nuclei, you must remember that the drawings of atomic nuclei in Figure 3-2 correspond to a magnification ten thousand times greater than the drawings of atoms and molecules that are shown elsewhere in this book. The nuclei are very small, even compared with atoms.

We shall continue the discussion of atomic nuclei of different kinds, and atoms of different kinds, in the following chapter.

3-7. The Experiments That Led to the Discovery of the Electron

Many interesting experiments involving electricity were carried out by physicists during the nineteenth century. These experiments ultimately led to the discovery of the electron. In order to understand them it is necessary to know something about the way in which the motion of an electrically charged particle is affected by other electric charges or by a magnet.

The Interaction of an Electric Charge with Other Electric Charges and with Magnets.   An electric charge is said to be surrounded by an *electric field*, which exercises a force, either of attraction or of repulsion, on any other electric charge in its neighborhood. The strength of an electric field can be measured by determining the force that operates on a unit of electric charge.

In experimental work use is often made of an apparatus like that shown in Figure 3-3, in which two large parallel plates of metal are held a small, constant distance from one another. By use of a battery or generator of electricity, one of these parallel plates is charged positively (that is, some electrons are taken away from it), and the other is charged negatively.

A wire or plate that has an excess of positive charge is called an *anode*. A wire or plate that has an excess of negative electric charge is called a cathode. In Figure 3-3 the upper plate is the anode and the lower plate is the cathode.

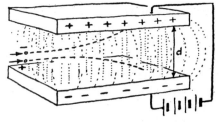

A particle with negative electric charge placed between the plates would be attracted toward the upper plate and repelled from the lower plate. It would accordingly move in the direction of the upper plate. Similarly, a particle with positive electric charge placed between the plates would move toward the lower plate.

Figure 3-3 *The motion of an electrically charged particle in the uniform electric field between charged plates.*

The force exerted on a positive charge by the electric field between the plates has the same effect as the force exerted on a mass by the gravitational field of the earth. Accordingly, a positively charged particle shot into the region between the plates, as indicated in Figure 3-3, would fall to the bottom plate along the path indicated by the dashed line, in the same way that a rock thrown horizontally would fall toward the surface of the earth.

You know that a piece of iron or steel can be magnetized, to form a *magnet*, and that the magnet has the power of attracting other pieces of iron. A magnet also has the power of exerting a force on any electrically charged particle that shoots by it. A magnet can therefore also be used to study charged particles.

No force is exerted on a stationary electric charge by a constant magnetic field. A force is exerted on an electric charge moving in a magnetic field. This is illustrated in Figure 3-4. The poles of the magnet are marked *N* (north-seeking pole) and *S* (south-seeking pole); the lines of force are indicated as going from the north-seeking pole to the south-seeking pole. A positively charged particle is shown as moving through the field from the left to the right. The nature of electricity and magnetism is such that a force operates that is proportional to the strength of the magnetic field, the quantity of electric charge on the particle, and the speed of the particle; the direction of this force is at right angles to the plane formed by the direction of motion of the moving particle and the direction of the lines of force of the magnetic field, its sense being out of the plane of the paper. This causes the moving charged particle to be deflected to the front, as indicated in the drawing.

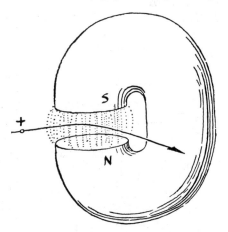

Figure 3-4 *The path of a moving electric charge in a magnetic field.*

The Explanation of Electricity and Magnetism. You may well ask how scientists explain the fact that an electron is repelled by another electron, that in general two electrically charged bodies repel or attract one another. How do scientists explain the still more extraordinary fact that an electric charge that is moving through a magnetic field is pushed to one side by interaction of its charge with the field? The answer to these questions is that there is no explanation. These properties of electric charges and of electric and magnetic fields are simply a part of the world in which we live.

The discovery that a lateral force is exerted on an electric charge moving through a magnetic field has led to very important practical applications. The ordinary electric generator (dynamo) produces electricity because of this fact. In an electric generator a wire is moved rapidly through a magnetic field, in a direction perpendicular to the lengthwise direction of the wire. Moving the wire (including the electrons in it) through the electric field causes the electrons to be set in motion, relative to the atoms in the wire, in the direction toward one end of the wire—namely, the end indicated by the rule of Figure 3-4. In this way a flow of electrons (current of electricity) is produced in the wire. Practically all the electric power that is used in the world is produced by this method, the energy for operating the electric generators (for moving the wire through the magnetic field) being provided by the fall of water in the earth's gravitational field, by the combustion of coal or oil to drive steam engines, or by nuclear reactions. A small amount of electric power is produced directly from chemical energy, as will be discussed in Chapter 8.

Figure **3-5** *The construction of an electromagnetic pump. When electric current flows through the liquid alloy in the region between the poles of the magnet, a force operates on the moving charges, and hence on the alloy, in the direction indicated.*

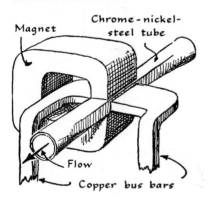

The Electromagnetic Pump. An interesting new device that makes use of the force that acts on a moving electric charge in a magnetic field is the electromagnetic pump. This pump was devised to pump the liquid metal (such as sodium-potassium alloy) that is used as a heat-transfer agent to carry the heat from a nuclear reactor to an external boiler. The liquid metal is in a pipe (made of a nickel-chromium alloy steel) between the poles of a large permanent magnet. An electric current of about 20,000 amperes, at 1 volt potential difference, passes through the liquid metal, as indicated in Figure 3-5. The lateral force that is exerted on the electrons moving through the magnetic field causes the metal to flow in the indicated direction, at right angles to the direction of the electric current and the direction of the magnetic field.

The Discovery of the Electron. During the nineteenth century many physicists carried out experiments on the conduction of electricity through gases. For example, if a glass tube about 50 cm long is fitted with electrodes, as shown in Figure 3-6, and a potential of about 10,000 volts is applied between the electrodes, no electricity is at first conducted between the electrodes. If, however, some of the air in the tube is pumped out, by use of pumps such as

Figure **3-6**

> *Apparatus used to observe the discharge of electricity in a gas at low pressure. The dark space around the cathode is called the Crookes dark space; at still lower pressures the Crookes dark space fills the whole tube.*

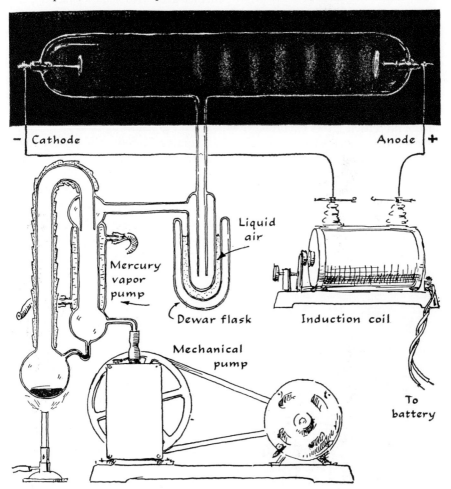

Figure **3-7** *Experiment showing that cathode rays, starting from the cathode at the left, move through the Crookes tube in straight lines.*

those indicated in the lower part of the figure, electricity begins to be conducted through the tube. While the electricity is being conducted through the tube light is emitted by the gas in the tube. You are familiar with this phenomenon, because you have seen many neon lamps in street signs. These neon lamps contain the gas neon, or some other gas, which is caused to emit light when electricity is conducted through the gas.

As the pressure of gas in the tube is further decreased, a dark space appears in the neighborhood of the cathode, and alternate light and dark regions are observed in the rest of the tube, as shown in Figure 3-6. At still lower pressure the dark space increases in size until it fills the whole tube. At this pressure no light is given out by the gas that is still present in very small quantity within the tube, but the glass of the tube itself glows (*fluoresces*) with a faint greenish light.

It was discovered that the greenish light coming from the glass is due to the bombardment of the glass by rays liberated at the cathode. These rays, called *cathode rays*, travel in straight lines from the cathode to the glass. This is shown by the experiment illustrated in Figure 3-7: an object placed within the tube, such as the cross shown in this figure, casts a shadow on the glass—the glass fluoresces everywhere except in the region of this shadow.

Figure **3-8** *Experiment showing that the cathode rays have a negative charge.*

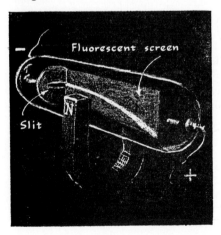

It was shown by the French scientist Jean Perrin (1870–1942) in 1895 that these cathode rays consist of particles with a negative electric charge, rather than a positive charge. His experiment is illustrated in Figure 3-8. He introduced a shield with a slit in the tube, so as to form a beam of cathode rays. He also placed a fluorescent screen* in the tube, so that the path of the beam could be followed by the trace of the

* A fluorescent screen is a sheet of paper or glass coated with a substance that shines when it is struck by electrons.

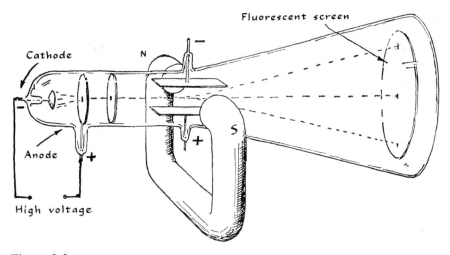

Figure **3-9**

> *The apparatus used by J. J. Thomson to determine the ratio of electric charge to mass of the cathode rays, through the simultaneous deflection of the rays by an electric field and a magnetic field.*

fluorescence. When a magnet was placed near the tube the beam was observed to be deflected in the direction corresponding to the presence of a negative charge on the particles.

J. J. Thomson then carried out some experiments that permitted him to make some quantitative statements about the particles that constitute the cathode rays. He used the apparatus shown in Figure 3-9, in which a beam of cathode rays can be affected by either a magnet that is brought up beside the tube, or by an electric field, produced by applying an electric potential to the two metal plates in the tube, or by both the magnet and the electric field. The effect on the beam of cathode rays was observed by use of a fluorescent screen. The results of his experiment convinced Thomson that the cathode-ray particles constitute a form of matter different from ordinary forms of matter. The particles were indicated by Thomson's experiments to be much lighter than atoms. Later and more accurate experiments showed that the mass of the cathode-ray particle is only 1/1837 times the mass of the hydrogen atom.

Although other investigators had carried out important experiments on cathode rays, the quantitative experiments by Thomson provided the first convincing evidence that these rays consist of particles (electrons) much lighter than atoms, and Thomson is hence given the credit for discovering the electron.

The Determination of the Charge of the Electron. After the discovery of the electron by Thomson, many investigators worked on the problem of determining accurately the charge of the electron. The American physicist R. A. Millikan (1868–1953), who began his experiments in 1906, was the most successful of the earlier experimenters. By means of his oil-drop experiment he determined in 1909 the value of the charge of the electron to within 1%.

The apparatus that he used is illustrated in Figure 3-10. Small drops of oil are formed by a sprayer, and some of them attach themselves to electrons that have been separated from molecules by action of a beam of x-rays. The experimenter watches one of these small oil drops through a microscope. He first measures the rate at which it falls in the earth's gravitational field. The small drops fall at a rate determined by their size, and measurement of the rate of fall of a drop permits the investigator to calculate the size.

When the electric field is turned on, by charging the plates above and below the region where the oil drops are moving, some of the drops, which carry no electric charge, continue to fall as before. Other drops, carrying electric charges, change their speed, and may rise, being pulled up by the attraction of the electric charge for the oppositely charged upper plate in the apparatus. The rate of a drop that has been watched falling is then observed. From these measurements, the magnitude of the electric charge on the drop can be calcu-

Figure **3-10**

A diagram of the apparatus used by R. A. Millikan in determining the charge of the electron by the oil-drop method.

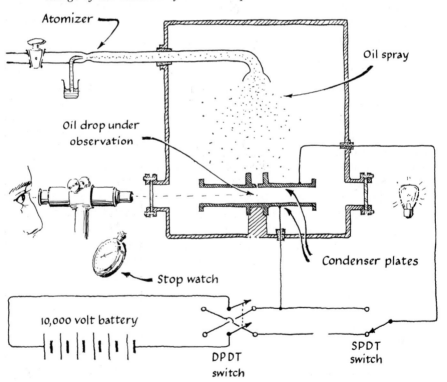

lated. In various experiments with different oil drops, values such as the following were obtained for the electric charge on the drop:

$$\text{Charge} = 4.8 \times 10^{-10} \text{ statcoulombs}$$
$$\text{Charge} = 9.6 \times 10^{-10} = 2 \times 4.8 \times 10^{-10}$$
$$\text{Charge} = 4.8 \times 10^{-10}$$
$$\text{Charge} = 24.0 \times 10^{-10} = 5 \times 4.8 \times 10^{-10}$$

All of these values have a common factor, 4.8×10^{-10} statcoulombs. Millikan accordingly concluded that this is the smallest electric charge that can occur under these conditions, and he identified it with the charge of the electron.

Since Millikan carried out his work, a number of other methods have been developed for determining the charge of the electron, and its value is now known to about 0.01 %.

3-8. The Discovery of X-Rays and Radioactivity

Several great scientific discoveries were made in a period of a few years, beginning in 1895. These discoveries made great changes in chemistry as well as in physics. X-rays were discovered in 1895, radioactivity was discovered in 1896, the new radioactive elements polonium and radium were isolated in the same year, and the electron was discovered in 1897.

Wilhelm Konrad Röntgen (1845–1923), Professor of Physics in the University of Würzburg, Germany, reported in 1895 that he had discovered a new kind of rays, which he called x-rays. These rays are produced when electricity is passed through a tube such as that shown in Figure 3-6. The rays are outside of the tube; they radiate from the place where the cathode-ray electrons strike the glass. They have the power of passing through matter that is opaque to ordinary light, and of exposing a photographic plate. Within a few weeks after the announcement of this great discovery, x-rays were being used by physicians for the investigation of patients with broken bones and other disorders.

Soon after the discovery of x-rays the French physicist Henri Becquerel (1852–1908) investigated some minerals containing uranium. He found that these minerals emit rays that, like x-rays, can pass through black paper and other opaque materials and expose a photographic plate. He also found that the radiation produced by the uranium minerals could, like x-rays, discharge an electroscope (Figure 3-11), by making the air conductive.

Marie Sklodowska Curie (1867–1934) then began a systematic investigation of "Becquerel radiation," using the electroscope as a test. She investigated many substances, to see if they were similar to uranium in producing rays. She found that natural pitchblende, an ore of uranium, is several times more active than purified uranium oxide.

With her husband, Professor Pierre Curie (1859–1906), she began to separate

Figure 3-11   *A simple electroscope. When an electric charge is present on the gold foil and its support, the two leaves of the foil separate, because of the repulsion of like electric charges.*

pitchblende into fractions and to determine their activity in discharging the electroscope. She isolated a fraction that was 400 times more active than uranium. This fraction consisted largely of bismuth sulfide. Since pure bismuth sulfide is not radioactive, she assumed that a new, strongly radioactive element, similar in chemical properties to bismuth, was present as a contaminant. This element, which she named *polonium*, was the first element discovered through its properties of radioactivity. In the same year, 1898, the Curies isolated another new radioactive element, which they named *radium*.

In 1899 Ernest Rutherford, working in McGill University, Montreal, Canada, reported that the radiation from uranium is of at least two distinct types, which he called alpha radiation and beta radiation. A French investigator, P. Villard, soon reported that a third kind of radiation, gamma radiation, is also emitted.

Alpha, Beta, and Gamma Rays.   The experiments showing the presence of three kinds of rays emitted by natural radioactive materials are illustrated by Figure 3-12. The rays, formed into a beam by passing along a narrow hole in a lead block, traverse a strong magnetic field. They are affected in three different ways, showing that the three kinds of rays have different electric charges. Alpha rays carry a positive electric charge. Beta rays carry a negative electric charge, and are deflected by a magnet in the opposite direction to the alpha rays. Gamma rays do not carry an electric charge, and are not deflected by the magnet.

Figure **3-12**

The deflection of alpha rays and beta rays by a magnetic field.

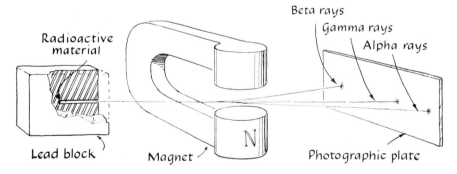

Rutherford found that the alpha rays, after they are slowed down, produce the gas helium. Further studies made by him showed definitely that the *alpha rays are the positively charged parts of helium atoms*, moving at high speeds. The *beta rays are electrons*, also moving at high speeds—they are similar in nature to the cathode rays produced in an electric discharge tube. *Gamma rays are a form of radiant energy, similar to visible light.* They are identical with x-rays produced in an x-ray tube operated at very high voltage.

The identification of the positively charged alpha particles with helium atoms was made by Rutherford by an experiment in which he allowed alpha particles to be shot through a thin metal foil into a chamber, and later was able to show that helium was present in the chamber. He could, moreover, correlate the amount of helium in the chamber with the number of alpha particles that had passed through the foil.

3-9.   The Discovery of the Nuclei of Atoms

In 1911 Rutherford carried out the experiment that showed that most of the mass of atoms is concentrated in particles that are very small in size compared with the atoms themselves.

His experiment consisted in bombarding a film of some substance, a piece of metal foil, with a stream of fast-moving alpha particles, and observing the direction in which the alpha particles rebound from the atoms. The nature of the experiment is indicated by the drawing in Figure 3-13. A piece of radium emits alpha particles in all directions. A narrow hole in a lead block defines a

Figure **3-13**

> *A diagram representing the experiment carried out by Rutherford, which showed that atoms contain very small, heavy atomic nuclei.*

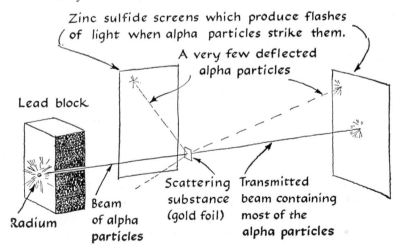

beam of the alpha particles. This beam of alpha particles then passes through the metal foil, and the directions in which the alpha particles continue to move are observed. The direction in which an alpha particle moves can be detected by use of a screen coated with zinc sulfide. When an alpha particle strikes the screen a flash of light is sent out.

If the atoms bombarded with alpha particles were solid throughout their volume we should expect all of the alpha particles in the beam to be deflected to some extent. Actually, however, Rutherford observed that most of the alpha particles passed through the metal foil without appreciable deflection: in one experiment, in which the alpha particles were sent through a gold foil 4000 Å thick, so that they penetrated about 1000 layers of atoms, only about one alpha particle in 100,000 was deflected. This one usually showed a great deflection, often through more than 90°, as indicated in the figure. When foil twice as thick was taken, it was found that about twice as many alpha particles showed deflection through large angles, with most of them still passing straight through.

These experimental results can be understood if the assumption is made that *most of the mass of the atom is concentrated into a very small particle,* which Rutherford called the atomic nucleus. If the alpha particle were also very small, then the chance of collision of these two very small particles as the alpha particle passed through the atom would be small. Most of the alpha particles could pass through the foil without striking any atomic nucleus, and these alpha particles would not then be deflected.

Since about one particle in 100,000 is deflected on passing through a foil consisting of 1000 atom layers, only about one particle in 100,000,000 would be deflected by a single layer of atoms. Rutherford concluded from this that the heavy nucleus has a cross-sectional area only 0.00000001 as great as the cross-sectional area of the atom, and hence that the diameter of the nucleus is only 1/10,000 as great as the diameter of the atom (the square root of 0.00000001 is 1/10,000).

Since atoms are a few Ångströms in diameter, the diameter of the nucleus is indicated to be approximately 10^{-4} Å or 10^{-12} cm.

The picture of the atom that has been developed from this experiment and similar experiments is indeed an extraordinary one. If we could magnify a piece of gold leaf by the linear factor 1,000,000,000—a billionfold—we would see it as an immense pile of atoms about two feet in diameter, each atom thus being about as big as a bushel basket. Practically the entire mass of each atom would, however, be concentrated in a single particle, the nucleus, about 0.001 inch in diameter, like an extremely small grain of sand. This nucleus would be surrounded by electrons, equally small, and moving very rapidly about. Rutherford's experiment would correspond to shooting through a pile of these bushel-basket atoms a stream of minute grains of sand, each of which would continue in a straight line unless it happened to collide with one of the minute grains of sand representing the nuclei of the atoms. It is obvious that the chance of such a collision would be very small. (The alpha particles are not deflected by the electrons in the atoms, because they are very much heavier than the electrons.)

Because of the new knowledge about the nature of atoms that it led to, Rutherford's experiment must be considered one of the most important experiments that any man has ever made.

3-10. The Quantum Theory of Light. The Photon

Light (electromagnetic radiation) plays such an important part in many of the phenomena of chemistry that it is necessary to discuss its nature and some of its properties.

The wave character of light was mentioned in Section 2-10. The wavelengths in the radio region are 1 meter or more, in the microwave region around 1 cm, in the infrared region about 8000 Å to 0.1 cm, in the visible region 3800 Å to 8000 Å, in the ultraviolet region about 100 Å to 3800 Å, in the x-ray region about 0.1 Å to 100 Å, and in the gamma-ray region less than about 0.1 Å. In the infrared, visible, and ultraviolet regions the wavelengths have been determined by the use of a prism or a ruled grating (Figure 3-14), and the wavelengths of x-rays and gamma rays have been determined by diffraction from a crystal grating (Section 2-10). The whole spectrum of light waves (electromagnetic waves) is shown in Figure 25-1, and the sequence of colors in the visible region is also shown, in the diagram next to the top one in this figure.

When gases are heated or are excited by the passage of an electric spark, the atoms and molecules in the gases emit light of definite wavelengths. The light that is emitted by an atom or molecule under these conditions is said to constitute its *emission spectrum*. The emission spectra of the alkali metals, mercury, and neon are shown in Figure 25-1. The emission spectra of elements, especially of the metals, can be used for identifying them, and *spectroscopic*

Figure **3-14**

A simple spectroscope. The light from the source is refracted into a spectrum by use of a glass prism; it could instead be diffracted into a spectrum by use of a ruled grating, in place of the prism.

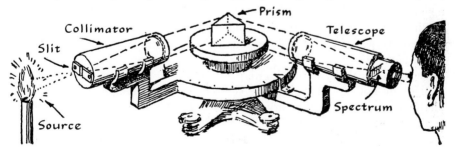

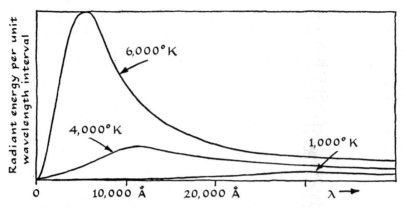

Figure 3-15

Curves showing the distribution of energy as a function of wave-length in the light in equilibrium with a hot body, at three different temperatures. Through the analysis of experimental curves of this sort Max Planck was led to the discovery of the quantum theory in 1900.

chemical analysis is an important technique of analytical chemistry. The *spectroscope* is an instrument, using a ruled grating or a prism, for analyzing light into its constituent wavelengths and determining their values. A simple spectroscope is shown in Figure 3-14. An instrument of this sort was used by the German chemist Robert Wilhelm Bunsen (1811–1899) to discover rubidium and cesium, in 1860. The instrument had been invented by the physicist Kirchhoff just the year before, and cesium was the first element to be discovered with its use.

During the last years of the nineteenth century it was found that the light that emerges through a hole from the hollow center of a hot body does not show characteristic emission lines, but has a smooth distribution of intensity with wavelength, characteristic of the temperature but independent of the nature of the hot body. This distribution is indicated, for three temperatures, in Figure 3-15. It is seen that at low temperatures, below 4000°K, most of the energy is in the infrared region and only a small amount is in the visible region, between 4000 Å and 8000 Å. At 6000°K the wavelength with the maximum amount of energy is about 5000 Å, and a large fraction of the emitted energy is in the visible region. This is the temperature of the surface of the sun.

The theoretical physicists who were interested in the problem of the emission of light by hot bodies, during the years before 1900, found that they were unable to account for the curves shown in Figure 3-15 on the basis of the emission and absorption of light by vibrating molecules in the hot body. The German physicist Max Planck (1858–1947) then discovered that a satisfactory theory could be formulated if the assumption were made that the hot body cannot emit or absorb light of a given wavelength in arbitrarily small amount, but must emit or absorb a certain quantum of energy of light of that wavelength. Although Planck's theory did not require that the light itself be considered as consisting of bundles of energy—*light quanta* or *photons*—it was soon pointed out by Einstein (in 1905) that other evidence supports this concept.

The amount of light energy of wavelength λ absorbed or emitted by a solid body in a single act was found by Planck to be proportional to the frequency v (equal to c/λ):

$$E = hv \tag{1}$$

In this equation E is the amount of energy of light with frequency v emitted or absorbed in a single act, and h is the constant of proportionality. *This constant h is a very important constant; it is one of the fundamental constants of nature, and the basis of the whole quantum theory.* It is called **Planck's constant.** Its value is

$$h = 6.6252 \times 10^{-27} \text{ erg sec} \tag{2}$$

(The units of h, erg sec, have the dimensions of energy times time, as is required by Equation 1.)

We see that light of short wavelength consists of large bundles of energy and light of long wavelength of small bundles of energy. Some of the experiments in which these bundles of energy express their magnitudes will be discussed in the following section.

The Photoelectric Effect. In 1887 the German physicist Heinrich Hertz (1857–1894), who discovered radiowaves, observed that a spark passes between two metal electrodes at a lower voltage when ultraviolet light is shining on the electrodes than when they are not illuminated. It was then discovered by J. J. Thomson in 1898 that negative electric charges are emitted by a metal surface on which ultraviolet light impinges. A simple experiment to show this effect is represented in Figure 3-16. An electroscope is negatively charged, and ultraviolet light is allowed to fall on the zinc plate in contact with it. The leaves of the electroscope fall, showing that the negative electric charge is being removed under the action of the ultraviolet light. If the electroscope has a large positive charge the leaves do not fall, showing that positive charges

Figure **3-16** *A simple experiment showing the photoelectric effect. A negative charge is emitted by a zinc plate upon which ultraviolet light impinges.*

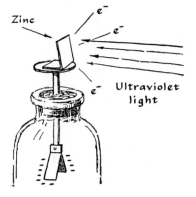

are not emitted under similar conditions. An uncharged electroscope becomes charged when the metal plate is illuminated with ultraviolet light, and the charge that remains on the leaves of the electroscope is a positive charge, showing that negative charges have left the metal.

J. J. Thomson was able to show that the negative electric charge that leaves the zinc plate under the influence of ultraviolet light consists of electrons. The emission of electrons by action of ultraviolet light or x-rays is called the *photoelectric effect*. The electrons that are given off by the metal plate are called *photoelectrons;* they are not different in character from other electrons.

A great deal was learned through study of the photoelectric effect. It was soon found that visible light falling on a zinc plate does not cause the emission of photoelectrons, whereas ultraviolet light with a wavelength shorter than about 3500 Å does cause their emission. The maximum wavelength that is effective is called the *photoelectric threshold.*

Substances differ in their photoelectric thresholds: the alkali metals are especially good photoelectric emitters, and their thresholds lie in the visible region; that for sodium is about 6500 Å, so that visible light is effective with this metal except at the red end of the spectrum.

It was discovered that the photoelectrons are emitted with extra kinetic energy, depending upon the wavelength of the light. An apparatus somewhat like the photoelectric cell shown in Figure 3-17 can be used for this purpose. In this apparatus the photoelectrons that are emitted when the metal is illuminated are collected by a collecting electrode, and the number of them that strike the electrode can be found by measuring the current that flows along the wire to the electrode. A potential difference can be applied between the electrode and the emitting metal. If the collecting electrode is given a slight negative potential, which requires work to be done on the electrons to transfer them from the emitting metal to the collecting electrode, the flow of photoelectrons to the collecting electrode is stopped if the incident light has a wavelength close to the threshold, but it continues if the incident light has a wavelength much shorter than the threshold wavelength. By increasing the negative charge on the collecting electrode the potential difference can be made great enough to stop the flow of photoelectrons to the electrode.

Figure **3-17** *A photoelectric cell.*

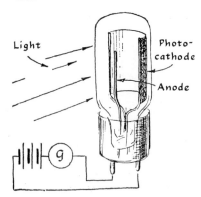

Light

Photo-cathode

Anode

g

These observations were explained by Einstein in 1905, by his theory of the photoelectric effect. He assumed that the light that impinges on the metal plate consists of photons with energy $h\nu$, and that when the light is absorbed by the metal all of the energy of one photon is converted into energy of a photoelectron. However, the electron must use a certain amount of energy to escape from the metal. This may be represented by the symbol E_i (the energy of ionizing the metal). The remaining energy is kinetic energy of the photoelectron. The *Einstein photoelectric equation* is

$$hv = E_i + \tfrac{1}{2}mv^2 \qquad (3)$$

This famous equation states that the energy of the light quantum, hv, is equal to the energy required to remove the electron from the metal, E_i, plus the kinetic energy imparted to the electron, $\tfrac{1}{2}mv^2$. The success of this equation in explaining the observations of the photoelectric effect was largely responsible for the acceptance of the idea of light quanta.

It is difficult to measure the velocity of the electrons directly. Instead, the energy quantity $\tfrac{1}{2}mv^2$ is measured by measuring the potential difference, V, which is necessary to keep the photoelectrons from striking the collecting electrode; the product of the potential difference V and the charge of the

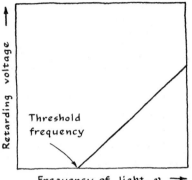

Figure **3-18** *Curve representing the result of experiments on the retarding voltage necessary to prevent the flow of photoelectrons to the anode, as a function of the frequency of light producing the photoelectrons. The threshold frequency is the frequency of light such that one quantum has just enough energy to remove an electron from the metal; a quantum of light with larger frequency is able to remove the electron from the metal and give it some kinetic energy.*

electron, e, is the amount of work done against the electrostatic field, and when V has just the value required to prevent the electrons from reaching the collecting plate the following relation holds:

$$eV = \tfrac{1}{2}mv^2$$

Introducing this in the preceding equation, we obtain

$$eV = hv - E_i$$

or

$$V = \frac{hv}{e} - \frac{E_i}{e} \qquad (4)$$

In Figure 3-18 this equation is plotted. The equation expresses a linear relation between the retarding voltage and the frequency of the light. The experimental observations lie on a line of just this sort. The intercept on the frequency axis, v_o, corresponds to the photoelectric threshold for the metal. The slope of the curve is seen from Equation 4 to be equal to h/e—that is, to the ratio of Planck's constant, h, to the charge of the electron, e. R. A.

Millikan in 1912 carried out careful measurements on the retarding voltage, in order to verify the Einstein equation. He used an apparatus similar to that shown in Figure 3-17, and his measurements led to a value of h/e which he could combine with his value of e to obtain a value for Planck's constant; this value for many years was the most accurate known.

The Photoelectric Cell.   The photoelectric cell is used in talking motion pictures, television, automatic door-openers, and many other practical applications. The cell may be made by depositing a thin layer of an alkali metal on the inner surface of a small vacuum tube, as shown in Figure 3-17. The collecting electrode is positively charged, so that the photoelectrons are attracted to it. Illumination of the metal surface by any radiation with wavelength shorter than the photoelectric threshold causes the emission of photoelectrons and a consequent flow of electric current through the circuit. The current may be registered on an ammeter. It is found that the magnitude of the current is proportional to the intensity of the light.

Example 1.   How much energy is there in one photon with wavelength 6500 Å?

Solution.   The amount of energy in a photon is $h\nu$, where h is Planck's constant and ν is the frequency of the light. The frequency of light of wavelength λ is c/λ; hence

$$\nu = \frac{3 \times 10^{10}}{6500 \times 10^{-8}} = 4.62 \times 10^{14} \text{ cycles/sec}$$

Thus we obtain

energy of photon $= h\nu = 6.625 \times 10^{-27}$
$$\times 4.62 \times 10^{14} = \mathbf{3.06 \times 10^{-12}} \textbf{ erg}$$

Example 2.   What retarding voltage would be required to stop the flow of photoelectrons produced by light of wavelength 6500 Å from a sodium metal surface?

Solution.   The photoelectric threshold of sodium metal is 6500 Å. Accordingly, the photoelectrons that are produced have no kinetic energy; the amount of energy in the photon is just enough to remove the electron from the metal. Hence an extremely small retarding potential would stop the flow of photoelectrons under these conditions.

Example 3.   What retarding potential would be required to stop the flow of photoelectrons in a photoelectric cell with sodium metal illuminated with light of wavelength 3250 Å?

Solution.   If, using the method of the solution of Example 1, we calculate the energy of a light quantum with wavelength 3250 Å, we obtain the value 6.12×10^{-12} erg. This result can be obtained, in fact, with little calculation by noting that this wavelength is just half that of the photoelectric threshold, 6500 Å; hence the frequency ν is twice as great and the energy $h\nu$ is also twice as great as in Example 1.

Of this total amount of energy in the light quantum, the amount 3.06×10^{-12} erg is used to remove the electron from the metal. The remaining amount, 3.06×10^{-12} erg, is kinetic energy of the photoelectron. The retarding potential that would slow the electron down to zero speed is such that its product with the charge of the electron is equal to this amount of energy:

$$eV = 3.06 \times 10^{-12} \text{ erg}$$

$$V = \frac{3.06 \times 10^{-12}}{4.80 \times 10^{-10}} = 6.38 \times 10^{-3} \text{ statvolt}$$

To convert statvolts into volts we multiply by 300 (1 statvolt = 300 volts); hence the retarding potential necessary to prevent the flow of photoelectrons in the sodium photoelectric cell illuminated with wavelength 3250 Å is $300 \times 6.38 \times 10^{-3} =$ **1.91 volts.**

The Production of X-rays. An x-ray tube is shown in Figure 2-25. In the tube electrons from the cathode (the lower electrode in the figure) are speeded up to high velocity by a potential difference V. Their kinetic energy then becomes equal to the energy quantity eV. When such a fast-moving electron strikes the anode it is quickly brought down to low velocity, perhaps to velocity zero. If it is brought to velocity zero, the whole of its energy eV is converted into x-radiation (light), with energy $h\nu$ and corresponding frequency ν. The frequency of this radiation can hence be calculated from the photoelectric equation, $eV = h\nu$. (The ionization energy of the metal, E_i, can be neglected in this case, because it is a small energy quantity in comparison with the others.) If the electron is not slowed down completely the frequency of the x-ray quantum that is emitted will be somewhat smaller than the limiting value.

This process of creation of photons from the energy of fast-moving electrons is called the *inverse photoelectric effect.*

Example 4. An x-ray tube is operated at 50,000 volts. What is the short-wavelength limit of the x-rays that are produced?

Solution. The energy of an electron that strikes the anode in the x-ray tube is eV. The value of e is 4.80×10^{-10} statcoulombs and that of V is $50,000/300 = 166.7$ statvolts. The value of eV is accordingly $4.80 \times 10^{-10} \times 166.7 = 8.01 \times 10^{-8}$ erg. This is equal to $h\nu$; hence for ν we have

$$\nu = \frac{8.01 \times 10^{-8}}{6.625 \times 10^{-27}} = 1.208 \times 10^{19} \text{ cycles/sec}$$

The wavelength λ is obtained by dividing the velocity of light by this quantity:

$$\lambda = \frac{c}{\nu} = \frac{3 \times 10^{10}}{1.208 \times 10^{19}} = 2.48 \times 10^{-9} \text{ cm} = \textbf{0.248 Å}$$

Hence the short-wavelength limit of an x-ray tube operated at 50,000 volts is calculated to be 0.248 Å.

It is interesting to note that the preceding calculation can be simplified by combining all the steps into a single equation:

$$\text{short-wavelength limit (in Å)} = \frac{12,398 \text{ Å volt}}{\text{accelerating potential (in volts)}} \tag{5}$$

This equation states that a quantum of light with wavelength 12,398 Å (in the near infrared) has the same energy as an electron that has been accelerated by a potential difference of 1 volt. This energy quantity is sometimes called 1 *electron volt*, with abbreviation 1 eV.

The relations among the commonly used units of energy are summarized in Appendices I and II of this book.

Equation 5 may be derived in the following way. From the equations $\lambda = c/\nu$ and $h\nu = eV$, we obtain $\lambda = ch/eV$. Replacing c, h, and e by their numerical values, $c = 3 \times 10^{10}$ cm sec^{-1}, $h = 6.625 \times 10^{-27}$ erg sec, and $e = 4.80 \times 10^{-10}$ erg statvolt^{-1}, we write

$$\lambda = \frac{3 \times 10^{10} \times 6.625 \times 10^{-27}}{4.80 \times 10^{-10}V} = \frac{4.15 \times 10^{-7} \text{ cm statvolt}}{V}$$

The statvolt is 300 volts; hence $1/V$ can be replaced by 300/(accelerating potential in volts); and the factor 10^8 is needed if λ is to be in Å rather than cm. Hence we obtain

$$\lambda \text{ (in Å)} = \frac{4.15 \times 10^{-7} \times 300 \times 10^8}{\text{accelerating potential in volts}}$$

$$= \frac{12,398 \text{ Å volt}}{\text{accelerating potential in volts}}$$

Example 5. A beam of light with wavelength 6500 Å and carrying the energy 1×10^5 ergs per second falls on a photoelectric cell, and is completely used in the production of photoelectrons. (This is about the energy of the light from the sun and sky on a bright day that strikes an area of 1 cm^2.) What is the magnitude of the photoelectric current that then flows in the circuit of which the photoelectric cell is a part?

Solution. The energy of one quantum of light with wavelength 6500 Å is 3.06×10^{-12} erg. Hence there are $1 \times 10^5/3.06 \times 10^{-12} = 0.327 \times 10^{17}$ photons in the amount of light carrying 1×10^5 ergs of radiant energy, and this number of photons impinges on the metal of the photoelectric cell every second. The same number of photoelectrons would be produced. Multiplying by the charge of the electron, 4.80×10^{-10} statcoulomb, we obtain 1.57×10^7 statcoulombs as the amount of electric charge transferred from the sodium metal surface in the photoelectric cell to the collecting electrode each second. Dividing by 3×10^9, the number of statcoulombs in one coulomb, we obtain 5.22×10^{-3} as the number of coulombs transferred per second. One ampere is a flow of electricity at the rate of 1 coulomb per second; hence the current that is produced by the beam of light is 5.22×10^{-3} amp—that is, **5.22 milliamperes.**

3-11.   The Wave Character of the Electron

Until 1924 the observed properties of the electron were considered to justify describing it as a small electrically charged particle, similar except for size to a ball bearing carrying an electric charge. In that year the wave character of the electron was discovered by the French physicist Louis de Broglie (born 1892). While making a theoretical study of the quantum theory, to serve as his thesis for the doctor's degree from the University of Paris, he found that a striking analogy between the properties of electrons and the properties of photons could be recognized if a moving electron were to be assigned a wavelength. This wavelength is now called the de Broglie wavelength of the electron.

The equation for the wavelength of the electron is

$$\lambda = \frac{h}{mv} \tag{6}$$

In this equation λ is the wavelength of the electron, h is Planck's constant, m is the mass of the electron, and v is the velocity of the electron. It is seen that according to this equation a stationary electron has infinite wavelength, and the wavelength decreases with increase in the velocity of the electron.

Example 6.   What is the wavelength of an electron with 13.6 eV of kinetic energy?

   Solution.   One volt is 1/300 statvolt. The energy of a 13.6-eV electron is accordingly

$$E = 13.6 \times 4.80 \times 10^{-10}/300 = 0.218 \times 10^{-10} \text{ erg}$$

This is equal to $\frac{1}{2}mv^2$, the kinetic energy of an electron moving with velocity v; accordingly,

$$mv^2 = 0.436 \times 10^{-10} \text{ erg}$$

Multiplying both sides of this equation by m, we obtain

$$m^2v^2 = 0.436 \times 10^{-10} \times m = 0.436 \times 10^{-10}$$
$$\times 9.107 \times 10^{-28} = 3.96 \times 10^{-38}$$

By taking the square root of each side of this equation we obtain

$$mv = 1.99 \times 10^{-19} \text{ g cm sec}^{-1}$$

By use of the de Broglie equation we can now obtain the value for the wavelength:

$$\lambda = \frac{h}{mv} = \frac{6.624 \times 10^{-27} \text{ g cm}^2 \text{ sec}^{-1}}{1.99 \times 10^{-19} \text{ g cm sec}^{-1}} = 3.33 \times 10^{-8} \text{ cm} = \mathbf{3.33} \text{ Å}$$

Accordingly, we have found that the de Broglie wavelength of an electron that has been accelerated by a potential difference of 13.6 V is 3.33 Å.

We can now calculate easily the wavelength of an electron with 100 times as much kinetic energy—that is, an electron that has been accelerated by a potential difference of 1360 V. Since the energy is proportional to the square of the velocity, such an electron has a velocity ten times that of a 13.6-eV electron, and, according to the de Broglie equation, its wavelength is $1/10$ as great. Thus the wavelength of a 1360-eV electron is 0.333 Å.

The Analogy Between the Photon and the Electron. One part of the argument carried out by de Broglie in his discovery of the wavelength of the electron can be easily presented. The energy of a photon with frequency ν is $h\nu$. The mass of the photon is related to the energy by the Einstein equation

$$mc^2 = h\nu$$

where m represents the mass of the photon. Dividing each side of this equation by c, we obtain

$$mc = \frac{h\nu}{c}$$

In this equation ν/c can be replaced by $1/\lambda$, giving

$$mc = \frac{h}{\lambda}$$

or

$$\lambda = \frac{h}{mc}$$

De Broglie pointed out that the same equation might be applied to an electron, by using m for the mass of the electron instead of the mass of the photon, and replacing c, the velocity of the photon, by v, the velocity of the electron. In this way the de Broglie equation is obtained.

The Direct Experimental Verification of the Wavelength of the Electron. The wave character of moving electrons was established beyond question by the work of the American physicist C. J. Davisson (1881–1958) and the English physicist G. P. Thomson (born 1892). These investigators found that electrons that are scattered by crystals produce a diffraction pattern, similar to that produced by x-rays scattered by crystals (Section 2-10), and, moreover, that the diffraction pattern, interpreted by the Bragg law, corresponds to the wavelength given by the de Broglie equation.

The penetrating power of electrons through matter is far less than that of x-rays with the same wavelength. It is accordingly necessary to reflect the beam of x-rays from the surface of a crystal (as was done by Davisson and his collaborators, using a single crystal of nickel), or to shoot a stream of high-speed electrons through a very thin crystal or layer of crystalline powder (as was done by Thomson).

The structure of crystals can be investigated by the electron-diffraction method as well as by the x-ray-diffraction method. The electron-diffraction method has been especially useful in studying the structure of very thin films on the surface of a crystal. For example, it has been shown that when argon is adsorbed on a clean face of a nickel crystal the argon atoms occupy only one-quarter of the positions formed by triangles of nickel atoms (in the octahedral face of the cubic closest-packed crystal; Figure 2-5). The structure of very thin films of metal oxide that are formed on the surface of metals, and that protect them against further corrosion, has been studied by this method.

The electron-diffraction method is also very useful for determining the structure of gas molecules. The way in which the diffraction pattern is formed is illustrated by Figure 2-23, which corresponds to the scattering of waves by a diatomic molecule. The molecules in a gas have different orientations, and the diffraction pattern is accordingly somewhat blurred. It consists of a series of rings. Knowledge of the wavelength of the electrons and measurement of the diameters of these rings permit calculation of the interatomic distances in the molecules. Since the discovery of the electron-diffraction method the structures of several hundred molecules have been determined in this way.

The Wavelength of the Neutron. Neutron Diffraction. Not only electrons, but also protons and neutrons (Section 3-5) and other particles have wave character. Their wavelength is given by the de Broglie equation with use of the appropriate value for the mass. The relative scattering powers of atoms of different kinds in a crystal for neutrons are different from those for x-rays. In consequence, the study of the neutron diffraction patterns of crystals gives information supplementing that given by the x-ray diffraction patterns. Neutron diffraction has been found to be especially valuable for locating hydrogen atoms in a crystal containing heavier atoms and for the study of magnetic substances.

3-12. What Is Light? What Is an Electron?

During recent years many people have asked the following questions: Does light *really* consist of waves, or of particles? Is the electron *really* a particle, or is it a wave?

These questions cannot be answered by one of the two alternatives. Light is the name that we have given to describe a part of nature. The name refers to all of the properties that light has, to all of the phenomena that are observed in a system containing light. Some of the properties of light resemble those of waves, and can be described in terms of a wavelength. Other properties of light resemble those of particles, and can be described in terms of a light quantum, having a certain amount of energy, $h\nu$, and a certain mass, $h\nu/c^2$. A beam of light is neither a sequence of waves nor a stream of particles; it is both.

In the same way, an electron is neither a particle nor a wave, in the ordinary sense. In many ways the behavior of electrons is similar to that expected of small particles, with mass m and electric charge $-e$. But electrons differ from ordinary particles, such as ball bearings, in that they also behave as though they had wave character, with wavelength given by the de Broglie equation. The electron, like the photon, has to be described as having the character both of a particle and of a wave.

After the first period of adjustment to these new ideas about the nature of light and of electrons, scientists became accustomed to them, and found that they could usually predict when, in a certain experiment, the behavior of a beam of light would be determined mainly by its wavelength, and when it would be determined by the energy and mass of the photon; that is, they would know when it was convenient to consider light as consisting of waves, and when to consider it as consisting of particles, the photons. Similarly, they learned when it was convenient to consider an electron as a particle, and when as a wave. In some experiments the wave character and the particle character both contribute significantly, and it is then necessary to carry out a careful theoretical treatment, using the equations of quantum mechanics, in order to predict how the light or the electron will behave.

You may ask two other questions: Do electrons exist? What do they look like?

The answer to the first question is that electrons do exist: "electron" is the name that scientists have used in discussing certain phenomena, such as the beam in the electric discharge tube studied by J. J. Thomson, the carrier of the unit electric charge on the oil drops in Millikan's apparatus, the part that is added to the neutral fluorine atom to convert it into a fluoride ion. The second question—what does the electron look like?—cannot be answered. No one knows how to look at an electron—it is too small to be seen by scattering ordinary visible light from it, and unless somebody discovers some better way of studying nature than is now known, this question will remain unanswered. However, it is possible to say some things about what the proton and the neutron look like. By the study of the scattering of rapidly moving electrons by protons and neutrons information has been obtained about the distribution in space of the electric charge in these particles. The results of these studies are described in Section 29-4.

EXERCISES

3-3. State the law of attraction or repulsion between two electrically charged particles. How is the force between the two charged particles changed

(a) if the distance between them is doubled?
(b) if the charge of one particle is doubled?
(c) if the charges of both particles are doubled?

3-4. Discuss the motion of an electron moving transversely between two parallel plates carrying opposite electric charges. Also discuss the motion of an electron moving transversely between the poles of a magnet.

3-5. Describe the electromagnetic pump, used to pump sodium-potassium alloy in nuclear power plants. Why is the electromagnetic pump not used as a water pump?

3-6. Describe the experiments of Jean Perrin and J. J. Thomson that led to the discovery of the electron.

3-7. Calculate the velocity with which the electrons would move in the apparatus used by J. J. Thomson, operated at an accelerating voltage of 6000 V. Assume that each electron has kinetic energy equal to eV, where e is the charge of the electron in statcoulombs and V is the accelerating potential in statvolts.

3-8. Before a correction was made in the charge of the electron, the formula for the minimum wavelength of x-rays produced by an x-ray tube at voltage V was $12345/V$ instead of $12398/V$ (Example 4, Section 3-10). By what percent has the charge on the electron been corrected? (Answer: 0.43%.)

3-9. Describe Millikan's oil-drop experiment. Why is a knowledge of the value of the viscosity of air needed in order for the value of the charge of the electron to be calculated from the measurements?

3-10. Briefly summarize the history of the discovery of x-rays by Röntgen, the discovery of radioactivity by Becquerel, and the discovery of polonium and radium by the Curies.

3-11. Describe the Rutherford experiment, and explain why the observations indicate that most of the mass of an atom is concentrated in a very small particle, the nucleus.

3-12. The principal alpha particles from radium have an energy of 4.79 MeV (4.79 million electron volts). With what velocity are they moving? What is the ratio of their velocity to the velocity of light? The mass of the alpha particle is 6.66×10^{-24} g. (Answer: Velocity $= 1.5 \times 10^9$ cm/sec.) (Note that if the velocity of a particle is less than 10% of the velocity of light the expression $\frac{1}{2}mv^2$ for its kinetic energy can be used with error less than 1%. For larger values of the velocity the theory of relativity must be used to obtain the correct answers.)

3-13. Calculate the energy, in ergs, of alpha particles of radium, which have energy 4.79 MeV. The nucleus of an atom of gold has the electric charge $79e$, in which e is the magnitude of the charge of the electron. The alpha particle has the charge $2e$. At what distance is the mutual potential energy of the alpha particle and the nucleus of an atom of gold (equal, in ergs, to the product of the two charges, in statcoulombs, divided by the distance between them, in centimeters) equal to the kinetic energy of the alpha particle? This radius may be taken as indicating how closely the alpha particle must approach the atom of gold in order to experience a large deflection. (Answer: 4.75×10^{-12} cm.)

3-14. What is the minimum wavelength of the x-rays emitted by a million-volt x-ray tube? (Answer: 0.012398 Å.)

3-15. According to the law of gravitation, the gravitational force of attraction between two particles with masses m_1 and m_2 a distance r apart is Gm_1m_2/r^2, where G, the constant of gravitation, has been found by experiment to have the value 6.673×10^{-8}; that is, the force of attraction between two particles each with mass 1 g and the distance 1 cm apart is 6.673×10^{-8} dyne.

(a) Calculate the force of electrostatic attraction between an electron and a proton 10 Å apart.

(b) Calculate the force of gravitational attraction between an electron and a proton 10 Å apart. What is the relationship of the electrostatic attraction to the gravitational attraction at this distance?

(c) What is the dependence on distance of the ratio of electrostatic attraction and gravitational attraction of an electron and a proton?

[Answer: (a) 2.31×10^{-5} dyne; (b) 1.02×10^{-44} dyne; Ratio 2.27×10^{39}.]

3-16. While the ancient Greeks argued about the existence or nonexistence of atoms of matter, they appear never to have concerned themselves about "atoms" (i.e., quanta) of energy. Can you suggest an explanation of their failure to do so?

CHAPTER 4

Elements, Elementary Substances,

and Compounds

One of the most important parts of chemical theory is the division of substances into the two classes *elementary substances* and *compounds*. This division was achieved about a century and a half ago, principally through the efforts of the French chemist Lavoisier.

The arguments used by Lavoisier and other early chemists to decide whether a substance is an elementary substance or a compound have been briefly discussed in Chapter 1. During recent years more straightforward and definite methods have been found for identifying elementary substances. These methods, developed by physicists, involve the determination of the electric charge of the atomic nuclei (the number of unit electric charges). The power of the new methods has caused the definitions of the words element, elementary substance, and compound to be changed in recent years.

4-1. The Chemical Elements

A kind of matter consisting of atoms that all have nuclei with the same electric charge is called an **element.**

For example, all of the atoms that contain nuclei with the charge $+e$, each nucleus having one electron attached to it to neutralize its charge, comprise the element hydrogen, and all of the atoms that contain nuclei with the charge $+92e$ comprise the element uranium.

All pure substances can be divided into two classes: elementary substances and compounds.

*An **elementary substance** is a substance that is composed of atoms of one element only.* An elementary substance is commonly called an element.

Hydrogen, carbon, nitrogen, oxygen, sodium, iron, copper, zinc, lead, tin, silver, gold, chlorine, iodine, sulfur, and phosphorus are well-known elements; 103 different elements in all are known at the present time.

*A **compound** is a substance that is composed of atoms of two or more different elements.* These atoms of two or more different elements must be present in a definite numerical ratio, since compounds are defined as having a definite composition (Sections 1-3, 2-2).

Common salt, sugar, and baking soda are well-known compounds. Common salt contains atoms of two elements—atoms of sodium and atoms of chlorine. Sugar contains atoms of carbon, hydrogen, and oxygen, and baking soda contains atoms of sodium, hydrogen, carbon, and oxygen. Several hundred thousand different chemical compounds are now known, and many new ones are made every year.

Atomic Number.   The electric charge of the nucleus of an atom, in units equal to the charge on the proton, is called the *atomic number* of the atom. It is usually given the symbol Z, the electric charge of a nucleus with atomic number Z being Z times e, with the charge of the proton equal to e, and the charge of the electron equal to $-e$. Thus the simplest atom, that of hydrogen, has atomic number 1; it consists of a nucleus with electric charge e, and an electron with electric charge $-e$.

The elements that have so far been discovered or made by scientists represent all the atomic numbers from 1 to 103.

The Assignment of Atomic Numbers to the Elements.   Soon after the discovery of the electron as a constituent of matter it was recognized that elements might be assigned atomic numbers, representing the number of electrons in an atom of each element, but the way of doing this correctly was not known until 1913. In that year, H. G. J. Moseley (1887–1915), a young English physicist working in the University of Manchester, found that the atomic number of any element could be determined by the study of the x-rays emitted by an x-ray tube containing the element. By a few months of experimental work he was able to assign their correct atomic numbers to many elements.

A brief account of Moseley's experiment is given in Section 4-9.

Isotopes.   It was mentioned in Chapter 3 that sometimes different atomic nuclei (with different mass) have the same electric charge. For example, the proton has electric charge $+e$, and the deuteron, which is built of a proton and a neutron, also has electric charge $+e$. The two nuclei differ in their mass, the deuteron having about twice the mass of the proton. When the proton combines with an electron a hydrogen atom is formed. Similarly, when a deuteron combines with an electron a hydrogen atom is formed that differs from the light hydrogen atom in having a heavier nucleus. A third kind of hydrogen atom is also known. Its nucleus, called the *triton*, consists of a proton and two neutrons. Each of these three nuclei contains one proton, and hence has the electric charge $+e$ and atomic number 1.

The *protium* atom, containing a proton as its nucleus, the *deuterium* atom, containing a deuteron as its nucleus, and the *tritium* atom, containing a triton as its nucleus, are three different kinds of hydrogen atoms, all equal in atomic number ($Z = 1$) and electric charge ($+e$) of their nuclei, but differing in mass. These three kinds of atoms are called the *isotopes* of hydrogen.*

The **isotopes** *of an element are atoms whose nuclei contain the same number of protons (equal to the atomic number of the element) but different numbers of neutrons.*

All known elements have two or more isotopes. In some cases (such as aluminum) only one isotope occurs naturally, the others being unstable. The maximum number of stable isotopes of any element is 10, possessed by tin. Natural hydrogen consists almost entirely of protium, with about 0.02% of deuterium, which is a stable isotope. Tritium is unstable, but a small amount, formed by cosmic rays in the upper atmosphere (Section 29-2), is found in natural hydrogen.

The chemical properties of all the isotopes of an element are essentially the same. These properties are determined in the main by the atomic number of the nucleus, and not by its mass.

The different nuclear species, such as the proton, the deuteron, etc., are called *nuclides*. The word nuclide is used in referring to a kind of nucleus and the word isotope in referring to a kind of atom (the nucleus plus one or more electrons, to neutralize the nuclear charge).

The Names and Symbols of the Elements. The names of the elements are given in order of atomic number in Table 4-1. The chemical symbols of the elements, used as abbreviations for their names, are also given in the table. These symbols are usually the initial letters of the names, plus another letter when necessary. In some cases the initial letters of Latin names are used: Na for sodium (natrium), K for potassium (kalium), Fe for iron (ferrum), Cu for copper (cuprum), Ag for silver (argentum), Au for gold (aurum), Hg for mercury (hydrargyrum), Sn for tin (stannum), Sb for antimony (stibium), W for tungsten (wolfram), and Pb for lead (plumbum). The system of chemical symbols was proposed by the Swedish chemist Jöns Jakob Berzelius (1779–1848) in 1811.

* The word isotope is from the Greek *isos*, the same, and *topos*, place; isotopes occupy the same place in the sequence of elements and in the periodic table (Chapter 7). The first indication of the existence of isotopes was obtained in the course of studies of radioactive substances. The American chemist Theodore William Richards in 1914 found the atomic weight of lead in an ore of uranium to be about 206 and that of lead in an ore of thorium to be about 208. J. J. Thomson discovered neon 20 and neon 22 in 1913 by use of a simple form of the mass spectrograph (Section 5-5). The name isotope was proposed by F. W. Aston, who improved the mass spectrograph and used it to determine the isotopic composition of many elements.

Table **4-1**

The Names, Atomic Numbers, and Symbols of the Elements

ATOMIC NUMBER	SYMBOL	ELEMENT	ATOMIC NUMBER	SYMBOL	ELEMENT
1	H	Hydrogen	53	I	Iodine
2	He	Helium	54	Xe	Xenon
3	Li	Lithium	55	Cs	Cesium
4	Be	Beryllium	56	Ba	Barium
5	B	Boron	57	La	Lanthanum
6	C	Carbon	58	Ce	Cerium
7	N	Nitrogen	59	Pr	Praseodymium
8	O	Oxygen	60	Nd	Neodymium
9	F	Fluorine	61	Pm	Promethium
10	Ne	Neon	62	Sm	Samarium
11	Na	Sodium	63	Eu	Europium
12	Mg	Magnesium	64	Gd	Gadolinium
13	Al	Aluminum	65	Tb	Terbium
14	Si	Silicon	66	Dy	Dysprosium
15	P	Phosphorus	67	Ho	Holmium
16	S	Sulfur	68	Er	Erbium
17	Cl	Chlorine	69	Tm	Thulium
18	Ar	Argon	70	Yb	Ytterbium
19	K	Potassium	71	Lu	Lutetium
20	Ca	Calcium	72	Hf	Hafnium
21	Sc	Scandium	73	Ta	Tantalum
22	Ti	Titanium	74	W	Tungsten
23	V	Vanadium	75	Re	Rhenium
24	Cr	Chromium	76	Os	Osmium
25	Mn	Manganese	77	Ir	Iridium
26	Fe	Iron	78	Pt	Platinum
27	Co	Cobalt	79	Au	Gold
28	Ni	Nickel	80	Hg	Mercury
29	Cu	Copper	81	Tl	Thallium
30	Zn	Zinc	82	Pb	Lead
31	Ga	Gallium	83	Bi	Bismuth
32	Ge	Germanium	84	Po	Polonium
33	As	Arsenic	85	At	Astatine
34	Se	Selenium	86	Rn	Radon
35	Br	Bromine	87	Fr	Francium
36	Kr	Krypton	88	Ra	Radium
37	Rb	Rubidium	89	Ac	Actinium
38	Sr	Strontium	90	Th	Thorium
39	Y	Yttrium	91	Pa	Protactinium
40	Zr	Zirconium	92	U	Uranium
41	Nb	Niobium	93	Np	Neptunium
42	Mo	Molybdenum	94	Pu	Plutonium
43	Tc	Technetium	95	Am	Americium
44	Ru	Ruthenium	96	Cm	Curium
45	Rh	Rhodium	97	Bk	Berkelium
46	Pd	Palladium	98	Cf	Californium
47	Ag	Silver	99	Es	Einsteinium
48	Cd	Cadmium	100	Fm	Fermium
49	In	Indium	101	Mv	Mendelevium
50	Sn	Tin	102	No	Nobelium
51	Sb	Antimony	103	Lw	Lawrencium
52	Te	Tellurium			

The elements are shown in a special arrangement, the *periodic table*, at the front of the book and in Table 7-1, and are also given in alphabetical order in Table 5-1, as well as in the order of their atomic numbers in Table 4-1.

You may find it useful at this stage in your study of chemistry to memorize the atomic numbers, names, and symbols of the first eighteen elements.

A symbol is used to represent an atom of an element, as well as the element itself. The symbol I represents the element iodine, and also may be used to mean the elementary substance. However, I_2 is the customary formula for the elementary substance, because it is known that elementary iodine consists of molecules containing two atoms in the solid and liquid states as well as in the gaseous state (except at very high temperature).

An isotope or nuclide is often represented by the symbol of the element with the atomic number as a subscript to the left and the mass number as a super-script to the right; for example, $_6C^{13}$ is the isotope of carbon with mass number 13 (6 protons and 7 neutrons in the nucleus). Often the atomic number is omitted, and the isotope or nuclide is referred to as C^{13}, C 13, or carbon 13. Sometimes the neutron number is introduced as a right subscript: $_6C_7^{13}$, for example.

These symbols are especially useful in discussing nuclear reactions. The symbol n or $_0n_1^1$ is used for the neutron, and the symbol p or $_1p_0^1$ for the proton. As an example we may write the equation for the reaction of a nitrogen-14 nucleus and a neutron to form a carbon-14 nucleus and a proton:

$$_7N_7^{14} + {}_0n_1^1 \longrightarrow {}_6C_8^{14} + {}_1p_0^1$$

Many nuclear reactions will be mentioned in Chapter 30.

Illustrative Exercises

4-1. The atomic number of oxygen is 8. What is the electric charge on the nucleus of the oxygen atom, in units e? How many electrons are there in the oxygen atom? Note that every electrically neutral atom must have a number of electrons around the nucleus equal to the atomic number of the atom; the negative charges of these electrons then exactly neutralize (balance) the total positive charge, $+Ze$, of the nucleus.

4-2. (a) What is the complete symbol (showing atomic number, mass number, and neutron number) of uranium 235? (b) Under certain conditions the nuclide U^{235} undergoes fission (splitting into two or three nuclides, Chapter 30). If a U^{235} nucleus reacts with a neutron to form two neutrons and two nuclei, one of which is xenon 144, what is the other? Write a nuclear equation for this reaction, and show that electric charge, proton number, and neutron number are conserved. (c) Xenon 144 is unstable; it decomposes by convert-ing a neutron into a proton, which is retained, and an electron, which is emitted. What is the nuclide that is formed? Write the nuclear reaction.

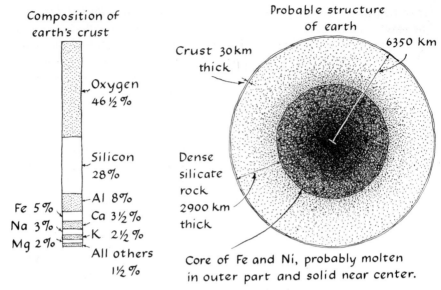

Figure 4-1

The composition of the earth's crust.

4-2.   The Distribution of the Elements

You may be interested to know how the different elements are distributed throughout the earth and the universe.

The structure of the earth, as indicated by the analysis of evidence from records of earthquakes, study of rocks, and other observations, is shown in Figure 4-1. There is an outer crust, about 30 km thick, then an inner shell of denser rock, and a metallic core.

The estimated composition of the outer crust of the earth is shown in Figure 4-1 and the occurrence of the ten most common elements in it is given in Table 4-2.

Table **4-2**

The Estimated Composition by Weight of the Earth's Crust*

Oxygen	46.5%	Sodium	3.0%
Silicon	28.0%	Potassium	2.5%
Aluminum	8.1%	Magnesium	2.2%
Iron	5.1%	Titanium	0.5%
Calcium	3.5%	Hydrogen	0.2%

* This is the composition of the solid (rocky) crust of the earth, not including the ocean and the atmosphere. The ocean contains 85.79% oxygen, 10.67% hydrogen, 1.14% sodium, 2.07% chlorine, 0.14% magnesium, and 0.19% other elements.

In some regions of the earth's surface there are denser rocks that are thought to be like the material in the shell under the earth's crust. On the assumption that the composition of these rocks is the same as the composition of this shell, and that the metallic core of the earth is an iron-nickel alloy resembling the metallic meteorites, the percentages given in Table 4-3 have been calculated for the distribution of elements in the whole earth.

Table 4-3

The Estimated Composition by Weight of the Entire Earth

Iron	39.8%	Calcium	2.5%
Oxygen	27.7%	Aluminum	1.8%
Silicon	14.5%	Sulfur	0.6%
Magnesium	8.7%	Sodium	0.4%
Nickel	3.2%	All others	0.8%

Astronomers have studied the light from the sun and stars, and have found that the same elements are present in these heavenly bodies as in the earth, but in different relative amounts. The sun and the stars contain great amounts of the two lightest elements, hydrogen and helium, which are relatively rare in the earth.

4-3. The Formulas of Compounds

Compounds are represented by formulas. These formulas are made up of the symbols of the elements contained in the compounds. For example, NaCl is the formula for sodium chloride, which consists of equal numbers of sodium and chlorine atoms. When the atoms of the different elements are not present in the compound in equal numbers, their ratios are indicated by the use of subscripts. Thus H_2O is the formula for water, each molecule of which contains two hydrogen atoms and one oxygen atom.

If the true molecular structure of a substance is known, it is proper to indicate it in the formula. Hydrogen peroxide is a compound of hydrogen and oxygen which differs from water in that two hydrogen atoms and two oxygen atoms are contained in its molecule. The formula for hydrogen peroxide is H_2O_2, and not HO.

Sometimes parentheses are used in a formula, to indicate how the atoms are grouped together in the molecule or crystal. For example, the formula $Ca(OH)_2$ means one calcium atom, two oxygen atoms, and two hydrogen atoms. Also, a number may appear in front of a group of symbols; it serves as a factor. For example, the substance $Na_2CO_3 \cdot 10H_2O$ consists of ten water molecules (twenty hydrogen atoms and ten oxygen atoms) in addition to two sodium atoms, one carbon atom, and three oxygen atoms.

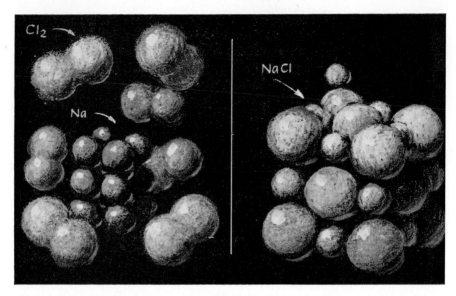

Figure 4-2

At the left there are represented chlorine gas molecules (Cl_2) and metallic sodium, and at the right the same system after chemical reaction, with the formation of common salt, sodium chloride.

Atomic Ratios in Compounds.   In the crystal of sodium chloride there are atoms of two different kinds, arranged in the regular pattern shown at the right of Figure 4-2. The smaller atoms are those of sodium and the larger ones are those of chlorine. The surface layers shown, which are the cube faces of the sodium chloride crystal, contain both kinds of atoms in equal numbers, when the pattern is repeated a great number of times.

The numerical ratio of sodium and chlorine atoms in solid sodium chloride is fixed at 1:1 by the structure of the crystal, and that for sodium chloride gas is likewise fixed at 1:1 by the structure of the gas molecule, which contains one sodium atom and one chlorine atom. Similarly the numerical ratio of hydrogen atoms and oxygen atoms in water is fixed at 2:1 by the structure of the water molecule. *It is the definite structure of crystals and molecules that causes compounds in general to contain elements in definite atomic ratios.*

Illustrative Exercises

4-3.   The formula of ethyl alcohol is C_2H_5OH. What elements are present in this compound? How many atoms of each element are there in one molecule of the compound?

4-4.   The front layer of atoms in the drawing of the crystal of sodium chloride, Figure 4-2, contains four sodium atoms and five chlorine atoms. Show that if this layer were very large (say 1000 atoms on edge) the ratio of the numbers of sodium and chlorine atoms would be very close to 1:1, and not 4:5. (Note that sodium atoms and chlorine atoms alternate in each row.)

4-5. Write the formula for the substance nitric acid; its molecule contains one hydrogen atom, one nitrogen atom, and three oxygen atoms.

4-4.   The Atomic and Molecular Nature of Chemical Reactions

In Chapter 1 it was pointed out that a chemical reaction is a process in which certain substances, the reactants, are converted into other substances, the products. We shall now discuss chemical reactions in relation to the atomic theory.

During a **chemical reaction** *there occurs a* **rearrangement of atoms.**

For example, let us consider again the reaction of sodium and chlorine to form sodium chloride. The metal sodium consists of sodium atoms arranged in a regular structure which is similar to that described in Chapter 2 for copper, but is not identical with it. The gas chlorine consists of molecules, as shown in Figure 4-2. During the reaction of sodium and chlorine the sodium atoms in the metal separate from one another and the two chlorine atoms in the molecules of chlorine separate from one another. The atoms of sodium and chlorine then arrange themselves in a new structure, in which the atoms

Figure **4-3**

At the left there is represented a gas containing hydrogen molecules (H_2) and oxygen molecules (O_2), and at the right the same system after chemical reaction, leading to the formation of water molecules, H_2O.

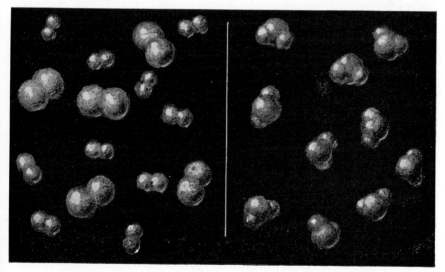

of the two kinds alternate, as shown at the right in Figure 4-2. This arrangement of sodium and chlorine atoms constitutes the new substance, sodium chloride, that has formed during the chemical reaction.

The gas hydrogen consists of molecules H_2. Oxygen also consists of molecules O_2. If two flasks, one containing hydrogen and one containing oxygen, are connected together, the two gases mix with each other quietly, to produce a gaseous mixture (left side of Figure 4-3). If, however, a flame is brought into contact with the gaseous mixture a violent explosion occurs, and afterward the presence of water can be shown. This explosion is the result of the combination of hydrogen and oxygen to form a new substance, water (right side of Figure 4-3), with the emission also of heat and light.

4-5.   How to Balance the Equation for a Chemical Reaction

The chemical reaction of the formation of water from hydrogen and oxygen can be represented by an equation:

$$2H_2 + O_2 \longrightarrow 2H_2O$$

On the left side of this equation we have the formula H_2 for hydrogen and the formula O_2 for oxygen, and on the right side the formula H_2O for water. It would not, however, be correct to write this equation without the numerical prefixes that are indicated, because we use the formulas to indicate relative numbers of atoms, as well as to describe the reactants and the products of the chemical reaction. The water molecule contains twice as many hydrogen atoms as oxygen atoms, and accordingly the equation should show that twice as many hydrogen atoms as oxygen atoms are needed for the reaction. This can be achieved by introducing the coefficient (multiplier) 2 in front of the symbol for the hydrogen molecule. If four hydrogen atoms (two molecules) and two oxygen atoms (one molecule) react, two water molecules are formed. This is indicated by use of the coefficient 2 in front of the formula for water.

It is a good practice to check every chemical equation that you write, to be sure that it agrees with the **"law of the conservation of atoms of every element."**

Illustrative Exercises

4-6.   (a) How many atoms of hydrogen and how many atoms of oxygen are there in 100 molecules of water?

(b) How many molecules of hydrogen and how many molecules of oxygen would be required to produce 100 molecules of water?

(c) Write the equation for the reaction, with 100 H_2O as the product.

(d) Reduce this equation to its simplest form, by dividing by the greatest common divisor of the coefficients of the three terms.

4-7.   Hydrogen peroxide, H_2O_2, easily decomposes into water and oxygen. Write a balanced equation for this reaction.

4-8.   Balance the following equations (the formulas are correct):

$$Fe + H_2SO_4 \longrightarrow FeSO_4 + H_2$$
$$C_{10}H_8 + O_2 \longrightarrow CO_2 + H_2O$$
$$C_6H_{14} + O_2 \longrightarrow CO_2 + H_2O$$
$$C_6H_{14} + O_2 \longrightarrow CO + H_2O$$
$$C_2H_5OH + O_2 \longrightarrow CO_2 + H_2O$$
$$AgNO_3 + CaCl_2 \longrightarrow AgCl + Ca(NO_3)_2$$

4-6. The Naming of Chemical Compounds

Compounds consisting of two elements are called *binary compounds*. For example, water, H_2O, is a binary compound of hydrogen and oxygen, and sodium chloride, NaCl, is a binary compound of sodium and chlorine.

The chemical name of a binary compound is obtained by stating the name of one of the elements, usually the more metallic of the two elements, and adding the name of the second element, with its ending changed to *ide*.

Sodium chloride, for example, is a compound of sodium and chlorine. Sodium is a metal, and chlorine is a nonmetal. It is accordingly the word chlorine that is modified by the use of the ending ide; it becomes chloride, and this word follows the word sodium in the name sodium chloride.

The symbols for the elements should be written in the same order in the formula, the symbol for the more metallic of the two elements coming first, and that for the less metallic second; for example, NaCl for sodium chloride.

Sometimes the number of atoms in the formula of a compound is indicated by the use of a prefix. For example, the two oxides, SO_2 and SO_3, of sulfur are called sulfur dioxide and sulfur trioxide, respectively. The prefixes *mono, di, tri, tetra, penta, hexa, hepta,* and *octa* are used to indicate one atom, two atoms, and so on to eight atoms. For example, the molecule N_2O_3 is called dinitrogen trioxide; the prefixes di and tri indicate that the molecule contains two atoms of nitrogen and three atoms of oxygen.

Many metals form two oxides (some of them form more than two). It is customary in the case of metals to make use of a suffix to the name of the metal in order to distinguish between the oxides. The suffix *ous* is used for the compound containing the smaller amount of oxygen (or other nonmetallic element), and the suffix *ic* is used for the compound containing the larger amount of oxygen (or other nonmetallic element). Often these suffixes are used with the Latin name of the element, rather than the English name. For example, the metal tin (Latin name *stannum*, symbol Sn) forms two oxides, SnO and SnO_2. These are named stannous oxide and stannic oxide, respectively.

Illustrative Exercises

4-9. Assign names to the following binary compounds: MgO, NaH, KCl, CaH_2, Al_2O_3, SiO_2, CaS, Na_2O, Li_3N, AlF_3.

4-10. The following pairs of elements form binary compounds in which the atoms of the two elements occur in equal numbers

Write formulas for them, and assign names to them: cesium and fluorine; nitrogen and boron; oxygen and beryllium; carbon and silicon; aluminum and phosphorus; chlorine and fluorine.

4-11. Using prefixes to indicate the number of atoms of different kind, assign names to the following binary compounds: $MgCl_2$, BF_3, SiO_2, PCl_5, SF_6, CO, CO_2, SO_2, SO_3, $SiCl_4$.

4-7. The Difference in Chemical Properties of Elements and Compounds

It is only recently that methods have become available for determining directly whether a substance contains atoms of only one kind or of two or more kinds. For two hundred years, since 1741, when M. V. Lomonosov (1711–1765), an imaginative Russian poet and chemist, published his new ideas about the nature of matter, and especially since 1789, when Lavoisier published such a clear discussion of the question as to convince nearly all of his fellow chemists, substances had undergone classification as elements or compounds on the basis of chemical reactions, as was briefly discussed in Chapter 1. Definite chemical evidence for the compound nature of a substance could be obtained, by decomposing it into two or more substances; if it was lacking, the substance was presumed to be an element.

There are two chemical tests for the compound nature of a substance.

First: if a substance can be decomposed (that is, if it can be made to undergo reaction in which it alone is destroyed) to form two or more product substances,* the original substance must be a compound. For example, molten salt can be decomposed completely into sodium and chlorine by passing an electric current through it; hence it is a compound. Similarly, mercuric oxide, HgO, can be decomposed into mercury and oxygen simply by heating it; hence it is a compound.

The second chemical test for the compound nature of a substance is this: if two or more substances react to form a single product substance, that substance is a compound. Thus sodium and chlorine, in the proper relative amounts, will react completely to form common salt; hence common salt is a compound.

It is interesting to note that *until the new physical methods, especially the x-ray method* (Section 4-9), *were developed, there was no way of rigorously proving a substance to be an element.* In the early years of the science of chemistry a substance was accepted as an element so long as no reaction showing it to be a compound had been observed. At first some mistakes were made: lime (calcium oxide, CaO) was considered to be an element until the English chemist Sir Humphry Davy reduced it to calcium metal in 1808; and uranium dioxide, UO_2, was accepted as an element from 1789 to 1841. By

---

* Here it is assumed that the different products are essentially different, and do not contain the same atoms (as do oxygen and ozone, Chapter 6).

1900, however, all but about a score of the elements that are now known had been recognized and correctly identified as elements.

This chemical method of classifying substances is interesting as an example of logical argument. A *single experiment* in which a substance is decomposed into two or more other substances or is alone formed from them *proves* that it is a compound; this conclusion is inescapable. The *failure* of such an experiment, however, *does not prove* that the substance is an element. It is, indeed, not possible to prove that a substance is an element by tests of this kind, no matter how many are made. It may be convenient to assume it to be an element, in case that there is no evidence to the contrary; but if this is done it should not be forgotten that the assumption is not necessarily true.

It was not until the present century, when powerful methods of studying atoms were discovered, that scientists could be sure that the forms of matter which they called elements were all really elements, and that some were not compounds.

4-8. Note on Radioactivity and the Transmutation of Elements

For centuries, before the development of chemistry as a science, the alchemists strove to carry out the transmutation of elements, in particular to change mercury into gold with the aid of the "philosopher's stone." Then, as scientific chemistry developed and success in transmutation eluded the investigators, the opinion gained firm hold that the conversion of one element into another was impossible, and that atoms were immutable and indestructible. The definitions of element and elementary substance accepted during the nineteenth century were based upon this belief.

In 1896 there came the discovery of radioactivity by Henri Becquerel and the discovery of radium by Pierre and Marie Curie. Soon thereafter it was recognized that *radioactive changes involve the spontaneous conversion of atoms of one element into those of another.* It then became necessary to change the definition of element; this was done by saying that one element could not be converted into another *by artificial means.*

It has now become necessary to make another change in the definition. In 1919 Lord Rutherford and his collaborators at the Cavendish Laboratory in Cambridge, England, where active study of radioactive phenomena was under way, reported that they had succeeded in converting nitrogen atoms into oxygen atoms by bombarding nitrogen with high-speed alpha particles, which are given off by radium. The nitrogen nucleus, with charge $+7e$, and the alpha particle (helium nucleus), with charge $+2e$, react to produce an oxygen nucleus, with charge $+8e$, and a proton, with charge $+e$.

Since 1930 there has been very great progress in this field of artificial radioactivity, which now is one of the most actively prosecuted research fields in physics. Every element has now been rendered radioactive and converted into other elements by bombardment with particles moving at high speed, and a great body of information about the properties of atomic nuclei is being gathered.

These developments necessitate another change in the concept of element: it is now said that *an element cannot be transmuted into another element by ordinary chemical methods.* The discovery of these new phenomena might have led to confusion regarding the validity of the classification of substances as elementary substances and compounds were it not for the fact that our knowledge of the structure and properties of atoms has also increased rapidly in recent years.

4-9. Moseley's Experiment

It was mentioned in Section 4-1 that Moseley determined the atomic numbers of elements by the study of the x-rays emitted by an x-ray tube containing the element. The apparatus that might be used to repeat Moseley's experiment is shown in Figure 2-25. The x-ray tube is drawn at the left side of this figure. Electrons that come from the cup near the bottom of the tube (as drawn) are speeded up by the electric potential (several thousand volts) applied to the two ends of the tube, and strike the target, which is near the center of the tube. The x-rays are emitted by the atoms of the target when they are struck by the fast-moving electrons.

It was found that the x-rays produced by an x-ray tube contain lines of definite wavelengths, characteristic of the material in the target of the x-ray

Figure 4-4

Diagram showing regular change of wavelength of x-ray emission lines for a series of elements.

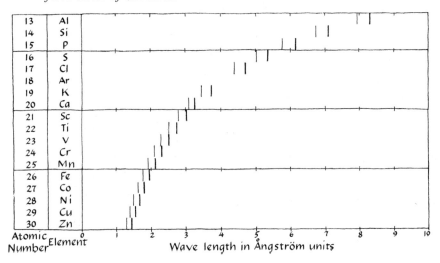

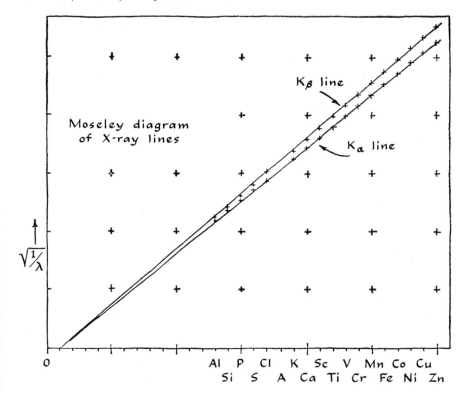

Figure 4-5

A graph of the reciprocal of the square root of the wavelengths of x-ray lines, for the K_α line and the K_β line, of elements, plotted against the order of the elements in the periodic table. This graph, called the Moseley diagram, was used by Moseley in determining the atomic numbers of the elements.

tube. Moseley measured the wavelengths produced by a number of different elements, and found that they change in a regular way. The wavelengths of the two principal x-ray lines of the elements from aluminum to zinc (omitting the gas argon) are shown in Figure 4-4.

The regularity in the wavelengths can be shown more strikingly by plotting the square root of the reciprocals of the wavelengths of the two x-ray lines for the various elements arranged in the proper sequence, which is the sequence of the atomic numbers of the elements. In a graph of this sort, called a Moseley diagram, the points for a given x-ray line lie on a straight line. The Moseley diagram for the elements from aluminum to zinc is shown in Figure 4-5. It was easy for Moseley to assign the correct atomic numbers to the elements with use of a diagram of this sort.

EXERCISES

4-12. Define atomic number. Define elementary substance in terms of atoms.

4-13. When sugar is strongly heated, water vapor is driven off and a black residue, carbon, is left. Does this experiment prove rigorously that sugar is not an element?

4-14. Balance the following equations:

$$CuO + NH_3 = N_2 + Cu + H_2O$$
$$Al + O_2 = Al_2O_3$$
$$Na + H_2O = NaOH + H_2$$
$$H_3PO_4 + NaOH = Na_3PO_4 + H_2O$$
$$KClO_3 = KCl + O_2$$
$$H_3BO_3 = B_2O_3 + H_2O$$
$$HCl + Ba(OH)_2 = BaCl_2 + H_2O$$
$$C_{12}H_{22}O_{11} + O_2 = H_2O + CO_2$$
$$N_2 + H_2 = NH_3$$

4-15. How was the definition of element affected by the discovery of radioactivity in 1896?

4-16. What are the atomic number and approximate atomic weight of the element each of whose nuclei contains 79 protons and 118 neutrons? By reference to Table 4-1 identify this element.

4-17. How many protons and how many neutrons are in the nucleus of the isotope of chlorine with mass 35? of the isotope of chlorine with mass 37? of the isotope of plutonium with mass 239?

4-18. Use the Moseley diagram (Figure 4-5) to make a rough prediction of the wavelength of the $K\alpha$ x-ray line for argon. Can you surmise why it was not measured by Moseley?

4-19. An atom of Sr^{90} emits a beta ray. What are the atomic number and mass number of the resulting nucleus? What element is it? This nucleus also emits a beta ray. What nucleus does it produce?

4-20. Argon, potassium, and calcium all have nuclides with mass 40. How many protons and how many neutrons constitute each of the three nuclei?

REFERENCE

Mary E. Weeks, *Discovery of the Elements*, Journal of Chemical Education, Easton, Pa., 1945.

2

Some Aspects of

Chemical Theory

In Chapter 1 we discussed different kinds of matter—homogeneous materials and heterogeneous materials, mixtures, solutions, and pure substances. In Chapter 2 a beginning was made on the correlation of the properties of substances and their structure, especially in relation to the atomic theory. We have seen that the characteristic properties of crystals are a consequence of their regular structure. A crystal of copper, which was discussed as an example, contains atoms of copper packed closely together in a regular three-dimensional arrangement, and a crystal of iodine, discussed as an example of a molecular crystal, contains molecules, each made of two iodine atoms, packed closely together in another regular arrangement. In a liquid the atoms or molecules are packed together, but not in a regular arrangement, and they are able to move around one another, permitting the liquid to flow and to adjust its shape to its container. In a gas the atoms or molecules are free to move away from one another, permitting the gas to expand to fill the volume of its container.

In Chapter 3 the study of structure was carried one step further, to the structure of the atom itself. An account was given of the experiments that led to the discovery that the atom is not a fundamental particle of matter, incapable of subdivision, but is itself composed of simpler particles: each atom contains one nucleus, which has a positive electric charge, and one or more electrons, which have negative electric charges. Atoms are known in which the nucleus has a single unit of positive electric charge (hydrogen), two units of positive electric charge (helium), and so on, without a gap, to 103 units of positive electric charge. The number of electric charges on the nucleus is called the atomic number of the atom. The structure of the nucleus itself was also discussed: every nucleus can be described as composed of protons and neutrons (except the simplest one, the proton itself). The number of protons in the nucleus is equal to the atomic number of the atom. All of the atoms with a given atomic number constitute an element; 103 elements are known.

A substance composed only of atoms of one element is called an element or elementary substance, and a substance composed of atoms of two or more elements, in definite proportions, is called a compound; a discussion of the nature of elements and compounds was presented in Chapter 4.

We are now ready to embark upon a further study of chemical theory, which is presented in the following five chapters. We have learned, in the earlier chapters, that compounds are formed of atoms of different elements, in definite proportions: water, for example, consists of molecules containing two atoms of hydrogen and one atom of oxygen. We see that if we knew the relative weights of the atoms we could calculate the weights of hydrogen and oxygen in water—that is, the composition of water. The first part of Chapter 5 is devoted to this quantitative aspect of chemistry—weight relations in chemical reactions. Some energy relations of chemical reactions are then discussed, especially in relation to change in state of a system, and to the nature of energy, heat, and work.

In Chapter 3 some mention was made of quantum effects—the quantum character of light as evidenced in the photoelectric effect, and the wave character of the electron and the neutron. We recognize now that chemistry is largely a quantum subject, and that to understand chemistry some knowledge of quantum mechanics is needed, including quantum statistical mechanics. In the second part of Chapter 5 there are presented the quantum theory of the harmonic oscillator and the Boltzmann distribution law in its quantum-theory form. These theories are then used to explain the surprising behavior of the heat capacity of solids and of gases at low temperature.

In Chapter 6, after a section on the chemistry of hydrogen and oxygen, the properties of gases are discussed, especially in relation to the Maxwell-Boltzmann distribution law for molecular velocities.

The 103 elements differ greatly from one another in their properties, and the task of learning and remembering many of the important facts about them would be an appalling one if it could not be systematized. It is fortunate that the properties of the elements depend upon their atomic numbers in a systematic way, as expressed in the periodic law. This important generalization is discussed in detail in Chapter 7, with special reference to its relation to the electronic structure of the elements. A detailed discussion of valence and the nature of the chemical bond in relation to the electronic structure of molecules and crystals follows, in Chapters 8 and 9.

When you have completed the study of Part 2 of this book, and have gained an understanding of these more quantitative and precise aspects of chemical theory, you will be in a position to proceed more effectively than before with the study of the properties and reactions of chemical substances.

CHAPTER 5

Weight and Energy Relations

In Chemical Reactions

In every branch of chemistry it is necessary to make calculations about the weights of substances involved in chemical reactions. Often calculations of this sort are of interest in everyday life.

These calculations can always be carried out by considering the atoms involved and using their atomic weights. No new principles are needed.

Analyze each problem that you meet; do not memorize rules for solving these problems. When you have a problem to solve, think about it until you are sure that you understand it; in particular, consider the behavior of the atoms involved. Then formulate an equation containing the unknown quantities, making use of atomic weights, and solve it. It is often helpful to solve a problem in steps.

5-1. The Atomic Weights of the Elements

All of the weight relations in chemical reactions depend upon the weights of the atoms of the elements. These weights (or masses) are called *atomic weights*. They are very important in the study and practice of chemistry.

The Meaning of Atomic Weights. The fact that many elements consist of a mixture of stable isotopes (Section 4-1) complicates the discussion of atomic weights.

The chemical atomic weights of elements are the average relative weights (masses) of atoms of the elements, the average being for the usual isotopic composition of each element.

Until 1961 the base of atomic weights was the element oxygen, with its atomic weight arbitrarily taken as 16.00000. Oxygen had been chosen as the base by general agreement of chemists for the reason that it combines with most of the elements, whose atomic weights can then be evaluated by the experimental determination of the weight relations involved in the oxygen compounds. The choice of 16.00000 for its mass was due to the facts that with this standard an astonishingly large number of elements have nearly integral atomic weights and that none has atomic weight less than one unit. Then in 1961, by action of the International Union of Pure and Applied Physics and the International Union of Pure and Applied Chemistry, the isotope carbon 12 was taken as the base, with atomic weight 12.00000. The *atomic weight unit* (abbreviation awu) is defined as *exactly 1/12 of the mass of the carbon-12 atom. The atomic weight of an element is the average mass of an atom of the element measured in this unit, with the isotopic composition usually found in nature.*

An atomic weight on the old (oxygen-16) scale is converted to its value on the new (carbon-12) scale by dividing by 1.000043. Thus the revised atomic weight of oxygen is 15.9994.

Ordinary hydrogen contains about one deuterium atom (2.0143 awu) to every 5000 protium atoms (1.00777 awu). We see that the extra weight, approximately 1 awu, of one deuterium atom to every 5000 protium atoms would cause an increase in the average weight of 1/5000, or 0.00020 awu. Accordingly, the chemical atomic weight of ordinary hydrogen is 1.0078 + 0.0002 = 1.0080 (more accurately, 1.00797).

The chemical atomic weight defined in this way, as the average for the usual isotopic composition of the element, would not be very useful unless the isotopic composition were constant. But it is in fact found that the isotopic composition of most elements (the proportion of different isotopes) is the same for all natural occurrences of the element, to within the precision of experimental determination of atomic weights. One exception is lead, which is found in certain minerals (where it was formed by radioactive decomposition of thorium) with atomic weight 205.96 and in others (where it was formed from uranium) with atomic weight 208.0. The atomic weight of ordinary lead, from the common mineral galena, PbS, is 207.19. Since galena is the source of almost all the lead that is used, this is the value given in the table of atomic weights. Other exceptions are given in a footnote to Table 5-1.

The History of the Atomic Weight Scale. John Dalton, who in 1803 made the old atomic hypothesis into a useful scientific theory by developing the concept of atomic weights, chose as the base the value 1 for hydrogen. Later Berzelius, who made many atomic-weight determinations, used 100 for oxygen as the base, but his choice was not accepted. The Belgian chemist J. S. Stas, in his careful work from 1850 on, used the value 16 for oxygen, considering it to be equivalent to 1 for hydrogen. By 1905 it was recognized that the ratio of atomic weights for hydrogen and oxygen, as determined by measuring

Table **5-1** *International Atomic Weights*

ELEMENT	SYM-BOL	ATOMIC NUMBER	ATOMIC WEIGHT	ELEMENT	SYM-BOL	ATOMIC NUMBER	ATOMIC WEIGHT
Actinium	Ac	89	[227]	Mercury	Hg	80	200.59
Aluminum	Al	13	26.9815	Molybdenum	Mo	42	95.94
Americium	Am	95	[243]	Neodymium	Nd	60	144.24
Antimony	Sb	51	121.75	Neon	Ne	10	20.183
Argon	Ar	18	39.948	Neptunium	Np	93	[237]
Arsenic	As	33	74.9216	Nickel	Ni	28	58.71
Astatine	At	85	[210]	Niobium	Nb	41	92.906
Barium	Ba	56	137.34	Nitrogen	N	7	14.0067
Berkelium	Bk	97	[247]	Nobelium	No	102	
Beryllium	Be	4	9.0122	Osmium	Os	76	190.2
Bismuth	Bi	83	208.980	Oxygen	O	8	15.9994*
Boron	B	5	10.811*	Palladium	Pd	46	106.4
Bromine	Br	35	79.909†	Phosphorus	P	15	30.9738
Cadmium	Cd	48	112.40	Platinum	Pt	78	195.09
Calcium	Ca	20	40.08	Plutonium	Pu	94	[242]
Californium	Cf	98	[249]	Polonium	Po	84	[210]
Carbon	C	6	12.01115*	Potassium	K	19	39.102
Cerium	Ce	58	140.12	Praseodymium	Pr	59	140.907
Cesium	Cs	55	132.905	Promethium	Pm	61	[147]
Chlorine	Cl	17	35.453†	Protactinium	Pa	91	[231]
Chromium	Cr	24	51.996†	Radium	Ra	88	[226]
Cobalt	Co	27	58.9332	Radon	Rn	86	[222]
Copper	Cu	29	63.54	Rhenium	Re	75	186.2
Curium	Cm	96	[247]	Rhodium	Rh	45	102.905
Dysprosium	Dy	66	162.50	Rubidium	Rb	37	85.47
Einsteinium	Es	99	[254]	Ruthenium	Ru	44	101.07
Erbium	Er	68	167.26	Samarium	Sm	62	150.35
Europium	Eu	63	151.96	Scandium	Sc	21	44.956
Fermium	Fm	100	[253]	Selenium	Se	34	78.96
Fluorine	F	9	18.9984	Silicon	Si	14	28.086*
Francium	Fr	87	[223]	Silver	Ag	47	107.870†
Gadolinium	Gd	64	157.25	Sodium	Na	11	22.9898
Gallium	Ga	31	69.72	Strontium	Sr	38	87.62
Germanium	Ge	32	72.59	Sulfur	S	16	32.064*
Gold	Au	79	196.967	Tantalum	Ta	73	180.948
Hafnium	Hf	72	178.49	Technetium	Tc	43	[97]
Helium	He	2	4.0026	Tellurium	Te	52	127.60
Holmium	Ho	67	164.930	Terbium	Tb	65	158.924
Hydrogen	H	1	1.00797*	Thallium	Tl	81	204.37
Indium	In	49	114.82	Thorium	Th	90	232.038
Iodine	I	53	126.9044	Thulium	Tm	69	168.934
Iridium	Ir	77	192.2	Tin	Sn	50	118.69
Iron	Fe	26	55.847†	Titanium	Ti	22	47.90
Krypton	Kr	36	83.80	Tungsten	W	74	183.85
Lanthanum	La	57	138.91	Uranium	U	92	238.03
Lawrencium	Lw	103		Vanadium	V	23	50.942
Lead	Pb	82	207.19	Xenon	Xe	54	131.30
Lithium	Li	3	6.939	Ytterbium	Yb	70	173.04
Lutetium	Lu	71	174.97	Yttrium	Y	39	88.905
Magnesium	Mg	12	24.312	Zinc	Zn	30	65.37
Manganese	Mn	25	54.9380	Zirconium	Zr	40	91.22
Mendelevium	Md	101	[256]				

* The atomic weight varies because of natural variations in the isotopic composition of the element. The observed ranges are boron, ±0.003; carbon, ±0.00005; hydrogen, ±0.00001; oxygen, ±0.0001; silicon, ±0.001; sulfur, ±0.003.

† The atomic weight is believed to have an experimental uncertainty of the following magnitude: bromine, ±0.002; chlorine, ±0.001; chromium, ±0.001; iron, ±0.003; silver, ±0.003. For other elements the last digit given is believed to be reliable to ±0.5.

experimentally the ratio of weights of hydrogen and of oxygen that combine with one another to form water, differs from 1:16 by nearly 1%. Most of the experimental values of atomic-weight ratios had been determined relative to oxygen, for which 16 had been used: hence by accepting 16.00000 for oxygen as base, no change in the older tables was needed, except for hydrogen. The change to 12.00000 for carbon 12 in 1961 required only a very small revision of the chemists' atomic weights: division by 1.000043.

The Einstein Equation and the Masses of Nuclei. A striking property of nuclei is that *the mass of a heavy nucleus is slightly less than the sum of the masses of the protons and neutrons that combine to form it.* The reason for this is that during combination of the protons and neutrons a large amount of energy is released in the form of radiation. In consequence of the relativistic relation (the *Einstein equation*) between mass and energy, which is $E = mc^2$ (E = energy, m = mass, c = velocity of light), this release of radiation leads to a corresponding decrease in mass by about 1% (see Chapter 30); there is *conservation of mass-energy.* The change in mass that accompanies ordinary chemical reactions as a result of the emission or absorption of heat is too small to be detected.

The Values of the Atomic Weights. The atomic weights of the elements are given in Table 5-1. A simpler table, giving approximate atomic weights for the common elements, is opposite the inside of the front cover. The values in this table are good enough for most purposes.

5-2. The Quantitative Meaning of Chemical Symbols and Formulas

A symbol such as Cu is used to indicate the element copper, either in the elementary substance or in compounds. It also means a definite amount of copper—one atom or one atomic weight (63.54) in any weight unit (such as 63.54 g or 63.54 pounds). In particular, however, it is often used to mean one *gram-atom* of copper, 63.54 g.

Similarly, a formula such as $CuSO_4 \cdot 5H_2O$ represents the compound copper sulfate pentahydrate, which contains the four elements whose symbols are involved in the atomic ratios indicated by the formula. These ratios are 1Cu:1S:9O:10H. The formula also means one formula weight (in arbitrary units) of the substance. In particular, the formula is often used to mean one *gram-formula weight*, 249.69 g, and hence to mean 1 gram-atom of copper, plus 1 gram-atom of sulfur, 9 gram-atoms of oxygen, and 10 gram-atoms of hydrogen. The abbreviation for gram-formula weight is gfw.

The *molecular weight* of a substance is the average weight* in atomic weight

---

* The expression "average weight" is used here because of the existence of stable isotopes of most of the elements.

units of a molecule of a substance. If the molecular formula of the substance is known, the molecular weight is calculated by adding the atomic weights of the elements as given in the formula of the substance. Inasmuch as the true formula of a substance may not be known, it is often convenient to use the *formula weight*, the sum of the atomic weights of the atoms in an assumed formula for a substance, which may not be the correct molecular formula (an example: HO for hydrogen peroxide instead of H_2O_2). A gram-formula weight is then the amount of the substance with weight equal to the formula weight in grams, as indicated above for copper sulfate pentahydrate.

A *mole* of any substance is the amount of the substance with weight equal to the molecular weight in grams. When it is known that the formula written for a substance is its correct molecular formula, the molecular weight and the formula weight are of course the same, and the mole equals the gram formula weight.

Often the state of aggregation of a substance is represented by appended letters: Cu(*s*) refers to crystalline copper (*s* standing for solid; sometimes *c* is used), Cu(*l*) to liquid copper, and Cu(*g*) to gaseous copper. Sometimes a substance is indicated as solid or crystalline by a line drawn under its formula; both AgCl and AgCl(*s*) mean solid silver chloride. A substance in solution is sometimes represented by its formula followed by *aq* (for aqueous solution).

5-3. Examples of Weight-relation Calculations

The way to work a weight-relation problem is to think about the problem, in terms of atoms and molecules, and then to decide how to carry out the calculations. You should not memorize any rule about these problems —such rules are apt to confuse you, and to cause you to make mistakes.

The way to work these problems is best indicated by some examples.

In general, chemical problems may be solved by using a slide rule for the numerical work. This gives about three reliable figures in the answer, which is often all that is justified by the accuracy of the data. Sometimes the data are more reliable, and logarithms or long-hand calculations might be used to obtain the answer with the accuracy called for. Unless the problem requires unusual accuracy, you may round values of atomic weights off to the first decimal point.

Example 1. What is the percentage of lead in galena, PbS? Calculate to 0.1%.

    Solution. The formula weight of PbS is obtained by adding the atomic weights of lead and sulfur, which we obtain from the table inside the front cover:

$$\begin{aligned}
\text{Weight of one lead atom (1 Pb)} &= 207.2 \text{ awu} \\
\text{Weight of one sulfur atom (1 S)} &= 32.1 \text{ awu} \\
\hline
\text{Weight of 1 PbS} &= 239.3 \text{ awu}
\end{aligned}$$

Hence 239.3 awu of PbS contains 207.2 awu of lead. We see that 100.0 g of PbS would contain

$$\frac{207.2 \text{ awu of lead}}{239.3 \text{ awu of galena}} \times 100.0 \text{ g of galena} = 86.6 \text{ g of lead}$$

Hence the percentage of lead in galena is **86.6%**.

Note that on the left side of the above equation the units awu in numerator and denominator cancel, and also the names (galena) cancel.

You may prefer to work examples of this sort by use of *proportion*. It is good practice in using this method to write the definition of the un-known quantity, usually represented by the letter x.

Let x = percentage of lead in galena; that is, x = grams of lead in 100 g of galena.

We may now write two ratios (two fractions), each being the ratio of the weight of lead to the weight of PbS containing it; these ratios must be equal, because of the constancy of composition of the compound lead sulfide:

$$\frac{207.2 \text{ awu}}{239.3 \text{ awu}} = \frac{x}{100.0 \text{ g}}$$

The ratio on the left is the ratio of the atomic weight of lead to the formula weight of PbS. That on the right is the ratio of the weight of lead in 100.0 g of galena to the weight of the galena. On solving this equation we obtain the answer given above.

Example 2. A propellant for rockets can be made by mixing powdered potassium perchlorate, $KClO_4$, and powdered carbon (carbon black), C, with a little adhesive to bind the powdered materials together. What weight of carbon should be mixed with 1000 g of potassium perchlorate in order that the products of the reaction be KCl and CO?

Solution. Taking the equation for the reaction as

$$KClO_4 + 4C \longrightarrow KCl + 4CO$$

we first calculate the formula weight of $KClO_4$:

$$
\begin{aligned}
\text{Weight of K} &= 39.1 \text{ awu} \\
\text{Weight of Cl} &= 35.5 \text{ awu} \\
\text{Weight of 4O} = 4 \times 16.0 &= 64.0 \text{ awu} \\
\hline
\text{Weight of } KClO_4 &= 138.6 \text{ awu}
\end{aligned}
$$

The atomic weight of carbon is 12.0; the weight 4C is 48.0 awu. Hence the weight of carbon required is 48.0/138.6 times the weight of potassium perchlorate:

$$\frac{48.0 \text{ awu (C)}}{138.6 \text{ awu } (KClO_4)} \times 1000 \text{ g } (KClO_4) = 346 \text{ g (C)}$$

Hence about **346 g** of carbon* is required for 1000 g of potassium perchlorate.

Example 3. How much iron can be obtained by the reduction of one ton of hematite iron ore, assuming it to be pure Fe_2O_3?

Solution. We assume that all the iron atoms in ferric oxide (hematite) can be converted into elementary iron by reduction; and we write the corresponding equation:

$$Fe_2O_3 + \text{reducing agent} \longrightarrow 2Fe + \text{product}$$

From this equation we see that one formula Fe_2O_3 of hematite gives on reduction two atoms of iron. The formula weight of Fe_2O_3 is 159.7 awu, as is found in the following way:

$$\text{Weight of 2Fe} = 2 \times 55.85 = 111.7 \text{ awu}$$
$$\text{Weight of 3O} = 3 \times 16.0 = 48.0 \text{ awu}$$
$$\overline{}$$
$$\text{Formula weight of } Fe_2O_3 = 159.7 \text{ awu}$$

It is evident that the ratio of the weight of iron that can be obtained from hematite to the weight of hematite is 111.7/159.7. Accordingly, if we multiply the weight of hematite (1 ton) by this quantity we obtain the weight in tons of iron that could be produced from the hematite:

$$\frac{111.7 \text{ awu (iron)}}{159.7 \text{ awu } (Fe_2O_3)} \times 1 \text{ ton } (Fe_2O_3) = \textbf{0.699} \text{ ton (iron)}$$
$$= \textbf{1398} \text{ pounds of iron}$$

Example 4. An oxide of arsenic contains 65.2% arsenic. What is its simplest formula?

Solution. In 100 g of this oxide of arsenic there are contained, according to the reported analysis, 65.2 g of arsenic and 34.8 g of oxygen. If we divide 65.2 g by the gram-atomic weight of arsenic, 74.9 g, we obtain 0.871 as the number of gram-atoms of arsenic. Similarly, by dividing 34.8 g by the gram-atomic weight of oxygen, 16 g, we obtain 2.17 as the number of gram-atoms of oxygen in 100 g of this oxide of arsenic. Hence the numbers of atoms of arsenic and oxygen in the compound are in the ratio 0.871 to 2.17. If we set this ratio, 0.871/2.17, on the slide rule, we see that it is very close to 2/5, being 2/4.97. Hence the simplest formula is As_2O_5.

We say that this is the simplest formula in order not to rule out the possibility that the substance contains more complex molecules, such as As_4O_{10}, in which case it would be proper to indicate in the formula the larger numbers of atoms per molecule.

* Note the convention in chemistry that "346 g of carbon" is singular in number; it means a quantity of carbon weighing 346 g, rather than 346 separate grams of carbon.

Example 5. A substance is found by qualitative tests to consist of only carbon and hydrogen (it is a hydrocarbon). A quantitative analysis is made of the substance by putting a weighed amount, 0.2822 g, in a tube which can be strongly heated from outside, and then burning it in a stream of dry air. The air containing the products of combustion is passed first through a weighed tube containing calcium chloride, which absorbs the water vapor, and then through another weighed tube containing a mixture of sodium hydroxide and calcium oxide, which absorbs the carbon dioxide. When the first tube is weighed, after the combustion is completed, it is found to have increased in weight by 0.1598 g, this being accordingly the weight of water produced by the combustion of the sample. The second tube is found to have increased in weight by 0.9768 g. What is the simplest formula of the substance?

    Solution. It is convenient to solve this problem in steps. Let us first find out how many moles of water were produced. The number of moles of water produced is found by dividing 0.1598 g by 18.02 g, the weight of a mole of water; it is 0.00887. Each mole of water vapor contains two gram-atoms of hydrogen; hence the number of gram-atoms of hydrogen in the original sample is twice this number, or 0.01774.

    Similarly, the number of moles of carbon dioxide in the products of combustion is obtained by dividing the weight of carbon dioxide, 0.9768 g, by the molar weight of the substance, 44.01 g. It is 0.02219, which is also the number of gram-atoms of carbon in the sample of substance, because each molecule of carbon dioxide contains one atom of carbon.

    The original substance accordingly contained carbon atoms and hydrogen atoms in the ratio 0.02219 to 0.01774. This ratio is found on calculation to be 1.251, which is equal to 5/4, to within the accuracy of the analysis. Accordingly the simplest formula for the substance is C_5H_4.

    If the analyst had smelled the substance, and noticed an odor resembling moth balls, he would have identified the substance as naphthalene, $C_{10}H_8$.

Illustrative Exercises

5-1. Calculate, to 0.1%, the percentage composition of water.

5-2. The atomic weight of calcium is 40.0 and that of carbon is 12.0; what is the formula weight of calcium carbonate, $CaCO_3$? What is the percentage of calcium in it? How much lime, CaO, could be made by heating 100 tons of limestone in a limekiln?

5-3. What amount of tin is contained in one ton of its ore cassiterite, SnO_2?

5-4. An oxide of mercury contains 7.4% oxygen and 92.6% mercury. What is its formula?

5-5. What is the weight of chloroform, $CHCl_3$, that might be made by reaction of 1000 g of methane with chlorine? The reaction is $CH_4 + 3Cl_2 \longrightarrow CHCl_3 + 3HCl$.

5-6. How many pounds of water and how many pounds of carbon dioxide are produced by burning a tankful (20 gallons) of gasoline? Assume gasoline to have the formula C_8H_{14} and density 5.7 pounds per gallon.

5-7. In 1825 Michael Faraday discovered a new compound of carbon and hydrogen, which was later given the name benzene. On analysis it was found to contain 7.8% hydrogen and 92.2% carbon. What is its simplest formula?

5-4. Determination of Atomic Weights by the Chemical Method

It is hard to overestimate the importance of the table of atomic weights. Almost every activity of a chemist involves the use of atomic weights in some way. During the past 150 years successive generations of chemists have carried out experiments in the effort to provide more and more accurate values of the atomic weights, in order that chemical calculations could be carried out with greater accuracy.

Until recently almost all atomic weight determinations were made by the chemical method. This method consists in determining the amount of the element that will combine with one gram-atom of oxygen or of another element with known atomic weight. The method is illustrated by the following examples.

Example 6. During the period 1882 to 1895 Professor E. W. Morley (1838–1923) of Western Reserve University carried out the first experiments that showed definitely that the ratio of atomic weights of hydrogen and oxygen is not exactly 1:16. In one such experiment he found that 1.8467 g of hydrogen combines with 14.656 g of oxygen to form water. What is the atomic weight of hydrogen, calculated from the result of this experiment?

Solution. Water has the formula H_2O. Hence the observed weights of the two gases are the relative weights of two atoms of hydrogen and one atom of oxygen. If the weight of oxygen, 14.656, is multiplied by the fraction 15.999/14.656 it becomes 15.999, which is the atomic weight of oxygen. Accordingly, if the weight of hydrogen were to be multiplied by the fraction, the answer would be the weight of 2 atoms of hydrogen:

$$1.8467 \times \frac{15.999}{14.656} = 2.01594$$

This is the weight of two atoms of hydrogen, relative to $O = 15.999$. Hence the weight of one atom of hydrogen on this scale is one-half of 2.01594, or **1.0080**. This is the atomic weight of hydrogen as given by the result of this experiment.

5-5. Determination of Atomic Weights by Use of the Mass Spectrograph

In 1907 J. J. Thomson developed a method of determining the *ratio of charge to mass* of an ionized atom (or ionized gas molecule) by measuring the deflection of a beam of the ionized atoms in electric and magnetic fields. The apparatus is called a *mass spectrograph*. It has become useful in several ways in attacking chemical problems. Its principal uses have been for the discovery of isotopes and the determination of atomic weights. The importance of these uses justifies a brief discussion of the apparatus and the way it works.

Let us consider, as an example, the element iodine, which was used as an example also in Chapter 2. Iodine gas at ordinary temperatures consists of diatomic molecules, I_2. As the temperature is raised, some of these molecules respond to the greatly increased thermal agitation by being broken into separate atoms. This partial dissociation of a gas into atoms can also be achieved at room temperature by passing an electric discharge through the gas. A fast-moving electron (or ion) in the electric discharge may strike a molecule of iodine so vigorously as to cause it to split into atoms:

$$I_2 \longrightarrow 2I$$

Ions of iodine also are formed in such an electric discharge. An iodine molecule may be struck such a blow as to cause the two nuclei to separate with unequal numbers of electrons; that is, the molecule may be caused to dissociate into one negative ion, with an extra electron, and one positive ion, with an electron missing:

$$I_2 \xrightarrow[\text{collision}]{} I^- + I^+$$

Negative ions are called *anions*, and positive ions are called *cations*. A cation I^+ might suffer another collision that would cause it to lose a second electron, converting it into a doubly charged cation:

$$I^+ \xrightarrow[\text{collision}]{} I^{++} + e^-$$

All atoms, even such stable atoms as those of the inert gases, can be made to form gaseous cations in an electric discharge through a gas at low pressure. Some atoms also form stable singly charged gaseous anions, such as the ion I^-. Molecules also form ions under these circumstances: an electric discharge through methane, CH_4, produces gaseous molecular ions such as CH_4^+, CH_3^+, CH_2^+, and CH^+, as well as atomic ions such as H^+, C^+, C^{++}, C^{+++}, and C^{++++}.

The principle of the mass spectrograph can be illustrated by the simple apparatus shown in Figure 5-1.

At the left is a chamber in which positive ions are formed by an electric discharge, and then accelerated toward the right by an electric potential. The ions passing through the first pinhole have different velocities; in the second

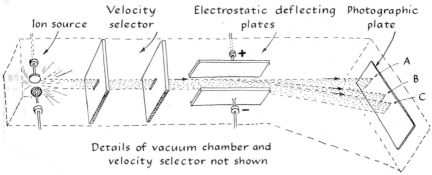

Figure 5-1

Diagram of a simple mass spectrograph.

part of the apparatus a beam of ions with approximately a certain velocity is selected, and allowed to pass through the second pinhole, the ions with other velocities being stopped. (We shall not attempt to describe the construction of the velocity selector.) The ions passing through the second pinhole then move on between two metal plates, one of which has a positive electric charge and the other a negative charge. The ions accordingly undergo an acceleration toward the negative plate, and are deflected from the straight path A that they would pursue if the plates were not charged.

The force acting on an ion between these plates is proportional to $+ne$, its electric charge (n being the number of missing electrons), and its inertia is proportional to its mass M. The amount of deflection is hence determined by ne/M, the ratio of the charge of the ion to its mass.

Of two ions with the same charge, the lighter one will be deflected in this apparatus by the greater amount. The beam C might accordingly represent the ion C^+, with charge $+e$ and mass 12 atomic weight units (the atomic weight of carbon), and the beam B the heavier ion O^+, with the same charge but with mass 16.

Of two ions with the same mass, the one with the greater charge will be deflected by the greater amount. Beams B and C might represent O^{++} and O^{+++}, respectively.

By measuring the deflection of the beams, relative values of ne/M for different ions can be determined. Since e is constant, relative values of ne/M for different ions are also inverse relative values of M/n: therefore this method permits the direct experimental determination of the relative masses of atoms, and hence of their atomic weights. By this method Thomson discovered the first known nonradioactive isotopes, those of neon, in 1913.

The value of the integer n—the degree of ionization of the ions—can usually be fixed from knowledge of the substances present in the discharge tube; thus neon gives ions with $M/n = 20$ and $22(n = 1)$, 10 and $11(n = 2)$, etc.

Instead of the mass spectrograph described above, others of different design,

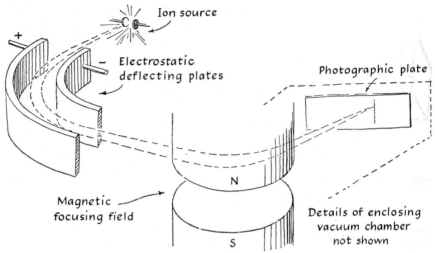

Figure **5-2**

A focusing mass spectrograph, using both electrostatic and magnetic deflection of the beam of ions.

using both an electric field and a magnetic field, are usually used. These instruments are designed so that they focus the beam of ions with a given value of M/n into a sharp line on a photographic plate. An instrument of this sort, using both an electric field, with curved plates, and a magnetic field, is sketched in Figure 5-2. Focusing mass spectrographs can also be made with the direction of magnetic deflection opposite to that of electric deflection.

Modern types of mass spectrographs have an accuracy of about one part in 200,000 and a resolving power of 20,000 (that is, they are able to separate ion beams with values of M/n differing by only one part in 20,000). The great accuracy of modern mass spectrographs makes the mass-spectrographic method of determining atomic weights more useful and important at present than the chemical method.

Mass-spectrographic comparisons with C^{12} or O^{16} are made in the following way. An ion source that produces ions both of carbon (or oxygen) and of the element to be investigated is used; the lines of carbon or oxygen and of the element in such states of ionization that their ne/M values are nearly the same are then obtained—thus for S^{32}, S^{33}, and S^{34} the lines for the doubly ionized atoms would lie near the line for singly ionized oxygen. Accurate relative measurements of these lines can then be made.

The Oxygen-16 Atomic-weight Scale.   Until 1961 atomic masses obtained with the mass spectrograph were reported relative to $O^{16} = 16.00000$. These atomic masses are called the *atomic weights on the physicists' old scale.* Since ordinary oxygen contains 0.2% of O^{18} and 0.04% of O^{17}, these mass values had to be corrected by division by a suitable divisor to give the values on the chemists' old scale, based on the average weight 16.00000 for ordinary oxygen, or on the C^{12} scale. The value of this conversion divisor is 1.000275 for the chemists' old scale and 1.000318 for the C^{12} scale.

Examples of the Determination of Atomic Weights with the Mass Spectrograph. For a simple element, with only one isotope, the value of the atomic mass of that isotope is the atomic weight of the element. Thus for gold, which consists entirely of one stable isotope, Au^{197}, the mass-spectrographic mass (relative to $C^{12} = 12.00000$) is reported to be 196.967. This value has been accepted by the International Committee on Atomic Weights.

For elements with two or more stable isotopes the atomic weight can be calculated from the masses of the isotopes and values of their relative amounts, as shown in the following example.

Example 7. Silver has two stable isotopes. Their masses on the O^{16} scale, as determined by use of the mass spectrograph, were found to be 106.936 and 108.935, with relative amounts (numbers of nuclei) 51.35% and 48.65%, respectively. What is the atomic weight of silver, from this investigation?

> **Solution.** The average atomic weight on the O^{16} scale is $0.5135 \times 106.936 + 0.4865 \times 108.935$. We see that this can be rewritten as $106.936 + 0.4865 \times (108.935 - 106.936) = 106.936 + 0.4865 \times 1.999 = 106.936 + 0.968 = 107.904$. To convert this value to the C^{12} scale we must divide by 1.000318. This we can do* by multiplying by $1 - 0.000318$:

$$1 \times 107.904 = 107.904$$
$$-0.000318 \times 107.904 = -0.034$$
$$\overline{107.870}$$

The value of the atomic weight of silver is accordingly calculated to be **107.870.**

Illustrative Exercise	**5-8.** Gallium has two stable isotopes, with atomic abundances 60% and 40% and masses on the O^{16} scale 68.955 and 70.953, respectively. Evaluate the atomic weight of the element.

5-6. The Discovery of the Correct Atomic Weights. Isomorphism

In the early years of the atomic theory there was no secure knowledge of the true relative weights of different elements. As mentioned in Section 2-2, Dalton assigned atomic weights in such a way as to lead to simple formulas for compounds. Many chemists continued to write HO for water until 1858.

---

* Remember that $(1 + x)^{-1} = 1 - x + x^2 - \cdots$, and is hence approximated by $1 - x$ when x is small.

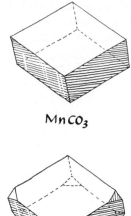

MnCO₃

CaCO₃

Figure **5-3** *Isomorphous crystals of rhodochrosite and calcite (hexagonal system).*

In that year a principle discovered much earlier (1811) by Avogadro was applied so effectively by Cannizzaro as to convince most chemists that the atomic weights obtained by its use could be accepted as correct. This principle will be discussed in the next chapter (Sections 6-7 and 6-8).

Some other methods for assigning correct atomic weights were also developed during the first half of the nineteenth century. One of them (the rule of Dulong and Petit) will be discussed in Section 5-8.

In 1819 the German chemist Eilhard Mitscherlich (1794–1863) discovered the phenomenon of **isomorphism,** *the existence of different crystalline substances with essentially the same crystal form,* and suggested his **rule of isomorphism,** which states that *isomorphous crystals have similar chemical formulas.*

As an example of isomorphism, we may consider the minerals rhodochrosite, $MnCO_3$, and calcite, $CaCO_3$. Crystals of these two substances resemble one another closely, as shown in Figure 5-3. They both belong to the hexagonal crystal system (Section 2-5), and they both have excellent rhombohedral cleavage. The larger of the two angles of a rhombic face of the cleavage rhombohedron has the value 102°50' for rhodochrosite and 101°55' for calcite. These facts justified the description of the two crystals as isomorphous more than a century ago. When x-ray diffraction was discovered it was possible to verify that the crystals have the same structure.

An illustration of the use of the rule of isomorphism is given by the work of the English chemist Henry E. Roscoe in determining the correct atomic weight of vanadium. Berzelius had attributed the atomic weight 68.5 to vanadium in 1831. In 1867 Roscoe noticed that the corresponding formula for the hexagonal mineral vanadinite was not analogous to the formulas of other hexagonal minerals apparently isomorphous with it:

		Axial ratio
Apatite	$Ca_5(PO_4)_3F$	$c/a = 1.363$
Hydroxyapatite	$Ca_5(PO_4)_3OH$	1.355
Pyromorphite	$Pb_5(PO_4)_3Cl$	1.362
Mimetite	$Pb_5(AsO_4)_3Cl$	1.377
Vanadinite	$Pb_5(VO_3)_3Cl$ (wrong)	1.404

The formula for vanadinite analogous to the other formulas is $Pb_5(VO_4)_3Cl$. On reinvestigating the compounds of vanadium Roscoe found that this latter formula is indeed the correct one, and that Berzelius had accepted the oxide VO, vanadium monoxide, as the elementary substance. The atomic weight of vanadium now accepted is 50.942.

There are occasional exceptions to the rule of isomorphism. An example is provided by hydroxyapatite, which in the form of its crystals is classed as isomorphous with apatite, but which has an extra atom in its formula. The explanation of this deviation from the rule is that the hydrogen atom is smaller than other atoms, and in the hydroxyapatite crystal the hydrogen atoms occupy interstices among the larger atoms that are vacant in the apatite crystal.

Illustrative Exercise	**5-9.** A compound containing only barium, phosphorus, hydrogen, and oxygen is found to form hexagonal crystals resembling those of apatite in shape and with axial ratio $c/a = 1.33$. What is its probable formula?

5-7. Energy and Chemical Change. Enthalpy of Reaction

Some chemical reactions take place with the evolution of heat, and some with the absorption of heat. The reactions that take place with the evolution of heat are called *exothermic reactions,* and those that take place with the absorption of heat are called *endothermic reactions.* Of course, any reaction that is exothermic when it takes place in one direction is endothermic when it takes place in the reverse direction.

The relation of energy to chemical change is important both in the science of chemistry and in its industrial applications. For example, in the construction of very large concrete dams the heat that is evolved during the setting of the Portland cement may cause the concrete to crack, and it is accordingly necessary to include a system of pipes in the mass of concrete, in order to cool the concrete by a stream of water. We can see that it would be useful if a method could be devised to permit this reaction, the setting of Portland cement, to occur without the evolution of heat; but unfortunately the nature of the relation between energy and chemical change is such that it is not possible to achieve this result.

The branch of chemistry dealing with heats of reaction and closely related subjects is called *thermochemistry.* The more general study of the relations between energy and chemical change, including such questions as the electric potential that can be obtained from an electrolytic cell (Chapter 8) and the amount of work that can be done by chemical means, is called *thermodynamic chemistry.* Thermochemistry and thermodynamic chemistry are a part of physical chemistry.

Heat of Reaction. The heat of a chemical reaction is the quantity of heat that is evolved or absorbed when the reaction takes place at constant temperature and constant pressure.* If heat is evolved, the reaction is exothermic. If heat is absorbed by the reaction, the reaction is endothermic.

We can tell whether a chemical reaction is exothermic or endothermic by causing the reactants, at a certain temperature, to undergo reaction, and then determining the temperature of the products. If the products are warmer than the reactants were, the reaction is exothermic; if they are colder, the reaction is endothermic. For example, we know that when a fuel burns in air the products are very hot. This reaction, the combustion of a fuel, is a strongly exothermic reaction. But when common salt is dissolved in water the solution is cooled somewhat below room temperature. This reaction, the solution of sodium chloride in water, is endothermic.

Measuring the Heat of a Reaction. An instrument used to measure the heat of a reaction is called a *calorimeter*. Calorimeters are made of various designs, corresponding to the nature of the reaction to be studied. A calorimeter of simple design is shown in Figure 5-4. This calorimeter consists of a reaction vessel in the center of a larger vessel filled with water and provided with a stirrer and a sensitive thermometer. The larger vessel is surrounded by insulating material.

If it is desired to obtain the *heat of combustion* of carbon (the heat of its reaction with oxygen), a weighed quantity of carbon is placed in the reaction vessel and oxygen gas is forced into the vessel under pressure. A reaction vessel for this purpose is strongly built of steel, to stand high pressure; it is called a *combustion bomb*. After the passage of enough time for the materials inside the insulation to have reached a uniform temperature, the temperature is recorded, and the sample of carbon is ignited by passing an electric current through a wire embedded in it. The heat liberated by the reaction causes the entire system inside the insulating material to increase in temperature. When the temperature of this material has again become uniform, it is again recorded. From the rise in temperature and the total water equivalent of the calorimeter (that is, the weight of water that would

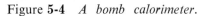

Figure 5-4 *A bomb calorimeter.*

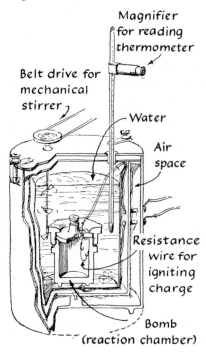

Magnifier
for reading
thermometer

Belt drive for
mechanical
stirrer

Water

Air
space

Resistance
wire for
igniting
charge

Bomb
(reaction chamber)

* The definition of heat of reaction is discussed in the paragraphs on enthalpy later in this section.

require the same amount of heat to cause the temperature to rise one degree as is required to cause a rise in temperature of one degree of the total material of the calorimeter inside of the insulation), the amount of heat liberated in the reaction can be calculated. A correction must of course be made for the amount of heat introduced by the electric current that produced the ignition.

It has been found by experiments of this sort that the heat evolved on combustion of carbon (graphite) to carbon dioxide is 94,052 calories per gram-atom of carbon:

$$C \text{ (graphite)} + O_2(g) \longrightarrow CO_2(g) + 94{,}052 \text{ cal/mole}$$

With a limited supply of oxygen, carbon monoxide, CO, is formed. The heat evolved on combustion of graphite to carbon monoxide is 26,416 cal/mole:

$$C \text{ (graphite)} + \tfrac{1}{2}O_2(g) \longrightarrow CO(g) + 26{,}416 \text{ cal/mole}$$

The heat of solution of sodium chloride in water might be determined by use of a calorimeter similar to that shown in Figure 5-4, but provided with a central container in which water is placed, with a little bucket of salt crystals arranged in such a way as to permit the bucket to be dropped into the water during the experiment. A stirrer for the salt solution would also be needed in order to cause the salt to dissolve sufficiently rapidly. When this experiment is carried out, it is found that the process of solution of 1 gfw of sodium chloride in water is accompanied by the absorption of approximately 1,200 cal. The heat of the reaction depends slightly on the concentration of the solution that is produced.

Heat Content, Enthalpy. It has been found by experiment that it is possible to assign to every substance at standard conditions a numerical value of a certain quantity, represented by the symbol H, such that the heat absorbed during a chemical reaction carried out at constant temperature and constant pressure can be found by subtracting the sum of the values of H for the reactants from the sum for the products of the reaction. The names used for the quantity H are *heat content* and *enthalpy*. These names are equivalent to one another.

The symbol ΔH is used to express the change in enthalpy (or heat content) of a system accompanying a change in state, such as a chemical reaction. Thus a positive value of ΔH means that heat is absorbed from the surroundings during the reaction. The symbol ΔH°_{298} is used for the change in enthalpy accompanying a change (reaction) at 298.16°K (25°C) and 1 atm pressure. For example, we may write the equations for the combustion of carbon as follows:

$$C \text{ (graphite)} + O_2(g) \longrightarrow CO_2(g) \qquad \Delta H^\circ_{298} = -94{,}052 \text{ cal/mole}$$
$$C \text{ (graphite)} + \tfrac{1}{2}O_2(g) \longrightarrow CO(g) \qquad \Delta H^\circ_{298} = -26{,}416 \text{ cal/mole}$$

(The temperature 25°C has been accepted by chemists as the customary one for determination of thermochemical quantities.)

The name *enthalpy of reaction* is used for the quantity ΔH°. (ΔH°_{298} is the enthalpy of reaction at 298.16°K.) We see that the enthalpy of reaction is negative for exothermic reactions and positive for endothermic reactions.

In a preceding paragraph we have described the heat of a reaction as the amount of heat evolved or absorbed when the reaction takes place at constant temperature and pressure. Two mutually contradictory definitions of heat of reactions are used at the present time in textbooks and reference books. For over a century it has been customary to define the heat of a reaction (heat of combustion, heat of formation, heat of solution) as the heat evolved in the process; that is, as $-\Delta H^\circ$. On the other hand, heats of fusion and vaporization (Section 5-8) have been defined as the heat absorbed during fusion or vaporization. During the last few years many chemists have adopted the definition of heat of reaction as the heat absorbed in the process. This usage is to be found, for example, in the valuable reference book *Selected Values of Chemical Thermodynamic Properties*, Circular of the U.S. Bureau of Standards No. 500 (1952), in which values of heats of formation of compounds from elements in their standard states and some other properties of substances are given.

In order to avoid the confusion that might result from the present lack of agreement about the sign in the definition of heat of reaction, we shall in this textbook make use instead of the term enthalpy of reaction, defined as ΔH°.

The Use of Enthalpy Values. In *Selected Values of Chemical Thermodynamic Properties* the experimental values are given for the enthalpy of formation of about 5000 compounds from the elements in their standard states. These values may be combined to obtain the enthalpy of any reaction involving these compounds (and elementary substances) as reactants and products.

The use of values of enthalpy of formation in this way is an application of the principle of conservation of energy. A further discussion of this question is given in Section 5-9.

Example 8. What is the enthalpy change in the combustion of carbon monoxide to carbon dioxide?

Solution. The standard enthalpy of formation at 25°C of CO(g) from the elements is $-26,416$ cal/mole, and that of $CO_2(g)$ is $-94,052$ cal/mole (given above in

Figure **5-5** *Diagram showing the standard enthalpy of formation of carbon monoxide and carbon dioxide from the elements at 25°C.*

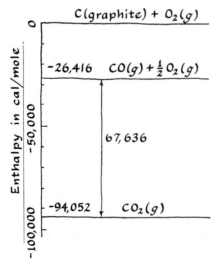

text). We may represent these values on an enthalpy diagram, Figure 5-5. We see that $CO(g) + \frac{1}{2}O_2(g)$ has $-26,416 - (-94,052) = 67,636$ cal/mole more enthalpy than $CO_2(g)$. Hence we write

$$CO(g) + \tfrac{1}{2}O_2(g) \longrightarrow CO_2(g) \qquad \Delta H° = -67,636 \text{ cal/mole}$$

Another method is the following: we write

$$C \text{ (graphite)} + O_2(g) \longrightarrow CO_2(g) + 94,052 \text{ cal/mole}$$
$$C \text{ (graphite)} + \tfrac{1}{2}O_2(g) \longrightarrow CO(g) + 26,416 \text{ cal/mole}$$

Subtracting the second equation from the first, we obtain

$$CO(g) + \tfrac{1}{2}O_2(g) \longrightarrow CO_2(g) + 67,636 \text{ cal/mole}$$

There is evolution of heat, 67,636 cal/mole. The change in enthalpy of the system, $\Delta H°$, is accordingly negative; its value is **$-67,636$ cal/mole.**

Illustrative Exercises

5-10. The enthalpy of formation of diamond from graphite at 25°C is 576 cal/mole. What is the enthalpy change on burning diamond to $CO_2(g)$?

5-11. When carbon dioxide is passed over red-hot charcoal it reacts to form carbon monoxide. Write the equation for the reaction, showing the amount of heat absorbed or evolved (as calculated for 25°C). Is the reaction exothermic or endothermic?

5-12. The heat evolved on combustion of methane, $CH_4(g)$, to carbon dioxide and water vapor is 191,762 cal/mole. The standard enthalpy of formation of $H_2O(g)$ is $-57,800$ cal/mole. Using information about carbon dioxide given in the text, determine whether the formation of $CH_4(g)$ from graphite and $H_2(g)$ is exothermic or endothermic, and by how much.
(Answer: Exothermic; heat liberated, 17,890 cal/mole.)

5-8. Heat Capacity. Heats of Fusion, Vaporization, and Transition

The amount of heat required to raise the temperature of unit quantity (1 mole or 1 g) of a substance by 1°C without change in phase is called the *heat capacity* (sometimes called *specific heat*) of the substance. Values of the heat capacity of substances are given in tables which may be found in reference books. The heat capacity is usually measured at constant pressure. The heat capacity per mole is equal to the heat capacity per gram multiplied by the molecular weight.

It was pointed out in 1819 by Dulong and Petit in France that for the heavier solid elementary substances (with atomic weights above 35) the product of the heat capacity per gram and the atomic weight is approximately constant, with value about 6.2 cal per degree. This is called the *rule of Dulong and Petit.* The extent of validity of the rule is indicated by the following examples:

EXPERIMENTAL VALUES OF HEAT
CAPACITY AT 20°C

ELEMENT	per gram	per mole
Al	0.214 cal deg^{-1} g^{-1}	5.8 cal deg^{-1} mole^{-1}
Fe	.107	6.0
Ni	.105	6.2
Ag	.0565	6.1
Au	.0312	6.1
Pb	.0305	6.3

The low value for aluminum (atomic weight 27) illustrates the deviation from the rule that occurs for elements with low atomic weight.

During the first half of the nineteenth century the rule was used to get rough values of the atomic weight of some elements, by dividing 6.2 by the measured heat capacity per gram of the solid elementary substance. For example, the heat capacity of bismuth is 0.0294 cal/g. By dividing this into 6.2 we obtain 211 as the rough value of the atomic weight of bismuth given by the rule of Dulong and Petit; the actual atomic weight of bismuth is 209.

Kopp's Rule. A rough estimate of the molar heat capacity of a solid substance can be obtained by adding the following values for the various atoms in the formula of the substance (this procedure is called *Kopp's rule*):

H	Li	Be	B	C	N	O	F	All others	
2.5	5.0	3.5	3.0	2.0	3.0	4.0	5.0	6.2	cal deg^{-1} mole^{-1}

These values are for room temperature. Liquids have somewhat larger heat capacity than the crystalline substances, usually about 15% larger. The heat capacity of liquid water is unusually large; it is 18 cal deg^{-1} mole^{-1}, whereas that of ice is 9 cal deg^{-1} mole^{-1}, agreeing with the rule. The interpretation of the large value for water is given in Chapter 16.

Example 9. When a mixture of iron filings and sulfur is ignited by a bit of burning magnesium ribbon, the mixture reacts to form iron sulfide, with enthalpy of reaction -22.7 kcal/mole:

$$Fe(c) + S(c) \longrightarrow FeS(c) + 22.7 \text{ kcal/mole}$$

If the reaction were complete, would the product reach its melting point (1193°C)?

   Solution. The heat available for heating the reaction mixture above 25°C is 22.7 kcal/mole, which is 22,700 cal/mole. The heat capacity of FeS(c) is given by Kopp's rule as about $2 \times 6.2 = 12.4$ cal deg^{-1} mole^{-1}. To heat FeS(c) to its melting point would require about 12.4 cal deg^{-1} mole^{-1} $\times$ (1193 $-$ 25) deg $= 12.4 \times 1168$ cal mole^{-1} $= 14,500$ cal mole^{-1}.

The heat available is larger than this amount. Hence if the reaction were complete and all of the heat released were used to heat the product, its melting point would be reached and some or all of it would be melted.

Heat Capacity at Low Temperatures. The low values of the molar heat capacity found for light elements at room temperature are shown by all elements at sufficiently low temperatures. Experimental curves of the heat capacity of diamond, aluminum, and lead are given in Figure 5-6. It is seen that for each element the heat capacity is very small at low temperature, and with increasing temperature increases toward an asymptote of about 6 kcal/mole; the value 5.5 is reached by diamond at 1000°K. The curves for different elements are similar, except for the scale along the temperature axis. By changing the scale by dividing the temperature by a suitable value for each element, called the *Debye characteristic temperature*, the curves can be made to coincide. The characteristic temperature was defined by P. Debye in 1912 in such a way that it is 4 times the absolute temperature at which the heat capacity reaches 3 cal/mole deg, half its maximum value.

The characteristic temperature has the value 90° for lead, 390° for aluminum, and 1890° for diamond. It increases with decrease in atomic weight and increase in strength of the bonds between the atoms.

The decrease of the heat capacity of solids toward zero at low temperatures is a quantum phenomenon. We shall discuss it further in Section 5-12.

Gases also show quantum effects in their heat-capacity values. Curves representing the heat capacities at constant pressure of some diatomic gases are shown in Figure 5-7. It is seen that at high temperatures the values approach 9 cal deg^{-1} mole^{-1}, and at lower temperatures 7 cal deg^{-1} mole^{-1}. Diatomic hydrogen falls to the value 5 cal deg^{-1} mole^{-1} at very low temper-

Figure **5-6**

Experimental values of heat capacity of diamond, aluminum, and lead.

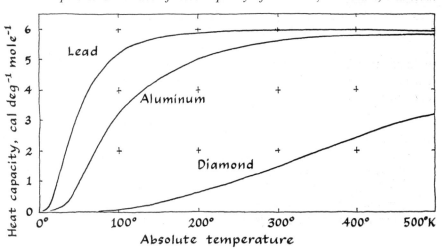

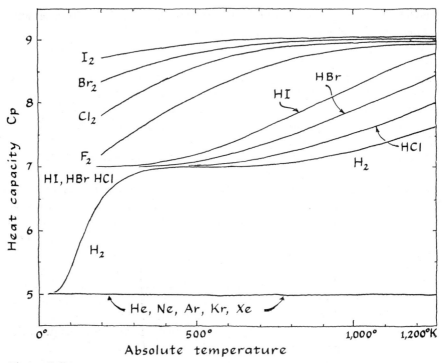

Figure 5-7

Experimental values of the heat capacity at constant pressure of some diatomic gases.

atures; this is the value found for monatomic gases. The interpretation of these phenomena will be presented in Section 5-12.

Heat of Fusion.   A definite amount of heat is required to convert a crystal into the liquid at the melting point; this is called the *heat of fusion*. The heat of fusion of ice is 79.7 cal/g or 1,436 cal/mole.

Heat of Vaporization.   The heat absorbed on vaporization at the boiling point is the *heat of vaporization;* for water its value is 539.6 cal/g or 9,710 cal/mole.

For many substances a rough value of the heat of vaporization can be predicted from *Trouton's rule,* which states that the quotient of the molar heat of vaporization by the absolute boiling point has a constant value, about 20 cal deg^{-1} mole^{-1}. For example, this rule predicts that the molar heat of vaporization of carbon disulfide, b.p. 319°K, is 20 × 319 = 6,380 cal/mole; the experimental value is 6,391 cal/mole. The heat of vaporization of water is larger than expected from Trouton's rule because of the strong intermolecular forces in the liquids, which result from the action of hydrogen bonds (see Section 16-10 for a more detailed discussion of the relation between the heat of vaporization and the boiling point).

Heat of Transition. The transition of a substance from one crystalline modification to another crystalline modification stable in a higher temperature range is accompanied by the absorption of the *heat of transition*. The value of this quantity for the transition of red phosphorus to white phosphorus, for example, is 3,700 cal/mole, and for red mercuric iodide to yellow mercuric iodide it is 3,000 cal/mole.

The use of these thermal quantities in calculations is illustrated below.

Example 10. What products would result from adding 100 ml of water to 56g of powdered lime, CaO, in an open insulated vessel of small heat capacity, with initial temperature 20°C? The enthalpy change for the reaction

$$CaO(c) + H_2O(l) \longrightarrow Ca(OH)_2(c)$$

is -16.0 kcal/mole.

> **Solution.** The products are one mole of $Ca(OH)_2$, with molar heat capacity (Kopp's rule) 19.2 cal/deg, and 82 ml of water. The heat required to increase the temperature of this system by 1° is $19.2 + 82 = 101$ cal. The 16,000 cal of heat liberated by the reaction would accordingly raise the temperature by $16,000/101 = 158°C$; that is, to the final temperature 178°C, if the vessel were sealed. However, on reaching 100°C some of the water would evaporate. The amount of heat needed to reach 100° is $(100 - 20)$ deg $\times$ 101 cal deg^{-1} = 80 $\times$ 101 cal = 8,080 cal. The amount available to evaporate some of the water is $16,000 - 8,080 = 7,920$ cal. The amount of water evaporated is 7,920 cal/539.6 cal g^{-1} = 14.7 g.
>
> Hence the products would be 74 g of $Ca(OH)_2$, 67.3 g of water, and 14.7 g of water vapor, all at 100°C.

5-9. Heat and Work. Energy and Enthalpy

The relation between heat and work is treated in courses in physics, and may be briefly reviewed here. Work is done by a directed force acting through a distance; the amount of work done by a force of one dyne acting through a distance of one centimeter is called one erg. If this amount of work is done in putting an object initially at rest into motion, we say that the moving object has a *kinetic energy* of 1 erg. All of this kinetic energy may be used to do work, as the moving object is slowed down to rest; for example, a string attached to the moving object might serve to lift a small weight to a certain height above its original position.

Another way in which the moving object can be slowed down to rest is through *friction*. The process that then occurs is that the kinetic energy of the directed motion of the moving body is converted into energy of randomly directed motion of the molecules of the bodies between which friction occurs.

This increase in vigor of molecular motion corresponds to an increase in temperature of the bodies. We say that heat has been added to the bodies, causing their temperatures to rise. Thus if one of the bodies was 1 g of water, and if its temperature rose by 1 deg, we would say that 1 cal of heat had entered it.

The question at once arises as to how much work must be done to produce this much heat. This question was answered by experiments carried out in Manchester, England, between 1840 and 1878 by James Prescott Joule (1818–1889), after Count Rumford (Benjamin Thompson, 1753–1814, an American Tory) had shown in 1798 that the friction of a blunt borer in a cannon caused an increase in temperature of the cannon. Joule's work led to essentially the value now accepted for the mechanical equivalent of heat; that is, for the relation between heat and work:

$$\textbf{1 cal = 4.1840 joule = 4.1840} \times \textbf{10}^7 \textbf{ erg}$$

The large unit of energy introduced here, the *joule*, is 1×10^7 ergs. One joule is also equal to the work done by the flow of one coulomb of electricity through a potential difference of one volt:

$$\textbf{1 joule = 1 volt-coulomb = 1 watt-sec = 1} \times \textbf{10}^7 \textbf{ erg}$$

The relation between heat and work can be illustrated by asking how great the height is at which the potential energy of a quantity of water in the earth's gravitational field would be equivalent to the heat required to raise its temperature by 1°C. The force of gravity on 1 g of water is 980 dynes. Hence the water would have to fall through a height of $4.184 \times 10^7/980 = 42{,}690$ cm, which is 1,400 feet, to get enough kinetic energy to raise its temperature by 1°C when converted into heat.

Energy and Enthalpy.   The energy E of a system is determined by the state of the system (composition, pressure, temperature; sometimes other factors, such as strength of gravitational field, electric field, magnetic field). The change in energy ΔE accompanying change of a system from an initial state to a final state is determined exactly by the initial state and the final state, and is independent of the path by way of which this change is effected.

The foregoing statement is a statement of the law of conservation of energy.

It is not true, however, that the *heat* evolved or absorbed by a system during a change from an initial state to a final state is independent of the path by way of which the change is effected. The change may take place by a path such that the system does work on the environment or work is done on the system by the environment.

In general, we may express the law of conservation of energy in the following way:

ΔE = heat transferred to the system from the environment
                     + work done on the system by the environment

The sum of the heat transferred to the system and the work done on the system constitutes the change in energy of the system. This sum is independent of the path between the initial state and the final state. The heat transferred depends on the path, and the work done depends on the path.

To illustrate, let us consider the reaction of liquid nitrogen trichloride at 25°C and 1 atm pressure to form nitrogen and chlorine at the same temperature and pressure:

$$2NCl_3(l) \longrightarrow N_2(g) + 3Cl_2(g)$$

The value of ΔE for this change in state is found by experiment to be $-108,000$ cal for 2 moles of NCl_3.

At 25°C and 1 atm pressure two moles of liquid nitrogen trichloride occupy the volume 148 ml. Under the same conditions the reactants, which are gases, occupy the volume 97,900 ml. We may carry out the change from the initial state to the final state in such a way that no work is done on the system by the environment or on the environment by the system. Two moles (240.8 g) of nitrogen trichloride at 25°C and 1 atm is sealed in a thin glass bulb, which is placed in a steel vessel with volume 97,900 ml. The vessel is then evacuated, and the nitrogen trichloride is exploded (caused to react) by passing a spark between two wires sealed into the bulb. When thermal equilibrium has been reached with the environment (at 25°C), the pressure inside the steel vessel is 1 atm. No work has been done. The amount of heat transferred to the system by the environment is exactly ΔE, which is $-108,000$ cal; that is, 108,000 cal of heat has been transferred from the system to the environment.

Another path from the same initial state of the system to the same final state is the following. Let us place a small internal-explosion engine inside the steel vessel, with 240.8 g of nitrogen trichloride (at 25°C) in its fuel tank, and with a shaft passing through the wall of the vessel to permit work to be done on the environment. The vessel, with volume 97,900 ml (not including the solid parts of the engine), is evacuated. The engine is then allowed to operate until the fuel is exhausted, and the system is allowed to stand until thermal equilibrium with the environment (at 25°C) is reached.

Let us assume that the engine resembles good Diesel engines in having 43% efficiency. The work done by the system on the environment would then be 43% × 108,000 cal = 46,440 cal. The heat transferred from the system to the environment would be 108,000 − 46,440 = 61,560 cal.

The change from the same initial state to the same final state of the system by other paths would in general involve different values of the heat exchanged with the environment and of the work done.

Most changes in state that are studied in the laboratory are carried out at 1 atm pressure, under conditions such that the volume of the system can change (rather than in an evacuated vessel, as described above). The system may increase in volume, by the amount ΔV; it then does the work $P \Delta V$ on the environment, in which P is the pressure. For example, if $2NCl_3(l)$ were to decompose slowly at 25°C and 1 atm pressure, in a cylinder with movable piston, the work 1 atm $\times$ (97,900 − 148) ml = 97,852 atm ml would be done by the system on the environment. (This work consists in pushing back the atmosphere.) Using the relation 1 atm ml = 0.0242 cal, we find that the pressure-volume work done by the system is 2,370 cal. The heat transferred to the environment during the change in state by this path is hence 108,000 − 2,370 = 105,630 cal.

The enthalpy H of a system is defined as the energy E plus the term PV:

$$H = E + PV \tag{1}$$

For any change of a system from an initial state to a final state carried out at constant pressure P in such a way that the only work done is the pressure-volume work, the value of ΔH is exactly equal to the heat transferred from the environment to the system. To obtain ΔE, it is necessary to measure also the change in volume and to apply the corresponding correction for the pressure-volume work.

The simplification resulting from the use of enthalpy (with the PV term) rather than energy was first recognized by the great American scientist J. Willard Gibbs (1839–1903) in the course of his theoretical studies, published in 1876 and 1878 under the title *On the Equilibrium of Heterogeneous Substances*, in which he laid the foundations of the whole field of chemical thermodynamics.

Gibbs and other workers in this field also attacked and solved the question of the maximum amount of work that can be done by a system on the environment during a change in state of the system. We shall return to this question in Chapters 11 and 18.

Example 11. If it were possible for all the heat of the reaction to be converted into kinetic energy of the jet of water molecules, what is the jet velocity that would result from using hydrogen and oxygen as rocket fuel?

    Solution. The heat evolved in the formation of one mole of water vapor is 57,800 cal (Exercise 5-12). This is equal to $57,800 \times 4.184 \times 10^7$ erg, which is 2.42×10^{12} erg. The kinetic energy in ergs of a mass of m grams at velocity v cm/sec is $\frac{1}{2}mv^2$. Hence we write

$$\tfrac{1}{2}mv^2 = 2.42 \times 10^{12} \text{ erg}$$

Placing $m = 18$ g, for one mole of water vapor, we solve for v and obtain

$$v^2 = 2 \times 2.42 \times 10^{12}/18 = 0.269 \times 10^{12}$$
$$v = 5.1 \times 10^5 \text{ cm/sec} = 5.1 \text{ km/sec} = 11,400 \text{ mph}$$

Example 12. If it were possible for all the heat of the reaction to be converted into the work of overcoming the earth's gravitation, what would be the maximum weight of a rocket ship powered by hydrogen and oxygen that could escape from the earth? The earth's field produces a force of 980 dynes on a mass of 1 g at the earth's surface, and requires 6.24×10^{11} erg of work to remove 1 g to infinity.*

Solution. The heat of the reaction is $2.42 \times 10^{12}/18 = 1.34 \times 10^{11}$ erg per gram of fuel (preceding example). But 6.24×10^{11} erg is needed to lift one gram to infinity. Hence 1.34×10^{11} erg would lift only $1.34 \times 10^{11}/6.24 \times 10^{11} = 0.215$ g to infinity. Hence one ton of fuel could lift only about one-fifth of a ton of ship out of the earth's field. The fuel would hence have to be burned in such a way that most of the products remained close to the earth's surface. (It is in fact not possible to convert all the heat of the reaction into the work of overcoming the earth's gravitation; about 65% is the maximum ordinarily achieved in rocket propulsion.)

Illustrative Exercises

5-13. The heat evolved on formation at room temperature of $H_2O(g)$ from $H_2(g)$ and $\frac{1}{2}O_2(g)$ is 57,800 cal/mole. Calculate the temperature of the water vapor produced in this reaction, if the entire heat of reaction were to be used to raise the temperature of the water molecules. Use the value 0.60 cal deg^{-1} g^{-1} for the heat capacity of water vapor. (The calculated value of the temperature is high, because some of the water dissociates at high temperatures into hydrogen and oxygen, absorbing heat in this process and thus decreasing the value of the temperature that is produced by the reaction.)

5-14. Use Kopp's rule to estimate values of the heat capacity (per gram) at room temperature of $AlCl_3(c)$, $CuI(c)$, $CaSO_4 \cdot 2H_2O(c)$, $C_{14}H_{10}(c)$ (anthracene, an organic compound), and $C_6H_6(l)$ (benzene). Experimental values are 0.188, 0.066, 0.265, 0.306, and 0.406 cal deg^{-1} g^{-1}, respectively.

5-15. (a) A piece of metal weighing 200 g was removed from boiling water and placed in a vacuum bottle containing some ice water and a piece of ice weighing 38.0 g. After a few minutes the piece of ice was removed and weighed; its weight was found to be 26.7 g. What is the approximate atomic weight of the metal?

(b) The oxide of this metal contains 10.44% oxygen. Calculate a more exact value of the atomic weight.

5-16. The enthalpy of formation of $HF(g)$ from $\frac{1}{2}H_2(g)$ and $\frac{1}{2}F_2(g)$ is $-64,200$ cal/mole. Compare the effectiveness for rocket propulsion of liquid hydrogen with liquid oxygen as oxidant and with liquid fluorine as oxidant. (See Example 11.) The comparison should be on the basis of heat liberated per unit weight of fuel plus oxidant. Ignore the difference in heats of vaporization.

* The mutual gravitational potential energy of two spherical masses m and M the distance R apart (measured between their centers) is $-mMg/R$ (g is the gravitational constant). The force, which is the derivative of this quantity with respect to R, is mMg/R^2. Hence the product of the force and R is the energy required to separate the two masses to infinity. The radius of the earth is 6.37×10^8 cm, and the product is $980 \times 6.37 \times 10^8 = 6.24 \times 10^{11}$ erg/g.

5-10. The Quantum Theory

Theoretical chemistry is largely based upon the quantum theory. It has been discovered during the twentieth century that objects with very small mass—atoms, molecules, electrons, atomic nuclei—do not behave in accordance with the laws of classical physics that describe adequately the behavior of ordinary objects, objects that weigh a milligram, a gram, a kilogram. Some of the laws that describe the behavior of electrons, atoms, and other objects with very small mass have been discovered; others, especially some of those pertaining to the interactions of nucleons (protons and neutrons in nuclei) and other fundamental particles (Chapter 29), remain to be discovered.

It was mentioned in Section 3-10 that Max Planck first introduced the idea of the emission and absorption of light in quanta in 1900, and that Einstein in 1905 suggested that light of frequency ν consists of particles (photons) with energy $h\nu$. The value of Planck's constant h is 6.6252×10^{-27} erg sec.

The development of quantum theory was at first slow. In 1907 Einstein pointed out that the quantum theory provides an explanation of the surprising temperature dependence of the heat capacity of solids (Figure 5-6, Section 5-12). The great importance of the quantum theory to chemistry was revealed in 1913 by Bohr's quantum theory of atomic structure, which we shall discuss in Chapter 7.

The Harmonic Oscillator in One Dimension. Planck suggested that a particle (an atom or electron) in a crystal might be thought of as carrying out vibrations about its equilibrium position, with its vibrational energy restricted to certain values differing by the amount $h\nu$. In the modern form of quantum theory (*quantum mechanics* or *wave mechanics*, developed by W. Heisenberg, E. Schrödinger, and P. A. M. Dirac in 1925), the equation for the allowed energy values of a one-dimensional harmonic oscillator with characteristic frequency of oscillation ν is

$$E_v = (v + \tfrac{1}{2})h\nu \qquad (2)$$

with $v = 0, 1, 2, 3, \cdots$. The number v is called the *vibrational quantum number*. We see (Figure 5-8) that the allowed energy values, which are called *energy levels*, for this system (the one-dimensional harmonic oscillator) constitute a series, with difference $h\nu$ between successive terms.

Let us consider a particle free to move in one dimension (the x axis), and bound to the point $x = 0$ by a force proportional to its displacement. Let k be the force constant, such that the restoring force for displacement x is $-kx$ and the potential energy is $\tfrac{1}{2}kx^2$. It is shown in courses in chemical physics that the motion of the particle is simple harmonic, described by the equation

$$x = a \sin 2\pi\nu t \qquad (3)$$

Here a is the amplitude and ν is the frequency of the oscillation. The frequency ν is related to the force constant k and the mass m of the particle by the relation

$$k = 4\pi^2 m\nu^2 \qquad (4)$$

and the energy is given by the equation

$$E = 2\pi^2 m\nu^2 a^2 \qquad (5)$$

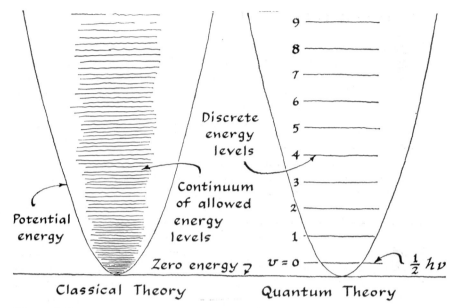

Discrete
energy
levels

Continuum
of allowed
energy
levels

Potential
energy

Zero energy

$v = 0$

$\frac{1}{2}h\nu$

Classical Theory   **Quantum Theory**

Figure 5-8

Quantized energy levels for the harmonic oscillator. The parabola repre-
sents the potential energy as a function of the displacement of the particle
from its equilibrium position.

It is easily shown that for the harmonic oscillator in any state of motion the
time-average potential energy (time average of $\frac{1}{2}kx^2$) and the time-average kinetic
energy (time average of $\frac{1}{2}mv^2$, with v here the velocity) are equal; each is equal to
one-half of the total energy, E. (This is called the *virial theorem* for the harmonic
oscillator; it holds for both classical mechanics and quantum mechanics.)

Degenerate Quantum States.   For many systems two or more quantum states
may have the same energy. These states are called *degenerate states*; a quantum
state that does not have the same energy as any other quantum state is called
nondegenerate.

The one-dimensional harmonic oscillator was described above as having quantum states represented by the values 0, 1, 2, 3, $\cdots$ of the vibrational quantum
number v, with energy values $E_v = (v + \frac{1}{2})h\nu$. An atom in a crystal may occupy a position with orthorhombic symmetry (Section 2-5). Its motion relative
to its neighbors might then be described as approximately that of an anisotropic
three-dimensional harmonic oscillator. Its vibration along the x axis, the y axis,
and the z axis would involve three different frequencies, ν_x, ν_y, and ν_z, respectively. A quantum state for the three-dimensional oscillator is described by the
values of three quantum numbers, v_x, v_y, and v_z, each of which can assume the
values 0, 1, 2, 3, $\cdots$. The energy $E_{v_x v_y v_z}$ of the state $v_x v_y v_z$ is the sum of three
terms:

$$E_{v_x v_y v_z} = (v_x + \tfrac{1}{2})\nu_x + (v_y + \tfrac{1}{2})\nu_y + (v_z + \tfrac{1}{2})\nu_z \tag{6}$$

The normal state 000 and the other states, 100, 010, 001, 200, 020, 002, 110, etc., are all nondegenerate, unless the frequencies ν_x, ν_y, ν_z are in the ratio of integers.

If the atom is in a position with cubic symmetry the three frequencies ν_x, ν_y, and ν_z are equal. The motion of the atom is then approximately that of an isotropic three-dimensional harmonic oscillator; with $\nu_x = \nu_y = \nu_z = \nu$, the energy levels are

$$E_{v_x v_y v_z} = (v_x + v_y + v_z + \tfrac{3}{2})h\nu \qquad (7)$$

The normal state, 000, is nondegenerate, with energy $E_{000} = \tfrac{3}{2}h\nu$. The first excited energy level is triply degenerate, with $v_x v_y v_z = 100$, 010, and 001, and $E_{100} = E_{010} = E_{001} = \tfrac{5}{2}h\nu$. The second excited energy level has sixfold degeneracy (200, 020, 001, 011, 101, 110), and so on.

A System of Coupled Equivalent Harmonic Oscillators.   A crystal (such as a copper crystal) containing N atoms in equivalent positions with cubic symmetry may be described as a system of $3N$ harmonic oscillators, each with frequency ν, coupled with one another (that is, interacting with one another). If the coupling is weak (interaction energy small enough to be neglected), the energy of the system is equal to the sum of the energy values $(v_i + \tfrac{1}{2})h\nu$, with $v_i = v_1, v_2, \cdots, v_{3N}$, the quantum numbers for the $3N$ oscillators. (Each atom is considered to be equivalent to three oscillators.) All of the quantum states of the system with the same value of the sum $\sum v_i$ of the $3N$ quantum numbers have the same energy.

A system of this sort is used in the following section in the discussion of the theory of statistical mechanics.

5-11.   The Boltzmann Distribution Law

Statistical mechanics is one of the most interesting and valuable branches of physical and chemical theory. It is a large subject, and in part difficult, as you will find if you examine a treatise on it. Nevertheless, you can obtain some knowledge about it in the course of your study of general chemistry, and you can use this knowledge to obtain increased insight about the world.

Statistical mechanics is based almost entirely on the *Boltzmann distribution law*. In its classical form this law was developed during the decades preceding 1900, largely by the German physicist Ludwig Boltzmann (1844–1906), and in its quantum form shortly after the discovery of quantum theory (1900) and quantum mechanics (1925). The quantum form is more easily presented than the classical form.

The Boltzmann Distribution Law in Quantum Theory.   The distribution law deals with the relative probabilities of different states of a system (atom, molecule, group of atoms or molecules) in thermodynamic equilibrium at absolute temperature T. It involves an important quantity called the *Boltzmann exponential factor* (or *Boltzmann factor*):

$$\text{Boltzmann factor} = e^{-E/kT} = \exp\left(-E/kT\right) \qquad (8)$$

Here E is the energy of the system in the state under consideration, and k is the *Boltzmann constant*, with value 1.3805×10^{-16} erg deg^{-1}.

It will be pointed out in the following chapter that the Boltzmann constant is the gas constant R divided by Avogadro's number; k is the gas constant per molecule, whereas R is the gas constant per mole. The Boltzmann factor can be rewritten with the energy per mole ($E_{\text{molar}} = NE$) and the molar gas constant ($R = Nk$):

$$\text{Boltzmann factor} = \exp\left(-E_{\text{molar}}/RT\right) \qquad (9)$$

The value of R is 1.9872 cal deg^{-1} mole^{-1} or 22.413 liter atm deg^{-1} mole^{-1}.

We now give the Boltzmann distribution law in its quantum form: *the probabilities of two quantum states A and B of a system, with energy values E_A and E_B, in thermodynamic equilibrium at absolute temperature T, are proportional to their Boltzmann exponential factors $e^{-E_A/kT}$ and $e^{-E_B/kT}$.*

We may rewrite the law as follows:

$$\frac{\text{Probability of quantum state } A}{\text{Probability of quantum state } B} = \frac{\exp\left(-E_A/kT\right)}{\exp\left(-E_B/kT\right)} = \exp\left[-(E_A - E_B)/kT\right] \qquad (10)$$

If the energy levels A and B are degenerate, with p_A and p_B quantum states, respectively, the Boltzmann distribution law as given above can be extended to the form

$$\frac{\text{Probability of energy level } A}{\text{Probability of energy level } B} = \frac{p_A \exp\left(-E_A/kT\right)}{p_B \exp\left(-E_B/kT\right)} = \frac{p_A}{p_B} \exp\left[-(E_A - E_B)/kT\right] \qquad (11)$$

The quantity p_A is called the quantum weight of the energy level A. Its value is unity for nondegenerate energy levels.

Derivation of the Boltzmann Distribution Law. Let us consider a large system, such as a crystal that can be described as a collection of weakly coupled equivalent harmonic oscillators. We assume that the total energy of the system is known, and we ask what the properties of the system are—for example, how many of the individual oscillators are in the lowest state ($v = 0$), how many in the next state ($v = 1$), and so on.

This question can be answered by use of the following theorem of quantum mechanics: *In calculating average values of the properties of a system with energy E_{total}, the same weight is to be assigned to each quantum state with this value of the energy.*[*]

For example, let us consider the system of three equivalent harmonic oscillators, A, B, and C, interacting weakly with one another. Let the total energy be $7\frac{1}{2}h$, corresponding to the average energy $2\frac{1}{2}h$ per oscillator. We ask: What are the probabilities that the first oscillator, A, will be in the quantum state with value 0, or 1, or 2, $\cdots$, for its quantum number v_A?

The total energy of the system is given by the equation

_____

* This theorem can be derived from the basic principles of quantum mechanics together with the assumption that the interactions involved in the transition from one quantum state to another operate in a random way.

$$E_{\text{total}} = (v_A + v_B + v_C + \tfrac{3}{2})h\nu \tag{12}$$

The various quantum states with this energy have $v_A + v_B + v_C = 6$.

We see that one such state is the one with $v_A = 6$, $v_B = 0$, and $v_C = 0$. Two similar ones are those with $v_A = 0$, $v_B = 6$, $v_C = 0$ and $v_A = 0$, $v_B = 0$, $v_C = 6$. These three states are represented by the first line, 6 0 0 etc. (3), in Table 5-2. Sim-

Table **5-2**

Sets of Quantum Numbers for Three Coupled
Equivalent Harmonic Oscillators with
Total Quantum Number 6

v_A	v_B	v_C		VALUE OF v_A	NUMBER OF TIMES IT OCCURS
6	0	0 etc.*	(3)	0	7
5	1	0	(6)	1	6
4	2	0	(6)	2	5
4	1	1	(3)	3	4
3	3	0	(3)	4	3
3	2	1	(6)	5	2
2	2	2	(1)	6	1

* The other sets indicated by "etc." are in this case 0 6 0 and 0 0 6, giving a total of three, as shown by the number in parentheses.

ilarly, the second line represents the six states in which one oscillator has $v = 5$, one has $v = 1$, and one has $v = 0$. You can easily verify that there are 28 quantum states for the energy level $E_{\text{total}} = 7\tfrac{1}{2}h\nu$.

By counting the number of times that $v_A = 0$ occurs in these 28 sets of quantum numbers, we find it to be 7. The probability of the state $v_A = 6$ for the oscillator A is accordingly $\tfrac{7}{28} = 0.250$. This value and the values for $v_A = 1, 2, \cdots$ are listed in the second column of Table 5-3.

A similar calculation can be made for larger systems, and for the same average energy $2\tfrac{1}{2}h\nu$ per oscillator. Values calculated for the system of five oscillators and total energy $12\tfrac{1}{2}h\nu$ are also given in Table 5-3.

For a very large number of oscillators this calculation leads to values in close agreement with those given by the Boltzmann factor, Equation 8, with a suitable normalization constant, C, chosen to make $\sum_{v=0}^{\infty} p_v = 1$ (that is, the sum of the probabilities is unity—this is the customary convention in defining probability), and with kT replaced by $\tfrac{5}{2}h\nu$, the average energy per oscillator. The details of the calculation are given in Example 13.

The three sets of calculated values for p_v are represented in Figure 5-9.

The discussion of the Boltzmann distribution law is continued in the following examples, in Section 5-12 (quantum effects on heat capacity), in the next chapter (the distribution law for molecular velocities), in later chapters, and in Appendix V, in which some of the special aspects of the law in classical mechanics are taken up. You will find that with practice you can obtain a good understanding of this important principle of nature, and that you can often apply it to in-

Table **5-3**

Probabilities of Quantum States of an Individual
Harmonic Oscillator in a System of Harmonic
Oscillators with Average Vibrational Quantum Number 2

VALUE OF QUANTUM NUMBERS v	CALCULATED PROBABILITY FOR		
	3 OSCILLATORS p_v	5 OSCILLATORS* p_v	INFINITE NUMBER p_v
0	0.250	0.286	0.3295
1	.214	.220	.2209
2	.179	.165	.1481
3	.143	.120	.0993
4	.107	.084	.0666
5	.071	.056	.0447
6	.036	.035	.0299
7	.000	.020	.0201
8		.010	.0135
9		.004	.0091
10		.001	.0061
11		.000	.0041
12			.0027
13			.0018
14			.0012
15			.0008
16			.0006
17			.0004
18			.0002
19			.0002
20			.0001
21			.0001
22			.0000
Total	1.000	1.001	1.0000

* From Linus Pauling and E. Bright Wilson, Jr., *Introduction to Quantum Mechanics*, McGraw-Hill Book Co., Inc., 1935, p. 400.

crease your insight into natural phenomena, including those classed as chemical thermodynamics. Many questions can be given a satisfactory approximate answer simply by consideration of the magnitude of the Boltzmann exponential factor. It is especially important to realize that this factor is squared when the energy is doubled. If the factor has the value 0.1 for energy (or difference in energy of two states) E, its value is 0.01 for $2E$, 0.001 for $3E$, 0.0001 for $4E$, etc.

The foregoing discussion of quantum theory and statistical mechanics and the later discussions in this book are superficial and inadequate. A scientist who strives to attain a deep understanding of the nature of the world must have detailed knowledge of quantum theory, statistical mechanics, and thermodynamics.

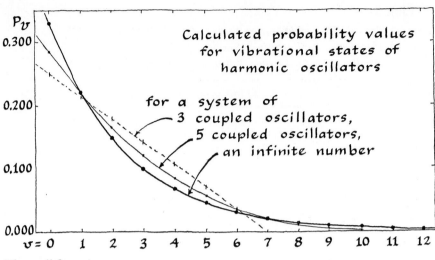

Figure 5-9

Calculated values of probability of different quantum numbers for a system of 3, 5, or infinite number of harmonic oscillators with average vibrational quantum number 2.

I hope that you are planning to study these subjects, and that in the meantime you are obtaining the knowledge of mathematics that is needed for their mastery.

Example 13.   Apply the Boltzmann distribution law to obtain the probability p_v of the state v of the harmonic oscillator.

Solution.   From Equation 8 we write

$$p_v = Cx^v \tag{13}$$

for the probability. Here C is a normalizing factor and x has the value

$$x = \exp\left(-h\nu/kT\right) \tag{14}$$

To evaluate C we note that the sum of p_v for all values of v is

$$\sum_{v=0}^{\infty} p_v = C(1 + x + x^2 + x^3 + \cdots) \tag{15}$$

We recognize that the series $1 + x + x^2 + x^3 + \cdots$ is $(1 - x)^{-1}$. [This can be verified by expanding $(1 - x)^{-1}$ by the binomial theorem.] The sum of probabilities $\sum_{v=0}^{\infty} p_v$ is unity; hence we obtain

$$C(1 - x)^{-1} = 1$$

or

$$C = 1 - x = 1 - \exp\left(-h\nu/kT\right)$$

The probability p_v hence has the value

$$p_v = (1 - x)x^v = [1 - \exp\left(-h\nu/kT\right)]\exp\left(-vh\nu/kT\right) \tag{16}$$

It will be shown in the following example that for $kT = \frac{5}{2}h\nu$ the average value of the energy is $\frac{5}{2}h\nu$ (i.e., $v = 2$), corresponding to Figure 5-9. For this value of kT, x has the value $e^{-2/5} = e^{-0.400}$. We note that the relation

$$e = 10^{-1/2.303}$$

permits us to evaluate $x = e^{-0.400}$ easily, by use of a table of common logarithms:

$$x = e^{-0.400} = 10^{-0.400/2.303} = 10^{-0.1736}$$
$$\log x = -0.1736 = -1 + 0.8264$$
$$x = 0.6705$$

From Equation 16 we obtain

$$p_v = 0.3295(0.6705)^v$$

The values of p_v obtained in this way are given in the last column of Table 5-3. Note that the probability of each state is 67% of that of the next more stable state (v less by 1).

Example 14. What is the average energy of a harmonic oscillator with frequency ν at temperature T?

Solution. The energy E_v of the vth state is $(v + \frac{1}{2})h\nu$. The average energy $\overline{E}$ is the sum of the products $p_v E_v$:

$$\overline{E} = \sum_{v=0}^{\infty} p_v E_v$$

$$= h\nu \sum_{v=0}^{\infty} p_v v + \frac{1}{2}h\nu \sum_{v=0}^{\infty} p_v \qquad (17)$$

Introducing $(1 - x)x^v$ for p_v (Equation *16*) and noting that $\sum p_v = 1$ (in the second term), we obtain

$$\overline{E} = h\nu(1 - x)\left(\sum_{v=0}^{\infty} vx^v \right) + \frac{1}{2}h\nu$$

The sum is easily evaluated by use of the binomial theorem:

$$\sum_{v=0}^{\infty} vx^v = x + 2x^2 + 3x^3 + \cdots$$
$$= x(1 + 2x + 3x^2 + \cdots)$$
$$= x(1 - x)^{-2}$$

Hence we obtain the result

$$\overline{E} = \frac{h\nu \exp(-h\nu/kT)}{1 - \exp(-h\nu/kT)} + \frac{1}{2}h\nu \qquad (18)$$

Let us place $kT = \frac{5}{2}h\nu$, as in the preceding example. The value of the Boltzmann factor is then $e^{-2/5} = 0.6705$, and the value of the average energy is

$$\overline{E} = h\nu\left(\frac{0.6705}{1 - 0.6705} + \frac{1}{2} \right) = h\nu\left(\frac{0.6705}{0.3295} + \frac{1}{2} \right)$$
$$= (2.03 + 0.50)h\nu = 2.53h\nu$$

Hence $\bar{E}$, the average energy at temperature T with $kT = \frac{5}{2}h\nu$, is very nearly equal to $\frac{5}{2}h\nu$, and hence to kT.

It is found that at high temperature ($kT > h\nu$) the average energy is approximately kT. The average kinetic energy and the average potential energy are each equal to $\frac{1}{2}kT$. This is called the *principle of equipartition of energy.**

Example 15. The vibrational frequency of the HCl molecule is found by analysis of the infrared absorption spectrum of hydrogen chloride gas to have the value $\nu = 8.97 \times 10^{13}$ sec^{-1} (i.e., vibrations per second). What fraction of the gas molecules at room temperature (293°K) are in the first excited vibrational state? What is the fraction at four times this absolute temperature?

Solution. The HCl molecule can be treated as a one-dimensional harmonic oscillator, with vibrational energy $E_v = (v + \frac{1}{2})h\nu$. The value of $h\nu/kT$ is

$$\frac{h\nu}{kT} = \frac{6.625 \times 10^{-27} \text{ erg sec} \times 8.97 \times 10^{13} \text{ sec}^{-1}}{1.380 \times 10^{-16} \text{ erg deg}^{-1} \times 293 \text{ deg}} = 14.7$$

Hence the Boltzmann factor $e^{-h\nu/kT}$ has the value $e^{-14.7} = 10^{-14.7/2.303} = 10^{-6.4} = 10^{-7} \times 10^{0.6} = 4 \times 10^{-7}$. We conclude that only four molecules in ten million are in the first excited state at room temperature.

At a temperature four times as great (1152°K) the Boltzmann exponent is $\frac{1}{4}$ as large, and the factor becomes $10^{-1.6} = 10^{-2} \times 10^{0.4} = 2.5 \times 10^{-2}$. Hence at this temperature about 2.5% of the molecules are in the first excited state.

Example 16. The nucleus Se^{80} has an excited state 665 keV (kilo electron volts; 1 keV = 1000 eV) above the normal state. Would some Se^{80} nuclei be raised to this level at atomic-bomb temperature, 50,000,000°K?

Solution. The energy 665,000 eV is 0.665×10^6 eV $\times 1.602 \times 10^{-12}$ erg/eV $= 1.065 \times 10^{-6}$ erg. (The conversion factor from eV to erg is given in Appendix II.) The value of kT at 50,000,000°K is 1.380×10^{-16} erg deg^{-1} $\times 5 \times 10^7$ deg $= 6.9 \times 10^{-9}$ erg. The value of E/kT is $1.065 \times 10^{-6}/6.9 \times 10^{-9} = 154$, and the value of the Boltzmann factor is $e^{-154} = 10^{-154/2.303} = 10^{-67}$. The ratio of quantum weights of the excited state and normal state is not likely to be more than 5. Hence no excited Se^{80} is present in thermodynamic equilibrium with normal Se^{80} at 50,000,000°K.

An alternative method of calculation is by use of molar quantities. With 1 eV = 23,063 cal/mole, $E_{\text{molar}} = 0.665 \times 10^6 \times 2.3063 \times 10^4 = 1.53 \times 10^{10}$ cal/mole, $RT = 1.987 \times 50,000,000 = 0.993 \times 10^8$ cal/mole, and $E_{\text{molar}}/RT = 153/0.993 = 154$, as above.

5-12. The Quantum Theory of Low-temperature Heat Capacity

One of the early successes of the quantum theory was the explanation, by Einstein, of the decrease in heat capacity toward zero observed for solids at low temperature (Figure 5-6).

*For other systems this principle applies to the kinetic energy, but in general not to the potential energy.

In the preceding section we have shown (Equation 17) that the average energy of a harmonic oscillator at temperature T has the value kT if the temperature is high, so that kT is greater than $h\nu$, the energy difference of adjacent energy levels. For a classical harmonic oscillator this energy difference of adjacent energy levels is zero, and the expression $\bar{E} = kT$ should be valid at all values of the temperature.

A crystal containing N atoms (one mole) may be described as equivalent to $3N$ harmonic oscillators (Section 5-10). The molar energy of vibration is then

$$E_{\text{molar}} = 3NkT = 3RT \tag{19}$$

The heat capacity at constant volume can be obtained by differentiating with respect to T:

$$c_v = \frac{dE_{\text{molar}}}{dT} = 3R = 6 \text{ cal deg}^{-1} \text{ mole}^{-1} \tag{20}$$

Thus the classical theory of statistical mechanics leads directly to the conclusion that the molar heat capacity at constant volume for elements should have the value 6 cal deg^{-1} mole^{-1}; the value at constant pressure should be about 0.2 cal deg^{-1} mole^{-1} larger. As mentioned in Section 5-8, this agrees with the experimental values at room temperature for elements with large atomic weight, but the light elements at room temperature and all elements at sufficiently low temperature are observed to have much smaller values, approaching zero as the temperature approaches 0°K.

The force constant for the bonds between each atom and its neighboring atoms in a crystal can be calculated from the measured value of the compressibility of the crystal. From the value of the force constant and the mass of the atom the frequency of the vibration of the atom relative to its neighbors can be calculated. The value of ν found in this way for aluminum is 4 times that for lead, and the value for diamond is 20 times that for lead. The corresponding energy levels (relative to the state with $v = 0$ for each element) are shown in Figure 5-10. We see that if a piece of lead, a piece of aluminum, and a diamond were in contact with a substance at such a temperature that the average collision between atoms could provide the amount of energy indicated by the horizontal arrow, the lead atoms could accept the energy. On the other hand, this amount of energy would be far less than needed

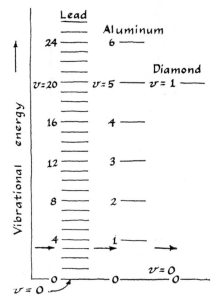

Figure 5-10 *Diagram showing relative vibrational energy levels for crystals of diamond, aluminum, and lead.*

to raise a carbon atom of diamond from the lowest vibrational state ($v = 0$) to the first excited level ($v = 1$). Hence increase in the temperature would not cause the diamond to accept energy from the surroundings, and its heat capacity would be close to zero.

In Example 17, given below, the expression for the heat capacity for $3N$ quantized harmonic oscillators is evaluated. It is found that the heat capacity is calculated to be $1.5R$, half the normal value, when T has approximately the value $\frac{1}{3}h\nu/k$.

Einstein calculated the heat-capacity function in this way, in 1907. The calculated curves were found to fall off with decreasing temperature more rapidly than the experimental values. P. Debye then developed a more refined theory. He took into consideration the vibrational motion of a group of two or more atoms relative to the surrounding atoms. His theoretical heat-capacity function was found to be in complete agreement with experiment, and scientists then recognized (in 1912) that it is necessary to use the quantum theory to understand the properties of substances in terms of their atomic and molecular structures. In the Debye theory the heat capacity is $1.5R$ when T has approximately the value $\frac{1}{4}h\nu/k$.

Quantum effects were also recognized in the observed heat capacities of gases. Classical statistical mechanics (Section 6-11) leads to the value 5 cal deg^{-1} mole^{-1} for monatomic gases (heat capacity at constant pressure), as observed for the noble gases and metal vapors. For diatomic gases the value 9 cal deg^{-1} mole^{-1} is expected from classical theory; 5 cal deg^{-1} mole^{-1} for translational motion (as for monatomic gases), 2 cal deg^{-1} mole^{-1} for rotational motion, and 2 cal deg^{-1} mole^{-1} for vibrational motion. The Einstein theory accounts quantitatively, with use of the vibrational frequencies given by the spectra of the molecules, for the change from 9 to 7 cal deg^{-1} mole^{-1} shown in Figure 5-7. A further decrease to the value 5 cal deg^{-1} mole^{-1} characteristic of monatomic molecules is found for H_2; this effect shows that the rotational motion of molecules is also quantized.

Example 17. At what value of the temperature does the heat capacity of a quantized harmonic oscillator have half the equipartition value?

Solution. The average energy of a quantized harmonic oscillator at temperature T is given in Equation 17:

$$\overline{E} = \frac{h\nu \exp(-h\nu/kT)}{1 - \exp(-h\nu/kT)} + \frac{1}{2}h\nu$$

The heat capacity is $d\overline{E}/dT$. On carrying out the differentiation, we obtain the result

$$\frac{d\overline{E}}{dT} = k\frac{u^2 e^u}{(e^u - 1)^2} \tag{21}$$

with $u = h\nu/kT$. To find the value of u at which the heat capacity has the value $\frac{1}{2}k$, we substitute numerical values of u in the expression on the right side of Equation 21. The values that are obtained for this expression (not including k) are given in the following table:

u	$\dfrac{1}{k}\dfrac{d\bar{E}}{dT}$
0	1.000
1	0.921
2	.724
3	.496
4	.304
5	.171
6	.090
7	.045
8	.022

Hence the heat capacity has half its high-temperature value (2 cal deg^{-1} mole^{-1} for the contribution of the vibrational motion of diatomic molecules) when $u = 3$ (more accurately, 2.98); that is, when T is approximately equal to $\frac{1}{3}h\nu/k$. (The Debye theory gives $T = \frac{1}{4}h\nu/k$ as the temperature at which the heat capacity of a solid element reaches half its high-temperature value of 6 cal deg^{-1} mole^{-1}.)

Illustrative Exercises

5-17. In Figure 5-7 the curve for HCl indicates that at about 1300°K the vibrational heat capacity for the molecule has reached 1 cal deg^{-1} mole^{-1}, which is half the equipartition value. Using the result of Example 17, evaluate the vibrational frequency for the HCl molecule, and compare with the observed frequency 8.97×10^{13} sec^{-1} (Example 15).

5-18. From the heat-capacity curves of Figure 5-6 it can be determined that the vibrational frequencies for diamond, aluminum, and lead are in the ratios 20:4:1. What are the ratios of the force constants in the three elements? (Note the relation connecting frequency, force constant, and mass, Equation 4.)   (Answer: 23:2:1.)

5-19. By reference to Figure 5-7, state whether the vibrational frequency of the Cl_2 molecule is greater than or less than that of the HCl molecule. By about what factor?
[Answer: Less, 0.21; the observed (spectroscopic) value is 0.218.]

5-20. If a hydrogen atom in the cubic crystal Pd_2H can be treated as an isotropic three-dimensional harmonic oscillator with vibrational frequency $\frac{1}{4}$ that of the HCl molecule, what fraction of the hydrogen atoms would be in the first excited vibrational level at room temperature? In the second excited vibrational level? Remember that the hydrogen atom in the crystal is a three-dimensional oscillator.   (Answer: 7%; 0.33%.)

5-21. It is evident from Figure 5-6 that for lead at room temperature $h\nu$ is much smaller than kT. What is the approximate ratio of the number of lead atoms in the first excited vibrational level to the number in the normal state?   (Answer: 3.)

EXERCISES

Note: Slide-rule accuracy is usually sufficient for chemical problems. This is not so for atomic-weight problems, which contain data given to five or six significant figures; for these problems five-place or seven-place logarithms or some equivalent method of calculation must be used, and the atomic weights should be calculated to five or six significant figures.

5-22. How much sulfuric acid, H_2SO_4, could be obtained from 100 lbs of sulfur? (Answer: 306 lbs.)

5-23. The density of oxygen at 20°C and 1 atm is 1.33 g/liter. What weight of mercuric oxide, HgO, would have to be decomposed to produce 5 liters of oxygen at this temperature and pressure?

5-24. Calculate the elementary composition of sugar (sucrose), $C_{12}H_{22}O_{11}$; that is, calculate the percentage of each element in this substance. (Answer: 42.1 % C, 6.5 % H, 51.4 % O.)

5-25. What is the elementary composition of chrome alum, $KCr(SO_4)_2 \cdot 12H_2O$?

5-26. Kernite, $Na_2B_4O_7 \cdot 4H_2O$, can be shipped to its destination and there treated with water to form borax, $Na_2B_4O_7 \cdot 10H_2O$. What saving in freight cost results from doing this, instead of converting it to borax before shipping? (Answer: 28.4 %.)

5-27. How much baking soda should be mixed with 1 level teaspoonful (4 g) of cream of tartar to make baking powder? Cream of tartar is potassium hydrogen tartrate, $KHC_4H_4O_6$, and baking soda is sodium hydrogen carbonate, $NaHCO_3$. The reaction that takes place in rising dough made with baking powder is

$$KHC_4H_4O_6 + NaHCO_3 \longrightarrow KNaC_4H_4O_6 + H_2O + CO_2$$

5-28. Platinum forms two chlorides, one of which contains 26.7 % chlorine and the other 42.1 % chlorine. What are the formulas of the two substances? (Answer: $PtCl_2$, $PtCl_4$.)

5-29. What is the percentage of oxygen in water, H_2O? In heavy water, D_2O (deuterium oxide)?

5-30. On combustion of a hydrocarbon (a substance containing only hydrogen and carbon), 0.04497 g gave 0.02381 g H_2O and 0.15503 g CO_2. What are possible formulas of the substance?

5-31. A sample of cheese weighing 0.1103 g was ignited (heated strongly in a crucible until the organic matter has been burned off), and the ash was dissolved in water and precipitated with silver nitrate, forming 0.00283 g AgCl. Assuming the chloride in the cheese to be sodium chloride, calculate the percentage of sodium chloride in the cheese. (Answer: 1.05 %.)

5-32. A known fluoride of silver contains 85.1 % silver. What is its simplest formula?

5-33. Two chlorides of a metal were found on analysis to contain 50.91 % and 46.37 %, respectively, of the metal. What are the possible values of the atomic weight of the metal? What is the metal? (Refer to the atomic-weight table.)

5-34. An oxychloride of vanadium is found on analysis to have the elementary composition V 60.17 %, O 18.89 %, Cl 20.94 %. What is the simplest formula which can be assigned to it? (Answer: V_2O_2Cl.)

5-35. Potassium and cadmium form an intermetallic compound containing 2.61 % potassium. What is its simplest formula?

5-36. By dissolving aluminum in hydrochloric acid, precipitating $Al(OH)_3$ with sodium hydroxide, and heating the collected precipitate to convert it to the oxide, the ratio of aluminum to oxygen in the oxide was found to be 1.124015. Calculate from this experimental value the atomic weight of aluminum. (Answer: 26.976.)

5-37. On complete combustion 3.03162 g of

anthracene, $C_{14}H_{10}$, gave 10.48035 g of carbon dioxide. Calculate the atomic weight of carbon, using 1.0080 for hydrogen. (Answer: 12.011.)

5-38. A certain substance containing only carbon, hydrogen, and oxygen gave 0.6179 g of carbon dioxide and 0.1264 g of water on combustion of a sample weighing 0.2200 g. What is the empirical formula of the substance?

5-39. The appearance of a rock indicates that it is a mixture of magnesite (magnesium carbonate, $MgCO_3$) and quartz (SiO_2). It is found that 1.00 g of the rock, on treatment with hydrochloric acid, yields 0.430 g of carbon dioxide. Write the equation for the reaction, and calculate the percentage of magnesite and the percentage of quartz in the rock.

5-40. The combustion of diborane is exothermic:

$$B_2H_6(g) + 3O_2(g) \longrightarrow B_2O_3(c) \\ + 3H_2O(g) + 482{,}900 \text{ cal/mole}$$

Compare diborane and hydrogen as rocket fuels, on the basis of heat production per unit weight of fuel and oxidant (see Exercise 5-8). (Answer: Diborane-oxygen liberates 21% more heat per gram than hydrogen-oxygen.)

5-41. The heat of combustion of decaborane, $B_{10}H_{14}(c)$, is 1922 kcal/mole. Compare decaborane and diborane (preceding exercise) as rocket fuels, on the basis of heat production per unit weight of fuel and oxidant.

REFERENCES

The following *Scientific American* offprints (see Appendix VI) are of interest to this chapter:

256. The Mass Spectrometer

205. The Quantum Theory

CHAPTER 6

Hydrogen and Oxygen. The

Properties of Gases

Hydrogen and oxygen form a great many compounds with other elements, and take part in a great number of chemical reactions. We shall begin our detailed study of descriptive chemistry in this chapter with the study of these two elements.

Both hydrogen and oxygen are gases at room temperature and atmospheric pressure. It is interesting that it was not until the early years of the seventeenth century that the word "gas" was used. This word was invented by a Belgian physician, J. B. van Helmont (1577–1644), to fill the need caused by the new idea that different kinds of "airs" exist. Van Helmont discovered that a gas (the gas that we now call carbon dioxide) is formed when limestone is treated with acid, and that this gas differs from air in that when respired it does not support life and that it is heavier than air. He also found that the same gas is produced by fermentation, and that it is present in the Grotto del Cane, a cave in Italy in which dogs were observed to become unconscious (carbon dioxide escaping from fissures in the floor displaces the air in the lower part of the cave).

During the seventeenth and eighteenth centuries other gases were discovered, including hydrogen, oxygen, and nitrogen, and many of their properties were investigated. However, it was not until nearly the end of the seventeenth century that these three gases were recognized as elements. When Lavoisier recognized that oxygen is an element, and that combustion is the process of combining with oxygen, the foundation of modern chemistry was laid.

Gases differ remarkably from liquids and solids in that the volume of a sample of gas depends in a striking way on the temperature of the gas and the applied pressure. The volume of a sample of liquid water, say 1 kg of water, remains essentially the same when the temperature and pressure are changed somewhat. Increasing the pressure from 1 atm to 2 atm causes the volume of a sample of liquid water to decrease by less than 0.01% and increasing the temperature from 0°C to 100°C causes the volume to increase by only 2%. On the other hand, the volume of a sample of air is cut in half when the pressure is increased from 1 atm to 2 atm, and it increases by 36.6% when the temperature is changed from 0°C to 100°C.

We can understand why these interesting phenomena attracted the attention of scientists during the early years of development of modern chemistry through the application of quantitative experimental methods of investigation of nature, and why many physicists and chemists during the past century have devoted themselves to the problem of developing a sound theory to explain the behavior of gases. This theory is presented in the second part of this chapter.

6-1. Hydrogen

Hydrogen is a very widely distributed element. It is found in most of the substances that constitute living matter, and in many inorganic substances. There are more compounds of hydrogen known than of any other element, carbon being a close second.

Free hydrogen, H_2, is a colorless, odorless, and tasteless gas. It is the lightest of all gases, its density being about one-fourteenth that of air. Its melting point ($-259°C$ or $14°A$) and boiling point ($-252.7°C$) are very low, only those of helium being lower. Liquid hydrogen, with density 0.070 g/cm^3, is, as might be expected, the lightest of all liquids. Crystalline hydrogen, with density 0.088 g/cm^3, is also the lightest of all crystalline substances. Hydrogen is very slightly soluble in water; one liter of water at 0°C dissolves only 21.5 ml of hydrogen gas under 1 atm pressure. The solubility decreases with increasing temperature, and increases with increase in the pressure of the gas.

In the laboratory hydrogen may be easily made by the reaction of an acid such as sulfuric acid, H_2SO_4, with a metal such as zinc. Figure 6-1 represents apparatus used for this purpose. The equation for the reaction is

$$H_2SO_4 + Zn \longrightarrow ZnSO_4 + H_2$$

Hydrogen can also be prepared by the reaction of some metals with water or steam. Sodium and its related elements react very vigorously with water, so vigorously as to generate enough heat to ignite the liberated hydrogen. An alloy of lead and sodium, which reacts less vigorously, is sometimes used for the preparation of hydrogen. The equation for the reaction of sodium with water is the following:

$$2Na + 2H_2O \longrightarrow 2NaOH + H_2$$

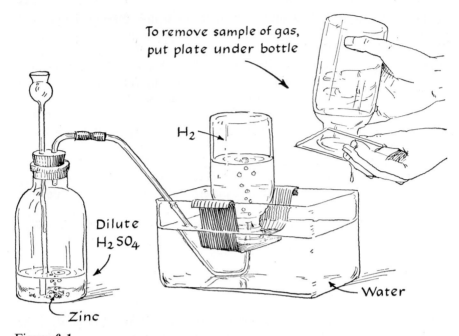

To remove sample of gas, put plate under bottle

H_2

Dilute H_2SO_4

Zinc

Water

Figure 6-1

The preparation of hydrogen in the laboratory.

The substance NaOH produced in this way is called *sodium hydroxide.*

Calcium also reacts with water, but with less vigor. The reaction of metallic calcium with cold water provides a simple and safe way of preparing hydrogen in the laboratory. The equation for this reaction is

$$Ca + 2H_2O \longrightarrow Ca(OH)_2 + H_2$$

The substance $Ca(OH)_2$ is called *calcium hydroxide.* Calcium hydroxide is not very soluble in water, and in the course of the reaction of calcium with water a white precipitate of calcium hydroxide is formed.

It is to be seen from the equations above that each of the metals sodium and calcium liberates only half of the hydrogen contained in the water with which it reacts.

Much of the hydrogen that is used in industry is produced by the reaction of iron with steam. The steam from a boiler is passed over iron filings heated to a temperature of about 600°C. The reaction that occurs is

$$3Fe + 4H_2O \longrightarrow Fe_3O_4 + 4H_2$$

After a mass of iron has been used in this way for some time, it is largely converted into iron oxide, Fe_3O_4. The iron can then be regenerated by passing carbon monoxide, CO, over the heated oxide:

$$Fe_3O_4 + 4CO \longrightarrow 3Fe + 4CO_2$$

The carbon monoxide is changed by this reaction into CO_2, carbon dioxide. In this way the iron can be used over and over again.

Hydrogen can also be made by the reaction of a *metallic hydride* (a compound of a metal and hydrogen) with water. Thus calcium hydride, CaH_2, produces hydrogen according to the following reaction:

$$CaH_2 + 2H_2O \longrightarrow Ca(OH)_2 + 2H_2$$

Hydrogen (together with oxygen) can also be made by the *electrolysis* of water. Pure water hardly conducts an electric current at all, but it becomes a good conductor if salt is dissolved in it. When two electrodes are introduced into such a solution and a suitable potential difference of electricity (voltage difference) is applied, hydrogen is liberated at one electrode (the cathode) and oxygen at the other electrode (the anode); this phenomenon of decomposition of a substance by an electric current is called electrolysis. The theory of this phenomenon will be discussed in a later chapter (Chapter 8). The over-all reaction that takes place (Figure 6-2) is represented by the equation

$$2H_2O \longrightarrow 2H_2 + O_2$$

The Discovery of Hydrogen. It was discovered early in the sixteenth century that a combustible gas is formed when sulfuric acid acts upon steel filings or iron nails. Robert Boyle of Oxford observed that hydrogen would not burn in the rarefied atmosphere produced by his air pump. Henry Cavendish in 1781 showed that water is produced when hydrogen combines with oxygen. He did not, however, recognize that the hydrogen had originally been produced from water or acid, but thought that it had come from the metal that reacted with the acid. Cavendish's name for hydrogen was "inflammable air." Lavoisier named the element hydrogen (water-former, from Greek *hydor*, water, and *genon*, to form).

The Compounds of Hydrogen. Hydrogen forms binary compounds with all of the metalloids and nonmetals except the noble gases. It also combines with many of the metals.

The compounds of hydrogen with metals and metalloids are called *hydrides:* an example is lithium hydride, LiH.

Many of the compounds of hydrogen with nonmetallic elements have special names; for example, CH_4, methane; NH_3, ammonia; H_2O, water; SiH_4, silane; PH_3, phosphine; and AsH_3, arsine.

6-2. Oxygen

Occurrence of Oxygen. Oxygen is the most abundant element in the earth's crust. It constitutes by weight 89% of water, 23% of air (21% by volume), and nearly 50% of the common minerals (silicates). The average composition of the atmosphere is given in Table 6-1.

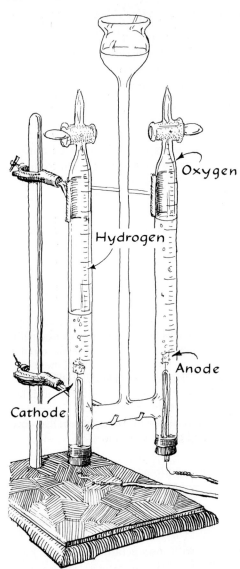

Figure **6-2** *Apparatus for the electrolysis of water.*

The Discovery of Oxygen. Joseph Priestley (1733–1804), of Manchester, England, announced in 1774 the discovery of a gas with the ability to support combustion better than air. He had prepared the gas by heating some red mercuric oxide which was confined in a cylinder over mercury. K. W. Scheele of Sweden seems to have prepared and investigated oxygen before 1773, but an account of his work was not published until 1777.

Red mercuric oxide, HgO, is made by heating mercuric nitrate, $Hg(NO_3)_2$, which itself is made by the action of nitric acid (HNO_3) on mercury. Priestley found that when mercuric oxide is heated to a high temperature it decomposes with the liberation of oxygen:

$$2HgO \longrightarrow 2Hg + O_2$$

In 1775 Lavoisier, having learned about Priestley's work, reported his own work on the nature of combustion and the oxidation of metals, and advanced his new theory of combustion. He showed that $\frac{1}{5}$ of the volume of air is removed by phosphorus or by mercury (when heated for a long time), and that by strongly heating the mercuric oxide formed in this way a gas with volume equal to the volume lost from the air could be recovered. He showed that this gas supported combustion vigorously. Lavoisier named the new gas oxygen (Greek, *oxys*, acid, and *genon*, to form) because he thought, mistakenly, that it was a constituent of all acids.

Preparation and Properties. Ordinary oxygen consists of diatomic molecules, O_2. It is a colorless, odorless gas, which is slightly soluble in water—1 liter of water at 0°C dissolves 48.9 ml of oxygen gas at 1 atm pressure. Its density at 0°C and 1 atm is 1.429 g/liter. Oxygen condenses to a pale blue liquid at its boiling point, $-183.0°C$; and on further cooling freezes, at $-218.4°C$, to a pale blue crystalline solid.

Oxygen may be easily prepared in the laboratory by heating potassium chlorate, $KClO_3$:

$$2KClO_3 \longrightarrow 2KCl + 3O_2$$

The reaction proceeds readily at a temperature just above the melting point of potassium chlorate if a small amount of manganese dioxide, MnO_2, is mixed with it. Although the manganese dioxide accelerates the rate of evolution of oxygen from the potassium chlorate, it itself is not changed.

Table **6-1**

Composition of the Atmosphere

SUBSTANCE	VOLUME PERCENT IN DRY AIR	SUBSTANCE	VOLUME PERCENT IN DRY AIR
Nitrogen	78.03	Neon	0.0018
Oxygen	20.99	Helium	0.0005
Argon	0.93	Krypton	0.0001
Carbon dioxide	0.03	Ozone	0.00006
Hydrogen	0.01	Xenon	0.000009

A substance with this property of accelerating a chemical reaction without itself undergoing significant change is called a **catalyst,** *and is said to* **catalyze** *the reaction.*

Oxygen is made commercially mainly by the distillation of liquid air. Nitrogen is more volatile than oxygen, and tends to evaporate first from liquid air. By properly controlling the conditions of the evaporation nearly pure oxygen can be obtained. The oxygen is stored and shipped in steel cylinders, at pressures of 100 atm or more. Some oxygen is also made commercially, together with hydrogen, by the electrolysis of water.

The Compounds of Oxygen. Oxides of all the elements have been prepared, except the lighter noble gases. Examples are sodium oxide, Na_2O; magnesium oxide, MgO; aluminum oxide, Al_2O_3; sulfur dioxide, SO_2. Most of the elementary substances combine so vigorously with oxygen that they will burn, either spontaneously (phosphorus) or after they have been ignited (sulfur, hydrogen, sodium, magnesium, iron, etc.). A few metals, such as copper and mercury, form oxides only slowly, even when heated; in some cases it is necessary to prepare oxides by indirect methods, rather than by direct reaction with oxygen. The properties of oxides are discussed in later sections of the book.

The Uses of Oxygen. A considerable part of the energy liberated by an ordinary flame is required to heat the nitrogen of the air to the flame temperature, and hence much higher flame temperatures can be reached by using pure oxygen instead of air. An oxygen flame (oxygen and illuminating gas) is used for working glass of high softening point (such as Pyrex glass), and an oxyhydrogen flame is used for working silica. The oxyacetylene flame (acetylene is a compound of hydrogen and carbon, with formula C_2H_2) and the oxyhydrogen flame are used for welding iron and steel, and for cutting iron and steel plates as much as several inches thick.

About 4×10^{10} cu ft of oxygen was used in industrial processes in the U.S. in 1962, two-thirds of the total in the manufacture of iron and steel (Chapter 24).

The energy required to keep the human body warm and to carry on the chemical and physical processes involved in life is obtained from chemical reaction of oxygen with organic material derived from or contained in the food that we eat. The oxygen required for this process enters the lungs, is picked up by a protein, hemoglobin, in the red cells of the blood, and is carried by the blood to the tissues, where part of it is released. In case the lungs are damaged by noxious gases or by disease, such as pneumonia, and it becomes difficult for the oxygen of the air to be transferred to the blood at the proper rate, a patient may be aided by being placed in an oxygen-rich atmosphere (40 to 60% oxygen) either in an "oxygen tent" or by use of an oxygen mask. Aviators breathe pure oxygen at high altitudes, where the pressure of oxygen in the air is insufficient for human needs, and oxygen tanks and helmets are used by rescue workers in gas-filled mines and buildings.

Oxidation and Reduction. Hydrogen combines with oxygen with great vigor. A stream of hydrogen when ignited burns in oxygen or air with a very hot, almost colorless flame, and a mixture of hydrogen and oxygen when ignited explodes with great violence.

When hydrogen burns in air or oxygen, forming hydrogen oxide (water), the hydrogen is said to have been *oxidized*. The process is called *oxidation*, and oxygen is called the *oxidizing agent*.

The tendency of hydrogen to combine with oxygen to form water is so great that the gas will even remove oxygen from many metallic oxides. Thus when a stream of hydrogen is passed over hot copper oxide, CuO, in a heated tube, the copper oxide is converted into metallic copper (Figure 6-3):

$$CuO + H_2 \longrightarrow Cu + H_2O$$

This reaction is described as the *reduction* of copper oxide by hydrogen. Hydrogen is called the *reducing agent* in the reaction. Copper oxide is said to have been *reduced* to metallic copper.

In the reaction of hydrogen and copper oxide the copper oxide is the oxidizing agent. In every reaction of this sort there is a reducing agent that is oxidized and an oxidizing agent that is reduced.

Enthalpy Values.   Values of the enthalpy of formation of some atoms, ions, and molecules are given in Table 6-2. These values have been found by experiment—by measurement of heats of reaction or (especially for ions) by the analysis of spectroscopic data. They can be used to calculate the heat of any reaction involving only substances for which the enthalpies are known.

The heat evolved on formation of any substance from the elements in their standard states is equal to the standard enthalpy of formation of the substance with its sign changed. For example, from Table 6-2 we may write

Figure **6-3**

The reduction of a metal oxide by hydrogen.

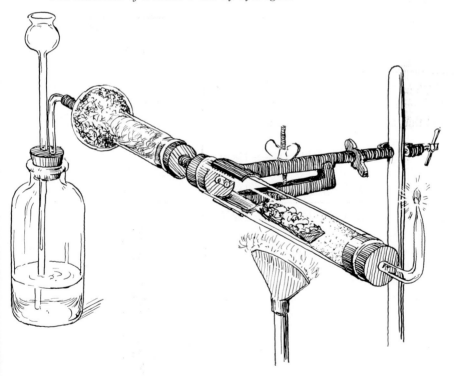

$$H_2(g) + \tfrac{1}{2}O_2(g) \longrightarrow H_2O(g) + 57.80 \text{ kcal/mole}$$
$$\tfrac{3}{2}O_2(g) \longrightarrow O_3(g) - 34.0 \text{ kcal/mole}$$
$$\tfrac{1}{2}H_2(g) \longrightarrow H(g) - 52.09 \text{ kcal/mole}$$

We see that the formation of water vapor from hydrogen and oxygen occurs by an exothermic reaction, whereas the formation of ozone (O_3) from ordinary oxygen (O_2) and the formation of atomic hydrogen from molecular hydrogen are endothermic.

Table 6-2

Standard Enthalpy of Formation of Compounds of Hydrogen and Oxygen at 25°C, in kcal/mole

$e^-(g)$	0.00*	$O^+(g)$	374.61	$OH^-(g)$	−76.4
$H_2(g)$	0.00*	$O^-(g)$	−13.12	$OH^-(aq)$	−54.96
$O_2(g)$	0.00*	$O_2^+(g)$	283.1	$H_2O(g)$	−57.80
$H^+(aq)$	0.00*	$O_2(aq)$	−3.8	$H_2O(l)$	−68.32
$H(g)$	52.09	$O_3(g)$	34.0	$H_2O_2(g)$	−31.83
$O(g)$	59.16	$O_4(g)$	−0.16	$H_2O_2(l)$	−44.84
$H^+(g)$	367.09	$OH(g)$	10.06	$H_2O_2(aq)$	−45.68
$H^-(g)$	35.6				

* Values of the enthalpy of formation of elements in a standard state, of electron gas, and of hydrogen ion in aqueous solution are arbitrarily taken to be zero.

The effectiveness of hydrogen as a rocket fuel with oxygen as oxidizer is largely determined by the heat of reaction. We see from the values in Table 6-2 that atomic hydrogen and atomic oxygen would be much better:

$$2H(g) \longrightarrow H_2(g) \; + 104.18 \text{ kcal/mole}$$
$$O(g) \longrightarrow \tfrac{1}{2}O_2(g) \; + \; 59.16 \text{ kcal/mole}$$
$$H_2(g) + \tfrac{1}{2}O_2(g) \longrightarrow H_2O(g) + \; 57.80 \text{ kcal/mole}$$

$$\overline{2H(g) + O(g) \; \longrightarrow H_2O(g) + 221.14 \text{ kcal/mole}}$$

The fourth equation is obtained by adding the other three. The formation of water vapor from atomic hydrogen and atomic oxygen is accompanied by the liberation of nearly four times as much heat as its formation from molecular hydrogen and molecular oxygen. Atomic hydrogen and atomic oxygen are, however, very reactive; they cannot be stored and kept from forming the diatomic molecules.

6-1. Write the chemical equation for one reaction that might be used to prepare hydrogen in the laboratory and one that might be used to prepare oxygen. Why is manganese dioxide mixed with potassium chlorate in the usual laboratory procedure for preparing oxygen?

6-2. (a) Write the equation for the reaction of acetylene, C_2H_2, and oxygen, assuming that the products are water and carbon dioxide, CO_2.

(b) Write the equation for the reaction of acetylene and oxygen with products water and carbon monoxide, CO.

(c) Under what conditions would you expect the products to be water and carbon dioxide? Water and carbon monoxide?

6-3. How many pounds of zinc and sulfuric acid would be needed to make hydrogen to fill a balloon 25 feet in diameter? The density of hydrogen at room temperature is 0.083 g per liter.

6-4. Nearly pure liquid hydrogen peroxide, H_2O_2, is used as a propellant or fuel for engines; in the presence of a catalyst it forms oxygen and water. Write the equation for this reaction.

6-5. From values given in Table 6-2, find the heat evolved during the reaction of $H_2O_2(l)$ to form oxygen and water vapor.

6-3.   Ozone. The Phenomenon of Allotropy

Ozone is a blue gas which has a characteristic odor (its name is from the Greek *ozein*, to smell) and is a stronger oxidizing agent than ordinary oxygen. It is formed when an electric current is passed through oxygen (Figure 6-4).

Ozone is formed in air by the passage of electric sparks or an electric arc. It is largely the cause of the odor that is observed around electrical machinery. Most people can detect the odor of ozone at a concentration of one part in 100,000,000 in air. Ozone is a normal constituent of the upper atmosphere (Section 18-9). It oxidizes organic substances in the atmosphere, and by reacting with hydrocarbons (gasoline vapor) probably produces the irritating substances in the smog of Los Angeles and other regions.

The density of ozone at 0°C and 1 atm is 2.144 g/liter. On cooling, the gas condenses to a deep blue liquid (boiling point −111.5°C) and then freezes to a deep blue crystalline solid (melting point −249.6°C). The liquid and solid are explosive.

Although its properties are different from those of ordinary oxygen, ozone is not a compound, but is elementary oxygen in a different form—a form with three atoms in the molecule (O_3) instead of two, as in ordinary oxygen (Figure 6-5).

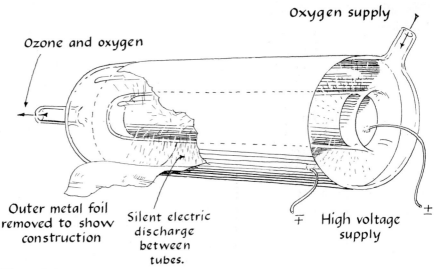

Oxygen supply

Ozone and oxygen

Outer metal foil removed to show construction | **Silent electric discharge between tubes.** | ∓ **High voltage supply** ±

Figure **6-4**

An ozonizer, for converting oxygen to ozone by use of a silent electric discharge.

The existence of an elementary substance in two or more forms is called **allotropy** (Greek *allotropia*, variety, from *allos*, other, and *tropos*, direction).

Ordinary oxygen and ozone are the **allotropes** of oxygen. Allotropy is shown by many elements; it is due either to the existence of two or more kinds of molecules (containing different numbers of atoms) or to the existence of two or more different crystalline forms; that is, of different arrangements of the atoms or molecules in a crystalline array.

Figure **6-5** *Molecules of oxygen and ozone. This drawing, like most of the drawings of atoms and molecules in this book, is made with linear magnification about 60,000,000.*

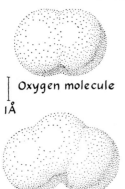

Oxygen molecule

1Å

Ozone molecule

Ozone contains more energy than oxygen: the heat evolved when one mole (48 g) of ozone decomposes to oxygen is 34,000 cal, and that amount of energy must have been given to the ozone molecule by the electric discharge when the ozone was formed. Because of its greater energy content, ozone is more reactive than oxygen. It converts mercury and silver into oxides, and it readily frees iodine from potassium iodide, whereas oxygen does not cause these reactions at room temperature.

Like some other oxidizing agents (such as chlorine), ozone has the power of converting many colored organic substances to colorless products; it accordingly finds use as a bleaching agent for oils, waxes, starch, and flour. It is also used instead of chlorine to sterilize drinking water, by destroying the bacteria in it.

The Tetratomic Oxygen Molecule. In 1924 G. N. Lewis pointed out that the magnetic properties of liquid oxygen indicate that molecules O_4 are present, with enthalpy of formation -0.16 kcal/mole from O_2 (Table 6-2). Crystalline oxygen consists of O_4 molecules, and these molecules are shown by the absorption spectrum to be present in small concentration in air. Tetratomic oxygen differs from ozone in that it is in rapid equilibrium with O_2 and its enthalpy of formation is close to zero. Because of the rapid equilibrium it is not usually described as an allotropic form of oxygen.

Illustrative Exercises

6-6. Write the equations for the reaction of liquid hydrazine, N_2H_4, with oxygen and with ozone, to form water vapor and nitrogen (N_2).

6-7. The standard enthalpy of formation of liquid hydrazine is 12.05 kcal/mole. Calculate the heat evolved in each of the two reactions of Exercise 6-6. By what factor would you describe the superiority of ozone and hydrazine over oxygen and hydrazine for rocket propulsion?

6-8. Assuming the heat capacity of $O_2(g)$ at constant pressure to be 7 cal deg^{-1} mole^{-1}, calculate the temperature of the oxygen formed by the rapid decomposition (explosion) of pure ozone, initially at 25°C. (Answer: About 3260°C.)

6-9. From enthalpy values in Table 6-2, calculate the heat of vaporization of hydrogen peroxide and the heat of solution of $H_2O_2(g)$ in water. (Answer: 13.01 and 13.85 kcal/mole.)

6-4. The Nature of the Gas Laws

It has been mentioned above that the interesting properties of gases attracted the attention of the early scientists, who devoted themselves to the problem of developing a theory to explain the observed regularities.

In addition to the desire to understand this part of the physical world, there is another reason, a practical one, for studying the gas laws. This reason is concerned with the *measurement of gases*. The most convenient way to determine the amount of material in a sample of a solid is to weigh it on a balance. This can also be done conveniently for liquids; or we may measure the volume of a sample of a liquid, and, if we want to know its weight, multiply the volume by its density, as found by a previous experiment. The method of weighing is usually not conveniently used for gases, because their densities are very small; volume measurements can be made much more accurately and easily by the use of containers of known volume. But the volume of a sample of gas depends greatly on both the pressure and the temperature, and to calculate the weight of gas in a measured volume the law of this dependence must be known. It is partly for this reason that study of the pressure-volume-temperature properties of gases is a part of chemistry.

Another important reason for studying the gas laws is that the *density* of a dilute gas is related in a simple way to its *molecular weight*, whereas there is no similar simple relation for liquids and solids. This relation for gases (*Avogadro's law*) was of great value in the original decision as to the correct atomic weights of the elements, and it is still of great practical significance, permitting the direct calculation of the approximate density of a gas of known molecular composition, or the experimental determination of the effective (average) molecular weight of a gas of unknown molecular composition by the measurement of its density. These uses are discussed in detail in the following sections.

It has been found by experiment that **all ordinary gases behave in nearly the same way.** The nature of this behavior is described by the *perfect-gas laws* (often referred to briefly as the *gas laws*).

It is found experimentally that—to within the reliability of the gas laws (better than 1% under ordinary conditions)—the volume of a sample of any gas is determined by only three quantities: the *pressure* of the gas, the *temperature* of the gas, and the *number of molecules* in the sample of the gas. The law describing the dependence of the volume of the gas on the pressure is called *Boyle's law;* that describing the dependence of the volume on the temperature is called the *law of Charles and Gay-Lussac;* and that describing the dependence of the volume on the number of molecules in the sample of gas is called *Avogadro's law.*

In the following sections of this chapter these three laws are formulated and applied in the solution of some problems. It is also shown that they can be combined into a single equation, which is called the *perfect-gas equation.*

6-5.   The Dependence of Gas Volume on Pressure. Boyle's Law

An investigation of the dependence of the volume of a sample of gas on the applied pressure can be carried out with the simple apparatus shown at the left side of Figure 6-6, a long glass tube, with one end turned up. A sample of air is trapped in the upturned closed end by means of mercury. When the level of the mercury in the two arms of the tube is the same, as shown at the far left of the figure, the sample of gas is under a pressure of 1 atm.

It has been pointed out in Chapter 1 that the standard atmospheric pressure is just equal to the pressure exerted by a column of mercury 760 mm high. Accordingly if mercury is poured into the open end of our tube until the mercury levels in the two arms differ by 760 mm, the pressure exerted on the gas will be equal to 2 atm, 1 atm being due to the weight of the column of mercury and 1 atm to the pressure of the atmosphere on the top of this column. It is found that under this pressure the volume of the sample of air

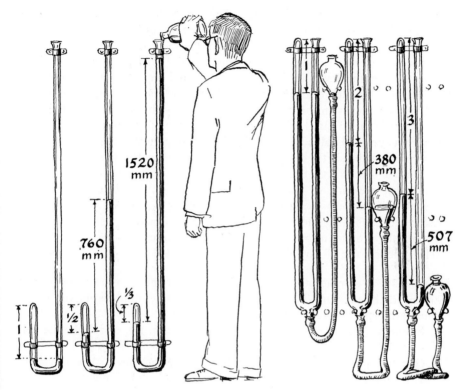

Figure **6-6**

A simple apparatus for demonstrating Boyle's law of the dependence of volume of a gas on the applied pressure.

is reduced to one-half the original volume. If more mercury is poured into the tube, until the difference in level of the two columns of mercury is 1520 mm, or 2 atm, the total pressure exerted on the sample of air is then 3 atm, and the volume of the enclosed air is found to be one-third the original volume.

Experiments such as this one have shown that **for nearly all gases, the volume of a sample of gas at constant temperature is inversely proportional to the pressure;** that is, the product of pressure and volume under these conditions is constant:

$$PV = \text{constant (temperature constant, moles of gas constant)}$$

This equation expresses Boyle's law. The law was inferred from experimental data by the English natural scientist Robert Boyle (1627–1691) in 1662.

Boyle's law describes the behavior of gases under reduced pressure as well as under increased pressure. An investigation of the behavior of a sample of gas under reduced pressure can be carried out with an apparatus such as that shown at the right side of Figure 6-6. This apparatus closely resembles that shown at the left side, the attached rubber tube with the glass reservoir serving as a convenient means of removing some of the mercury.

If the volume of a sample of gas enclosed in the tube is measured at 1 atm (when the mercury levels in the two arms of tube are the same, as shown in the diagram at the left of the figure), and then mercury is removed, permitting the level of mercury in the open arm to fall below that in the closed arm of the tube, it is found that the volume of the sample of gas becomes just equal to twice its original value when the level of the mercury in the open arm lies 380 mm below that in the closed arm. The pressure due to 380 mm of mercury is $\frac{1}{2}$ atm; it is seen that this pressure, due to the mercury, is opposing the atmospheric pressure, so that the pressure acting on the enclosed sample of gas is the difference between 1 atm and $\frac{1}{2}$ atm, or $\frac{1}{2}$ atm. Accordingly under these conditions also there is an inverse proportionality of volume and pressure, the product of pressure and volume remaining constant.

The practical use of Boyle's law may be illustrated by some examples.

Example 1. A sample of gas is found by measurement to have the volume 1000 ml at the pressure 730 mm of mercury. What would be its volume at normal atmospheric pressure, 760 mm of mercury?

Solution. Let P_1 be the initial pressure, 730 mm Hg, and V_1 be the volume, 1000 ml. Let P_2 be the changed pressure, 760 mm Hg, and V_2 be the changed volume, which we wish to determine. From Boyle's law, Equation 1, we know that the product PV remains constant; hence we write

$$P_1V_1 = P_2V_2 \tag{1}$$

or

$$730 \text{ mm Hg} \times 1000 \text{ ml} = 760 \text{ mm Hg} \times V_2$$

Solving for V_2, we obtain

$$V_2 = \frac{730 \text{ mm Hg}}{760 \text{ mm Hg}} \times 1000 \text{ ml} = \textbf{960 ml}$$

There is another way of solving the problem that involves more thinking, and that may help to prevent errors. We know that Boyle's law is of such a form that the volume changes by a factor equal to the ratio of the two pressures. We can hence obtain the final volume by multiplying the initial volume by the ratio $\frac{730}{760}$. (We know that the ratio $\frac{760}{730}$ is not the correct one to multiply by, because *increase* in pressure always causes a *decrease* in volume, and the factor must accordingly be *less* than 1.) Thus we obtain as the desired volume

$$\frac{730}{760} \times 1000 \text{ ml} = \textbf{960 ml}$$

It is good practice to *work every problem in your head*, in a rough numerical way, in order to verify that the answer that you have obtained by your calculation is a reasonable one. In the present problem we note that the pressure is increased by 30 mm of Hg, which is about 4%. Hence the volume must decrease by about 4%. Since 4% of 1000 ml is 40 ml, the answer should be about 960 ml.

In the second calculation above there occurs the fraction $\frac{730}{760}$, without the units mm Hg after either of the two numbers. When a ratio of two quantities measured in the same units occurs in an expression, as in this case, it is not necessary to show the units. Thus, when a ratio of two temperatures or of two pressures occurs in the solution of later problems only the ratio of the numbers will in general be written.

Example 2.   What is the weight of oxygen that can be put in an oxygen tank with volume 2 cu ft under pressure of 500 lbs per sq in? The density of oxygen at 1 atm pressure and room temperature (18°C) is 1.34 g/liter.

Solution.   Let us convert the volume of the tank to liters and the pressure to atmospheres. The number of liters in 1 cu ft can be found by remembering that 2.54 cm = 1 inch. The number of cm^3 in 1 cu ft is accordingly $(12 \times 2.54)^3 = 30.48^3 = 28316\ cm^3$. Hence 1 cu ft = 28.3 liters, and 2 cu ft, the volume of the tank, is 56.6 liters. We also remember, from Chapter 1, that 1 atm pressure is equal to 14.7 lbs per sq in. Hence the pressure in the tank in atmospheres is 500/14.7 = 34 atm. By application of Boyle's law we see that a volume of 56.6 liters of gas at 34 atm will become much larger, by the factor 34, when the pressure is decreased to 1 atm; the volume at 1 atm is accordingly

$$\frac{34}{1} \times 56.61 = 1920 \text{ liters}$$

The weight of this volume of oxygen in grams is the product of the volume by the density, 1.34 g/liter, which is 2570 g or, dividing by 454, the number of grams in a pound, 5.7 lb. The weight of oxygen that the tank will hold under this pressure is accordingly **5.7 lbs.**

Illustrative Exercises

6-10.   If the pressure on a sample of gas (held at constant temperature) were to be doubled, how would its volume change? If the volume were doubled, how would the pressure change?

6-11.   A sample of gas in a glass apparatus being used by a chemist was found to have volume 2000 ml at pressure 0.1000 mm of mercury. What would its volume be when the pressure is increased to 1 atm?

The Partial Pressures of Components of a Gas Mixture.   It is found by experiment (Dalton, 1801) that when two samples of gas at the same pressure are mixed there is no change in volume. If the two samples of gas were originally present in containers of the same size, at a pressure of 1 atm, each container after the mixing was completed would contain a mixture of gas molecules, half of them of one kind and half the other. It is reasonable to assume that each gas in this mixture exerts the pressure of $\frac{1}{2}$ atm, as it would if the other gas were not present. Dalton's **law of partial pressures** states that *in a gas mixture the molecules of gas of each kind exert the same pressure as they would if present alone*, and that *the total pressure is the sum of the partial pressures exerted by the different gases in the mixture.*

Correction for the Vapor Pressure of Water. When a sample of gas is collected over water, the pressure of the gas is due in part to the water vapor in it. The pressure due to the water vapor in the gas in equilibrium with liquid water is equal to the vapor pressure of water. Values of the vapor pressure at different temperatures are given in Appendix III.

The way in which a correction for the vapor pressure of water can be made is illustrated in the following example.

Example 3. An experiment is made to find out how much oxygen is liberated from a given amount of potassium chlorate, $KClO_3$. The quantity 2.00 g of this salt is weighed out, mixed with some manganese dioxide, to serve as catalyst, and introduced into a test tube, which is provided with a cork and delivery tube leading to a bottle filled with water and inverted in a trough. The test tube is heated, and the heating is continued until the evolution of gas ceases. The volume of the liberated gas was determined to be 591 ml. The temperature was 18°C, and the pressure was 748.3 mm Hg. What was the weight of oxygen liberated? How does this compare with the theoretical yield?

    Solution. The atmospheric pressure, 748.3 mm Hg, is balanced in part by the pressure of the oxygen collected in the bottle, and in part by the pressure of the water vapor dissolved by the oxygen as it bubbles through the water. By reference to Appendix III we see that the vapor pressure of water at 18°C is 15.5 mm Hg. Accordingly the pressure due to the oxygen in the bottle is less than 748.3 mm by this amount, and is equal to 748.3 − 15.5 = 732.8 mm Hg.

    Let us now find what volume the liberated oxygen would occupy at standard pressure, 760 mm Hg. The volume at the pressure 732.8 mm Hg is 591 ml. We know that gases become smaller in volume when they are compressed; the volume at the higher pressure, 760 mm, will hence be less than 591, and we see that the volume 591 must be multiplied by the fraction 732.8/760:

$$\text{Volume of oxygen at 760 mm Hg} = \frac{732.8}{760} \times 591 \text{ ml} = 570 \text{ ml}$$

    In Example 2 the density of oxygen at 1 atm pressure and 18°C was given as 1.34 g/liter; that is, 1.34 g per 1000 ml. The weight of 570 ml of oxygen under these conditions is easily calculated; this is the answer to the first question in our example.

$$\text{Weight of oxygen liberated} = \frac{570}{1000} \times 1.34 \text{ g} = \mathbf{0.76 \text{ g}}$$

Note how simple the means are by which the weight of liberated oxygen was found, to 1 mg accuracy—only rough volume measurements (to 1 ml) needed to be made.

To answer the second question, let us calculate the theoretical yield of oxygen from 2.00 g of potassium chlorate. The equation for the decomposition of potassium chlorate is

$$KClO_3 \longrightarrow KCl + \tfrac{3}{2}O_2$$

(Note that it is sometimes convenient to represent a fractional number of molecules in an equation.) We see that 1 gram formula weight of $KClO_3$, 122.5 g, should liberate 3 gram-atoms of oxygen, 48.0 g. Hence the amount of oxygen that should be liberated from 2.00 g of potassium chlorate is $48.0/122.5 \times 2.00$ g $= 0.786$ g.

The observed amount of oxygen liberated is seen to be less than the theoretical amount by 0.022 g, or **2.8%**.

Illustrative **Exercise**	6-12. (a) A volume of gas was collected over water at 25°C. The measured pressure was 750.0 mm Hg. How much of this pressure was due to water vapor, and how much to the gas? (b) What would be the pressure of the gas if the water vapor were to be removed by use of a drying agent, the volume and temperature being kept the same?

6-6. The Dependence of Gas Volume on Temperature. The Law of Charles and Gay-Lussac

After the discovery of Boyle's law, it was more than one hundred years before the dependence of the volume of a gas on the temperature was investigated. Then in 1787 the French physicist Jacques Alexandre Charles (1746–1823) reported that different gases expand by the same fractional amount for the same rise in temperature. Dalton in England continued these studies in 1801, and in 1802 Joseph Louis Gay-Lussac (1778–1850) extended the work, and determined the amount of expansion per degree Centigrade. He found that all gases expand by $\frac{1}{273}$ of their volume at 0°C for each degree Centigrade that they are heated above this temperature. Thus a sample of gas with volume 273 ml at 0°C has the volume 274 ml at 1°C and the same pressure, 275 ml at 2°C, 373 ml at 100°C, etc.

We now state the law of the dependence of the volume of a gas on temperature, the **law of Charles and Gay-Lussac,** in the following way. **If the pressure and the number of moles of a sample of gas remain constant, the volume of the sample of gas is proportional to the absolute temperature:**

$$V = \text{constant} \times T \text{ (pressure constant, number of moles constant)}$$

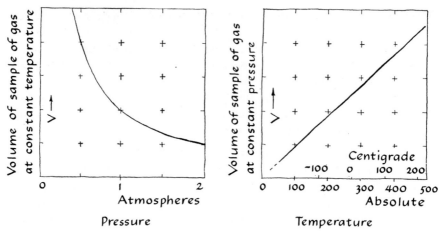

Figure 6-7

Curves showing, at the left, the dependence of the volume of a sample of gas at constant temperature and containing a constant number of molecules on the pressure, and, at the right, the dependence of the volume of a sample of gas at constant pressure and containing a constant number of molecules on the temperature.

You will note that the dependence of volume on the absolute temperature is a direct proportionality, whereas the volume is inversely proportional to the pressure. The nature of these two relations is illustrated in Figure 6-7.

The use of the law of Charles and Gay-Lussac in working problems is illustrated by the example given below.

Standard Conditions. It is customary to refer the volumes of gases to 0°C and a pressure of 1 atm. This temperature and pressure are called **standard conditions.** A sample of gas is said to be *reduced to standard conditions* when its volume is calculated at this temperature and pressure.

Example 4. One gram of methane has volume 1513 ml at 25°C and 1 atm. What is its volume at standard conditions?

Solution. Our problem is to find the volume of a sample of gas at 0°C which has the volume 1513 ml at 25°C; or, changing to the absolute temperature scale, to find the volume of a sample of gas at 273°K that has volume 1513 ml at 298°K.

Cooling a gas causes its volume to decrease. Accordingly we know that we must multiply the volume at the higher temperature by $\frac{273}{298}$, rather than by the reciprocal of this fraction. Thus we have

$$\text{Volume of gas at standard conditions} = \frac{273}{298} \times 1513 \text{ ml} = \textbf{1386 ml}$$

Correction of the Volume of a Gas for Change in Both Pressure and Temperature. Boyle's law and the law of Charles and Gay-Lussac can be applied in a straightforward manner to calculate the change in volume of a sample of gas from one pressure and temperature to another pressure and temperature, as is illustrated by the following example.

Example 5. A sample of gas has volume 1200 ml at 100°C and 800 mm pressure. Reduce to standard conditions.

Solution. We may solve this problem by multiplying the original volume by a ratio of pressures to correct for the change in pressure, and by a ratio of temperatures to correct for the change in temperature. We must decide for each ratio whether the correction is greater or less than one.

In this case the sample is initially at a greater pressure than 1 atm (760 mm) and hence it will expand when the pressure is reduced to 1 atm. Accordingly the pressure factor must be $\frac{800}{760}$, and not $\frac{760}{800}$. Also the sample will contract (decrease in volume) when it is cooled, and hence the temperature factor must be $\frac{273}{373}$, and not $\frac{373}{273}$. Therefore we write

$$V = \frac{800}{760} \times \frac{273}{373} \times 1200 \text{ ml} = \textbf{925 ml}$$

This method is to be used in solving any pressure-volume-temperature problem for a sample of gas, provided that the number of molecules in the sample remains constant.

Illustrative Exercises

6-13. To what temperature would a sample of gas, held at constant pressure, have to be heated in order to have double the volume that it has at 0°C?

6-14. A sample of carbon dioxide is found to have volume 450 ml at 21°C and 780 mm of mercury. What would be its volume at standard conditions?

6-15. (a) A balloon contains 10,000 m³ of hot air, at temperature 200°C and pressure 1 atm. What volume would it have at 18°C and 1 atm?

(b) How much does this amount of air weigh? The density of air is 1.21 g/liter at 18°C and 1 atm.

(c) How much does 10,000 m³ of air at 18°C and 1 atm weigh? (This is the amount of air displaced by the balloon; the difference of the two weights is the lifting power of the balloon.)

6-7. Avogadro's Law

In 1805 Gay-Lussac began a series of experiments to find the volume percentage of oxygen in air. In the course of this work he made a very important discovery. The experiments were carried out by mixing a certain volume of hydrogen with air and exploding the mixture, and then testing the remaining gas to see whether oxygen or hydrogen had been present in excess. He was surprised to find a very simple relation: 1000 ml of oxygen required just 2000 ml of hydrogen, to form water. Continuing the study of the volumes of gases that react with one another, he found that 1000 ml of hydrogen chloride combines exactly with 1000 ml of ammonia, and that 1000 ml of carbon monoxide combines with 500 ml of oxygen to form 1000 ml of carbon dioxide. On the basis of these observations he formulated the **law of combining volumes:** *the volumes of gases that react with one another or are produced in a chemical reaction are in the ratios of small integers.*

Figure 6-8

The relative volumes of gases involved in chemical reactions.

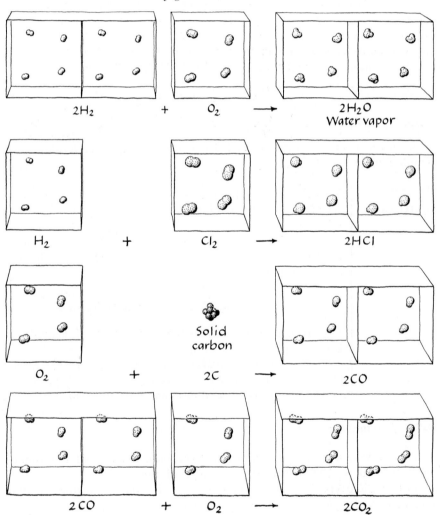

Such a simple empirical law as this called for a simple theoretical interpretation, and in 1811 Amedeo Avogadro (1776–1856), professor of physics in the University of Turin, Italy, proposed a hypothesis to explain the law. Avogadro's hypothesis was that **equal numbers of molecules are contained in equal volumes of all gases under the same conditions.** This hypothesis has been thoroughly verified to within the accuracy of approximation of real gases to ideal behavior, and it is now called a law—**Avogadro's law.***

> During the last century Avogadro's law provided the most satisfactory and the only reliable way of determining which multiples of the equivalent weights of the elements should be accepted as their atomic weights; the arguments involved are discussed in the following sections. But the value of this law remained unrecognized by chemists from 1811 until 1858. In this year Stanislao Cannizzaro (1826–1910), an Italian chemist working in Geneva, showed how to apply the law systematically, and immediately the uncertainty about the correct atomic weights of the elements and the correct formulas of compounds disappeared. Before 1858 many chemists used the formula HO for water and accepted 8 as the atomic weight of oxygen; since that year H_2O has been accepted as the formula for water by everyone.†

Avogadro's Law and the Law of Combining Volumes. Avogadro's law requires that the volumes of gaseous reactants and products (under the same conditions) be approximately in the ratios of small integers; the numbers of molecules of reactants and products in a chemical reaction are in integral ratios, and the same ratios represent the relative gas volumes. Some simple diagrams illustrating this for several reactions are given in Figure 6-8. Each cube in these diagrams represents the volume occupied by four gas molecules.

6-8. The Use of Avogadro's Law in the Determination of the Correct Atomic Weights of Elements

The way in which Avogadro's law was applied by Cannizzaro in 1858 for the selection of the correct approximate atomic weights of elements was essentially the following. Let us accept as the molecular weight of a substance the weight in grams of 22.4 liters of the gaseous substance reduced to standard conditions. (Any other volume could be used—this would correspond to the selection of a different base for the atomic weight scale.) *Then it is probable that of a large number of compounds of a particular element at least one compound will have only one atom of the element per molecule; the weight of the element in the standard gas volume of this compound is its atomic weight.*

---

* Dalton had considered and rejected the hypothesis that equal volumes of gases contain equal numbers of atoms; the idea that elementary substances might exist as polyatomic molecules (H_2, O_2) did not occur to him.

† The failure of chemists to accept Avogadro's law during the period from 1811 to 1858 seems to have been due to a feeling that molecules were too "theoretical" to deserve serious consideration.

For gaseous compounds of hydrogen the weight per standard volume and the weight of the contained hydrogen per standard volume are as follows:

	WEIGHT OF GAS, IN GRAMS	WEIGHT OF CONTAINED HYDROGEN, IN GRAMS
Hydrogen (H_2)	2	2
Methane (CH_4)	16	4
Ethane (C_2H_6)	30	6
Water (H_2O)	18	2
Hydrogen sulfide (H_2S)	34	2
Hydrogen cyanide (HCN)	27	1
Hydrogen chloride (HCl)	36	1
Ammonia (NH_3)	17	3
Pyridine (C_5H_5N)	79	5

In these and all other compounds of hydrogen the minimum weight of hydrogen in the standard gas volume is found to be 1 g, and the weight is always an integral multiple of the minimum weight; hence 1 can be accepted as the atomic weight of hydrogen. The elementary substance hydrogen then is seen to consist of diatomic molecules H_2, and water is seen to have the formula H_2O_x, with x still to be determined.

For oxygen compounds the following similar table of experimental data can be set up:

	WEIGHT OF GAS, IN GRAMS	WEIGHT OF CONTAINED OXYGEN, IN GRAMS
Oxygen (O_2)	32	32
Water (H_2O)	18	16
Carbon monoxide (CO)	28	16
Carbon dioxide (CO_2)	44	32
Nitrous oxide (N_2O)	44	16
Nitric oxide (NO)	30	16
Sulfur dioxide (SO_2)	64	32
Sulfur trioxide (SO_3)	80	48

From the comparison of oxygen and water in this table it can be concluded rigorously that the oxygen molecule contains two atoms or a multiple of two atoms; we see that the standard volume of oxygen contains twice as much oxygen (32 g) as is contained by the standard volume of water vapor (16 g of oxygen). The data for the other compounds provide no evidence that the atomic weight of oxygen is less than 16; hence this value may be adopted. Water thus is given the formula H_2O.

Note that this application of Avogadro's law provided rigorously only a maximum value of the atomic weight of an element. The possibility was not eliminated that the true atomic weight was a submultiple of this value.

6-9. The Complete Perfect-gas Equation

Boyle's law, the law of Charles and Gay-Lussac, and Avogadro's law can be combined into a single equation,

$$PV = nRT \tag{2}$$

In this equation P is the pressure acting on a given sample of gas, V is the volume occupied by the sample of gas, n is the number of moles of gas in the sample, R is a quantity called the *gas constant*, and T is the absolute temperature.

The gas constant R has a numerical value depending on the units in which it is measured (that is, the units used for P, V, n, and T). If P is measured in atmospheres, V in liters, n in moles, and T in degrees Kelvin, the value of R is **0.0820 liter atmospheres per degree mole.**

If the number of moles in a sample of gas, n, remains constant and the temperature T remains constant, the perfect-gas equation simplifies to

$$PV = \text{constant}$$

The value of the constant in this equation is nRT. This equation is seen to be just the equation expressing Boyle's law.

Similarly, if the pressure P is constant and the number of moles in the sample of gas is constant, the perfect-gas equation simplifies to

$$V = \frac{nR}{P} T = \text{constant} \times T$$

This is the expression of the law of Charles and Gay-Lussac.

The perfect-gas equation can also be written in the form

$$n = \frac{PV}{RT}$$

This equation states that the number of moles of any gas is equal to a product of quantities independent of the nature of the gas, but depending only on the pressure, volume, and temperature; accordingly equal volumes of all gases under the same condition are stated by this equation to contain the same number of moles (molecules). This equation accordingly expresses Avogadro's law.

The value of the gas constant R is found experimentally by determining the volume occupied by 1 mole of a perfect gas at standard conditions. One mole of oxygen weighs exactly 32 g, and the density of oxygen gas at standard conditions is found by experiment to be 1.429 g/liter. The quotient

$32/1.429 = 22.4$ liters is accordingly the volume occupied by 1 mole of gas at standard conditions.

The volume 22.4 liters is the volume of one mole of gas at standard conditions (0°C, 1 atm).

More accurate determinations, involving the measurement of the density of oxygen at low pressure, where it approaches a perfect gas more closely, have led to the value **22.4130 liters** for the molal gas volume.

The volume occupied by one mole of gas at standard conditions is seen from the perfect-gas equation to be just the product of R and the temperature 0°C on the absolute scale. The value of R can hence be found by dividing 22.4 by 273:

$$R = \frac{1 \text{ atm} \times 22.4 \text{ liter}}{1 \text{ mole} \times 273 \text{ deg}}$$

$$= \textbf{0.0820 liter atm deg}^{-1} \textbf{ mole}^{-1} = \textbf{1.987 cal deg}^{-1} \textbf{ mole}^{-1}$$

Avogadro's Number. *Avogadro's number N is defined as the number of carbon atoms in a gram-atom of carbon.* It is, of course, also the number of atoms of any element in a gram-atom of that element, and the number of molecules in a mole of any substance. The volume 22.4 liters of any gas at standard conditions contains Avogadro's number of molecules.

The value of Avogadro's number was known to within an accuracy of about 30% in 1875. It was then determined to within 1% by Millikan in 1909, and then more accurately (to within 0.01%) in the period between 1930 and 1940 through the work of several experimental physicists. It is*

$$N = \textbf{0.6022} \times \textbf{10}^{24}$$

It is difficult to imagine such a large number as Avogadro's number. Some idea of its magnitude is given by the following calculation. Let us suppose that the entire state of Texas, with area 262,000 square miles, were covered with a layer of fine sand 50 feet thick, each grain of sand being 1/100 of an inch in diameter. There would then be Avogadro's number of grains of sand in this immense sandpile. There is the same number of molecules of water in one mole of water—18 g, 1/25 of a pint.

---

* It may be pointed out that Avogadro's number as written above, 0.6022×10^{24}, differs from the usual convention about writing large numbers, according to which one integer is introduced before the decimal point. With this convention Avogadro's number would be expressed as 6.022×10^{23}—this is, in fact, the usual way of writing the number. However, there is a great convenience in learning Avogadro's number as 0.6022×10^{24}. An important use of this number involves the conversion of the volume of a gram-atom of an element into the volume per atom. The first volume is expressed in cm³, and the second in Å³. The relation between cm³ and Å³ involves the factor 10^{24}; indeed, 1 cm³ = 10^{24} Å³. Accordingly, in case that Avogadro's number has been taken as 0.6022×10^{24} there is no trouble whatever in deciding on the position of the decimal point, whereas if 6.022×10^{23} is used for Avogadro's number it is always necessary to decide whether the decimal point should be moved one place to the right or one place to the left.

6-10. Calculations Based on the Perfect-gas Equation

Some of the ways in which the perfect-gas equation can be used in the solution of chemical problems are discussed in the following paragraphs.

The Calculation of the Density of a Gas or the Weight of a Sample of Gas from Its Molecular Formula.   If the molecular formula of a gaseous substance is known, an approximate value of its density can be calculated. This calculation can also be carried out for a mixture of known composition of gases of known molecular formulas. The method to be used is illustrated in the following examples.

Example 6.   What is the density of carbon dioxide at standard conditions?
   Solution.   The molecular weight of carbon dioxide, CO_2, is 44. The volume occupied by 1 mole, 44 g, of carbon dioxide at standard conditions is 22.4 liters. The density is the weight per unit volume; that is,

$$\text{Density of carbon dioxide} = \frac{44 \text{ g/mole}}{22.4 \text{ liters/mole}} = \textbf{1.96 g/liter}$$

Example 7.   What is the approximate value of the density of air at 25°C?
   Solution.   Air is a mixture of oxygen and nitrogen, being mainly (about 80%) nitrogen. The molecular weight of oxygen is 32, and that of nitrogen is 28; we see that the average molecular weight of the mixture is 28.8. The weight of 1 liter of air at standard conditions is accordingly 28.8/22.4 = 1.29 g/liter.

   When air is heated from 0°C (273°K) to 25°C (298°K) it increases in volume, and accordingly decreases in density. The fraction by which the density at 0°C must be multiplied to obtain the density at 25°C is seen to be 273/298; hence

$$\text{Density of air at 25°C} = \frac{273}{298} \times 1.29 \text{ g/liter} = \textbf{1.17 g/liter}$$

The Determination of the Molecular Weight of a Gas.   In the investigation of a new substance, one of the first things that a chemist does is to determine its molecular weight. If the substance can be vaporized without decomposing it, the density of its vapor provides a value of the molecular weight, and this method is usually used for volatile substances.

   The density of a substance that is a gas under ordinary conditions is usually determined by the simple method of weighing a flask of known volume filled with the gas under known pressure, and then weighing the flask after it has been evacuated with a vacuum pump. In ordinary work the second weighing may be replaced by a weighing of the flask filled with air, oxygen, or other gas of known density. The volume of the flask is determined by weighing it filled with water.

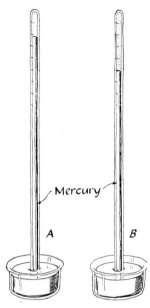

Figure **6-9** *The Hof-mann method for determining the density of a vapor.*

Example 8. Determination of the Molecular Weight of a Substance by the Hofmann Method. A chemist isolated a substance in the form of a yellow oil. He found on analysis that the oil contained only hydrogen and sulfur, and the amount of water obtained when a sample of the substance was burned showed that it consisted of about 3% hydrogen and 97% sulfur. To determine the molecular weight he prepared a very small glass bulb, weighed the glass bulb, filled it with the oil, and weighed it again; the difference in the two weighings, which is the weight of the oil, was 0.0302 g. He then introduced the filled bulb into the evacuated space above the mercury column in a tube, as shown in Figure 6-9. The level of the mercury dropped to 118 mm below its original level, after the oil had been completely vaporized. The temperature of the tube was 30°C. The volume of the gas phase above the mercury at the end of the experiment was 73.2 ml. Find the molecular weight and formula of the substance.

Solution. The vapor of the substance is stated to occupy the volume 73.2 ml at temperature 30°C and pressure 118 mm Hg. Its volume corrected to standard conditions is seen to be

$$73.2 \text{ ml} \times \frac{273}{303} \times \frac{118}{760} = 10.24 \text{ ml}$$

One mole of gas at standard conditions occupies 22,400 ml; hence the number of moles in the sample of the substance is $10.24/22,400 = 0.000457$. The weight of this fraction of a mole is stated to be 0.0302 g; hence the weight of one mole is this weight divided by the number of moles:

$$\text{Molar weight of substance} = \frac{0.0302 \text{ g}}{0.000457 \text{ mole}} = \textbf{66.0 g/mole}$$

The substance was found by analysis to contain 3% hydrogen and 97% sulfur. If we had 100 g of the oil, it would contain 3 g of hydrogen, which is 3 gram-atoms, and 97 g of sulfur, which is also 3 gram-atoms (the atomic weight of sulfur is 32). Hence the molecule contains equal numbers of hydrogen atoms and sulfur atoms. If its formula were HS, its molecular weight would be the sum of the atomic weights of hydrogen and sulfur, 33. It is evident from the observed molecular weight that the formula is H_2S_2, the molecular weight of which is 66.15.

Illustrative Exercises

6-16. Calculate the density of uranium hexafluoride gas, UF_6, at 100°C and 500 mm Hg. (This gas is used at Oak Ridge, Tenn., in the gaseous diffusion plant for separating U^{235} from U^{238}.)

6-17. (a) The vapor density of a metal at 819°C and 76.0 mm Hg is measured, and found to be 0.1483 g/liter. What is the molecular weight of the metal?

(b) The heat capacity of the solid metal is 0.047 cal/g. Calculate a rough value of the atomic weight of the metal, and an accurate value.

6-11. The Kinetic Theory of Gases

During the nineteenth century the concepts were developed that atoms and molecules are in continual motion and that the temperature of a body is a measure of the intensity of this motion. The idea that the behavior of gases could be accounted for by considering the motion of the gas molecules had occurred to several people (Daniel Bernoulli in 1738, J. P. Joule in 1851, A. Kronig in 1856), and in the years following 1858 this idea was developed into a detailed kinetic theory of gases by R. J. E. Clausius, Clerk Maxwell, L. Boltzmann, and many later investigators. Boltzmann then expanded it into the important part of the branch of theoretical science called statistical mechanics, which we have already discussed in Section 5-11.

In a gas at temperature T the molecules are moving about, different molecules having at a given time different speeds v and different kinetic energies of translational motion $\frac{1}{2}mv^2$ (m being the mass of a molecule). It has been found that *the average kinetic energy per molecule*, $\frac{1}{2}m[v^2]_{average}$, *is the same for all gases at the same temperature, and that its value increases with the temperature, being equal to* $\frac{3}{2}kT$. (Here k is the Boltzmann constant, Section 5-11, equal to R/N.) We shall discuss this principle further in Section 11-12.

The average (root-mean-square*) velocity of hydrogen molecules at 0°C is 1.84×10^5 cm/sec—over a mile per second. At higher temperatures the average velocity is greater; it reaches twice as great a value, 3.68×10^5 cm/sec, for hydrogen molecules at 820°C, corresponding to an absolute temperature four times as great.

Since the average kinetic energy, $\frac{1}{2}m[v^2]_{average}$, is equal for different molecules, the average value of the square of the velocity is seen to be inversely proportional to the mass of the molecule, and hence the average velocity (root-mean-square average) is inversely proportional to the square root of the molecular weight. The molecular weight of oxygen is just 16 times that of hydrogen; accordingly molecules of oxygen move with a speed just one quarter as great as molecules of hydrogen at the same temperature. The average speed of oxygen molecules at 0°C is 0.46×10^5 cm/sec.

The explanation of Boyle's law given by the kinetic theory is simple. A molecule striking the wall of the container of the gas rebounds, and contributes momentum to the wall; in this way the collisions of the molecules of the gas with the wall

---

* The root-mean-square average of a quantity is the square root of the average value of the square of the quantity.

produce the gas pressure that balances the external pressure applied to the gas. If the volume is decreased by 50%, molecules strike a unit area of the wall twice as often, and hence the pressure is doubled. The explanation of the law of Charles and Gay-Lussac is equally simple. If the absolute temperature is doubled, the speed of the molecules is increased by the factor $\sqrt{2}$. This causes the molecules to make $\sqrt{2}$ times as many collisions as before, and each collision is increased in force by $\sqrt{2}$, so that the pressure itself is doubled by doubling the absolute temperature. Avogadro's law is also explained by the fact that the average kinetic energy is the same at a given temperature for all gases.

The Effusion and Diffusion of Gases. The Mean Free Paths of Molecules.   There is an interesting dependence of the *rate of effusion* of a gas through a small hole on the molecular weight of the gas. The speeds of motion of different molecules are inversely proportional to the square roots of their molecular weights. If a small hole is made in the wall of a gas container, the gas molecules will pass through the hole into an evacuated region outside at a rate determined by the speed at which they are moving (these speeds determine the probability that a molecule will strike the hole). Accordingly the kinetic theory requires that the rate of effusion of a gas through a small hole be inversely proportional to the square root of its molecular weight. This law was discovered experimentally before the development of the kinetic theory—it was observed that hydrogen effuses through a porous plate four times as rapidly as oxygen.

In the foregoing discussions we have ignored the appreciable sizes of gas molecules, which cause the molecules to collide often with one another. In an ordinary gas, such as air at standard conditions, a molecule moves only about 500 Å on the average between collisions—that is, its *mean free path* under these conditions is only about two hundred times its own diameter.

The value of the mean free path is significant for phenomena that depend on molecular collisions, such as the viscosity and the thermal conductivity of gases. Another such phenomenon is the *diffusion* of one gas through another or through itself (such as of radioactive molecules of a gas through the nonradioactive gas). In the early days of kinetic theory it was pointed out by skeptics that it takes minutes or hours for a gas to diffuse from one side of a quiet room to the other, even though the molecules are attributed velocities of about a mile per second. The explanation of the slow diffusion rate is that a molecule diffusing through a gas is not able to move directly from one point to another a long distance away, but instead is forced by collisions with other molecules to follow a tortuous path, making only slow progress in its resultant motion. Only when diffusing into a high vacuum can the gas diffuse with the speed of molecular motion.

The Distribution Law for Molecular Velocities.   In 1860 the English physicist James Clerk Maxwell (1831–1879) derived an equation that correctly gives the fraction of gas molecules with velocities in the range v to $v + dv$. This equation is called the *Maxwell distribution law* (or *Maxwell-Boltzmann distribution law*) *for molecular velocities.* In a perfect gas at temperature T, containing N molecules, each with mass m, we ask how many molecules dN have velocities lying between v and $v + dv$. The velocity v may be described as a vector with components v_x,

v_y, and v_z in velocity space. The volume of the spherical shell bounded by the surfaces v and $v + dv$ is $4\pi v^2 \, dv$. It was found by Maxwell through analysis of the transfer of momentum from one molecule to another during a molecular collision that this volume element must be multiplied by the exponential factor $\exp(-\frac{1}{2}mv^2/kT)$. (This factor is, of course, now called the Boltzmann factor, which we have discussed in Section 5-11; see also Appendix V.) The normalizing factor $(m/2\pi kT)^{3/2}$ is also needed in order that the integral of dN over all velocities ($v = 0$ to $v = \infty$) should be equal to N. The distribution law for molecular velocities is

$$dN = 4\pi N \left(\frac{m}{2\pi kT}\right)^{3/2} \exp\left(\tfrac{1}{2}mv^2/kT\right)v^2 \, dv \qquad (3)$$

The distribution function calculated for helium atoms at 100°K and also for helium atoms at 400°K is shown as Figure 6-10. We see that in Equation 3 the mass and the absolute temperature occur only in the ratio m/T. Accordingly, the two curves that are shown apply also to methane, CH_4, with molecular weight four times that of helium, at temperatures four times as great, 400°K and 1600°K, respectively.

The maximum for the distribution function occurs at the value of v called the most probable velocity, v_{mp}; it is equal to $(2kT/m)^{1/2}$, which has the value $12{,}895(T/M)^{1/2}$ cm/sec (here M is the molecular weight). This value is represented by a vertical line on the curve for helium at 400°K.

The average value of the velocity is $(8kT/\pi m)^{1/2}$, which is equal to $14{,}551(T/M)^{1/2}$. The root-mean-square value of the velocity, which is the square root of the average value of v^2, is equal to $(3kT/m)^{1/2}$, with value $15{,}794(T/M)^{1/2}$.

We see that **the average kinetic energy per molecule, $\frac{1}{2}m(v^2)_{average}$, is equal to $\frac{3}{2}kT$.** It accordingly has the same value for all gases at the same temperature, as stated in the second paragraph of this section.

Figure 6-10

The velocity distribution function for helium atoms at 100°K and also for helium atoms at 400°K. These two curves also apply to methane at temperatures 400°K and 1600°K, respectively.

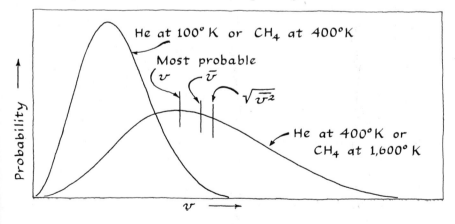

This result, called the *equipartition of energy*, is one of the most important consequences of the kinetic theory. Some of the ways in which it can be used in the discussion of the properties of gases have been mentioned above.

The law of equipartition of energy is sometimes expressed in the following words: *The average kinetic energy of molecules or other particles in the region in which classical theory applies is $\frac{1}{2}kT$ per degree of freedom.* A molecule is considered to have three degrees of freedom of translational motion, corresponding to the three components of velocity v_x, v_y, and v_z, and the average kinetic energy of the molecule at temperature T is accordingly $\frac{3}{2}kT$. This value for the average kinetic energy applies also to liquids and crystals, if the temperature is high enough for the classical theory to be valid. At lower temperatures, where the quantum effect of decrease in heat capacity below the equipartition value occurs (Section 5-8), the average energy per degree of freedom is less than the equipartition value.

Example 9. What is the heat capacity of helium gas at constant volume?

Solution. In helium gas the molecules (atoms of helium) interact with one another only very weakly, and we need to consider only the kinetic energy of the molecules. The average value of the kinetic energy is $\frac{3}{2}kT$ per molecule, which is equal to $\frac{3}{2}RT$ per mole. The increase in energy accompanying an increase by dT in temperature is

$$\frac{d}{dT}(\tfrac{3}{2}RT) = \tfrac{3}{2}R$$

The value of R is 1.987 cal deg^{-1} mole^{-1}; accordingly the heat capacity at constant volume, C_V, is $\frac{3}{2} \times 1.987 = 2.98$ cal deg^{-1} mole^{-1}, approximately 3 cal deg^{-1} mole^{-1}. This value is found by experiment for all monatomic gases.

Example 10. What is the heat capacity of a diatomic gas at constant volume, at room temperature?

Solution. A diatomic molecule consists of two atoms, each with three degrees of freedom. Accordingly, if the properties of the molecule corresponded to classical theory, there would be six degrees of freedom, and the contribution of kinetic energy to the energy would be $6 \times \frac{1}{2}kT = 3kT$. In addition, the equipartition of energy would require some potential energy, amounting to $\frac{1}{2}kT$, for the vibrational motion of the molecule. For a molecule such as HCl the vibrational frequency is so high that at room temperature the vibration is not excited—the molecules are almost entirely in the lowest vibrational state (Sections 5-8, 5-12). Hence only the other five degrees of freedom are excited, and the energy becomes $\frac{5}{2}kT$, or $\frac{5}{2}RT$ per mole. By differentiating with respect to T, we thus obtain the heat capacity at constant volume as $\frac{5}{2}R$, approximately 5 cal deg^{-1} mole^{-1}.

Pressure-Volume Work. When the volume of a system changes by amount dV at constant pressure P, an amount of work $P\,dV$ is done (Section 5-9). The gas law equation $PV = nRT$ shows that the work associated with the volume V at pressure P is equal to nRT, which is RT per mole. When a gas is heated at constant pressure it expands, and energy is required to produce the expansion. The amount of this energy (for a mole of gas) corresponding to the increase in temperature dT, with pressure held constant at the value P, is found to be R by differentiating the expression for the energy. Accordingly the heat capacity of a mole of gas at constant pressure is greater than that at constant volume by the amount R, about 2 cal deg^{-1} mole^{-1}.

This conclusion agrees with experiment. The heat capacity of a monatomic gas such as helium is 3 cal deg^{-1} mole^{-1} at constant volume and 5 cal deg^{-1} mole^{-1} at constant pressure, and that of a diatomic gas such as HCl at low temperatures where vibration is not excited is 5 cal deg^{-1} mole^{-1} at constant volume and 7 cal deg^{-1} mole^{-1} at constant pressure.

Experimental Verification of the Distribution Law.   Many deductions from the distribution law were found to be in agreement with experiment, and none in disagreement. For example, Maxwell showed that according to kinetic theory the viscosity of a gas should be independent of pressure (except at very small and very large pressures), and should increase with increasing temperature, rather than decrease. These surprising properties were verified by experiment, and the kinetic theory of gases, including the distribution law for molecular velocities, was accepted long before a direct experimental determination of the velocity distribution function could be carried out. By 1920 the experimental techniques of physics, especially the ability to obtain a high vacuum, had developed enough to permit direct determinations to be made. Otto Stern (born 1888) carried out the first experiment of this sort. He studied a beam of silver atoms emitted from the silver coating on a tungsten wire heated to about 1200°C. The beam was defined by a system of slits, and it then impinged on the surface of a rotating drum. One of the slits was also rotating in such a way that the atoms of silver could pass through the slit only during a small fraction of the time of revolution of the drum. The fast atoms struck the inside of the drum very quickly, before it had rotated far, whereas the slow atoms were delayed in striking the drum. This experiment gave a rough verification of the distribution function.

Figure **6-11**

Apparatus used in experimental test of the distribution law for molecular velocities.

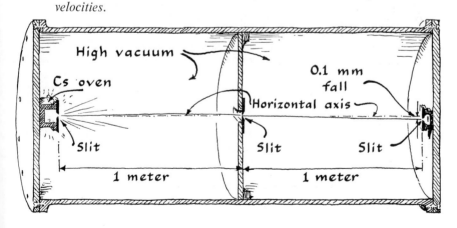

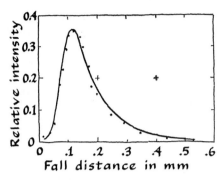

Figure 6-12 *Velocity distribution of cesium atoms, determined experimentally by use of the apparatus of Figure 6-11.*

Later experiments have led to essentially complete experimental verification of the distribution function. One of these experiments, carried out by I. Estermann, O. C. Simpson, and O. Stern in 1947, is illustrated in Figure 6-11. The entire apparatus is evacuated. At the left there is shown an oven containing some cesium metal. The oven is heated to a temperature of about 450°K, at which the vapor pressure of cesium is sufficiently great to cause many cesium atoms to be present in the gas phase. A beam of cesium atoms coming from a small horizontal slit in the oven is further defined by another slit, 100 cm away. It consists of a fine horizontal tungsten wire, electrically heated, and an adjacent curved plate with a negative electric charge. Whenever a cesium atom strikes the wire it is ionized; it leaves the wire as a cesium ion, Cs^+, and is attracted to the negatively charged plate. The number of cesium ions reaching the plate can be measured by measuring the electric current between the wire and the plate.

The atoms of cesium constituting the beam defined by the slit in the oven and the slit in the center of the tube move along parabolic paths under the influence of the earth's gravitational attraction. The average amount of deflection in this apparatus is about 2 mm for cesium atoms at 450°K.

The distribution observed—the number of cesium ions reaching the plate as a function of the vertical coordinate of the tungsten wire—is shown in Figure 6-12. From this distribution the distribution of velocities of the molecules (atoms) of cesium in the oven can be calculated. It is found to be that given by the Maxwell-Boltzmann distribution law for molecular velocities, Equation 3. The experiments provide verification of the law to within about 1%.

Example 11.   At what height above sea level is the atmospheric pressure 0.5 atm? Assume the temperature to be constant, 20°C.

  Solution.   This problem illustrates another way of using the Boltzmann distribution law in classical mechanics. From Equation 2 of Appendix V we see that the number of molecules in unit volume, n, is proportional to $\exp(-E_{pot}/kT)$. The value of E_{pot} is mgz, with g equal to 981 cm sec^{-2}. For m we use $M/$Avogadro's number. M may be taken as 28.8 g mole^{-1} (average for N_2 and O_2, Table 6-1), giving $m = 28.8$ g mole$^{-1}/0.602 \times 10^{24}$ mole$^{-1} = 47.8 \times 10^{-24}$ g. Let $z = 0$ at sea level; the corresponding values of $\exp(-E_{pot}/kT)$ is 1. The ratio $n(z)$ to $n(0)$ is $\exp(-mgz/kT)$, which is equal to 0.5 if the pressure is 0.5 atm. The value of mg/kT is

$$\frac{4718 \times 10^{-24}\,\text{g} \times 981\,\text{cm sec}^{-2}}{1.380 \times 10^{-16}\,\text{erg deg}^{-1} \times 293\,\text{deg}} = 1.16 \times 10^{-6}\,\text{cm}^{-1}$$

We hence write

$$\exp(-1.16 \times 10^{-6} z) = 0.5$$
$$-1.16 \times 10^{-6} z = \ln 0.5 = 2.303 \log 0.5 = -2.303 \log 2$$
$$= -2.303 \times 0.301$$

Hence

$$z = \frac{2.303 \times 0.301}{1.16 \times 10^{-6} \text{ cm}^{-1}} = \textbf{0.6} \times \textbf{10}^{\textbf{6}} \textbf{ cm}$$

We accordingly have calculated that the atmospheric pressure is 0.5 atm at 6 km above sea level.

Example 12. Assuming thermodynamic equilibrium and temperature 20°C, at about what height would the partial pressure of hydrogen in the atmosphere be half that at sea level? What is the fraction of H_2 in the air at that height?

Solution. We may solve this problem with little effort by making use of the result of Example 11. The mass of H_2 is 1/7.2 that of the average N_2 and O_2 molecule in the atmosphere. Hence the partial pressure of hydrogen is one-half that at sea level at the height $7.2 \times 6 = \textbf{43 km}$. (Note that the exponent in the Boltzmann factor then has the same value as in Example 11.)

At 43 km the exponent in the Boltzmann factor for the average mass for oxygen and nitrogen in air has value 7.2 times that used in Example 11, which reduces the atmospheric pressure by the factor $\frac{1}{2}$. The value of the Boltzmann factor is thus $(\frac{1}{2})^{7.2}$ or approximately $(\frac{1}{2})^7 = 1/2^7 = 1/128$. We accordingly calculate that hydrogen composes about $0.005 \times 128 = 0.6\%$ by volume of the air at elevation 43 km, instead of the value 0.01% at sea level (Table 6-1).

6-12. Deviations of Real Gases from Ideal Behavior

Real gases differ in their behavior from that represented by the perfect-gas equation for two reasons. First, the molecules have a definite size, so that each molecule prevents others from making use of a part of the volume of the gas container. This causes the volume of a gas to be larger than that calculated for ideal behavior. Second, the molecules even when some distance apart do not move independently of one another, but attract one another slightly. This tends to cause the volume of a gas to be smaller than the calculated volume.

The amounts of the deviation for some gases are shown in Figure 6-13. It is seen that for hydrogen at 0°C the deviation is positive at all pressures—it is due essentially to the volume of the molecules, as the effect of their attraction at this high temperature (relative to the boiling point, -252.8°C) is extremely small.

At pressures below 120 atm, nitrogen (at 0°C) shows negative deviations from ideal behavior, intermolecular attraction having a greater effect than the finite size of the molecules.

The deviation of hydrogen and nitrogen at 0°C from ideal behavior is seen to be less than 10% at pressures less than 300 atm. Oxygen, helium, and other

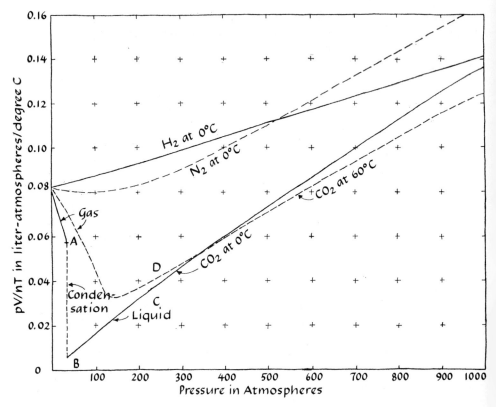

Figure 6-13

The value of PV/nT for some gases, showing deviation from the perfect-gas law at high pressures.

gases with low boiling points also show small deviations from the perfect-gas law. For these gases the perfect-gas law holds to within 1% at room temperature or higher temperatures and at pressures below 10 atm.

Larger deviations are shown by gases with higher boiling points—in general, the deviations from ideal behavior become large as the gas approaches condensation. It is seen from the figure that for carbon dioxide at 60°C the volume of the gas is only about 30% as great at 120 atm pressure as the volume calculated by the perfect-gas equation.

If the temperature is low the deviations are shown in a pronounced way by the condensation of the gas to a liquid (see the curve for carbon dioxide at 0°C). After carbon dioxide has been compressed to about 40 atm at 0°C, the effect of the attraction of the molecules for one another becomes so great that they cling together, forming a liquid, the system then consisting of two phases, the gaseous phase and the liquid phase. On further compression the volume decreases without change in pressure (region A of the figure) until all the gas is condensed (point **B**). The volume of the liquid decreases much less rapidly with increase in pressure from point **B** on than would that of a gas, because the molecules of the liquid are effectively in contact; hence the curve rises (region C).

An extraordinary phenomenon, the **continuity of the liquid and gaseous states,** was discovered about eighty years ago by Thomas Andrews (1813–1885). He found that above a temperature characteristic of the gas, called the *critical temperature*, the transition from the gaseous state to the liquid state occurs without a sharp change in volume on increasing the pressure.

The critical temperature of carbon dioxide is 31.1°C. Above this temperature (at 60°C, for example, corresponding to the curve shown in the figure), all the properties of the substance change continuously, showing no signs that the gas has condensed to a liquid. Nevertheless, when the pressure becomes greater than about 200 atm the substance behaves like carbon dioxide liquid, rather than like a gas (region D of Figure 6-13). It is, indeed, possible to change from the gas at 0°C and 1 atm pressure to the liquid at 0°C and 50 atm either by the ordinary process of condensing the gas to the liquid, passing through the two-phase stage, or, without condensation or any discontinuity, by heating to 60°, increasing the pressure to about 200 atm, cooling to 0°, and then reducing the pressure to 50 atm. The liquid could then be made to boil, simply by reducing the pressure and keeping the temperature at 0°C; and then, by repeating the cycle, it could be brought back to 0°C and 50 atm pressure without condensation, and be made to boil again.

Values of the critical temperature, critical pressure, and critical density of some substances are given in Table 6-3.

The possibility of continuous transition from the gaseous to the liquid state is understandable in view of the mutual characteristic of randomness of structure of these phases, as discussed in Chapter 2. It is, on the other hand, difficult to imagine the possibility of a gradual transition from a disordered state (liquid) to a completely ordered state (crystal); and correspondingly it has not been found possible to crystallize substances or to melt crystals without passing through a discontinuity at the melting point—there is no critical temperature for melting a crystal.

The van der Waals Equation of State. An equation relating the volume of a sample of substance to the temperature and pressure is called an *equation of state* for the substance.

The perfect-gas equation has only limited applicability to real gases, and many other equations, involving constants characteristic of the substance in addition to the general constant R, have been proposed.

The most useful simple equation of this sort was discovered in 1873 by the Dutch physicist Johannes Diderik van der Waals (1837–1923). It is

$$\left(P + \frac{n^2 a}{V^2}\right)(V - nb) = nRT \qquad (4)$$

Table **6-3**

Van der Waals Constants and Critical Constants of Some Substances

SUB-STANCE	a	b	CRITICAL TEMPER-ATURE	CRITICAL PRESSURE	CRITICAL VOLUME
He	0.0341 l² atm mole⁻²	0.0237 l mole⁻¹	5.3°K	2.26 atm	58 ml mole⁻¹
Ne	.211	.0171	44.5	25.9	42
Ar	1.35	.0322	151	48	75
Kr	2.32	.0398	210	54	107
Xe	4.19	.0550	300	58	112
H₂	0.244	.0266	73.3	12.8	65
N₂	1.39	.0391	126.1	33.5	90
O₂	1.36	.0318	154.4	49.7	74
Cl₂	6.49	.0562	417	76	125
CO	1.49	.0399	134	35	90
CO₂	3.59	.0427	304	73	96
N₂O	3.78	.0441	309.7	72.6	98
CH₄	2.25	.0428	91	46	99
C₂H₆	5.49	.0638	305	49	143
SO₂	6.71	.0564	430	78	123
CCl₄	20.39	.138	556	45	276
SnCl₄	26.91	.164	592	37	352
H₂O	5.46	.0305	647.2	217.7	45
NH₃	4.17	.0371	406	112	72
Hg	8.09	.0170	1823	200	45

This equation contains two constants, characteristic of the substance, a and b. (They are usually called van der Waals' a and van der Waals' b.) Values of a and b found by experiment (measurement of the deviation from the perfect-gas law) for several substances are given in Table 6-3.

The constant a is a measure of the energy of attraction between the molecules. Its numerical value, in l^2 atm mole⁻², is roughly equal to the heat of vaporization of the liquid substance in kcal/mole (examples: He, 0.034, 0.020; Ar, 1.35, 1.56; CO, 1.49, 1.44; CH₄, 2.25, 1.96; N₂O, 3.78, 3.96).

Van der Waals' b has the dimensions of volume. It is usually considered to be $4N$ times the volume of a molecule. For example, for the noble gases the values of b in Table 6-3 lead to the following values of the atomic radii: He, 1.33 Å; Ne, 1.19 Å; Ar, 1.47 Å; Kr, 1.58 Å; Xe, 1.76 Å. Except for helium,* these values agree roughly with those estimated in other ways (Section 9-15).

The van der Waals equation provides an interesting explanation of the transition between the gaseous state and the liquid state and of the critical point. In Figure 6-14 there are shown four curves of the volume per mole as a function of the pressure, calculated by Equation 4, with a and b given the values for N₂O, for four values of T in the neighborhood of the critical temperature. The calculated curve for 308.7°K, one degree less than the critical temperature, shows a

_____
* Many properties of helium show abnormalities that are attributed to quantum effects, related to its small atomic weight.

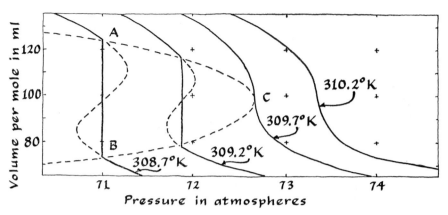

Figure **6-14**

Curves calculated by use of the van der Waals equation, giving the molar volume of nitrous oxide for four values of the temperature.

region in which the pressure would decrease with decrease in volume (center of dashed portion). Instead, the fluid separates into two phases, and with decreasing volume the pressure remains constant as the phase point moves along the straight line from *A* to *B*, until only one phase remains (at *B*, liquid phase only).

The point *C* is the critical point, at which the properties of the gaseous phase and the liquid phase become identical. This is a point of inflection for the curve. By evaluating the point of inflection of Equation 4, the following expressions are found for the critical constants:

$$\text{Critical temperature} \quad = \frac{8a}{27bR} \tag{5}$$

$$\text{Critical pressure} \quad = \frac{a}{27b^2} \tag{6}$$

$$\text{Critical molar volume} = 3b \tag{7}$$

It can be seen by reference to the values in Table 6-3 that these relations are satisfied only roughly.

EXERCISES

6-18. What are allotropes? What differences in properties and structure between oxygen and ozone can you mention?

6-19. Do you know any elements other than oxygen that exist in allotropic forms?

6-20. What is the lightest gas? The lightest liquid? The lightest crystalline substance?

6-21. The molecular weight of hydrogen is 2, and hence hydrogen gas is lighter than helium, which has molecular weight 4 (monatomic molecules). What property of hydrogen makes it less desirable than helium for inflating balloons?

6-22. Explain why helium, though twice as heavy as hydrogen, has a lifting power (in balloons) 92% as great as hydrogen.

6-23. How much helium should be put into

a balloon of 10,000-liter capacity that is meant to rise without loss of gas to a height where the pressure is 200 mm of mercury and the temperature is $-10°C$, if it starts at sea level (1 atm pressure) at a temperature of 25°C? (Answer: 3,080 liters.)

6-24. The number of people on the earth is about 4×10^9. What volume of gas at standard conditions contains this number of molecules?

6-25. A certain compound of carbon and hydrogen contains 81.8% carbon. This compound is a gas with density 1.96 g per liter at standard conditions. What is its formula?

6-26. Disulfur decafluoride, S_2F_{10}, has standard boiling point 29°C. What is the density of the gas at this temperature (1 atm pressure)? What is the ratio of its density to that of hydrogen?

6-27. Calculate the volume occupied at 20°C and 1 atm pressure by the gas evolved from 100 cm³ of solid carbon dioxide, which has density 1.53 g/cm³.

6-28. What weight of gasoline, approximately C_8H_{14}, would be needed to combine with the oxygen in a cylinder with volume 30 cubic inches containing air and the proper amount of gasoline vapor at 1 atm and 20°C to produce H_2O and CO_2? (Note that a correction should be made for the partial pressure of the gasoline vapor.)

6-29. What is the volume in cubic feet at standard conditions of one ounce-molecular-weight of a gas?* (Answer: 22.4.)

6-30. What is the weight in ounces of 22.4 cu ft of carbon dioxide at standard conditions? (Answer: 44.)

6-31. The density of hydrogen cyanide at standard conditions is 1.29 g/liter. Calculate the apparent molecular weight of hydrogen cyanide vapor.

6-32. The volume of an ordinary hand-operated bicycle pump is about 0.01 cu ft, and the volume of a bicycle tire is about 0.08 cu ft. At what point in the stroke of the pump does air start to enter a tire which

is at a gage pressure of 47 lbs per sq in? Does the pressure in the tire change more per stroke when the tire is at gage pressure of 50 lbs/sq in than at 20 lbs/sq in?

6-33. A bromide of silicon is found on analysis to contain 89.5% bromine. Its measured gas density at 240°C and 1 atm is 12.7 g/liter. What is its formula?

6-34. (a) If pure ozone at room temperature (20°C) and 1 atm were to explode, forming oxygen, what would be the temperature of the product in a well-insulated closed vessel? Use 0.20 cal deg^{-1} g^{-1} for the heat capacity of oxygen at constant volume and enthalpy values from Table 6-2.

(b) What would be the pressure reached, with volume held constant?

(c) What would be the pressure after the temperature had returned to 20°C?
[Answer: (c) 1.5 atm.]

6-35. Liquid hydrogen peroxide has density 1.47 g cm^{-3} at 25°C. If all the heat of its decomposition were used to raise the temperature of the products of decomposition (Exercises 6-4, 6-5), what would be the increase in volume on decomposition at 1 atm pressure? For the heat capacity at constant pressure use 7 cal deg^{-1} mole^{-1} for oxygen and 9 cal deg^{-1} mole^{-1} for water vapor.

6-36. In Section 6-11 it is stated that the average speed of a hydrogen molecule at 0°C is 1.84×10^5 cm/sec. What is the average speed at this temperature of a molecule of uranium hexafluoride?

6-37. In the gas-diffusion U^{235} plant at Oak Ridge, uranium hexafluoride is used as the gas in the separation of U^{235} from U^{238}. Natural uranium contains 0.71% U^{235}. If the diffusion through a porous metal diaphragm were perfectly efficient, what increase in U^{235} content would occur in diffusion of some of the gas through one membrane? How many diffusion stages would be needed to double the U^{235} content of the gas? (Answer: By factor 1.0043; about 162.)

6-38. The atmosphere might arbitrarily be

* It is interesting in this connection that the master craftsmen of Lübeck defined the ounce as one one-thousandth of the weight of one cubic foot of ice-cold water.

defined as extending above the earth to the height where there is only about one molecule of nitrogen or oxygen per milliliter. Using the Boltzmann distribution law as in Example 13, make a rough calculation of this height. (Answer: About 385 km.)

6-39. In the fission of U^{235} or Pu^{239}, about 0.1% of the mass is converted into energy (Chapter 30). Assuming that 1% of the released energy becomes kinetic energy of the particles released from the fission process (atomic nuclei, neutrons, electrons), and that the molecular weight of the average particle is 1, calculate the average kinetic energy per particle and the temperature of the material after the explosion. (Answer: About 70,000,000°C.)

6-40. During much of the nineteenth century hydrogen, nitrogen, oxygen, carbon monoxide, and methane were called permanent gases, whereas other gases (chlorine, carbon dioxide, ethane) were not put in this category. Can you explain this classification? (See Table 6-3.)

6-41. By graphical integration under one of the curves of Figure 6-10, estimate what fraction of molecules in a gas have velocity greater than twice the root-mean-square average, and what fraction have less than half.

REFERENCES

R. D. Present, *Kinetic Theory of Gases*, McGraw-Hill Book Company, Inc., New York, 1958.

Norman Davidson, *Statistical Mechanics*, McGraw-Hill Book Company, Inc., New York, 1962.

Allen L. King, *Thermophysics*, W. H. Freeman and Co., San Francisco, 1962.

CHAPTER 7

The Chemical Elements,

the Periodic Law, and

the Electronic Structure of Atoms

The 103 known elements include some with which everyone is familiar and many that are rare. At room temperature some of the elementary substances are gases, some are liquids, and some are solids.* They show great variety in their chemical properties and in the nature of the compounds that they form. In consequence, the study of chemistry is not simple or easy; to obtain a reasonably broad knowledge of general chemistry it is necessary to learn many facts.

The facts of chemistry cannot be completely coordinated by a unifying theory. Nevertheless, the development of chemical theories has now proceeded far enough to be of great aid to the student, who can simplify his task of learning about the properties and reactions of substances by correlating this information with theories, such as the theory of atomic structure, which has been discussed in the preceding chapters, and the periodic law, which we shall now consider.

7-1. The Periodic Law

Let us first recall from Chapters 3 and 4 that atoms are built of particles of three kinds: protons, neutrons, and electrons. The nucleus of each atom is

---

* The elements that are gases at standard conditions (0°C and 1 atm) are hydrogen, helium, nitrogen, oxygen, fluorine, neon, chlorine, argon, krypton, xenon, and radon. The only elements that are liquids at standard conditions are bromine and mercury.

made of protons and neutrons. The number of protons (the atomic number) determines the electric charge of the nucleus, and the total number of protons and neutrons (the mass number) determines its mass. In a neutral atom the number of electrons surrounding the nucleus is equal to the atomic number.

The periodic law states that *the properties of the chemical elements are not arbitrary, but depend upon the structure of the atom and vary with the atomic number in a systematic way.* The important point is that this dependence involves a crude periodicity that shows itself in the recurrence of characteristic properties.

For example, the elements with atomic numbers 2, 10, 18, 36, 54, and 86 are all chemically inert gases. Similarly, the elements with atomic numbers one greater—namely, 3, 11, 19, 37, 55, and 87—are all light metals that are very reactive chemically. These six metals, lithium (3), sodium (11), potassium (19), rubidium (37), cesium (55), and francium (87), all react with chlorine to form colorless compounds that crystallize in cubes and show a cubic cleavage. The chemical formulas of these salts are similar: $LiCl$, $NaCl$, KCl, $RbCl$, $CsCl$, and $FrCl$. The composition and properties of other compounds of these six metals are correspondingly similar, and different from those of other elements.

The comparison of the observed chemical and physical properties of elements and their compounds with the atomic numbers of the elements accordingly indicates that, after the first two elements, hydrogen and helium, which constitute the **very short period** (the word period is used for a sequence of elements), there are the **first short period** of eight elements (from helium, atomic number 2, to neon, 10), the **second short period** of eight elements (to argon, 18), the **first long period** of eighteen elements (to krypton, 36), the **second long period** of eighteen elements (to xenon, 54), and then the **very long period** of 32 elements (to radon, 86). In case that enough new elements of very large atomic number are made in the future it may well be found that there is another very long period of 32 elements ending in another inert gas, with atomic number 118.

7-2. The Periodic Table

The periodic recurrence of properties of the elements with increasing atomic number may be effectively emphasized by arranging the elements in a table, called the *periodic table* or *periodic system* of the elements. Several alternative forms of the periodic table have been proposed and used. We shall base the discussion of the elements and their properties in this book on the table shown as Table 7-1 (it is also reproduced inside the front cover of the book).

The Development of the Periodic Table. The differentiation of chemical substances into two groups, elements and compounds, was achieved at the end of the eighteenth century. A long time was required for the recognition of the fact

Table 7-1

The Periodic System of the Elements

	Group 0
H 1	He 2

p-block (periods 2 and 3):

	III	IV	V	VI	VII	0
						He 2
	B 5	C 6	N 7	O 8	F 9	Ne 10
	Al 13	Si 14	P 15	S 16	Cl 17	Ar 18

Main block:

0	I	II	III	IVa	Va	VIa	VIIa	VIII			Ib	IIb	IIIb	IVb	Vb	VIb	VIIb	0
	Li 3	Be 4																
	Na 11	Mg 12																
Ar 18	K 19	Ca 20	Sc 21	Ti 22	V 23	Cr 24	Mn 25	Fe 26	Co 27	Ni 28	Cu 29	Zn 30	Ga 31	Ge 32	As 33	Se 34	Br 35	Kr 36
Kr 36	Rb 37	Sr 38	Y 39	Zr 40	Nb 41	Mo 42	Tc 43	Ru 44	Rh 45	Pd 46	Ag 47	Cd 48	In 49	Sn 50	Sb 51	Te 52	I 53	Xe 54
Xe 54	Cs 55	Ba 56	La 57 *	Hf 72	Ta 73	W 74	Re 75	Os 76	Ir 77	Pt 78	Au 79	Hg 80	Tl 81	Pb 82	Bi 83	Po 84	At 85	Rn 86
Rn 86	Fr 87	Ra 88	Ac 89 ◆	Th 90	Pa 91	U 92	Np 93	Pu 94										

* Lanthanons

Ce 58	Pr 59	Nd 60	Pm 61	Sm 62	Eu 63	Gd 64	Tb 65	Dy 66	Ho 67	Er 68	Tm 69	Yb 70	Lu 71

◆ Actinons

Th 90	Pa 91	U 92	Np 93	Pu 94	Am 95	Cm 96	Bk 97	Cf 98	Es 99	Fm 100	Md 101	No 102	Lw 103

that the elements can be classified in the way now described by the periodic law. The first step was taken in 1817, when the German chemist J. W. Döbereiner (1780–1849) showed that the combining weight of strontium lies midway between the combining weights of the two related elements calcium and barium. Some years later he recognized the existence of other "triads" of similar elements (chlorine, bromine, and iodine; lithium, sodium, and potassium).

Other chemists then showed that the elements could be classified into groups consisting of more than three similar elements. Fluorine was added to the triad chlorine, bromine, and iodine, and magnesium to the triad calcium, strontium, and barium. By 1854, oxygen, sulfur, selenium, and tellurium had been classed as one group, and nitrogen, phosphorus, arsenic, antimony, and bismuth as another group of elements.

In 1862 the French chemist A. E. B. de Chancourtois arranged the elements in the order of atomic weights (the masses of their atoms). He noticed that elements differing by about 16 in atomic weight sometimes had similar properties, and suggested that "the properties of elements are the properties of numbers." The English chemist J. A. R. Newlands in 1863 proposed a system of classification of the elements in order of atomic weights, in which the elements were divided into seven groups of seven elements each. He termed his relation the *law of octaves*, by analogy with the seven intervals of the musical scale. His proposal was ridiculed, however, and he did not develop it further.

The most important step in the development of the periodic table was taken in 1869, when the Russian chemist Dmitri I. Mendelyeev (1834–1907) made a thorough study of the relation between the atomic weights of the elements and their physical and chemical properties. Mendelyeev proposed a periodic table containing seventeen columns, resembling Table 7-1 with the end columns (labeled 0) missing (these elements had not yet been discovered at that time). In 1871 Mendelyeev and the German chemist Lothar Meyer (1830–1895), who was working independently, proposed another table, with eight columns, obtained by splitting each of the long periods into a period of seven elements, an eighth group containing the three central elements (such as iron, cobalt, nickel), and a second period of seven elements. The first and second periods of seven were later distinguished by use of the letters "a" and "b" attached to the group symbols, which were the Roman numerals. This nomenclature of the periods (Ia, IIa, IIIa, IVa, Va, VIa, VIIa, VIII, Ib, IIb, IIIb, IVb, Vb, VIb, VIIb) appears, slightly revised, in the present periodic table.

The periodic table in the second form proposed by Mendelyeev (the "short-period" form) remained popular for many years, but has now been largely replaced by the "long-period" form, used in this book, which is in better agreement with the new knowledge about the electronic structure of atoms.

The periodic law was accepted immediately after its proposal by Mendelyeev because of his success in making predictions with its use which were afterward verified by experiment. In 1871 Mendelyeev found that by changing seventeen elements from the positions indicated by the atomic weights that had then been assigned to them into new positions, their properties could be better correlated with the properties of the other elements. He pointed out that this change indicated the existence of small errors in the previously accepted atomic weights of several of the elements, and large errors for several others, to the compounds of which incorrect formulas had been assigned. Further experimental work verified Mendelyeev's revisions.

A very striking application of the periodic law was made by Mendelyeev. He was able to predict the existence of six elements that had not yet been discovered, corresponding to vacant places in his table. He named these elements eka-boron, eka-aluminum, eka-silicon, eka-manganese, dvi-manganese, and eka-tantalum (Sanskrit: *eka*, first; *dvi*, second).

Three of these elements were soon discovered (they were named scandium, gallium, and germanium by their discoverers), and it was found that their properties and the properties of their compounds are very close to those predicted by Mendelyeev for eka-boron, eka-aluminum, and eka-silicon, respectively. Since then the elements technetium, rhenium, and protactinium have been discovered or made artificially, and have been found to have properties similar to those predicted for eka-manganese, dvi-manganese, and eka-tantalum. A comparison of the properties predicted by Mendelyeev for eka-silicon and those determined experimentally for germanium is given below.

MENDELYEEV'S PREDICTIONS FOR EKA-SILICON (*1871*)	OBSERVED PROPERTIES OF GERMANIUM (*discovered in 1886*)
Atomic weight about 72.	Atomic weight 72.59.
Es will be obtained from EsO_2 or K_2EsF_6 by reaction with sodium.	Ge is obtained by reaction of K_2GeF_6 and sodium.
Es will be a dark gray metal, with high melting point and density 5.5 g/cm³.	Ge is gray, with melting point 958°C and density 5.36 g/cm³.
Es will be slightly attacked by acids, such as hydrochloric acid, HCl, and will resist alkalies, such as sodium hydroxide, NaOH.	Ge is not dissolved by HCl or NaOH, but is dissolved by concentrated nitric acid, HNO_3.
On heating Es, it will form the oxide EsO_2, with high melting point and density 4.7 g/cm³.	Ge reacts with oxygen to give GeO_2, m.p. 1100°C, density 4.70 g/cm³.
A hydrated EsO_2 soluble in acid and easily reprecipitated is expected.	$Ge(OH)_4$ dissolves in dilute acid and is reprecipitated on dilution or addition of base.
The sulfide, EsS_2, will be insoluble in water but soluble in ammonium sulfide.	GeS_2 is insoluble in water and dilute acids, but readily soluble in ammonium sulfide.
$EsCl_4$ will be a volatile liquid, with boiling point a little under 100°C and density 1.9 g/cm³.	$GeCl_4$ is a volatile liquid, with b.p. 83°C and density 1.88 g/cm³.

Illustrative Exercises

7-1. In the article on "Chemistry" in the Ninth Edition of *The Encyclopaedia Britannica* (published in 1878) the author (H. A. Armstrong) says that Mendelyeev had recently proposed that uranium be assigned the atomic weight 240 in place of the old value 120 that had been assigned to it by Berzelius, but that he himself preferred 180. Mendelyeev was right. The correct formula of pitchblende, an important ore of uranium, is U_3O_8. What formula was written for pitchblende by (a) Berzelius, (b) Armstrong?

7-2. By extrapolation from the values given in Table 22-2 for the other alkali metals, estimate values of the melting point, boiling point, and density of francium.

7-3. Description of the Periodic Table

The horizontal rows of the periodic table consist of a very short period (containing hydrogen and helium, atomic numbers 1 and 2), two short periods of 8 elements each, two long periods of 18 elements each, a very long period of 32 elements, and an incomplete period.

The properties of elements change in a systematic way through a period: this is indicated in Figure 7-1, which shows the density of the elements, in the crystalline state, as a function of the atomic number. It is seen that there are five pronounced minima (low points) in the density curve. They occur for the elements sodium (11), potassium (19), rubidium (37), cesium (55), and francium (87). It was mentioned in Section 7-1 that these five elements together with lithium constitute a group of elements that are strikingly similar in their properties.

The **vertical columns** *of the periodic table*, with connections between the short and long periods as shown, *are the* **groups** *of chemical elements.* Elements

Figure **7-1**

The density of the elements in the solid state, in g/cm³. The symbols of the elements at high and low points of the jagged curve are shown.

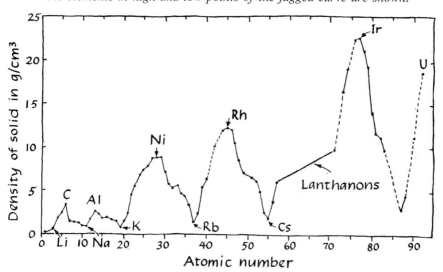

in the same group may be called *congeners;* these elements have closely related physical and chemical properties.

The groups I, II, and III are considered to include the elements in corresponding places at the left side of all the periods in Table 7-1, and IV, V, VI, and VII the elements at the right side. The central elements of the long periods, called the *transition elements*, have properties differing from those of the elements of the short periods; these elements are discussed separately, as groups IVa, Va, VIa, VIIa, VIII (which, for historical reasons, includes three elements in each long period), Ib, IIb, and IIIb.

The very long period is compressed into the table by removing fourteen elements, the *rare-earth metals* or *lanthanons* (elements resembling lanthanum, $Z = 57$), from $Z = 58$ to $Z = 71$, and representing them separately below. The elements from $Z = 90$ to $Z = 103$, called the *actinons* (elements resembling actinium, $Z = 89$), are listed below the lanthanons; those from $Z = 90$ to $Z = 94$ are also listed in the main body of the table.

The elements on the left side and in the center of the periodic table are **metals.** These elementary substances have the characteristic properties called *metallic properties*—high electric and thermal conductivity, metallic luster, the capability of being hammered or rolled into sheets (malleability) and of being drawn into wire (ductility). The elements on the right side of the periodic table are **nonmetals,** the elementary substances not having metallic properties.

The metallic properties are most pronounced for elements in the lower left corner of the periodic table, and the nonmetallic properties are most pronounced for elements in the upper right corner (omitting the noble gases). The transition from metals to nonmetals is marked by the *elements with intermediate properties*, which occupy a diagonal region extending from a point near the upper center to the lower right corner. These elements, which are called **metalloids,** include boron, silicon, germanium, arsenic, antimony, tellurium, and polonium.

The groups of elements may be described briefly in the following way:

Group 0, the noble gases: The elements of this group, helium, neon, argon, krypton, xenon, and radon, are nearly completely unreactive chemically; they form only a few chemical compounds. A discussion of the noble gases is given in the following sections of this chapter.

Group I, the alkali metals: The alkali metals—lithium, sodium, potassium, rubidium, cesium, and francium—are light metals which are very reactive chemically. Many of their compounds have important uses in industry and in life. The alkali metals and their compounds are discussed in Chapter 22. The word alkali is derived from an arabic word meaning ashes (compounds of these metals were obtained from wood ashes).

Group II, the alkaline-earth metals: These metals—beryllium, magnesium, calcium, strontium, barium, and radium—and their compounds are discussed in Chapter 22.

Group III, the boron or aluminum group: Boron is a metalloid, whereas aluminum and its other congeners are metals. The properties of boron and its congeners are discussed in Chapter 22.

Group IV, carbon and silicon: The chemistry of carbon is described in Chapter 10 and in greater detail in Chapters 27 and 28. The chemistry of silicon and the other elements of this group is described in Chapter 22.

Group V, the nitrogen or phosphorus group: Nitrogen and phosphorus are nonmetals, their congeners arsenic and antimony are metalloids, and bismuth is usually classed as a metal. The chemistry of nitrogen is described in Chapter 14 and that of phosphorus and the other elements of the group in Chapter 15.

Group VI, the oxygen group: Oxygen and its congeners sulfur and selenium are nonmetals, whereas tellurium and polonium are classed as metalloids. The chemistry of oxygen is discussed in Chapter 6, and that of sulfur and its congeners in Chapter 13.

Group VII, the halogen group: The halogens—fluorine, chlorine, bromine, iodine, and astatine—are the class of the most strongly nonmetallic elements. They are very reactive chemically, and form many compounds. Their chemistry is discussed in Chapter 12. The word halogen is from the Greek words *hals*, salt, and *genes*, producing.

The discussion in the immediately following chapters will be largely restricted to these elements, whose chemistry can be systematized by comparison of their electronic structures with those of the noble gases. The remaining elements are called the transition elements. They are discussed in Chapters 23 to 26.

7-4. The Noble Gases

The first element in the periodic table, hydrogen, is a reactive substance that forms a great many compounds. The chemistry of hydrogen was discussed in the preceding chapter. Helium, the second element (atomic number 2), is much different; it is a gas with the very striking chemical property that *it forms no chemical compounds whatever*, but exists only in the free state. Its atoms will not even combine with one another to form polyatomic molecules, but remain as separate atoms in the gas, which is hence described as containing monatomic molecules. Because of its property of remaining aloof from other elements it is called a "noble" gas.

This lack of chemical reactivity is the result of an extraordinary stability of the electronic structure of the helium atom. This stability is characteristic of the presence of two electrons close to an atomic nucleus.

The other elements of the zero group—neon, argon, krypton, xenon, and radon—are also chemically inert.* The small tendency of these inert elements

---

* Some recently prepared compounds of the noble gases are mentioned toward the end of this Section. See also the discussion of clathrate compounds of the noble gases, Section 16-8.

to form chemical compounds is similarly due to the great stability of their electronic structures. These extremely stable electronic structures are formed by 2, 10, 18, 36, 54, and 86 electrons about a nucleus.

These six gases are called the *noble gases* (or sometimes the *rare gases* or *inert gases*). Their names, except radon, are from Greek roots: *helios*, sun: *neos*, new; *argos*, inert; *kryptos*, hidden; *xenos*, stranger. Radon is named after radium, from which it is formed by radioactive decomposition. The properties of the noble gases are given in Table 7-2. Note the regular dependence of melting point and boiling point on atomic number.

Table **7-2**

Properties of the Noble Gases

	SYMBOL	ATOMIC NUMBER	ATOMIC WEIGHT	MELTING POINT	BOILING POINT
Helium	He	2	4.003	$-272.2°C*$	$-268.9°C$
Neon	Ne	10	20.183	$-248.67°$	$-245.9°$
Argon	Ar	18	39.944	$-189.2°$	$-185.7°$
Krypton	Kr	36	83.80	$-157°$	$-152.9°$
Xenon	Xe	54	131.30	$-112°$	$-107.1°$
Radon	Rn	86	222	$-77°$	$-61.8°$

* At 26 atm pressure. At smaller pressures helium remains liquid at still lower temperatures.

Helium.   Helium is present in very small quantities in the atmosphere. Its presence in the sun is shown by the occurrence of its spectral lines in sunlight. These lines were observed in 1868, long before the element was discovered on earth, and the lines were ascribed to a new element, which was named helium* by Sir Norman Lockyer (1836–1920).

Helium occurs as a gas entrapped in some uranium minerals, from which it can be liberated by heating. It is also present in natural gas from some wells, especially in Texas and Canada; this is the principal source of the element.

Helium is used for filling balloons and dirigibles and for mixing with oxygen (in place of the nitrogen of the air) for breathing by divers, in order to avoid the "bends," caused by gas bubbles formed by release of the nitrogen of the atmosphere that had dissolved in the blood under increased pressure, and to avoid the narcotic action (anesthetizing action) of nitrogen under pressure.

Neon.   The second noble gas, neon, occurs in the atmosphere to the extent of 0.002 %. It is obtained, along with the other noble gases (except helium), by the distillation of liquid air (air that has been liquefied by cooling).

When an electric current is passed through a tube containing neon gas at

* The ending "ium," which is otherwise used only for metallic elements, is due to Lockyer's incorrect surmise that the new element was a metal. "Helion" would be a better name, as its ending is consistent with those of the names of the other noble gases.

low pressure, the atoms of neon are caused to emit light with their characteristic spectral lines. This produces a brilliant red light, used in advertising signs (neon signs). Other colors for signs are obtained by the use of helium, argon, and mercury, sometimes in mixtures with neon or with one another.

Argon. Argon composes about 1% of the atmosphere. It is used in incandescent light bulbs to permit the filament to be heated to a higher temperature, and thus to produce a whiter light than would be practical in a vacuum. The argon decreases the rate at which the metallic filament evaporates, by keeping vaporized metal atoms from diffusing away from the filament and permitting them to reattach themselves to it. Argon is also extensively used in industry to provide a chemically inert atmosphere, especially in welding and in making pure metals and alloys. The total production of argon for these purposes in the year 1963 was about 10^9 cu ft.

Krypton, Xenon, and Radon. Krypton and xenon, which occur in very small quantities in the air, have not found any significant use. Xenon is a good anesthetic agent, but it is too expensive for general use (it has been used in two major operations on human beings).

In 1962 and 1963 several compounds of xenon were synthesized. The first one to be reported (by the Canadian chemist Neil Bartlett) was xenon hexafluoroplatinate, $XePtF_6$, a yellow crystalline substance. Later (1963) he reported the synthesis of the corresponding rhodium compound, $XeRhF_6$. Scientists in the Argonne National Laboratory, and later other investigators, prepared several xenon fluorides, including XeF_2, XeF_4, and XeF_6. Each compound is a colored solid substance that reacts vigorously with water. The products of the reaction of XeF_4 and XeF_6 with water are unstable (explosive) solid substances with composition $Xe(OH)_4$, XeO_3, and H_4XeO_6 (perxenic acid). It is likely that other compounds of xenon can be made. Some compounds of radon and krypton (RnF_4, KrF_4) have also been synthesized.*

Radon, which is produced steadily by radium, is used in the treatment of cancer. It has been found that the rays given off by radioactive substances are often effective in controlling this disease. A convenient way of administering this radiation is to pump the radon that has been produced by a sample of radium into a small gold tube, which is then placed in proximity to the tissues to be treated.

The Discovery of the Noble Gases. The story of the discovery of argon provides an interesting illustration of the importance of attention to minor discrepancies in the results of scientific investigations.

For over a hundred years it was thought that atmospheric air consisted, aside

---

* The possibility of synthesizing fluorides and oxygen compounds of xenon (XeF_6, XeF_8, KrF_6, H_4XeO_6, and others) was predicted long ago from structural arguments [Linus Pauling, *J. Am. Chem. Soc.* **55**, 1895 (1933)]. An early effort to make xenon fluoride was unsuccessful [D. M. Yost and A. L. Kaye, *ibid.* **55**, 3890 (1933)].

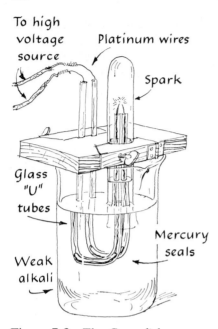

To high
voltage   Platinum wires
source

Spark

Glass
"U"
tubes

Mercury
seals

Weak
alkali

Figure **7-2**   *The Cavendish appara-tus, used in the investigation of the composition of air.*

from small variable amounts of water va-por and carbon dioxide, solely of oxygen (21% by volume) and nitrogen (79%). In 1785 the English scientist Henry Caven-dish (1731–1810) investigated the com-position of the atmosphere. He mixed oxygen with air and then passed an electric spark through the mixture, to form a com-pound of nitrogen and oxygen, which was dissolved in a solution in contact with the gas (Figure 7-2). The sparking was con-tinued until there was no further decrease in volume, and the oxygen was then re-moved from the residual gas by treatment with another solution. He found that after this treatment only a small bubble of air remained unabsorbed, not more than $\frac{1}{120}$ of the original air. Although Cavendish did not commit himself on the point, it seems to have been assumed by chemists that if the sparking had been continued for a longer time there would have been no residue, and Cavendish's experiment was accordingly interpreted as showing that only oxygen and nitrogen were pres-ent in the atmosphere.

Then in 1894, more than 100 years later, Lord Rayleigh began an investigation involving the careful determination of the densities of the gases hydrogen, oxygen, and nitrogen. To prepare nitrogen he mixed dried air with an excess of ammonia, NH_3, and passed the mixture over red-hot copper. Under these conditions the oxygen reacts with ammonia, according to the equation

$$4NH_3 + 3O_2 \longrightarrow 6H_2O + 2N_2$$

The excess ammonia is then removed by bubbling the gas through sulfuric acid. The remaining gas, after drying, should have been pure nitrogen, derived in part from the ammonia and in part from air. The density of this gas was deter-mined. Another sample of nitrogen was made simply by passing air over red-hot copper, which removed the oxygen by combining with it to form copper oxide:

$$O_2 + 2Cu \longrightarrow 2CuO$$

When the density of this gas was determined it was found to be about 0.1% greater than that from the sample of ammonia and air. In order to investigate this dis-crepancy, a third sample of nitrogen was made by the reaction of ammonia and pure oxygen. It was found that this sample of nitrogen had a density 0.5% less than that of the second sample.

Further investigations showed that nitrogen prepared entirely from air had a density 0.5% greater than nitrogen prepared from ammonia or in any other chemical way. Nitrogen obtained from air was found to have density 1.2572 g/liter at 0°C and 1 atm, whereas nitrogen made by chemical methods has density 1.2505 g/liter. Rayleigh and Ramsay then repeated Cavendish's experiment, and showed by spectroscopic analysis that the residual gas was indeed not nitrogen but a new element. They then searched for the other noble gases and discovered them.

7-5. The Electronic Structure of Atoms

The noble gases are strange elements. They are different from all other elements—they form very few compounds, whereas every other element forms many compounds.

This peculiarity of the noble gases is explained by the **electronic structure** of the noble-gas atoms—the way in which the electrons move about the atomic nuclei. This is the subject that we shall now consider, beginning with the electronic structure of the simplest element, hydrogen.

The knowledge about the structure of atoms that is presented in the following paragraphs has been obtained largely by physicists from the study of spectral lines. The understanding of atomic structure was obtained during the years between 1913 and 1925. It was in 1913 that Niels Bohr (1885–1962), the great Danish physicist, developed his simple theory of the hydrogen atom (Section 7-7), which during the following twelve years was expanded and refined into our present theory of atomic structure.

The detailed mathematical theory of quantum mechanics—the modern mathematical theory of the properties of electrons and other small particles—is not suited to study by the beginning student. However, the picture of the electronic structure of atoms that is provided by this theory is easy to understand and to learn. Knowledge of this electronic structure is important to the student of chemistry.

The Electronic Structure of the Hydrogen Atom. The smallest and lightest nucleus is the proton. The proton carries one unit of positive charge, and with one electron, which carries one unit of negative charge, it forms a hydrogen atom.

Soon after the development of the concept of the nuclear atom some idea was gained as to the way in which a proton and an electron are combined to form a hydrogen atom. Because of the attraction of the oppositely charged electron and proton, the electron might be expected to revolve in an orbit about the much heavier proton in a way similar to that in which the earth revolves about the sun. Bohr suggested that the orbit of the electron in the normal hydrogen atom should be circular, with radius 0.530 Å (see Section 7-7). The electron was calculated to be going around in this orbit with the constant speed 2.18×10^8 cm/sec, which is a little less than 1% of the speed of light (3×10^{10} cm/sec, about 186,000 miles per second).

As a result of studies made by many physicists, this picture is now known to be nearly but not quite right. The electron does not move in a definite orbit, but rather in a somewhat random way, so that it is sometimes very close to the nucleus and sometimes rather far away. Moreover, it moves mainly toward the nucleus or away from it, and it travels in all directions about the nucleus instead of staying in one plane. Although it does not stay just 0.530 Å from the nucleus, this is its most probable distance. By moving around rapidly it effectively occupies all the space within about 1 Å from the nucleus, and so gives the hydrogen atom an effective radius of about 1 Å. It is because of this motion of electrons that atoms, which are made of particles only about 0.00001 to 0.0001 Å in diameter, act as solid objects several Å in diameter. The speed of the electron in the hydrogen atom is not constant; but its root-mean-square average is the Bohr value 2.18×10^8 cm/sec.

Thus we can describe the free hydrogen atom as having a heavy nucleus at the center of a sphere defined by the space filled by the fast-moving electron in its motion about the nucleus. This sphere is about 2 Å in diameter.

Because of the nature of the equations of quantum mechanics that describe the electron in the normal hydrogen atom, it has been decided that it is not right to say that the electron moves about the nucleus in an orbit. Instead, the electron is said to occupy an *orbital*. The orbital that is occupied by the electron in the normal state (most stable state) of the hydrogen atom is called the 1*s* orbital. The number 1 is the value of the *principal quantum number n*.

There is only one orbital for $n = 1$. There are other possible orbitals for the hydrogen atom, corresponding to $n = 2$, $n = 3$, etc. A hydrogen atom in which the electron occupies one of these other orbitals is unstable; it is said to be in an *excited state*. A large amount of energy is required to change the hydrogen atom from its normal state to the first excited state ($n = 2$)—three-quarters as much as to remove the electron completely. The diameter of the atom for this excited state is about 8 Å, four times as great as for the normal state. The orbitals with $n = 2, 3, 4$, etc. are occupied by electrons in heavier atoms.

The Spin of the Electron.   It was discovered in 1925 by two Dutch physicists, G. E. Uhlenbeck and S. A. Goudsmit, that *the electron has a spin*—it rotates about an axis in a way that can be compared with the rotation of the earth about an axis through its north pole and south pole. The amount of the spin (angular momentum) is the same for all electrons, but the orientation of the axis can change. With respect to a specified direction, such as the direction of the earth's magnetic field, a free electron can orient itself in either one of only two ways: either it lines up parallel to the field, or antiparallel (with the opposite orientation).

In general the motion of electricity produces a magnetic field. The spin of the electron is no exception—the electron produces a magnetic field corresponding to the magnetic moment that would be expected for the rotation of negative electricity. The spinning electron can be described as a small magnet that can orient itself in a magnetic field so that its component along the field direction is either $+\mu_B$ or $-\mu_B$, where μ_B is the Bohr magneton, 0.927×10^{-20} erg/gauss. The spin of an electron in a magnetic field can be made to change from positive to negative orientation by absorption of microwave radiation of suitable frequency. This is the basis of the technique of *electron spin resonance spectroscopy*, which during the years since 1945 has provided much information about electronic structure.

The Pauli Exclusion Principle. *Two electrons can occupy the same orbital only if their spins are opposed;* that is, oriented in opposite directions.

This sentence is a statement of the *Pauli exclusion principle*. W. Pauli (Austrian physicist, 1900–1959) was the first man to notice that an electron excludes another electron with the same spin orientation from the orbital it occupies. Only two electrons can occupy one orbital, and they must have opposite spins.

The Electronic Structure of the Noble Gases. The distributions of electrons in atoms of the noble gases have been determined by physicists by experimental and theoretical methods that are too complex to be discussed here. The results obtained are shown in Figure 7-3. It is seen that *for the atoms neon, argon, krypton, and xenon the electrons are arranged about the atomic nuclei in two or more concentric shells.*

The **helium atom** contains two electrons, each of which carries out motion about the helium nucleus similar to that of the one electron in the hydrogen atom. These two electrons occupy the same orbital, the 1s orbital, and in accordance with the Pauli exclusion principle their spins are opposed.

The symbol $1s^2$ is used to express the electron configuration of the normal helium atom. The superscript 2 means that two electrons occupy the 1s orbital.

Two electrons with opposed spins occupying the same orbital are called an *electron pair*. The electrons can be described as forming a ball of negative electricity near the nucleus. Its diameter is only about half that of the hydrogen atom, because of the doubled value of the nuclear charge.

These two electrons are said to constitute a **completed helium shell** (also called a **completed K shell**).

All of the atoms heavier than hydrogen have a completed helium shell, consisting of two 1s electrons ($1s^2$) close to the nucleus. The diameter of the helium shell is inversely proportional to the atomic number; for radon ($Z = 86$) it is only about 0.02 Å.

The **neon atom** has two shells. First, it has a helium shell of two electrons, with diameter about 0.2 Å, as shown in Figure 7-3, and around this shell an **outer shell of eight electrons,** called the **neon shell** or **L shell.** The diameter of this outer shell is about 2 Å.

These two shells, reduced in size, appear in argon, krypton, and xenon

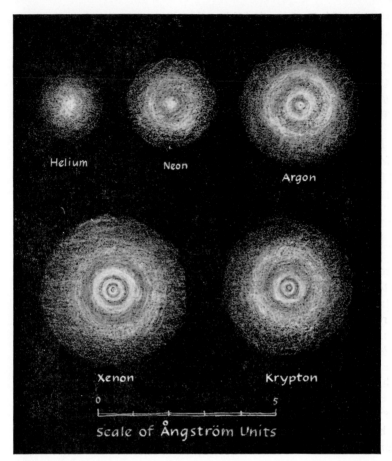

Figure **7-3**

  Drawing of electron distributions in noble-gas atoms, showing successive electron shells.

(Figure 7-3), together with additional shells. The nature of these shells is discussed in the following paragraphs.

Shells and Subshells of Electrons.   Around 1920, while they were developing the theory of atomic spectra (line spectra and x-ray spectra of the elements), physicists discovered that the successive shells, after the helium shell, contain orbitals of more than one kind.

The K shell consists of only one orbital, the $1s$ orbital, described in the preceding section. The L shell consists of four orbitals and two subshells. The $2s$ subshell consists of only one orbital, the $2s$ orbital. The $2p$ subshell consists of three $2p$ orbitals. An electron in a $2s$ orbital is somewhat more stable and somewhat closer to the nucleus than an electron in one of the $2p$ orbitals, as is indicated in the energy diagram, Figure 7-4. The three $2p$ orbitals have the same energy.

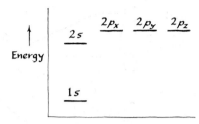

The $2s$ orbital, like the $1s$ orbital, corresponds to an electron distribution that is spherically symmetrical. The electron distribution for a $2p$ orbital is not spherically symmetrical, but is concentrated about an axis, as shown in Figure 7-5. The characteristic axes of the three $2p$ orbitals in an atom are at right angles to one another, and they can be taken as the x axis, the y axis, and the z axis, respectively, as indicated in Figure 7-5. The three $2p$ orbitals can be given the symbols $2p_x$, $2p_y$, and $2p_z$.

Figure 7-4 *Diagram showing the relative stability of the 1s, 2s, $2p_x$, $2p_y$, and $2p_z$ orbitals. The vertical coordinate also measures the relative average distances of the electrons from the nucleus.*

In accordance with the Pauli exclusion principle, each of these orbitals can be occupied by two electrons, which must have their spins opposed. Hence the completed $2s$ subshell contains two electrons (one electron pair) and the complete $2p$ subshell contains six electrons (three electron pairs, one for each of the three $2p$ orbitals). The completed L shell accordingly contains eight electrons (four electron pairs).

The symbol for the completed $2s$ subshell is $2s^2$ and that for the completed $2p$ subshell is $2p_x^2 2p_y^2 2p_z^2$, which is usually simplified to $2p^6$. The symbol for the completed L shell is $2s^2 2p_x^2 2p_y^2 2p_z^2$, usually written as $2s^2 2p^6$.

The M shell, with total quantum number $n = 3$, consists of nine orbitals

Figure 7-5

Representation of the relative magnitudes of the s orbital and the three p orbitals in dependence on angle.

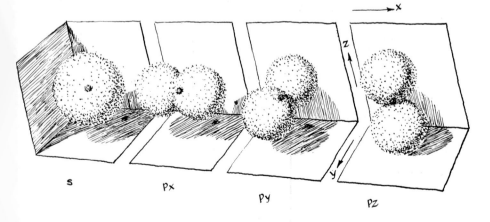

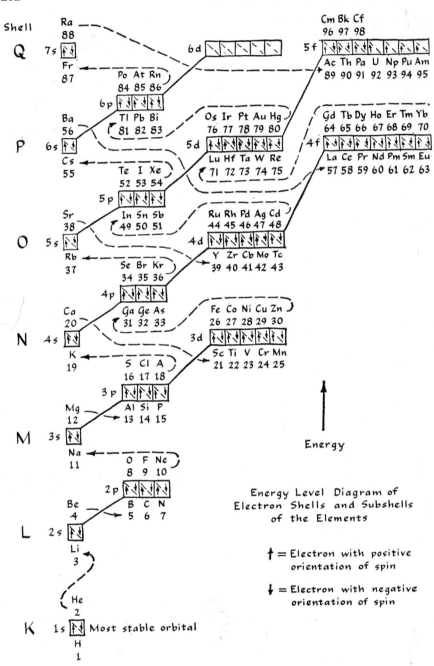

Figure 7-6

and three subshells. In addition to the 3s subshell (one orbital) and the 3p subshell (three orbitals), it contains a 3d subshell, with five 3d orbitals.

The next shell, the *N* shell, contains these subshells plus an additional one, the 4f subshell, which has seven orbitals.

The letters *K, L, M, N, O, P* that are used for electron shells correspond to the successive values of the principal quantum number *n*: *K* to $n = 1$, *L* to $n = 2$, *M* to $n = 3$, and so on. It is as a result of·historical accident that this sequence of letters begins with *K* rather than *A*. Also, the letters *s, p, d, f* have a curious origin: they are the initial letters of the adjectives *sharp, principal, diffuse,* and *fundamental*, which happened to be used by the spectroscopists to describe the spectra that they had observed. These letters accordingly are not abbreviations of words that describe the orbitals or subshells in a significant way.

The successive electron shells (*K, L, M*, etc.) described above are those used by physicists. Chemists have found it convenient to use a different classification, corresponding to a different way of grouping the subshells together. In Figure 7-6 the approximate sequence of energy values for all orbitals that are occupied by electrons in atoms in their normal states are shown. It is seen that the energy values for the physicists' shells overlap. For example, the energy of a 3d electron (in the *M* shell) is about the same as that of a 4s electron (in the *N* shell). Because of their interest in sets of electrons with the same energy, chemists have found it convenient to assign the five 3d orbitals to 4s and 4p, rather than to 3s and 3p, and to make similar assignments of 4d, 5d, 6d, 4f, and 5f, as indicated in Figure 7-6.

The successive shells are named for the noble gases in which they first are completed. The number of electrons in each shell is equal to the number of elements in the period of the periodic table that is completed by the corresponding noble gas: 2 for the helium shell, 8 each for the neon shell and the argon shell, 18 each for the krypton shell and the xenon shell, and 32 each for the radon shell and the eka-radon shell. The symbols for the completed shells are given in Table 7-3.

Table **7-3**

Shells and Subshells of Electrons

CHEMISTS' NAME FOR SHELL	SYMBOL FOR ELECTRON CONFIGURATION OF COMPLETED SHELL, SHOWING SUBSHELLS
Helium shell	$1s^2$
Neon shell	$2s^2 2p^6$
Argon shell	$3s^2 3p^6$
Krypton shell	$3d^{10} 4s^2 4p^6$
Xenon shell	$4d^{10} 5s^2 5p^6$
Radon shell	$4f^{14} 5d^{10} 6s^2 6p^6$
Eka-radon shell	$5f^{14} 6d^{10} 7s^2 7p^6$

Electron Shells and the Periods of the Periodic Table. The successive electron shells listed in Table 7-3 involve the following numbers of electrons: 2, 8, 8, 18, 18, 32, 32.

These numbers are equal to the numbers of elements in the successive periods of the periodic system (the last period incomplete).

We see that each of the two short periods, with eight elements, corresponds to the filling of two subshells, an s subshell (one orbital) and a p subshell (three orbitals).

The next two periods, the long periods, correspond to the filling not only of the next sets of these orbitals (giving $4s^2 4p^6$ and $5s^2 5p^6$), but also of sets of d orbitals ($3d^{10}$ and $4d^{10}$). It is the introduction of the ten d electrons that increases these periods to 18 elements each.

The very long period, which ends in radon, involves not only $5d^{10}$ and $6s^2 6p^6$, but also $4f^{14}$.

The Octet. In every one of the noble gases except helium the outermost electrons, with the maximum value of the principal quantum number, are a set of eight (four pairs) with the symbol $ns^2 np^6$. This set of eight electrons is called an *octet*.

It is found that most of the properties of elements close to the noble gases in the periodic table can be discussed in a simple and satisfactory way in terms of the octet and the four corresponding orbitals ns, np_x, np_y, and np_z. (For other elements, discussed for the most part in the final chapters of this book, the d orbitals must also be taken into consideration.)

The Electronic Structure of the Elements of the First Short Period. Each of the elements from lithium to fluorine has an inner shell, $1s^2$. Lithium has in addition a $2s$ electron. Accordingly its electron configuration is $1s^2 2s$.

The electronic structure of an atom may be represented by an *electron-dot symbol*, in which the electrons of the other shell (or outer octet) are represented by dots and the nucleus and inner electrons by the chemical symbol of the element. The electron-dot symbol of lithium, Li · , shows only the outermost electron, which is called the valence electron.

The next element, beryllium, has two valence electrons, both of which occupy the $2s$ orbital if the atom is in its normal state. The normal beryllium atom has the electron-dot symbol Be : and the electron configuration $1s^2 2s^2$. The two dots together represent two electrons with opposed spins in one orbital.

The electron-dot symbols for the normal states of the eight elements of the first short period are

Li ·   Be :   : B ·   : C ·   : N ·   : O ·   : F ·   : Ne :

Note that two or three $2p$ electrons occupy different orbitals, and remain unpaired. The normal state of carbon corresponds to the configuration $1s^22s^22p_x2p_y$, and not to $1s^22s^22p_x^2$.

The electron configurations for the normal states of the elements lithium to neon are given in Table 7-4.

Table **7-4**

Electron Configurations, Li to Ne

ATOM	NUMBER OF ELECTRONS PER ORBITAL*				ELECTRON CONFIGURATION*
	$2s$	$2p_x$	$2p_y$	$2p_z$	
Li	1				$2s$
Be	2				$2s^2$
B	2	1			$2s^22p$
C	2	1	1		$2s^22p^2$
N	2	1	1	1	$2s^22p^3$
O	2	2	1	1	$2s^22p^4$
F	2	2	2	1	$2s^22p^5$
Ne	2	2	2	2	$2s^22p^6$

* The inner electrons are not shown; for all of these atoms they are a $1s^2$ pair.

The electron configurations for the congeners of these elements are the same except for the increased value of the quantum number n. For example, sulfur, the congener of oxygen in the next period, has the configuration $3s^23p^4$ for its valence electrons.

The use of electronic structures in correlating the properties of substances will be illustrated in the following chapters.

Electron-spin Multiplets. In 1925 the American astronomer Henry Norris Russell and the American physicist F. A. Saunders made an important discovery about the electronic structure of atoms. While they were trying to find the principles determining the wavelengths of the spectral lines emitted by atoms that have been excited by an electric discharge or in some other way, they discovered that the spins of the electrons in an atom may combine to form a resultant spin, which is designated by the resultant electron-spin quantum number S. Similarly, the orbital angular momenta of the several electrons can combine to form a resultant, designated by the orbital quantum number L. These two angular momentum vectors then combine to form a resultant total angular momentum vector, designated by the quantum number J. This sort of interaction of the electrons is called *Russell-Saunders coupling*.

For example, the normal boron atom, with electron configuration $1s^22s^22p$, contains two pairs of electrons, and the two electrons of each pair, occupying the same orbit, have their spins opposed (Pauli exclusion principle). Hence the total resultant spin is just that of the fifth electron, and therefore the value of S is that of one electron: $S = \frac{1}{2}$. Also, the $1s$ and $2s$ electrons have zero orbital angular momentum, and the 2p electron has one unit of orbital angular momentum, corresponding to the quantum number $l = 1$; hence the value of L is the same, $L = 1$.

The states of an atom with Russell-Saunders coupling are represented by *Russell-Saunders symbols*. The symbol for the normal state of the boron atom is $^2P_{1/2}$.

In this symbol the capital letter gives the value of L. The letters $S, P, D, F, G, \cdots$ correspond to $L = 0, 1, 2, 3, \cdots$, just as for one electron the letters $s, p, d, f, \cdots$ correspond to the values $0, 1, 2, 3, \cdots$ for the orbital angular momentum quantum number l.

The superscript on the left of the letter is a quantity called the *multiplicity* of the state. Its value is $2S + 1$, where S is the resultant electron-spin quantum number. The multiplicity represents the number of ways in which the resultant electron spin can orient itself relative to a magnetic field or to the orbital angular momentum vector. For $S = \frac{1}{2}$ there are two orientations, corresponding to the component $+\frac{1}{2}$ or $-\frac{1}{2}$ relative to L. For $L = 1$, as in the normal state of the boron atom, these two orientations of the electron spin lead to two values of J: $1 + \frac{1}{2} = \frac{3}{2}$ and $1 - \frac{1}{2} = \frac{1}{2}$. These values of J are given as a subscript in the symbol; the two states are $^2P_{3/2}$ and $^2P_{1/2}$. These two states are nearly equal in energy; they differ by only 14.9 cal/mole, with $^2P_{1/2}$ the more stable. The two states are described as forming the two components of a *doublet*.

Similarly, the normal state of the carbon atom has the Russell-Saunders symbol $^3P_0$, corresponding to $S = 1, L = 1, J = 0$. It is a component of a triplet, the other two components being $^3P_1$ and $^3P_2$. The two p electrons of the carbon configuration $1s^22s^22p^2$ (Table 7-4) can combine their spins to the resultant $S = 0$ (which gives singlet states) or the resultant $S = 1$ (which gives triplet states, corresponding to the components $+1, 0,$ and -1). Similarly, the two orbital angular momenta with value 1 (for the two p electrons) can combine to $L = 0, 1,$ or 2, giving $S, P,$ and D states. The Pauli exclusion principle operates in such a way (too complicated for discussion in an elementary course) that the actual states are $^1S, ^3P,$ and ^1D, and of these the triplet state, ^3P, is the most stable.

The Russell-Saunders symbols for the normal states of some atoms are given in tables in later chapters.

The idea of multiplets has been extended in an interesting way in the theory of electric-charge multiplets, described in Chapter 29 in the discussion of the fundamental particles.

Illustrative Exercises

7-3. (a) Without referring to the text, draw electron-dot symbols of normal states of atoms of the elements from sodium to argon, showing 1 to 8 electrons of the outer shell.

(b) What electrons in these atoms are not represented by dots in these symbols?

7-4. The alkali metals, group I of the periodic table, are Li, Na, K, Rb, Cs, and Fr. Their atomic numbers are 3, 11, 19, 37, 55, and 87, respectively. How do they differ in electronic structure from the noble gases that precede them in the periodic table?

7-5. Write electron-dot symbols for the alkali metals.

7-6. The halogens, group VII of the periodic table, are F, Cl, Br, I, and At, with atomic numbers 9, 17, 35, 53, and 85, respectively. Write electron-dot symbols for them, showing only electrons of the outermost shell.

7-7. In an electric arc between carbon electrodes some of the carbon atoms are raised to an excited state to which the spectroscopists have assigned the electron configuration $1s^22s2p_x2p_y2p_z$ (also written $2s2p^3$). What electron-dot symbol would you write for this state of the carbon atom?

7-6. An Energy-level Diagram

A diagram representing the distribution of all electrons in all atoms is given in Figure 7-6.

Each orbital is represented by a square. The most stable orbital (its electrons being held most tightly by the nucleus) is the $1s$ orbital, at the bottom of the diagram. Energy is required to lift an electron from a stable orbital to a less stable one, above it in the diagram.

The electrons are shown being introduced in sequence; the first and second in the $1s$ orbital, the next two in the $2s$ orbital, the next six in the $2p$ orbitals, and so on. The sequence is indicated by arrows. The symbol and atomic number of each element are shown adjacent to the outermost electron (least tightly held electron) in the neutral atom.

The electron configuration is indicated by the sequence along this path, up to the symbol of the element. Thus the electron configuration of nitrogen is $1s^22s^22p^3$ and that of scandium is $1s^22s^22p^63s^23p^64s^23d$.

For the heavier atoms two or more electron configurations may have nearly the same energy, and there is some arbitrariness in the diagram shown in Figure 7-6. The configuration shown for each element is either that of the most stable state of the free atom (in a gas) or of a state close to the most stable state.

Illustrative Exercises

7-8. (a) What is the electron configuration of fluorine? (Refer to Figure 7-6, and show all nine electrons. Remember that there are three $2p$ orbitals in the subshell.)

(b) How many electron pairs are there in the atom? Which orbitals do they occupy?

(c) How many unpaired electrons are there? Which orbital does it occupy?

7-9. (a) What are the electron configurations of beryllium and boron, as shown in Figure 7-6?

(b) What electron-dot symbols do they correspond to?

(c) What are the customary chemical electron-dot symbols for these atoms? (They show a larger number of unpaired electrons.)

7-10. Write the electron configuration for the element with $Z = 103$, showing all 103 electrons. To what orbital do you assign the last electron? Why?

7-7. The Bohr Theory of the Structure of the Hydrogen Atom

Most of our knowledge of the electronic structure of atoms has been obtained by the study of the light given out by atoms when they are excited by high temperature or by an electric arc or spark. The light that is emitted by atoms consists of lines of certain frequencies; it is described as the *line spectrum* of the atom (see Figure 25-1).

The careful study of line spectra began about 1880. Early investigators made some progress in the interpretation of spectra, in recognizing regularities in the frequencies of the lines: the frequencies of the spectral lines of the hydrogen atom, for example, show an especially simple relationship with one another, which will be discussed below. The regularity is evident in the reproduction of a part of the spectrum of hydrogen in Figure 7-7. It was not until 1913, however, that the interpretation of the spectrum of hydrogen in terms of the electronic structure of the hydrogen atom was achieved. In this year Niels Bohr successfully applied the quantum theory to this problem, and laid the basis for the extraordinary advance in our understanding of the nature of matter that has been made during the past forty years.

The Quantum Theory of the Hydrogen Atom. The hydrogen atom consists of an electron and a proton. The interaction of their electric charges, $-e$ and $+e$, respectively, corresponds to inverse-square attraction, in the same way that the gravitational interaction of the earth and the sun corresponds to inverse-square attraction. If Newton's laws of motion were applicable to the hydrogen atom we should accordingly expect that the electron, whose mass is small compared with that of the nucleus, would revolve about the nucleus in an elliptical orbit, in the same way that the earth revolves about the sun. The simplest orbit for the electron about the nucleus would be a circle, and Newton's laws of motion would permit the circle to be of any size, as determined by the energy of the system.

Figure **7-7**

The Balmer series of spectral lines of atomic hydrogen. The line at the right, with the longest wavelength, is H_α. It corresponds to the transition from the state with $n = 3$ to the state with $n = 2$.

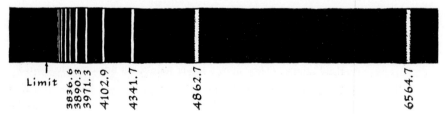

After the discovery of the electron and the proton, this model was considered by physicists interested in atomic structure, and it became evident that the older theories of the motion of particles (Newton's laws of motion) and of electricity and magnetism could not apply to the atom. If the electron were revolving around the nucleus it should, according to electromagnetic theory, produce light, with the frequency of the light equal to the frequency of revolution of the electron in the atom. This emission of light by the moving electron is similar to the emission of radiowaves by the electrons that move back and forth in the antenna of a radio station. However, with the continued emission of energy by the atom, in the form of light, the electron would move in a spiral approaching more and more closely to the nucleus, and the frequency of its motion about the nucleus would become greater and greater. Accordingly, the older (classical) theories of motion and of electromagnetism would require that hydrogen atoms produce a spectrum of light of all wavelengths (a *continuous spectrum*). This is contrary to observation: the spectrum of hydrogen, produced in a discharge tube containing hydrogen atoms (formed by dissociation of hydrogen molecules), consists of lines, as shown in Figure 7-7. Moreover, it is known that the volume occupied by a hydrogen atom in a solid or liquid substance corresponds to a diameter of about 2 Å, whereas the older theory of the hydrogen atom contained no mechanism for preventing the electron from approaching more and more closely to the nucleus, and the atom from becoming far smaller than 2 Å in diameter.

A hint as to the way to solve this difficulty had been given to Bohr by Planck's quantum theory of emission of light by a hot body, and by Einstein's theory of the photoelectric effect and the light quantum. Both Planck and Einstein assumed that light of frequency ν is not emitted or absorbed by matter in arbitrarily small amounts, but only in quanta of energy $h\nu$. If a hydrogen atom in which the electron is revolving about the nucleus in a large circular orbit emits a quantum of energy $h\nu$, the electron must then be in a much different (smaller) circular orbit, corresponding to an energy value of the atom $h\nu$ less than its initial energy. Bohr accordingly assumed that *the hydrogen atom can exist only in certain states*, which are called the **stationary states** of the atom. He assumed that one of these states, the *ground state* or *normal state*, represents the minimum energy possible for the atom; it is accordingly the most stable state of the atom. The other states, with an excess of energy relative to the ground state, are called the *excited states* of the atom. He further assumed, in agreement with the earlier work of Planck and Einstein, that when an atom changes from a state with energy E'' to a state with energy E' the difference in energy $E'' - E'$ is equal to the energy of the light quantum that is emitted. This equation,

$$h\nu = E'' - E' \tag{1}$$

is called the **Bohr frequency rule;** it gives the value of the frequency of the light that is emitted when an atom changes from an excited state with energy E'' to a lower state with energy E'.

The same equation also applies to the absorption of light by atoms. The frequency of the light absorbed in the transition from a lower state to an upper state is equal to the difference in energy of the upper state and the lower state divided by Planck's constant. The equation also applies to the emission and absorption of light by molecules and more complex systems.

Example 1. It is found that a tube containing hydrogen atoms in their normal state does not absorb any light in the visible region, but only in the far ultra-violet. The absorption line of longest wavelength has $\lambda = 1,216$ Å. What is the energy of the excited state of the hydrogen atom that is produced from the normal state by the absorption of a quantum of this light?

Solution. The frequency of the absorbed light is $\nu = c/\lambda = (2.998 \times 10^{10}$ cm/sec)/$(1.216 \times 10^{-5}$ cm$) = 2.467 \times 10^{15}$ sec^{-1}. The energy of a light quantum is $h\nu$. This is just the energy of the excited state relative to the normal state of the hydrogen atom. Accordingly, the answer to our problem is

Energy of excited state relative to normal state

$$= h\nu = 6.624 \times 10^{-27} \text{ erg sec} \times 2.467 \times 10^{15} \text{ sec}^{-1}$$

$$= 1.634 \times 10^{-11} \text{ erg}$$

This can be converted into electron volts in the usual way; the answer is **10.20 eV.** This result is also obtained simply by applying Equation 5 of Chapter 3:

$$12,372/1,216 \text{ Å} = 10.20 \text{ eV.}$$

Bohr also discovered a method of calculating the energy of the stationary states of the hydrogen atom, with use of Planck's constant. He found that the correct values of the energies of the stationary states were obtained if he assumed that the orbits of the electrons are circular and that the angular momentum of the electron has for the normal state the value $h/2\pi$, for the first excited state the value $2h/2\pi$, for the next excited state the value $3h/2\pi$, and so on.

In general, the angular momentum of the electron in the circular orbit about the nucleus (the *Bohr orbit*) was represented by Bohr as having the value

$$\text{Angular momentum} = \frac{nh}{2\pi}, \quad \text{with } n = 1, 2, 3, \cdots \tag{2}$$

The number n introduced in this way in the Bohr theory is called the *principal quantum number* of the Bohr orbit.

The radius of the Bohr orbit is found to be equal to $n^2 a_0$, in which

$$a_0 = h^2/4\pi^2 m e^2 = 0.530 \text{ Å}$$

In this equation m is the mass of the electron and e is the electronic charge. Thus the radius of the Bohr orbit for the normal state of the hydrogen atom is 0.530 Å, that for the first excited state is four times as great, that for the

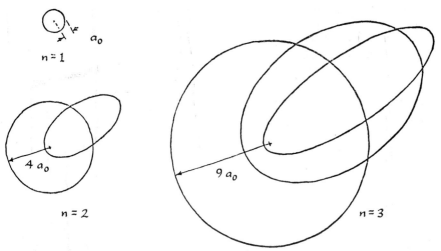

Figure **7-8**

Bohr orbits for an electron in the hydrogen atom. These circular and elliptical orbits were involved in the Bohr theory. They do not provide a correct description of the motion of the electron in the hydrogen atom. According to the theory of quantum mechanics, which seems to be essentially correct, the electron moves about the nucleus in the hydrogen atom in roughly the way described by Bohr, but the motion in the normal state (n = 1) is not in a circle, but is radial (in and out, toward the nucleus and away from the nucleus). The average distance of the electron from the nucleus, according to quantum mechanics, is the same as the radius of the Bohr orbit.

next excited state nine times as great, and so on, as illustrated in Figure 7-8.

The energy-level diagram for the hydrogen atom is shown in Figure 7-9. The energy of the atom in the *n*th stationary state is given by the Bohr theory (as described in the following section) by the equation

$$E_n = -\frac{2\pi^2 m e^4}{n^2 h^2} \tag{3}$$

Making use of the Bohr frequency rule, we obtain from this expression the following equation for the wavelength of the light emitted or absorbed on transition between the *n′* stationary state and the *n″* stationary state:

$$\frac{1}{\lambda} = \frac{2\pi^2 m e^4}{c h^3} \left(\frac{1}{n'^2} - \frac{1}{n''^2} \right) \tag{4}$$

On introducing the numerical values of the mass of the electron, the charge of the electron, the velocity of light, and Planck's constant, we obtain

$$\frac{1}{\lambda} = 109{,}678 \left(\frac{1}{n'^2} - \frac{1}{n''^2} \right) \mathrm{cm}^{-1} \tag{5}$$

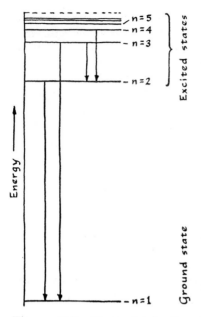

Figure **7-9** *Energy-level dia-*
gram for the hydrogen atom.

This equation, with n'' and n' given various integral values, accounts for the line spectrum of hydrogen. There was great excitement in 1913 when Bohr developed this theory, because the theory permitted him to calculate the spectral lines of hydrogen completely from physical quantities that had been determined by the use of other experiments. The charge of the electron had been determined by Millikan's oil-drop method; the mass of the electron had been determined by experiments such as that of J. J. Thomson, described in Chapter 3; Planck's constant had been determined by Planck from the experimental measurements of the distribution of intensity with wavelengths in the light given out by a hot body, and more accurately by Millikan through his experiments on the photoelectric effect; and the velocity of light had been determined by Albert A. Michelson. Many investigators immediately began to extend the theory and to check it by further experiment.

The spectrum shown in Figure 7-7 does not contain the lines representing transitions to the normal state of hydrogen ($n' = 1$), but rather the lines representing transitions from the higher excited states to the first excited state ($n' = 2$) (Figure 7-9). The equation for these lines is

$$\frac{1}{\lambda} = 109{,}678 \left(\frac{1}{4} - \frac{1}{n''^2} \right) \text{cm}^{-1}, \qquad n'' = 3, 4, 5, \cdots$$

That is, the value of n' has been placed equal to 2, corresponding to the first excited state. This series of lines is called the *Balmer series* of spectral lines of hydrogen. The series involving as its lower state the state with $n = 3$, and that involving the state with $n = 4$, were also known at the time that Bohr carried out his work. The series with the ground state, $n = 1$, as the lower state for the transition had not, however, been recognized. Bohr predicted that this series would exist, and he calculated the wavelengths of the lines ($\lambda = 1{,}216$ Å, etc.). Experimental physicists immediately began the search for these lines, lying in the far ultraviolet region, which involved difficult experimental techniques, and in 1915 Professor Theodore Lyman of Harvard University discovered the lines, which are called the Lyman series.

Bohr's Mathematical Theory of the Hydrogen Atom. We may calculate the properties of the hydrogen atom in the way first carried out by Bohr. In Figure 7-10, representing the motion of the electron about the nucleus in the circular orbit, we see that the velocity of the electron, which at any instant is in a direction tangent to the circular orbit, changes as the electron proceeds around the circle. This requires that the electron be accelerated toward the nucleus. The amount of the acceleration is calculated from the geometry of the figure to be v^2/r, and hence the force required to produce it is mv^2/r. This force is the coulomb force of attraction, e^2/r^2. We thus have the equation

$$\frac{mv^2}{r} = \frac{e^2}{r^2}$$

or, multiplying by r,

$$mv^2 = \frac{e^2}{r} \tag{6}$$

Note that this equation gives a relation between the kinetic energy, which is $\frac{1}{2}mv^2$, and the potential energy, which is $-e^2/r$; namely, the kinetic energy is equal to $\frac{1}{2}$ the potential energy, with the sign changed.

The angular momentum of the electron in its circular orbit is the linear momentum times the radius; that is, it is equal to mvr. Bohr made the assumption that the angular momentum must be equal to $nh/2\pi$:

$$mvr = \frac{nh}{2\pi} \tag{7}$$

Multiplying Equation 6 by mr^2, we obtain

$$m^2v^2r^2 = e^2mr$$

The left side of this equation is just the square of the quantity on the left side of Equation 7; accordingly, it is equal to the square of the right side of this equation, which is $n^2h^2/4\pi^2$. Thus we obtain the equation

$$\frac{n^2h^2}{4\pi^2} = e^2mr$$

The equation for the radius of the orbit is given by solving this for r:

$$r = \frac{n^2h^2}{4\pi^2me^2} = n^2 \times 0.530 \text{ Å} \tag{8}$$

With use of Equation 7, we can solve for the velocity, obtaining

$$v = \frac{2\pi e^2}{nh} = \frac{2.18 \times 10^8}{n} \text{ cm/sec} \tag{9}$$

The total energy, which is the sum of the kinetic energy and the potential energy, is seen to be given by the expression quoted above (Equation 3).

Figure **7-10** *Diagram illustrating the calculation of centrifugal force to balance the centripetal force of electrostatic attraction, in the Bohr theory of the hydrogen atom.*

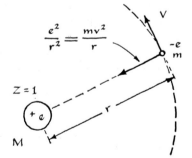

The Wavelength of the Electron and the Bohr Orbit. In Section 3-11 it was stated that an electron moving with velocity v has the wavelength $\lambda = h/mv$. De Broglie, who discovered this equation, pointed out that the wavelength of the electron as given by his equation has just the value to give reinforcement of electron waves in the circular Bohr orbits. An example is the circular Bohr orbit with total quantum number n equal to 5. The length of the orbit, 2π times the radius, is just equal to five times the de Broglie wavelength for an electron moving with the velocity given by Bohr's theory for the electron in this orbit. Thus the electron waves could be considered to reinforce one another as the electron moves about the nucleus in this orbit, whereas in slightly smaller or slightly larger orbits the waves would interfere.

The calculation verifying this statement has been made in Example 6 of Chapter 3. The kinetic energy of an electron in the first Bohr orbit, the normal state of the hydrogen atom, is 13.60 eV. In the solution of this example we found the wavelength of the electron to be 3.33 Å. The radius of the first Bohr orbit is 0.530 Å. When this is multiplied by 2π, the value 3.33 Å is obtained. Hence in the first Bohr orbit there is, according to de Broglie's calculation, just one wavelength in the circumference of the orbit. According to the Bohr theory the velocity of the electron in the nth Bohr orbit is just $1/n$ times the velocity in the first Bohr orbit, and the wavelength is accordingly $n \times 3.33$ Å. The circumference of the Bohr orbit is, however, proportional to n^2 (Equation 8), being equal to $n^2 \times 3.33$ Å. This calculation hence shows, as de Broglie discovered, that there are n electron wavelengths in the circumference of the nth Bohr orbit.

This discovery was interesting in suggesting that the wave character of the electron was involved in determining the stationary states of the hydrogen atom, but there is no close connection between this relation of the de Broglie wavelength to the circumference of the Bohr orbits and the description of the hydrogen atom given by quantum mechanics.

7-8. The Uncertainty Principle

The **uncertainty principle,** an important relation that is a consequence of quantum mechanics, was discovered by the German physicist Werner Heisenberg (born 1901) in 1927. Heisenberg showed that in consequence of the wave-particle duality of matter it is impossible to carry out simultaneously a precise determination of the position of a particle and of its velocity. He also showed that it is impossible to determine exactly the energy of a system at an instant of time.

The uncertainty principle in quantum mechanics is closely related to an uncertainty equation between frequency and time for any sort of waves. Let us consider, for example, a train of ocean waves passing a buoy that is anchored at a fixed point. An observer on the buoy could measure the frequency (number of waves passing the buoy per unit time) at time t_0 by counting the number of crests and troughs passing the buoy between the times $t_0 - \Delta t$ and $t_0 + \Delta t$, dividing by 2 to obtain the number of waves in time $2\Delta t$, and by $2\Delta t$ to obtain the frequency (ν), which is defined as the number of waves in unit time:

$$\nu = \frac{\text{number of crests plus number of troughs}}{2 \times 2\Delta t}$$

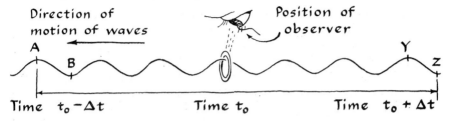

Figure **7-11**

A diagram illustrating the uncertainty in determining the frequency by counting the number of waves passing a point during a period of time.

This measurement is an average for a period of time $2\Delta t$ in the neighborhood of t_0; we may describe it as being for the time t_0 with uncertainty Δt. There is also an uncertainty in the frequency. The crest A (Figure 7-11) might or might not be counted, and similarly the trough Z. Hence there is an uncertainty of about 2 in the number of crests plus the number of troughs, and hence of about $1/2\Delta t$ in the frequency:

$$\Delta \nu = \frac{2}{2 \times 2\Delta t} = \frac{1}{2\Delta t}$$

We may rewrite this equation as $\Delta \nu \times \Delta t = \frac{1}{2}$. A more detailed discussion based on an error-function definition of $\Delta \nu$ and Δt leads to the *uncertainty equation for frequency and time* in its customary form:

$$\Delta \nu \times \Delta t = \frac{1}{2\pi} \qquad (10)$$

By use of quantum theory this equation can be at once converted into the uncertainty equation for energy and time for photons. The energy of a photon with frequency ν is $h\nu$. The uncertainty in frequency $\Delta \nu$ when multiplied by h is the uncertainty in energy ΔE:

$$\Delta E = h\Delta \nu$$

By substituting this relation in Equation 10 we obtain the energy-time uncertainty equation:

$$\Delta E \times \Delta t = \frac{h}{2\pi} \qquad (11)$$

It has been found by analysis of many experiments on the basis of quantum theory that this relation holds for any system. Only by making the measurement of the energy of any system over a long period of time can the error in the measured energy of the system be made small.

Example 2. The yellow D lines, with wavelengths 5890 and 5896 Å, are emitted by sodium gas when it is excited by an electric discharge. They result from the transition of the atom from the excited states $3p\ ^2P_{3/2}$ and $3p\ ^2P_{1/2}$ to the normal state $3s\ ^2S_{1/2}$ (the other electrons have configuration $1s^2 2s^2 2p^6$ in these excited states as well as the normal state). The rate at which the D lines are emitted has been determined by measuring the intensity of the lines as absorption lines in sodium gas. It is such as to correspond to a mean life of the excited states of 1.6×10^{-8} sec. (Most excited states of atoms have about this mean life.) Does this value of the mean life lead to a broadening of the spectral lines?

Solution. We use the uncertainty principle here on the argument that the train of waves corresponding to the photon emitted by an atom is emitted during a period of time approximately equal to the mean life of the excited state of the atom. The frequency corresponding to wavelength $\lambda = 0.589 \times 10^{-4}$ cm is $\nu = c/\lambda = 3 \times 10^{10}/0.589 \times 10^{-4} = 5.09 \times 10^{14}$ sec^{-1}. The uncertainty in frequency corresponding to the uncertainty in time $\Delta t = 1.6 \times 10^{-8}$ sec is given by Equation 10 as $\Delta \nu = 1/(2\pi \Delta t) = 1/(2\pi \times 1.6 \times 10^{-8}) = 1.00 \times 10^7$ sec^{-1}. Hence the relative uncertainty in frequency is $\Delta \nu/\nu = 1.00 \times 10^7/5.09 \times 10^{14} = 1.96 \times 10^{-8}$. This is also the value of $\Delta \lambda/\lambda$, the relative uncertainty in wavelength. Hence we obtain $\Delta \lambda = 1.96 \times 10^{-8} \times 0.589 \times 10^{-4} = 1.15 \times 10^{-12}$ cm $= 0.0001$ Å.

The uncertainty in frequency of these lines thus gives a line width that is only about 1/50,000,000 of the wavelength. This line broadening is usually masked by other effects. However, some excited states of atoms, with energy greater than the ionization energy, have mean life only 10^{-12} sec, because of very rapid decomposition into an electron and a positive ion, and the spectral lines with one of these states as upper state are about 1 Å broad.

The uncertainty principle between position and momentum of a particle states that the product of the uncertainty in one of the coordinates x, y, z describing the position, such as Δx, and the uncertainty in the corresponding component of the momentum, $\Delta(mv_x)$, is equal to or greater than $h/2\pi$:

$$\Delta x \times \Delta(mv_x) \geq \frac{h}{2\pi} \tag{12}$$

For example, the uncertainty in the position of the electron in the hydrogen atom in its normal state is about equal to its average distance from the nucleus, 0.530×10^{-8} cm. The electron moves with the root-mean-square speed 2.18×10^8 cm/sec. This quantity may be taken roughly as the uncertainty in the component of its velocity along the x-axis. Accordingly, the uncertainty in the x component of the momentum is 2.18×10^8 cm/sec multiplied by the mass, 9.1×10^{-28} g, which is 1.99×10^{-19}. The product of the two uncertainties is accordingly 1.05×10^{-27} erg sec, which is just equal to $h/2\pi$.

7-9. Excitation and Ionization Energies

Interesting verification of Bohr's idea about stationary states of atoms and molecules was provided by some electron-impact experiments carried out by James Franck (born 1882) and Gustav Hertz (1887–1963) during the years 1914 to 1920. They were able to show that when a fast-moving electron collides with an atom or molecule it bounces off with only small loss of kinetic energy, unless it has a high enough speed to be able to raise the atom or molecule from its nor-

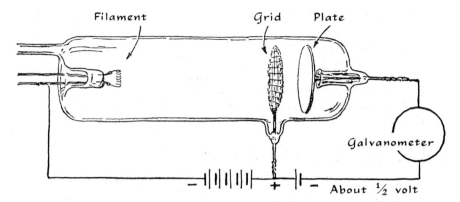

Figure **7-12**

Apparatus for electron-impact experiments of the sort carried out by Franck and Hertz.

mal electronic state to an excited electronic state, or even to ionize the atom or molecule, by knocking an electron out of it.

The apparatus that they used is indicated diagrammatically in Figure 7-12. Electrons are boiled out of the hot filament, and are accelerated toward the grid by the accelerating potential difference V_1. Many of these electrons pass through the perforations in the grid, and strike the collecting plate, which is held at a negative voltage relative to the grid. The electrons are able to move against the electrostatic field between the grid and the collecting plate because of the kinetic energy that they have gained while being accelerated from the filament to the grid. Even if there are some atoms or gas molecules in the space between the filament and the grid, the electrons may bounce off from them without much loss in energy.

If, however, the accelerating voltage V_1 is great enough that the kinetic energy picked up by the electron exceeds the excitation energy of the atom or molecule with which the electron may collide, then the electron on impact with the atom or molecule may raise it from the normal state to the first excited state. The colliding electron will retain only the kinetic energy equal to its original kinetic energy minus the excitation energy of the atom or molecule with which it has collided. It may then not have enough residual kinetic energy to travel to the plate, against the opposing field, and the current registered by the galvanometer to the plate may show a decrease, as the accelerating voltage is increased.

With hydrogen atoms in the tube, for example, no change in the plate current would be registered on the galvanometer until the accelerating voltage reaches 10.2 V. At this accelerating voltage the electrons obtain from the field between the filament and the grid just enough energy to raise a normal hydrogen atom to the first excited state—that is, to change the quantum number from $n = 1$ to $n = 2$. There then occurs a decrease in the plate current. The voltage 10.2 V is called a *critical voltage* or *critical potential* for atomic hydrogen. Other critical potentials occur, corresponding to the other excited states, and a large one occurs at 13.60 V. This critical voltage, 13.60 V, corresponds to the energy, 13.60 eV, required to remove an electron completely from the hydrogen atom; that is, it corresponds to the energy required to convert a normal hydrogen atom into a proton plus an electron far removed from it. The voltage 13.60 V is called the *ionization potential* of the hydrogen atom, and the amount of energy 13.60 eV is called the *ionization energy* of the hydrogen atom.

The discussion of ionization energies of atoms will be continued in the next chapter.

7-10.   Magnetic Moments of Atoms and Molecules

It was discovered by Faraday that most substances when placed in a magnetic field develop a magnetic moment opposed to the field. Such a substance is said to be diamagnetic. Substances that develop a moment parallel to the field are called paramagnetic substances (or ferromagnetic substances, if the amount of magnetic polarization is large in weak fields and approaches a constant value as the field strength increases).

A sample of a diamagnetic substance placed in an inhomogeneous magnetic field is acted on by a force that tends to push it into the region where the field is weaker. A sample of paramagnetic substance is pulled into the stronger field.

The explanation of diamagnetism is that the application of a magnetic field induces a motion of the electrons in an atom or monatomic ion in a direction such as to give rise to a magnetic dipole with orientation opposed to the field. All substances show this diamagnetic effect.

The magnetic susceptibility of a diamagnetic or paramagnetic substance is defined by the equation

$$M = \chi H$$

in which M is the induced moment in unit amount (unit volume, unit mass, or one mole) of substance, χ is the magnetic susceptibility (χ_v, χ_m, or χ_{molar}, respectively), and H is the strength of the magnetic field.

It was shown by Pierre Curie in 1895 that paramagnetic susceptibility is strongly dependent on temperature, and for many substances is inversely proportional to the absolute temperature. The equation

$$\chi_{molar} = \frac{C_{molar}}{T} + D$$

is called Curie's Law, and the constant C_{molar} is called the molar Curie constant; D, which is usually negative, represents the contribution of diamagnetism.

The first term in this equation can be evaluated by use of the Boltzmann principle, with the assumption that the substance contains permanent magnetic dipole moments that can orient themselves in the magnetic field. This theoretical treatment was carried out by the French scientist Paul Langevin in 1905. He derived the equation

$$C_{molar} = \frac{N\mu^2}{3k}$$

in which μ is the value of the magnetic dipole moment per atom or molecule.

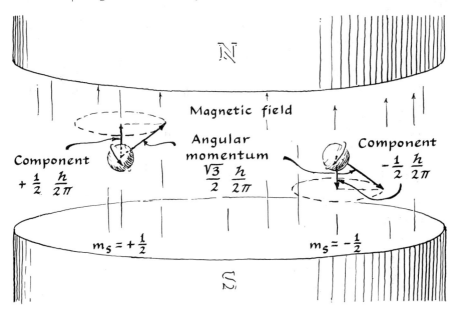

Figure **7-13**

Diagram illustrating spatial quantization of the spin of an electron. The spin quantum number is $s = \frac{1}{2}$, leading to angular momentum $\frac{\sqrt{3}}{2}\frac{h}{2\pi}$. The magnetic quantum number m_s can be either $+\frac{1}{2}$ or $-\frac{1}{2}$, with values $+\frac{1}{2}\frac{h}{2\pi}$ and $-\frac{1}{2}\frac{h}{2\pi}$, respectively, for the component of the angular momentum in the direction of the magnetic field.

By application of this equation to the observed magnetic susceptibilities of paramagnetic substances, measured over a range of temperature, the values of magnetic moments can be determined.

The electron spin is assigned a magnetic moment such that the value of the component of the magnetic moment in the field direction is ± 1 Bohr magneton. The Bohr magneton, μ_B, has the value $he/4\pi mc = 0.927 \times 10^{-20}$ erg/gauss. The magnitude of the magnetic moment of the electron spin is considered to be $\sqrt{3}$ times this quantity. Accordingly, the magnetic moment of the electron makes an angle with the field direction, with two alternative values of the angle, as shown in Figure 7-13.

In general, the magnetic moment of an atom, ion, or molecule with total angular moment quantum number J is given by the equation

$$\mu = g[J(J + 1)]^{1/2} \mu_B$$

Here g is the Landé g-factor, with value 1 for the part of the magnetic moment that is due to orbital motion of the electron and 2 for electron spin.

For example, for one electron the value of J is just equal to the spin quantum number, $s = \frac{1}{2}$. The value of magnetic moment in Bohr magnetons is accordingly $2(\frac{1}{2} \times \frac{3}{2})^{1/2} = \sqrt{3}$.

The Stern-Gerlach Experiment. The idea that a magnetic moment (produced, for example, by the motion of an electron in a circular orbit in the hydrogen atom or other atom, as given by the old Bohr theory) could be oriented in a small number of definite orientations in a magnetic field, rather than being free to assume all orientations, was suggested by the old quantum theory. Scientists were skeptical about this idea of spatial quantization of electron orbits, which had been originated by the German physicist Arnold Sommerfeld (1868–1951), until in 1921 Otto Stern suggested an experiment designed to test it, and then carried it out in collaboration with W. Gerlach.

The experiment carried out by Stern and Gerlach is represented in Figure 7-14. Silver vapor emanates from a furnace in an evacuated chamber. A narrow stream of silver atoms, defined by a slit, is then passed through a highly inhomogeneous

Figure 7-14

Diagram illustrating the Stern-Gerlach experiment, showing quantized orientation of the magnetic moment of an atom in a magnetic field.

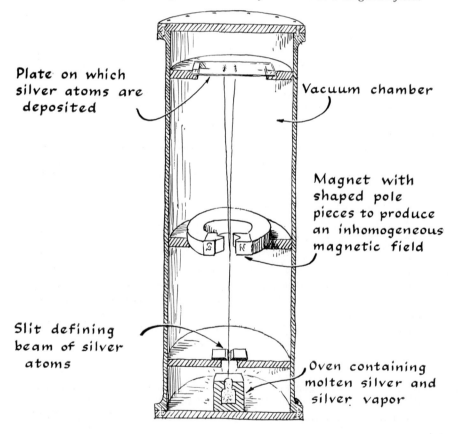

Plate on which silver atoms are deposited

Vacuum chamber

Magnet with shaped pole pieces to produce an inhomogeneous magnetic field

Slit defining beam of silver atoms

Oven containing molten silver and silver vapor

magnetic field produced by the shaped pole pieces of a magnet. The magnetic moments orient themselves in the magnetic field, and the inhomogeneity of the magnetic field causes a force to operate on each magnetic moment, proportional to the gradient of the field and to the component of magnetic moment in the direction of the field. For one electron spin, with two orientations possible, the beam of atoms is deflected in two directions, as indicated in the diagram. It was found that beams of silver, hydrogen, copper, gold, sodium, and potassium atoms were split into two beams, corresponding to a component of $+1$ Bohr magneton or -1 Bohr magneton in the field direction.

This experiment provided a striking example of a successful prediction by the quantum theory. The spin of the electron had at that time not yet been discovered, and it was thought that the magnetic moment was due to the orbital motion of the electron; that is, to a state with $J = 1$ and $g = 1$. The orientations of J should correspond to a component M_J of $+1$, 0, or -1, and for a few years, until the spin of the electron was discovered, the results of the experiment were interpreted by a special assumption, that the orientation with $M_J = 0$ for some reason did not occur. The discovery of the spin of the electron and other developments in the theory of atomic structure in the period around 1925 led to an essentially complete theory of the magnetic moments of atoms and molecules.

EXERCISES

7-11. Without looking at the periodic table, but by remembering the number of elements in each row (2, 8, 8, 18, 18, 32), deduce what elements have atomic numbers 9, 10, 11, 17, 19, 35, 37, 54.

7-12. Sketch a plan of the periodic table, and fill in from memory the symbols and atomic numbers of the first eighteen elements and the remaining alkali metals, halogens, and noble gases.

7-13. By extrapolation with use of the data given in Table 7-2, predict approximate values of the atomic weight, melting point, and boiling point of element 118. What would you expect its chemical properties to be?

7-14. Where was helium first detected? What is the principal source of this element at present?

7-15. List as many uses as you can for the various noble gases.

7-16. What predictions would you make about the formula, color, solubility, taste, and melting point of the compound that would be formed by reaction of chlorine and element 119?

7-17. What are the most important metallic properties? In what part of the periodic table are the elements with metallic properties?

7-18. Classify the following elements as metals, metalloids, or nonmetals: potassium, arsenic, aluminum, xenon, bromine, silicon, phosphorus.

7-19. Neon, argon, krypton, and xenon crystallize in cubic closest packing (Section 2-4), with $a = 4.52$ Å, 5.43 Å, 5.59 Å, and 6.18 Å, respectively. To what values of the density do these values of the edge of the unit cube correspond?

7-20. What are the values of the effective atomic radius of neon, argon, krypton, and xenon given by the information in the preceding Exercise?

7-21. In Section 7-9 it is pointed out that the first change in plate current in the Franck-Hertz experiment with atomic hydrogen in the apparatus would occur when the voltage reached 10.2 V. To what change in principal quantum number of the electron in the hydrogen atom does this excitation correspond? At what voltage would the next excitation occur? (Answer: $n = 1$ to $n = 2$; 12.1 V.)

7-22. The Bohr orbit for the normal hydrogen atom has radius 0.530 Å. What is the radius for the first excited orbit, with $n = 2$? For the orbit with $n = 3$?

7-23. By using Ze^2/r^2 in place of e^2/r^2 for the force of attraction of the electron by a nucleus with charge $+Ze$, show that the Bohr orbits of hydrogen-like ions (He^+, Li^{++}, etc.) have energy Z^2 times the value for hydrogen (Equation 3) and radii Z^{-1} times the value for hydrogen; i.e., n^2a_0/Z (Equation 8). What is the diameter of the smallest Bohr orbit of an electron around a uranium nucleus? (Answer: 0.0058 Å.)

7-24. Using the result of the preceding Exercise, calculate the ionization energy of He^+. (Answer: 54.2 eV.)

REFERENCE

Scientific American offprint (see Appendix VI):
212. The Principle of Uncertainty

CHAPTER 8

Ionic Valence and Electrolysis

In Chapter 4 it was pointed out that the formulas of compounds can be systematized by assigning certain combining powers, valences, to the elements. The valence of an element was described as the number of valence bonds formed by an atom of the element with other atoms.

The effort to obtain a clear understanding of the nature of valence and of chemical combination in general has led in recent years to the dissociation of the concept of valence into several new concepts—especially *ionic valence* and *covalence*. We shall examine these concepts in this chapter and the following one. The related concept of *oxidation number* will be discussed in Chapter 11, and *metallic valence* will be discussed in Chapter 20.

In addition to ionic valence, there are given in the following sections of this chapter discussions of electrolysis, electrochemical processes, and acids, bases, and salts.

8-1. The Discovery of Ions

Two hundred years ago, during the eighteenth century, scientists (they were then called natural philosophers) were making many discoveries about the nature and properties of electricity. An Italian scientist named Beccaria discovered that pure water is a very poor conductor of electricity. In 1771 the British scientist Henry Cavendish reported that he had found that salt dissolved in water causes the electric conductivity to increase very greatly. Many scientists then carried on investigations of the conductance of electricity by salt solutions and of chemical reactions produced by electricity, but the discovery of the way in which salt solutions carry an electric current was not made for over one hundred years.

In 1884 a young Swedish scientist Svante Arrhenius (1859–1927), then twenty-five years old, published his doctor's dissertation, which included measurements of the electric conductivity of salt solutions and his ideas as to their interpretation. These ideas were rather vague, but he later made them more precise and then published a detailed paper on ionic dissociation in 1887.

The hypothesis made by Arrhenius is that a solution of salt, such as sodium chloride, contains electrically charged particles, which are called ions (Section 5-5). This hypothesis was not accepted at first, but before long chemists found that it explained so many of the facts of chemistry in a simple way that it was accepted; it is now an important part of chemical theory.

The electron had not yet been discovered when Arrhenius proposed his theory, but we shall discuss the theory in terms of the electronic structure of ions.

Sodium has atomic number 11. The nucleus of a sodium atom has electric charge $+11e$, and the atom is electrically neutral when the nucleus is surrounded by 11 electrons. If an electron were to be removed from the sodium atom, leaving only 10 electrons around the nucleus, the resulting particle would have a positive charge, $+e$. This particle, composed of a sodium nucleus and 10 electrons, is called a *sodium ion*. Similarly, a chlorine atom, with 17 electrons surrounding a nucleus with charge $+17e$, is converted into a *chloride ion*, with negative charge $-e$, by the addition of an eighteenth electron. The transfer of an electron from a sodium atom to a chlorine atom produces a sodium ion, Na^+, and a chloride ion, Cl^-.

Arrhenius assumed that in a solution of sodium chloride in water there are present sodium ions, Na^+, and chloride ions, Cl^-. When electrodes are put into such a solution, the sodium ions are attracted toward the cathode, and move in that direction, and the chloride ions are attracted toward the anode, and move in the direction of the anode. The motion of these ions through the solution, in opposite directions, provides the mechanism of conduction of the current of electricity by the solution.

The word ion is derived from the Greek word meaning to go, to move.

Because of the importance of ions in chemistry, it is worth while to define the word ion: *an* **ion** *is an atom or group of atoms that is not electrically neutral, but instead carries a positive or negative electric charge.*

An atom (or group of atoms) is electrically neutral when the number of electrons surrounding the nucleus (or nuclei) is exactly equal to the atomic number (or sum of the atomic numbers). It is a positive ion (cation) if one or more electrons are missing, and it is a negative ion (anion) if it has one or more extra electrons.

While chemists were investigating the properties of aqueous solutions containing ions, physicists were making similar investigations of ions in gases at low pressures, especially in relation to the passage of an electric discharge through the gas (Chapter 3) and to the nature of the spectral lines emitted or absorbed by the gas atoms or ions. These physical methods have permitted the determination of the amount of energy required to remove an electron from an atom (the ionization energy) and the amount liberated when an atom attaches an electron to itself (the electron affinity). These energy quantities are discussed in the following sections.

8-2. Ionization Energies of Atoms

Ionization is the process of producing ions from neutral atoms or molecules, by removing electrons or adding electrons.

The amount of energy required to remove an electron is called the *ionization energy* of the atom (Section 7-8). It is customary to give values of this quantity in electron-volts (eV); one electron-volt is equal to 23,053 cal/mole.

The first ionization energy of helium (removing one electron) is 24.58 eV, and the second (removing the second electron) is 54.40 eV. Many other values have also been determined by study of the spectra of the atoms.

Ionization energies of the elements from hydrogen to argon are given in Table 8-1, and values of the first ionization energy for the first sixty elements are plotted in Figure 8-1.

Table 8-1

Ionization Energies of Atoms

Z	ELE- MENT	NUMBERS OF ELECTRONS					IONIZATION ENERGIES (electron-volts)			
		$1s$	$2s$	$2p$	$3s$	$3p$	1st	2nd	3rd	4th
1	H	1					13.60			
2	He	2					24.58	54.40		
3	Li	2	1				5.39	75.62	122.42	
4	Be	2	2				9.32	18.21	153.85	217.66
5	B	2	2	1			8.30	25.15	37.92	259.30
6	C	2	2	2			11.26	24.38	47.86	64.48
7	N	2	2	3			14.54	29.61	47.43	77.45
8	O	2	2	4			13.61	35.15	54.93	77.39
9	F	2	2	5			17.42	34.98	62.65	87.23
10	Ne	2	2	6			21.56	41.07	64.0	97.16
11	Na	2	2	6	1		5.14	47.29	71.65	98.88
12	Mg	2	2	6	2		7.64	15.03	80.12	109.29
13	Al	2	2	6	2	1	5.98	18.82	28.44	119.96
14	Si	2	2	6	2	2	8.15	16.34	33.46	45.13
15	P	2	2	6	2	3	11.0	19.65	30.16	51.35
16	S	2	2	6	2	4	10.36	23.4	35.0	47.29
17	Cl	2	2	6	2	5	13.01	23.80	39.90	53.5
18	Ar	2	2	6	2	6	15.76	27.62	40.90	59.79

It is seen that there is a striking correlation of these values with the periodic table. The ionization-energy curve has sharp maxima at $Z = 2$, 10, 18, 36, and 54; that is, at the noble gases. These are immediately followed by deep

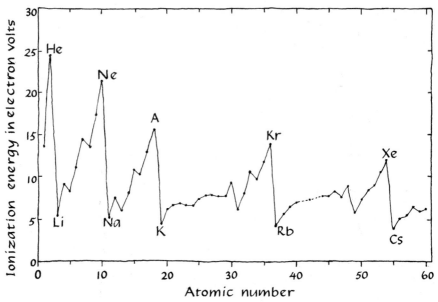

Figure 8-1

The ionization energy, in electron-volts, of the first electron of atoms from hydrogen, atomic number 1, to neodymium, atomic number 60. Symbols of the elements with very high and very low ionization energy are shown in the figure.

minima, for the soft metals lithium, sodium, potassium, rubidium, and cesium, which were described in Section 7-1 as being closely similar to one another in properties.

We may well feel that the resistance that atoms of the noble gases offer to giving up any of their electrons is closely related to their striking chemical inertness.

Illustrative Exercises

8-1. The first ionization energy of helium is 24.58 eV, and the second is 54.40 eV. In each case a $1s$ electron is removed. Can you explain why the second $1s$ electron is held so much more tightly than the first?

8-2. What are the electron configurations of Li^+ and Be^+? Why does the second ionization energy have a much larger value for lithium than for beryllium?

8-3. Ionic Crystals and Ionic Valence

The Structure of an Ionic Crystal.   When metallic sodium and gaseous chlorine react each sodium atom transfers an electron to a chlorine atom:

$$2Na + Cl_2 \longrightarrow 2Na^+ + 2Cl^-$$

Table **8-2**

*Ionization Energies of the Alkali Metals
and Electron Affinities of the Halogens*

ALKALI METAL	IONIZATION ENERGY (kcal/mole)	HALOGEN	ELECTRON AFFINITY (kcal/mole)
Lithium	124.3		
Sodium	118.5	Fluorine	90
Potassium	100.1	Chlorine	92
Rubidium	95.9	Bromine	89
Cesium	89.2	Iodine	79

There occurs a strong electrostatic attraction between each sodium ion and every chloride ion in its neighborhood. There also occurs repulsion between ions of like sign. In consequence of these forces and the repulsive forces that operate between all ions or molecules when they get so close to one another that their electronic structures are in contact, the ions pile up together in a regular way, each sodium ion surrounding itself with six chloride ions as nearest neighbors, and keeping all other sodium ions somewhat farther away. The structure of the sodium chloride crystal is represented in Figure 4-2.

The Ionic Bond; Ionic Valence. The strong electrostatic forces acting between anions and cations are called *ionic bonds*. The magnitude of the electric charge on an ion (in units e) is called its *ionic valence*. Thus sodium has ionic valence $+1$ in sodium chloride and is said to be *unipositive*, chlorine has ionic valence -1 and is said to be *uninegative*.

Any specimen of matter big enough to be seen by the eye must be essentially electrically neutral. It might have an excess of either positive or negative ions, and thus be charged positively or negatively, but the amount of charge, measured in units e, is always small compared with the number of atoms. Hence a crystal of sodium chloride must contain substantially as many Na^+ ions as Cl^- ions, and its formula must be Na^+Cl^-. The composition of the crystal and the formula of the compound are thus determined by the ionic valences of the constituent elements: these ionic valences must add up to zero.

Ionic Valence and the Periodic Table. It is a striking fact that *every alkali ion and every halogenide ion contains the same number of electrons as one of the noble gases*. The stability of these ions and the lack of chemical reactivity of the noble gases can thus be attributed to the same cause—*the extraordinary stability of configurations of 2, 10, 18, 36, 54, and 86 electrons about an atomic nucleus.*

The alkali metals (in group I of the periodic table) are unipositive because their atoms contain one more electron than a noble-gas atom, and this electron is easily removed, to produce the corresponding cation, Li^+, Na^+, K^+, Rb^+, and Cs^+. The ease with which the outermost electron can be removed from an atom of an alkali metal, compared with other atoms, is shown by the values of the first ionization potentials given in Table 8-2 and Figure 8-1. The values of the first ionization potentials of the alkali metals are less than those for any other elements. Less energy is required to ionize these atoms than any others. The amount of energy, in kcal/mole, required to ionize gas atoms of the alkali metals is given in Table 8-2.

The halogens (in group VII of the periodic table) are uninegative because each of their atoms contains one less electron than a noble-gas atom, and readily gains an electron, producing the corresponding anion, F^-, Cl^-, Br^-, and I^-. The energy that is liberated when an extra electron is attached to an atom to form an anion is called the *electron affinity* of the atom. Values of electron affinities of the halogens, given in Table 8-2, are larger than those of other atoms.

The atoms of group II of the periodic table, by losing two electrons, can also produce ions with the noble-gas structures: these ions are Be^{++}, Mg^{++}, Ca^{++}, Sr^{++}, and Ba^{++}. The alkaline-earth elements are hence bipositive in valence. The elements of group III are tripositive, those of group VI are binegative, etc.

The formulas of binary salts of these elements can thus be written from knowledge of the positions of the elements in the periodic table:

$$Na^+F^- \qquad Na^+Br^- \qquad K^+I^- \qquad Ca^{++}(F^-)_2 \qquad Ba^{++}(Cl^-)_2$$
$$Al^{+++}(Cl^-)_3 \qquad (Na^+)_2O^{--} \qquad Ca^{++}O^{--} \qquad (Al^{+++})_2(O^{--})_3$$

Ionic compounds are formed between the strong metals in groups I and II and the strong nonmetals in the upper right corner of the periodic table. In addition, ionic compounds are formed containing the cations of the strong metals and the anions of acids, especially of the oxygen acids.

It will be pointed out in the following chapter that the description of compounds as aggregates of ions is an approximation. The electronic structure of molecules and crystals usually described as ionic involves only a partial transfer of electrons from the metal atoms to the nonmetal atoms. Nevertheless, the discussion of ionic valence in relation to the noble-gas electron configurations, as given above, is an important and useful part of chemical theory.

Illustrative Exercises

8-3. What ions can atoms of magnesium and oxygen form, by assuming the configuration of the nearest noble gas (neon)? What are the ionic valences of magnesium and oxygen? What is the predicted composition of magnesium oxide?

8-4. Assign ionic valences to the atoms in the following compounds: Na_2O, $MgCl_2$, Al_2O_3, CsF, SiO_2, PF_5. For each ion, state what noble-gas configuration has been assumed.

8-5. What is the electron configuration of the aluminum atom? Of the tripositive aluminum ion, Al^{+++}? From what orbitals were the three valence electrons removed? Why are there no compounds containing the ion Al^{++++}?

8-4. Ionic Radii

The electron distributions in alkali ions and halogenide ions are shown in Figure 8-2. It is seen that these ions are closely similar to the corresponding noble gases, which are shown, on a somewhat larger scale, in Figure 7-3. With increase in nuclear charge from $+9e$ for fluoride ion to $+11e$ for sodium ion the electron shells are drawn closer to the nucleus, so that the sodium ion is about 30% smaller than the fluoride ion. The neon atom is intermediate in size.

Atoms and ions do not have a sharply defined outer surface. Instead, the electron distribution function usually reaches a maximum for the outer shell and then decreases asymptotically toward zero with increasing distance from the nucleus. It is possible to define a set of *crystal radii* for ions such that the radii of two ions with similar electronic structures are proportional to the relative extensions in space of the electron distribution functions for the two ions, and that the sum of two radii is equal to the contact distance of the two ions in the crystal. Figure 8-3 shows the relative sizes of various ions with noble-gas structures, chosen in this way. Some values of ionic radii are given in Table 8-3.

These radii give the observed cation-anion distance in crystals in which cation and anion have the structure of the same noble gas, such as Na^+F^- (both ions with the neon structure) and K^+Cl^- (both with the argon structure). The observed distances, $Na^+—F^- = 2.31$ Å and $K^+—Cl^- = 3.14$ Å, are equal to the sums of the corresponding radii. In other crys-

Figure **8-2** *The electron distribution in alkali ions and halogenide ions.*

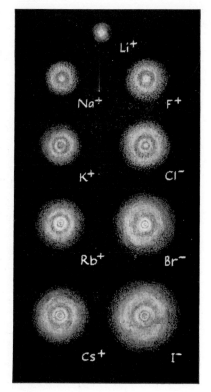

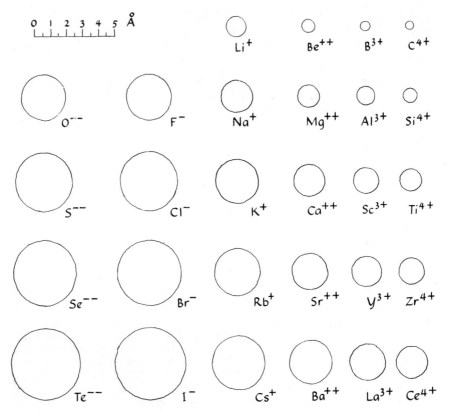

Figure 8-3

A drawing representing the ionic radii of ions.

tals, in which the anions are almost in contact, the observed distance is larger than the radius sum.

An extreme case is that of lithium iodide. In this crystal, as shown in Figure 8-4, the iodide ions are in contact with one another, and the lithium ions are not in contact with the surrounding iodide ions. In consequence of the contact of the large iodide ions with one another the Li^+—I^- distance in the crystal, 3.02 Å, is nearly 10% greater than the radius sum, 2.76 Å. In con-

Table 8-3

Crystal Radii of Some Ions

ION	RADIUS	ION	RADIUS	ION	RADIUS	ION	RADIUS	ION	RADIUS	ION	RADIUS
				Li^+	0.60 Å	Be^{++}	0.31 Å	B^{3+}	0.20 Å	C^{4+}	0.15 Å
O^{--}	1.40 Å	F^-	1.36 Å	Na^+	.95	Mg^{++}	.65	Al^{3+}	.50	Si^{4+}	0.41
S^{--}	1.84	Cl^-	1.81	K^+	1.33	Ca^{++}	.99	Sc^{3+}	.81	Ge^{4+}	.53
Se^{--}	1.98	Br^-	1.95	Rb^+	1.48	Sr^{++}	1.13	Y^{3+}	.93	Sn^{4+}	.71
Te^{--}	2.21	I^-	2.16	Cs^+	1.69	Ba^{++}	1.35	La^{3+}	1.15	Pb^{4+}	.84

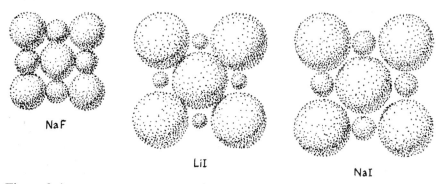

NaF

LiI

NaI

Figure 8-4

The arrangement of lithium ions and iodide ions in the lithium iodide crystal, showing that the iodide ions are in contact with one another.

sequence the substance is softer than the other alkali halogenides, and also has lower melting point, boiling point, heat of fusion, and heat of vaporization. Figure 8-5 shows the effect on the melting point of the large ratio of radius of anion to radius of cation. The crystals containing the smallest cation, with each anion, would be expected to have the highest melting point, because of the stronger attraction. But the salts of lithium show large deviation from this expectation. Sodium iodide also has a lower melting point than expected. In this crystal both the anion-anion contact and the cation-anion contact are operating, and in consequence the crystal lattice is expanded somewhat.

These radius-ratio effects do not occur in the gas molecules, such as LiI. For all the alkali halogenide gas molecules for which the cation-anion distance has been determined (by microwave spectroscopy), as given in Table 8-4, the distance is equal to about 86% of the sum of the crystal ionic radii.

The decrease in cation-anion distance from an alkali halogenide crystal to the gas molecule can be explained as corresponding to an increase in the strength of the ionic bond. In the gas molecule, such as Na^+Cl^-, we may say that there is a single bond between the unipositive cation and the uninegative anion. In the crystal we may say that each cation divides its power of attraction among the six anions that sur-

Figure **8-5** *The observed melting points of the alkali halogenides, showing the effect of anion contact in the lithium salts and sodium iodide.*

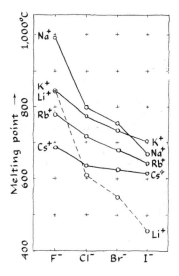

Table 8-4

Cation-anion Distances in Alkali Halogenide Gas Molecules

	Li$^+$	Na$^+$	K$^+$	Rb$^+$	Cs$^+$
Cl$^-$	2.03 Å	2.36 Å	2.67 Å	2.79 Å	2.91 Å
Br$^-$	2.17	2.50	2.82	2.95	3.07
I$^-$	2.39	2.71	3.05	3.18	3.32

round it, and that in consequence each cation-anion contact represents one-sixth of a bond, a $\frac{1}{6}$th bond. This weaker bond is longer (by 0.4 to 0.6 Å) than the full bond in the gas molecule.

Illustrative Exercises

8-6. The observed Li$^+$—I$^-$ distance in the lithium iodide crystal is 3.02 Å. Assuming that the iodide ions are in contact, calculate a value for the iodide ion radius. (Answer: 2.13 Å.)

8-7. (a) At what value of ratio of cation radius to anion radius would the anions in a crystal with the sodium chloride structure (Figures 4-2, 8-4) be in contact with one another and also with the cations? (Consider the ions to be hard spheres.)

(b) Which alkali halogenides have a smaller ratio?

(c) Which have a ratio within 10% of this value, and hence have some anion-anion contact as well as cation-anion contact? Compare your answer with the alkali halogenides showing abnormal melting points (Figure 8-5).

8-5. The Electrolytic Decomposition of Molten Salts

The discovery of ions resulted from the experimental investigations of the interaction of an electric current with chemical substances. These investigations were begun early in the nineteenth century, and were carried on effectively by Michael Faraday (1791–1867), in the period around 1830.

The Electrolysis of Molten Sodium Chloride. Molten sodium chloride (the salt melts at 801°C) conducts an electric current, as do other molten salts. During the process of conducting the current a chemical reaction occurs— the salt is *decomposed*. If two electrodes (carbon rods) are dipped into a crucible containing molten sodium chloride and an electric potential (from a battery or generator) is applied, metallic sodium is produced at the negative electrode—the cathode—and chlorine gas at the positive electrode—the anode. Such electric decomposition of a substance is called *electrolysis*.

The Mechanism of Ionic Conduction. Molten sodium chloride, like the crystalline substance, consists of equal numbers of sodium ions and chloride ions.

These ions are very stable, and do not gain electrons or lose electrons easily. Whereas the ions in the crystal are firmly held in place by their neighbors, those in the molten salt move about with considerable freedom.

An electric generator or battery forces electrons into the cathode and pumps them away from the anode—electrons move freely in a metal or a semi-metallic conductor such as graphite. But electrons cannot ordinarily get into a substance such as salt; the crystalline substance is an insulator, and the electric conductivity shown by the molten salt is not electronic conductivity (metallic conductivity), but is conductivity of a different kind, called *ionic conductivity* or *electrolytic conductivity*. This sort of conductivity results from the motion of the ions in the liquid; the cations, Na^+, are attracted by the negatively charged cathode and move toward it, and the anions, Cl^-, are attracted by the anode and move toward it (Figure 8-6).

The Electrode Reactions. The preceding statement describes the mechanism of the conduction of the current through the liquid. We must now consider the way in which the current passes between the electrodes and the liquid; that is, we consider the *electrode reactions*.

The process that occurs at the cathode is this: sodium ions, attracted to the cathode, combine with the electrons carried by the cathode to form sodium atoms; that is, to form sodium metal. The *cathode reaction* accordingly is

$$Na^+ + e^- \longrightarrow Na \tag{1}$$

The symbol e^- represents an electron, which in this case comes from the cathode. Similarly, at the anode chloride ions give up their extra electrons to the anode, and become chlorine atoms, which are combined as the molecules of chlorine gas. The *anode reaction* is

$$2Cl^- \longrightarrow Cl_2 + 2e^- \tag{2}$$

The Over-all Reaction. The whole process of electric conduction in this system thus occurs in the following steps.

1. An electron is pumped into the cathode.
2. The electron jumps out of the cathode onto an adjacent sodium ion, converting it into an atom of sodium metal.
3. The charge of the electron is conducted across the liquid by the motion of the ions.
4. A chloride ion gives its extra electron to the anode, and becomes half of a molecule of chlorine gas.
5. The electron moves out of the anode toward the generator or battery.

The student should note that there is nothing mysterious about this complex phenomenon, after it is separated into its parts and the individual processes are analyzed. If the phenomenon seems mysterious, he should study it further, and if necessary ask the instructor to explain it.

Anode   Cathode

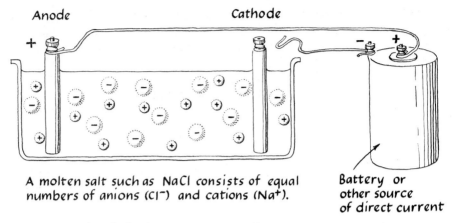

A molten salt such as NaCl consists of equal
numbers of anions (Cl⁻) and cations (Na⁺).

Battery or
other source
of direct current

When the circuit is closed electrons flow as through a tube.

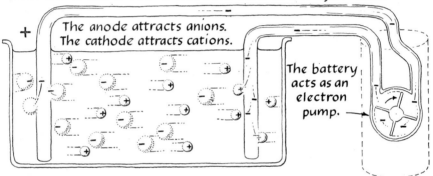

The anode attracts anions.
The cathode attracts cations.

The battery
acts as an
electron
pump.

Anions give up their extra
electrons to the anode
and become neutral atoms.

Cations receive electrons from
the cathode and also become
neutral atoms.

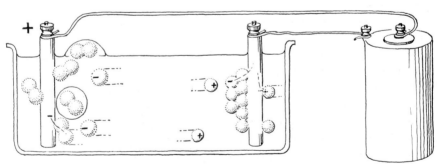

Neutral atoms of chlorine
unite to form bubbles of
chlorine gas (Cl₂).

Neutral sodium atoms
form a layer of
metallic sodium.

Figure 8-6

Electrolysis of molten sodium chloride.

The over-all reaction for the electrolytic decomposition is the sum of the two electrode reactions. Since two electrons are shown on their way around the circuit in Equation 2, we must double Equation 1:

$$
\begin{aligned}
2Na^+ + 2e^- &\longrightarrow 2Na \\
2Cl^- &\longrightarrow Cl_2 + 2e^- \\
\hline
2Na^+ + 2Cl^- &\xrightarrow{\text{electr.}} 2Na + Cl_2
\end{aligned}
$$
(3)

or

$$2NaCl \xrightarrow{\text{electr.}} 2Na + Cl_2 \tag{4}$$

The Equations 3 and 4 are equivalent; they both represent the decomposition of sodium chloride into its elementary constituents. The abbreviation "electr." (for electrolysis) is written beneath the arrow to indicate that the reaction occurs on the passage of an electric current.

Illustrative Exercises

8-8. Molten magnesium chloride, $MgCl_2$, can be electrolyzed, forming magnesium and chlorine. Write equations for the cathode reaction, the anode reaction, and the over-all reaction.

8-6. The Electrolysis of an Aqueous Salt Solution

Although pure water does not conduct electricity in any significant amount, a solution of salt (or acid or base) is a good conductor. During electrolysis chemical reactions take place at the electrodes; often these reactions lead to the production of gaseous hydrogen and oxygen, as described in Chapter 6.

The phenomena that occur when a current of electricity is passed through such a solution are analogous to those described in the preceding section for molten salt. The five steps are the following.

1. Electrons are pumped into the cathode.
2. Electrons jump from the cathode to adjacent ions or molecules, producing the cathode reaction.
3. The current is conducted across the liquid by the motion of the dissolved ions.
4. Electrons jump from ions or molecules in the solution to the anode, producing the anode reaction.
5. The electrons move out of the anode toward the generator or battery.

Let us consider a dilute solution of sodium chloride (Figure 8-7). The process of conduction through this solution (step 3) is closely similar to that for molten sodium chloride. Here it is the dissolved sodium ions that move toward the cathode and the dissolved chloride ions that move toward the anode. By the motion of the ions in this way, negative electric charge is carried toward the anode and away from the cathode.

But the electrode reactions for dilute salt solutions are entirely different from those for molten salts. Electrolysis of dilute salt solution produces

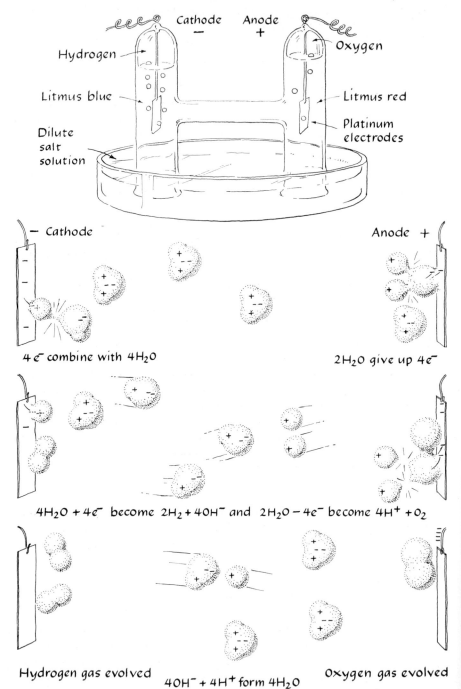

Figure 8-7

Electrolysis of dilute aqueous salt solution.

hydrogen at the cathode and oxygen at the anode, whereas electrolysis of molten salt produces sodium and chlorine.

The *cathode reaction* for a dilute salt solution is

$$2e^- + 2H_2O \longrightarrow H_2 + 2OH^- \tag{5}$$

Two electrons from the cathode react with two water molecules to produce a molecule of hydrogen and two hydroxide ions. The molecular hydrogen bubbles off as hydrogen gas (after the solution near the cathode has become saturated with hydrogen) and the hydroxide ions stay in the solution. The *anode reaction* is

$$2H_2O \longrightarrow O_2 + 4H^+ + 4e^- \tag{6}$$

Four electrons enter the anode from two water molecules, which decompose to form an oxygen molecule and four hydrogen ions.

These electrode reactions, like other chemical reactions, may occur in steps; the description given in the preceding sentence of the course of the anode reaction is not to be interpreted as giving the necessary sequence of events.

The *over-all reaction* is obtained by multiplying Equation 5 by 2 and adding Equation 6:

$$6H_2O \xrightarrow{\text{electr.}} \underset{\text{Cathode}}{2H_2} + \underset{\text{Anode}}{O_2} + \underset{\text{Anode}}{4H^+} + \underset{\text{Cathode}}{4OH^-} \tag{7}$$

It is seen that in the electrolysis of the salt solution the solution around the anode becomes acidic, because of the production of hydrogen ions, and that around the cathode becomes basic, because of the production of hydroxide ions. This reaction could accordingly be used for the manufacture of acids such as hydrochloric acid and bases such as sodium hydroxide.

In the course of time, if the system were allowed to stand, the hydrogen ions produced near the anode and the hydroxide ions produced near the cathode would diffuse together and combine to form water:

$$H^+ + OH^- \longrightarrow H_2O$$

This reaction would, in particular, occur if the solution of electrolytes were to be stirred during the electrolysis. If this reaction of neutralization of hydrogen ion by hydroxide ion occurs completely, the over-all electrolysis reaction is

$$2H_2O \xrightarrow{\text{electr.}} \underset{\text{Cathode}}{2H_2} + \underset{\text{Anode}}{O_2} \tag{8}$$

In discussing the electrode reactions we have made little use of the fact that the electrolyte is sodium chloride. Indeed, *the electrode reactions are the same for almost all dilute aqueous electrolytic solutions*, and even for pure water as well. When electrodes are placed in pure water and an electric potential is applied, the electrode reactions shown in Equations 5 and 6 begin to take place. Very soon, however, a large enough concentration of hydroxide ions is built up near the cathode and of hydrogen ions near the anode to produce a back electric potential that tends to stop the reactions. Even in pure water there are a few ions (hydrogen ions and hydroxide ions); these ions move slowly toward the electrodes, and neutralize the ions (OH^- and H^+, respectively) formed by the electrode reactions. It is the smallness of the current which the very few ions that are present in pure water can carry through the region between the electrodes that causes the electrolysis of pure water to proceed only very slowly.

Equations 5 and 6 show water molecules undergoing decomposition at the electrodes. These equations probably represent the usual molecular reactions in neutral salt solutions. However, in acidic solutions, in which there is a high concentration of hydrogen ions, the cathode reaction may well be simply the reaction

$$2H^+ + 2e^- \longrightarrow H_2$$

and in basic solutions, in which there is a high concentration of hydroxide ions, the anode reaction may be

$$4OH^- \longrightarrow O_2 + 2H_2O + 4e^-$$

The ions in an electrolytic solution can carry a larger current between the electrodes than can the very few ions in pure water. In a sodium chloride solution undergoing electrolysis, sodium ions move to the cathode region, where their positive electric charges compensate the negative charges of the hydroxide ions that have been formed by the cathode reaction. Similarly, the chloride ions that move toward the anode compensate electrically the hydrogen ions that have been formed by the acid reaction.

Production of hydroxide ions at the cathode and of hydrogen ions at the anode during the electrolysis can be demonstrated by means of litmus or a similar indicator (see Section 8-9).

The electrolysis of dilute aqueous solutions of other electrolytes is closely similar to that of sodium chloride, producing hydrogen and oxygen gases at the electrodes. Concentrated electrolytic solutions may behave differently; concentrated brine (sodium chloride solution) on electrolysis produces chlorine at the anode, as well as oxygen. We may understand this fact by remembering that in concentrated brine there are a great many chloride ions near the anode, and some of these give up electrons to the anode, and form chlorine molecules.

8-7. Faraday's Laws of Electrolysis

In 1832 and 1833 Michael Faraday, a great English chemist and physicist, reported his discovery by experiment of the fundamental laws of electrolysis.

1. **The weight of a substance produced by a cathode or anode reaction in electrolysis is directly proportional to the quantity of electricity passed through the cell.**

2. **The weights of different substances produced by the same quantity of electricity are proportional to the equivalent weights of the substances.**

These laws are now known to be the result of the fact that electricity is composed of individual particles, the electrons. Quantity of electricity can be expressed as number of electrons. The *equivalent weight* mentioned in the second of Faraday's laws is the formula weight or atomic weight of the substance divided by the number of electrons occurring with one formula of the substance in the electrode reaction. For example, in the electrolysis of a solution containing cupric ion, copper is deposited at the cathode; the electrode reaction is

$$Cu^{++} + 2e^- \longrightarrow Cu$$

Since two electrons occur in this equation with one formula Cu, the equivalent weight of copper for this reaction is the atomic weight divided by 2.

The magnitude of the charge of one mole of electrons (Avogadro's number of electrons) *is 96,500 coulombs of electricity*. This is called a *faraday*.

1 faraday = 96,500 coulombs = 96,500 ampere seconds.

Note that the charge of an electron (Chapter 3) is -1.602×10^{-19} coulombs, as determined by the Millikan oil-drop experiment and other methods. Avogadro's number is 0.6022×10^{24}. The product of these numbers is $-96,500$ coulombs of electricity. This is accordingly the electric charge, the quantity of electricity, of Avogadro's number of electrons, 1 mole of electrons. It is customary to define the faraday as this quantity of positive electricity, rather than of negative electricity.[*]

It is not difficult to make calculations involving weights of chemical substances and the amount of electricity passing through an electrolytic cell, if you keep clearly in mind what the relation between the number of atoms and the number of electrons is. You must remember that the *current* of electricity, measured in amperes, is the quantity of electricity that flows through the cell in unit time. To find the *amount* of electricity, the current must be multiplied by the *time* measured in seconds. *One ampere flowing for one second is the quantity 1 coulomb of electricity.*

The quantitative treatment of electrochemical reactions is made in the same way as the calculation of weight relations in ordinary chemical reactions, with use of the faraday to represent one mole of electrons.

It will be noted by the student that the voltage at which the cell operates does not affect the weights of different substances reacting in the cell. The weights of substances involved in electrode reactions are determined solely by the quantity of electricity that passes through the cell. If the voltage applied to the cell is too low, current will not flow through the cell; but if the

---

[*] The value of the faraday may be determined by measuring the amount of electricity needed to deposit one gram-atom of silver from a solution containing silver ion, Ag^+. After Millikan had determined the value of the charge of the electron by his oil-drop experiment, he calculated the value of Avogadro's number by dividing this value into the faraday.

voltage is large enough to produce a current through the cell, the amount of reaction produced in a given time is determined only by the current, and not by the voltage.*

Example 1.   For how long a time would a current of 20 amperes have to be passed through a cell containing fused sodium chloride to produce 23 g of metallic sodium at the cathode? How much chlorine would be produced at the anode?

Solution.   The cathode reaction is

$$Na^+ + e^- \longrightarrow Na$$

Hence 1 mole of electrons passing through the cell would produce 1 mole of sodium atoms. One mole of electrons is 1 faraday, and 1 mole of sodium atoms is a gram-atom of sodium, 23.00 g. Hence the amount of electricity required is 96,500 coulombs, 1 faraday. One coulomb is 1 ampere second. Hence 96,500 coulombs of electricity passes through the cell if 1 ampere flows for 96,500 sec, or 20 amperes for $96,500/20 =$ **4825 sec,** or 1 hour 20 min 25 sec.

The anode reaction is

$$2Cl^- \longrightarrow Cl_2 + 2e^-$$

To produce 1 mole of molecular chlorine, Cl_2, 2 faradays must pass through the cell. One faraday would hence produce 1 gram-atom of chlorine, which is **35.46 g.**

Example 2.   Two cells are set up in series, and a current is passed through them. (Cells are said to be set up in series when all of the electrons that flow along the wire from the generator or battery must pass first through the first cell, from the negative electrode to the positive electrode, and then through the second cell, from its negative electrode to the positive electrode, and so on.) Cell A contains an aqueous solution of silver sulfate, Ag_2SO_4, which forms silver ions, Ag^+, and sulfate ions, SO_4^{--}, in the solution. This cell has platinum electrodes, which are unreactive. Cell B contains a copper sulfate solution, $CuSO_4$, and has copper electrodes. The current is passed through until 1.600 g of oxygen has been liberated at the anode of cell A. What has occurred at the other electrodes? (See Figure 8-8.)

Solution.   At the anode of cell A the reaction is

$$2H_2O \longrightarrow O_2 + 4H^+ + 4e^-$$

Hence 4 faradays of electricity would liberate 32 g of oxygen. The amount of oxygen liberated, 1.600 g, is seen to be $\frac{1}{20}$ of 32 g; accordingly the amount of electricity that passed through the cell is $\frac{1}{20}$ of 4 faradays or

* It is assumed in making this statement that the nature of the chemical reaction that takes place in the cell is not changed by a change in the voltage.

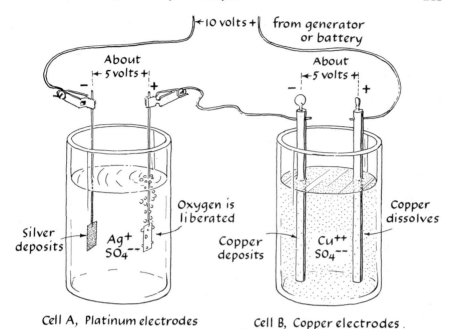

Cell A, Platinum electrodes   Cell B, Copper electrodes.

Figure 8-8

Two electrolytic cells in series.

0.2 faradays. This amount of electricity must have taken part in the electrode reaction at each of the other three electrodes.

Let us now consider the reaction at the cathode of cell A. At this electrode metallic silver is deposited. The cathode reaction is accordingly

$$Ag^+ + e^- \longrightarrow Ag$$

One gram-atom of silver, 107.880 g, would be deposited by 1 faraday, and the passage of 0.200 faraday through the cell would accordingly deposit $0.2 \times 107,880 =$ **21.576 g** of silver on the platinum cathode.

At the cathode in cell B the reaction is

$$Cu^{++} + 2e^- \longrightarrow Cu$$

One gram-atom of copper, 63.57 g, would be deposited on the cathode by 2 faradays of electricity, and **6.357 g** by 0.200 faraday.

At the anode of this cell copper dissolves from the copper electrode, to form Cu^{++} ions in solution. The same number of electrons flows through the anode as through the cathode. Hence the same amount of copper, **6.357 g**, is dissolved from the anode as is deposited on the cathode. The anode reaction is

$$Cu \longrightarrow Cu^{++} + 2e^-$$

It may be mentioned that the total voltage difference supplied by the generator or battery (shown in the figure as 10 volts) is divided between the two cells coupled in series. The division need not be equal, as indicated, but is determined by the properties of the two cells.

| Illustrative Exercise | 8-9. How many grams of magnesium and how many grams of chlorine would be liberated by passing one faraday of electricity through molten magnesium chloride, $MgCl_2$? |

8-8. Electrolytic Production of Elements

Many metals and some nonmetals are made by electrolytic methods. Hydrogen and oxygen are produced by the electrolysis of water containing an electrolyte. The alkali metals, alkaline-earth metals, magnesium, aluminum, and many other metals are manufactured either entirely or for special uses by electrochemical reduction of their compounds.

The Production of Sodium and Chlorine.   Many electrochemical processes depend for their success on ingenious devices for securing the purity of the product. As an illustration we may consider a cell used for making metallic sodium and elementary chlorine from sodium chloride.

The molten sodium chloride (usually with some sodium carbonate added to reduce its melting point) is in a vessel containing a carbon anode and iron cathode, separated by an iron screen which leads to pipes, as indicated in Figure 8-9. The gaseous chlorine is led off through one pipe, and the molten sodium, which is lighter than the electrolyte, rises and is drawn off into a storage tank.

Only about 8% of the chlorine used in the United States is produced in this way. Most of it is produced in connection with the production of sodium hydroxide and hydrogen by electrolysis of brine.

The Cost of Electrochemical Processes.   Faraday's laws do not tell us enough to determine the cost of the electric energy required to carry out an electrochemical process. The cost of electricity is determined by the electric energy used, the energy being the product of the quantity of electricity, in coulombs, and the potential difference, in volts. The unit of electric energy is the watt second (1 watt sec = 1 coulomb volt = 1 ampere volt second), or, more customarily, the kilowatt hour. Calculations such as those given in Examples 1 and 2 determine the quantity of electricity required to produce a given amount of substance electrolytically, but not the voltage at which it must be supplied. The principles determining the voltage that a cell provides or needs for its operation are more complicated; a brief description of them is given in Chapter 18.

In any commercial process a considerable fraction of the required voltage

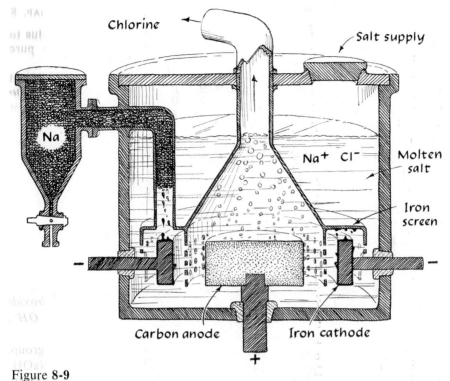

Figure 8-9

A cell used for making sodium and chlorine by electrolysis of fused sodium chloride.

is that needed to overcome the electric resistance of the electrolyte in the cell. The corresponding energy is converted into heat, and sometimes serves to keep the electrolyte molten. If the operating voltage of a cell is known, and the cost of electric power, per kilowatt hour (kwh), is known, a calculation of the electric cost can be made. In some industrial processes, such as the production of aluminum, the cost of electricity is such a large factor in the total cost of operation that the industrial plants are located near the sources of hydroelectric power. It is for this reason that important electrochemical industrial plants have been built near Niagara Falls and in the Pacific Northwest.

8-9. Acids, Bases, and Salts

The Nature of Acids and Bases. The alchemists observed that many different substances when dissolved in water give solutions with certain properties in common, such as acidic taste and the property of reacting with metals such as zinc with liberation of hydrogen. These substances were classed as *acids.* It is now known that the acidic properties of the solutions are due to the presence of *hydrogen ion,* H^+, in concentration greater than in pure water.

The usage of the word acid is variable. For many purposes it is convenient to say that *an acid is a hydrogen-containing substance that dissociates on solution in water to produce hydrogen ion.*

Examples of acids are

Hydrochloric acid, HCl (hydrogen chloride)
Hydrobromic acid, HBr (hydrogen bromide)
Hydrosulfuric acid, H_2S (hydrogen sulfide)
Sulfuric acid, H_2SO_4
Sulfurous acid, H_2SO_3
Phosphoric acid, H_3PO_4
Nitric acid, HNO_3
Perchloric acid, $HClO_4$
Chloric acid, $HClO_3$
Carbonic acid, H_2CO_3

A base is a substance containing the hydroxide ion, OH^-, or the hydroxide group, OH, that can dissociate in aqueous solution as the hydroxide ion, OH^-. Basic solutions have a characteristic brackish taste.

Hydroxides of metals are compounds of metals with the hydroxide group, OH. The hydroxides of the metals are bases. The hydroxides LiOH, NaOH, KOH, RbOH, and CsOH are called *alkalies;* and the hydroxides $Be(OH)_2$, $Mg(OH)_2$, $Ca(OH)_2$, $Sr(OH)_2$, and $Ba(OH)_2$ are called *alkaline earths.* A basic solution is also called an *alkaline solution.*

Acids and bases react to form compounds that are called *salts.* Thus the reaction of sodium hydroxide and hydrochloric acid produces the salt sodium chloride, NaCl, and water:

$$NaOH + HCl \longrightarrow NaCl + H_2O$$

Similarly, the reaction of calcium hydroxide and phosphoric acid produces water and calcium phosphate, $Ca_3(PO_4)_2$:

$$3Ca(OH)_2 + 2H_3PO_4 \longrightarrow Ca_3(PO_4)_2 + 6H_2O$$

Hydrogen Ion (Hydronium Ion) and Hydroxide Ion. The hydrogen ion, H^+, has a very simple structure: it consists of a bare proton, without the electron that is attached to it in a hydrogen atom. The hydrogen ion has a positive electric charge of one unit. The bare proton, H^+, does not exist in appreciable concentration in aqueous solutions, but instead exists attached to a water molecule, forming the *hydronium ion,* H_3O^+. The structure of the hydronium ion will be discussed in the following chapter.

Because of the additional complexity introduced into chemical equations by use of H_3O^+ in place of H^+, it is customary for the sake of convenience to write equations for reactions of acids in aqueous solution with use of the symbol H$^+$. It is to be understood that this is a shorthand device, and that the molecular species present is the hydronium ion, H$_3$O$^+$.

The hydroxide ion, which is present in basic solutions, carries a negative charge: its formula is OH$^-$.

Indicators. Acids and bases have the property of causing many organic substances to change in color. Thus if lemon juice is added to a cup of tea, the tea becomes lighter in color; a dark brown substance in the tea is converted into a light yellow substance. That this change is reversible may be shown by adding an alkaline substance, such as common baking soda (sodium hydrogen carbonate, NaHCO$_3$) to the tea; this will restore the original dark color. A substance that has this property of changing color when acid or base is added to it is called an *indicator*.

A very common indicator is *litmus*, a dye obtained from certain lichens. Litmus assumes a red color in acidic solution and a blue color in basic solution. A useful way of testing the acidity or basicity of a solution is by use of paper in which litmus has been absorbed, called *litmus paper*. A solution that gives litmus paper a color intermediate between blue and red is called a *neutral solution*. Such a solution contains hydrogen ions and hydroxide ions in equal (extremely small) concentrations.

Nomenclature of Acids, Bases, and Salts. Acids with 1, 2, and 3 replaceable hydrogen atoms are called *monoprotic*, *diprotic*, and *triprotic acids*, respectively, and bases with 1, 2, and 3 replaceable hydroxide groups are called *monohydroxic*, *dihydroxic*, and *trihydroxic bases*. For example, HCl is a monoprotic acid, H$_2$SO$_4$ a diprotic acid, and H$_3$PO$_4$ a triprotic acid. NaOH is a monohydroxic base, and Ca(OH)$_2$ a dihydroxic base.

Salts such as Na$_2$SO$_4$, which result from complete neutralization of an acid by a base, are called *normal salts;* those containing more acid are called *acid salts*.

The ways of naming salts are illustrated by the following examples:

Na$_2$SO$_4$: sodium sulfate, normal sodium sulfate
NaHSO$_4$: sodium hydrogen sulfate; sodium acid sulfate
Na$_3$PO$_4$: normal sodium phosphate; trisodium phosphate
Na$_2$HPO$_4$: disodium monohydrogen phosphate; sodium monohydrogen phosphate
NaH$_2$PO$_4$: sodium dihydrogen phosphate

There are three kinds of names given in the list of acids at the beginning of this section. A name of one kind, illustrated by hydrochloric acid, has the prefix *hydro* and the suffix *ic* attached to the name of the element characteristic of the acid. The molecules of acids with names of this kind do not contain oxygen. The salts are named by omitting the prefix *hydro*, and replacing the suffix *ic* by the suffix *ide*. Thus the sodium salt of hydrochloric acid is sodium chloride.

The names of some other acids, such as sulfuric acid, have the same suffix, *ic*, but no prefix. The molecules of these acids contain oxygen atoms. The salts are named simply by changing the suffix to *ate*. Thus the normal sodium salt of sulfuric acid is sodium sulfate.

Sulfurous acid is a representative of another class of acids, the names of which have the suffix *ous*. In general these acids have fewer oxygen atoms in the molecule than the corresponding *ic* acids. The salts are named by changing the suffix *ous* to *ite*. Thus the normal sodium salt of sulfurous acid is sodium sulfite.

A few acids have names that do not fit into this classification, but they are not very important.

Acidic Oxides and Basic Oxides.   An oxide such as sulfur trioxide, SO_3, or diphosphorus pentoxide, P_2O_5, which does not contain hydrogen but which with water forms an acid, is called an *acidic oxide* or *acid anhydride*. The equations for the reactions of formation of the corresponding acids from these oxides are the following:

$$SO_3 + H_2O \longrightarrow H_2SO_4$$
$$P_2O_5 + 3H_2O \longrightarrow 2H_3PO_4$$

The oxides of most of the nonmetallic elements are acidic oxides.

An oxide that with water forms a base is called a *basic oxide*. The oxides of the metals are basic oxides (even though some of them are very little affected by water). Thus sodium oxide, Na_2O, reacts with water to form a base, sodium hydroxide:

$$Na_2O + H_2O \longrightarrow 2NaOH$$

Acidic oxides and basic oxides may combine directly with one another to form salts:

$$Na_2O + SO_3 \longrightarrow Na_2SO_4$$
$$3CaO + P_2O_5 \longrightarrow Ca_3(PO_4)_2$$

Illustrative Exercises

8-10.   Write the equation for the reaction of sodium hydroxide and perchloric acid to form sodium perchlorate.

8-11.   Write equations for three reactions of potassium hydroxide and phosphoric acid to form three potassium salts of phosphoric acid, representing replacement of 1, 2, and 3 atoms of hydrogen by atoms of potassium. Write names for the three salts.

8-12.   What is the formula of normal calcium sulfide?

8-13.   Nitrous acid has the formula HNO_2. Write an equation for the reaction of formation of its sodium salt. What is the name of this salt?

8-14.   Dichlorine heptoxide, Cl_2O_7, is the anhydride of perchloric acid. Write the equation for the reaction of the heptoxide with water to form the acid.

8-15.   What is the anhydride of carbonic acid, H_2CO_3?

8-10. The Proton Theory of Acids and Bases

In the preceding section an acid has been defined as a hydrogen-containing substance that in water dissociates to produce a hydrogen ion (a proton), and a base as a substance containing the hydroxide group that in water dissociates to produce the hydroxide ion, OH^-. A somewhat more general pair of definitions was proposed in 1923 by the Danish chemist J. N. Brønsted and the English chemist T. M. Lowry. This theory, called the *Brønsted-Lowry theory* or the *proton theory* of acids and bases, states that *an acid is any molecule or ion that can give up a proton* (serve as a *proton donor*) and *a base is any molecule or ion that can take up a proton* (serve as a *proton acceptor*).

Thus the ammonium ion is called an acid, since it can give up a proton:

$$NH_4^+ \longrightarrow NH_3 + H^+$$

and ammonia is called a base, since it can take up a proton:

$$NH_3 + H^+ \longrightarrow NH_4^+$$

Ammonium ion and ammonia, which differ only in the presence or absence of a proton, are called a *conjugate acid-base pair*.

Ammonia can also act as an acid. The substance potassium amide, KNH_2, dissociates when dissolved in liquid ammonia, forming potassium ion, K^+, and amide ion, NH_2^-. The amide ion is the conjugate base to ammonia:

$$NH_3 \longrightarrow H^+ + NH_2^-$$

A substance, such as ammonia, that can either lose or gain a proton is said to be *amphiprotic* (from Greek *ampho*, both). With a base stronger than itself it acts as an acid and with a stronger acid it acts as a base.

Water is also amphiprotic:

$$H_2O \longrightarrow H^+ + OH^-$$
$$H_2O + H^+ \longrightarrow H_3O^+$$

The reaction between an acid and a base leads to the formation of the conjugate base and the conjugate acid. Thus hydrogen chloride, the acid for which chloride ion, Cl^-, is the conjugate base, reacts with water to produce its conjugate acid H_3O^+:

$$HCl + H_2O \longrightarrow Cl^- + H_3O^+$$

The use of the proton theory of acids and bases will be illustrated in later chapters of this book, especially Chapter 19.

Illustrative Exercises

8-16. What is the conjugate base of hydrobromic acid, HBr? Of perchloric acid, $HClO_4$?

8-17. What is the conjugate acid of water? Of hydroxide ion? iodide ion, I^-? Of sulfate ion, SO_4^{--}? Of hydrogen sulfate ion, HSO_4^-?

8-18. The hydrogen carbonate ion, HCO_3^-, is amphiprotic. What is its conjugate acid? What is its conjugate base?

8-19. Phosphoric acid, H_3PO_4, is a triprotic acid. What is the acid conjugate to the base HPO_4^{--}? What is the base conjugate to the acid HPO_4^{--}?

8-20. The base OH^- has a greater affinity for protons than any of the bases $H_2PO_4^-$, HPO_4^{--}, or PO_4^{---}. Write equations for the three reactions of OH^- with the acids conjugate to these three bases. Also write equations for three successive reactions of H_3PO_4 with NaOH. Compare the two sets of reactions on the assumption that NaOH consists of Na^+ ions and OH^- ions.

8-11.   The Ionization of Acids, Bases, and Salts

Most salts, like sodium chloride, dissolve in water to form solutions with large electric conductivity. The conductivity of the solutions is so large as to show that the *salts are completely ionized* in aqueous solution. For example, the substance sodium sulfate, Na_2SO_4, dissolves in water to form a solution containing sodium ions, Na^+, and sulfate ions, SO_4^{--}.

Some acids and bases are also completely ionized in aqueous solution. For example, a dilute solution of hydrogen chloride, HCl, in water, contains hydrogen ion, H^+, and chloride ion, Cl^-, and only a few undissociated hydrogen chloride molecules, HCl. Similarly, a solution of sodium hydroxide, NaOH, contains the sodium ion, Na^+, and the hydroxide ion, OH^-.

Some acids and bases, and also a few salts, are, however, only partially ionized in solution. For example, acetic acid when dissolved in water produces a solution containing rather small amounts of hydrogen ion, H^+, and acetate ion, $C_2H_3O_2^-$, and a large amount of undissociated molecules of acetic acid, $HC_2H_3O_2$. The acids and bases that are completely ionized in aqueous solution are called *strong acids* and *strong bases*. Those that are only partially ionized are called *weak acids* and *weak bases*.

An example of a salt that is only partially ionized in aqueous solution is mercuric chloride, $HgCl_2$. A solution of mercuric chloride contains the molecular species* $HgCl_2$, $HgCl^+$, Hg^{++}, and Cl^-, all in appreciable concentrations. This substance is exceptional—most salts are completely ionized.

Acids, bases, and salts that are completely ionized are called *strong electrolytes*; those that are only partially ionized are called *weak electrolytes*. The difference between a solution of a strong electrolyte and a solution of a weak electrolyte is illustrated in Figure 8-10.

Writing Equations for Ionic Reactions.   In writing an equation for a chemical reaction between strong electrolytes in solution, *ions* should usually be

* It is customary to use the term "molecular species" to refer to ions as well as neutral molecules.

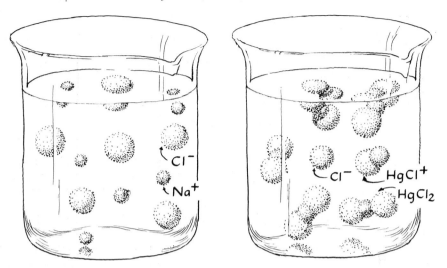

Figure **8-10**

A solution of a completely dissociated salt (at the left) and of a partially dissociated salt (at the right).

written as reactants and products.* Thus the precipitation of silver chloride on the addition of a solution of hydrochloric acid to a solution of silver nitrate should be written

$$Ag^+ + Cl^- \longrightarrow AgCl(c)$$

and not

$$AgNO_3 + HCl \longrightarrow AgCl(c) + HNO_3$$

Silver nitrate, hydrochloric acid, and nitric acid are all strong electrolytes, and their solutions consist nearly entirely of the dissociated ions. The ionic equation written above accordingly represents the actual reaction that takes place in the beaker, which is simply the combination of silver ion and chloride ion to form the product, silver chloride. It is true that nitrate ion was present in solution with the silver ion, and that hydrogen ion was present with the chloride ion; but these ions remain in essentially their original state after the reaction has occurred, and there is hence usually no reason to indicate them in the equation.

The same equation,

$$Ag^+ + Cl^- \longrightarrow AgCl(c)$$

is, moreover, applicable also to the precipitation of, say, silver perchlorate solution (containing Ag^+ and ClO_4^-) by sodium chloride solution (containing Na^+ and Cl^-).

* Sometimes the use of molecular formulas in equations is advantageous, in that it shows what reagents are to be used in an experiment.

A good rule to follow is *to write the chemical equation to correspond as closely as possible to the actual reaction, showing the molecules or ions that actually react and are formed.*

In accordance with this rule, either the ions or the molecules might be shown for reactions involving weak electrolytes. If a substance is not ionized at all, the formula for its molecules should be used in the equation.

EXERCISES

8-21. (a) Hydrochloric acid, HCl, is a strong acid. What molecular species are present in a dilute aqueous solution of this acid? (b) Sodium hydroxide, NaOH, is a strong base. What molecular species are present in its solution? (c) Write an equation for the reaction that occurs when these two solutions are mixed.

8-22. When a solution of silver nitrate, containing the ions Ag^+ and NO_3^- (nitrate ion), is added to a solution of sodium chloride, a white precipitate of the insoluble substance silver chloride, AgCl, is formed. (a) Write the equation for this reaction. (b) What molecular species remain in the solution?

8-23. Assuming that their atoms can lose enough electrons to reach the electronic structure of neon, what would be the charges on the positive ions with this structure of the elements sodium to chlorine inclusive? Write the formulas of the corresponding oxides of these elements.

8-24. Assign values of the ionic charge to the elements in the following compounds, by writing the corresponding number of plus signs or minus signs as a superscript to the symbol for the element:

LiF	LiI	Na_2O
$CaCl_2$	$MgCl_2$	$FeCl_2$
B_2O_3	KBr	Na_2S
$FeCl_3$	CaH_2	HCl
TiO_2	BaO	SiF_4
$RaCl_2$	CaS	LiH

By reference to the periodic table, find which ions in these compounds do not have a noble-gas structure, and underline them in the formulas.

8-25. What forces hold a sodium chloride crystal together? Compare the bond between the sodium ion and the chloride ion in the crystal with that in the gas molecule.

8-26. Magnesium oxide and sodium fluoride have the same crystal structure as sodium chloride (shown in Figure 4-2). Magnesium oxide is very much harder than sodium fluoride. Can you explain why the two substances differ so much in hardness? Can you also explain why the melting point of magnesium oxide (2800°C) is much higher than that of sodium fluoride (992°C)? Note that the ions in the two substances have the same electronic structure.

8-27. How is electric current conducted along a metallic wire? How is the current conducted from an inert cathode, such as the carbon cathode, through molten sodium chloride? From molten sodium chloride into an inert anode?

8-28. Why does molten sodium chloride conduct a current much better than solid sodium chloride?

8-29. What substance would be formed at each electrode on electrolysis of molten lithium hydride, Li^+H^-, with inert electrodes? What is the electronic structure of the H^- ion?

8-30. Outline the complete mechanism of conduction of electricity between inert electrodes in a dilute solution of potassium sulfate.

8-31. Write equations for the anode reaction, the cathode reaction, and the over-all reaction for electrolysis of the following systems, with inert electrodes:

(a) Molten sodium bromide.

(b) Molten potassium oxide.

(c) Dilute aqueous solution of sodium hydroxide.

(d) Dilute aqueous solution of hydrochloric acid.

(e) Molten silver bromide, Ag^+Br^-.

(f) Dilute solution of silver nitrate, $AgNO_3$ (metallic silver deposits on the cathode).

8-32. How much copper would be deposited from a solution of copper sulfate, $CuSO_4$, by a current of 1 ampere in the time 1 hour? (Answer: 1.18 g.)

8-33. Sodium metal is sometimes made commercially by the electrolysis of fused sodium hydroxide, NaOH.

(a) Write equations for the anode and cathode reactions and the over-all reaction.

(b) Calculate the weight of sodium formed per hour in a cell through which 2000 amperes is flowing.

8-34. A current operating for a period of 5 hours deposited 0.800 g of silver. Calculate the average current in amperes. (Answer: 0.0398.)

8-35. The annual production of chlorine in the United States (1962) is approximately 3,500,000 tons. Assuming no loss, how many faradays of electricity and how many tons of sodium chloride would be required to produce this much chlorine by electrolysis? If the cells are operated at 2.4 volts, what fraction of the total hydroelectric power of the country, about 100,000,000 kilowatts, would be required to produce the chlorine?

8-36. Write the equation for the reaction of citric acid, $H_3C_6H_5O_7$ (the acid present in citrus fruits), and potassium hydroxide to form water and potassium citrate, $K_3C_6H_5O_7$. Is citric acid a monoprotic acid, a diprotic acid, or a triprotic acid?

8-37. Write equations for the neutralization of ammonium hydroxide, NH_4OH, with hydrochloric acid, sulfuric acid, and nitric acid.

8-38. Write the equation for the neutraliza-tion of acetic acid, $HC_2H_3O_2$, by sodium hydroxide. Write the equation for the neutralization of this acid by calcium hydroxide.

8-39. Write equations to represent the formation from sodium hydroxide and phosphoric acid of normal sodium phosphate, disodium monohydrogen phosphate, and sodium dihydrogen phosphate.

8-40. What relative amounts of sodium hydroxide would be required for the three reactions of Exercise 8-39, with the same amount of phosphoric acid?

8-41. What are the acid anhydrides of nitric acid, sulfuric acid, and phosphoric acid? Write the equation for the reaction of the anhydride of nitric acid with water to form the acid.

8-42. When sulfur is burned in air it forms the gas sulfur dioxide, SO_2. What is the formula of the acid of which this gas is the anhydride?

8-43. How long would it take to prepare 30 liters of hydrogen, measured over water at 720 mm Hg pressure and 20°C, by electrolysis of a dilute sodium chloride solution, with current 5 amperes?

8-44. The following reactions occur:

$$HCl + H_2O \longrightarrow H_3O^+ + Cl^-$$
$$NH_3 + H_2O \longrightarrow NH_4^+ + OH^-$$

Using the proton theory of acids and bases, what would you expect to happen when HCl is dissolved in liquid ammonia?

8-45. (a) In 1912 R. A. Millikan reported -1.59×10^{-19} coulombs as the value of the charge of the electron. Show, with use of the value of the faraday (96,500 coulombs per mole), that this value leads to 0.607×10^{24} for Avogadro's number.

(b) With use of this value of Avogadro's number and the density 2.16 g/cm^3 of sodium chloride, verify the statement made in Example 3 of Section 2-10 that the corresponding value of the spacing d_1 of the NaCl crystal is 2.81 Å.

CHAPTER 9

Covalence and Electronic Structure

In the preceding chapter we have discussed chemical compounds that contain *ions*, and that owe their stability to the tendency of certain atoms to lose electrons and of others to gain them. When these ionic substances are melted or are dissolved in water the ions become able to move about independently in the molten substance or solution, which for this reason is a conductor of electricity.

There are many other substances, however, that do not have these properties. These nonionic substances are so numerous that it is not necessary to search for examples—nearly every substance except the salts is in this class. Thus molten sulfur, like solid sulfur, is an electric insulator; it does not conduct electricity. Liquid air (liquid oxygen, liquid nitrogen), bromine, gasoline, carbon tetrachloride, and many other liquid substances are insulators. Gases, too, are insulators, and do not contain ions, unless they have been ionized by an electric discharge or in some similar way.

These nonionic substances consist of *molecules* made of atoms that are bonded tightly together. Thus the pale straw-colored liquid that is obtained by melting sulfur contains S_8 molecules, each molecule being built of eight sulfur atoms; liquid air contains the stable diatomic molecules O_2 and N_2, bromine the molecules Br_2, carbon tetrachloride the molecules CCl_4, and so on.

9-1. The Nature of Covalence

The atoms of these molecules are held tightly together by a very important sort of bond, the *shared-electron-pair bond* or *covalent bond*. This bond is so important, so nearly universally present in substances that Professor Gilbert Newton Lewis of the University of California (1875–1946), who discovered its electronic structure, called it *the* chemical bond.

It is the covalent bond that is represented by a dash in the valence-bond

formulas, such as Br—Br and

$$Cl-\overset{\displaystyle Cl}{\underset{\displaystyle Cl}{|}}-Cl,$$

that have been written by chemists

for nearly a hundred years. We have described these formulas in Chapter 4.

Modern chemistry has been greatly simplified through the development of the theory of the covalent bond. It is now easier to understand and to remember chemical facts—by connecting them with our knowledge of the nature of the chemical bond and the electronic structure of molecules—than was possible fifty years ago. It is accordingly wise for the student of chemistry to study this chapter carefully, and to get a clear picture of the covalent bond.

9-2. Covalent Molecules

The Hydrogen Molecule. The simplest example of a covalent molecule is the hydrogen molecule, H_2. For this molecule the electronic structure H : H is written, indicating that the two electrons are shared between the two hydrogen atoms, forming the bond between them. This structure corresponds to the valence-bond structure H—H.

By the study of its spectrum and by calculations made on the basis of the theory of quantum mechanics, the hydrogen molecule has been shown to have the structure represented in Figure 9-1. The two nuclei are firmly held at a distance of about 0.74 Å apart—they oscillate relative to each other with

Figure **9-1**

The electron distribution in a hydrogen molecule. The two nuclei in the molecule are 0.74 Å apart.

an amplitude of a few hundredths of an Ångström at room temperature, and with a somewhat larger amplitude at higher temperatures. The two electrons move very rapidly about in the region of the two nuclei, their time-average distribution being indicated by the shading in the figure. It can be seen that the motion of the two electrons is largely concentrated into the small region between the two nuclei. (The nuclei are in the positions where the electron density is greatest.) *The two electrons held jointly by the two nuclei constitute the chemical bond between the two hydrogen atoms in the hydrogen molecule.*

We have seen in the consideration of ionic valence that there is a very strong tendency for atoms of the stronger metals and the nonmetals to achieve the electron number of an inert gas by losing or gaining one or more electrons. It was pointed out by Lewis that the same tendency is operating in the formation of molecules containing covalent bonds, and that the electrons in a covalent bond are to be counted for each of the bonded atoms.

Thus the hydrogen atom, with one electron, can achieve the helium structure by taking up another electron, to form the hydride anion, $H:^-$, as in the salt lithium hydride, Li^+H^-. But the hydrogen atom can also achieve the helium structure by sharing its electron with the electron of another hydrogen atom, to form a shared-electron-pair bond. Each of the two atoms thus contributes one electron to the shared electron pair. The shared electron pair is to be counted first for one hydrogen atom, and then for the other; if this is done, it is seen that in the hydrogen molecule each of the atoms has the helium structure:

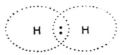

The Covalent Bond in Other Molecules. The covalent bond in other molecules is closely similar to that in the hydrogen molecule. For each covalent bond a pair of electrons is needed; also, two orbitals are needed, one of each atom.

The covalent bond consists of a pair of electrons shared between two atoms, and occupying two stable orbitals, one of each atom.

For example, reference to the energy-level diagram (Figure 7-7 or inside the back cover) shows that the carbon atom has four stable orbitals in its *L* shell, and four electrons that may be used in bond formation. Hence it may combine with four hydrogen atoms, each of which has one stable orbital (the 1s orbital) and one electron, forming four covalent bonds:

$$
\begin{array}{ccc}
& H & \\
& \overset{\cdot\cdot}{\underset{\cdot\cdot}{H:C:H}} & \qquad \text{equivalent to} \qquad
\begin{array}{c}
H \\
| \\
H-C-H \\
| \\
H
\end{array}
\\
& H &
\end{array}
$$

In this molecule each atom has achieved a noble-gas structure; the shared electron pairs are to be counted for each of the atoms sharing them. The carbon atom, with four shared pairs in the *L* shell and one unshared pair in the *K* shell, has achieved the neon structure, and each hydrogen atom has achieved the helium structure.

It has been found that the atoms of the principal groups of the periodic table (that is, all atoms except the transition elements) usually have a noble-gas structure in their stable compounds.

Stable molecules and complex ions usually have structures such that each atom has the electronic structure of a noble-gas atom, the shared electrons of each covalent bond being counted for each of the two atoms connected by the covalent bond.

The noble-gas atoms, except for helium, have eight electrons in the outermost shell, occupying four orbitals (one *s* orbital and three *p* orbitals). These eight electrons are called the *octet*. When an atom achieves a noble-gas structure, either by transferring electrons to or from other atoms or by sharing electron pairs with other atoms, it is said to *complete the octet*.

9-3. The Structure of Covalent Compounds

The electronic structure of molecules of covalent compounds involving the principal groups of the periodic table can usually be written by counting the number of valence electrons in the molecule and then distributing the valence electrons as unshared electron pairs and shared electron pairs in such a way that each atom achieves a noble-gas structure.

It is often necessary to have some experimental information about the way in which the atoms are bonded together. This is true especially of organic compounds. Thus there are two compounds with the composition C_2H_6O, ethyl alcohol and dimethyl ether. The chemical properties of these two substances show that one of them, ethyl alcohol, contains one hydrogen atom attached to an oxygen atom, whereas dimethyl ether does not contain such a hydroxyl group. The structures of these two isomeric molecules are shown in Figure 9-2.

Compounds of Hydrogen with Nonmetals. Let us consider first the structure expected for a compound between hydrogen and fluorine, the lightest element of the seventh group. Hydrogen has a single orbital and one electron. Accordingly, it could achieve the helium configuration by forming a single covalent bond with another element. Fluorine has seven electrons in its outer shell, the *L* shell. These seven electrons occupy the four orbitals of the *L* shell.

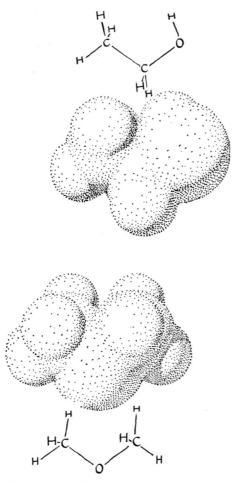

Figure **9-2** *The structures of the iso-meric molecules ethyl alcohol, C_2H_5OH, and dimethyl ether, $(CH_3)_2O$.*

They accordingly constitute three electron pairs in three of the orbitals and a single electron in the fourth orbital. Hence fluorine also can achieve a noble-gas configuration by forming a single covalent bond with use of its odd electron. We are thus led to the following structure for the hydrogen fluoride molecule:

$$H : \ddot{\underset{..}{F}} :$$

In this molecule, the hydrogen fluoride molecule, there is a single covalent bond that holds the hydrogen atom and the fluorine atom firmly together.

It is often convenient to represent this electronic structure by using a dash as a symbol for the covalent bond instead of the dots representing the shared electron pair. Sometimes, especially when the electronic structure of the molecule is under discussion, the unshared pairs in the outer shell of each atom are represented, but often they are omitted:

$$H{-}\ddot{\underset{..}{F}} : \qquad \text{or} \qquad H{-}F$$

The other halogens form similar compounds:

$$H{-}\ddot{\underset{..}{Cl}} : \qquad\qquad H{-}\ddot{\underset{..}{Br}} : \qquad\qquad H{-}\ddot{\underset{..}{I}} :$$

Hydrogen chloride   Hydrogen bromide   Hydrogen iodide

These substances are strong acids: when they are dissolved in water the proton leaves the molecule, and attaches itself to a water molecule to form a hydronium ion, H_3O^+, the halogen being left as a halogenide ion,

$$: \ddot{\underset{..}{Cl}} : ^- \qquad : \ddot{\underset{..}{Br}} : ^- \qquad \text{or} \qquad : \ddot{\underset{..}{I}} : ^-$$

Hydrogen fluoride is a weak acid.

Elements of the sixth group (oxygen, sulfur, selenium, tellurium) can achieve the noble-gas structure by forming two covalent bonds. Oxygen has six electrons in its outer shell. These can be distributed among the four orbitals by putting two unshared pairs in two of the orbitals and an odd electron in each of the other two orbitals. These two odd electrons can be used in forming covalent bonds with two hydrogen atoms, to give a water molecule, with the following electronic structure:

$$
\begin{array}{ccc}
\text{H} & & \text{H} \\
\ddots & & | \\
:\text{O}:\text{H} & \text{or} & :\text{O}-\text{H} \\
\ddots & & \ddots
\end{array}
$$

If a proton is removed, a hydroxide ion, OH^-, is formed:

$$
\left[\, : \ddot{\text{O}} - \text{H} \right]^{-}
$$

If a proton is added to a water molecule (attaching itself to one of the unshared electron pairs), a hydronium ion, OH_3^+, is formed:

$$
\left[
\begin{array}{c}
\text{H} \\
| \\
:\text{O}-\text{H} \\
| \\
\text{H}
\end{array}
\right]^{+}
$$

All three of the hydrogen atoms in the hydronium ion are held to the oxygen atom by the same kind of bond, a covalent bond.

In hydrogen peroxide, H_2O_2, each oxygen atom achieves the neon configuration by forming one covalent bond with the other oxygen atom and one covalent bond with a hydrogen atom:

$$
\begin{array}{cc}
\text{H} & \text{H} \\
| & | \\
:\text{O}-\text{O}: \\
\ddots & \ddots
\end{array}
$$

Hydrogen sulfide, hydrogen selenide, and hydrogen telluride have the same electronic structure as water:

$$
\begin{array}{ccc}
\text{H} & \text{H} & \text{H} \\
| & | & | \\
:\text{S}-\text{H} \quad & :\text{Se}-\text{H} \quad & :\text{Te}-\text{H} \\
\ddots & \ddots & \ddots
\end{array}
$$

Nitrogen and the other fifth-group elements, with five outer electrons, can achieve the noble-gas configuration by forming three covalent bonds. The structures of ammonia, phosphine, arsine, and stibine are the following:

$$
\begin{array}{cccc}
\text{H} & \text{H} & \text{H} & \text{H} \\
| & | & | & | \\
:\text{N}-\text{H} \quad & :\text{P}-\text{H} \quad & :\text{As}-\text{H} \quad & :\text{Sb}-\text{H} \\
| & | & | & | \\
\text{H} & \text{H} & \text{H} & \text{H}
\end{array}
$$

The ammonia molecule can attach a proton to itself, to form an ammonium ion, NH_4^+, in which all four hydrogen atoms are held to the nitrogen atom by covalent bonds:

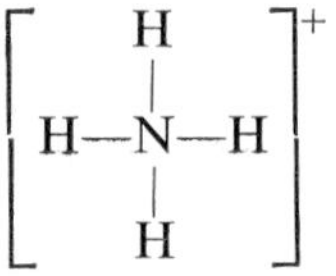

$$\left[\begin{array}{c} H \\ | \\ H-N-H \\ | \\ H \end{array} \right]^+$$

In the ammonium ion all four of the L orbitals are used in forming covalent bonds. The formation of the ammonium ion from ammonia is similar to the formation of the hydronium ion from water.

The Electronic Structure of Some Other Compounds.   Electronic structures of other molecules containing covalent bonds may be readily written, by keeping in mind the importance of completing the octets of atoms of non-metallic elements. The structures of some compounds of nonmetallic elements with one another are shown below:

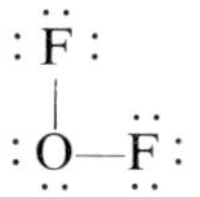

:F:
|
:O—F: Oxygen difluoride
··

:Cl:
|
:S—Cl: Sulfur dichloride
··

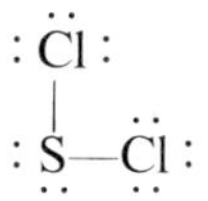

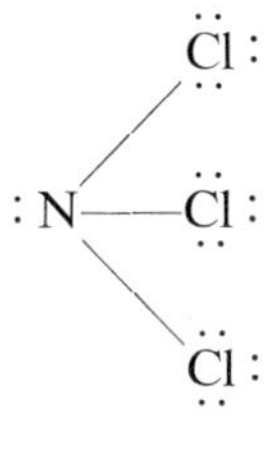

              Cl:
             /
:N————Cl: Nitrogen trichloride*
             \
              Cl:

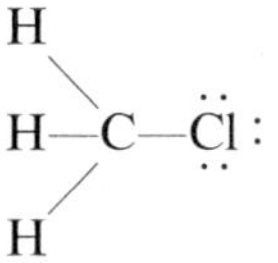

H
 \
H—C—Cl: Methyl chloride
 /
H

* Note that sometimes an effort is made in drawing the structure of a molecule to indicate the spatial configuration; the structure shown here for nitrogen trichloride is supposed to indicate that the molecule is pyramidal, with the chlorine atoms approximately at three corners of a tetrahedron about the nitrogen atom. The spatial configuration of molecules is discussed in the following section,

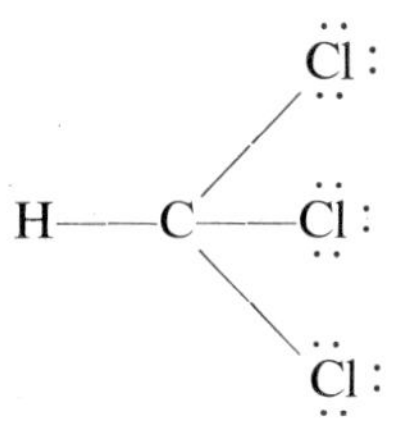

$$H\!-\!\overset{\displaystyle \nearrow \ddot{\ddot{C}}l:}{\underset{\displaystyle \searrow \ddot{\ddot{C}}l:}{C}\!-\!\ddot{C}l:} \qquad \text{Chloroform}$$

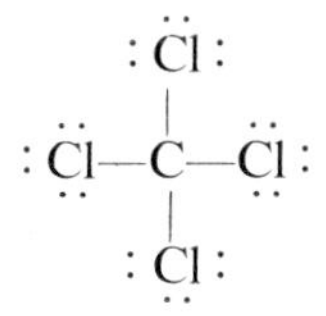

$$:\!\ddot{C}l\!-\!\overset{\displaystyle :\ddot{C}l:}{\underset{\displaystyle :\ddot{C}l:}{C}}\!-\!\ddot{C}l: \qquad \text{Carbon tetrachloride}$$

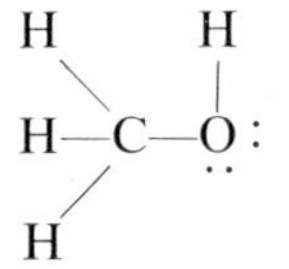

$$H\!-\!\overset{\displaystyle \overset{H}{\big|}}{\underset{\displaystyle H \nearrow}{C}}\!-\!\ddot{O}: \qquad \text{Methyl alcohol}$$

$$H\!-\!\overset{\displaystyle H}{\underset{\displaystyle H \nearrow}{C}}\!-\!\overset{\displaystyle \nearrow H}{\underset{\displaystyle \searrow H}{C}}\!-\!H \qquad \text{Ethane}$$

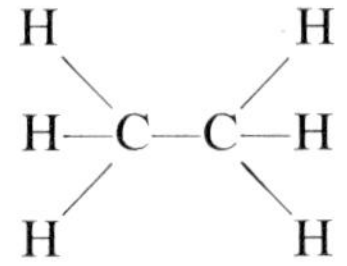

Illustrative Exercises

9-1. Silicon and hydrogen form the compound silane, SiH_4.
(a) What is its electronic structure?
(b) What orbitals of the silicon atom are used in forming the four covalent bonds?

9-2. Write electronic structures for silicon tetrachloride, $SiCl_4$, and phosphorus trichloride, PCl_3, showing all electron pairs in the outermost shell of each atom.

9-3. Write the electronic structure of ethyl chloride, C_2H_2Cl. What noble-gas structure does each atom achieve?

9-4. In the second paragraph of Section 9-3 it is said that there are two compounds with the composition C_2H_6O. Can you prove that there are only two ways of connecting these atoms together into one molecule and keeping carbon quadrivalent, oxygen bivalent, and hydrogen univalent?

9-4. The Direction of Valence Bonds in Space

In 1874 it was discovered that the four bonds formed by a carbon atom are directed in space toward the four corners of a tetrahedron. This discovery was made through the effort to explain the observed effects of some substances on polarized light, as described in the following paragraphs.

Optical Activity.   When a beam of ordinary light is passed through a crystal of calcite, it is split into two beams. Each of these beams is a beam of plane-polarized light; the vibrating electric field of the light lies in one plane for one of the beams and in the plane at right angles to it for the other beam.

A prism made of two pieces of calcite cut in a certain way and cemented together has the property of permitting only one beam to pass through; the other is reflected to the side and absorbed in the darkened side of the prism. Such a prism (called a Nicol prism) can be used to form a beam of plane-polarized light, and also to determine the orientation of the plane of polarization. In the instrument called the polarimeter, shown in Figure 9-3, the first prism defines the beam. If there is nothing between the two prisms to rotate the plane of polarization, the beam will pass through the second prism if it has the same orientation as the first, but will be absorbed if it is oriented at right angles to the first.

In 1811 the French physicist Dominique François Jean Arago (1786–1853) discovered that a quartz crystal has the power of rotating the plane of polarization of the beam of polarized light passing through it. Some quartz crystals were found to rotate the plane of polarization to the right (so that the second prism has to be turned clockwise, viewed in the direction opposite to the path of the light, in order that the beam pass through it), and others to the left.

Figure **9-3**

The polarimeter, an instrument used to determine the rotation of the plane of polarization of a beam of plane-polarized light by an optically active substance.

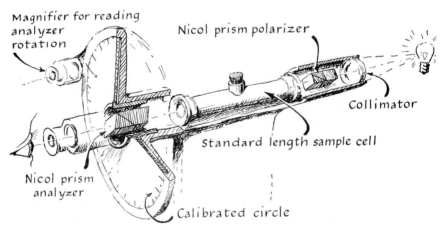

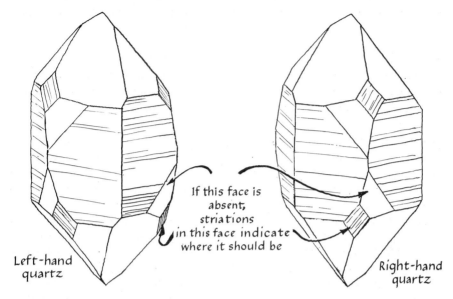

Figure **9-4**

Right-handed and left-handed quartz crystals.

These are called dextrorotatory crystals and levorotatory crystals, respectively.

The two kinds of quartz crystals also differ in their face development, as shown in Figure 9-4. They are mirror images of one another—one can be described as a right-handed crystal and one as a left-handed crystal.

Right-handed and Left-handed Molecules. The French physicist Jean Baptiste Biot (1774–1862) then found that some liquids are optically active (that is, have the power of rotating the plane of polarization). For example, turpentine was found to be levorotatory, and an aqueous solution of sucrose (cane sugar, $C_{12}H_{22}O_{11}$) was found to be dextrorotatory. The substances that were found to be optically active in solution were all organic compounds, produced by plants or animals.

A puzzling observation was then made. It was found that two kinds of tartaric acid were deposited from wine lees. These two kinds of tartaric acid are closely similar in their properties, but they show the astounding difference that one is dextrorotatory, and the other is completely without rotatory power. How could there be two molecules with the same composition but with such greatly different power of interacting with polarized light?

The answer to this puzzle was found in 1844 by the great French chemist Louis Pasteur (1822–1895). He added sodium hydroxide and ammonium

hydroxide to the solution of the optically inactive tartaric acid and allowed
the solution to evaporate, so that crystals of sodium ammonium tartrate,
$NaNH_4C_4H_4O_6$, were formed. On examining the crystals he first noticed that
they appeared to be identical with the crystals similarly made from the optically active tartaric acid. Then, as he continued to scrutinize them carefully,
he suddenly recognized that only half of them were truly identical; the others
were their mirror images (Figure 9-5). He separated the two kinds of crystals
by hand and dissolved them in water. One of the solutions was dextrorotatory
and the other levorotatory, with the same rotatory power, except for sign.

It was accordingly evident that the atoms in the tartaric acid molecule
arrange themselves in a structure that does not have a plane of symmetry or
a center of symmetry; hence there is a right-handed arrangement of atoms
and there also is a left-handed arrangement, the mirror image of the first.

In 1844 the possibility of discovering these arrangements (the three-dimensional structures of the molecules) was so small that neither Pasteur nor any
other chemist attacked the problem. But within fifteen years the correct
atomic weights were accepted and the correct formulas were assigned, the
concept of the chemical bond was developed, and the quadrivalence of carbon
was established. The term "chemical structure" was used for the first time
in 1861 by the Russian chemist Alexander M. Butlerov (1828–1886), who
wrote that it is essential to find the way in which each atom is linked to other
atoms in the molecules of substances.

A few more years passed. Many students of chemistry learned about the
quadrivalence of carbon, about structural formulas, and about right-handed
and left-handed molecules. Then two of them, the young Dutch chemist
Jacobus Hendricus van't Hoff (1852–1911) and the young French chemist

Figure **9-5**

Right-handed and left-handed crystals of sodium ammonium tartrate.

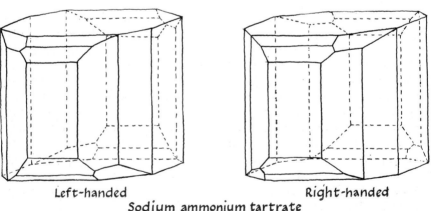

Left-handed   Right-handed
Sodium ammonium tartrate

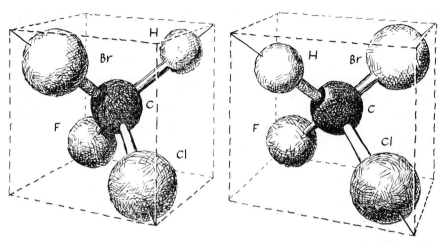

Figure **9-6**

Right-handed and left-handed molecules of fluorochlorobromomethane.

Jules Achille le Bel (1847–1930), saw in 1874 that *no* structure in which the atoms lie in a single plane can lead to optical activity. A planar molecule is its own mirror image, because the plane is itself a plane of symmetry for the molecule. For example, the substance fluorochlorobromomethane, CHFClBr, can be resolved into a dextrorotatory variety and a levorotatory variety. Hence it cannot be correctly represented by the planar formula

$$
\begin{array}{c}
\text{F} \\
| \\
\text{Cl}-\text{C}-\text{H} \\
| \\
\text{Br}
\end{array}
$$

The four bonds formed by the carbon atom in this molecule cannot lie in one plane, but instead must extend toward the corners of a tetrahedron. There must be two kinds of fluorochlorobromomethane molecules, identical except for handedness, each the exact mirror image of the other (Figure 9-6).

This was the birth of the tetrahedral carbon atom and of stereochemistry (the chemistry of three-dimensional space, structural chemistry). It led to the rapid development of chemical structure theory and of chemistry as a whole.

A pair of right-handed and left-handed molecules are called an *enantiomeric pair,* and the two substances they compose are called *enantiomers* (from the Greek *enantios,* opposite, and *meros,* part). The symbols D and L are used as prefixes to distinguish the two substances that constitute an enantiomeric pair.

A discussion of right-handed and left-handed molecules in living organisms is given in Chapter 28.

9-5. Fluorochloromethane, CH_2FCl, does not comprise an enantiomeric pair of substances; it is a single optically inactive substance. Explain this fact by making a drawing of the molecule and indicating its plane of symmetry.

9-6. Three substances correspond to the following formula:

$$\begin{array}{ccc} H & & H \\ \diagdown & & \diagup \\ F-C & - & C-F \\ \diagup & & \diagdown \\ Cl & & Cl \end{array}$$

Two of them constitute an enantiomeric pair and the third is optically inactive. Make a drawing of the three-dimensional structure of the molecule of the inactive substance.

9-5.   Tetrahedral Bond Orbitals

In a molecule such as methane (Figure 9-7) or carbon tetrachloride, in which the four bonds are equivalent, the bond angles have the value 109°28′. In an asymmetric molecule such as CHFClBr the angles differ somewhat from this value, but only by a few degrees. It has been found by experiment (x-ray diffraction, electron diffraction, microwave spectroscopy) that these angles usually lie between 106° and 113°, with the average value for the six bond angles close to 109°28′.

Each of the four bonds formed by the carbon atom involves one of the four orbitals of the L shell (Section 9-2). These orbitals are given in Chapter 7 as the $2s$ orbital and the three $2p$ orbitals. We might hence ask whether or not the bonds to the four hydrogen atoms are all alike. Would not the $2s$ electron form a bond of one kind, and the three $2p$ electrons form bonds of a different kind?

Figure **9-7** *The methane molecule,* CH_4.

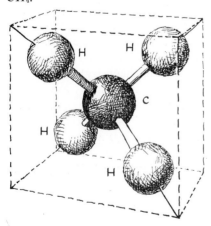

Chemists have made many experiments to answer this question, and have concluded that the four bonds of the carbon atom are alike. A theory of the tetrahedral carbon atom was developed in 1931. According to this theory, the *theory of hybrid bond orbitals*, the $2s$ orbital and the three $2p$ orbitals of the carbon atom are hybridized (combined) to form four *tetrahedral bond orbitals*. They are exactly equivalent to one another, and are directed toward the corners of a regular tetrahedron, as shown in Figure 9-8. Moreover, the nature of s and p

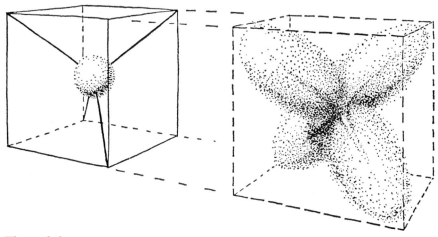

Figure **9-8**

> *Diagram illustrating (left) the 1s orbital in the K shell of the carbon atom, and (right) the four tetrahedral orbitals of the L shell.*

orbitals and their hybrids is such that of all possible hybrid orbitals of s and p the tetrahedral orbitals are the best suited for forming strong bonds. Accordingly the tetrahedral arrangement of the bonds is the stable one.

Some molecules are known in which the bond angles are required by the molecular structure to differ greatly from the tetrahedral value. These molecules can be described as containing bent bonds, and as being strained. The substance cyclopropane, C_3H_6, is an example. The cyclopropane molecule contains a ring of three carbon atoms, as shown in Figure 9-9. Each bond is bent through nearly 50°. The molecules are less stable by about 24 kcal/mole (8 kcal/mole per bond) than corresponding unstrained molecules, such as those of cyclohexane, C_6H_{12}.

The Carbon-carbon Double Bond. Sometimes two valence bonds of an atom are used in the formation of a double bond with another atom. There is a double bond between two carbon atoms in the molecules of ethylene, C_2H_4:

$$
\begin{array}{ccc}
H & & H \\
\diagdown & & \diagup \\
& C\!=\!C & \\
\diagup & & \diagdown \\
H & & H
\end{array}
$$

Ethylene

Such a double bond between two atoms may be represented by two tetrahedra sharing two corners: that is, sharing an edge, as shown in Figure 9-10. The amount of bending of the two bonds constituting the double bond is indicated in Figure 9-11.

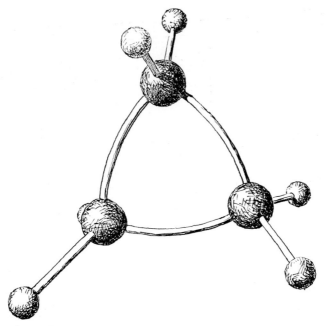

Figure **9-9**

> *The molecule of cyclopropane, C_3H_6, showing the bent carbon-carbon bonds.*

It is interesting to note that the four other bonds that the two carbon atoms in ethylene can form lie in the same plane, at right angles to the plane containing the two bent bonds.

The Carbon-carbon Triple Bond.   In acetylene, C_2H_2, there is a triple bond between the two carbon atoms:

$$H—C\equiv C—H$$
Acetylene

Figure **9-10**

> *Tetrahedral atoms forming single, double, and triple bonds.*

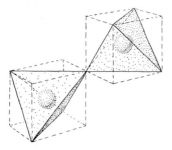
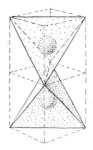
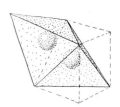

Single bond   Double bond   Triple bond

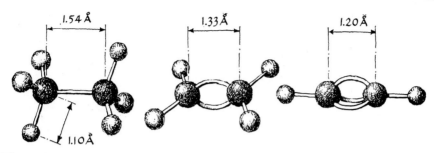

Figure 9-11

Valence-bond models of ethylene, C_2H_4, and acetylene, C_2H_2.

The triple bonds between two atoms may be represented by two tetrahedra sharing a face (Figures 9-10 and 9-11). This causes the acetylene molecule to be linear.

Bond Lengths. Spectroscopic studies have led to the determination of the carbon-carbon bond length (distance between the nuclei of the two carbon atoms) in ethane, ethylene, and acetylene. The values are 1.54 Å for the single bond in ethane (and also in other molecules containing the C—C bond), 1.33 Å for the double bond, and 1.20 Å for the triple bond.

It is interesting that these values for C=C and C≡C are within 0.02 Å of the values that correspond to bent bonds with the normal single-bond length 1.54 Å and at tetrahedral angles, as indicated in Figure 9-11. This agreement supports the bent-bond description of the double bond and the triple bond.

Illustrative Exercises

9-7. The diacetylene molecule has the formula C_4H_2. What is its structural formula? What is the spatial arrangement of the six atoms in the molecule relative to one another?

9-8. Cyclopropane has the formula C_3H_6. One other substance (called propylene) has the same formula. What is its structural formula? How many of the six hydrogen atoms lie in the plane of the three carbon atoms? (Answer: Three must, a fourth may.)

9-9. Three different substances are known with the molecular formula C_3H_4. Draw their structural formulas and describe their spatial arrangements.

9-10. Allene has the structural formula $H_2C=C=CH_2$. Do all of the atoms lie in the same plane? Would you predict that 1,3-difluoroallene, HFC=C=CHF, exists as an enantiomeric pair of substances or as a single optically inactive substance?

9-11. Three isomers of dichloroethylene, $C_2H_2Cl_2$, exist. Can you assign structural formulas to them?

9-12. If you have studied trigonometry, verify that the angle between two tetrahedral bonds is 109°28'. Refer to Figure 9-12, and note that the distance from the central atom (at the center of the cube, not shown) to a corner atom is one half of the body diagonal of the cube, and hence equal to $\sqrt{3}\, a/2$, where a is the length of the edge of the cube, and the distance between two corner atoms is the face diagonal of the cube, equal to $\sqrt{2}\, a$.

Figure 9-12

Drawing showing the relation of the tetrahedron and the octahedron to the cube. These polyhedra are important in molecular structure.

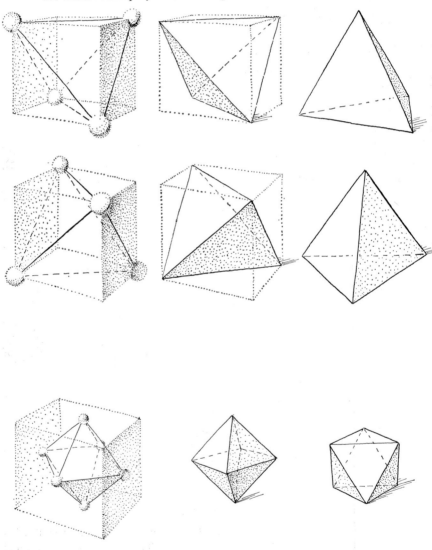

9-6. Bond Orbitals with Large *p* Character

In a molecule such as ammonia, NH_3, with structural formula

the bond orbitals of the nitrogen atom are not tetrahedral orbitals, but instead have mainly the character of the three $2p$ orbitals. Quantum-mechanical calculations and nuclear magnetic resonance experiments (which measure the interaction energy of the nuclear spin magnetic moment with the valence electrons) agree in allocating the unshared electron pair to a hybrid orbital that is largely $2s$ in character (about 79%). The three bond orbitals have about 93% $2p$ character and 7% $2s$ character.

It was pointed out in Chapter 7 that a $2s$ electron is more stable than a $2p$ electron. The difference in energy is about 180 kcal/mole. The nitrogen atom, $: \overset{\cdot}{N} \cdot$, is 180 kcal/mole more stable if the pair of electrons is in the $2s$ orbital ($2s^2 2p_x 2p_y 2p_z$) than if it is in one of the $2p$ orbitals ($2s 2p_x^2 2p_y 2p_z$). Hence it tends to retain the $2s$ pair in forming compounds, and to use the $2p_x$, $2p_y$, and $2p_z$ orbitals for the bonding electrons.

The three $2p$ orbitals are represented in Figure 7-5. The $2p_x$ orbital extends in two opposite directions along the x axis, and can be used in forming a bond in either direction. The $2p_y$ orbital can be used in forming a bond along the y axis, and the $2p_z$ orbital in forming a bond along the z axis. Hence *the bonds formed by p orbitals are approximately at 90° to one another.** With some s character to the bond orbitals the bond angles increase, reaching 109°28′ for tetrahedral orbitals, which have 25% s character.

The experimental values of bond angles for atoms with unshared electron pairs usually lie between 90° and 109°. For example, the spectroscopically determined value for NH_3 is 107°, for H_2O 104.5°, for PH_3 93°, for H_2S 92°, and for H_2Se 91°.

9-7. Molecules and Crystals of the Nonmetallic Elements

The Halogen Molecules.   A halogen atom such as fluorine can achieve the noble-gas structure by forming a single covalent bond with another halogen atom:

$$: \overset{\cdot\cdot}{\underset{\cdot\cdot}{F}} - \overset{\cdot\cdot}{\underset{\cdot\cdot}{F}} : \qquad : \overset{\cdot\cdot}{\underset{\cdot\cdot}{Cl}} - \overset{\cdot\cdot}{\underset{\cdot\cdot}{Cl}} : \qquad : \overset{\cdot\cdot}{\underset{\cdot\cdot}{Br}} - \overset{\cdot\cdot}{\underset{\cdot\cdot}{Br}} : \qquad : \overset{\cdot\cdot}{\underset{\cdot\cdot}{I}} - \overset{\cdot\cdot}{\underset{\cdot\cdot}{I}} :$$

---

* The 90° bond angle for *p* bonds was discovered by J. C. Slater in 1931.

This single covalent bond holds the atoms together into diatomic molecules, which are present in the elementary halogens in all states of aggregation— crystal, liquid, and gas.

The Elements of the Sixth Group.   An atom of a sixth-group element, such as sulfur, lacks two electrons of having a completed octet. It can complete its octet by forming single covalent bonds with two other atoms. These bonds may hold the molecule together either into a ring, such as an S_8 ring, or into a very long chain, with the two end atoms having an abnormal structure:

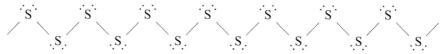

The elementary substance **sulfur** occurs in both these forms. Ordinary sulfur (orthorhombic sulfur) consists of molecules made of eight atoms. The molecule S_8 has the configuration shown in Figure 9-13. It is a staggered octagonal ring, with S—S—S bond angle 102°. When sulfur is melted, it is converted into a straw-colored liquid, which also consists of the staggered ring S_8. However, when molten sulfur is heated to a temperature considerably above its melting point it becomes deep red in color and extremely viscous, so that it will not pour out of the test tube when it is inverted. This change in properties is the result of the formation of very large molecules containing hundreds of atoms into a long chain—the S_8 rings break open, and then combine

Figure **9-13**

   The S_8 ring, and a long chain of sulfur atoms.

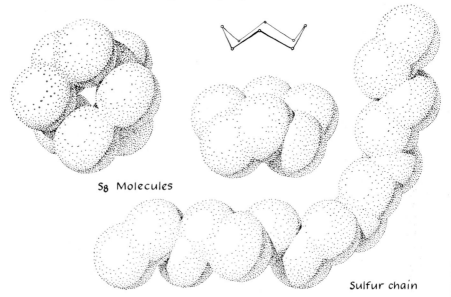

S₈ Molecules

Sulfur chain

together in a "high polymer."* The deep red color is due to the abnormal atoms at the end of the chains, which are forming only one bond instead of the two bonds that a sulfur atom is expected to form. The great viscosity of the liquid is due to the interference with molecular motion caused by entanglement of the long chains of atoms with one another.

Selenium, which is just under sulfur in the periodic table, crystallizes as red crystals containing Se_8 molecules, and also as semimetallic gray crystals which contain long staggered chains, stretching from one end of the crystal to the other. **Tellurium** crystals also contain long chains.

Ordinary **oxygen** consists of diatomic molecules with an unusual electronic structure. We might expect these molecules O_2 to contain a double bond:

$$: \overset{..}{O} : : \overset{..}{O} : \qquad \text{or} \qquad : \overset{..}{O} = \overset{..}{O} :$$

Instead, only one shared pair is formed, leaving two unshared electrons:

$$: \overset{..}{\underset{.}{O}} - \overset{.}{\underset{..}{O}} :$$

These two unshared electrons are responsible for the paramagnetism of oxygen. It has been found by study of the oxygen spectrum that the force of attraction between the oxygen atoms is much greater than that expected for a single covalent bond. This shows that the unpaired electrons are really involved in the formation of bonds of a special sort. The oxygen molecule may be said to contain a single covalent bond plus two *three-electron bonds*, and its structure may be written as

$$: O \overset{..}{\underset{..}{:}} O :$$

Ozone, the triatomic form of oxygen, has the electronic structure

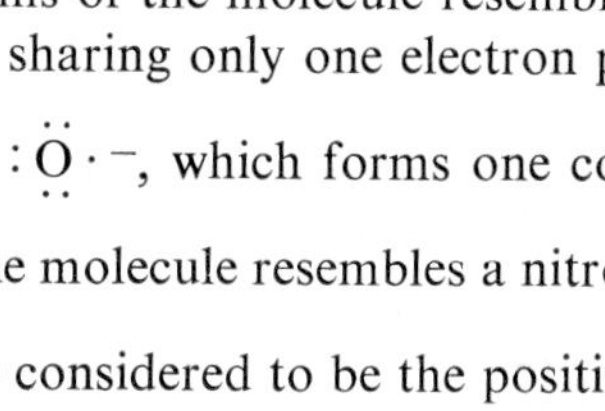

Here one of the end atoms of the molecule resembles a fluorine atom in that it completes its octet by sharing only one electron pair. It may be considered

to be the negative ion: $: \overset{..}{O} \cdot ^-$, which forms one covalent bond. The central

oxygen atom of the ozone molecule resembles a nitrogen atom (see the follow-

ing section), and may be considered to be the positive ion $: \overset{.}{O} \cdot ^+$, which forms

three covalent bonds (one double bond and one single bond).

---

* A *polymer* is a molecule made by combination of two or more identical smaller molecules. A *high polymer* is made by the combination of a great many smaller molecules. The words dimer, trimer, tetramer, etc., are used for molecules obtained by combining two, three, four etc., identical smaller molecules.

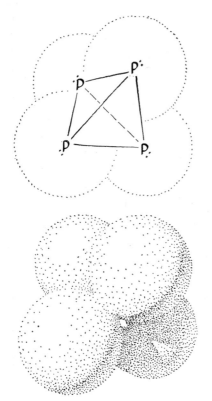

Figure **9-14**   *The P₄ molecule.*

Two structures for ozone are shown in braces (p. 271). This indicates that the two end oxygen atoms are not different, but are equivalent. The molecule has a structure represented by the superposition of the two structures shown; that is, each bond is a *hybrid* of a single covalent bond and a double covalent bond.

Nitrogen and Its Congeners. The nitrogen atom, lacking three electrons of a completed octet, may complete the octet by forming three covalent bonds. It does this in elementary **nitrogen** by forming a triple bond in the molecule N_2. Three electron pairs are shared by the two nitrogen atoms:

$$: N : : : N :   \text{or}   : N \equiv N :$$

This bond is extremely strong, and the N_2 molecule is a very stable molecule.

Phosphorus gas at very high temperatures consists of P_2 molecules, with a similar structure, $: P \equiv P :$. At lower temperatures, however, phosphorus forms a molecule containing four atoms, P_4. This molecule has the structure shown in Figure 9-14. The four phosphorus atoms are arranged at the corners of a regular tetrahedron. Each phosphorus atom forms covalent bonds with the three other phosphorus atoms. This P_4 molecule exists in phosphorus vapor, in solutions of phosphorus in carbon disulfide and other nonpolar solvents, and in solid white phosphorus. In other forms of elementary phosphorus (red phosphorus, black phosphorus) the atoms are bonded together into larger aggregates.

Arsenic and **antimony** also form tetrahedral molecules, As_4 and Sb_4, in the vapor phase. At higher temperatures these molecules dissociate into diatomic molecules, As_2 and Sb_2. Crystals of these elementary substances and of bismuth, however, contain high polymers—layers of atoms in which each atom is bonded to three neighbors by single covalent bonds, as shown in Figure 9-15.

Carbon and Its Congeners.   The structures of diamond and graphite will be discussed in Section 10-2. **Silicon, germanium,** and **gray tin** crystallize with the diamond structure. Ordinary tin (white tin) and lead have metallic structures (see Chapter 20).

9-13. Write the electronic structures of P_2, As_4, S_8, and S_x (x very large), showing all electron pairs in the outermost shell of each atom. Which noble-gas structure is assumed, in each case?

9-14. An orange-red crystalline form of sulfur can be made by treating a solution of sodium thiosulfate with acetic acid. The molecular weight corresponds to the formula S_6. What electronic structure would you assign to the molecules?

9-15. The heat of combustion of white phosphorus is 6 kcal/mole (per P) greater than that of black phosphorus. Which is the more stable of the two forms of phosphorus? Black phosphorus has a layer structure somewhat similar to the arsenic structure, Figure 9-15. The P—P—P bond angles have the normal value for p bonds with a small amount of s character, about 100°. Can you explain in a qualitative way the difference in stability of white and black phosphorus?

9-8. Resonance

In the foregoing section it was mentioned that ozone has the structure

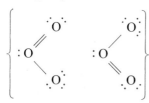

The reason for this statement is that it is known from experiment that the two oxygen-oxygen bonds in ozone are not different, but are equivalent. Equivalence of the bonds can be explained by the assumption of a *hybrid structure*. Each of the bonds in ozone is a hybrid between a single bond and a double bond, and its properties are intermediate between those of these two kinds of bonds.

It is customary to say that the double bond *resonates* between the two positions in ozone. *The resonance of molecules between two or more electronic structures* is an important concept. Often it is found difficult to assign to a molecule a single electronic structure of the valence-bond type which repre-

Figure **9-15** *A puckered layer of atoms from the arsenic crystal. Each atom is attached by single bonds to three other atoms.*

sents its properties satisfactorily. Often, also, two or more electronic structures seem to be about equally good. In these cases it is usually wise to say that the actual molecule resonates among the reasonable structures, and to indicate the molecule by writing the various resonating structures together in brackets. These various structures do not correspond to different kinds of molecules; there is only one kind of molecule present, with an electronic structure that can be described as a hybrid structure of two or more valence bond structures.

The following resonating structures represent important molecules:

$$\{ :C-\overset{..}{\underset{..}{O}}: \qquad :C=\overset{..}{O}: \qquad :C\equiv O: \} \qquad \text{Carbon monoxide}$$

$$\left\{ :\overset{..}{O}=C=O: \qquad :\overset{..}{\underset{..}{O}}-C\equiv O: \qquad :O\equiv C-\overset{..}{\underset{..}{O}}: \right. \qquad \begin{array}{l}\text{Carbon dioxide}\\ \text{(linear molecule)}\end{array}$$

$$\left\{ :\overset{..}{S}=C=\overset{..}{S}: \qquad :\overset{..}{\underset{..}{S}}-C\equiv S: \qquad :S\equiv C-\overset{..}{\underset{..}{S}}: \right. \qquad \begin{array}{l}\text{Carbon disulfide}\\ \text{(linear molecule)}\end{array}$$

$$\left\{ :\overset{..}{N}=N=\overset{..}{\underset{..}{O}}: \qquad :N\equiv N-\overset{..}{\underset{..}{O}}: \right\} \qquad \begin{array}{l}\text{Nitrous oxide}\\ \text{(linear molecule)}\end{array}$$

There is experimental evidence showing that these molecules have the resonating structures indicated above. Perhaps the simplest evidence is that given by the distances between the atoms. It has been observed that in general the distance between two atoms connected by a double bond is approximately 0.21 Å less than the distance between the same two atoms connected by a single bond, and that the distance for a triple bond is approximately 0.13 Å less than that for a double bond. For example, the single-bond distance between two carbon atoms (as in diamond or ethane, H_3C-CH_3) is 1.54 Å; the double-bond distance is 1.33 Å, and the triple-bond distance is 1.20 Å. The distance between a carbon atom and an oxygen atom connected by a double bond as found in compounds such as formaldehyde,

is 1.22 Å. In carbon dioxide, however, for which the structure O=C=O was accepted for many years, the distance between the carbon atom and an oxygen atom has been found to be 1.16 Å. The shortening of 0.06 Å is due to the triple-bond character introduced by the two structures O≡C—O and O—C≡O (the effect of the triple bond on the interatomic distance is greater than the effect of the single bond).

9-9. The Partial Ionic Character of Covalent Bonds

Often a decision must be made as to whether a molecule is to be considered as containing an ionic bond or a covalent bond. There is no question about a salt of a strong metal and a strong nonmetal; an ionic structure is to be written for it. Thus for lithium chloride we write

$$Li^+Cl^- \qquad or \qquad Li^+ : \overset{..}{\underset{..}{Cl}} : {}^-$$

Similarly there is no doubt about nitrogen trichloride, NCl_3, an oily molecular substance composed of two nonmetals. Its molecules have the covalent structure

$$
\begin{array}{c}
\overset{..}{Cl} : \\
\diagup \\
: N \!\!-\!\!-\!\! \overset{..}{\underset{..}{Cl}} : \\
\diagdown \\
\overset{..}{\underset{..}{Cl}} :
\end{array}
$$

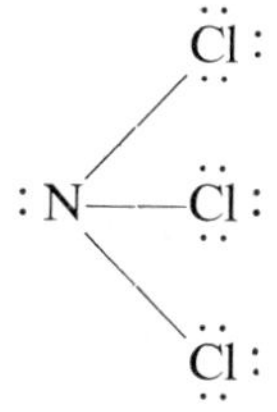

Between LiCl and NCl_3 there are the three compounds $BeCl_2$, BCl_3, and CCl_4. Where does the change from an ionic structure to a covalent structure occur?

The answer to this question is provided by the theory of resonance. *The transition from an ionic bond to a normal covalent bond in a series of compounds such as those mentioned in the preceding sentence does not occur sharply, but gradually.*

Often only the covalent structure is shown, and the chemist bears in mind that the covalent bonds have a certain amount of ionic character. These bonds are called *covalent bonds with partial ionic character.*

For example, the hydrogen chloride molecule may be assigned the resonating structure

$$\left\{ H^+ : \overset{..}{\underset{..}{Cl}} : {}^- \qquad H\!\!-\!\!\overset{..}{\underset{..}{Cl}} : \right\}$$

This is usually represented by the simple structural formula

$$H\!\!-\!\!\overset{..}{\underset{..}{Cl}} : \qquad or \qquad H\!\!-\!\!Cl$$

In practice it is customary to indicate bonds between the highly electropositive metals and the nonmetals as ionic bonds, and bonds between nonmetals and nonmetals or metalloids as covalent bonds, which are understood to have a certain amount of partial ionic character.

9-10. The Electric Dipole Moment of Molecules and the Partial Ionic Character of Bonds

About fifty years ago it was noticed that some liquids have a small dielectric constant (1.5 to 2.5) that is nearly independent of the temperature, and that others have a larger value that decreases rapidly with increase in the temperature. The idea was developed that the liquids of the first kind, called *nonpolar liquids*, consist of molecules with no electric dipole moment, and that the liquids of the second kind, called *polar liquids*, consist of molecules that have a dipole moment.

A molecule has an electric dipole moment if its center of positive charge does not coincide with its center of negative charge. The magnitude of the dipole moment is equal to the charge e multiplied by the distance between the charges. For example, a proton (charge $+e = 4.80 \times 10^{-10}$ statcoulomb) and an electron (charge $-e$) held 2 Å (2×10^{-8} cm) apart would have the dipole moment $4.80 \times 10^{-10} \times 2 \times 10^{-8} = 9.60 \times 10^{-18}$ statcoulomb cm. This is usually written as 9.60 D; D is the symbol for the unit the debye.

The water molecule has a considerable amount of ionic character; it can be thought of (somewhat idealized) as an oxygen ion O^{--} with two hydrogen ions H^+ attached near its surface. These hydrogen ions are 0.96 Å from the oxygen nucleus, and on the same side of the oxygen atom. Hence there is a separation of positive charge and negative charge within the molecule, causing the center of the positive charge in the molecule to be to one side of the center of the negative charge (Figure 9-16).

Figure **9-16** *Two water molecules with their electric dipole moment vectors oriented in opposite directions.*

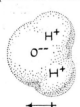

Dipole moment

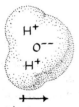

Dipole moment

In an electric field, as between the electrostatically charged plates of a condenser, water molecules tend to orient themselves, pointing their positive ends toward the negative plate and their negative ends toward the positive plate (Figure 9-17). This partially neutralizes the applied field, an effect described by saying that the medium (water) has a *dielectric constant* greater than unity.

The voltage required to put a given amount of electric charge on the plates of a condenser is inversely proportional to the dielectric constant of the medium surrounding the condenser plates. In this way the dielectric constant of the substance can be determined, and from its value, by use of a theory developed by P. P. Debye in 1914, the dipole moment of the molecules can be evaluated. Values of dipole moments can also be determined with great accuracy by microwave spectroscopy and molecular beam resonance methods.

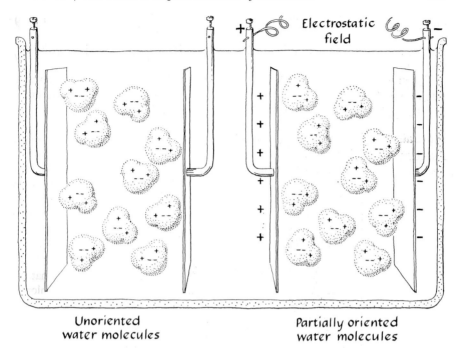

Unoriented
water molecules
     Partially oriented
water molecules

Figure 9-17

Orientation of polar molecules in an electrostatic field, producing the effect of a high dielectric constant.

The value of the dipole moment of the water molecule in water vapor is 1.86 D. This value corresponds to the charge $+0.33e$ on each hydrogen atom and $-0.66e$ on the oxygen atom, if the electrons are assumed to be arranged with spherical symmetry around each nucleus. The statement can hence be made that each of the O—H bonds in the water molecule has about one-third ionic character and two-thirds covalent character.

An extreme case is the lithium fluoride gas molecule, which has dipole moment 6.7 D, equal to 92% of the value for Li^+ and F^- at the internuclear distance 1.52 Å. This molecule is accordingly well represented by the symbol Li^+F^-, and the bond may be described as an ionic bond with only a small amount of covalent character (about 8%).

On the other hand, the observed dipole moment for hydrogen iodide, 0.38 D. with the internuclear distance 1.62 Å, corresponds to only 5% of ionic character. The HI molecule is well represented by the normal covalent structure

H : Ï : .

Hydrogen fluoride has dipole moment 1.98 D and internuclear distance 0.92 Å. These correspond to a 45% contribution of the ionic structure H^+F^-

and 55% contribution of the covalent structure H : F̈ :. The H—F bond may thus be described as about midway between the ionic extreme and the covalent extreme

The amounts of ionic character and covalent character of a bond between two atoms A and B can be estimated with use of quantity called the electronegativity. This quantity will be discussed in the following section.

Illustrative Exercises

9-16. The observed internuclear distance in the HCl molecule is 1.28 Å.

(a) Calculate the value of the electric dipole moment of the HCl molecule corresponding to the extreme ionic structure H^+Cl^-, assuming the chloride ion to be spherically symmetrical, so that the center of charge for the 18 electrons coincides with the chlorine nucleus.

(b) The observed value of the dipole moment is 1.03 D. To what amount of partial ionic character of the H—Cl bond does this value correspond? (Answer: 6.07 D, 17%.)

9-17. The dimensions of the water molecule (O—H bond length 0.96 Å, H—O—H angle 104.5°) make the distance between the oxygen nucleus and the point midway between the protons equal to 0.79 Å. To what value of the partial ionic character of the O—H bond does the observed value of the electric dipole moment (1.86 D) correspond?

9-11. The Electronegativity Scale of the Elements

It has been found possible to assign to the elements numbers representing their power of attraction for the electrons in a covalent bond, by means of

Table **9-1**

Values of the Electronegativity of Elements

													H				
													2.1				
Li	Be	B												C	N	O	F
1.0	1.5	2.0												2.5	3.0	3.5	4.0
Na	Mg	Al												Si	P	S	Cl
0.9	1.2	1.5												1.8	2.1	2.5	3.0
K	Ca	Sc	Ti	V	Cr	Mn	Fe	Co	Ni	Cu	Zn	Ga	Ge	As	Se	Br
0.8	1.0	1.3	1.5	1.6	1.6	1.5	1.8	1.8	1.8	1.9	1.6	1.6	1.8	2.0	2.4	2.8
Rb	Sr	Y	Zr	Nb	Mo	Tc	Ru	Rh	Pd	Ag	Cd	In	Sn	Sb	Te	I
0.8	1.0	1.2	1.4	1.6	1.8	1.9	2.2	2.2	2.2	1.9	1.7	1.7	1.8	1.9	2.1	2.5
Cs	Ba	La–Lu	Hf	Ta	W	Re	Os	Ir	Pt	Au	Hg	Tl	Pb	Bi	Po	At
0.7	0.9	1.0–1.2	1.3	1.5	1.7	1.9	2.2	2.2	2.2	2.4	1.9	1.8	1.9	1.9	2.0	2.2
Fr	Ra	Ac	Th	Pa	U	Np–No										
0.7	0.9	1.1	1.3	1.5	1.7	1.5–1.3										

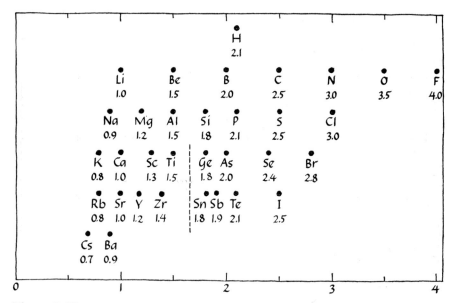

Figure **9-18**

The electronegativity scale. The dashed line indicates approximate values for the transition metals.

which the amount of partial ionic character of the bond may be estimated. This power of attraction for the electrons in a covalent bond is called the *electronegativity* of the element. In Figure 9-18 the elements other than the transition elements and the rare-earth metals are shown on an *electronegativity* scale. The electronegativity values are also given in Table 9-1. The symbol x is used for electronegativity.

The scale extends from cesium, with electronegativity 0.7, to fluorine, with electronegativity 4.0. Fluorine is by far the most electronegative element, with oxygen in second place, and nitrogen and chlorine in third place. Hydrogen and the metalloids are in the center of the scale, with electronegativity values close to 2. The metals have values about 1.7 or less.

The electronegativity scale as drawn in Figure 9-18 is seen to be similar in a general way to the periodic table, but deformed by pushing the top to the right and the bottom to the left. In describing the periodic table we have said that the strongest metals are in the lower left corner and the strongest nonmetals in the upper right corner of the table; because of this deformation, the electronegativity scale shows the metallic or nonmetallic character of an element simply as a function of the value of the horizontal coordinate, the electronegativity.

A rough relation between the electronegativity difference $x_A - x_B$ (or $x_B - x_A$) and the amount of partial ionic character of the bond between atoms A and B can be found by plotting the partial ionic character as given

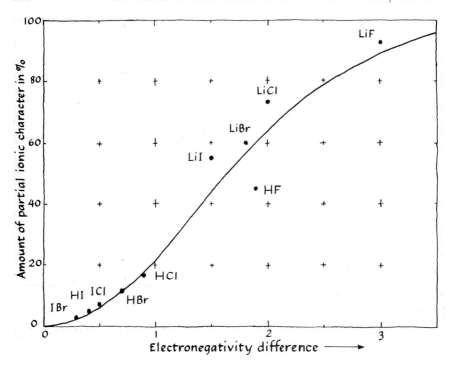

Figure 9-19

A diagram showing the relation between the ionic character of a bond and the electronegativity difference of the two atoms that are bonded together.

by the observed values of the electric dipole moment and the internuclear distance for diatomic molecules (Section 9-10) against the electronegativity difference. Such a diagram is shown in Figure 9-19. Experimental points are shown for iodine bromide, iodine chloride, the hydrogen halogenides, and the lithium halogenides (gas molecules). The smooth curve that is drawn is seen to approximate the experimental points to within about $\pm 2\%$ for $x_A - x_B$ less than 1 and about $\pm 10\%$ for larger values.

Numerical values corresponding to the curve are given in Table 9-2.

The dipole moment is a vector, and can be represented by an arrow. The convention has been adopted of drawing the arrow from the positive charge to the negative charge. Sometimes a special arrow, $\leftrightarrow$, is used.

The dipole moment of a polyatomic molecule is found to be roughly equal to the vector sum of the moments calculated from the partial ionic character of the bonds in the molecule. When the experimental value shows large disagreement with the value calculated in this way, it is likely that the electronic structure of the molecule is somewhat different from that used in making the calculation.

Table **9-2**

Relation between Electronegativity Difference and
Amount of Partial Ionic Character of Bonds

$x_A - x_B$	AMOUNT OF IONIC CHARACTER	$x_A - x_B$	AMOUNT OF IONIC CHARACTER
0.2	1%	1.8	55%
.4	4	2.0	63
.6	9	2.2	70
.8	15	2.4	76
1.0	22	2.6	82
1.2	30	2.8	86
1.4	39	3.0	89
1.6	47	3.2	92

The farther away two elements are from one another in the electronegativity scale (horizontally in Figure 9-18), the greater is the amount of ionic character of a bond between them. When the separation on the scale is 1.7 the bond has about 50% ionic character. If the separation is greater than this, it would seem appropriate to write an ionic structure for the substance, and if it is less to write a covalent structure. However, it is not necessary to adhere rigorously to this rule.

Example 1. Describe the electronic structure of the NaCl gas molecule (the boiling point of NaCl at 1 atm is 1430°C). What is the predicted value of its electric dipole moment?

Solution. The electronegativity difference for chlorine ($x = 3.0$) and sodium ($x = 0.9$) is 2.1. Hence the molecule is largely ionic, Na^+Cl^-, with only about 33% covalent character (67% ionic character, Table 9-2). The bond length is given in Table 8-4 as 2.36 Å. Hence the dipole moment for 100% ionic character would be $2.36 \times 4.80 = 11.3$ D. (The electronic charge is 4.80×10^{-10} statcoulomb and unit 1 D is 1×10^{-18} statcoulomb). For 67% partial ionic character the predicted value of the dipole moment is 0.67×11.3 D = **7.6 D.** (The observed value is somewhat larger—8.3 D—corresponding to 75% of partial ionic character for the bond.)

Example 2. What is the electric dipole moment of acetylene, C_2H_2?

Solution. The acetylene molecule, $H-C{\equiv}C-H$, is linear (Section 9-5). Hence the two H—C dipole moments oppose one another,

$$\overset{+\!\!\rightarrow}{}\quad\overset{\leftarrow\!\!+}{}$$
$$H-C{\equiv}C-H$$

and have the resultant zero. Thus the answer is **0.**

Illustrative Exercises

9-18.   In which of the following molecules are the bonds largely ionic, and in which are they largely covalent? PF_3, PI_3, NCl_3, SiF_4, $MgCl_2$, CsF, CsI, CCl_4.

9-19.   Predict a value for the electric dipole moment of the LiBr molecule with use of Table 9-2. The bond length is 2.17 Å.   (Answer: 5.7 D. The observed value is 6.2 D.)

9-12.   Heats of Formation and Relative Electronegativity of Atoms

Atoms of hydrogen and iodine, although quite different in general, are approximately equal in electronegativity. In the molecule H—I⋮ the two atoms exert about the same attraction on the shared electron pair that constitutes the covalent bond between them. This bond is accordingly much like the covalent bonds in the elementary molecules H—H and ⋮I—I⋮. It is hence not surprising that the energy of the H—I bond is very nearly the average of the energies of the H—H bond and the I—I bond. The heat of formation of HI from the gas molecules H_2 and I_2

$$\tfrac{1}{2}H_2 + \tfrac{1}{2}I_2 \longrightarrow HI + 1.5 \text{ kcal/mole}$$

is only 1.5 kcal/mole.

The other hydrogen halogenide molecules have larger amounts of electronegativity difference (0.7 for HBr, 0.9 for HCl, 1.9 for HF) and of partial ionic character (12%, 17%, and 45%, respectively), and their heats of formation also increase greatly in the same order:

$$\tfrac{1}{2}H_2 + \tfrac{1}{2}Br_2 \longrightarrow HBr + 12.3 \text{ kcal/mole}$$
$$\tfrac{1}{2}H_2 + \tfrac{1}{2}Cl_2 \longrightarrow HCl + 22.1 \text{ kcal/mole}$$
$$\tfrac{1}{2}H_2 + \tfrac{1}{2}F_2 \longrightarrow HF + 64.2 \text{ kcal/mole}$$

This means that the bonds in these hydrogen halogenide molecules are stronger than the average of the bonds in the molecules of the elementary substances, and that the increased strength (bond energy) is determined by the electronegativity difference of the two atoms. *The greater the separation of two elements on the electronegativity scale, the greater is the strength of the bond between them.*

Bond Energy.   The heat of formation of a compound from the elements composing it is a measure of the difference in energy of the bonds in the compound and the bonds in the elements. Values of the bond energy for simple molecules, such as H_2, F_2, Cl_2, Br_2, and I_2, have been determined by spectroscopic methods. These bond energies are equal to the heats of formation ($-\Delta H°$) of the diatomic molecules from atoms:

$$H + H \longrightarrow H_2 + 104.2 \text{ kcal/mole}$$
$$F + F \longrightarrow F_2 + 36.6 \text{ kcal/mole}$$
$$Cl + Cl \longrightarrow Cl_2 + 58.0 \text{ kcal/mole}$$
$$Br + Br \longrightarrow Br_2 + 46.1 \text{ kcal/mole}$$
$$I + I \longrightarrow I_2 + 36.1 \text{ kcal/mole}$$

The energy required to break an H—H bond and an F—F bond is $104.2 + 36.6 = 140.8$ kcal/mole. The bond energy of HF is 134.6 kcal/mole:

$$H + F \longrightarrow HF + 134.6 \text{ kcal/mole}$$

or

$$2H + 2F \longrightarrow 2HF + 269.2 \text{ kcal/mole}$$

We see that in forming two H—F bonds 269.2 kcal/mole of energy is released. Of this only 140.8 kcal/mole is needed to dissociate H_2 and F_2 into 2H and 2F. Hence the two H—F bonds are $269.2 - 140.8 = 128.4$ kcal/mole stronger than H—H and F—F. One H—F bond is 64.2 kcal/mole stronger than the average of H—H and F—F. This quantity is just the heat of formation of HF from $\frac{1}{2}H_2$ and $\frac{1}{2}F_2$.

The quantitative relation between bond energy and electronegativity difference may be expressed by an equation. For a single covalent bond between two atoms A and B the extra energy due to the partial ionic character is approximately $23(x_A - x_B)^2$ kcal/mole; that is, it is proportional to the square of the difference in electronegativity of the two atoms, and the proportionality constant has the value 23 kcal/mole. For example, chlorine and fluorine have electronegativity values differing by 1; hence the heat of formation of ClF (containing one Cl—F bond) is predicted to be 23 kcal/mole. The observed heat of formation of ClF is 25.7 kcal/mole. The agreement between the predicted and observed heat of formation is only approximate. For electronegativity differences of 1 or less there is usually agreement to within 2 or 3 kcal/mole, but for larger values of the difference the calculated value may show a larger error.

Heats of formation calculated in this way would refer to elements in states in which the atoms formed single bonds, as they do in the molecules P_4 and S_8. Nitrogen (N_2) and oxygen (O_2) contain multiple bonds, and the nitrogen and oxygen molecules are more stable, by 110 kcal/mole and 48 kcal/mole, respectively, than they would be if the molecules contained single bonds (as in P_4 and S_8). Hence we must correct for this extra stability by using the equation

$$Q = \text{heat of formation (in kcal/mole)} = 23 \sum (x_A - x_B)^2 - 55n_N - 24n_O \tag{1}$$

Here the summation indicated by $\sum$ is to be taken over all the bonds represented by the formula of the compound. The symbol n_N means the number of nitrogen atoms in the formula, and n_O the number of oxygen atoms.

As an example, we may consider the substance nitrogen trichloride,

$$
\begin{array}{c}
\text{Cl} \\
\diagup \\
\text{N}-\text{Cl} \\
\diagdown \\
\text{Cl}
\end{array}
$$

Nitrogen and chlorine have the same electronegativity; hence the first term contributes nothing. There is one nitrogen atom in the molecule. Hence $Q = -55$ kcal/mole. The minus sign shows that the substance is unstable, and that heat is liberated when it decomposes. Nitrogen trichloride is in fact an oil which explodes easily, with great violence:

$$2NCl_3 \longrightarrow N_2 + 3Cl_2 + 110 \text{ kcal}$$

The instability of nitrogen trichloride is due entirely to the great stability of the triple bond in the nitrogen molecule.

Equation 1 may be used to calculate rough values of the heat of formation of any compound in which the atoms are held together by single bonds. Its use may be illustrated by some examples and exercises.

Example 3.   Which of the two following substances is predicted to form from the elements by a strongly exothermic reaction: PI_3, PF_3?
    Solution.   Phosphorus and iodine differ by only 0.4 in electronegativity; hence the formation of PI_3 is predicted to be only slightly exothermic. The extra P—I bond energy due to partial ionic character, $23(x_A - x_B)^2$ kcal/mole, is $23 \times 0.4^2 = 3.7$ kcal/mole per P—I bond; hence we predict $P + \frac{3}{2}I_2 \longrightarrow PI_3 + 11$ kcal/mole.

    For formation of PF_3 a strongly exothermic reaction is expected, because of the large electronegativity difference, 1.9, which leads to $3 \times 23 \times 1.9^2 = 250$ kcal/mole: $P + \frac{3}{2}F_2 \longrightarrow PF_3 + 250$ kcal/mole.

Example 4.   Which compounds of nitrogen involving single bonds are predicted to be stable relative to the elements?
    Solution.   In general it is assumed that a compound that is formed from the elements by an exothermic reaction is stable relative to the elements (although the heat of formation is not the only factor determining stability; see Chapter 18). The formation of a compound of nitrogen with an element with the same electronegativity (3.0) is endothermic by 55 kcal/mole per N (Equation 1), because of the stability of the N≡N triple bond in N_2. Hence to be formed by an exothermic reaction the compound must be with an element differing in electronegativity by an amount such that the extra stability of the bonds due to partial ionic character overcomes this instability of 55 kcal/mole. There are three N—X bonds formed per nitrogen atom. Hence we write

$$
\begin{aligned}
3 \times 23 \times (x_X - x_N)^2 &= 55 \\
(x_X - x_N)^2 &= 55/(3 \times 23) = 0.80 \\
x_X - x_N &= \pm 0.80^{1/2} = \pm\,\mathbf{0.9}
\end{aligned}
$$

Hence compounds of nitrogen with chlorine and bromine (NCl_3 and NBr_3) are predicted to be unstable, and those with other elements are predicted to be stable.

Example 5. A mixture of aluminum powder and iron(III) oxide, Fe_2O_3, can be ignited; the reaction

$$2Al + Fe_2O_3 \longrightarrow 2Fe + Al_2O_3$$

then takes place, producing much heat (the product is molten iron). Would you predict that magnesium could be similarly made from MgO by use of aluminum?

Solution. We may consider the two reactions

$$4Al + 3O_2 \longrightarrow 2Al_2O_3 + Q_1$$

and

$$6Mg + 3O_2 \longrightarrow 6MgO + Q_2$$

Here Q_1 is the heat evolved in the first reaction and Q_2 is the heat evolved in the second reaction. In each reaction, as written, twelve metal-oxygen single bonds are formed. The electronegativity of Al is 1.5 and that of Mg is 1.2. Hence the electronegativity difference for Al—O, 2.0, is less than that of Mg—O, 2.3, and accordingly Q_1 is less than Q_2. By subtracting the second equation from the first we obtain the result

$$4Al + 6MgO \longrightarrow 6Mg + 2Al_2O_3 + Q_1 - Q_2$$

Since Q_1 is less than Q_2, this reaction is endothermic, and probably would not take place. Accordingly magnesium cannot be made by igniting a mixture of aluminum and magnesium oxide.

Illustrative Exercises

9-20. Explain why the heat of formation of beryllium chloride, $BeCl_2$, from beryllium and chlorine is very large (122 kcal/mole), and that of phosphine, PH_3, from red phosphorus and hydrogen is very small (2.2 kcal/mole).

9-21. Why is a great amount of heat liberated when metals combine with oxygen, but only a small amount when metals combine with other metals?

9-22. What metals might be used to react with $MgCl_2$ in order to make magnesium metal?

9-23. Calculate the heat of formation of beryllium sulfide, BeS, from beryllium and sulfur, using Equation 1. The experimental value is 55.9 kcal/mole.

9-13. The Electroneutrality Principle

A useful principle in writing electronic structures for substances is the *electroneutrality principle*. This principle is that *stable molecules and crystals have electronic structures such that the electric charge of each atom is close to zero.* "Close to zero" means between -1 and $+1$.

That this principle is a reasonable one may be seen by the consideration of values of the ionization energy and electron affinity of atoms. The electron affinity of atoms of nonmetals is 80 or 90 kcal/mole for the first electron added, to convert the atom $:\ddot{\text{F}}\cdot$ into the anion $:\ddot{\text{F}}:^-$ or the atom $:\ddot{\text{O}}\cdot$ into the anion $:\ddot{\text{O}}\cdot^-$ (Section 8-2). But there is in general no significant affinity for a second electron (to convert $:\ddot{\text{O}}\cdot^-$ into $:\ddot{\text{O}}:^{--}$), even when it would complete an octet. The repulsion of the two negative charges decreases the attraction for the second electron to nearly zero. Similarly, the values of the first ionization energy of metal atoms lies between 90 and 200 kcal/mole, but the second ionization energy is 350 kcal/mole or more (Tables 8-1 and 8-2). It is accordingly unlikely that an atom in a stable molecule would have either a double negative charge or a double positive charge.

The use of the electroneutrality principle in assigning electronic structures to molecules and crystals is discussed in the following examples and in the following section and later chapters (see Chapters 16, 23).

Example 6. Should the hydrogen cyanide molecule be assigned the structure HCN or the structure HNC?

  Solution. The electronic structure $\text{H---C}{\equiv}\text{N}:$ makes the atoms nearly neutral. The partial ionic character of the bonds (4% for H—C and 7% for each C—N) leads to the charge $+0.04$ on H, $+0.17$ on C, and -0.21 on N. These charges are small, and are compatible with the electroneutrality principle. For HNC the structure $\text{H---N}{\equiv}\text{C}:$, which completes the octet about N and C, assigns four valence electrons to N and five to C, and hence corresponds to N^+ and C^-. The partial ionic character of the bonds then leads to the charges $+0.04$ on H, $+0.75$ on N, and -0.79 on C. These charges on N and C are much larger than for the structure $\text{H---C}{\equiv}\text{N}:$, and correspond to instability. Hence **HCN** is the preferable structure.

Example 7. Methyl cyanide and methyl isocyanide have the same composition. Their heats of formation are -21.0 kcal/mole and -35.9 kcal/mole, respectively. Which of the two is $\text{H}_3\text{C---C}{\equiv}\text{N}:$?

  Solution. Methyl cyanide is more stable than methyl isocyanide by 14.9 kcal/mole. The two structures $\text{H}_3\text{C---C}{\equiv}\text{N}:$ and $\text{H}_3\text{C---N}{\equiv}\text{C}:$ contain the same number of bonds, but the first places smaller electric charges on the atoms than the second, and is accordingly the more stable of the two. Hence **methyl cyanide** is to be assigned the structure $\text{H}_3\text{C---C}{\equiv}\text{N}:$, and methyl isocyanide the structure $\text{H}_3\text{C---N}{\equiv}\text{C}:$.

Example 8. What is the electronic structure of carbon monoxide? Its observed electric dipole moment is very small, only 0.112 D.

Solution. The only electronic structure that completes the octet about both C and O is $:C\equiv O:$, which corresponds to C^- and O^+. The electronegativity difference 1.0 corresponds to 22% partial ionic character for each bond, and hence to the charges -0.36 for C and $+0.36$

for O. Another possible electronic structure, $:C\!\!=\!\!\overset{..}{O}:$, gives oxygen its normal covalence but does not complete the octet of carbon. The partial ionic character of the bonds leads to the charges $+0.44$ for C and -0.44 for O.

We conclude that the two structures contribute about equally to a hybrid structure, which has very small resultant electric charge on each atom, in agreement with the electroneutrality principle and the observed very small dipole moment. Hence we describe the molecule as the res-

onance hybrid $\{:C\equiv O:, :C\!\!=\!\!\overset{..}{O}:\}$.

Example 9. What is the electronic structure of the anesthetic gas nitrous oxide, N_2O? Its electric dipole moment is 0.166 D.

Solution. A ring structure is not likely, because of the strain of the bent

bonds. The linear structure $:\overset{--}{N}\!-\!\overset{+}{N}\!\!\equiv\!\!\overset{+}{O}:$ completes the octet for each

atom, but we reject it because of the double negative charge on the end nitrogen atom. The two other structures that complete the octet for each

atom are $:N\!\!\equiv\!\!\overset{+}{N}\!-\!\overset{..\,-}{O}:$ and $:\overset{-\,..}{N}\!\!=\!\!\overset{+}{N}\!\!=\!\!\overset{..}{O}:$, each of which has formal

charges on two atoms as shown. These two structures look equally good, and we conclude that the molecule can best be described as the resonance hybrid with the two structures contributing about equally. Each structure alone would give the molecule a large dipole moment, but since these two dipole moments point in opposite directions they cancel one another in the hybrid, in agreement with the small observed dipole moment.

9-14. Deviations from the Octet Rule

Sometimes heavy atoms form so many covalent bonds as to surround themselves with more than four electron pairs. An example is phosphorus pentachloride, PCl_5; in the molecule of this substance the phosphorus atom is surrounded by five chlorine atoms, with each of which it forms a covalent bond (with some ionic character):

$$: \overset{\cdot\cdot}{\underset{}{Cl}} :$$

$$: \overset{\cdot\cdot}{\underset{\cdot\cdot}{Cl}} \diagdown \Big|$$
$$P — \overset{\cdot\cdot}{Cl} :$$
$$: \overset{\cdot\cdot}{\underset{\cdot\cdot}{Cl}} \diagup \Big|$$

$$: \overset{}{\underset{\cdot\cdot}{Cl}} :$$

The phosphorus atom in this compound seems to be using five of the nine orbitals of the M shell, rather than only the four most stable orbitals, which are occupied by electrons in the argon configuration. It seems likely that of the nine or more orbitals in the M shell, the N shell, and the O shell four are especially stable, but that one or more others may occasionally be utilized.

The difference in electronegativity of chlorine and phosphorus is 0.9, which corresponds to 18% of partial ionic character. Accordingly, an alternative description of the PCl_5 molecule is that the phosphorus atom forms four covalent bonds, using only the four orbitals of the outer shell, and one ionic bond to Cl^-, and that the four covalent bonds resonate among the five positions, so that each chlorine atom is held by a bond with 80% covalent and 20% ionic character.

The oxygen acids, such as H_2SO_4, may be assigned similar structures, involving deviation from the octet rule:

$$H — \overset{\cdot\cdot}{O} :$$
$$: \overset{}{\underset{\cdot\cdot}{O}} = \overset{\cdot\cdot}{S} — \overset{\cdot\cdot}{O} :$$
$$: \overset{}{\underset{}{O}} \quad H$$

How to Make Use of Electronic Structures.   In the study of descriptive chemistry it is a good practice to write electronic structures for all the new substances encountered, and to see whether they fit into the simple scheme with all atoms having noble-gas structures, or whether they constitute exceptions. It is possible in this way to gain an understanding of chemical phenomena and a systematization of the facts of chemistry that should be useful in your work.

You should write the electronic structures in such a way as to reproduce the actual structure of the molecule as closely as can conveniently be done. For example, the angle between two valence bonds formed by an oxygen atom is about 105°; hence we write

$$H$$
$$|$$
$$: \overset{}{\underset{\cdot\cdot}{O}} — H$$

for the water molecule rather than $H — \overset{\cdot\cdot}{\underset{\cdot\cdot}{O}} — H$.

9-15. The Sizes of Atoms and Molecules. Covalent Radii and van der Waals Radii

Interatomic distances (bond lengths) in molecules and crystals can be determined by the methods of spectroscopy (including microwave spectroscopy), x-ray diffraction, electron diffraction, neutron diffraction, and nuclear magnetic resonance. The description of these methods is beyond the scope of this book. During the past forty years the bond lengths have been determined for many hundreds of substances, and their values have been found to be useful in the discussion of the electronic structures of molecules and crystals.

It has been found that usually the bond length for the single bond A—B is, to within about 0.03 Å, equal to the average of the bond lengths A—A and B—B. For example, the average of C—C (1.54 Å, Section 9-5) and Cl—Cl (1.98 Å) is $\frac{1}{2} \times (1.54 + 1.98) = 1.76$ Å. The value of C—Cl found by the investigation of CCl_4 by the electron diffraction method is 1.76 Å; hence the *single-bond covalent radii* 0.77 Å for C and 0.99 Å for Cl can be added together in three ways to give the three observed bond lengths C—C, Cl—Cl, and C—Cl.

Values of the single-bond covalent radii of nonmetallic elements are given in Table 9-3. The value for hydrogen is 0.30 Å, for all bonds other than H—H (the H—H bond length, 0.74 Å, corresponds to a larger radius for hydrogen than the value used for other bonds).

Table **9-3**

Single-bond Covalent Radii

C	0.77 Å	N	0.70 Å	O	0.66 Å	F	0.64 Å
Si	1.17	P	1.10	S	1.04	Cl	0.99
Ge	1.22	As	1.21	Se	1.17	Br	1.14
Sn	1.40	Sb	1.41	Te	1.37	I	1.33

It was mentioned in Section 9-5 that the C=C and C≡C bond lengths are 0.21 Å and 0.34 Å, respectively, less than the C—C bond length. Approximately the same shortening is found for other double and triple bonds. For example, for C—N the bond length 1.47 Å is given by the sum of the radii for carbon and nitrogen (Table 9-3), and the value $1.47 - 0.34 = 1.13$ Å would be expected for C≡N. The value observed in H—C≡N is 1.15 Å, in reasonably good agreement with the result of the calculation.

Bond lengths for hybrid structures have intermediate values.

Example 10. The bond lengths 1.13 Å for nitrogen-nitrogen and 1.19 Å for nitrogen-oxygen are observed in nitrous oxide, N_2O. What do these values indicate about the structure of the molecule?

Solution. Expected bond lengths (Table 9-3), with use of -0.21 Å for a double bond and -0.34 Å for a triple bond, are 1.19 Å for N=N, 1.06 Å for N≡N, 1.36 Å for N—O, and 1.15 Å for N=O. We see that the observed values indicate that the nitrogen-nitrogen bond is intermediate between a double bond and a triple bond and that the nitrogen-oxygen bond is intermediate between a single bond and a double bond. This comparison accordingly supports the conclusion reached in Example 9, that

the structure is a resonance hybrid of $: \text{N} \equiv \overset{+}{\text{N}} - \overset{..}{\underset{..}{\text{O}}} :^{-}$ and $:^{-} \overset{..}{\text{N}} = \overset{+}{\text{N}} = \overset{..}{\underset{..}{\text{O}}} :$.

Illustrative Exercise

9-24. The observed interatomic distance for carbon monoxide is 1.13 Å. Does this value agree with the value expected for the resonating structure described in Example 8?

Van der Waals Radii. Van der Waals found that in order to explain the deviations of real gases from ideal behavior (Section 6-12) it was necessary to assume that molecules have a well-defined size, so that two molecules begin to undergo strong repulsion when, as they approach, they reach a certain distance from one another. For example, the deviations of the noble gases from ideal behavior and other properties such as viscosity lead to the assignment of effective radii between 1 Å and 2 Å to their molecules. These radii are called the *van der Waals radii* of the atoms.

It has been found that the effective sizes of molecules packed together in liquids and crystals can be described by assigning similar van der Waals radii to each atom in the molecule. Values of these radii are given in Table 9-4.

Table **9-4**

Van der Waals Radii of Atoms

		H	1.1 Å		
N	1.5 Å	O	1.40	F	1.35 Å
P	1.9	S	1.85	Cl	1.80
As	2.0	Se	2.00	Br	1.95
Sb	2.2	Te	2.20	I	2.15

Radius of methyl group, —CH₃, 2.0 Å
Half-thickness of aromatic molecule (such as benzene or naphthalene), 1.7 Å

The values are seen to be about 0.8 Å larger than the corresponding single-bond covalent radii (Table 9-3). This difference is illustrated in Figure 9-20, which represents two chlorine molecules in van der Waals contact (packed together in a crystal or colliding in the liquid or gas—see Figure 2-6). Each chlorine atom is surrounded by four outer electron pairs. One pair is shared with the other chlorine atom in the same Cl_2 molecule. The point midway between the two nuclei, 0.99 A from each nucleus, represents the average

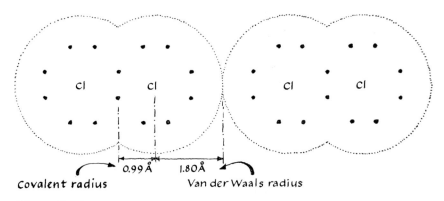

Figure **9-20**

Two chlorine molecules in van der Waals contact, illustrating the difference between van der Waals radius and covalent radius.

position of the shared pair. The three unshared pairs about each nucleus are also about the same distance, equal to the covalent radius, from the nucleus. When two nonbonded chlorine atoms are in contact there are two unshared pairs in the region between the nuclei; the van der Waals radius defines the region that includes the major part of the electron distribution function for the unshared pairs.

In making drawings of atoms or molecules, the van der Waals radii may be used in indicating the volume within which the electrons are largely contained. For ions, the ionic radii (crystal radii) discussed in Section 8-4 may be used. The van der Waals radius of an atom and the ionic radius of its negative ion are essentially the same. For example, the van der Waals radius of chlorine (Table 9-4) is 1.80 Å, and the ionic radius of the chloride ion (Table 8-3) is 1.81 Å.

The covalent radii have a different meaning and a different use. The sum of the single-bond covalent radii for two atoms is equal to the distance between the atoms when they are connected by a single covalent bond. The single-bond covalent radius of an atom may be considered to be the distance from the nucleus to the *average* position of the shared electron pair, whereas the van der Waals radius extends to the outer part of the region occupied by the electrons of the atom, as indicated in Figure 9-20.

Example 11. In making drawings of atoms of the noble gases, what values of the radius would you use?
   Solution. For this purpose the van der Waals radius is to be used. These values are not given for the noble gases in Table 9-4. However, from the sequence N 1.5, O 1.40, F 1.35, we may extrapolate to 1.30 Å for Ne, and similarly 1.75 A for Ar, 1.90 Å for Kr, and 2.10 Å for Xe. The value 1.1 Å for H suggests 1.0 Å for He.

Example 12. In a drawing in a textbook of college chemistry the chlorine atom is represented by a ball with radius about half of that for the chloride ion (radius 1.0 Å for Cl, 1.8 Å for Cl$^-$). Is this an acceptable representation? What are the relative sizes of Cl and Cl$^-$?

Solution. The chlorine atom has two $3s$ electrons and five $3p$ electrons in its outer shell. The chloride ion has two $3s$ electrons and six $3p$ electrons. Hence the atom and the ion have nearly the same electronic structure, and should be represented by spheres with nearly the same radius. In fact, the van der Waals radius for the atom is given as 1.80 Å in Table 9-4 and the crystal radius for the ion is given as 1.81 Å in Table 8-3. The representation of the chlorine atom as half the size of the chloride ion is erroneous, and is probably the result of a misunderstanding of the meaning of the covalent radius of the atom.

The effective radius of an atom in a direction that makes only a small angle with the direction of a covalent bond formed by the atom is smaller than the van der Waals radius in directions away from the bond. For example, in the carbon tetrachloride molecule the chlorine atoms are only 2.9 Å apart, and yet the properties of the substance indicate that there is no great strain, even though this distance is much less than the van der Waals diameter 3.6 Å.

EXERCISES

9-25. Make a drawing of each of the noble gases, He, Ne, Ar, Kr, and Xe, showing by dots the electrons in the outermost electron shell.

9-26. Write electronic structures for hydrogen iodide, HI; hydrogen selenide, H_2Se; phosphine, PH_3; arsenic trichloride, $AsCl_3$; chloroform, $HCCl_3$; ethane, C_2H_6. What are the expected values of the bond angles? Which of these molecules do you predict to have zero electric dipole moment?

9-27. Assuming that the following compounds contain ionic bonds only, write the electron-dot formula for each ion, and put in parentheses the symbol of the noble gas with the same structure:

HF   LiCl   Na$_2$O   MgO   KMgF$_3$

9-28. Write electronic structures for the following polyatomic ions, indicating all the electrons in the outer shell of each atom (assume that the various atoms of the ion are held together by covalent bonds):

Peroxide ion, O_2^{--}
Trisulfide ion, S_3^{--}
Borohydride ion, BH_4^-
Phosphonium ion, PH_4^+
Tetramethyl ammonium ion, $N(CH_3)_4^+$

For each of these ions, what corresponding neutral molecule has the same electronic structure? Example: HS$^-$, the hydrogen sulfide ion, has the same electronic structure as HCl.

9-29. Write electronic structures for the molecules NH$_3$ (ammonia) and BF$_3$ (boron trifluoride). When these substances are mixed they react to form a compound H$_3$NBF$_3$; such a compound is called an "addition compound." What is the electronic structure of this compound? What is the similarity in the electronic rearrangement in the following chemical reactions?

$$NH_3 + H^+ \longrightarrow NH_4^+$$
$$NH_3 + BF_3 \longrightarrow H_3NBF_3$$

9-30. Assuming covalent bonds, write electronic structures for the molecules ClF (chlorine fluoride), BrF$_3$ (bromine trifluoride), SbCl$_5$ (antimony pentachloride), H$_2$S$_2$

(hydrogen disulfide). In which of these molecules are there atoms with electron configurations that are not noble-gas configurations?

9-31. Write the resonating electronic structures for the nitrate ion, NO_3^-; the nitrite ion, NO_2^-; the carbonate ion, CO_3^{--}; ozone.

9-32. How does the difference in the structures of diamond and graphite manifest itself in some of the physical properties of these substances?

9-33. By reference to the electronegativity scale, arrange the following binary compounds in rough order of their stability, placing those you think would be especially stable at the top of the list, and the most unstable at the bottom of the list:

Phosphine, PH_3
Aluminum oxide, Al_2O_3
Hydrogen iodide, HI
Lithium fluoride, LiF
Cesium fluoride, CsF
Sodium iodide, NaI
Nitrogen trichloride, NCl_3
Selenium diiodide, SeI_2

9-34. What is the electronic structure of tin tetriodide, SnI_4? What noble-gas structure is assumed by each atom? What is the spatial configuration of the molecule? What is the value of its electric dipole moment? Of the Sn—I bond length?

9-35. What is the electronic structure of sulfur dichloride, SCl_2? What value do you predict for the bond length? For the amount of ionic character of the S—Cl bond? For the electric dipole moment of the S—Cl bond? For the electric dipole moment of the SCl_2 molecule, assuming 90° for the bond angle?

9-36. In Exercise 7-23 it is pointed out that the radius of the Bohr orbit with total quantum number n about a nucleus with charge Ze is $n^2 a_0/Z$, with $a_0 = 0.530$ Å. The van der Waals radius of hydrogen, 1.1 Å (Table 9-4), is twice the Bohr radius. Why is not 0.53 Å suggested above as the van der Waals radius of helium? (Answer: If there were only one electron, 0.53 Å would be right. But each electron moves in the electric field of the nucleus shielded to some extent by the other electron. The effective nuclear charge in the helium atom lies between 1 and 2.)

9-37. What electronic structure would you assign to SF_6? To S_2F_{10}? Note that sulfur has $3d$ orbitals available, which can be hybridized with the $3s$ and $3p$ orbitals to form bond orbitals.

9-38. Assign electronic structures to Si_2Cl_6 and Si_2Cl_6O. Would you expect both of these molecules to have an electric dipole moment differing from zero?

9-39. Phosphorus forms the halogen compounds PF_3Br_2, PCl_3Br_2, and PCl_3I_2, but not PF_2Br_3, PCl_2Br_3, and PCl_2I_3. Can you suggest an explanation of this fact?

9-40. From the values of single-bond covalent radii of Sb, Te, and I given in Table 9-3, estimate a value for Xe. What is the predicted value for the Xe—F bond length? (By x-ray diffraction of XeF_4 crystals the experimental value 1.92 ± 0.03 Å has been determined.)

9-41. Predict values for the single-bond covalent radius of krypton and for the Kr—F bond length. (No experimental value has yet been reported.)

REFERENCES

G. N. Lewis, *Valence and the Structure of Atoms and Molecules*, Chemical Catalog Co., 1923. This is a famous book, in which the author summarizes his work on the chemical bond.

L. Pauling, *The Nature of the Chemical Bond and the Structure of Molecules and Crystals*, Third Edition, Cornell University Press, Ithaca, N.Y., 1960. Later developments in chemical bond theory are described in this book.

3

Some Nonmetallic Elements

and Their Compounds

We have now obtained, through the study of the five chapters that constitute Part 2 of our book, an understanding of weight relations in chemical reactions and of the properties of gases that permits us to discuss such questions as the amount of a product that might be produced by the reaction of substances with one another, and also, through the study of thermochemistry, the quantum theory, the Boltzmann distribution law, the electronic structure of atoms, ionic valence, covalence, partial ionic character of bonds, the electronegativity scale of the elements, and the electroneutrality principle, an understanding of the structure of substances and the combining power of atoms that permits us to discuss the properties of substances in terms of their structure. With this background we may now continue the study of the chemistry of some of the nonmetallic elements, which was initiated in Chapter 6, where hydrogen and oxygen were discussed.

Chapter 10 deals with carbon and the compounds of carbon. This chapter is followed by a chapter on the use of oxidation numbers of atoms in balancing equations for oxidation-reduction reactions. The next four chapters of the book deal respectively with the chemistry of the halogens, of sulfur, selenium, and tellurium, of nitrogen, and of phosphorus, arsenic, antimony, and bismuth.

In the study of the chapters of Part 3 you may find it useful to correlate the properties of the elements and their compounds with the periodic system. The formulas and properties of the compounds of these nonmetallic elements change in a regular way from group to group (horizontally in the periodic system), and from period to period (vertically). The theory of electronic structure that has been developed during the past 60 years is still far from complete, and you will find that there are some compounds described that you have difficulty in fitting into the system. Nevertheless, even though it is not perfect, the present system of electronic structure can be of much value by serving as the framework to which you can tie the facts of chemistry in the course of your study.

10

Carbon and Compounds of Carbon

Carbon is the first element of the fourth group of the periodic table, the others being silicon, germanium, tin, and lead (Chapter 22). Carbon forms a great many compounds, and its chemistry is especially interesting to us because most of the substances that make up a human body (and other living organisms) are compounds of carbon. Moreover, the compounds of carbon illustrate the principles that have been discussed in the preceding chapters and others that need to be discussed. It is for these reasons that we now consider the chemistry of carbon.

The name *organic chemistry*, which was originally used to refer to the chemistry of substances that occur in living organisms (plants and animals), is now used for the chemistry of the compounds of carbon. The chemistry of the elements other than carbon is called *inorganic chemistry*.

Biochemistry may be considered to be a part of organic chemistry. It deals especially with the chemical reactions that take place in living organisms. The manufacture of the artificial fiber nylon, for example, is included in organic chemistry, but not in biochemistry; the structure, methods of synthesis, and general chemical properties of vitamin B_1 are a part of organic chemistry, and the special reactions of this substance in plants and animals are a part of biochemistry.

We shall consider some aspects of organic chemistry and biochemistry throughout this book, beginning in the following paragraphs. A more detailed discussion of organic chemistry will then be given in Chapter 27, and of biochemistry in Chapter 28.

10-1. The Electronic Structure and Properties of the Carbon Atom

The normal state of the carbon atom is represented by the symbol $1s^2 2s^2 2p^2 \, {}^3P$ (Section 7-5). In addition to the electron pair of the inner shell (the K shell), the atom has a pair of electrons in the $2s$ orbital and two valence electrons, with parallel spins, in two of the $2p$ orbitals. The first two excited states of the atom are ^1D at 29 kcal/mole and ^1S at 62 kcal/mole above the normal state; these states, like the normal state, are based on the configuration $1s^22s^22p^2$, with only the two $2p$ electrons available for use in forming covalent bonds (Section 9-2).

We would accordingly expect the carbon atom to retain an unshared pair of electrons in its outer shell and to use the other two electrons to form two covalent bonds. Known molecules containing carbon atoms with an unshared electron pair in the outer shell include CH_2, CCl_2, C_2, CO, and CS (Section 10-11). All of these substances except carbon monoxide are highly reactive.

In most of its compounds carbon is quadrivalent. It uses all four of its outer electrons in forming covalent bonds, and has no unshared electron pair in its outer shell. The four bond orbitals are the tetrahedral sp^3 hybrid orbitals described in Section 9-5.

The quadrivalent carbon atom is based upon the electron configuration $1s^22s2p^3$, in which the four electrons of the outer shell occupy four orbitals separately (the $2s$ orbital and the three $2p$ orbitals, or the four tetrahedral orbitals). The lowest state of the carbon atom based upon this configuration is ^5S, which lies 96 kcal/mole above the normal state. The quadrivalent state of the carbon atom is described as involving the *promotion* of one electron from the $2s$ orbital to a $2p$ orbital. The energy of the quadrivalent state is estimated to be about 100 kcal/mole above that of the bivalent state.*

Values of the standard enthalpy of formation (heat content relative to the elements in their standard states) for a few carbon compounds are given in

Table **10-1**

Standard Enthalpy of Formation of Carbon Compounds at 25°C (kcal/mole)

C(graphite)	0.00	$C_2H_2(g)$	54.19	$CH_2O(g)$	formaldehyde	−27.7
C(diamond)	0.45	$C_2H_4(g)$	12.50	$CH_3CHO(g)$	acetaldehyde	−39.67
$C(g)$	171.70	$C_2H_6(g)$	−20.24	$(CH_3)_2CO(g)$	acetone	−51.72
$C^+(g)$	431.65	$CF_4(g)$	−218	$HCOOH(g)$	formic acid	−86.67
$C_2(g)$	234.7	$CCl_4(g)$	−25.5	$CH_3COOH(g)$	acetic acid	−103.8
$CO(g)$	−26.42	$CHCl_3(g)$	−24	$CH_3OH(g)$	methanol	−48.08
$CO^+(g)$	292.5	$CH_2Cl_2(g)$	−21	$C_2H_5OH(g)$	ethanol	−56.63
$CO_2(g)$	−94.05	$CH_3Cl(g)$	−19.6	$(CH_3)_2O(g)$	dimethyl ether	−44.3
$CH(g)$	142.1	$CBr_4(g)$	12	$C_3H_6(g)$	cyclopropane	9.0
$CH_2(g)$	95	$CS_2(g)$	27.55	$C_6H_{12}(g)$	cyclohexane	−29.98
$CH_3(g)$	32.0	$COS(g)$	−32.80	$C_6H_{10}(g)$	cyclohexene	−1.39
$CH_4(g)$	−17.90	$(CH_3)_2S(g)$	−8.98	$C_6H_6(g)$	benzene	19.82

* The energy difference of a $2p$ electron and a $2s$ electron is about 180 kcal/mole. Quantum mechanical calculations have shown that the quadrivalent state does not require complete $2s \longrightarrow 2p$ promotion.

Table 10-1. These values are selected from those for hundreds of compounds that have been determined by experiment.

We may use these values to discuss the question of why carbon is usually quadrivalent rather than bivalent. Let us take CH_2 and CH_4 as examples. From Table 10-1 we obtain values for the heats of formation of the two substances (enthalpies of formation with changed sign):

$$C(\text{graphite}) + H_2 \longrightarrow CH_2(g) - 95 \text{ kcal/mole}$$
$$C(\text{graphite}) + 2H_2 \longrightarrow CH_4(g) + 17.90 \text{ kcal/mole}$$

By combining these two equations we obtain

$$CH_2 + H_2 \longrightarrow CH_4 + 113 \text{ kcal/mole}$$

and

$$2CH_2 \longrightarrow C(\text{graphite}) + CH_4 + 208 \text{ kcal/mole}$$

The reverse of the first equation is

$$CH_2 \longrightarrow C(\text{graphite}) + H_2 + 95 \text{ kcal/mole}$$

The driving force of a chemical reaction is not just the enthalpy change; another factor, the entropy change (a measure of probability, Section 18-10), is also involved. Nevertheless, the heat of reaction is very important and often predominant. Reactions that are highly exothermic often proceed with explosive violence. For example, the decomposition of acetylene, $H—C\equiv C—H$, into graphite and hydrogen is exothermic (Table 10-1):

$$C_2H_2(g) \longrightarrow 2C(\text{graphite}) + H_2 + 54.19 \text{ kcal/mole}$$

Liquid acetylene is a treacherously explosive substance. We would accordingly expect CH_2, if it could be made in concentrated form, to react to produce the elements or graphite and methane or some other products.

A further discussion of the stability of quadrivalent carbon is given in Section 10-11.

We do not need to know the electronic structure of the valence bond in order to use the chemical structure theory. Indeed, the quadrivalence of carbon was known and structural formulas (valence-bond formulas) of compounds were written by chemists for forty years before the electron was discovered, and another thirty years had gone by before a clear picture had been obtained of the electronic structure of the covalent bond. The development, a century ago, of the chemical structure theory as a correlating theory for the mass of information about the chemical properties of substances was one of the greatest of all intellectual feats.

10-2. Elementary Carbon

Carbon occurs in nature in its elementary state in two allotropic forms: **diamond,** the hardest substance known, which often forms beautiful transparent and highly refractive crystals, used as gems (Figure 10-1); and **graphite,**

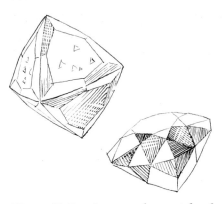

Figure **10-1** *A natural crystal of diamond, with octahedral faces and smaller faces rounding the edges, and a brilliant-cut diamond.*

a soft, black crystalline substance, used as a lubricant and in the "lead" of lead pencils. *Bort* and *black diamond* are imperfectly crystalline forms of diamond, which do not show the cleavage characteristic of diamond crystals. Their density is slightly less than that of crystalline diamond, and they are tougher and somewhat harder. They are used in diamond drills and saws and other grinding and cutting devices. Other uses of diamonds also depend upon their great hardness. For example, diamonds with a tapering hole drilled through them are used for drawing wires. Charcoal, coke, and carbon black (lampblack) are microcrystalline or amorphous forms of carbon. The density of diamond is 3.51 g/cm³ and that of graphite is 2.26 g/cm³.

The great hardness of diamond is explained by the structure of the diamond crystal, as determined by the x-ray diffraction method. In the diamond crystal (Figure 10-2) each carbon atom is surrounded by four other carbon atoms, which lie at the corners of a regular tetrahedron about it. A structural formula can be written for a small part of a diamond crystal:

$$
\begin{array}{ccc}
\diagdown\ \big|\ & & \big|\ \diagup \\
-C & & C- \\
\diagdown & & \diagup \\
& C & \\
\diagup & & \diagdown \\
-C & & C- \\
\diagup\ \big|\ & & \big|\ \diagdown
\end{array}
$$

Valence bonds connect each carbon atom with four others. Each of these four is bonded to three others (plus the original one), and so on throughout the crystal. The entire crystal is a giant molecule, held together by covalent bonds. To break the crystal, many of these bonds must be broken; this requires a large amount of energy, and hence the substance is very hard. The bond length in diamond has the single-bond value, 1.54 Å.

It was discovered in 1934 that natural diamonds can be divided into two classes on the basis of their ultraviolet and infrared absorption spectra. The type-I diamonds, which constitute about 99% of all natural diamonds, have a strong absorption band in the infrared region 7 to 10 μ [1 μ (micron) is 10,000 Å], whereas the type-II diamonds are transparent in this spectral range. The type-I diamonds also show extra x-ray diffraction spots, not accounted for by the structure shown in Figure 10-2. The properties of the type-I diamonds indicate that there are imperfections in the crystals, either foreign atoms or vacancies (missing carbon atoms), or possibly small groups of carbon atoms with changed positions replacing groups with the normal structure. It has been found that many type-I diamond crystals contain about 0.2% of nitrogen-14 atoms, but the way in which these atoms fit into the diamond structure has not yet been determined, nor is it known whether or not other atoms may be the important impurities in some type-I diamonds.

Most diamonds have extremely low electric conductivity, but a few type-II diamonds (called type-IIb) have been found to be semiconductors. The nature of the impurity or structural defect responsible for the conductivity is not known.

The French chemist Henri Moissan (1852–1907) and the English chemists Crookes and Hannay reported that they had made small diamonds by dropping a crucible containing liquid iron with some dissolved carbon into cold water. Recent work has indicated that they were not successful.

The commercial manufacture of diamonds was begun in the period around 1950, after techniques for obtaining very high pressures (over 70,000 atm) at high temperatures (2000°C) had been developed. The crystallization of the artificial diamonds is favored by the addition of a small amount of a metal such as nickel. It is significant that the length of the edge of the unit cube of the nickel crystal, containing four nickel atoms in cubic closest packing, is 3.52 Å, nearly equal to that, 3.56 Å, of the unit cube of the diamond crystal, which contains eight carbon atoms in the arrangement shown in Figure 10-2.

Figure **10-2**

The structure of diamond.

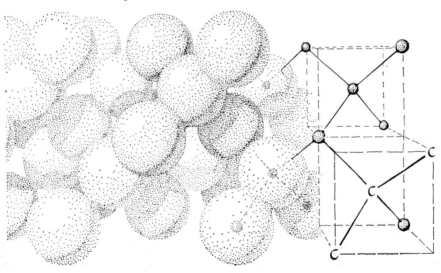

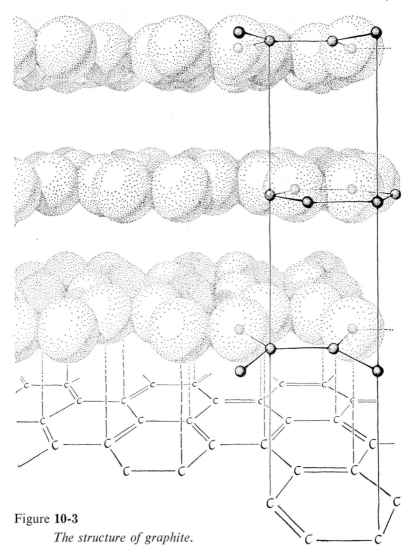

Figure **10-3**

The structure of graphite.

Artificial diamonds contain some nickel atoms replacing pairs of carbon atoms.

The structure of graphite is shown in Figure 10-3. It is a layer structure. Each atom forms two single bonds and one double bond with its three nearest neighbors, as shown in the lowest part of the drawing. The bonds resonate among the positions in each layer in such a way as to give each bond two-thirds single-bond character and one-third double-bond character. The interatomic distances in the layer are 1.42 Å, which is intermediate between the single-bond value, 1.54 Å, and the double-bond value, 1.33 Å. The distance between layers is 3.4 Å, over twice the bond length in a layer. The crystal of graphite can be described as built of giant flat molecules, loosely held together in a pile. The layers can be easily separated; hence graphite is a soft substance, which is even used as a lubricant.

Hardness. The property of hardness is not a simple one to define. It has probably evaded precise definition because the concept of hardness represents a composite of several properties (tensile strength, resistance to cleavage, etc.). Various scales of hardness and instruments for testing hardness have been proposed. One test consists of dropping a diamond-tipped weight on the specimen and measuring the height of rebound. In another test (the Brinell test) a hardened steel ball is pressed into the surface of the specimen, and the size of the produced indentation is measured.

A very simple test of hardness is the scratch test—a specimen that scratches another specimen and is not scratched by it is said to be harder than the second specimen. The scratch-test scale used by mineralogists is the *Mohs scale*, with reference points (the *Mohs hardness*) from 1 to 10, defined by the following ten minerals:

1. Talc, $Mg_3Si_4O_{10}(OH)_2$
2. Gypsum, $CaSO_4 \cdot 2H_2O$
3. Calcite, $CaCO_3$
4. Fluorite, CaF_2
5. Apatite, $Ca_5(PO_4)_3F$
6. Orthoclase, $KAlSi_3O_8$
7. Quartz, SiO_2
8. Topaz, $Al_2SiO_4F_2$
9. Corundum, Al_2O_3
10. Diamond, C

Diamond is indeed far harder than corundum, and modifications of the Mohs scale have been suggested that assign a much larger hardness number, such as 15, to diamond. The hardness of graphite is between 1 and 2.

10-3.   Carbon Monoxide and Carbon Dioxide

Carbon burns to form the gases *carbon monoxide*, CO, and *carbon dioxide*, CO_2, the former being produced when there is a deficiency of oxygen or when the flame temperature is very high.

Carbon Monoxide.   Carbon monoxide is a colorless, odorless gas with small solubility in water (35.4 ml per liter of water at 0°C and 1 atm). It is poisonous, because of its ability to combine with the hemoglobin in the blood in the same way that oxygen does; thus the carbon monoxide prevents the hemoglobin from combining with oxygen in the lungs and carrying it to the tissues. It causes death when about one-half of the hemoglobin in the blood has been converted into carbonmonoxyhemoglobin. The exhaust gas from automobile engines contains some carbon monoxide, and it is accordingly dangerous to be in a closed garage with an automobile whose engine is running. Carbon monoxide is a valuable industrial gas, for use as a fuel and as a reducing agent.

The heat of formation of carbon monoxide is 26.42 kcal/mole (Table 10-1), and its heat of combustion is 67.63 kcal/mole:

$$C(graphite) + \tfrac{1}{2}O_2(g) \longrightarrow CO(g) + 26.42 \text{ kcal/mole}$$
$$CO(g) + \tfrac{1}{2}O_2(g) \longrightarrow CO_2(g) + 67.63 \text{ kcal/mole}$$

The blue lambent flame seen over a charcoal fire involves the combustion of the carbon monoxide that has been formed by the surface combustion of the charcoal.

In Example 8 of Chapter 9 it was suggested from consideration of its electric dipole moment that the carbon monoxide molecule has an electronic structure that is a hybrid of $:C{\equiv}O:$ and $:C{=}\overset{..}{O}:$. Support for this structure is provided by the heats of formation from atoms of the three molecules C_2, O_2, and CO (Table 10-1):

$$2C(g) \longrightarrow C_2(g) + 108.7 \text{ kcal/mole}$$
$$2O(g) \longrightarrow O_2(g) + 118.32 \text{ kcal/mole}$$
$$C(g) + O(g) \longrightarrow CO(g) + 257.28 \text{ kcal/mole}$$

The bond energy of carbon monoxide, 257.28 kcal/mole, is larger than that for any other diatomic molecule. We may first estimate the energy of the double bond, $:C{=}\overset{..}{O}:$. Its value is approximately the average* of the values for C_2 and O_2, with the addition of $2 \times 23 = 46$ kcal/mole for the partial ionic character of the two single C—O bent bonds constituting the double bond (Equation 1 of Chapter 9): $\tfrac{1}{2}(108.7 + 118.3) + 46 = 159.5$ kcal/mole. This value is much less than the observed bond energy, and the structure $:C{=}\overset{..}{O}:$ for the CO molecule is accordingly not acceptable. (The observed bond length 1.13 Å also rules out the double-bond structure, which would give bond length 1.22 Å; Section 9-15.) For the triple-bond structure $:C{\equiv}O:$, in which all four orbitals of the carbon atom as well as of the oxygen atom are used, we estimate that the bond energy is about 240 kcal/mole, 50% greater than for the double-bond structure. The experimental value, 257 kcal/mole, is a little larger still; the difference is the resonance energy between the two structures (Section 10-9).

Carbon Dioxide. Carbon dioxide is a colorless, odorless gas with a weakly acid taste, due to the formation of some carbonic acid when it is dissolved in water. It is about 50% heavier than air. It is easily soluble in water, one liter of water at 0°C dissolving 1713 ml of the gas under 1 atm pressure. Its melting point (freezing point) is higher than the point of vaporization at 1 atm of the crystalline form. When crystalline carbon dioxide is heated from a very low temperature, its vapor pressure reaches 1 atm at −79°C, at which temperature it vaporizes (sublimes) without melting. If the pressure is increased to 5.2 atm, the crystalline substance melts to a liquid at −56.6°C. Under ordinary

---

* The oxygen molecule contains a single bond and two three-electron bonds (Section 9-7). Its bond energy is approximately that of a double bond, since a three-electron bond (as well as a one-electron bond) is about half as strong as an electron-pair bond. The C_2 molecule also has a triplet structure, with two one-electron bonds and a single bond, $:C{\div}C:$.

pressure, then, the solid substance is changed directly to a gas. This property has made solid carbon dioxide (dry ice) popular as a refrigerating agent.

Carbon dioxide combines with water to form *carbonic acid*, H_2CO_3, a weak acid whose salts are the *carbonates*. The carbonates are important minerals (see calcium carbonate, Section 10-5).

The enthalpy of formation of carbon dioxide is -94.05 kcal/mole. Its heat of sublimation at $-78.48°C$ (1 atm pressure) is 6.031 kcal/mole. The molecule is linear, with carbon-oxygen bond length 1.159 Å.

Uses of Carbon Dioxide. Carbon dioxide is used for the manufacture of *sodium carbonate*, $Na_2CO_3 \cdot 10H_2O$ (washing soda); *sodium hydrogen carbonate*, $NaHCO_3$ (baking soda); and carbonated water, for use as a beverage (soda water). Carbonated water is charged with carbon dioxide under a pressure of 3 or 4 atm.

Carbon dioxide can be used to extinguish fires by smothering them. One form of portable fire extinguisher is a cylinder of liquid carbon dioxide—the gas can be liquefied at ordinary temperatures under pressures of about 70 atm. Some commercial carbon dioxide (mainly solid carbon dioxide) is made from the gas emitted in nearly pure state from gas wells in the western United States. Most of the carbon dioxide used commercially is a by-product (subsidiary substance produced in the process) of cement mills, limekilns, iron blast furnaces, and breweries.

Illustrative Exercises	**10-1.** By use of the values of enthalpy of formation of CO and CO_2 given in Table 10-1, derive the value of the heat of combustion of carbon monoxide. (Answer: 67.63 kcal/mole.)
	10-2. From values given in Tables 6-1 and 10-1, calculate the heats of formation of C_2, O_2, and CO molecules from atoms. (Answer: 108.7, 118.32, 257.28 kcal/mole.)
	10-3. From the heat of sublimation of crystalline carbon dioxide given above and the heat of fusion of ice (1.4363 kcal/mole), determine (a) which of the two substances is the better cooling agent, and (b) by what amount. [Answer: (b) 72% better.]

10-4. Carbonic Acid and Carbonates

When carbon dioxide dissolves in water, some of it reacts to form carbonic acid:

$$CO_2 + H_2O \longrightarrow H_2CO_3$$

The structural formula of carbonic acid is

$$O=C\begin{smallmatrix} \nearrow O-H \\ \searrow O-H \end{smallmatrix}$$

The acid is diprotic; with a base such as sodium hydroxide it may form both a normal salt, Na_2CO_3, and an acid salt, $NaHCO_3$. The normal salt contains the carbonate ion, CO_3^{--}, and the acid salt contains the hydrogen carbonate ion, HCO_3^-.

For many years chemists assigned the structural formula

$$O=C \begin{matrix} O^- \\ \\ O^- \end{matrix}$$

to the carbonate ion. With this formula, one of the oxygen atoms is attached to the carbon atom by a double bond, and the other two are attached by single bonds. Then in 1914 W. L. Bragg carried out an x-ray diffraction study of calcite, $CaCO_3$, and found that the three bonds from the carbon atom to the three oxygen atoms in the carbonate ion in this crystal are identical. This new experimental fact required a change in the structural formula. The new structural formula was proposed in 1931, when the chemical resonance theory was developed (Section 9-8). For the carbonate ion the structure is a hybrid of three structures:

$$\left\{ O=C\begin{matrix} O^- \\ \\ O^- \end{matrix} \qquad -O-C\begin{matrix} O \\ \\ O^- \end{matrix} \qquad -O-C\begin{matrix} O^- \\ \\ O \end{matrix} \right\}$$

Each oxygen atom is attached to the carbon atom by a bond that is a hybrid of a double bond (one-third) and a single bond (two-thirds). The three carbon-oxygen bonds are thus identical.

Calcium Carbonate.   The most important carbonate mineral is calcium carbonate, $CaCO_3$. This substance occurs in beautiful colorless hexagonal crystals as the mineral *calcite* (Figure 10-4). *Marble* is a microcrystalline form of calcium carbonate, and *limestone* is a rock composed mainly of this substance. Calcium carbonate is the principal constituent also of pearls, coral, and most sea shells. It also occurs in a second crystalline form, as the orthorhombic mineral *aragonite* (Figure 10-5).

When calcium carbonate is heated (as in a limekiln, Figure 10-6, where limestone is mixed with fuel, which is burned), it decomposes, forming calcium oxide (*quicklime*):

$$CaCO_3 \longrightarrow CaO + CO_2(g)$$

Quicklime is slaked by adding water, to form calcium hydroxide:

$$CaO + H_2O \longrightarrow Ca(OH)_2$$

Slaked lime prepared in this way is a white powder that can be mixed with water and sand to form *mortar*. The mortar hardens by first forming crystals

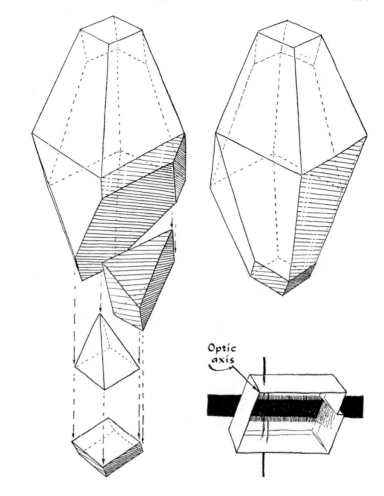

Figure **10-4**

> *Natural crystals of calcite, CaCO$_3$, showing planes of cleavage and how they produce the cleavage rhombohedron (left). The property of birefringence (double refraction) is possessed by calcite (lower right).*

of calcium hydroxide, which cement the grains of sand together; then on exposure to air the mortar continues to get harder by taking up carbon dioxide and forming calcium carbonate:

$$Ca(OH)_2 + CO_2 \longrightarrow CaCO_3 + H_2O$$

Large amounts of limestone are used also in the manufacture of Portland cement, described in Chapter 22.

Sodium carbonate (washing soda, sal soda), Na$_2$CO$_3\cdot$10H$_2$O, is a white, crystalline substance used as a household alkali, for washing and cleaning, and as an industrial chemical. The crystals of the decahydrate lose water readily,

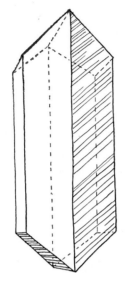

Figure **10-5** *Natural crystal of aragonite, another form of calcium carbonate, CaCO₃.*

forming the monohydrate, $Na_2CO_3 \cdot H_2O$. The monohydrate when heated to 100°C changes to anhydrous sodium carbonate (*soda ash*), Na_2CO_3.

Sodium hydrogen carbonate (*baking soda, bicarbonate of soda*), $NaHCO_3$, is a white substance usually available as a powder. It is used in cooking, in medicine, and in the manufacture of *baking powder*.

Baking powder is a leavening agent used in making biscuits, cakes, and other food. Its purpose is to provide bubbles of gas, to make the dough "rise." The same foods can be made by use of sodium hydrogen carbonate (baking soda) and sour milk, instead of baking powder. In each case the reaction that occurs involves the action of an acid on sodium hydrogen carbonate to form carbon dioxide. When sour milk is used, the acid that reacts with the sodium hydrogen carbonate is lactic acid, $HC_3H_5O_3$; the equation for the reaction is

$$NaHCO_3 + HC_3H_5O_3 \longrightarrow$$
$$NaC_3H_5O_3 + H_2O + CO_2(g)$$

The product $NaC_3H_5O_3$ is sodium lactate, the sodium salt of lactic acid. Cream of tartar baking powder consists of sodium hydrogen carbonate, potassium hydrogen tartrate ($KHC_4H_4O_6$, commonly known as cream of tartar), and starch, the starch being added to keep the powder from forming a solid cake. The reaction that occurs when water is added to a cream of tartar baking powder is

$$NaHCO_3 + KHC_4H_4O_6 \longrightarrow NaKC_4H_4O_6 + H_2O + CO_2(g)$$

Baking powders are also made with calcium dihydrogen phosphate, $Ca(H_2PO_4)_2$, sodium dihydrogen phosphate, NaH_2PO_4, or sodium aluminum sulfate, $NaAl(SO_4)_2$, as the acidic constituent.

The leavening agent in ordinary bread dough is *yeast*, a microorganism. This microorganism produces an *enzyme* (an organic catalyst) that converts sugar into alcohol and carbon dioxide:

$$C_6H_{12}O_6 \longrightarrow 2C_2H_5OH + 2CO_2(g)$$

The formula $C_6H_{12}O_6$ in this equation represents glucose, a simple sugar.

The Ammonia-Soda Process. Sodium carbonate is a very important chemical, over four million tons being made every year. About a quarter of the total amount is used in making glass, and another quarter in making soap, the rest being required in the textile and paper industries and many others. Nearly all of this great quantity of sodium carbonate is made from sodium chloride by a process called the *ammonia-soda process* or *Solvay process*.

This process depends upon the fact that sodium hydrogen carbonate is less soluble in water than are sodium chloride, ammonium hydrogen carbonate (NH_4HCO_3), and ammonium chloride.

The raw materials used in the process are sodium chloride and calcium carbonate (limestone), as well as coal to supply power and heat. The limestone is heated in a kiln, to produce carbon dioxide and lime (calcium oxide):

$$CaCO_3 \longrightarrow CaO + CO_2(g)$$

The carbon dioxide is allowed to react with a solution of sodium chloride that has been saturated with ammonia; ammonium ion and hydrogen carbonate ion are formed in the solution:

$$NH_3 + H_2O + CO_2 \longrightarrow NH_4^+ + HCO_3^-$$

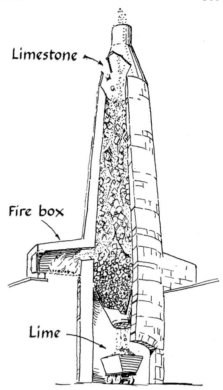

Figure **10-6** *A limekiln.*

When a sufficiently large amount of carbon dioxide has dissolved in the solution, the solution becomes saturated with sodium hydrogen carbonate, which precipitates out:

$$Na^+ + HCO_3^- \longrightarrow NaHCO_3(c)$$

The solid sodium hydrogen carbonate is filtered off, purified by recrystallization, and dried. Most of it is converted into sodium carbonate, by heating it:

$$2NaHCO_3 \longrightarrow Na_2CO_3 + H_2O + CO_2(g)$$

The carbon dioxide formed in this reaction is used along with that made from limestone to make more sodium hydrogen carbonate.

The low cost of sodium carbonate made by this process depends upon the fact that the ammonia can be nearly completely recovered. At the end of the process, after the sodium hydrogen carbonate has precipitated out and has been filtered off, a solution of ammonium chloride remains. The calcium oxide obtained from the limekiln is converted into calcium hydroxide by the addition of water, and the calcium hydroxide when added to the solution of ammonium chloride liberates ammonia:

$$CaO + H_2O \longrightarrow Ca(OH)_2$$
$$Ca(OH)_2 + 2NH_4Cl \longrightarrow CaCl_2 + 2H_2O + 2NH_3(g)$$

Hence the only substances used up in the process are limestone and common salt, and the only by-product is calcium chloride.

10-5. The Alkanes

The *hydrocarbons* are compounds composed of hydrogen and carbon alone. The simplest hydrocarbon is **methane,** CH_4. The methane molecule is tetrahedral, the four hydrogen atoms lying at the corners of a regular tetrahedron about the carbon atom, and connected with the carbon atom by single bonds (Figure 9-7).

Methane is a colorless, odorless gas. Some of its properties, and those of some other hydrocarbons, are given in Table 10-2.

Table **10-2**

Some Physical Properties of Normal Alkanes

SUBSTANCE	FORMULA	MELTING POINT	BOILING POINT	DENSITY OF LIQUID
Methane	CH_4	$-183°C$	$-161°C$	0.54 g/ml
Ethane	C_2H_6	-172	-88	.55
Propane	C_3H_8	-190	-45	.58
Butane	C_4H_{10}	-135	-1	.60
Pentane	C_5H_{12}	-130	36	.63
Hexane	C_6H_{14}	-95	69	.66
Heptane	C_7H_{16}	-91	98	.68
Octane	C_8H_{18}	-57	126	.70
Nonane	C_9H_{20}	-54	151	.72
Decane	$C_{10}H_{22}$	-30	174	.73
Pentadecane	$C_{15}H_{32}$	10	271	.77
Eicosane	$C_{20}H_{42}$	38		.78
Triacontane	$C_{30}H_{62}$	70		.79

Natural gas, from oil wells or gas wells, is usually about 85% methane. The gas that rises from the bottom of a marsh is methane (plus some carbon dioxide and nitrogen), formed by the anaerobic (air-free) fermentation of vegetable matter.

Methane is used as a fuel. It is also used in large quantities for the manufacture of carbon black, by combustion with a limited supply of air:

$$CH_4 + O_2 \longrightarrow 2H_2O + C$$

The methane burns to form water, and the carbon is deposited as very finely divided carbon, which finds extensive use as a filler for rubber for automobile tires.

Methane is the first member of a series of hydrocarbons called the *methane series* or *paraffin series*. Some of these compounds are listed in Table 10-2. They are called *alkanes*.

The name paraffin means "having little affinity." The compounds of this series are not very reactive chemically. They occur in petroleum. **Ethane** has the structure

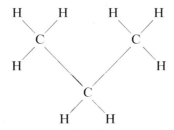

It is a gas (Table 10-2), which occurs in large amounts in natural gas from some wells. Propane, the third member of the series, has the structure

It is an easily liquefied gas, used as a fuel.

In the structural formula for propane there is a chain of three carbon atoms bonded together. The next larger alkane, **butane,** C_4H_{10}, can be obtained by replacing a hydrogen atom at one end of the chain by a methyl group,

Its formula is obtained by adding CH_2 to that of propane. These hydrocarbons, with longer and longer chains of carbon atoms, are called the *normal alkanes.*

The lighter members of the paraffin series are gases, the intermediate members are liquids, and the heavier members are solid substances. The common name *petroleum ether* refers to the pentane-hexane-heptane mixture, used as a solvent and in dry cleaning. *Gasoline* is the heptane-to-nonane mixture (C_7H_{16} to C_9H_{20}), and *kerosene* the decane-to-hexadecane mixture ($C_{10}H_{22}$ to $C_{16}H_{34}$). *Heavy fuel oil* is a mixture of paraffins containing twenty or more carbon atoms per molecule. The *lubricating oils, petroleum jelly* ("Vaseline"), and *solid paraffin* are mixtures of still larger paraffin molecules.

Isomerism. The phenomenon of isomerism is shown first in the paraffin series by butane, C_4H_{10}. *Isomerism is the existence of two or more compound substances having the same composition but different properties.* The difference in properties is usually the result of difference in the structure of the molecule, that is, in the way that the atoms are bonded together. There are two isomers of butane, called *normal butane* (*n*-butane) and *isobutane.* These substances have the structures shown in Figure 10-7; normal butane has a "straight chain" (actually the carbon chain is a zigzag chain, because of the tetrahedral nature of the carbon atom), and the isobutane molecule contains a branched chain. In general, the properties of these isomers are rather similar; for example, their melting points are $-135°C$ and $-145°C$, respectively. The branched-chain hydrocarbons are more stable than their straight-chain isomers [standard

Figure **10-7**

The structure of the isomers normal butane and isobutane.

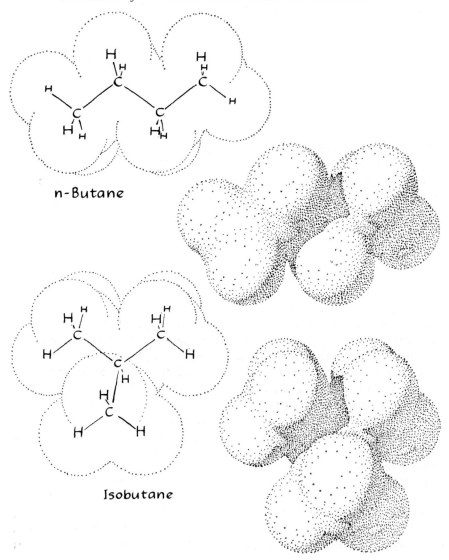

n-Butane

Isobutane

enthalpy of formation -30.15 kcal/mole for n-$C_4H_{10}(g)$, -32.15 for *iso*-$C_4H_{10}(g)$; -35.00 for n-$C_5H_{12}(g)$, -36.92 for *iso*-$C_5H_{15}(g)$, -39.67 for *neo*-$C_5H_{12}(g)$; neopentane is tetramethylmethane, $C(CH_3)_4$].

The normal (straight-chain) hydrocarbons "knock" badly when burned in a high-compression gasoline engine, whereas the highly branched hydro-carbons, which burn more slowly, do not knock. The "octane number" (the antiknock rating) of a gasoline is measured by comparing it with varying mixtures of n-heptane and a highly branched octane, with name 2,2,4-tri-methylpentane and structural formula

The octane number is the percentage of this octane in the mixture that has the same knocking properties as the gasoline being tested.

The substance *tetraethyl lead*, $Pb(C_2H_5)_4$, is widely used in gasoline as an antiknock agent. Gasoline containing it is called *ethyl gasoline*.

Names of Organic Compounds. Chemists have developed a rather compli-cated system of names for organic compounds. But the student of general chemistry needs to know only a small part of this system.

The simpler substances usually have special names; for example, methane, ethane, propane, butane. From pentane on (Table 10-2), the names of the alkanes give the number of carbon atoms, with use of the Greek prefixes for the numbers.

The group obtained by removing a hydrogen atom from an alkane has the name of the alkane with the ending *ane* changed to *yl*. Thus the methyl group is —CH_3, the ethyl group is —C_2H_5 (as in lead tetraethyl, above), and so on. These groups are called *alkyl groups*.

A branched hydrocarbon is given a name that is based on the longest chain of carbon atoms in it. The carbon atoms are numbered from one end $(1, 2, 3, \cdots)$, and groups attached to them, in place of hydrogen atoms, are indicated. For example, the substance called isobutane above (in the discussion of isomerism) may be called 2-methylpropane. Another example is 2,2,4-tri-methylpentane, the structural formula of which is given above.

Restricted Rotation about Single Bonds. Until about twenty-five years ago chemists assumed that the two ends of a molecule such as ethane, H_3C—CH_3, could rotate freely about the single bond connecting them. This assumption of free rotation about single bonds was made because all efforts to obtain isomers of substances such as 1,2-dichloroethane, H_2ClC—CH_2Cl, had failed.

Then in 1937 the American chemists J. D. Kemp and K. S. Pitzer showed that the experimental value of the entropy of ethane requires that there be an energy barrier with height about 3 kcal/mole restricting rotation of one methyl group in ethane relative to the other.

Many experimental values of the height of the potential barrier have been obtained, especially by E. B. Wilson, Jr., and his collaborators, through use of the techniques of microwave spectroscopy (study of absorption spectra of gas molecules in the wavelength region about 1 cm). The values 3.30 kcal/mole for H_3C—CH_2F and 3.18 kcal/mole for H_3C—CHF_2 are nearly the same as for ethane; those for H_3C—CH_2Cl and H_3C—CH_2Br are somewhat higher, 3.56 and 3.57 kcal/mole, respectively. In every case the stable configuration is the *staggered configuration* (bonds on opposite sides of the C—C axis, as illustrated in Figure 10-7). The unstable configuration, obtained by rotating a methyl group 60°, is called the *eclipsed configuration*.

Spectroscopic studies have shown that 1,2-dichloroethane in the gas phase or in the solution is a mixture of three isomers. All three have staggered configurations; viewed along the C—C axis, they have the following aspects:

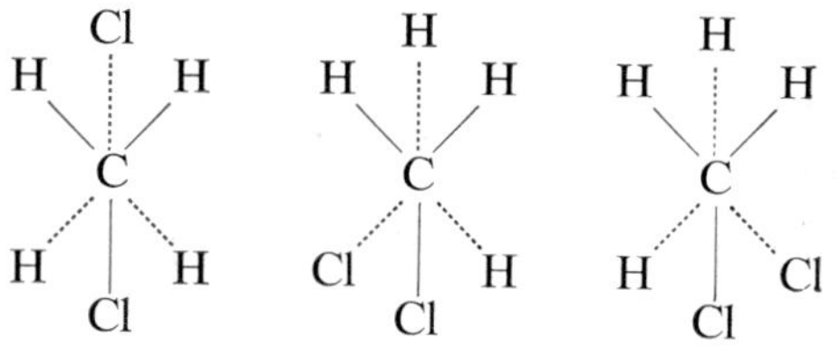

(The second and third constitute an enantiomeric pair, Section 9-4.) The energy restricting rotation is so low that the isomers are converted into one another too rapidly to permit their separation in the laboratory.

The cause of restricted rotation is still somewhat uncertain. The small dependence on the size of the atoms attached to the carbon atoms indicates that it is not mainly steric hindrance (hindrance resulting from contact of the atoms). The most likely explanation is that the barrier results from the repulsion of the H—C bond electrons of one methyl group and those of the other; that is, repulsion of the outer bonds. This explanation is supported by the values of the barrier height for H_3C—NH_2 and H_3C—OH, 1.90 and 1.07 kcal/mole, respectively.

Cyclic Hydrocarbons. It was mentioned in Section 9-5 that some hydrocarbon molecules involve rings of carbon atoms. The simplest cyclic hydrocarbon is *cyclopropane* (also called trimethylene), C_3H_6, with the structure shown in Figure 9-9. It is a colorless gas, with melting point $-126.6°C$, boiling point $-34.4°C$, and standard enthalpy of formation 4.88 kcal/mole. It is a good anesthetic agent, but has the disadvantage that its mixtures with air may explode if ignited by an electrostatic spark and thus cause the death of the patient.

The cyclopropane molecule is unstable relative to cyclohexane, C_6H_{12}, by 24.0 kcal/mole, as is seen by comparing the heats of formation (Table 10-1):

$$3C \text{ (graphite)} + 3H_2(g) \longrightarrow C_3H_6(g) - 9.0 \text{ kcal/mole}$$
$$3C \text{ (graphite)} + 3H_2(g) \longrightarrow \tfrac{1}{2}C_6H_{12}(g) + 15.0 \text{ kcal/mole}$$

This instability is due in part to the bent bonds in the three-membered ring and in part to the unfavorable configuration around the single bonds in cyclopropane. The cyclohexane molecule involves a puckered ring of six carbon atoms, with all bond angles tetrahedral (no bent bonds) and with the stable (staggered) configuration around each C—C bond. In the cyclopropane molecule, however, the configuration around each C—C bond is the unstable one (eclipsed). The amount of instability for each eclipsed C—C is about 3 kcal/mole. Hence we may conclude that the cyclopropane molecule is rendered unstable by about 9 kcal/mole by the eclipsed configuration around the three C—C bonds and by about 15 kcal/mole by the strain in the three bent bonds.

The discussion of cyclic compounds will be continued in Section 10-9 and Chapters 27 and 28.

10-6. Bond Energy and Bond-dissociation Energy

In Section 9-12 it was mentioned that a set of bond-energy values can be found such that their sum over all the bonds of a molecule that can be satisfactorily represented by a single valence-bond structure is equal to the heat of formation of the gaseous substance from atoms of the elements. Such a set of bond-energy values is given in Table 10-3. Most of the values are reliable to 0.5 kcal/mole, and calculations made with their use can be trusted to within about 0.5 kcal/mole per bond (see the examples at the end of this section).

Values for single bonds not given in the table can be estimated roughly from the relation to the electronegativity difference (Section 9-12):

$$E(A—B) = \tfrac{1}{2}\{E(A—A) + E(B—B)\} + 23(x_A - x_B)^2 \text{ kcal/mole} \qquad (1)$$

For example, as yet no determination has been made of the heat of formation of Br_2O, which is an unstable substance for which the structure

$$: \overset{..}{Br} :$$
$$\vert \quad \overset{..}{}$$
$$: \overset{..}{\underset{..}{O}}—\overset{..}{\underset{..}{Br}} :$$

may be written with confidence. From Equation 1 and the electronegativity values (Table 9-1) we obtain the value 50.9 kcal/mole for the Br—O bond energy:

$$E(Br—O) = \tfrac{1}{2}(33.2 + 46.1) + 23(3.5 - 2.8)^2$$
$$= 39.65 + 11.27 = 50.9 \text{ kcal/mole}$$

Table **10-3**

Energy Values of Bonds (kcal/mole)

BOND	BOND ENERGY	BOND	BOND ENERGY	BOND	BOND ENERGY
H—H	104.2	Si—H	70.4	Si—O	88.2
C—C	83.1	N—H	93.4	Si—S	54.2
C=C	147	P—H	76.4	Si—F	129.3
C≡C	194	As—H	58.6	Si—Cl	85.7
Si—Si	42.2	O—H	110.6	Si—Br	69.1
Ge—Ge	37.6	S—H	81.1	Si—I	50.9
Sn—Sn	34.2	Se—H	66.1	Ge—Cl	97.5
N—N	38.4	Te—H	57.5	N—F	64.5
N=N	100	H—F	134.6	N—Cl	47.7
N≡N	226.2	H—Cl	103.2	P—Cl	76.1
P—P	51.3	H—Br	87.5	P—Br	65.4
P=P	117	H—I	71.4	P—I	51.4
As—As	32.1	C—Si	69.3	As—F	111.3
Sb—Sb	30.2	C—N	69.7	As—Cl	68.9
Bi—Bi	25	C=N	147	As—Br	56.5
O—O	33.2	C≡N	213	As—I	41.6
S—S	50.9	C—O	84.0	O—F	44.2
Se—Se	44.0	C=O	172	O—Cl	48.5
Te—Te	33	C—S	62.0	S—Cl	59.7
F—F	36.6	C=S	114	S—Br	50.7
Cl—Cl	58.0	C—F	115.8	Cl—F	60.6
Br—Br	46.1	C—Cl	78.5	Br—Cl	52.3
I—I	36.1	C—Br	65.9	I—Cl	50.3
C—H	98.8	C—I	57.4	I—Br	42.5

Hence we obtain 101.8 kcal/mole for the heat of formation of $Br_2O(g)$ from atoms. By use of the values of the enthalpy of the atoms relative to the elements in their standard states (Tables 6-1 and 12-2) we can then obtain a predicted value of the standard heat of formation:

$$2Br(g) + O(g) \longrightarrow Br_2O(g) + 101.8 \text{ kcal/mole}$$
$$Br_2(l) \longrightarrow Br(g) - 39.4 \text{ kcal/mole}$$
$$\tfrac{1}{2}O_2(g) \longrightarrow O(g) - 59.2 \text{ kcal/mole}$$

$$Br_2(l) + \tfrac{1}{2}O_2(g) \longrightarrow Br_2O(g) + 3.2 \text{ kcal/mole}$$

The heat of formation is thus predicted to have a small positive value. The small value may explain the ease with which the substance decomposes.

Bond-dissociation Energy.   The *bond-dissociation energy* of a bond in a molecule is the energy required to break that bond alone—that is, to split the molecule into the two parts that were previously connected by that bond. For example, the bond-dissociation energy of the C—C bond in ethane, H_3C—CH_3, is the enthalpy of dissociation of ethane into two methyl radicals, · CH_3.

For diatomic molecules the bond energy and the bond-dissociation energy are the same. For polyatomic molecules they are in general different. The sum of successive bond-dissociation energies is, of course, equal to the sum of the bond energies.

The differences between values of bond-dissociation energies and bond energies can usually be interpreted in terms of known features of the electronic structure of the products of dissociation, as illustrated by the following example.

Example 1. What are the values of the O—H bond dissociation energy for H_2O and for OH? To what structural feature is the difference between the two values to be ascribed?

Solution. From the enthalpy values of Table 6-1 we obtain the following heats of reaction:

$$\tfrac{1}{2}H_2(g) + \tfrac{1}{2}O_2(g) \longrightarrow OH(g) - 10.06 \text{ kcal/mole}$$
$$H(g) \longrightarrow \tfrac{1}{2}H_2(g) + 52.09$$
$$O(g) \longrightarrow \tfrac{1}{2}O_2(g) + 59.16$$

$$H(g) \; + \; O(g) \longrightarrow OH(g) + 101.19 \text{ kcal/mole}$$

and

$$H_2(g) + \tfrac{1}{2}O_2(g) \longrightarrow H_2O(g) + 57.80 \text{ kcal/mole}$$
$$OH(g) \longrightarrow \tfrac{1}{2}H_2(g) + \tfrac{1}{2}O_2(g) + 10.06$$
$$H(g) \longrightarrow \tfrac{1}{2}H_2(g) + 52.09$$

$$H(g) \; + \; OH(g) \longrightarrow H_2O(g) + 119.95 \text{ kcal/mole}$$

Thus we find that on breaking the two O—H bonds in the water molecule in succession the bond-dissociation energy for the first is **119.95 kcal/mole** and that for the second is only **101.19 kcal/mole.** (The average of the two, 110.6 kcal/mole, is the value given in Table 10-3 for the O—H bond energy.)

To answer the question about what structural feature the difference is to be ascribed to, we examine the electronic structures of H_2O, OH, and O (the hydrogen atom has the same structure, $1s\,^2S$, whether it is the first one or the second one removed from the molecule, and hence it does not determine the difference in the two bond-dissociation energies). The water molecule,

H
|
: O—H
··

contains two unshared electron pairs on the oxygen atom, one occupying the $2s$ orbital and one a $2p$ orbital. The other two $2p$ orbitals of the oxygen atom are used in forming the two O—H bonds. Each bond consists of two electrons, with opposite spins; they may be described as interchanging their places between the two atoms.

The OH radical, produced when the first hydrogen atom is removed, has the structure :Ö—H. Again there are two unshared pairs, a $2s$ pair and a $2p$ pair, on the oxygen atom; of the other two $2p$ orbitals, one, as before, is involved in forming an O—H bond and the other is occupied by an odd electron. This odd electron may have its spin oriented in either a positive or negative direction, with no difference in energy, because the other electrons in the molecule are paired.

When the second hydrogen atom is removed an oxygen atom, :Ö· , remains. It has a $2s$ pair, a $2p$ pair, and two odd electrons in the other two $2p$ orbitals.

When these two odd electrons were serving as bonding electrons, the spins were essentially equally often parallel and opposed. But in the oxygen atom the parallel orientation of the spins gives rise to a triplet state, ^3P, and the opposed orientation gives rise to two singlet states, ^1D and ^1S (see Russell-Saunders coupling, Section 7-5). The interaction between electrons in an atom is such as to make the state with parallel spins (maximum multiplicity) more stable than the states with anti-parallel spin. Hence the normal state of the oxygen atom is the triplet state, ^3P, which we may represent as :Ö↑ . The two excited states, ^1D and ^1S (both :Ö↓), lie 45 kcal/mole and 96 kcal/mole above the ^3P normal state. The valence state of the oxygen atom in H_2O and OH corresponds to an average of these three states of the oxygen atom. The valence state is not changed when the first hydrogen atom is removed from the water molecule, and the bond-dissociation energy 120.0 kcal/mole might well be considered the true bond energy. If the oxygen atom remained in its valence state when the second hydrogen was removed, the second bond-dissociation energy would be expected to be about 120 kcal/mole; but the atom assumes the structure :Ö↑ ^3P, more stable than the valence state by about 20 kcal/mole, and the value of the second bond-dissociation energy is accordingly decreased by this amount, to 101.2 kcal/mole.

Illustrative Exercises

10-4. Using the bond energy from Table 10-3, calculate a value for the heat of formation of cyclohexane(g) from carbon and hydrogen atoms. With use of the standard enthalpies of C(g) and H(g), evaluate the heat of formation of cyclohexane(g) from graphite and molecular hydrogen, and compare it with the enthalpy value for $C_6H_{12}(g)$ in Table 10-1.

10-5. Would you expect the reaction $CH_4 + Cl_2 \longrightarrow CH_3Cl + HCl$ to be exothermic or endothermic? Use bond-energy values to obtain a value of the heat of the reaction.

10-7. Fuels

Carbon and hydrogen are the principal constituents of the solid fuels coal and wood. Coal has been formed in nature by the slow decomposition of vegetable matter, in the presence of water and absence of air. Most of it was formed during the Carboniferous Period of geologic time, about 250 million years ago (the method of measuring geologic times by use of radioactivity is described in Section 30-2). Coal consists of free carbon mixed with various carbon compounds and some mineral matter. *Anthracite coal* (hard coal) contains only a small amount of volatile matter, and burns with a nearly colorless flame; *bituminous coal* (soft coal) contains much volatile matter, and burns with a smoky flame.

Bituminous coal can be converted into *coke* by heating without access of air. When the heating is carried out in a by-product coke oven, many substances distill out, including gas for fuel, ammonia, and a complex mixture of liquid and solid organic compounds. The solid material remaining in the ovens, consisting mainly of carbon, is called coke. It burns with a nearly colorless flame, and is used in great amounts in metallurgical processes.

Petroleum is a very important liquid fuel. It is a complex mixture of compounds of carbon and hydrogen.

The gas obtained from a coke furnace (*coal gas*) consists of hydrogen (about 50% by volume), methane, CH_4 (30%), carbon monoxide (10%), and minor components. This coal gas was the original illuminating gas.

Natural gas, from gas wells and oil wells, consists largely of methane.

Producer gas is made by passing a limited supply of air through hot coal or coke. The layer of coal or coke that first comes into contact with the stream of air is oxidized to carbon dioxide:

$$C + O_2 \longrightarrow CO_2$$

As the carbon dioxide rises through the incandescent coke it is reduced to carbon monoxide, which, mixed with nitrogen of the air, escapes from the furnace:

$$CO_2 + C \longrightarrow 2CO$$

Producer gas contains about 25% of carbon monoxide by volume, the rest being nitrogen. Its fuel value is low (Exercise 10-7).

Water gas is made by passing steam through incandescent coke:

$$C + H_2O \longrightarrow CO + H_2$$

This reaction absorbs heat, so that the coke becomes cool. An air blast is then substituted for the steam until the fuel is heated to a temperature at which it is bright red, and then steam is blown in again. Sometimes a mixture of steam and air is used, instead of alternating the two gases. Water gas and producer gas are used in industrial processes and for domestic heating. Propane and butane, stored in tanks under pressure, are also used for fuel.

The method of determining heats of combustion has been described in Section 5-7. This method, with use of a bomb calorimeter, is the customary basis for determining the value of a fuel such as coal or oil. A weighed sample of the fuel is placed in the bomb calorimeter, the bomb is filled with oxygen, and the fuel is burned. When large amounts of fuel are purchased, the price may be determined by the result of tests in a calorimeter or by the result of chemical analyses and calculation of the heat of combustion.

In reporting the calorific value of fuels it is customary to use the *British thermal unit* (B.T.U.) instead of the calorie as the unit of heat. The British thermal unit is the amount of heat required to raise the temperature of 1 pound of water by 1 degree Fahrenheit. Since a pound is 453 g and 1 degree F is $\frac{5}{9}$ degrees C, the British thermal unit is equal to $\frac{5}{9} \times 453 = 252$ cal. The calorific value of a fuel expressed in B.T.U. per pound of fuel has a numerical value $\frac{5}{9}$ as great as that expressed in calories per gram.

Illustrative Exercises

10-6. From enthalpy values (Tables 6-2 and 10-1) calculate the heat values of hydrogen, methane, and carbon monoxide in kcal/m³ (standard conditions).

10-7. Using the results of Exercise 10-6, calculate the heat values in kcal/m³ of coal gas, producer gas, natural gas, and water gas (see text above for composition).

10-8. Hydrocarbons Containing Double Bonds and Triple Bonds

The substance **ethylene,** C_2H_4, consists of molecules

in which there is a double bond between the two carbon atoms. This double bond confers upon the molecule the property of much greater chemical reactivity than is possessed by the alkanes. For example, whereas chlorine, bromine, and iodine do not readily attack the alkane hydrocarbons, they easily react with ethylene; a mixture of chlorine and ethylene reacts readily at room temperature in the dark, and with explosive violence in light, to form the substance *dichloroethane*, $C_2H_4Cl_2$:

$$C_2H_4 + Cl_2 \longrightarrow C_2H_4Cl_2$$

or

$$\underset{H}{\overset{H}{\diagdown}} C=C \underset{H}{\overset{H}{\diagup}} + Cl-Cl \longrightarrow \underset{H}{\overset{Cl}{\diagdown}} H-C-C-H \underset{Cl}{\overset{H}{\diagup}}$$

In the course of this reaction the double bond between the two carbon atoms has become a single bond, and the single bond between the two chlorine atoms has been broken. Two new bonds—single bonds between a chlorine atom and a carbon atom—have been formed. We may use the bond-energy values of Table 10-3 to estimate the heat of the reaction:

Reactant bond energies		Product bond energies	
C=C	147	C—C	83
Cl—Cl	58	2C—Cl	157
	205 kcal/mole		240 kcal/mole

We see that the bonds in the product molecules are more stable than those in the reactant molecules by 35 kcal/mole. Hence this reaction is exothermic, with a moderately large amount of heat evolved on reaction, 35 kcal/mole.

A reaction of this sort is called an *addition reaction*. *An addition reaction is a reaction in which a molecule adds to a molecule containing a double bond, converting the double bond into a single bond.*

Because of this property of readily combining with other substances such as the halogens, ethylene and related hydrocarbons are said to be *unsaturated*. Ethylene is the first member of a homologous series of hydrocarbons, called the *alkenes*.

Ethylene is a colorless gas (b.p. $-104°C$) with a sweetish odor. It can be made in the laboratory by heating ethyl alcohol, C_2H_5OH, with concentrated sulfuric acid, preferably in the presence of a catalyst (such as silica) to increase the rate of the reaction. Concentrated sulfuric acid is a strong dehydrating agent, which removes water from the alcohol molecule:

$$C_2H_5OH \xrightarrow[H_2SO_4]{} C_2H_4 + H_2O$$

The formula H_2SO_4 is written below the arrow in this equation to show that sulfuric acid is needed to cause the reaction to take place.

Ethylene is made commercially by passing alcohol vapor over a catalyst (aluminum oxide) at about 400°C. The reaction is endothermic; a small amount of heat is absorbed when it takes place:

$$C_2H_5OH \longrightarrow C_2H_4 + H_2O - 11.33 \text{ kcal/mole}$$

Endothermic chemical reactions are in general favored by heating the reactants.

Ethylene has the interesting property of causing green fruit to ripen, and it is used commercially for this purpose. It is also used as an anesthetic.

Cis and Trans Isomers.   The ethylene molecule is planar (Section 9-5), with greatly restricted rotation around the double bond. In consequence, a disubstituted ethylene such as 1,2-dichloroethylene, CHCl=CHCl, exists as two isomers, called *cis*-1,2-dichloroethylene and *trans*-1,2-dichloroethylene:

Cis   *Trans*

These two substances have different properties: the *cis* isomer has m.p. −80.5°C, b.p. 59.8°C, density of liquid 1.291 g/ml, and electric dipole moment 1.89 D; and the *trans* isomer has m.p. −50°C, b.p. 48.5°C, density of liquid 1.265 g/ml, and electric dipole moment 0.

The potential energy barrier restricting rotation about the double bond has been found by experiment to be about 50 kcal/mole.*

A third isomer also exists, 1,1-dichloroethylene, $Cl_2C=CH_2$.

Acetylene, H—C≡C—H, is the first member of a homologous series of hydrocarbons containing triple bonds. Aside from acetylene, these substances (called *alkynes*) have not found wide use, except for the manufacture of other chemicals.

Acetylene is a colorless gas (b.p. −84°C), with a characteristic garliclike odor. It is liable to explode when compressed in the pure state, and is usually kept in solution under pressure in acetone. It is used as a fuel, in the oxyacetylene torch and the acetylene lamp, and is also used as the starting material for making other chemicals.

Acetylene is most easily made from **calcium carbide** (calcium acetylide, CaC_2). Calcium carbide is made by heating lime (calcium oxide, CaO) and coke in an electric furnace:

$$CaO + 3C \longrightarrow CaC_2 + CO(g)$$

* The height of the barrier can be estimated from the spectroscopic value of the frequency of the torsional vibration of the molecule (twisting vibration of one end relative to the other end), and from the activation energy (Chapter 18) of the cis-trans isomerization reaction.

Calcium carbide is a gray solid that reacts vigorously with water to produce calcium hydroxide and acetylene:

$$CaC_2 + 2H_2O \longrightarrow Ca(OH)_2 + C_2H_2(g)$$

The existence of calcium carbide and other carbides with similar formulas and properties shows that acetylene is an acid, with two replaceable hydrogen atoms. It is an extremely weak acid, however, and its solution in water does not taste acidic.

Acetylene and other substances containing a carbon-carbon triple bond are very reactive. They readily undergo addition reactions with chlorine and other reagents, and they are classed as unsaturated substances.

Illustrative Exercises

10-8. Using bond-energy values from Table 10-3, evaluate the heat of addition of F_2, Br_2, and I_2 to a double bond in an alkene. Would you expect these halogens to react with alkenes more vigorously or less vigorously than chlorine?

10-9. Write the equation for two successive addition reactions of chlorine with acetylene. Evaluate the heat of each reaction by use of bond-energy values.

10-10. The hydrogenation of unsaturated compounds is an important reaction both in the laboratory and in industry. The reaction is usually carried out in the presence of a catalyst, such as finely divided nickel. Using bond-energy values from Table 10-3, calculate the heat of addition of H_2 to the carbon-carbon double bond. (A representative experimental value is 29.70 kcal/mole for the hydrogenation of propene, $H_2C{=}CH{-}CH_3$, to propane.)

10-9. Aromatic Hydrocarbons. Benzene

An important hydrocarbon is **benzene,** which has the formula C_6H_6. It is a volatile liquid (m.p. 5.5°C, b.p. 80.1°C, density 0.88 g/ml). Benzene and other hydrocarbons similar to it in structure are called the *aromatic hydrocarbons.* Their derivatives are called aromatic substances—many of them have a characteristic aroma (agreeable odor). Benzene itself was discovered in 1825 by Faraday, who found it in the illuminating gas made by heating oils and fats.

For many years there was discussion about the structure of the benzene molecule. The German chemist August Kekulé in 1862 proposed that the six carbon atoms form a regular hexagon in space, the six hydrogen atoms being bonded to the carbon atoms, and forming a larger hexagon. Kekulé suggested that, in order for a carbon atom to show its normal quadrivalence, the ring contains three single bonds and three double bonds in alternate positions, as shown below. A structure of this sort is called a Kekulé structure.

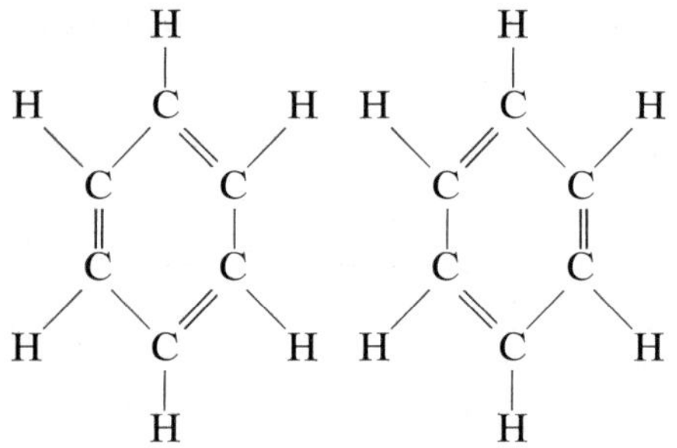

Other hydrocarbons, derivatives of benzene, can be obtained by replacing the hydrogen atoms by methyl groups or similar groups. Coal tar and petroleum contain substances of this sort, such as **toluene**, C_7H_8, and the three **xylenes**, C_8H_{10}. These formulas are usually written $C_6H_5CH_3$ and $C_6H_4(CH_3)_2$, to indicate the structural formulas, as shown below.

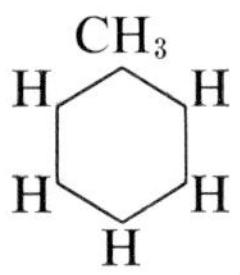

Toluene 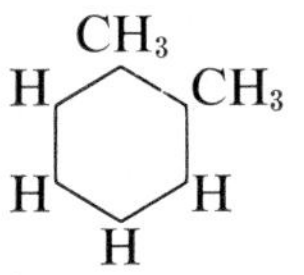   Ortho-xylene (o-xylene)   Meta-xylene (m-xylene)   Para-xylene (p-xylene)

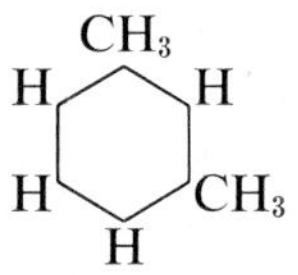

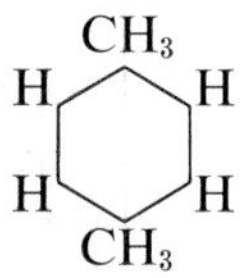

In these formulas the benzene ring of six carbon atoms is shown simply as a hexagon. This convention is used by organic chemists, who often also do not show the hydrogen atoms, but only other groups attached to the ring.

It is to be noted that we can draw two Kekulé structures for benzene and its derivatives. For example, for ortho-xylene the two Kekulé structures are

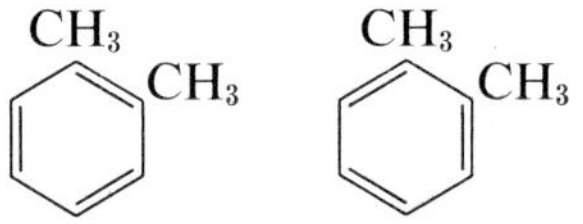

In the first structure there is a double bond between the carbon atoms to which methyl groups are attached, and in the second there is a single bond in this position. The organic chemists of a century ago found it impossible, however, to separate two isomers corresponding to these formulas. In order to explain this impossibility of separation Kekulé suggested that the molecule does not retain one Kekulé structure, but rather slips easily from one to the other. In the modern theory of molecular structure the ortho-xylene molecule is described as a hybrid of these two structures, with each bond between two carbon atoms in the ring intermediate in character between a single bond and a double bond. Even though this resonance structure is accepted for benzene and related compounds, it is often convenient simply to draw one of the Kekulé structures, or just a hexagon, to represent a benzene molecule.

The structure of the benzene molecule was determined by the electron diffraction method in 1929 and the following years. It is a planar hexagon with carbon-carbon bond length 1.40 Å (C—H bond length 1.06 Å). This value for a bond with 50% double-bond character is reasonable in comparison with the values 1.54 Å for C—C, 1.33 Å for C=C, and 1.42 Å for $33\frac{1}{3}$% double-bond character (graphite). The planar configuration is required by the properties of the double bond (Section 9-5).

Benzene and its derivatives are extremely important substances. They are used in the manufacture of drugs, explosives, photographic developers, plastics, synthetic dyes, and many other substances. For example, the substance **trinitrotoluene**, $C_6H_2(CH_3)(NO_2)_3$, is an important explosive (TNT). The structure of this substance is

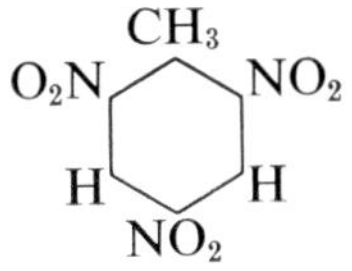

$$
\begin{array}{c}
CH_3 \\
O_2N \diagup \diagdown NO_2 \\
H \diagdown \diagup H \\
NO_2
\end{array}
$$

In addition to benzene and its derivatives, there exist many other aromatic hydrocarbons, containing two or more rings of carbon atoms. **Naphthalene,** $C_{10}H_8$, is a solid substance with a characteristic odor; it is used as a constituent of moth balls and in the manufacture of dyes and other organic compounds. **Anthracene,** $C_{14}H_{10}$, and **phenanthrene,** $C_{14}H_{10}$, are isomeric substances containing three rings fused together. These substances are also used in making dyes, and derivatives of them are important biological substances (cholesterol, sex hormones; see Chapter 28). For naphthalene, anthracene, and phenanthrene we may write the following structural formulas:

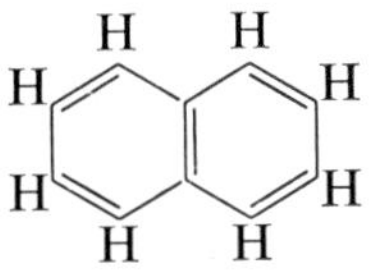

Naphthalene 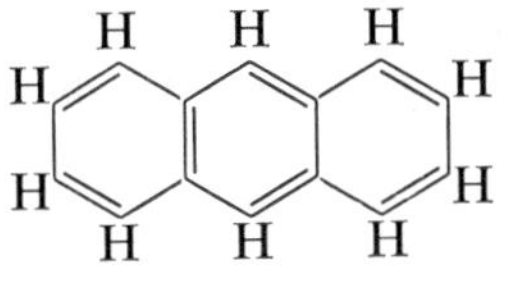   Anthracene 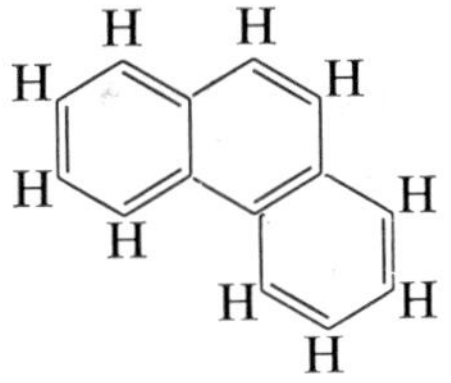   Phenanthrene

These molecules also have hybrid structures: the structural formulas shown above do not represent the molecules completely, but are analogous to one Kekulé structure for benzene.

Resonance Energy. The heat evolved when a molecule of hydrogen is added to a double bond is about 30 kcal/mole. For cyclohexane, for example, the value determined by experiment is 28.59 kcal/mole:

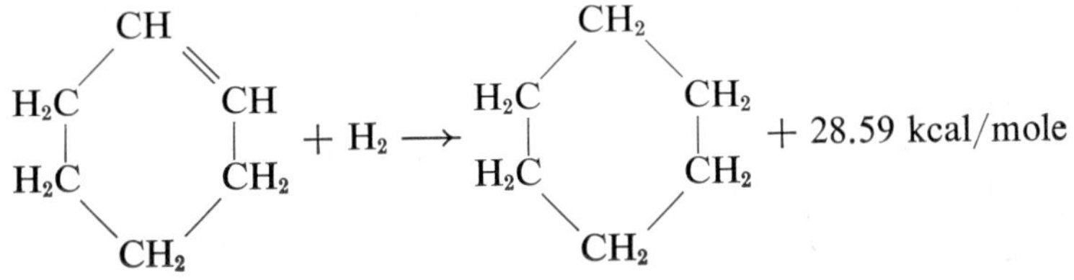

$$
\begin{array}{c}
CH \\
H_2C \diagup \diagdown CH \\
H_2C \diagdown \diagup CH_2 \\
CH_2
\end{array}
+ H_2 \longrightarrow
\begin{array}{c}
CH_2 \\
H_2C \diagup \diagdown CH_2 \\
H_2C \diagdown \diagup CH_2 \\
CH_2
\end{array}
+ 28.59 \text{ kcal/mole}
$$

If the benzene molecule had one Kekulé structure, [structure], we might well expect

that the heat of hydrogenation of its three double bonds would be approximately three times the heat of hydrogenation of the one double bond in cyclohexene, $3 \times 28.59 = 85.77$ kcal/mole:

$$
\begin{array}{c}
\text{CH} \\
\text{HC} \quad \text{CH} \\
\text{HC} \quad \text{CH} \\
\text{CH}
\end{array}
+ 3H_2 \longrightarrow
\begin{array}{c}
\text{CH}_2 \\
\text{H}_2\text{C} \quad \text{CH}_2 \\
\text{H}_2\text{C} \quad \text{CH}_2 \\
\text{CH}_2
\end{array}
+ 85.77 \text{ kcal/mole (incorrect)}
$$

The experimental value of the heat of hydrogenation is, however, 36 kcal/mole smaller:

$$C_6H_6(g) + 3H_2(g) \longrightarrow C_6H_{12}(g) + 49.80 \text{ kcal/mole}$$

We conclude that *the benzene molecule is 36 kcal/mole more stable than it would be if it were represented by a single Kekulé structure, with each of the three double bonds similar to the double bond in cyclohexene.* This extra stabilizing energy of 36 kcal/mole per mole is called the *resonance energy* of benzene. It is attributed to the fact that the benzene molecule is not satisfactorily represented by a single Kekulé structure, but instead can be reasonably well described as a hybrid of the two Kekulé structures.*

The resonance energy of benzene makes the substance far less reactive chemically than alkenes or other unsaturated substances. For example, the reaction of addition of one hydrogen molecule to benzene to form cyclohexadiene,

$$
\begin{array}{c}
\text{CH} \\
\text{HC} \quad \text{CH}_2 \\
\text{HC} \quad \text{CH}_2 \\
\text{CH}
\end{array}
$$

is endothermic, not exothermic. The properties of benzene and other aromatic substances reflect the stability conferred upon them by the resonance energy.

Illustrative Exercise

10-11. In how many ways can you write valence-bond structures for naphthalene? (One way is given in the text.) How many for anthracene? For phenanthrene?

---

* It would, of course, be surprising if the benzene molecule in its normal state were actually *less* stable than the hypothetical molecule with a single Kekulé structure; we would then ask why the molecule was prevented from assuming this more stable structure. The theory of resonance is based upon a theorem in quantum mechanics that the normal state of an atom or molecule is the most stable of all possible states.

10-10. Some Other Organic Compounds

The Chloromethanes. Methane and other paraffins will react with chlorine and bromine when exposed to sunlight or when heated to a high temperature. When a mixture of methane and chlorine is passed through a tube containing a catalyst (aluminum chloride, $AlCl_3$, mixed with clay) heated to about 300°C, the following reactions occur:*

$$CH_4 + Cl_2 \longrightarrow CH_3Cl + HCl$$
$$CH_3Cl + Cl_2 \longrightarrow CH_2Cl_2 + HCl$$
$$CH_2Cl_2 + Cl_2 \longrightarrow CHCl_3 + HCl$$
$$CHCl_3 + Cl_2 \longrightarrow CCl_4 + HCl$$

In each of these reactions a chlorine molecule, with structural formula Cl—Cl, is split into two chlorine atoms; one chlorine atom takes the place of a hydrogen atom bonded to carbon, and the other combines with the displaced hydrogen atom to form a molecule of hydrogen chloride, H—Cl. By use of values of bond energies from Table 10-3, we calculate for the heat of each of these reactions the value $78.5 + 103.2 - (58.0 + 98.8) = 24.9$ kcal/mole. The reactions are not so strongly exothermic as the reaction of addition of chlorine to a double bond (35 kcal/mole).

The four chlorine derivatives of methane, which are called the *chloromethanes*, have the following individual names:

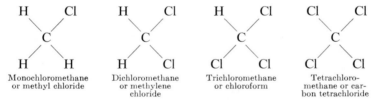

Monochloromethane or methyl chloride   Dichloromethane or methylene chloride   Trichloromethane or chloroform   Tetrachloromethane or carbon tetrachloride

Chemical reactions such as these four are called *substitution reactions. A* **substitution reaction** *is the replacement of one atom or group of atoms in a molecule by another atom or group of atoms.* The four chloromethanes are *substitution products* of methane. Substitution reactions and addition reactions (Section 10-8) are extensively used in practical organic chemistry.

Some physical properties of the chloromethanes are given in Table 10-4; their enthalpies of formation from the elements are given in Table 10-1. All four are colorless, with characteristic odors, and with low boiling points, increasing with the number of chlorine atoms in the molecule. The chloromethanes do not ionize in water.

Chloroform and carbon tetrachloride are used as solvents; carbon tetrachloride is an important dry-cleaning agent. Chloroform is also used as a general anesthetic.

---

* The relative amounts of the four products may be varied somewhat by changing the ratio of methane and chlorine in the gas mixture used.

Table **10-4**

Some Physical Properties of the Chloromethanes

SUBSTANCE	FORMULA	MELTING POINT	BOILING POINT	DENSITY OF LIQUID
Methyl chloride	CH_3Cl	$-98°C$	$-24°C$	0.92 g/ml
Dichloromethane	CH_2Cl_2	-97	40	1.34
Chloroform	$CHCl_3$	-64	61	1.50
Carbon tetrachloride	CCl_4	-23	77	1.60

Care must be taken in the use of carbon tetrachloride that no large amount of its vapor is inhaled, because it damages the liver.

Methyl Alcohol and Ethyl Alcohol. An *alcohol* is obtained from a hydrocarbon by replacing one hydrogen atom by a hydroxyl group, —OH. Thus methane, CH_4, gives *methyl alcohol*, CH_3OH, and ethane, C_2H_6, gives *ethyl alcohol*, C_2H_5OH. The names of the alcohols are often written by using the ending *ol*; methyl alcohol is called **methanol,** and ethyl alcohol **ethanol.** They have the following structural formulas:

Methyl alcohol   Ethyl alcohol

To make methyl alcohol from methane, the methane may be converted to methyl chloride by treatment with chlorine, as described above, and the methyl chloride then converted to methyl alcohol by treatment with sodium hydroxide:

$$CH_3Cl + NaOH \longrightarrow CH_3OH + NaCl$$

Methyl alcohol is made by the destructive distillation of wood; it is sometimes called wood alcohol. It is a poisonous substance, which on ingestion causes blindness and death. It is used as a solvent and for the preparation of other organic compounds.

The most important method of making ethyl alcohol is by the fermentation of sugars with yeast. Grains and molasses are the usual raw materials for this purpose. Yeast produces an enzyme that catalyzes the fermentation reaction. In the following equation the formula $C_6H_{12}O_6$ is that of a sugar—glucose (also called dextrose and grape sugar; Chapter 27):

$$C_6H_{12}O_6 \longrightarrow 2CO_2 + 2C_2H_5OH$$

Ethyl alcohol is a colorless liquid (m.p. $-117°C$, b.p. $79°C$) with a characteristic odor. It is used as a fuel, as a solvent, and as the starting material for preparing other compounds. Beer contains 3 to 5% alcohol, wine usually

10 to 12%, and distilled liquors such as whiskey, brandy, and gin 40 to 50%.

The *ethers* are compounds obtained by reaction of two alcohol molecules, with elimination of water. The most important ether is **diethyl ether** (ordinary ether), $(C_2H_5)_2O$. It is made by treating ethyl alcohol with concentrated sulfuric acid, which serves as a dehydrating agent:

$$2C_2H_5OH \xrightarrow[H_2SO_4]{} C_2H_5OC_2H_5 + H_2O$$

It is used as a general anesthetic and as a solvent.

The Organic Acids. Ethyl alcohol can be oxidized by oxygen of the air to **acetic acid,** $HC_2H_3O_2$ or CH_3COOH:

$$C_2H_5OH + O_2 \longrightarrow CH_3COOH + H_2O$$

This reaction occurs easily in nature. If wine, containing ethyl alcohol, is allowed to stand in an open container, it undergoes acetic-acid fermentation and changes into vinegar by the above reaction. The change is brought about by microorganisms ("mother of vinegar"), which produce enzymes that catalyze the reaction.

Acetic acid has the following structural formula:

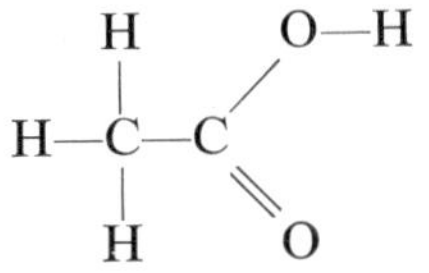

$$\begin{array}{ccc} H & & O-H \\ | & & / \\ H-C-C & & \\ | & \backslash\backslash & \\ H & & O \end{array}$$

It contains the group

$$\begin{array}{c} O-H \\ / \\ -C \\ \backslash\backslash \\ O \end{array}$$

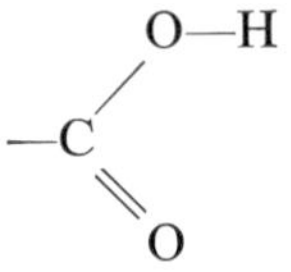

which is called the *carboxyl group*. It is this group that gives acidic properties to the organic acids.

Acetic acid melts at 17°C and boils at 118°C. It is soluble in water and alcohol. The molecule contains one hydrogen atom that ionizes from it in water, producing the *acetate ion*, $C_2H_3O_2^-$. The acid reacts with bases to form salts. An example is sodium acetate, $NaC_2H_3O_2$, a white solid:

$$HC_2H_3O_2 + NaOH \longrightarrow NaC_2H_3O_2 + H_2O$$

Formic acid, HCOOH, is the simplest of the carboxylic acids. Some others are discussed in Chapter 27.

Chemical Reactions of Organic Substances. In the above paragraphs we have discussed derivatives of methane and ethane in which a hydrogen atom is replaced by a chlorine atom, —Cl, a hydroxyl group, —OH, or a carboxyl group, —COOH. There are many other groups that can replace a hydrogen atom, to form other substances.

In general, the chemical reactions that can be used to convert methane into its derivatives can be applied also to the other hydrocarbons. By chemical analysis and the study of the chemical reactions of a new substance the chemist can determine its formula. For example, if a substance contains only carbon, hydrogen, and oxygen, and has acidic properties like those of acetic acid, the chemist assumes that it contains a carboxyl group, —COOH. An important part of organic chemistry is the use of special reactions that identify different groups in a molecule.

Illustrative Exercises

10-12. Write the equation for the reaction of ethane and chlorine to form monochloroethane (C_2H_5Cl, also called ethyl chloride, a colorless gas, b.p. 12°C). What is its structural formula? Is there more than one isomer of C_2H_5Cl?

10-13. Write the equation for the reaction of monochloroethane with chlorine to form dichloroethane. How many isomers of dichloroethane do you predict? What are their structural formulas?

10-14. What would you expect to be formed by the reaction of monochloroethane and sodium hydroxide? Write the equation for the reaction.

10-15. Write the equation for the reaction of addition of bromine to ethylene, showing the structural formulas. How many isomers of the product are obtained? Estimate the heat of the reaction by use of bond-energy values.

10-16. What is the structural formula of the compound C_3H_8O that has the name methyl ethyl ether? How many other substances with formula C_3H_8O are there?

10-17. Write the equation for the reaction of 1,2-dichloroethane with a large amount (an excess) of a strong solution of sodium hydroxide. (The product, called ethylene glycol, is used as an antifreeze agent in automobile radiators.)

10-11.   Molecules Containing Bivalent Carbon. Free Radicals

Carbon monoxide may be considered to be a compound of bivalent carbon. The valence state of the carbon atom in this molecule is based upon the electron configuration $2s^2 2p^2$, involving an unshared pair of electrons in the 2s orbital and two valence electrons occupying separate 2p orbitals.

There are only a few other substances containing bivalent carbon. The isocyanides constitute a class of substances of this sort. The isocyanides are substances that are less stable than the corresponding isomeric substances called the cyanides. For example, methyl cyanide, which is assigned the electronic structure $CH_3—C\equiv N:$, has enthalpy of formation 21.0 kcal/mole, whereas its isomer methyl isocyanide, $CH_3—N\equiv C:$, has enthalpy of formation 35.9 kcal/mole. Methyl isocyanide is a volatile liquid (b.p. 59.6°C) with an evil odor, far more pungent than that of methyl cyanide. The alkyl isocyanides with small side chains (methyl, ethyl, isopropyl, *tert*-butyl) have the property of combining with hemoglobin. There are only a few substances with this property, including molecular oxygen and carbon monoxide; this property is important in the functioning of hemoglobin, in combining with oxygen in the lungs and releasing it in the tissues. The alkyl isocyanides, like carbon monoxide, are poisonous because of the property of combining with the hemoglobin in the blood and inhibiting its use as an oxygen carrier.

The cyanide ion, $[:C\equiv N:]^-$, and the fulminate ion, $[:C\equiv N-\overset{..}{\underset{..}{O}}:]^-$, may also be considered to involve bivalent carbon.

The molecules C_2 and C_3 are present in the vapor of graphite at very high temperature. C_2 in its normal state has two unpaired electrons; its electronic structure can be written $:C\dot{-}\dot{-}C:$, with two one-electron bonds plus a single bond. A possible structure for C_3 is $:C=C=C:$.

Carbene or *methylene*, CH_2, can be made as a dilute gas by the photolysis of diazomethane, CH_2N_2:

$$CH_2N_2 + h\nu \longrightarrow CH_2 + N_2$$

The symbol $h\nu$ is used to represent a photon (ultraviolet light, wavelength about 1415 Å). Substituted carbenes can be made by a similar reaction; for example, diphenylcarbene, $(C_6H_5)_2C:$, by the photolysis of diazodiphenyl methane, $(C_6H_5)_2CN_2$.

Dichlorocarbene, CCl_2, is a useful chemical reagent. It cannot be prepared and stored in concentrated form, but it is easily generated in solution and it shows consistently characteristic properties of a highly reactant transient molecule (a molecule with a short lifetime). A convenient way of generating it is by the reaction of sodium ethoxide, C_2H_5ONa (the sodium derivative of ethanol), and chloroform:

$$C_2H_5ONa + CHCl_3 \longrightarrow C_2H_5OH + NaCl + CCl_2$$

Dichlorocarbene can be used to carry out many organic reactions that are hard to carry out in other ways. For example, it adds easily to a double bond, to form cyclopropane derivatives:

Cyclohexene   Dichloronorcarane

Free Radicals. An atom or group of atoms with one or more unshared electrons, which may enter into chemical-bond formation, is called a *free radical*.

(The same group in a molecule is called a radical; for example, the methyl radical in methyl cyanide or other molecules.) Free radicals are usually highly reactive and difficult to prepare in any except low concentration.

One way of making the methyl radical as a dilute gas is by heating mercury dimethyl, $Hg(CH_3)_2$, which decomposes to give metallic mercury and methyl radical. Methyl radical can also be made conveniently by the decomposition of diacetyl, $(CH_3CO_2)_2$, by either heat or ultraviolet light. The diacetyl molecule liberates two molecules of carbon dioxide and two methyl radicals.

The American chemist Moses Gomberg discovered in 1900 that some hydrocarbon free radicals are stable. He attempted to synthesize the substance hexaphenylethane, $(C_6H_5)_3C-C(C_6H_5)_3$, which he expected to be a stable, white crystalline substance. Instead, he obtained a strongly colored solution, with the property of combining readily with oxygen. He concluded correctly that the solution did not contain the hexaphenyl derivative of ethane, but instead the free radical triphenylmethyl, with the formula $(C_6H_5)_3C \cdot$. Many similar hydrocarbon free radicals have been made, and it has been shown that they are paramagnetic, and accordingly contain unpaired electrons (the paramagnetism is due to the magnetic moment of the electron spin of the unpaired electron). The stability of the triphenylmethyl radical, which is responsible for the low bond energy of the carbon-carbon bond in the substituted ethane, is attributed to the resonance energy of the unpaired electron among the various carbon atoms of the molecule. Note that you can write eight valence-bond structures of type A, each involving nine double bonds with the unpaired electron on the central carbon atom in the triphenylmethyl radical, and 36 similar structures of type B, with the unpaired electron on one of the ring carbon atoms.

A   B

The Structure of Carbene. There are two reasonable electronic structures that might be suggested for the normal state of the carbene molecule. One is the structure

based upon the configuration $2s^22p^2$ for the carbon atom. The bonds from the carbon atom to the hydrogen atoms for this structure would involve carbon bond orbitals $2p$ in character. The other structure that can be suggested is the triplet structure,

$$\uparrow \quad \overset{\displaystyle H}{\underset{\displaystyle H}{\overset{\diagup}{\underset{\diagdown}{C}}}}$$
$$\uparrow$$

With this structure the carbon atom is in the electron configuration $2s2p^3$, and the unshared electrons occupy two tetrahedral orbitals, the other two being occupied by the bond electrons. The carbon-hydrogen bonds are expected to be stronger for this structure than for the singlet structure, but this triplet structure requires promotion energy from the bivalent state of carbon to the quadrivalent state. Spectroscopic studies indicate that the normal state of the molecule is the triplet state, and that the singlet state is somewhat less stable; the relative energy of the two states has not yet been determined by experiment.

We can estimate the energy of the singlet state by use of bond-energy values. From the standard enthalpy of $CH(g)$ given in Table 10-1 we may calculate that the heat of formation of CH from atoms is 81.7 kcal/mole. We might expect the energy of the second C—H bond in the singlet state of CH_2 to be the same; the heat of formation of $:CH_2$ from atoms would then be predicted to be about 163.4 kcal/mole. The observed heat of formation of the normal state ($\overset{\uparrow}{\underset{\uparrow}{}} CH_2$, triplet state) from atoms is 181 kcal/mole (calculated from the value of the enthalpy of formation given in Table 10-1). This value is 18 kcal/mole greater than the value predicted for the singlet state, and accordingly we estimate that the singlet state lies about 18 kcal/mole above the triplet state.

The C—H bond in CH has length 1.12 Å, essentially the same as in methane (1.11 Å). In the normal (triplet) state CH_2 has bond length 1.07 Å and bond angle 140°; in the singlet state the values are 1.12 Å and 103°.

10-12. The Carbon Cycle in Nature

The atmosphere contains about 0.03% carbon dioxide. Additional carbon dioxide is being poured into the atmosphere all of the time—all animals exhale carbon dioxide, which has been produced by the oxidation of carbon compounds in their tissues, and carbon dioxide is also produced by the burning of wood and coal and the slow decay of plant and animal remains. If there were not some mechanism for removing carbon dioxide from the atmosphere, the composition of the atmosphere would in the course of time change enough to make the earth unsatisfactory for life in its present form.

There is a mechanism for the removal of carbon dioxide from the atmosphere: this mechanism is the utilization of atmospheric carbon dioxide by plants. The amount of plant life on the earth is such that a steady state has been reached in which the content of carbon dioxide in the atmosphere has remained nearly constant for tens of millions of years. Through the interplay of plants and animals there has been achieved a *carbon cycle* in nature.

Carbon dioxide is taken from the air by the plants, and broken down into carbon (in the form of *carbohydrates*, compounds of carbon with hydrogen and oxygen in the ratio 2H to O, as in water) and free oxygen, which is liberated into the air. Some of the plants are burned or are oxidized during the process of decay, their carbon being returned to the atmosphere as carbon dioxide. Others are eaten by animals, and the carbon compounds in the plant tissues are changed into carbon compounds in the animal tissues. Ultimately the compounds of carbon in the animal tissues are oxidized, and the carbon is returned to the atmosphere as carbon dioxide in the exhaled breath of the animals, or the animal dies, and the carbon is ultimately returned to the atmosphere through oxidation to carbon dioxide during decay.

The carbon cycle in the form that is of most interest to man involves three steps: carbon dioxide in the atmosphere is converted into carbon compounds in the tissues of plants; the plants (or animals that have eaten the plants) are eaten by man and the carbon compounds are converted into carbon compounds in the tissues of man; the carbon compounds are oxidized in the tissues by oxygen that has been inhaled and the carbon dioxide that is produced is exhaled into the atmosphere.

Energy is required to convert carbon dioxide and water into carbohydrates (cellulose, starch, sugars) and free oxygen. This energy is obtained by the plant from sunlight. The process of using the energy of sunlight to carry out the reaction is called *photosynthesis:*

$$x\text{CO}_2 + x\text{H}_2\text{O} + \text{energy from sunlight} \longrightarrow (\text{CH}_2\text{O})_x + x\text{O}_2$$

The formula $(\text{CH}_2\text{O})_x$ is used to indicate that there are several units with composition CH_2O in the molecules of carbohydrates produced; a simple sugar such as glucose has the formula $\text{C}_6\text{H}_{12}\text{O}_6$. The reaction of photosynthesis that is carried out by plants is one of the most important of all chemical reactions.

It has not been found possible to carry out the reaction of photosynthesis in the laboratory. Early in the history of the world, however, nature found a way, by developing a special catalyst that is highly effective. This catalyst, called *chlorophyll*, is a complex substance containing magnesium ion. It is the green substance that gives the green color to the leaves of plants. Chlorophyll is green because it absorbs the light in the red-orange and blue regions of the spectrum and allows the green light to pass through or to be reflected. The energy of the absorbed light is used for the chemical reaction that is catalyzed by the chlorophyll.

We may calculate the amount of energy required for conversion of carbon dioxide and water into substances such as glucose. The heat of combustion of glucose is 672 kcal/mole. Hence we write $CO_2 + H_2O + 112$ kcal/mole $\longrightarrow \frac{1}{6}C_6H_{12}O_6$. From the heat absorbed by this endothermic reaction we can calculate the minimum number of photons (light quanta) needed. The only light quanta that can provide the energy are those absorbed by the chlorophyll. Chlorophyll has a strong absorption region at about 6600 Å (red) and another at about 4200 Å (blue). The energy of a photon with frequency ν is $h\nu$, which is equal to hc/λ. For 6600 Å this amount of energy is 43 kcal/mole, and for 4200 Å it is 68 kcal/mole. Hence two or three photons are needed per CO_2 molecule reduced. Experiments indicate that the process probably involves four photons.

There are great amounts of carbon dioxide, in combined form, in the sea and in rocks. Sea water contains about 0.15% of its weight in carbon dioxide, mainly as hydrogen carbonate ion, HCO_3^-. The amount of carbon dioxide contained in sea water is about 65 times as much as that in the atmosphere. Under changed climatic conditions large amounts of carbon dioxide might be released from the oceans, increasing the concentration in the air. It is probable that there were larger amounts of carbon dioxide in the atmosphere during the Carboniferous Period than at the present time, permitting plant life to flourish and the great coal beds to be laid down.

EXERCISES

10-18. Compare diamond and graphite as to composition, hardness, density, structure, and principal uses.

10-19. Compare carbon monoxide and carbon dioxide as to color, odor, solubility in water, physiological activity, and combustibility.

10-20. Write the equation for the reaction of sodium hydrogen carbonate with hydrochloric acid. Do you think that baking soda and dilute hydrochloric acid (added separately to the dough) could be used in cooking in place of baking powder?

10-21. What is an addition reaction? A substitution reaction? Write an equation to illustrate each, using bromine, Br_2, as one of the reactants.

10-22. How many isomers do you predict for hexane, C_6H_{14}? Draw their structural formulas.

10-23. Propene, C_3H_6, follows ethylene in the ethylene series. What is its structural formula? Write the equation, using structural formulas, for its addition reaction with iodine, I_2.

10-24. What product would you expect to get if ethylene were allowed to react with chlorine at room temperature in the dark? At high temperature, with an excess of chlorine? Write equations.

10-25. (a) How many isomers with formula C_3H_6 are there? (b) With formula C_3H_5Cl? (c) With formula $C_3H_4Cl_2$?

10-26. There is an isomer of benzene that has been given the name dimethyldiacetylene. From the name, what structural formula would you assign it? Compare the spatial arrangement of the six carbon atoms with that in benzene.

10-27. The standard enthalpy of formation of *n*-propane, $C_3H_8(g)$, is -24.82 kcal/mole. What is the heat of combustion in kcal/mole? In B.T.U. per pound?

10-28. (a) Show by building a ball-and-stick model that the strain-free puckered ring (called the chair form) of cyclohexane (with bond angles $109°28'$) has the staggered orientation around each C—C bond.

(b) Show that there is another structure (the boat form) in which there is no bond-angle strain but not all the C—C bonds have the staggered orientation. By how much do you estimate this form of the molecule to be less stable than the other? (Answer: 6 kcal/mole.)

10-29. By building a ball-and-stick model show that a planar 5-ring of tetrahedral carbon atoms for cyclopentane, C_5H_{10}, involves little strain. By how much do the C—C—C angles differ from the tetrahedral value? (Answer: $1°28'$.)

10-30. Calculate the instability of the C_5H_{10} molecule with a planar C_5 ring that would result from unfavorable orientation about the C—C bonds. [The cyclopentane molecule has in fact been shown by electron diffraction to have one carbon atom moved out of the plane of the other four. The heat of combustion of $C_5H_{10}(g)$ is not 15 kcal/mole greater than $\frac{5}{6}$ that of $C_6H_{12}(g)$, but only 5 kcal/mole greater.] (Answer: 15 kcal/mole.)

10-31. The electric dipole moment of the carbon monoxide molecule has been found by microwave spectroscopy to have the value 0.112 D, with direction corresponding to positive charge on the oxygen atom. The internuclear distance is 1.130 Å. Assuming that the atomic charges are the same distance apart as the nuclei, calculate the fraction of electronic charge on each atom. (Answer: 0.0206.)

10-32. In Example 8 of Chapter 9 it is mentioned that the structure $: C \equiv O :$ places the charge $+0.36$ on the oxygen atom and the structure $: C = O :$ places the charge -0.44 on the oxygen atom. Assuming additivity of charges, what relative contributions of the two structures would lead to observed dipole moment? (See the preceding exercise.) (Answer: 57%, 43%.)

10-33. (a) From enthalpy values (Tables 6-1 and 10-1) evaluate the heat of formation of the carbon dioxide molecule from atoms. (b) Is the molecule more stable or less stable than a hypothetical molecule with the structure $: O = C = O :$? (Use the C=O bond energy from Table 10-3.)

(c) To what do you attribute the energy difference found in (b)?

10-34. From values given in Table 10-1 calculate the bond-dissociation energy of ethylene into $2CH_2$. Compare with the bond energy of the carbon-carbon double bond (Table 10-3). To what feature of the electronic structure of CH_2 do you attribute the difference? (Answer: 136 kcal/mole; stability of triplet state.)

10-35. Assuming the zigzag configuration of the carbon atoms in the chain, evaluate the length of a long normal hydrocarbon chain containing n CH_2 groups. Use C—C bond length 1.54 Å and the tetrahedral angle. (Answer: 1.26 Å per CH_2.)

10-36. The long-chain normal alkanes have density about 0.99 g/cm³. To what value of the cross-sectional area of the extended (zigzag) hydrocarbon chain does this density correspond? (Use the result of the preceding Exercise.) (Answer: 18.7 Å².)

10-37. The crystal of the hydrocarbon normal hexatriacontane, $C_{36}H_{74}$, is orthorhombic, with $a = 7.38$ Å, $b = 4.94$ Å, and $c = 47.51$ Å. The unit contains two molecules extended along the c axis. What is the cross-sectional area per chain in this crystal? (Answer: 18.2 Å².)

10-38. Make a drawing showing the projection of a long extended alkane chain on the plane normal to the long axis. How far apart are the two carbon-atom positions in the projection? What are the dimensions of the rectangle defined by the four hydrogen-atom positions? What are the dimensions of the rectangle circumscribed about the projections of the van der Waals surfaces of the hydrogen atoms? What is the area of this rectangle? (Answer: 0.89 Å; 1.80 Å $\times$ 2.17 Å; 4.0 Å $\times$ 4.4 Å; 17.6 Å².)

10-39. A compound whose molecules consist of two rings of carbon atoms without any bond between the rings, but linked together in the way that two links in a chain are attached to one another, has been synthesized. (Compounds of this sort are called *catenanes*.) Making use of your knowledge about bond lengths, bond angles, and van der Waals radii of atoms (see the preceding Exercises), estimate the number of carbon atoms needed in a hydrocarbon ring $(CH_2)_n$ in order that there be a hole in the ring large enough to permit the insertion of a portion of another hydrocarbon chain. (The investigators who prepared the first catenane* made it with two 34-atom rings, but stated that 20 methylene groups would give a large enough ring.) (Answer: About 22.)

10-40. Using values of bond energies (Table 10-3), calculate the enthalpy of formation of C_2O_2, with structure $O{=}C{=}C{=}O$. Can you explain why C_2O_2 has not been synthesized?

REFERENCES

Scientific American offprints (see Appendix VI):

85. Organic Chemical Reactions
122. The Path of Carbon in Photosynthesis
263. Frozen Free Radicals
286. Chemical Topology

T. A. Geissman, *Principles of Organic Chemistry*, Second Edition, W. H. Freeman and Co., San Francisco, 1962.

D. J. Cram and G. S. Hammond, *Organic Chemistry*, McGraw-Hill Book Co., New York, 1959.

L. B. Clapp, *Chemistry of the Covalent Bond*, W. H. Freeman and Co., San Francisco, 1957.

L. F. and M. Fieser, *Introduction to Organic Chemistry*, D. C. Heath Co., Boston, 1957.

R. C. Fuson and H. R. Snyder, *Organic Chemistry*, Second Edition, John Wiley & Sons, New York, 1954.

H. J. Lucas, *Organic Chemistry*, American Book Co., New York, 1953.

* "Chemical topology," by E. Wasserman, *Scientific American*, November 1962.

CHAPTER **11**

Oxidation-reduction Reactions

In the development of the theory of valence it was found convenient to place chemical reactions in which elements undergo a change in valence in a special class, the class of *oxidation-reduction reactions*. The study of these reactions in relation to electronic structure then led to the introduction of a special kind of valence, called *oxidation number*. It is to these topics that we now turn our attention.

11-1. The Electronic Interpretation of Oxidation and Reduction

In Section 6-2 the reaction of combination with oxygen was described as oxidation, and the removal of oxygen from a compound was described as reduction. It was recognized by chemists many years ago that combination with a nonmetallic element other than oxygen closely resembles combination with oxygen. Hydrogen burns in fluorine even more vigorously than in oxygen:

$$H_2 + F_2 \longrightarrow 2HF$$

Iron burns in fluorine and when heated combines readily with chlorine and also with sulfur:

$$2Fe + 3F_2 \longrightarrow 2FeF_3$$
$$2Fe + 3Cl_2 \longrightarrow 2FeCl_3$$
$$Fe + S \longrightarrow FeS$$

Because of the similarity of these reactions to those involving combination with oxygen they have come to be described as involving a generalized sort of oxidation.

In accordance with this usage we say that metallic sodium is oxidized when it burns in chlorine to form sodium chloride:

$$2Na + Cl_2 \longrightarrow 2Na^+Cl^-$$

Here we have written sodium chloride as Na^+Cl^- to show that it consists of ions.

The oxidation of metallic sodium is the process of removing an electron from each sodium atom:

$$Na \longrightarrow Na^+ + e^-$$

The process reverse to that of oxidation is called reduction. In the electrolysis of molten sodium chloride there occurs at the cathode the reaction

$$Na^+ + e^- \longrightarrow Na$$

This reaction, the reduction of sodium ion to metallic sodium by the addition of an electron from the cathode, is called *cathodic reduction.*

The Electronic Definitions of Oxidation and Reduction.   From these examples we see the justification for the modern usage of the words oxidation and reduction:

Oxidation is the removal of electrons from an atom or group of atoms.
Reduction is the addition of electrons to an atom or group of atoms.

When molten sodium chloride is decomposed by electrolysis, free chlorine is formed at the anode:

$$2Cl^- \longrightarrow Cl_2 + 2e^-$$

This is an example of *anodic oxidation.* The electrons that are liberated in this reaction move into the anode and along the wire connecting the anode with the generator or battery.

Oxidation and reduction reactions can take place either at the electrodes, which supply electrons and take up electrons, or by direct contact of atoms or molecules, with direct transfer of electrons. Thus when sodium burns in chlorine the sodium atoms transfer their electrons directly to the chlorine atoms at the time that the molecule of chlorine strikes the surface of the metal (Figure 11-1):

$$2Na \longrightarrow 2Na^+ + 2e^-$$
$$Cl_2 + 2e^- \longrightarrow 2Cl^-$$
$$\overline{}$$
$$2Na + Cl_2 \longrightarrow 2Na^+Cl^-$$

Oxidation or reduction of a substance could be carried out without simultaneous reduction or oxidation of another substance if one had at hand a very large electric condenser from which to remove electrons or in which to store them. Ordinarily such an electron reservoir is not available; even the very largest electric condenser charged to its maximum potential holds so few electrons (compared with Avogadro's number) that only a very small amount of chemical reaction can be produced by it. *There accordingly occur equivalent processes of oxidation and reduction in every oxidation-reduction reaction.*

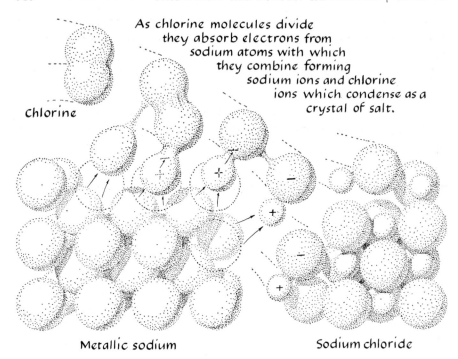

As chlorine molecules divide
they absorb electrons from
sodium atoms with which
they combine forming
sodium ions and chlorine
ions which condense as a
crystal of salt.

Chlorine

Metallic sodium   Sodium chloride

Figure **11-1**

The reaction of sodium and chlorine to form sodium chloride.

Oxidizing Agents and Reducing Agents. Oxidation-reduction Pairs. An atom, molecule, or ion that takes up electrons is called an *oxidizing agent*, and one that liberates electrons is called a *reducing agent*.

For example, in the formation of magnesium fluoride by combination of magnesium and fluorine, magnesium is the reducing agent and fluorine is the oxidizing agent:

$$Mg + F_2 \longrightarrow Mg^{++}(F^-)_2$$

Every electron reaction involves an oxidizing agent and a reducing agent, which are closely related to one another. Thus sodium ions in molten sodium chloride can be reduced to metallic sodium by the cathode of the cell:

$$Na^+ + e^- \longrightarrow Na$$

In this electron reaction the oxidizing agent Na^+ is reduced by the cathode. But when sodium combines with chlorine to form sodium chloride the metallic sodium Na is oxidized to Na^+, by giving its electron up to chlorine:

$$Na \longrightarrow Na^+ + e^-$$

In this reaction metallic sodium is the reducing agent. Metallic sodium and sodium ion are called an *oxidation-reduction pair*, or *oxidation-reduction couple*.

The interconversion of metallic sodium and sodium ion by an electron reaction can be expressed by a single equation, with a double arrow:

$$Na \rightleftarrows Na^+ + e^-$$

The direction in which this reaction proceeds in any system depends upon the nature of the system.

An example of the reversal of an electron reaction involving an oxidation-reduction pair is the bromine-bromide ion pair:

$$Br_2 + 2e^- \rightleftarrows 2Br^-$$

Here elementary bromine, Br_2, is the oxidizing agent of the pair and bromide ion is the reducing agent. Bromine is a strong enough oxidizing agent to liberate iodine from iodide ion—that is, to oxidize iodide ion to iodine:

$$Br_2 + 2e^- \longrightarrow 2Br^-$$
$$2I^- \longrightarrow I_2 + 2e^-$$

$$\overline{Br_2 + 2I^- \longrightarrow 2Br^- + I_2}$$

However, chlorine is a still stronger oxidizing agent; it is able to liberate bromine from bromide ion:

$$Cl_2 + 2e^- \longrightarrow 2Cl^-$$
$$2Br^- \longrightarrow Br_2 + 2e^-$$

$$\overline{Cl_2 + 2Br^- \longrightarrow 2Cl^- + Br_2}$$

Thus in one of these two oxidation-reduction reactions the bromine-bromide ion electron reaction proceeds in one direction, and in the other reaction it proceeds in the other direction.

The conditions determining the direction in which an electron reaction proceeds are discussed later in this chapter. It has been found that the oxidation-reduction pairs can be arranged in a series with increasing strength of the oxidizing agent and decreasing strength of the reducing agent. Thus as oxidizing agents the halogens lie in the order

$$F_2 > Cl_2 > Br_2 > I_2$$

and as reducing agents their ions lie in the reverse order:

$$I^- > Br^- > Cl^- > F^-$$

The nonmetallic elements are strong oxidizing agents, and the metals are strong reducing agents. There is rough correspondence between the strength of an elementary substance as an oxidizing or reducing agent and its electronegativity, discussed in the preceding chapter. Fluorine, the element with the greatest electronegativity, is also the strongest oxidizing agent known. The alkali metals, with the smallest electronegativity, are the strongest reducing agents.

Illustrative
Exercises

11-1. Write the equation for the reaction of carbon and fluorine to form carbon tetrafluoride. Is carbon serving here as an oxidizing agent or a reducing agent?

11-2. Aluminum wire will burn in an atmosphere of fluorine, forming aluminum fluoride.

(a) By reference to the periodic table, predict the ionic valence of aluminum and the formula of aluminum fluoride.

(b) What is the oxidizing agent and what is the reducing agent in this reaction?

11-3. (a) What halogen might you use to oxidize bromide ion to bromine?

(b) What halogenide ion might you use to reduce bromine to bromide ion?

(c) Write equations for the two reactions.

11-4. Write the anode reaction and the cathode reaction for the electrolysis of molten lanthanum chloride, $LaCl_3$. Is lanthanum metal produced at the anode or the cathode? By oxidation or reduction?

11-2. Oxidation Numbers of Atoms

The examples given above of oxidation-reduction reactions have involved the interconversion of atoms and monatomic ions. It is convenient to extend the idea of electron transfer in such a way as to permit it to be applied to all substances. This is done by introducing the concept of *oxidation number*.

For example, let us consider the reduction of the permanganate ion. Potassium permanganate, $KMnO_4$, is a purple crystalline substance soluble in water to produce a magenta solution. It is a strong oxidizing agent, and it is sometimes used in the jungle to disinfect water (it oxidizes the bacteria). The solution of potassium permanganate contains the magenta-colored permanganate ion, MnO_4^-. In the presence of alkali this ion is easily reduced to the manganate ion, MnO_4^{--}, which has a green color. The reduction can be carried out by electrolysis; the electrons are then transferred from the cathode to the permanganate ion to produce the manganate ion:

$$MnO_4^- + e^- \longrightarrow MnO_4^{--}$$

It is clear that the permanganate ion has served as the oxidizing agent in this electron reaction, having been reduced by the cathode, which transferred an electron to it. If we knew enough about the electronic structure of the permanganate ion and the manganate ion we might be able to say that the added electron had attached itself to a particular atom. It is, in fact, convenient to do so—we say that the added electron has attached itself to the manganese atom, which has been reduced; the oxygen atoms in the permanganate ion are considered not to have changed, in this respect, on conversion of the permanganate ion to the manganate ion. We say that the *oxidation number* of manganese has changed from $+7$ to $+6$, whereas that of oxygen has remained unchanged at -2.

The **oxidation number** *of an atom is a number that represents the electric charge that the atom would have if the electrons in a compound were assigned to the atoms in a certain way.*

The assignment of electrons is somewhat arbitrary, but the conventional procedure, described below, is useful because it permits a simple statement to be made about the valences of the elements in a compound without considering its electronic structure in detail and because it can be made the basis of a simple method of balancing equations for oxidation-reduction reactions.

An oxidation number may be assigned to each atom in a substance by the application of simple rules. These rules, while simple, are not completely unambiguous. Although their application is usually a straightforward procedure, it sometimes requires considerable chemical insight and knowledge of molecular structure. The rules are given in the following sentences:

1. *The oxidation number of a monatomic ion in an ionic substance is equal to its electric charge.*
2. *The oxidation number of an atom in an elementary substance is zero.*
3. *In a covalent compound of known structure, the oxidation number of each atom is the charge remaining on the atom when each shared electron pair is assigned completely to the more electronegative of the two atoms sharing it. An electron pair shared by two atoms of the same element is usually split between them.*
4. *The oxidation number of an element in a compound of uncertain structure may be calculated from a reasonable assignment of oxidation numbers to the other elements in the compounds.*

The application of the first three rules is illustrated by the following examples; the number by the symbol of each atom is the oxidation number of that atom:

$Na^{+1}Cl^{-1}$ $Mg^{+2}(Cl^{-1})_2$ $(B^{+3})_2(O^{-2})_3$

H_2^0 O_2^0 C^0 (diamond or graphite)

H^{+1} (hydrogen cation) $(O^{-2}H^{+1})^-$ (hydroxide ion)

$N^{-3}(H^{+1})_3$ $Cl^{+1}F^{-1}$ $C^{+4}(O^{-2})_2$

$C^{+2}O^{-2}$ $C^{-4}(H^{+1})_4$ $K^{+1}Mn^{+7}(O^{-2})_4$

Fluorine, the most electronegative element, has the oxidation number -1 in all of its compounds with other elements.

Oxygen is second only to fluorine in electronegativity, and in its compounds it usually has oxidation number -2; examples are $Ca^{+2}O^{-2}$, $(Fe^{+3})_2(O^{-2})_3$, $C^{+4}(O^{-2})_2$. Oxygen fluoride, OF_2, is an exception; in this compound, in which oxygen is combined with the only element that is more electronegative than it is, oxygen has the oxidation number $+2$. The peroxides, which are discussed in Section 11-5, are also exceptional; oxygen has the oxidation number -1 in these compounds.

Hydrogen when bonded to a nonmetal has oxidation number $+1$, as in $(H^{+1})_2O^{-2}$, $(H^{+1})_2S^{-2}$, $H^{+1}Cl^{-1}$, etc. In compounds with metals, such as $Li^{+1}H^{-1}$, its oxidation number is -1, corresponding to the electronic structure $H:^{-1}$ for a negative hydrogen ion with completed K shell (helium structure). On electrolysis of fused alkali hydride, hydrogen is liberated at the anode, according to the equation

$$2H^- \longrightarrow H_2 + 2e^-$$

Thiosulfuric acid, $H_2S_2O_3$, provides an example of a substance that is usually discussed by assigning different oxidation numbers to two atoms of the same element (sulfur). It is known that thiosulfuric acid is similar in structure to sulfuric acid, H_2SO_4. In sulfuric acid the sulfur atom is assigned oxidation number $+6$, with oxygen -2 and hydrogen $+1$. In thiosulfuric acid another sulfur atom takes the place of one of the oxygen atoms of sulfuric acid. It may be assigned the same oxidation number, -2, as oxygen, with the other sulfur atom retaining its oxidation number $+6$. Alternatives, such as assigning each sulfur atom the oxidation number $+2$, or assigning -1 to one and $+5$ to the other, can be accepted, provided that they agree with the total electric charge of the molecule.

Values of Oxidation Numbers of Elements.   Some of the elements are well-behaved in their compounds, in that they assume only certain standard oxidation numbers, whereas other elements are much more variable.

The elements of the first three groups of the periodic table have normal oxidation numbers, $+1$, $+2$, and $+3$, respectively, in all of their compounds, with rare exceptions. The processes of oxidation and reduction that these elements undergo are simply the interconversion of the elementary substances and their ions.

It will be found in later chapters that the nonmetals, in groups V, VI, and VII of the periodic table, show a variety of oxidation numbers, usually extending over a range of 8, with the important ones tending to differ by 2. Thus the halogens (aside from fluorine, which has oxidation numbers 0 and -1 only) have oxidation numbers ranging from -1 to $+7$, with $+1$, $+3$, and $+5$ the important intermediate values. The congeners of oxygen have oxidation numbers ranging from -2 to $+6$, and nitrogen and its congeners have oxidation numbers ranging from -3 to $+5$.

Each of the transition elements tends to have several oxidation numbers. Thus iron forms one series of compounds with oxidation number $+2$ (ferrous compounds) and another series with oxidation number $+3$ (ferric compounds). For chromium the principal oxidation numbers are $+3$ and $+6$, and for manganese they are $+2$ and $+7$. It would be of great value to chemistry if a simple and reliable theory of the oxidation states of the transition elements were to be developed; but this has not yet been done.

Illustrative Exercises

11-5. Verify that the oxidation number of manganese is $+7$ in permanganate ion, MnO_4^-, and $+6$ in manganate ion, MnO_4^{--}.

11-6. What is the oxidation number of sulfur in hydrogen sulfide, H_2S? In elementary sulfur, S_8? In sulfur dioxide, SO_2? In sulfuric acid, H_2SO_4? In the sulfate ion, SO_4^{--}?

11-7. What is the oxidation number of manganese in the elementary substance? In manganous chloride, $MnCl_2 \cdot 4H_2O$? In manganese dioxide, MnO_2?

11-3. Oxidation Number and Chemical Nomenclature

The principal classification of the compounds of an element is made on the basis of its oxidation state. In our discussions of the compounds formed by the various elements or groups of elements in the following chapters of this book we begin by a statement of the oxidation states represented by the compounds. The compounds are grouped together in classes, representing those with the principal element in the same oxidation state. For example, in the discussion of the compounds of iron, in Chapter 24, they are divided into two classes, representing the compounds of iron in oxidation state $+2$ and those in oxidation state $+3$, respectively.

The nomenclature of the compounds of the metals is also based upon their oxidation states. At the present time there are two principal nomenclatures in use. We may illustrate the two systems of nomenclature by taking the compounds $FeCl_2$ and $FeCl_3$ as examples. In the older system a compound of a metal in the lower of two important oxidation states is named by use of the name of the metal (usually the Latin name) with the suffix *ous*. Thus the salts of iron in oxidation state $+2$ are *ferrous* salts; $FeCl_2$ is called *ferrous chloride*. The compounds of a metal in the higher oxidation state are named with use of the suffix *ic*. The salts of iron in oxidation state $+3$ are called *ferric* salts; $FeCl_3$ is *ferric chloride*.

Note that the suffixes *ous* and *ic* do not tell what the oxidation states are. For copper compounds, such as $CuCl$ and $CuCl_2$, the compounds in which copper has oxidation number $+1$ are called cuprous compounds, and those in which it has oxidation number $+2$ are called cupric compounds.

A new system of nomenclature for inorganic compounds was drawn up by a committee of the International Union of Chemistry in 1940. According to this system the value of the oxidation number of a metal is represented by a Roman numeral given in parentheses following the name (usually the English name rather than the Latin name) of the metal. Thus $FeCl_2$ is given the name iron(II) chloride, and $FeCl_3$ is given the name iron(III) chloride. These names are read simply by stating the numeral after the name of the metal: thus iron(II) chloride is read as "iron two chloride."

It may be noted that it is not necessary to give the oxidation number of a metal in naming a compound if the metal forms only one principal series of compounds. The compound $BaCl_2$ may be called barium chloride rather than barium(II) chloride, because barium forms no compounds other than those in which it has oxidation number $+2$. Also, if one oxidation state is represented by many compounds, and another by only a few, the oxidation state does not need to be indicated for the compounds of the important series. Thus the compounds of copper with oxidation number $+2$ are far more important than those of copper with oxidation number $+1$, and for this reason $CuCl_2$ may be called simply copper chloride, whereas $CuCl$ would be called copper(I) chloride.

We shall in general make use of the new system of nomenclature in the following chapters of our book, except that, for convenience, we shall use the old nomenclature for the following common metals:

Iron: $+2$, ferrous; $+3$, ferric
Copper: $+1$, cuprous; $+2$, cupric (or copper)
Mercury: $+1$, mercurous; $+2$, mercuric
Tin: $+2$, stannous; $+4$, stannic

Compounds of metalloids and nonmetals are usually given names in which the numbers of atoms of different kinds are indicated by prefixes, as described in Chapter 4. The compounds PCl_3 and PCl_5, for example, are called phosphorus trichloride and phosphorus pentachloride, respectively.

11-4. How to Balance Equations for Oxidation-reduction Reactions

The principal use of the oxidation numbers that we have been discussing in the preceding section is in writing equations for oxidation-reduction reactions.

The first step in writing the equation for an oxidation-reduction reaction is the same as for any other chemical reaction: **be sure that you know what the reactants are and what the products are.**

The chemist finds what the reactants and the products are by studying the reaction as it occurs in the laboratory or in nature, or by reading in journals or books to find out what other chemists have learned about the reaction. Sometimes, of course, a knowledge of chemical theory permits a safe prediction about the nature of the reaction to be made.

The next step is to balance the equation for the reaction. In balancing the equation for an oxidation-reduction reaction it is often wise to write the electron reactions separately (as they would occur in an electrolytic cell), and then to add them so as to cancel out the electrons. For example, ferric ion,

Fe^{+++}, oxidizes stannous ion, Sn^{++}, to stannic ion, Sn^{++++}; that is, from the bipositive state to the quadripositive state. The ferric ion is itself reduced to ferrous ion, Fe^{++}. The two electron reactions are

$$Fe^{+++} + e^- \longrightarrow Fe^{++}$$

and

$$Sn^{++} \longrightarrow Sn^{++++} + 2e^-$$

Note that there is conservation of electric charge as well as conservation of atoms in each of these equations.

Before adding these two equations the first must be multiplied by 2 to use up the two electrons that are given by the second; then the two equations may be added together:

$$2Fe^{+++} + 2e^- \longrightarrow 2Fe^{++}$$
$$Sn^{++} \longrightarrow Sn^{++++} + 2e^-$$
$$\overline{}$$
$$2Fe^{+++} + Sn^{++} \longrightarrow 2Fe^{++} + Sn^{++++}$$

The consideration of the electrode reactions has shown that two ferric ions are required to oxidize one stannous ion, because the reduction of ferric ion requires only one electron, whereas in the oxidation of stannous ion two electrons are given up.

The process of balancing a more complicated equation is illustrated by the example given below.

Example 1. If potassium permanganate, $KMnO_4$, is dissolved in water, and a solution of ferrous salt, such as ferrous sulfate, $FeSO_4$, containing some sulfuric acid is added, the permanganate ion is reduced to manganese(II) ion, Mn^{++}, and the ferrous ion is oxidized to ferric ion. Write the equation for the reaction.

Solution. The oxidation number of manganese in permanganate ion, MnO_4^-, is $+7$. The oxidation number of manganese in manganese(II) ion, Mn^{++}, is $+2$. Hence 5 electrons are involved in the reduction of permanganate ion to manganese(II) ion. The electron reaction is accordingly

$$[Mn^{+7}(O^{-2})_4]^- + 5e^- + \text{other reactants} \longrightarrow Mn^{++} + \text{other products} \qquad (1a)$$

In reactions in aqueous solution water, hydrogen ion, and hydroxide ion may come into action as reactants or products. For example, in an acidic solution hydrogen ion may be either a reactant or a product, and water may also be either a reactant or a product in the same reaction. In an acidic solution hydroxide ion exists only in extremely low concentration and would hardly be expected to enter into the reaction. Hence water and hydrogen ion may enter into the reaction now under consideration.

Equation 1a is not balanced electrically; there are 6 negative charges on the left side and 2 positive charges on the right side. The only other ion that can enter into the reaction is hydrogen ion, H^+. The number of hydrogen ions needed to give conservation of electric charge is 8. Thus we obtain, as the second step in our process, the following equation:

$$MnO_4^- + 5e^- + 8H^+ \longrightarrow Mn^{++} + \text{other products} \qquad (1b)$$

Oxygen and hydrogen occur here on the left side and not on the right side of the equation; conservation of atoms is satisfied if $4H_2O$ is written in as the "other products":

$$MnO_4^- + 5e^- + 8H^+ \longrightarrow Mn^{++} + 4H_2O \qquad (1)$$

We now check this equation on three points—*proper change in oxidation number* (5 electrons were used, corresponding to the change of -5 in oxidation number of manganese from Mn^{+7} in permanganate ion to Mn^{+2} in manganese(II) ion), *conservation of electric charge* (from $-1 - 5 + 8$ to $+2$), and *conservation of atoms*—and convince ourselves that it is correct.

The electron reaction for the oxidation of ferrous ion to ferric ion is now written:

$$Fe^{++} \longrightarrow Fe^{+++} + e^- \qquad (2)$$

This equation checks on all three points.

The equation for the oxidation-reduction reaction itself is obtained by combining the two electron reactions in such a way that the electrons liberated in one are used up in the other. We see that this is to be achieved by multiplying Equation 2 by 5 and adding it to Equation 1:

$$5Fe^{++} \longrightarrow 5Fe^{+++} + 5e^-$$
$$MnO_4^- + 5e^- + 8H^+ \longrightarrow Mn^{++} + 4H_2O \qquad (3)$$
$$\overline{MnO_4^- + 5Fe^{++} + 8H^+ \longrightarrow Mn^{++} + 5Fe^{+++} + 4H_2O}$$

It is good practice to check this final equation also on all three points to be sure that no mistake has been made:

1. *Change in oxidation number:* Mn^{+7} to Mn^{+2}, change -5; $5Fe^{++}$ to $5Fe^{+++}$, change $+5$.
2. *Conservation of electric charge:* left side, $-1 + 10 + 8 = +17$; right side, $+2 + 15 = +17$
3. *Conservation of atoms:* Left side, 1Mn, 4O, 5Fe, 8H; right side, 1Mn, 5Fe, 8H, 4O

Illustrative Exercises

11-8. Balance the equation for the reaction of aluminum and fluorine to form aluminum fluoride, writing first the equations for the electron reactions and then that for the over-all reaction.

11-9. Ferric ion, Fe^{+++}, in aqueous solution is reduced to ferrous ion, Fe^{++}, by metallic zinc, which is oxidized to zinc ion, Zn^{++}. Write equations for the electron reactions and the over-all reaction.

11-10. Under certain conditions silver dissolves in nitric acid, HNO_3, to form silver ion, Ag^+, and nitric oxide gas, NO.

(a) What is the oxidation number of nitrogen in nitric acid? In nitric oxide?

(b) Balance the following equations for the electron reactions and the over-all reaction:

$$Ag \longrightarrow Ag^+ + e^-$$
$$H^+ + HNO_3 \longrightarrow H_2O + NO$$
$$\overline{Ag + H^+ + HNO_3 \longrightarrow Ag^+ + H_2O + NO}$$

11-5. An Example: The Reactions of Hydrogen Peroxide

When barium oxide, BaO, is heated to a dull red heat in a stream of air, it adds oxygen to form a higher oxide, BaO_2, *barium peroxide:*

$$2BaO + O_2 \longrightarrow 2BaO_2$$

This salt contains the *peroxide ion*, O_2^{--}, which has the electronic structure

$$\left[:\ddot{O}-\ddot{O}: \right]^{--}$$

There is a single covalent bond between the two oxygen atoms. The oxidation number of oxygen in the peroxide ion and in peroxides is -1. These substances represent an intermediate oxidation state between free oxygen (oxygen with oxidation number 0 in O_2) and oxides (O^{-2}).

The electrolysis of a peroxide solution leads to the liberation of one mole of oxygen at the anode by two moles of electrons, the anode reaction being

$$O_2^{--} \longrightarrow O_2 + 2e^-$$

Care must be taken to distinguish between *peroxides*, which contain two oxygen atoms with a single covalent bond between them, and *dioxides*. Thus BaO_2 is a peroxide, containing Ba^{++} and $\left[:\ddot{O}-\ddot{O}: \right]^{--}$, and TiO_2, titanium dioxide, is a dioxide, containing Ti^{++++} and two oxygen ions, O^{--}. A peroxide usually liberates hydrogen peroxide when treated with acid, whereas a dioxide does not.

Hydrogen peroxide, H_2O_2, is made by treating barium peroxide with sulfuric acid or phosphoric acid, and distilling:*

* A method involving organic compounds is used in industry.

$$BaO_2 + H_2SO_4 \longrightarrow BaSO_4 + H_2O_2$$

Pure hydrogen peroxide is a colorless, sirupy liquid, with density 1.47 g/cm^3, melting point $-1.7°C$, and boiling point 151°C. It is a very strong oxidizing agent, which spontaneously oxidizes organic substances. Its uses are in the main determined by its oxidizing power.

Commercial hydrogen peroxide is an aqueous solution, sometimes containing a small amount of a stabilizer, such as phosphate ion, to decrease its rate of decomposition to water and oxygen by the reaction

$$2H_2O_2 \longrightarrow 2H_2O + O_2$$

Drug-store hydrogen peroxide is a 3% solution (containing 3 g H_2O_2 per 100 g), for medical use as an antiseptic, or a 6% solution, for bleaching hair. A 30% solution and, in recent years, an 85% solution are used in chemical industries. The 85% solution (nearly pure hydrogen peroxide) has found some use as the oxidizing agent to burn fuel in rockets and for submarine propulsion.

The structure of the hydrogen peroxide molecule is

$$\begin{array}{cc} H & H \\ | & | \\ :\!O\!-\!O\!: \\ \cdot\cdot & \cdot\cdot \end{array}$$

Hydrogen Peroxide as an Oxidizing Agent.   It is the oxidizing power of hydrogen peroxide that causes it to be used for bleaching hair and other materials and that is responsible for its effectiveness as an antiseptic. Oil paintings that have been discolored by the formation of lead sulfide, PbS, which is black in color, from the white lead (a hydroxide-carbonate of lead) in the paint may be bleached by washing with hydrogen peroxide. The reaction that occurs is the oxidation of lead sulfide to lead sulfate (which is white):

$$PbS + 4H_2O_2 \longrightarrow PbSO_4 + 4H_2O$$

The electron reaction for the reduction of hydrogen peroxide in acidic solution is

$$H_2O_2 + 2H^+ + 2e^- \longrightarrow 2H_2O$$

Two electrons are required, because each of the two oxygen atoms of the H_2O_2 molecule changes its oxidation number from -1 to -2.

Hydrogen Peroxide as a Reducing Agent.   Hydrogen peroxide can also serve as a reducing agent, with increase in oxidation number of oxygen from -1 to 0, and the liberation of molecular oxygen.

This activity is shown, for example, by the decolorizing of an acidic solution of potassium permanganate by addition of hydrogen peroxide. The permanganate ion, MnO_4^-, is reduced to the manganese(II) ion, Mn^{++}, and free oxygen is liberated. The electron reactions are

$$H_2O_2 \longrightarrow O_2 + 2H^+ + 2e^-$$
$$MnO_4^- + 5e^- + 8H^+ \longrightarrow Mn^{++} + 4H_2O$$

or, with the proper factors to balance the electrons,

$$5H_2O_2 \longrightarrow 5O_2 + 10H^+ + 10e^-$$
$$2MnO_4^- + 10e^- + 16H^+ \longrightarrow 2Mn^{++} + 8H_2O$$
$$\overline{\phantom{2MnO_4^- + 5H_2O_2 + 6H^+ \longrightarrow 2Mn^{++} + 5O_2 + 8H_2O}}$$
$$2MnO_4^- + 5H_2O_2 + 6H^+ \longrightarrow 2Mn^{++} + 5O_2 + 8H_2O$$

Hydrogen peroxide also reduces permanganate ion in basic solution, forming a precipitate of MnO_2, manganese dioxide:

$$H_2O_2 + 2OH^- \longrightarrow O_2 + 2H_2O + 2e^-$$
$$MnO_4^- + 3e^- + 2H_2O \longrightarrow MnO_2 + 4OH^-$$

or

$$3H_2O_2 + 6OH^- \longrightarrow 3O_2 + 6H_2O + 6e^-$$
$$2MnO_4^- + 6e^- + 4H_2O \longrightarrow 2MnO_2 + 8OH^-$$

$$\overline{2MnO_4^- + 3H_2O_2 \longrightarrow 2MnO_2 + 3O_2 + 2H_2O + 2OH^-}$$

The Auto-oxidation of Hydrogen Peroxide. When hydrogen peroxide decomposes, by the reaction

$$2H_2O_2 \longrightarrow 2H_2O + O_2$$

it is carrying on an *auto-oxidation-reduction process* (usually called *auto-oxidation*), in which the substance acts simultaneously as an oxidizing agent and as a reducing agent; half of the oxygen atoms are reduced to O^{-2} (forming water), and the other half are oxidized to O^0 (free oxygen).

This process occurs only extremely slowly in pure hydrogen peroxide and its pure aqueous solutions. It is accelerated by catalysts, such as dust particles and active spots on ordinary solid surfaces. If some grains of a catalytic material such as manganese dioxide are dropped into a solution of hydrogen peroxide there is a vigorous evolution of free oxygen. The stabilizers that are added to hydrogen peroxide inactivate these catalysts.

It will be recalled that a catalyst is a substance that causes a chemical reaction to go faster than in its absence, but that is itself not changed by the reaction. It is probable that a catalyst for the hydrogen peroxide decomposition exerts its effect by attracting the molecules of hydrogen peroxide to its surface, and subjecting them to a strain, which causes the molecules to decompose. Presumably a stabilizer is attracted to the active surface of the catalyst, and firmly held there, thus preventing the hydrogen peroxide molecules from reaching this region.

The most effective catalysts for the decomposition of hydrogen peroxide are certain complex organic substances, with molecular weights of 100,000 or more, which occur in the cells of plants and animals. These substances, which are called *catalases* (a special kind of enzyme), have the specific job in the organism of causing the decomposition of peroxides.

The Peroxy Acids. Acids containing a peroxide group are called *peroxy acids.* Examples are

peroxysulfuric acid, H_2SO_5

$$
\begin{array}{c}
: \ddot{O} - H \\
| \\
: O = S - \ddot{O} : \\
\| \quad \diagdown \\
: \ddot{O} \quad : \ddot{O} - H
\end{array}
$$

peroxydisulfuric acid, $H_2S_2O_8$

$$
\begin{array}{c}
:\overset{..}{O}\!-\!H \\
| \\
:O\!=\!\overset{..}{\underset{\parallel}{S}}\!-\!\overset{..}{O}: \qquad \overset{..}{O}: \\
\overset{..}{\underset{}{O}} \qquad \diagdown \\
:\overset{}{\underset{..}{O}} \qquad :\overset{..}{O}\!-\!\overset{\parallel}{\underset{}{S}}\!=\!\overset{..}{O}: \\
\qquad\qquad H\!-\!\overset{}{\underset{..}{O}}:
\end{array}
$$

When moderately concentrated (50%) sulfuric acid is electrolyzed, hydrogen is formed at the cathode and peroxydisulfuric acid at the anode:

Cathode reaction: $2H^+ + 2e^- \longrightarrow H_2$

Anode reaction: $2H_2SO_4 \longrightarrow H_2S_2O_8 + 2H^+ + 2e^-$

When this solution is heated, peroxysulfuric acid is formed:

$$H_2S_2O_8 + H_2O \longrightarrow H_2SO_5 + H_2SO_4$$

If the solution is heated to a higher temperature it forms hydrogen peroxide, which can then be separated by distillation:

$$H_2SO_5 + H_2O \longrightarrow H_2SO_4 + H_2O_2$$

This method is used commercially for making 30% hydrogen peroxide.

The peroxy acids and their salts are strong oxidizing agents.

Illustrative Exercises

11-11. The over-all reaction of decomposition of hydrogen peroxide is described by the reaction

$$2H_2O_2 \longrightarrow 2H_2O + O_2$$

(a) Write equations for the two electron reactions.

(b) What is the oxidizing agent and what is the reducing agent? What is the oxidized product, and what is the reduced product?

(c) What changes in oxidation number have occurred?

11-12. How many liters of oxygen at standard conditions would be produced by complete decomposition of 10 kg (22 lbs) of 34% hydrogen peroxide?

11-6. The Electromotive-force Series of the Elements

If a piece of one metal is put into a solution containing ions of another metallic element the first metal may dissolve, with the deposition of the second metal from its ions. Thus a strip of zinc placed in a solution of copper salt causes a layer of metallic copper to deposit on the zinc, as the zinc goes into solution (Figure 11-2). The chemical reaction that is involved is the reduction of copper ion, Cu^{++}, by metallic zinc:

$$Zn + Cu^{++} \longrightarrow Zn^{++} + Cu$$

On the other hand, a strip of copper placed in a solution of zinc salt does not cause metallic zinc to deposit.* Many experiments of this sort have been carried out, and it has been found that the metallic elements can be arranged in a table showing their ability to reduce ions of other metals. This table is given as Table 11-1.

The metal with the greatest reducing power is at the head of the list. It is able to reduce the ions of all the other metals.

This series is called the *electromotive-force series* because the tendency of one metal to reduce ions of another can be measured by setting up an *electric cell* and measuring the voltage which it produces. (Electromotive force is here a synonym for voltage.) Thus

Figure **11-2** *Replacement of copper ion by zinc.*

the cell shown in Figure 11-3 would be used to measure the voltage between the electrodes at which occur the electrode reactions

$$Zn \longrightarrow Zn^{++} + 2e^-$$

and

$$Cu^{++} + 2e^- \longrightarrow Cu$$

This cell produces a voltage of about 1.1 volts, the difference of the values of $E°$ shown in the table. The cell is used to some extent in practice; it is called the *gravity cell* when it is made as shown in Figure 11-4.

The values of the voltages shown in Table 11-1 refer to an idealized cell in which each metal ion is present at an effective concentration of 1 mole per liter of solution, and in which interactions between ions, especially the effects of any anions present, have been neglected. Actually the presence of other substances in solution changes the voltage produced by a cell of this sort,

---

* It is not strictly correct to say that zinc can replace copper in solution and that copper cannot replace zinc. If a piece of metallic copper is placed in a solution containing zinc ions in appreciable concentration, say 1 mole per liter, and no cupric ion at all, the reaction

$$Cu + Zn^{++} \longrightarrow Cu^{++} + Zn$$

will occur to a very small extent, stopping when a certain very small concentration of copper ion has been produced. If metallic zinc is added to a solution of cupric ion, the reaction

$$Zn + Cu^{++} \longrightarrow Zn^{++} + Cu$$

will take place almost to completion, stopping when the concentration of cupric ion has become very small. It will be shown in a later chapter (Chapter 18) that the ratio of concentration of the two ions Cu^{++} and Zn^{++} in equilibrium with solid copper and solid zinc must be the same whether the equilibrium is reached by adding metallic copper to a zinc solution or metallic zinc to a copper solution. The statement "zinc replaces copper from solution" means that at equilibrium the amount of copper ion in the solution is very small relative to the amount of zinc ion.

Table **11-1**

*The Electromotive-Force Series of the Elements**

		$E°$			$E°$
1.	Li $\rightleftarrows$ Li$^+$ + e^-	3.05	17.	Cd $\rightleftarrows$ Cd^{++} + 2e^-	0.40
2.	Cs $\rightleftarrows$ Cs$^+$ + e^-	2.92	18.	Co $\rightleftarrows$ Co^{++} + 2e^-	.28
3.	Rb $\rightleftarrows$ Rb$^+$ + e^-	2.92	19.	Ni $\rightleftarrows$ Ni^{++} + 2e^-	.25
4.	K $\rightleftarrows$ K$^+$ + e^-	2.92	20.	Sn $\rightleftarrows$ Sn^{++} + 2e^-	.14
5.	Ba $\rightleftarrows$ Ba^{++} + 2e^-	2.90	21.	Pb $\rightleftarrows$ Pb^{++} + 2e^-	.13
6.	Sr $\rightleftarrows$ Sr^{++} + 2e^-	2.89	22.	H$_2$ $\rightleftarrows$ 2H$^+$ + 2e^-	0.00
7.	Ca $\rightleftarrows$ Ca^{++} + 2e^-	2.87	23.	Cu $\rightleftarrows$ Cu^{++} + 2e^-	−0.34
8.	Na $\rightleftarrows$ Na$^+$ + e^-	2.71	24.	2I$^-$ $\rightleftarrows$ I$_2$ + 2e^-	−0.53
9.	La $\rightleftarrows$ La^{+++} + 3e^-	2.52	25.	Ag $\rightleftarrows$ Ag$^+$ + e^-	−0.80
10.	Mg $\rightleftarrows$ Mg^{++} + 2e^-	2.34	26.	Hg $\rightleftarrows$ Hg^{++} + 2e^-	−0.85
11.	Be $\rightleftarrows$ Be^{++} + 2e^-	1.85	27.	2Br$^-$ $\rightleftarrows$ Br$_2$(*l*) + 2e^-	−1.06
12.	Al $\rightleftarrows$ Al^{+++} + 3e^-	1.67	28.	Pt $\rightleftarrows$ Pt^{++} + 2e^-	−1.2
13.	Mn $\rightleftarrows$ Mn^{++} + 2e^-	1.18	29.	2H$_2$O $\rightleftarrows$ O$_2$ + 4H$^+$ + 4e^-	−1.23
14.	Zn $\rightleftarrows$ Zn^{++} + 2e^-	0.76	30.	2Cl$^-$ $\rightleftarrows$ Cl$_2$ + 2e^-	−1.36
15.	Cr $\rightleftarrows$ Cr^{+++} + 3e^-	.74	31.	Au $\rightleftarrows$ Au$^+$ + e^-	−1.68
16.	Fe $\rightleftarrows$ Fe^{++} + 2e^-	.44	32.	2F$^-$ $\rightleftarrows$ F$_2$ + 2e^-	−2.65

← Strongest reducing action ——→

Strongest oxidizing action ——↓

* For a longer table, see Appendix IV. Note that it is customary in the United States to represent the electromotive force of a couple involving a strong reducing agent as positive in sign, as in this table, but that European scientists usually use the opposite convention, writing $E° = -3.05$ V for Li $\rightleftarrows$ Li$^+$ + e^- and $+2.65$ V for 2F$^-$ $\rightleftarrows$ F$_2$ + 2e^-.

The value 0.00 V is arbitrarily assumed for the standard hydrogen electrode, as the reference point for values of $E°$.

Figure **11-3**

A cell involving the Zn, Zn^{++} electrode and the Cu, Cu^{++} electrode.

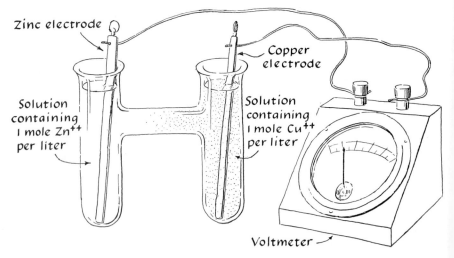

Zinc electrode

Copper electrode

Solution containing 1 mole Zn^{++} per liter

Solution containing 1 mole Cu^{++} per liter

Voltmeter

and often reverses the relative positions of two metals that are not far apart in the table. Nevertheless, the table is a very useful one in indicating whether an oxidation-reduction reaction involving two of the electron reactions shown is apt to take place or is apt not to take place.

The standard reference point in the electromotive-force series is the *hydrogen electrode*, which consists of gaseous hydrogen at 1 atm bubbling over a platinum electrode in an acidic solution (Figure 11-5). Similar electrodes can be made for some other nonmetallic elements, and a few of these elements are included in the table.

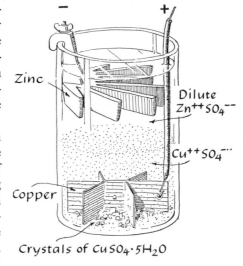

Figure **11-4**   *The gravity cell.*

Experimental values of standard oxidation-reduction potentials for many other pairs have also been obtained. Some of them are given in Appendix IV. They will be discussed further in Chapter 18.

Figure **11-5**

   A cell involving the zinc electrode and the hydrogen electrode.

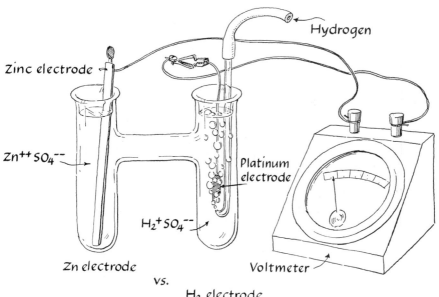

Electrode Potentials and Electronegativity. There is a good general correlation between standard electrode potentials and electronegativity values, illustrated for hydrogen and the halogens in Figure 11-6. It is seen that to within the uncertainty in the electronegativity values, ±0.05, the points for chlorine, bromine, and iodine lie on the straight line connecting the points for fluorine and hydrogen.

Illustrative Exercises

11-13. Would you expect iron to replace lead ion, Pb^{++}, from solution? Refer to Table 12-1. Write the equations for the electron reactions and the over-all reaction.

11-14. Which of the following metals would you expect to liberate hydrogen, if placed in a solution of sulfuric acid: zinc, gold, nickel, tin, platinum, silver, copper, iron, calcium, lanthanum?

11-15. (a) Write equations for the electrode reactions in the gravity cell, shown in Figure 11-4.

(b) Why is the zinc electrode marked negative and the copper electrode positive?

11-16. What voltage would you expect to read on the voltmeter in Figure 11-5? Would the zinc electrode be positive or negative?

Figure **11-6** *Diagram illustrating the relation between the standard electrode potentials of some elements and their electronegativity values.*

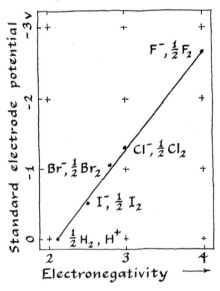

11-7. Primary Cells and Storage Cells

The production of an electric current through chemical reaction is achieved in *primary cells* and *storage cells.*

Primary cells are cells in which an oxidation-reduction reaction can be carried out in such a way that its driving force produces an electric potential. This is achieved by having the oxidizing agent and the reducing agent separated; the oxidizing agent then removes electrons from one electrode and the reducing agent gives electrons to another electrode, the flow of current through the cell itself being carried by ions.

Storage cells are similar cells, which, however, can be returned to their original state after current has been drawn from them (can be *charged*) by applying an impressed electric potential between the electrodes, and thus reversing the oxidation-reduction reaction.

The Common Dry Cell. One primary cell, the gravity cell, has been described in the preceding section. This cell is called a *wet cell*, because it contains a liquid electrolyte. A very useful primary cell is the *common dry cell*, shown in Figure 11-7. The common dry cell consists of a zinc cylinder that contains as electrolyte a paste of ammonium chloride (NH_4Cl), a little zinc chloride ($ZnCl_2$), water, and diatomaceous earth or other filler.* The central electrode is a mixture of carbon and manganese dioxide, embedded in a paste of these substances. The electrode reactions are

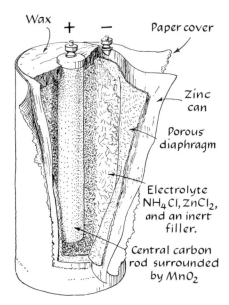

Figure **11-7** *The dry cell.*

$$Zn \longrightarrow Zn^{++} + 2e^-$$
$$2NH_4^+ + 2MnO_2 + 2e^- \longrightarrow 2MnO(OH) + 2NH_3$$

(The zinc ion combines to some extent with ammonia to form the zinc-ammonia complex ion, $Zn(NH_3)_4^{++}$.) This cell produces a potential of about 1.48 V.

The Lead Storage Battery. The most common storage cell is that in the *lead storage battery* (Figure 11-8). The electrolyte in this cell is a mixture of water and sulfuric acid with density about 1.290 g/cm^3 in the charged cell (38% H_2SO_4 by weight). The plates are lattices made of a lead alloy, the pores of one plate being filled with spongy metallic lead, and those of the other with lead dioxide, PbO_2. The spongy lead is the reducing agent and the lead dioxide the oxidizing agent in the chemical reaction that takes place in the cell. The electrode reactions that occur as the cell is being discharged are

$$Pb + SO_4^{--} \longrightarrow PbSO_4 + 2e^-$$
$$PbO_2 + SO_4^{--} + 4H^+ + 2e^- \longrightarrow PbSO_4 + 2H_2O$$

Each of these reactions produces the insoluble substance $PbSO_4$, lead sulfate, which adheres to the plates. As the cell is discharged sulfuric acid is removed from the electrolyte, which decreases in density. The state of charge or dis-

* The dry cell is not dry; water must be present in the paste that serves as electrolyte.

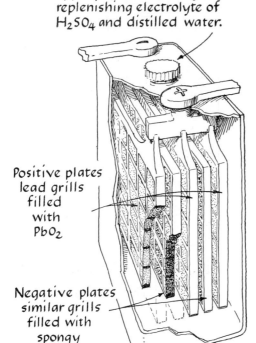

Capped hole for testing and
replenishing electrolyte of
H_2SO_4 and distilled water.

Positive plates
lead grills
filled
with
PbO_2

Negative plates
similar grills
filled with
spongy
lead

Figure **11-8**.
The lead storage cell.

charge of the cell can accordingly be determined with use of a hydrometer, by measuring the density of the electrolyte.

The cell can be charged again by applying an electric potential across the terminals, and causing the above electrode reactions to take place in the opposite directions. The charged cell produces an electromotive force of slightly over 2 volts.

It is interesting that in this cell the same element changes its oxidation state in the two plates: the oxidizing agent is PbO_2 (containing lead with oxidation number $+4$, which changes to $+2$ as the cell discharges), and the reducing agent is Pb (lead with oxidation number 0, which changes to $+2$).

Illustrative Exercises

11-17. Write equations for the electrode reactions that take place in a lead storage battery while it is being charged.

11-18. (a) If a fully charged lead storage battery has 3000 g of spongy lead on its plates, how much lead dioxide should it have on the other plates?

(b) How much sulfuric acid would it need in the electrolyte?

11-19. (a) How many faradays of electricity could a lead storage battery with 3000 g of spongy lead and a corresponding amount of lead dioxide produce?

(b) For how many hours could it deliver a current of 10 amperes?

EXERCISES

11-20. Give three examples of oxidation-reduction reactions in everyday life. In each case designate the oxidizing agent and the reducing agent.

11-21. Define an oxidation-reduction pair, and write an electron equation in illustration.

11-22. Assign oxidation numbers to elements in the following compounds:

Sodium peroxide, Na_2O_2
Permanganate ion, MnO_4^-
Cuprous oxide, Cu_2O
Ferrous oxide, FeO
Magnetite, Fe_3O_4
Garnet, $Ca_3Al_2Si_3O_{12}$
Sodium hydride, NaH
Nitric acid, HNO_3
Lead sulfate, $PbSO_4$
Potassium chromate, K_2CrO_4
Silica, SiO_2
Ammonium chloride, NH_4Cl
Sodium oxide, Na_2O
Peroxysulfate ion, SO_5^{--}
Cupric oxide, CuO
Ferric oxide, Fe_2O_3
Borax, $Na_2B_4O_7 \cdot 10H_2O$
Topaz, $Al_2SiO_4F_2$
Ammonia, NH_3
Lead sulfide, PbS
Phosphorus, P_4
Potassium dichromate, $K_2Cr_2O_7$
Nitrous acid, HNO_2
Ammonium nitrite, NH_4NO_2

11-23. Using the nomenclature described in Section 11-3, assign names to the following compounds:

$TiCl_3$	$AuCl$	$SnBr_2$
$FeSO_4 \cdot 7H_2O$	$AgNO_3$	$CuSO_4 \cdot 5H_2O$
$TiCl_4$	$AuCl_3$	SnI_4
$KFe(SO_4)_2 \cdot 12H_2O$	CuI	$MgCO_3$

11-24. Complete and balance the following oxidation-reduction equations:

$$Cl_2 + I^- \longrightarrow I_2 + Cl^-$$
$$Sn + I_2 \longrightarrow SnI_4$$
$$KClO_3 \longrightarrow KClO_4 + KCl$$
$$MnO_2 + H^+ + Cl^- \longrightarrow Mn^{++} + Cl_2$$
$$ClO_4^- + Sn^{++} \longrightarrow Cl^- + Sn^{++++}$$

11-25. Write electrode equations for the electrolytic production of (a) magnesium metal from molten magnesium chloride; (b) perchlorate ion, ClO_4^-, from chlorate ion, ClO_3^-, in aqueous solution; (c) permanganate ion, MnO_4^-, from manganate ion, MnO_4^{--}, in aqueous solution; (d) fluorine from fluoride ion in a molten salt. State in each case whether the reaction occurs at the anode or at the cathode.

11-26. What weight of 3.00% hydrogen peroxide solution would be required to oxidize 2.00 g of lead sulfide, PbS, to lead sulfate, $PbSO_4$?

11-27. Would you expect zinc to reduce cadmium ion? (Refer to the electromotive-force series.) Iron to reduce mercuric ion? Zinc to reduce lead ion? Potassium to reduce magnesium ion?

11-28. Which metal ions would you expect gold to reduce? Suggest a reason for calling gold and platinum noble metals.

11-29. What would you expect to happen if a large piece of lead were put in a beaker containing a solution of stannous salt? Note the values of the electromotive force in Table 11-1.

11-30. What would happen if chlorine gas were bubbled into a solution containing fluoride ion and bromide ion? If chlorine were bubbled into a solution containing both bromide ion and iodide ion?

11-31. Why are hydrogen peroxide and potassium permanganate both antiseptics?

Would you expect fluorine to be an antiseptic?

11-32. A sample of commercial hydrogen peroxide weighing 10.0 g was found to evolve 112 ml of oxygen (at standard conditions) when a little catalase was added to it. What was the strength of the hydrogen peroxide solution, in weight percentage? (Answer: 3.4%.)

11-33. Assign oxidation numbers to bromine in the bromate ion, BrO_3^-; the bromite ion, BrO_2^-; the hypobromite ion, BrO^-; the bromide ion, Br^-.

11-34. Write a balanced equation for the reaction of chromate ion, CrO_4^{--}, with stannite ion, $Sn(OH)_4^{--}$, in basic solution, to give stannate ion, $Sn(OH)_6^{--}$, and chromite ion, $Cr(OH)_4^-$.

11-35. A compound containing phosphorus and chlorine is found on analysis to contain 22.5% phosphorus. The molecular weight of the compound is about 137. What is the oxidation number of phosphorus in this compound, and what is the formula of the substance?

11-36. Write electronic formulas for calcium peroxide, CaO_2, and zirconium dioxide, ZrO_2. Write equations for the reactions of these two substances with sulfuric acid.

11-37. When a solution of a ferrous salt, containing the hydrated ferrous ion, Fe^{++}, is treated with sodium hydroxide, the precipitate of ferrous hydroxide that is first formed is rapidly oxidized by oxygen from the air, converting it into ferric hydroxide, $Fe(OH)_3$. Write the equation for this reaction.

11-38. What is the oxidation number of xenon in xenon hexafluoride, XeF_6? This substance reacts with an aqueous solution containing iodide ion to liberate free iodine and gaseous xenon. Balance the equation for the reaction.

CHAPTER 12

The Halogens

The halogens—fluorine, chlorine, bromine, and iodine—are the elements that immediately precede the noble gases in the periodic table. Their neutral atoms, with the electronic structures given in Table 12-1, have one electron less than the corresponding noble gas. They have a strong tendency to assume the electronic structure of the noble gas, either by adding an electron, to form a halogenide ion, as was discussed in Chapter 8, or by sharing an electron pair with another atom, forming a covalent bond (Chapter 9).

Table **12-1**

Electronic Structure of the Halogens

Z	ELEMENT	K	L		M			N			O	
		1s	2s	2p	3s	3p	3d	4s	4p	4d	5s	5p
9	Fluorine	2	2	5								
17	Chlorine	2	2	6	2	5						
35	Bromine	2	2	6	2	6	10	2	5			
53	Iodine	2	2	6	2	6	10	2	6	10	2	5

Sometimes more than one electron pair is shared by a halogen atom with other atoms, especially atoms of oxygen. The oxygen compounds of the halogens are important substances. A few of them, such as potassium chlorate, have been mentioned in earlier chapters. The chemistry of these substances is complex, but it can be systematized and clarified by correlation with the electronic theory of valence.

12-1. The Oxidation States of the Halogens

The oxidation states that are represented by known compounds of the halogens are shown in the diagram on the following page. It is seen that the range of the oxidation states extends from -1, corresponding to the achievement for each halogen atom of the structure of the adjacent noble gas, to $+7$, corresponding for chlorine to the inner noble-gas structure (neon). In general the odd oxidation states are represented by compounds. The importance of the odd oxidation states is the result of the stability of electronic structures involving pairs of electrons, either shared or unshared. Structures involving only pairs of electrons lead to even oxidation states for elements in even groups of the periodic system and to odd oxidation states for elements in odd groups. The exceptional compounds chlorine dioxide, ClO_2, bromine dioxide, BrO_2, and iodine dioxide, IO_2, corresponding to oxidation number $+4$, have molecules containing an odd number of electrons.

$+7$		$HClO_4$, Cl_2O_7		H_5IO_6
$+6$		Cl_2O_6		
$+5$		$HClO_3$	$HBrO_3$	HIO_3, I_2O_5
$+4$		ClO_2	BrO_2	IO_2
$+3$		$HClO_2$		
$+2$				
$+1$	HFO	$HClO$, Cl_2O	$HBrO$, Br_2O	HIO
0	F_2	Cl_2	Br_2	I_2
-1	HF, F^-	HCl, Cl^-	HBr, Br^-	HI, I^-

Fluorine differs significantly from the other halogens. Whereas chlorine, bromine, and iodine form many compounds with oxygen, fluorine forms very few.

This fact can be correlated with the position of fluorine in the electronegativity scale (Section 9-11). Fluorine, with electronegativity 4.0, is the most electronegative of the elements. It is more electronegative than oxygen (electronegativity 3.5), whereas the other halogens (chlorine 3.0, bromine 2.8, iodine 2.5) are less electronegative than oxygen. The large electronegativity of fluorine causes instability of positive oxidation states of fluorine, and great stability of its negative oxidation state.

The principal compound of fluorine and oxygen is OF_2. It is produced by reaction of fluorine with water containing a base, such as sodium hydroxide. Its electronic structure is

$$: \ddot{F} :$$
$$|$$
$$: \ddot{O} - \ddot{F} :$$

and it is considered to contain fluorine with oxidation number -1, because the electronegativity of fluorine is greater than that of oxygen; it is hence called *oxygen fluoride*, rather than fluorine oxide. The compounds O_2F_2, O_3F_2, and O_4F_2 have also been reported. Enthalpy values of some halogen compounds are given in Table 12-2.

Table **12-2**

Standard Enthalpy of Formation of Halogen Compounds at 25°C (kcal/mole)

	X = F	Cl	Br	I
$X_2(g)$	0.00	0.00	7.34	14.88
$X_2(l$ or $c)$			0.00(l)	0.00(c)
$X_2(aq)$		−6.0	−1.1	5.0
$X(g)$	18.3	29.01	26.71	25.48
$X^+(g)$	421.55	329.35	301.32	267.74
$X^-(g)$	−79.5	−58.3	−55.3	−50.2
$X^-(aq)$	−78.66	−40.02	−28.90	−13.37
$HX(g)$	−64.2	−22.06	−8.66	6.20
$KX(c)$	−134.46	−104.18	−93.73	−78.31
$X_2O(g)$	5.5	18.20		
$HXO(aq)$		−28.18		−38
$HXO_2(aq)$		−12.4		
$HXO_3(aq)$		−23.4	−9.5	−54.9
$HXO_4(aq)$		−31.41		
$H_5XO_6(aq)$				−183.0

Illustrative Exercises

12-1. Write the equation for the reaction of fluorine with water containing sodium hydroxide, producing oxygen fluoride. What is the other product of the reaction?

12-2. What are the oxidation numbers of hydrogen, oxygen, and fluorine in the reactants and the products of the reaction of Exercise 12-1? What is the oxidizing agent in this reaction? What has been oxidized?

12-3. How many liters of oxygen fluoride could be prepared by reaction of 20 liters of fluorine with water?

12-2. The Halogens and Halogenides

The halogens consist of diatomic molecules, F_2, Cl_2, Br_2, and I_2. Some physical properties of the halogens are given in Table 12-2.

Fluorine. Fluorine, the lightest of the halogens, is the most reactive of all the elements, and it forms compounds with all the elements except the lighter inert gases. Substances such as wood and rubber burst into flame when held in a stream of fluorine, and even asbestos (a silicate of magnesium and aluminum) reacts vigorously with it and becomes incandescent. Platinum is attacked only slowly by fluorine. Copper and steel can be used as containers for the gas; they are attacked by it, but become coated with a thin layer of copper fluoride or iron fluoride which then protects them against further attack.

Table **12-3**

Properties of the Halogens

	ATOMIC NUMBER	ATOMIC WEIGHT	COLOR AND FORM	MELTING POINT	BOILING POINT	IONIC RADIUS*	COVALENT RADIUS	HEAT OF DISSOCIATION
F₂	9	18.9984	Pale yellow gas	$-223°C$	$-187°C$	1.36 Å	0.64 Å	36.6 kcal/mole
Cl₂	17	35.453	Greenish yellow gas	$-101.6°$	$-34.6°$	1.81	.99	58.0
Br₂	35	79.909	Reddish brown liquid	$-7.3°$	$58.7°$	1.95	1.14	46.1
I₂	53	126.9044	Grayish black lustrous solid	$113.5°$	$184°$	2.16	1.27	36.1

* For negatively charged ion with ligancy 6, such as Cl⁻ in the NaCl crystal.

Fluorine was first made in 1886 by the French chemist Henri Moissan (1852–1907), by the method described in the following section. In recent years methods for its commercial production and transport (in steel tanks) have been developed, and it is now used in chemical industry in large quantities.

Fluorine occurs in nature in the combined state in minerals such as *fluorite* CaF_2; *fluor-apatite*, $Ca_5(PO_4)_3F$, which is a constituent of bones and teeth; and *cryolite*, Na_3AlF_6; and in small quantities in sea water and most supplies of drinking water, as fluoride ion. If there is not a sufficient (very small) quantity of fluoride ion in the drinking water of children, their teeth will not be properly resistant to decay.

The name fluorine, from Latin *fluere*, to flow, refers to the use of fluorite as a flux (a material that forms a melt with metal oxides).

Hydrogen fluoride, HF, can be made by treating fluorite with sulfuric acid:

$$H_2SO_4 + CaF_2 \longrightarrow CaSO_4 + 2HF$$

This method is used industrially. The reaction is usually carried out in the laboratory in a lead dish, because hydrogen fluoride attacks glass, porcelain, and other silicates. It is a colorless gas (m.p. $-92.3°C$, b.p. $19.4°C$), very soluble in water.

The solution of hydrogen fluoride in water is called hydrofluoric acid. This solution, and also hydrogen fluoride gas, may be used for etching glass. The glass is covered with a thin layer of paraffin, through which the design to be etched, such as the graduations on a buret, is scratched with a stylus. The object is then treated with the acid. The reactions that occur are similar to those for quartz, SiO_2:

$$SiO_2 + 4HF \longrightarrow SiF_4 + 2H_2O$$

The product, SiF_4, silicon tetrafluoride, is a gas.

Hydrofluoric acid must be handled with great care, because on contact with the skin it produces sores that heal very slowly. The acid is stored in bottles made of polyethylene (a resistant plastic).

The salts of hydrofluoric acid are called fluorides. Sodium fluoride, NaF, is used as an insecticide.

Chlorine.   Chlorine (from Greek *chloros*, greenish-yellow), the most common of the halogens, is a greenish-yellow gas, with a sharp irritating odor. It was first made by the Swedish chemist K. W. Scheele in 1774, by the action of manganese dioxide on hydrochloric acid. It is now manufactured on a large scale by the electrolysis of a strong solution of sodium chloride.

Chlorine is a very reactive substance, but less reactive than fluorine. It combines with most elements, to form chlorides, at room temperature or on gentle heating. Hydrogen burns in chlorine, after being ignited, to form hydrogen chloride:

$$H_2 + Cl_2 \longrightarrow 2HCl$$

Iron burns in chlorine, producing ferric chloride, a brown solid,

$$2Fe + 3Cl_2 \longrightarrow 2FeCl_3$$

and other metals react similarly with it.

Chlorine is a strong oxidizing agent, and because of this property it is effective in killing bacteria. It is used extensively to sterilize drinking water, and is also used in many ways throughout the chemical industry.

Hydrogen chloride, HCl, is a colorless gas (m.p. $-112°C$, b.p. $-83.7°C$) with an unpleasant sharp odor. It is easily made by heating sodium chloride with sulfuric acid:

$$NaCl + H_2SO_4 \longrightarrow NaHSO_4 + HCl$$

The gas dissolves readily in water, with the evolution of a large amount of heat. The solution is called hydrochloric acid. Hydrochloric acid is a strong acid—it has a very acidic taste, turns blue litmus paper red, dissolves zinc and other active metals with the evolution of hydrogen gas, and combines with bases to form salts. The salts formed by hydrochloric acid are called chlorides. A representative chloride is sodium chloride, which has been mentioned often in the preceding chapters; other chlorides will be discussed in later sections of the book.

Bromine.   The element bromine (from Greek *bromos*, stench) occurs in the form of compounds in small quantities in seawater and in natural salt deposits. It is an easily volatile, dark reddish-brown liquid with a strong, disagreeable odor and an irritating effect on the eyes and throat. It produces painful sores when spilled on the skin. The free element can be made by treating a bromide with an oxidizing agent, such as chlorine.

Hydrogen bromide, HBr, is a colorless gas (m.p. $-88.5°C$, b.p. $-67.0°C$). Its solution in water, hydrobromic acid, is a strong acid. The principal salts of hydrobromic acid are sodium bromide, NaBr, and potassium bromide, KBr, which are used in medicine, and silver bromide, AgBr, which, like silver chloride, AgCl, and silver iodide, AgI, is used in making photographic emulsions.

Iodine. The element iodine (from Greek *iodes*, violet) occurs as iodide ion, I⁻, in very small quantities in seawater, and, as **sodium iodate,** NaIO₃, in deposits of Chile saltpeter. It is made commercially from sodium iodate obtained from saltpeter, and also from kelp, which concentrates it from the seawater, and from oil-well brines.

The free element is an almost black crystalline solid with a slightly metallic luster. On gentle warming it gives a beautiful blue-violet vapor. Its solutions in chloroform, carbon tetrachloride, and carbon disulfide are also blue-violet in color, indicating that the molecules I_2 in these solutions closely resemble the gas molecules. The solutions of iodine in water containing potassium iodide and in alcohol (tincture of iodine) are brown; this change in color suggests that the iodine molecules have undergone chemical reaction in these solutions. The brown compound KI_3, potassium triiodide, is present in the first solution, and a compound with alcohol in the second.

Hydrogen iodide, HI, is a colorless gas (m.p. $-50.8°C$, b.p. $-35.3°C$), whose solution in water, called hydriodic acid, is a strong acid.

Illustrative Exercises	
	12-4. Write the equation for the reaction of methane with an excess of fluorine. What are the oxidation numbers of carbon, hydrogen, and fluorine in the reactants and the products?
	12-5. Write the electronic structure of silicon tetrafluoride.
	12-6. Can you explain by the consideration of electronegativities why hydrofluoric acid attacks glass, such as silica glass, SiO_2, whereas hydrochloric acid does not? (Compare the stability of the Si—F bond with that of the Si—Cl bond.)
	12-7. Assuming asbestos to have the formula $Ca_2Mg_5Si_8O_{24}H_2$, list the products that might be obtained by its reaction with an excess of fluorine. Write the equation for the reaction.
	12-8. How many grams of salt and how many grams of sulfuric acid (pure H_2SO_4) would be needed to prepare 22.4 liters (at standard conditions) of hydrogen chloride, by the reaction given above in the discussion of hydrogen chloride?

12-3. The Preparation of the Elementary Halogens

Since **fluorine** is the most electronegative of the elements, we can hardly expect that it could be prepared by reaction of another element with a fluoride. (Fluorine is the most powerful chemical oxidizing agent known—Table 11-1.) It can, however, be made by an electrode reaction, since the oxidizing power of an anode can be increased without limit by increasing the applied voltage.

The original method of preparing fluorine was the electrolysis of a solution

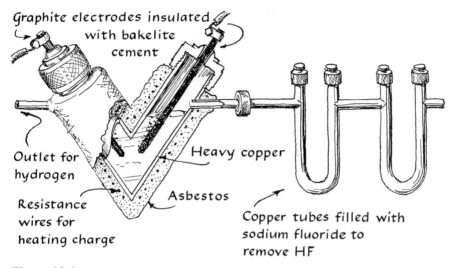

Graphite electrodes insulated with bakelite cement

Outlet for hydrogen

Resistance wires for heating charge

Heavy copper

Asbestos

Copper tubes filled with sodium fluoride to remove HF

Figure **12-1**

Apparatus used for preparing fluorine by electrolysis of potassium hydrogen fluoride.

of potassium fluoride, KF, in liquid hydrogen fluoride, HF, using as the material of the containing vessel an alloy of platinum and iridium. It has since been learned that copper can be used for this purpose. The copper is attacked by the fluorine, forming, however, a surface layer of copper fluoride that protects the tube from further corrosion.

The modern method of preparing fluorine in the laboratory is illustrated in Figure 12-1. The container is filled with dry potassium hydrogen fluoride, KHF_2, which is melted by passing an electric current through the resistance wires surrounding the copper tube. A direct potential is then applied between the two graphite electrodes, causing the liberation of hydrogen at the cathode, on the left, and fluorine at the anode. Hydrogen fluoride is removed from the fluorine gas by passage through a tube filled with sodium fluoride, which combines with hydrogen fluoride to form the crystalline substance sodium hydrogen fluoride, $NaHF_2$.

Chlorine is conveniently made in the laboratory by the oxidation of hydrochloric acid with either manganese dioxide or potassium permanganate. Manganese dioxide is placed in a flask and concentrated hydrochloric acid is added through a funnel. Chlorine is evolved according to the equation

$$MnO_2 + 4HCl \longrightarrow MnCl_2 + 2H_2O + Cl_2$$

This equation represents the over-all reaction, which in fact takes place in two stages. At room temperature manganese is reduced from the quadripositive state to the terpositive state, with liberation of a corresponding amount of chlorine:

$$2MnO_2 + 8HCl \longrightarrow 2MnCl_3 + 4H_2O + Cl_2$$

When the mixture is heated a further reaction takes place, with reduction of manganese to the bipositive state:

$$2MnCl_3 \longrightarrow 2MnCl_2 + Cl_2$$

The liberated chlorine is bubbled through a small amount of water, to remove hydrogen chloride, and then through concentrated sulfuric acid, to remove water vapor. The gas is over twice as heavy as air (molecular weight 71, as compared with average molecular weight 29 for air) and can accordingly be collected by upward displacement of air.

Chlorine for commercial use is made by electrolysis of molten sodium chloride, as described in Chapter 8, or of brine.

Bromine can be prepared in the laboratory by the action of sulfuric acid on a mixture of sodium bromide and manganese dioxide. Until recently most of the bromine used commercially was made in this way, from sodium bromide and potassium bromide mined from the Stassfurt deposits in Germany, or from brines pumped from wells in the eastern and central United States. During the past twenty-five years there has occurred a very great increase in the amount of bromine manufactured, until at present over 10,000 tons a year is being made.

Most of the bromine produced is converted into ethylene dibromide, $C_2H_4Br_2$, which is an important constituent of "ethyl gas," together with tetraethyl lead, $(C_2H_5)_4Pb$. Tetraethyl lead has valuable antiknock properties, but its continued use would cause damage to a motor through the deposition of metallic lead, unless some way were found to eliminate this deposit. The ethylene dibromide that is added to the gasoline provides bromine on combustion, which combines with the lead, permitting its elimination as lead bromide, $PbBr_2$.

The great amount of bromine required for this purpose and other uses at the present time is obtained by extraction of the element from seawater, which contains about 70 parts of bromine, as bromide ion, per million of water. The process of extraction involves four steps: oxidation with chlorine to convert the bromide ion to free bromine, removal of the bromine from the solution by bubbling a stream of air through it, absorption of the bromine from the air by bubbling through a solution of sodium carbonate, and treatment of the solution with sulfuric acid to liberate the elementary bromine. The equations for the successive reactions are

$$2Br^- + Cl_2 \longrightarrow Br_2 + 2Cl^-$$
$$3Br_2 + 6CO_3^{--} + 3H_2O \longrightarrow 5Br^- + BrO_3^- + 6HCO_3^-$$
$$5Br^- + BrO_3^- + 6H^+ \longrightarrow 3Br_2 + 3H_2O$$

The acidified reaction mixture is boiled, and the bromine is condensed from the vapor.

Iodine is conveniently made in the laboratory from sodium iodide, by the method described above for making bromine from a bromide.

Illustrative Exercises

12-9. Write the electrode reactions and the over-all reaction for the preparation of fluorine by electrolysis of potassium hydrogen fluoride.

12-10. How many liters of fluorine at 0°C and 1 atm would be produced by a current of 100 amperes in 16.1 minutes (965 seconds)?

12-11. Write the equation for production of chlorine by reaction of permanganate ion, MnO_4^-, with hydrogen ion and chloride ion, in aqueous solution. Manganese(II) ion, Mn^{++}, is also a product.

12-12. Write the equations for the combustion of tetraethyl lead to form carbon dioxide, water, and lead, the combustion of ethylene dibromide to form carbon dioxide, water, and bromine, and the reaction of lead and bromine to form lead(II) bromide. These reactions take place in a gasoline engine using ethyl gasoline.

12-13. How many grams of ethylene dibromide would you calculate to be needed in ethyl gasoline per gram of tetraethyl lead?

12-14. Write an equation for the reaction of sulfuric acid, manganese dioxide, and sodium iodide to prepare iodine.

12-4. The Preparation of the Hydrogen Halogenides

It was mentioned in Section 12-2 that **hydrogen fluoride,** HF, is made by treating fluorite with sulfuric acid. This reaction is usually carried out in a lead dish or a platinum dish; in the commercial manufacture of hydrofluoric acid it is carried out in an iron pot, which is connected with a series of lead boxes containing water, in which the hydrogen fluoride dissolves to form aqueous hydrofluoric acid. Pure, anhydrous hydrogen fluoride is best made by heating potassium hydrogen fluoride, KHF_2. This salt can be easily crystallized from a potassium fluoride solution to which hydrofluoric acid has been added.

Hydrogen chloride is made by the reaction of sodium chloride and sulfuric acid. The reaction between cold sulfuric acid and sodium chloride leads to the formation of sodium hydrogen sulfate, $NaHSO_4$.

Pure **hydrogen bromide** cannot be prepared by the same methods as used for hydrogen fluoride and hydrogen chloride, involving displacement of the acid from one of its salts by sulfuric acid. Sulfuric acid even at room temperature is a sufficiently strong oxidizing agent to oxidize some of the hydrogen bromide, causing it to be contaminated with bromine and sulfur dioxide. The reactions that take place when the effort is made to prepare hydrogen bromide in this way are the following:

$$KBr + H_2SO_4 \longrightarrow KHSO_4 + HBr$$
$$2HBr + H_2SO_4 \longrightarrow 2H_2O + SO_2 + Br_2$$

The preparation can be carried out with phosphoric acid in place of sulfuric acid, but it is customary instead to prepare hydrogen bromide in the laboratory by the hydrolysis of phosphorus tribromide, PBr_3. The reaction can be carried out by mixing red phosphorus with wet sand, placing the mixture in a flask equipped with a dropping funnel and an outlet tube, and allowing the bromine to drip onto the red phosphorus. Phosphorus and bromine immediately react, to form phosphorus tribromide, which at once hydrolyzes with the water present:

$$2P + 2Br_2 \longrightarrow 2PBr_3$$
$$PBr_3 + 3H_2O \longrightarrow P(OH)_3 + 3HBr$$

The gas that is evolved is passed through a U-tube containing glass beads mixed with red phosphorus, which combines with any bromine that may be carried along with it. The hydrogen bromide may be collected by upward displacement of air, or may be absorbed in water to form hydrobromic acid.

Hydrogen bromide can also be made by direct combination of the elements. If a stream of hydrogen is bubbled through bromine contained in a flask heated on a water bath to 38°C, the gas mixture that is produced contains hydrogen and bromine in approximately equimolecular proportions. This gas may be passed over platinized silicic acid, which acts as a catalyst, causing the combination of hydrogen and bromine:

$$H_2 + Br_2 \longrightarrow 2HBr$$

The reaction can also be made to take place in a heated tube filled with pieces of porous clay plate.

Hydrogen bromide can also be made by the reduction of bromine with hydrogen sulfide:

$$H_2S + Br_2 \longrightarrow 2HBr + S$$

The gas that is produced can be purified of bromine by passing over red phosphorus, as described in the first method.

Hydrogen iodide, which is still more easily oxidized than hydrogen bromide, can be prepared by similar methods. The customary method of preparation involves the reaction of water, iodine, and red phosphorus. Iodine and red phosphorus are mixed and placed in a flask, to which water is admitted from a dropping funnel. The reaction involved is

$$2P + 3I_2 + 6H_2O \longrightarrow 2P(OH)_3 + 6HI$$

Illustrative Exercises

12-15. Hydrogen chloride can be made by heating a mixture of sodium hydrogen sulfate and sodium chloride. Write the equation for the reaction.

12-16. Why cannot pure hydrogen iodide be made by use of sulfuric acid and sodium iodide? Write equations for two reactions that might take place if these substances were mixed.

12-17. It is stated above that when a stream of hydrogen is bubbled through bromine at 38°C the gas mixture produced is equimolecular in H_2 and Br_2. What is the vapor pressure of liquid bromine at 38°C? (Answer: About 380 mm Hg.)

12-18. In the reaction given above in the paragraph on hydrogen iodide, what is the oxidizing agent and what is the reducing agent? Assign oxidation numbers and write balanced equations for the two electron reactions.

12-5. The Oxygen Acids and Oxides of Chlorine

The oxygen acids of chlorine and their anions have the following formulas and names:

$HClO_4$, perchloric acid ClO_4^-, perchlorate ion
$HClO_3$, chloric acid ClO_3^-, chlorate ion
$HClO_2$, chlorous acid ClO_2^-, chlorite ion
$HClO$, hypochlorous acid ClO^-, hypochlorite ion

The structures of the four anions are shown in Figure 12-2.

The electronic structures shown at the top of the next page, which are in agreement with the electroneutrality principle but involve making use of the $3d$ orbitals for the chlorine atom (except for hypochlorous acid), may be assigned to the four acids:

Figure **12-2**

The structure of ions of the four oxygen acids of chlorine.

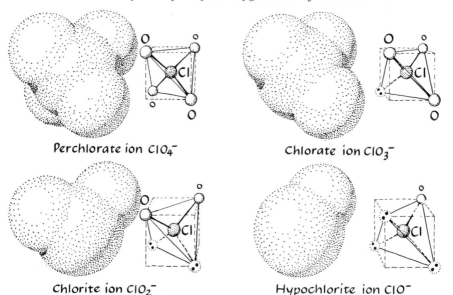

Perchlorate ion ClO_4^- Chlorate ion ClO_3^-

Chlorite ion ClO_2^- Hypochlorite ion ClO^-

$$
\begin{array}{cccc}
\ddot{O}-H & \ddot{O}-H & \ddot{O}-H & \ddot{O}-H \\
| & | & | & | \\
\ddot{O}=\overset{|}{Cl}=\ddot{O} & :\overset{|}{Cl}=\ddot{O} & :\overset{|}{Cl}=\ddot{O} & :\ddot{Cl}: \\
\| & \| & & \\
\ddot{O} & \ddot{O} & &
\end{array}
$$

Perchloric acid   Chloric acid   Chlorous acid   Hypochlorous acid

In the following sections these acids and their salts, and also the oxides of chlorine, are discussed in the order of increasing oxidation number of the halogen.

Hypochlorous Acid and the Hypochlorites. Hypochlorous acid, HClO, and most of its salts are known only in aqueous solution; they decompose when the solution is concentrated. A mixture of chloride ion and hypochlorite ion is formed when chlorine is bubbled through a solution of sodium hydroxide:

$$Cl_2 + 2OH^- \longrightarrow Cl^- + ClO^- + H_2O$$

A solution of **sodium hypochlorite,** NaClO, made in this way or by electrolysis of sodium chloride solution is a popular household sterilizing and bleaching agent. The hypochlorite ion is an active oxidizing agent, and its oxidizing power is the basis of its sterilizing and bleaching action.

Bleaching powder is a compound obtained by passing chlorine over calcium hydroxide:

$$Ca(OH)_2 + Cl_2 \longrightarrow CaCl(ClO) + H_2O$$

The formula CaCl(ClO), which approximates the composition of commercial bleaching powder, indicates it to be a calcium chloride-hypochlorite, containing the two anions Cl^- and ClO^-. Bleaching powder is a white, finely-powdered substance which usually smells of chlorine, because of its decomposition by water vapor in the air. It is often called by the incorrect name "chloride of lime." It is used as a household bleaching and sterilizing agent; in its former industrial use, for bleaching paper pulp and textile fabrics, it has been largely displaced by liquid chlorine. Pure **calcium hypochlorite,** $Ca(ClO)_2$, is also manufactured and used as a bleaching agent.

Hypochlorous acid is a weak acid. The solution obtained by adding another acid, such as sulfuric acid, to a solution of a hypochlorite contains molecules HClO, and very few hypochlorite ions ClO^-:

$$ClO^- + H^+ \longrightarrow HClO$$

Dichlorine monoxide, Cl_2O, is a yellow gas obtained by gently heating hypochlorous acid in a partially evacuated system (that is, under reduced pressure):

$$2HClO \longrightarrow H_2O + Cl_2O$$

or by passing chlorine over mercuric oxide:

$$2Cl_2 + HgO \longrightarrow HgCl_2 + Cl_2O$$

The gas condenses to a liquid at about 4°C. It is the anhydride of hypochlorous acid: that is, it reacts with water to give hypochlorous acid:

$$Cl_2O + H_2O \longrightarrow 2HClO$$

The electronic structure of chlorine monoxide is

$$: \ddot{\overset{\displaystyle ..}{Cl}} :$$
$$| \quad \overset{\displaystyle ..}{}$$
$$: \ddot{\underset{\displaystyle ..}{O}} - \ddot{\underset{\displaystyle ..}{Cl}} :$$

in which chlorine and oxygen have their normal covalences of 1 and 2, respectively.

Chlorous Acid and the Chlorites. When chlorine dioxide, ClO_2, is passed into a solution of sodium hydroxide or other alkali a chlorite ion and a chlorate ion are formed:

$$2ClO_2 + 2OH^- \longrightarrow ClO_2^- + ClO_3^- + H_2O$$

This is an auto-oxidation-reduction reaction, the chlorine with oxidation number $+4$ in chlorine dioxide being reduced and oxidized simultaneously to oxidation numbers $+3$ and $+5$. Pure sodium chlorite, $NaClO_2$, can be made by passing chlorine dioxide into a solution of sodium peroxide:

$$2ClO_2 + Na_2O_2 \longrightarrow 2Na^+ + 2ClO_2^- + O_2$$

In this reaction the peroxide oxygen serves as a reducing agent, decreasing the oxidation number of chlorine from $+4$ to $+3$.

Sodium chlorite is an active bleaching agent, used in the manufacture of textile fabrics.

Chlorine Dioxide. Chlorine dioxide, ClO_2, is the only known compound of quadripositive chlorine. It is a reddish-yellow gas, which is very explosive, decomposing readily to chlorine and oxygen. The violence of this decomposition makes it very dangerous to add sulfuric acid or any other strong acid to a chlorate or to any dry mixture containing a chlorate.

Chlorine dioxide can be made by carefully adding sulfuric acid to potassium chlorate, $KClO_3$. It would be expected that this mixture would react to produce chloric acid, $HClO_3$, and then, because of the dehydrating power of sulfuric acid, to produce the anhydride of chloric acid, Cl_2O_5:

$$KClO_3 + H_2SO_4 \longrightarrow KHSO_4 + HClO_3$$
$$2HClO_3 \longrightarrow H_2O + Cl_2O_5$$

However, dichlorine pentoxide, Cl_2O_5, is very unstable—its existence has never been verified. If it is formed at all, it decomposes at once to give chlorine dioxide and oxygen:

$$2Cl_2O_5 \longrightarrow 4ClO_2 + O_2$$

The over-all reaction may be written as

$$4KClO_3 + 4H_2SO_4 \longrightarrow 4KHSO_4 + 4ClO_2 + O_2 + 2H_2O$$

Chlorine dioxide is an **odd molecule;** that is, a molecule containing an odd number of electrons. It was pointed out by G. N. Lewis in 1916 that odd molecules (other than those containing transition elements) are rare, and that they are usually colored and are always paramagnetic (attracted by a magnet). Every electronic structure that can be written for chlorine dioxide contains one unpaired electron. This unpaired electron presumably resonates among the three atoms, the electronic structure of the molecule being a resonance hybrid:

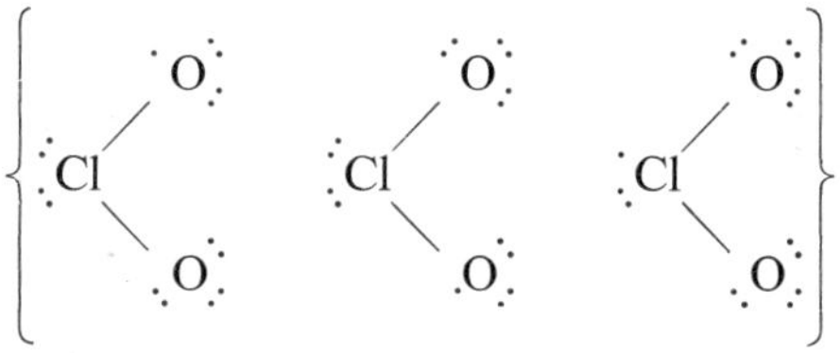

It was mentioned in the preceding section that when chlorine dioxide is dissolved in an alkaline solution chlorate ion and chlorite ion are formed.

Chloric Acid and Its Salts.   Chloric acid, $HClO_3$, is an unstable acid which, like its salts, is a strong oxidizing agent. The most important salt of chloric acid is **potassium chlorate,** $KClO_3$, which is made by passing an excess of chlorine through a hot solution of potassium hydroxide or by heating a solution containing hypochlorite ion and potassium ion:

$$3ClO^- \longrightarrow ClO_3^- + 2Cl^-$$

The potassium chlorate can be separated from the potassium chloride formed in this reaction by crystallization, its solubility at low temperatures being much less than that of the chloride (3 g and 28 g, respectively, per 100 g of water at 0°C). A cheaper way of making potassium chlorate is to electrolyze a solution of potassium chloride, using inert electrodes and keeping the solution mixed. The electrode reactions are

Cathode reaction: $2e^- + 2H_2O \longrightarrow 2OH^- + H_2$
Anode reaction: $Cl^- + 3H_2O \longrightarrow ClO_3^- + 6H^+ + 6e^-$

In the stirred solution the hydroxide ions and the hydrogen ions are brought into contact with one another, and combine to form water. The over-all reaction is

$$Cl^- + 3H_2O \xrightarrow[\text{electr.}]{} ClO_3^- + 3H_2$$

Potassium chlorate is a white crystalline substance, which is used as the oxidizing agent in matches and fireworks and in the manufacture of dyes.

A solution of the similar salt **sodium chlorate,** $NaClO_3$, is used as a weed killer. Potassium chlorate would be as good as sodium chlorate for this purpose; however, sodium salts are cheaper than potassium salts, and for this reason they are often used when only the anion is important. Sometimes the sodium salts have unsatisfactory properties, such as *deliquescence* (attraction of water from the air to form a solution), which make the potassium salts preferable for some uses, even though more expensive.

All the chlorates form sensitive explosive mixtures when mixed with reducing agents; **great care must be taken in handling them.** The use of sodium chlorate as a weed killer is attended with danger, because combustible material such as wood or clothing that has become saturated with the chlorate solution will ignite by friction after it has dried. Also, *it is very dangerous to grind a chlorate with sulfur, charcoal, or other reducing agent.*

Perchloric Acid and the Perchlorates. Potassium perchlorate, $KClO_4$, is made by heating potassium chlorate just to its melting point:

$$4KClO_3 \longrightarrow 3KClO_4 + KCl$$

At this temperature very little decomposition with evolution of oxygen occurs in the absence of a catalyst. Potassium perchlorate may also be made by long-continued electrolysis of a solution of potassium chloride, potassium hypochlorite, or potassium chlorate.

Potassium perchlorate and other perchlorates are oxidizing agents, somewhat less vigorous and less dangerous than the chlorates. Potassium perchlorate is used in explosives, such as the propellent powder of the bazooka and other rockets. This powder is a mixture of potassium perchlorate and carbon together with a binder; the equation for the principal reaction accompanying its burning is

$$KClO_4 + 4C \longrightarrow KCl + 4CO$$

Anhydrous **magnesium perchlorate,** $Mg(ClO_4)_2$, and **barium perchlorate,** $Ba(ClO_4)_2$, are used as drying agents (*desiccants*). These salts have a very strong attraction for water. Nearly all the perchlorates are highly soluble in water; potassium perchlorate is exceptional for its low solubility, 0.75 g/100 g at 0°C.

Sodium perchlorate, $NaClO_4$, made by the electrolytic method, is used as a weed killer; it is safer than sodium chlorate. In general the mixtures of perchlorates with oxidizable materials are less dangerous than the corresponding mixtures of chlorates.

Perchloric acid, $HClO_4 \cdot H_2O$, is a colorless liquid made by distilling, under reduced pressure, a solution of a perchlorate to which sulfuric acid has been added. The perchloric acid distills as the monohydrate, and on cooling it forms crystals of the monohydrate. These crystals are isomorphous with ammonium perchlorate, NH_4ClO_4, and the substance is presumably hydronium perchlorate, $(H_3O)^+(ClO_4)^-$.

Dichlorine heptoxide, Cl_2O_7, is the anhydride of perchloric acid. It can be made by heating perchloric acid with P_2O_5, a strong dehydrating agent:

$$2HClO_4 \cdot H_2O + P_2O_5 \longrightarrow 2H_3PO_4 + Cl_2O_7$$

It is a colorless liquid having a boiling point of 80°C. It is the most stable oxide of chlorine, but is exploded by heat or shock.

Illustrative Exercises

12-19. When chlorine is passed into a solution of potassium hydroxide, chloride ions and hypochlorite ions are formed. If the solution is heated the hypochlorite ions undergo auto-oxidation to chlorate ions and chloride ions. Write equations for the two reactions.

12-20. What reaction takes place when Cl_2O is added to water? When ClO_2 is added to water? When Cl_2O_7 is added to water? Would you consider each of these oxides to be an acid anhydride?

12-6. The Oxygen Acids and Oxides of Bromine

Bromine forms only two stable oxygen acids—hypobromous acid and bromic acid—and their salts:

.   HBrO, hypobromous acid   KBrO, potassium hypobromite
     $HBrO_3$, bromic acid $KBrO_3$, potassium bromate

Their preparation and properties are similar to those of the corresponding compounds of chlorine. They are somewhat weaker oxidizing agents than their chlorine analogs.

The bromite ion, BrO_2^-, has been reported to exist in solution. However, no effort to prepare perbromic acid or any perbromate has succeeded.

Three very unstable oxides of bromine, Br_2O, BrO_2, and Br_3O_8, have been described. The structure of Br_3O_8 is not known.

None of the oxygen compounds of bromine has found important practical use.

12-7. The Oxygen Acids and Oxides of Iodine

Iodine reacts with hydroxide ion in cold alkaline solution to form the **hypoiodite ion,** IO^-, and iodide ion:

$$I_2 + 2OH^- \longrightarrow IO^- + I^- + H_2O$$

On warming the solution it reacts further to form **iodate ion,** IO_3^-:

$$3IO^- \longrightarrow IO_3^- + 2I^-$$

The salts of hypoiodous acid and iodic acid may be made in these ways. **Iodic acid** itself, HIO_3, is usually made by oxidizing iodine with concentrated nitric acid:

$$I_2 + 10HNO_3 \longrightarrow 2HIO_3 + 10NO_2 + 4H_2O$$

Iodic acid is a white solid, which is only very slightly soluble in concentrated

Illustrative Exercises

12-21. Would you predict that iodine would react with chloride ion? With chlorate ion?

12-22. Write equations for the reaction of bromine with a solution of potassium hydroxide
    (a) to form hypobromous acid,
    (b) to form bromate ion.

12-23. Bromine forms only two oxygen acids, HBrO and $HBrO_3$. Write an equation for the reaction that you would expect to occur when the oxide BrO_2 is added to water.

12-24. From enthalpy values in Table 12-2, calculate the heat of the reaction

$$Cl_2(aq) + 2I^-(aq) \longrightarrow I_2(aq) + 2Cl^-(aq)$$

12-9. Compounds of Halogens with Nonmetals and Metalloids

The halogens form covalent compounds with most of the nonmetallic elements (including each other) and the metalloids. These compounds are usually molecular substances, with the relatively low melting points and boiling points characteristic of substances with small forces of intermolecular attraction.

An example of a compound involving a covalent bond between a halogen and a nonmetal is chloroform, $CHCl_3$ (Chapter 10). In this molecule, the structure of which is shown in Figure 12-4, the carbon atom is attached by single covalent bonds to one hydrogen atom and three chlorine atoms. Chloroform is a colorless liquid, with a characteristic sweetish odor, b.p. 61°C, density 1.498 g/ml. Chloroform is only slightly soluble in water, but it dissolves readily in alcohol, ether, and carbon tetrachloride.

The halogenides of carbon and its congeners are tetrahedral (sp^3 bond orbitals). Those of nitrogen and oxygen and their congeners have bond angles near 100°, corresponding to p bond orbitals with a small amount of s character (Section 9-6).

The melting points, boiling points, bond length, and bond angles of some chlorides are tabulated on p. 380.

In addition to these compounds, many compounds, such as PCl_5, ClF_3, SCl_4,

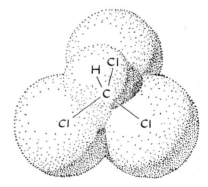

Figure **12-4** *The chloroform molecule, $CHCl_3$.*

	CCl$_4$	NCl$_3$	Cl$_2$O	ClF
m.p.	−23°	−40°	−20°	−154°C
b.p.	77°	70°	4°	−100°
Bond length	1.77 Å	1.73 Å	1.69 Å	1.63 Å
Bond angle	109.5°	110°	110°	

	SiCl$_4$	PCl$_3$	SCl$_2$	Cl$_2$
m.p.	−70°	−112°	−78°	−102°
b.p.	60°	74°	59°	−34°
Bond length	2.01 Å	2.04 Å	2.00 Å	1.99 Å
Bond angle	109.5°	100.0°	102°	

	GeCl$_4$	AsCl$_3$		BrCl
m.p.	−50°	−18°		
b.p.	83°	130°		
Bond length	2.09 Å	2.16 Å		2.14 Å
Bond angle	109.5°	99°		

	SnCl$_4$	SbCl$_3$	TeCl$_2$	ICl
m.p.	−33°	73°	209°	27°
b.p.	114°	223°	327°	97°
Bond length	2.32 Å	2.38 Å	2.34 Å	2.30 Å
Bond angle	109.5°	99°	99°	

etc., exist, to which a normal covalent structure with noble-gas configuration for the central atom cannot be assigned.

Many of these substances react readily with water, to form a hydride of one element and a hydroxide of the other:

$$ClF + H_2O \longrightarrow HClO + HF$$
$$PCl_3 + 3H_2O \longrightarrow P(OH)_3 + 3HCl$$

In general, in a reaction of this sort, called *hydrolysis*, the more electronegative element combines with hydrogen, and the less electronegative element combines with the hydroxide group. This rule is seen to be followed in the above examples.

The bond lengths in SiCl$_4$ and other halogenides (except of the first-row elements) are usually less than the sum of the single-bond radii; for SiCl$_4$ the difference is 0.16 Å. It is likely that this difference is to be interpreted as showing that the bonds have some double-bond character, involving use of the 3d orbitals.

EXERCISES

12-25. What chemical reaction takes place at each electrode in the electrolytic preparation of sodium hypochlorite from sodium chloride? Would a well-stirred solution become more acidic or more basic during the course of this electrolysis?

12-26. Which is the stronger oxidizing agent, hypochlorite ion, ClO⁻, or hypoiodite ion, IO⁻? Which is the stronger reducing agent?

12-27. Why is potassium chlorate rather than sodium chlorate usually used in the chemical laboratory when a chlorate is needed? Why is sodium chlorate solution, rather than potassium chlorate solution, used as a weed killer?

12-28. Write the equation for the formation of potassium iodate by the reaction of powdered iodine with a hot solution of potassium hydroxide.

12-29. Under what conditions does potassium chlorate decompose to give oxygen and potassium chloride, and under what conditions does it react to form potassium perchlorate and potassium chloride?

12-30. What is the equation for the hydrolysis of dichlorine monoxide? Is there any oxidation or reduction in this chemical reaction? If so, what element changes its oxidation number?

12-31. Write an equation for the reaction of chlorine with carbon disulfide, CS_2. The products of the reaction are carbon tetrachloride, CCl_4, and disulfur dichloride, S_2Cl_2. What do you think the structure of disulfur dichloride is?

12-32. The dangerously toxic substance phosgene, $COCl_2$, is made by mixing carbon monoxide with chlorine in the sunlight or in the presence of a catalyst. Write the equation for this reaction, assigning oxidation numbers to the elements in the reactants and the product. What do you think the electronic structure of phosgene is?

12-33. What are the names of the compounds $CaCl_2$, $Ca(ClO)_2$, $Ca(ClO_2)_2$, $Ca(ClO_3)_2$, $Ca(ClO_4)_2$? What is the oxidation number of chlorine in each compound?

12-34. If liquid chlorine costs 15 cents per pound, and bleaching powder approximating the formula $CaOCl_2$ costs 10 cents per pound, which would be the less expensive material to use to purify the water of a swimming pool?

12-35. In a mixture of sodium iodide, sodium bromide, sodium chloride, and sodium fluoride, what oxidizing agent could be used to oxidize the iodide to free iodine without affecting any of the others? After the oxidation of the iodide, what substance could be used to oxidize only the bromide? Then only the chloride? Can the fluoride be oxidized?

12-36. How can each of the four halogens be conveniently prepared from compounds in the laboratory? Write equations for all reactions.

12-37. How can each of the four hydrogen halogenides be prepared in moderately pure form in the laboratory? Write equations.

12-38. The German chemist Liebig is said to have prepared bromine several years before the discovery of this element, but to have failed to recognize it as a new element because of its close similarity in physical properties to ICl. How would you tell a sample of bromine from a sample of ICl?

12-39. It is stated in Section 12-9 that in hydrolysis of a binary compound the more electronegative element combines with hydrogen, and the less electronegative element combines with the OH group. Can you explain why this is to be expected? What would be the products of hydrolysis of ICl?

12-40. What do you suggest as the electronic structure of H_5IO_6? What orbitals are used in forming the hybrid bond orbitals of the iodine atom?

12-41. The enthalpy of formation of ClF(g) is -13.4 kcal/mole. What is the value of the Cl—F bond energy? (Answer: 60.7 kcal/mole.)

12-42. What is the structure of the ClF_3 molecule? What orbitals are used by the chlorine atom for outer unshared pairs of electrons, and what are used for bond orbitals?

12-43. The enthalpy of formation of $ClF_3(g)$ is -38.8 kcal/mole.
(a) What is the enthalpy of formation of ClF_3 from ClF and F_2?
(b) What is the effective bond energy of the two additional Cl—F bonds?
(c) The average bond energy of the three bonds? Why do you think the bonds are weaker than the bond in ClF?
(Answer: -25.4, 31.4, 40.9 kcal/mole; use of $3d$ orbital.)

12-44. The standard enthalpy of formation of $Cl_2O(g)$ is -18.20 kcal/mole. What is the enthalpy of formation of the molecule from atoms? To what value of the Cl—O bond energy does this value lead? (Answer: -99.0, 49.5 kcal/mole.)

12-45. No value has been reported for the standard enthalpy of formation of $Br_2O(g)$. What electronic structure would you assign to this molecule? Can you predict a value for the Br—O bond energy and the standard enthalpy of $Br_2O(g)$? (Answer: 51.2, -12.3 kcal/mole.)

12-46. The reactive molecule ClO, which has one unpaired electron, has been studied as a gas by spectroscopic methods. What electronic structure do you suggest for the molecule? Its standard enthalpy of formation is 33 kcal/mole. What is its enthalpy of formation from atoms? The three-electron bond (like the one-electron bond) is usually estimated to have about 50% or 60% of the bond energy of the corresponding electron-pair bond (single bond). What conclusion do you draw from the enthalpy of formation from atoms about the amount of three-electron-bond character in this molecule? (Answer: -55.2 kcal/mole.)

12-47. From enthalpy values in Table 12-2, calculate the ionization enthalpy and the electron affinity for atoms of the four halogens.

12-48. The American scientist R. S. Mulliken has suggested that for univalent elements the electronegativity is proportional to the sum of the first ionization energy and the electron affinity. Using the enthalpy values of the preceding Exercise, calculate the divisor that gives the same sum for the four halogens as the sum of the values in Table 9-1. To what values of the electronegativity does this relation lead? (Answer: 127 kcal/mole; 3.94, 3.05, 2.81, 2.50.)

CHAPTER 13

Sulfur, Selenium, and Tellurium

The sixth-group elements sulfur, selenium, and tellurium are much less electronegative than their congener oxygen, which was discussed in Chapter 6, and their chemical properties are correspondingly different.

The electronic structures of the atoms of these elements are given in Table 13-1. The normal state has the electron configuration $ns^2np^4(n = 3, 4, 5$, respec-

Table 13-1

Electronic Structures of Elements of Group VI

Z	ELEMENT	K	L		M			N			O	
		$1s$	$2s$	$2p$	$3s$	$3p$	$3d$	$4s$	$4p$	$4d$	$5s$	$5p$
8	Oxygen	2	2	4								
16	Sulfur	2	2	6	2	4						
34	Selenium	2	2	6	2	6	10	2	4			
52	Tellurium	2	2	6	2	6	10	2	6	10	2	4

tively) and the Russell-Saunders symbol ^3P, corresponding to two p electrons with parallel spin (a triplet state). The atoms have two electrons less than the corresponding noble gas. They can assume the electronic structure of the noble gas by adding two electrons, to form doubly charged anions, or by sharing two electron pairs with other atoms (that is, by forming two covalent bonds), or in other ways. When two covalent bonds are formed, use is made of two p orbitals (with some s character) as bond orbitals. In higher oxidation states the d orbitals are also involved in bond formation.

Some standard enthalpy values are given in Table 13-2.

Table **13-2**

Standard Enthalpy of Formation of Compounds of
Sulfur, Selenium, and Tellurium at 25°C (kcal/mole)

	X = S	Se	Te
$X(c)^*$	0.00	0.00	0.00
$X(g)$	66.7	48.37	47.6
$X^+(g)$	307.0	274.70	256.80
$X^{--}(g)$	125.2		
$X^{--}(aq)$	10.0	31.6	
$X_2(g)$	29.86	33.14	41.0
$X_6(g)$	25.3		
$X_8(g)$	24.1		
$XO(g)$	1.4	9.48	43.0
XO_2	$-70.96(g)$	$-55.00(c)$	$-77.69(c)$
$XO_3(g)$	-94.45		
$H_2X(g)$	-4.82	20.5	36.9
$H_2XO_3(aq)$	-151.36	-122.39	-144.7
H_2XO_4	$-193.91(l)$	$-128.6(c)$	
$H_2XO_4(aq)$	-216.90	-145.3	-166.7
$XCl_2(g)$		-9.7	
$X_2Cl_2(l)$	-14.4	-20.0	
$XF_6(g)$	-289	-246	-315

* The standard states are orthorhombic sulfur (S_8 molecules) and hexagonal selenium and tellurium (long chains of atoms).

13-1. The Oxidation States of Sulfur

The principal oxidation states of sulfur are -2, 0, $+4$, and $+6$. These states are represented by many important substances, including those given in the diagram in Section 13-2.

13-2. Elementary Sulfur

Orthorhombic and Monoclinic Sulfur. Sulfur exists in several allotropic forms. Ordinary sulfur is a yellow solid substance, which forms crystals with orthorhombic symmetry; it is called **orthorhombic sulfur** or, usually, **rhombic sulfur.** It is insoluble in water, but soluble in carbon disulfide (CS_2), carbon tetrachloride, and similar nonpolar solvents, giving solutions from which well-formed crystals of sulfur can be obtained (Figure 13-1). Some of its physical properties are given in Table 13-3.

At 112.8°C orthorhombic sulfur melts to form a straw-colored liquid. This liquid crystallizes in a monoclinic crystalline form, called β-sulfur or **monoclinic sulfur** (Figure 13-1). The sulfur molecules in both orthorhombic sulfur and monoclinic sulfur, as well as in the straw-colored liquid, are S_8

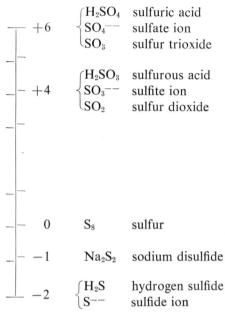

+6	H$_2$SO$_4$	sulfuric acid
	SO$_4$$^{--}$	sulfate ion
	SO$_3$	sulfur trioxide
+4	H$_2$SO$_3$	sulfurous acid
	SO$_3$$^{--}$	sulfite ion
	SO$_2$	sulfur dioxide
0	S$_8$	sulfur
−1	Na$_2$S$_2$	sodium disulfide
−2	H$_2$S	hydrogen sulfide
	S^{--}	sulfide ion

molecules, with a staggered-ring configuration (Figure 9-13). The formation of this large molecule (and of the similar molecules Se$_8$ and Te$_8$) is the result of the tendency of the sixth-group elements to form two single covalent bonds, instead of one double bond. Diatomic molecules S$_2$ are formed by heating sulfur vapor (S$_8$ at lower temperatures) to a high temperature, but these molecules are less stable than the large molecules containing single bonds.

This fact is not isolated, but is an example of the generalization that stable double bonds and triple bonds are formed readily by the light elements carbon, nitrogen, and oxygen, but only rarely by the heavier elements. Carbon disulfide, CS$_2$, and other compounds containing a carbon-sulfur double bond are the main exceptions to this rule.

Monoclinic sulfur is the stable form above 95.5°C, which is the *equilibrium temperature (transition temperature* or *transition point)* between it and the orthorhombic form. Monoclinic sulfur melts at 119.25°C.

Figure **13-1** *Crystals of orthorhombic and monoclinic sulfur.*

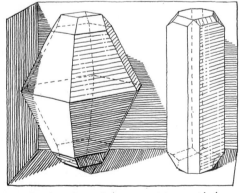

Orthorhombic   **Monoclinic**
Sulfur

Table 13-3

Properties of Oxygen, Sulfur, Selenium, and Tellurium

	ATOMIC NUMBER	ATOMIC WEIGHT	MELTING POINT	BOILING POINT	DENSITY	COVALENT RADIUS	IONIC RADIUS, X^{--}
Oxygen (gas)	8	15.9994	−218.4°C	−183.0°C	1.429 g/liter	0.66 Å	1.40 Å
Sulfur (orthorhombic)	16	32.064	119.25°, 112.8°*	444.6°	2.07 g/cm³	1.04	1.84
Selenium (gray)	34	78.96	217°	685°	4.79	1.17	1.98
Tellurium (gray)	52	127.60	450°	1087°	6.25	1.37	2.21

* For monoclinic sulfur and (rapidly heated) orthorhombic sulfur, respectively.

Liquid Sulfur.   Sulfur that has just been melted is a mobile, straw-colored liquid. The viscosity of this liquid is low because the S_8 molecules that compose it are nearly spherical in shape (Figure 9-13) and roll easily over one another. When molten sulfur is heated to a higher temperature, however, it gradually darkens in color and becomes more viscous, finally becoming so thick (at about 200°C) that it cannot be poured out of its container. Most substances decrease in viscosity with increasing temperature, because the increased thermal agitation causes the molecules to move around one another more easily. The abnormal behavior of liquid sulfur results from the production of molecules of a different kind—long chains, containing scores of atoms. These very long molecules get entangled with one another, causing the liquid to be very viscous. The dark red color is due to the ends of the chains, which consist of sulfur atoms with only one valence bond instead of the normal two.

The straw-colored liquid, S_8, is called λ-sulfur, and the dark red liquid consisting of very long chains is called μ-sulfur. When this liquid is rapidly cooled by being poured into water, it forms a rubbery *supercooled liquid,* insoluble in carbon disulfide. On standing at room temperature the long chains slowly rearrange into S_8 molecules, and the rubbery mass changes into an aggregate of crystals of orthorhombic sulfur.

A form of crystalline sulfur with rhombohedral symmetry can be made by extracting an acidified solution of sodium thiosulfate with chloroform and evaporating the chloroform solution. These crystals, which are orange in color, consist of S_6 molecules; they are unstable, and change into long chains and then into orthorhombic sulfur (S_8) in a few hours.

Sulfur boils at 444.6°C, forming S_8 vapor, which on a cold surface condenses directly to orthorhombic sulfur.

The Mining of Sulfur.   Free sulfur occurs in large quantities in Sicily, Louisiana, and Texas. The Sicilian deposits consist of rock (clay, gypsum, limestone) mixed with about 20% of free sulfur. The material is heated by burning part of the sulfur, and molten sulfur is drawn off, and then purified by sublimation.

Over 80% of the world's production of sulfur is mined in Louisiana and Texas by a very clever method, the Frasch process. The sulfur, mixed with limestone, occurs at depths of about one thousand feet, under strata of sand, clay, and rock. A boring is made to the deposit, and four concentric pipes are sunk (Figure 13-2). Superheated water (155°C) under pressure is pumped down the two outer pipes. This melts the sulfur, which collects in a pool around the open end. Air is forced down the innermost pipe, and a bubbly froth of air, sulfur, and water rises through the space between the innermost pipe and the next one. This mixture is allowed to flow into a very large wooden vat, where the sulfur hardens as a product 99.5% pure.

13-3. Hydrogen Sulfide and the Sulfides of the Metals

Hydrogen sulfide, H_2S, is analogous to water. Its electronic structure is

$$\overset{\displaystyle H}{\underset{\displaystyle}{\overset{|}{:\!S\!-\!H}}}$$

It is far more volatile (m.p. $-85.5°C$, b.p. $-60.3°C$) than water. It is appreciably soluble in cold water (2.6 liters of gas dissolves in 1 liter of water at 20°C), forming a slightly acidic solution. The solution is slowly oxidized by atmospheric oxygen, giving a milky precipitate of sulfur.

Hydrogen sulfide has a powerful odor, resembling that of rotten eggs. It is very poisonous, and care must be taken not to breathe the gas while using it in the analytical chemistry laboratory.

Hydrogen sulfide is readily prepared by action of hydrochloric acid on ferrous sulfide:

$$2HCl + FeS \longrightarrow FeCl_2 + H_2S$$

The **sulfides** of the alkali and alkaline-earth metals are colorless substances easily soluble in water. The sulfides of most other metals are insoluble or only very slightly soluble in water, and their precipitation under varying conditions is an important part of the usual scheme of qualitative analysis for the metallic ions. Many metallic sulfides occur in nature; important sulfide ores include FeS, Cu_2S, CuS, ZnS, Ag_2S, HgS, and PbS.

The Polysulfides. Sulfur dissolves in a solution of an alkali or alkaline-earth sulfide, forming a mixture of polysulfides:

$$S^{--} + S \longrightarrow S_2^{--}, \text{ disulfide ion}$$
$$S^{--} + 2S \longrightarrow S_3^{--}, \text{ trisulfide ion}$$
$$S^{--} + 3S \longrightarrow S_4^{--}, \text{ tetrasulfide ion}$$

The **disulfide ion** has a structure analogous to that of the peroxide ion, and the polysulfide ions have similar structures, involving chains of sulfur atoms connected by single covalent bonds:

$$\left[:\!\overset{..}{\underset{..}{S}}\!-\!\overset{..}{\underset{..}{S}}\!:\right]^{--} \qquad \left[\begin{array}{c} \overset{..}{S} \\ \diagup \quad \diagdown \\ :\!\overset{.}{S}\!. \qquad .\!\overset{.}{\underset{..}{S}}\!: \end{array}\right]^{--} \qquad \left[\begin{array}{c} \overset{..}{S} \qquad \overset{..}{\underset{.}{S}}\!: \\ \diagup \quad \diagdown \quad \diagup \\ :\!\overset{.}{S}\!. \qquad .\!\overset{.}{S}\!. \end{array}\right]^{--}$$

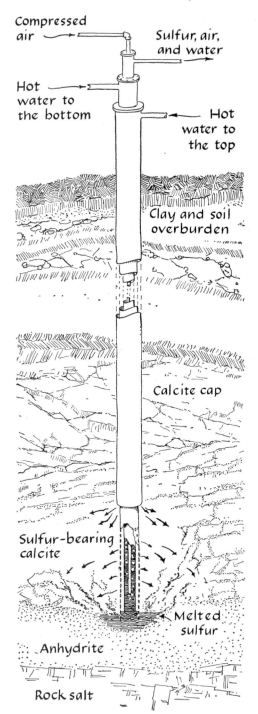

Compressed
air

Sulfur, air,
and water

Hot
water to
the bottom

Hot
water to
the top

Clay and soil
overburden

Calcite cap

Sulfur-bearing
calcite

Melted
sulfur

Anhydrite

Rock salt

Hydrogen disulfide, H_2S_2, analogous to hydrogen peroxide, can be made by careful treatment of a disulfide with acid; it is a pale yellow oily liquid. The hydrogen polysulfides readily decompose to hydrogen sulfide and sulfur.

The common mineral *pyrite*, FeS_2, is ferrous disulfide.

13-4. Sulfur Dioxide and Sulfurous Acid

Sulfur dioxide, SO_2, is the gas formed by burning sulfur or a sulfide, such as pyrite:

$$S + O_2 \longrightarrow SO_2$$
$$4FeS_2 + 11O_2 \longrightarrow 2Fe_2O_3 + 8SO_2$$

It is colorless, and has a characteristic choking odor.

Sulfur dioxide is conveniently made in the laboratory by adding a strong acid to solid sodium hydrogen sulfite:

$$H_2SO_4 + NaHSO_3 \longrightarrow$$
$$NaHSO_4 + H_2O + SO_2$$

It may be purified and dried by bubbling it through concentrated sulfuric acid, and, since it is over twice as dense as air, it may be collected by displacement of air.

Figure **13-2** *The Frasch process for mining sulfur. (The mineral anhydrite, which lies below the sulfur-calcite layer, is anhydrous calcium sulfate, $CaSO_4$.)*

A solution of **sulfurous acid,** H_2SO_3, is obtained by dissolving sulfur dioxide in water. Both sulfurous acid and its salts, the **sulfites,** are active reducing agents. They form sulfuric acid, H_2SO_4, and sulfates on oxidation by oxygen, the halogens, hydrogen peroxide, and similar oxidizing agents.

The electronic structure of sulfur dioxide is

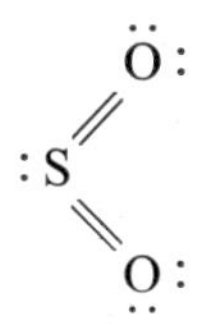

$$: S \diagdown \diagup \overset{\cdot\cdot}{O} : \quad \overset{\cdot\cdot}{O} :$$

In this structure use is made of one $3d$ orbital, as well as the $3s$ orbital and the three $3p$ orbitals. The observed sulfur-oxygen bond length, 1.43 Å, is a little less than the value 1.49 Å expected for a double bond (Section 9-15). The angle O—S—O has the value 119.5°.

The structure of sulfurous acid is

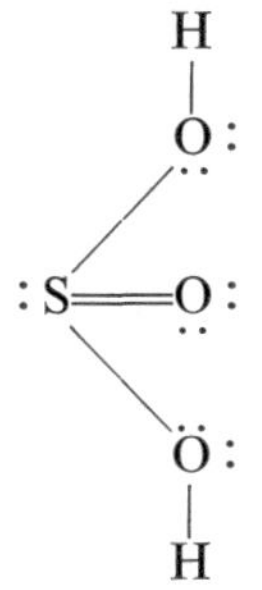

$$
\begin{array}{c}
H \\
| \\
\overset{\cdot\cdot}{O} : \\
\diagup \\
: S = \overset{\cdot\cdot}{\underset{\cdot\cdot}{O}} : \\
\diagdown \\
\overset{\cdot\cdot}{O} : \\
| \\
H
\end{array}
$$

In each of these molecules the sulfur atom has one unshared pair of electrons; this is characteristic of atoms with oxidation number two less than the maximum.

Sulfur dioxide is used in great quantities in the manufacture of sulfuric acid, sulfurous acid, and sulfites. It destroys fungi and bacteria, and is used as a preservative in the preparation of dried prunes, apricots, and other fruits. A solution of **calcium hydrogen sulfite,** $Ca(HSO_3)_2$, made by reaction of sulfur dioxide and calcium hydroxide, is used in the manufacture of paper pulp from wood. The solution dissolves lignin, a substance that cements the cellulose fibers together, and liberates these fibers, which are then processed into paper.

13-5. Sulfur Trioxide

Sulfur trioxide, SO_3, is formed in very small quantities when sulfur is burned in air. It is usually made by oxidation of sulfur dioxide by air, in the presence of a catalyst. The reaction

$$SO_2(g) + \tfrac{1}{2}O_2(g) \longrightarrow SO_3(g)$$

is exothermic, with heat of reaction 23.5 kcal/mole (Table 13-2). The nature of the equilibrium is such that at low temperatures a satisfactory yield can be obtained; the reaction proceeds nearly to completion. However, the rate of the reaction is so small at low temperatures as to make the direct combination of the substances unsuitable as a commercial process, and at higher temperatures, where the rate is satisfactory, the yield is low because of the unfavorable equilibrium.

The solution to this problem was the discovery of certain catalysts (platinum, vanadium pentoxide), which speed up the reaction without affecting the equilibrium. The catalyzed reaction proceeds not in the gaseous mixture, but on the surface of the catalyst, as the gas molecules strike it. In practice, sulfur dioxide, made by burning sulfur or pyrite, is mixed with air and passed over the catalyst at a temperature of 400° to 450°C. About 99% of the sulfur dioxide is converted into sulfur trioxide under these conditions. It is used mainly in the manufacture of sulfuric acid.

Sulfur trioxide is a corrosive gas, which combines vigorously with water to form sulfuric acid:

$$SO_3 + H_2O \longrightarrow H_2SO_4$$

It also dissolves readily in sulfuric acid, to form *oleum* or *fuming sulfuric acid*, which consists mainly of disulfuric acid, $H_2S_2O_7$ (also called *pyrosulfuric acid*):

$$SO_3 + H_2SO_4 \rightleftarrows H_2S_2O_7$$

Sulfur trioxide condenses at 44.5°C to a colorless liquid, which freezes at 16.8°C to transparent crystals. The substance is polymorphous, these crystals being the unstable form (the α-form). The stable form consists of silky asbestos-like crystals, which are produced when the α-crystals or the liquid stands for some time, especially in the presence of a trace of moisture. There exist also one or more other forms of this substance, which are hard to investigate because the changes from one form to another are very slow. The asbestos-like crystals slowly evaporate to SO_3 vapor at temperatures above 50°C.

The sulfur trioxide molecule—in the gas phase, the liquid, and the α-crystals —has the electronic structure

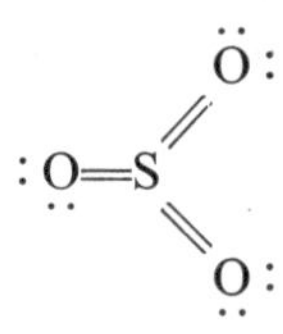

The molecule is planar, and the bonds have the same length, 1.43 Å, as in the sulfur dioxide molecule.

The properties of sulfur trioxide may be in large part explained as resulting from the instability of the sulfur-oxygen double bond. Thus by reaction with water the double bond can be replaced by two single bonds, in sulfuric acid:

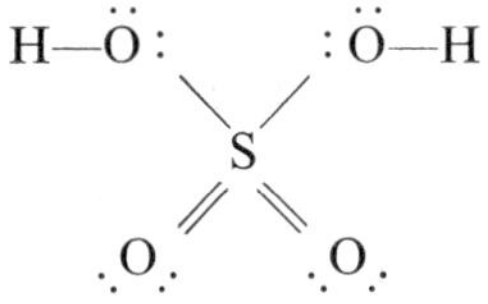

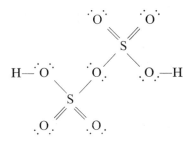

The increased stability of the product is reflected in the large amount of heat evolved in the reaction. A second sulfur trioxide molecule can eliminate its double bond by combining with a molecule of sulfuric acid to form a molecule of disulfuric acid:

Similarly, molecules of trisulfuric acid, $H_2S_3O_{10}$, tetrasulfuric acid, $H_2S_4O_{13}$, etc., can be formed (Figure 13-3), culminating in a chain $HO_3SO(SO_3)_\infty SO_3H$ of nearly infinite length—essentially a high polymer of sulfur trioxide, $(SO_3)_x$, with x large. It is these very long molecules that constitute the asbestos-like crystalline form of sulfur trioxide. We can understand why the crystals are fibrous, like asbestos—they consist of extremely long chain molecules, arranged together side by side, but easily separated into fibers, because, although the chains themselves are strong, the forces between them are relatively weak.

The molecular structures explain why the formation of the asbestos-like crystals, and also their decomposition to SO_3 vapor, are slow processes, whereas crystallization and evaporation are usually rapid. In this case these processes are really *chemical reactions*, involving the formation of new chemical bonds. The role of a trace of water in catalyzing the formation of the asbestos-like crystals can also be understood; the molecules of water serve to start the chains, which can then grow to great length.

In the long-chain polymer of sulfur trioxide (Figure 13-3) the sulfur-oxygen distance for the oxygen atoms bonded to two sulfur atoms in the chain is about 1.62 Å, and that for the oxygen atoms bonded to one sulfur atom is about 1.43 Å. These two bond lengths are a little less than the single-bond and double-bond values given by the covalent radii. We are accordingly led to assign to the sulfur trioxide polymer the structure

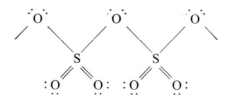

In this structure each sulfur atom is indicated as forming six bonds; the bond orbitals are hybrids of one $3s$ orbital, three $3p$ orbitals, and two $3d$ orbitals.

The observed heats of reaction also indicate that the bonds in the oxides of sulfur are double bonds. The heat of addition of an oxygen atom to the

Figure **13-3**

Sulfur trioxide and some oxygen acids of sulfur.

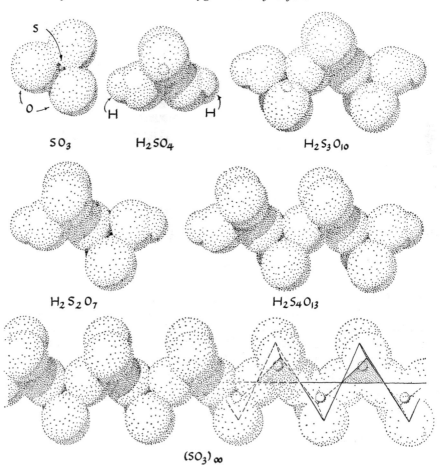

SO_3 H_2SO_4 $H_2S_3O_{10}$

$H_2S_2O_7$ $H_2S_4O_{13}$

$(SO_3)_\infty$

oxygen molecule to form ozone is only 25.2 kcal/mole (enthalpy values are given in Table 6-1):

$$O_2(g) + O(g) \longrightarrow O_3(g) + 25.2 \text{ kcal/mole}$$

This value is less than the O—O single-bond energy. The heat of the corresponding reaction for sulfur monoxide (Table 13-2) is 131.6 kcal/mole, which is even greater than the sulfur-oxygen double-bond energy:

$$S(g) + O(g) \longrightarrow SO(g) + 111.1 \text{ kcal/mole}$$
$$SO(g) + O(g) \longrightarrow SO_2(g) + 131.6 \text{ kcal/mole}$$

Large values of the heat of reaction are found also for other reactions of addition of an oxygen atom to sulfur:

$$(CH_3)_2S(l) + O(g) \longrightarrow (CH_3)_2SO(l) + 90 \text{ kcal/mole}$$
$$(CH_3)_2SO(l) + O(g) \longrightarrow (CH_3)_2SO_2(l) + 115 \text{ kcal/mole}$$
$$SCl_2O(l) + O(g) \longrightarrow SCl_2O_2(l) + 103 \text{ kcal/mole}$$
$$H_2SO_3(aq) + O(g) \longrightarrow H_2SO_4(aq) + 129 \text{ kcal/mole}$$
$$SO_2(g) + O(g) \longrightarrow SO_3(g) + 83 \text{ kcal/mole}$$

Illustrative Exercises

13-1. From enthalpy values (Table 13-2) calculate the heat of reaction of sulfurous acid to form sulfuric acid (aqueous solution). Would you expect sulfurous acid to be stable in the presence of air?

13-2. Write structural formulas, showing bonds and unshared outer electron pairs, for $(CH_2)_2S$ (dimethyl sulfide), $(CH_3)_2SO$ (dimethylsulfoxide), and $(CH_3)_2SO_2$ (dimethylsulfone).

13-3. From enthalpy values (Table 13-2) calculate
(a) the heat of the reaction of sulfide ion with molecular oxygen to form sulfate ion in aqueous solution;
(b) the heat of reaction with oxygen atoms;
(c) the average energy of addition of an oxygen atom to sulfide ion to form sulfate ion. (Answer: 227, 464, 116 kcal/mole.)

13-6. Sulfuric Acid and the Sulfates

Sulfuric acid, H_2SO_4, is one of the most important of all chemicals, finding use throughout the chemical industry and related industries. About 20,000,000 tons of the acid is made each year. It is a heavy, oily liquid (density 1.838 g/cm³), which fumes slightly in air, as the result of the liberation of traces of sulfur trioxide, which then combine with water vapor to form droplets of sulfuric acid. When heated, pure sulfuric acid yields a vapor rich in sulfur trioxide, and then boils, at 338°C with the constant composition 98% H_2SO_4, 2% water. This is the ordinary "concentrated sulfuric acid" of commerce.

Concentrated sulfuric acid is very corrosive. It has a strong affinity for water, and a large amount of heat is liberated when it is mixed with water, as the result of the formation of hydronium ion:

$$H_2SO_4 + 2H_2O \rightleftarrows 2H_3O^+ + SO_4^{--}$$

In diluting it, the concentrated acid should be poured into water in a thin stream, with stirring; *water should never be poured into the acid*, because it is apt to sputter and throw drops of acid out of the container. The diluted acid occupies a smaller volume than its constituents, the effect being a maximum at $H_2SO_4 + 2H_2O$ [$(H_3O)_2^+(SO_4)^{--}$].

The crystalline phases that form on cooling sulfuric acid containing varying amounts of sulfur trioxide or water are $H_2S_2O_7$, H_2SO_4, $H_2SO_4 \cdot H_2O$ [presumably $(H_3O)^+(HSO_4)^-$], $H_2SO_4 \cdot 2H_2O$ [$(H_3O)_2^+(SO_4)^{--}$], and $H_2SO_4 \cdot 4H_2O$.

The Manufacture of Sulfuric Acid.   Sulfuric acid is made by two processes, the *contact process* and the *lead-chamber process*, which are now about equally important.

In the **contact process** sulfur trioxide is made by the catalytic oxidation of sulfur dioxide (the name of the process refers to the fact that reaction occurs on contact of the gases with the solid catalyst). The catalyst formerly used was finely divided platinum; it has now been largely replaced by vanadium pentoxide, V_2O_5. The gas containing sulfur trioxide is then bubbled through sulfuric acid, which absorbs the sulfur trioxide. Water is added at the proper rate, and 98% acid is drawn off.

In the **lead-chamber process** oxygen, sulfur dioxide, nitric oxide, and a small amount of water vapor are introduced into a large lead-lined chamber (Figure 13-4). White crystals of nitrosulfuric acid, $NOHSO_4$ (sulfuric acid in which one hydrogen ion is replaced by the nitronium ion, $:N\equiv O:^+$), are formed. When steam is then introduced, the crystals react to form drops of sulfuric acid, liberating oxides of nitrogen. In effect, the oxides of nitrogen serve to catalyze the oxidation of sulfur dioxide by oxygen. The complex reactions that occur may be summarized as

$$2SO_2 + NO + NO_2 + O_2 + H_2O \longrightarrow 2NOHSO_4$$
$$2NOHSO_4 + H_2O \longrightarrow 2H_2SO_4 + NO + NO_2$$

The oxides of nitrogen, NO and NO_2, that take part in the first reaction are released by the second reaction, and can serve over and over again.

The acid produced, called *chamber acid*, is 65% to 70% H_2SO_4. It may be concentrated to 78% H_2SO_4 by the evaporation of water by the hot gases from the sulfur burner or pyrite burner. This process occurs as the acid trickles down over acid-resistant tile in a lead-lined tower. A similar tower is used to remove the nitrogen oxides from the exhaust gases; the oxides of nitrogen are then reintroduced into the chamber.

The Chemical Properties and Uses of Sulfuric Acid.   The uses of sulfuric acid are determined by its chemical properties—as an **acid**, a **dehydrating agent,** and an **oxidizing agent.**

Sulfuric acid has a high boiling point, 330°C, which permits it to be used

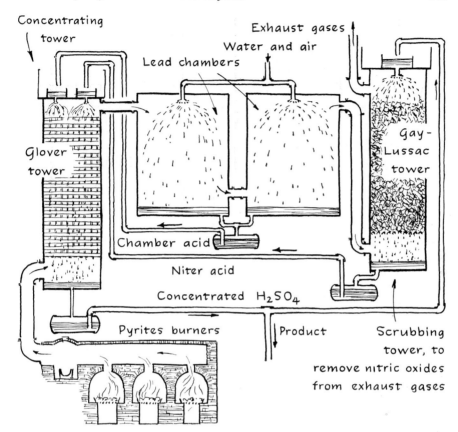

Concentrating tower

Exhaust gases

Water and air

Lead chambers

Glover tower

Gay-Lussac tower

Chamber acid

Niter acid

Concentrated H_2SO_4

Pyrites burners

Product

Scrubbing tower, to remove nitric oxides from exhaust gases

Figure 13-4

The lead-chamber process for making sulfuric acid.

with salts of more volatile acids in the preparation of these acids. Nitric acid, for example, can be made by heating a nitrate, such as sodium nitrate, with sulfuric acid:

$$NaNO_3 + H_2SO_4 \longrightarrow NaHSO_4 + HNO_3$$

The nitric acid distills off at 86°C. Sulfuric acid is also used for the manufacture of soluble phosphate fertilizers (Chapter 15), of ammonium sulfate for use as a fertilizer, of other sulfates, and in the manufacture of many chemicals and drugs. Steel is usually cleaned of iron rust (is "pickled") by immersion in a bath of sulfuric acid before it is coated with zinc, tin, or enamel. The use of sulfuric acid as the electrolyte in ordinary storage cells has been mentioned (Chapter 11).

Sulfuric acid has such a strong affinity for water as to make it an effective dehydrating agent. Gases that do not react with the substance may be dried by being bubbled through sulfuric acid. The dehydrating power of the concentrated acid is great enough to cause it to remove hydrogen and oxygen as water from organic compounds, such as sugar:

$$C_{12}H_{22}O_{11} \xrightarrow[H_2SO_4]{} 12C + 11H_2O$$

Sugar (sucrose)

(The symbol $\xrightarrow[H_2SO_4]{}$ is used to show that H_2SO_4 assists in causing the reaction to go to the right.) Many explosives, such as glyceryl trinitrate (nitroglycerine), are made by reaction of organic substances with nitric acid, producing the explosive substance and water:

$$C_3H_5(OH)_3 + 3HNO_3 \xrightarrow[H_2SO_4]{} C_3H_5(NO_3)_3 + 3H_2O$$

Glycerine · Glyceryl trinitrate

These reversible reactions are made to proceed to the right by mixing the nitric acid with sulfuric acid, which by its dehydrating action favors the products.

Hot concentrated sulfuric acid is an effective oxidizing agent, the product of its reduction being sulfur dioxide. It will dissolve copper, and will even oxidize carbon:

$$Cu + 2H_2SO_4 \longrightarrow CuSO_4 + 2H_2O + SO_2$$
$$C + 2H_2SO_4 \longrightarrow CO_2 + 2H_2O + 2SO_2$$

The solution of copper by hot concentrated sulfuric acid illustrates a general reaction—*the solution of an unreactive metal in an acid under the influence of an oxidizing agent.* The reactive metals, above hydrogen in the electromotive-force series, are oxidized to their cations by hydrogen ion, which is itself reduced to elementary hydrogen; for example,

$$Zn + 2H^+ \longrightarrow Zn^{++} + H_2$$

Copper is below hydrogen in the series, and does not undergo this reaction. It can be oxidized to cupric ion, however, by a stronger oxidizing agent, such as chlorine or nitric acid or, as illustrated above, hot concentrated sulfuric acid.

Sulfates.   Sulfuric acid combines with bases to form **normal sulfates,** such as K_2SO_4, potassium sulfate, and **hydrogen sulfates** or **acid sulfates,** such as $KHSO_4$, potassium hydrogen sulfate.

The less soluble sulfates occur as minerals: these include $CaSO_4 \cdot 2H_2O$ (gypsum), $SrSO_4$, $BaSO_4$ (barite), and $PbSO_4$. Barium sulfate is the least soluble of the sulfates, and its formation as a white precipitate is used as a test for sulfate ion.

Common soluble sulfates include $Na_2SO_4 \cdot 10H_2O$, $(NH_4)_2SO_4$, $MgSO_4 \cdot 7H_2O$ (Epsom salt), $CuSO_4 \cdot 5H_2O$ (blue vitriol), $FeSO_4 \cdot 7H_2O$, $(NH_4)_2Fe(SO_4)_2 \cdot 6H_2O$ (a well-crystallized, easily purified salt used in analytical chemistry in making standard solutions of ferrous ion), $ZnSO_4 \cdot 7H_2O$, $KAl(SO_4)_2 \cdot 12H_2O$ (alum), $NH_4Al(SO_4)_2 \cdot 12H_2O$ (ammonium alum), and $KCr(SO_4)_2 \cdot 12H_2O$ (chrome alum).

The Peroxysulfuric Acids. Sulfuric acid contains sulfur in its highest oxidation state. When a strong oxidizing agent (hydrogen peroxide or an anode at suitable electric potential) acts on sulfuric acid, the only oxidation which can occur is that of oxygen atoms, from -2 to -1. The products of this oxidation, **peroxysulfuric acid**, H_2SO_5, and **peroxydisulfuric acid**, $H_2S_2O_8$, have been mentioned in Chapter 11. These acids and their salts are used as bleaching agents.

13-7. The Thio or Sulfo Acids

Sodium thiosulfate, $Na_2S_2O_3 \cdot 5H_2O$ (incorrectly called "hypo," from an old name, sodium hyposulfite), is a substance used in photography (Chapter 25). It is made by boiling a solution of sodium sulfite with free sulfur:

$$SO_3^{--} + S \longrightarrow S_2O_3^{--}$$

Sulfite ion   Thiosulfate ion

Thiosulfuric acid, $H_2S_2O_3$, is unstable, and sulfur dioxide and sulfur are formed when a thiosulfate is treated with acid.

The structure of the thiosulfate ion, $S_2O_3^{--}$, is interesting in that the two sulfur atoms are not equivalent. This ion is a sulfate ion, SO_4^{--}, in which one of the oxygen atoms has been replaced by a sulfur atom. The central sulfur atom may be assigned oxidation number $+6$, and the attached sulfur atom oxidation number -2.

Thiosulfate ion is easily oxidized, especially by iodine, to **tetrathionate ion,** $S_4O_6^{--}$:

$$2S_2O_3^{--} \longrightarrow S_4O_6^{--} + 2e^-$$

or

$$2S_2O_3^{--} + I_2 \longrightarrow S_4O_6 + 2I^-$$

This reaction, between thiosulfate ion and iodine, is very useful in the quantitative analysis of oxidizing and reducing agents. The structure of tetrathionate ion is shown in Figure 13-5; it contains a disulfide group $-\overset{..}{\underset{..}{S}}-\overset{..}{\underset{..}{S}}-$ in place of the peroxide group of the peroxydisulfate ion. The oxidation of thiosulfate ion to tetrathionate ion is analogous to the oxidation of sulfide ion to disulfide ion:

$$2S^{--} \longrightarrow S_2^{--} + 2e^-$$

Thiosulfuric acid is representative of a general class of acids, called **thio acids** or **sulfo acids,** in which one or more oxygen atoms of an oxygen acid are replaced by sulfur atoms. For example, diarsenic pentasulfide dissolves in a sodium sulfide solution to form the thioarsenate ion, AsS_4^{---}, completely analogous to the arsenate ion, AsO_4^{---}:

$$As_2S_5 + 3S^{--} \longrightarrow 2AsS_4^{---}$$

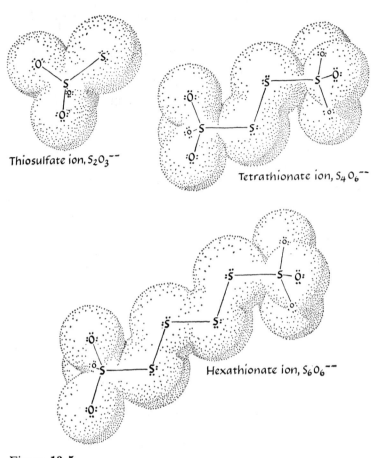

Figure 13-5

The thiosulfate ion and related ions.

Diarsenic trisulfide also dissolves, to form the thioarsenite ion:

$$As_2S_3 + 3S^{--} \longrightarrow 2AsS_3^{---}$$

If disulfide ion, S_2^{--}, is present in the solution, the thioarsenite ion is oxidized to thioarsenate ion:

$$AsS_3^{---} + S_2^{--} \longrightarrow AsS_4^{---} + S^{--}$$

An alkaline solution of sodium sulfide and sodium disulfide (or of the ammonium sulfides) is used in the usual systems of qualitative analysis as a means of separating the precipitated sulfides of certain metals and metalloids. This separation depends upon the ability of certain sulfides (HgS, As_2S_3, As_2S_5, Sb_2S_3, Sb_2S_5, SnS, SnS_2) to form thio anions (HgS$_2^{--}$, AsS$_4^{---}$, SbS$_4^{---}$, SnS$_4^{----}$), whereas others (Ag$_2$S, PbS, Bi$_2$S$_3$, CuS, CdS) remain undissolved.

13-8. Selenium and Tellurium

The elementary substances selenium and tellurium differ from sulfur in their physical properties in ways expected from their relative positions in the periodic table. Their melting points, boiling points, and densities are higher, as shown in Table 13-3.

The increase in metallic character with increase in atomic number is striking. Sulfur is a nonconductor of electricity, as is the red allotropic form of selenium. The gray form of selenium has a small but measurable electronic conductivity, and tellurium is a semiconductor, with conductivity a fraction of one percent of that of metals. An interesting property of the gray form of selenium is that its electric conductivity is greatly increased during exposure to visible light. This property is used in "selenium cells" for the measurement of light intensity.

Selenium is also used to impart a ruby-red color to glass, and to neutralize the green color in glass that is due to the presence of iron.

Selenium and tellurium are similar to sulfur in chemical properties, but are less electronegative (more metallic) in character. In addition, sexipositive

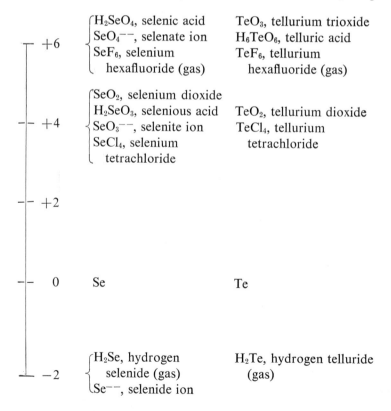

+6
H_2SeO_4, selenic acid
SeO_4^{--}, selenate ion
SeF_6, selenium
  hexafluoride (gas)

TeO_3, tellurium trioxide
H_6TeO_6, telluric acid
TeF_6, tellurium
  hexafluoride (gas)

+4
SeO_2, selenium dioxide
H_2SeO_3, selenious acid
SeO_3^{--}, selenite ion
$SeCl_4$, selenium
  tetrachloride

TeO_2, tellurium dioxide
$TeCl_4$, tellurium
  tetrachloride

+2

0   Se   Te

−2
H_2Se, hydrogen
  selenide (gas)
Se^{--}, selenide ion

H_2Te, hydrogen telluride
  (gas)

tellurium shows increase in ligancy from 4 to 6, telluric acid being H_6TeO_6. Representative compounds are shown in the chart on the preceding page.

EXERCISES

13-4. Write an oxidation-reduction equation for the formation of an acid of each of the important oxidation states of sulfur.

13-5. Describe the Frasch process of mining sulfur.

13-6. What is the electronic structure of H_2S_4? Give estimates of values of bond lengths and bond angles.

13-7. Write chemical equations for the preparation of each of the substances H_2S, SO_2, and SO_3 by
(a) a chemical reaction in which there is an oxidation or reduction of the sulfur atom;
(b) a chemical reaction in which there is no change in the oxidation number of the sulfur.

13-8. What is the role of a catalyst in the oxidation of SO_2 to SO_3? What is usually used as catalyst in the contact process? In the lead-chamber process?

13-9. List some examples of the use of concentrated sulfuric acid for the preparation of more volatile acids. Why cannot this method be applied to the preparation of hydrogen iodide gas?

13-10. Write chemical reactions illustrating the three important kinds of uses of sulfuric acid.

13-11. What is the electronic structure of pyrosulfuric acid?

13-12. What are the electronic structures of peroxysulfuric acid and peroxydisulfuric acid?

13-13. Write electronic-structure equations for
(a) sulfite ion and sulfur to give thiosulfate ion,

(b) thiosulfate ion and iodine to give tetrathionate ion plus iodide ion.

13-14. What volume of sulfur dioxide at standard conditions would be produced by burning 1 ton of pyrite, FeS_2?

13-15. A sample of an alloy of aluminum and copper weighing 1.000 g was dissolved in acid, the solution was saturated with hydrogen sulfide and filtered, and the precipitate, consisting of cupric sulfide, CuS, was dried and weighed. It was found to weigh 95.5 mg. What was the percentage of copper in the alloy?

13-16. From enthalpy values given in Table 13-2, evaluate the heat of the reaction $8S(g) \longrightarrow S_8(g)$. To what value of the S—S bond energy does this correspond?

13-17. The standard enthalpy of $H_2S_2(g)$ is 1 kcal/mole. Evaluate the heat of formation of H_2S_2 from atoms. Assuming the H—S bond energy to be the same as in H_2S, obtain a value for the S—S bond energy and compare with the value for the S_8 molecule.

13-18. From consideration of the bonds involved, estimate the heat of the reaction $H_2S(g) + \frac{1}{8}S_8(g) \longrightarrow H_2S_2(g)$. Compare with the experimental value given by the standard enthalpies in Table 13-2 and the preceding Exercise.

13-19. (a) Carbon disulfide, which has boiling point 46.3°C, is made by passing sulfur vapor over red-hot carbon. The carbon burns in the sulfur vapor, forming carbon disulfide. Write the equation for this reaction.
(b) The standard enthalpy of formation of $CS_2(g)$ is 27.55 kcal/mole. Using other values from Table 13-2, calculate the heat of the reaction

S₂(g) + C(graphite) ⟶ CS₂(g)

Is the reaction exothermic or endothermic? (Answer: 2.3 kcal/mole.)

13-20. In the presence of iodine as catalyst, carbon disulfide reacts with chlorine to form carbon tetrachloride and disulfur dichloride, S_2Cl_2. Write the equation for this reaction.

13-21. By microwave spectroscopy it has been found that in the sulfur dioxide molecule the bonds have length 1.432 Å, the bond angle has the value 119.5°, and the electric dipole moment is 1.59 D. What electric charges on the atoms (assumed to be at the nuclear positions) would account for the dipole moment? (Answer: +0.46 on S, −0.23 on each O.)

13-22. In the discussion of sulfur dioxide, Section 13-4, it is mentioned that the bond length 1.49 Å is expected for the S=O bond from Section 9-15. How is this value obtained?

13-23. Assuming that a double bond is two bent single bonds with the same properties as straight single bonds and that each of the two oxygen atoms is attached to the sulfur atom by a double bond, calculate from the electronegativity values for sulfur and oxygen (Section 9-11) the ionic character of each of the four bent single bonds in the sulfur dioxide molecule, and the corresponding value of the electric charge on the sulfur atom and on each oxygen atom. (Answer: 22%, +0.88, −0.44.)

13-24. The American chemists G. N. Lewis and Irving Langmuir assumed that the sulfur atom in its compounds would have the electronic structure of argon. What two resonance structures for SO_2 correspond to this postulate? To what electric charges on sulfur and oxygen do they correspond? (Answer: +1.66, −0.83.)

13-25. The observed sulfur-oxygen bond length in sulfur dioxide suggests that the bonds have some triple-bond character (Exercises 13-21, 13-22). To what bond length and what electric charge on the

sulfur atom would the pair of resonance structures

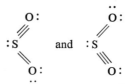

correspond? (Answer: 1.36 Å, −0.10 on sulfur.)

13-26. Using the results of Exercises 13-23 and 13-25, calculate the relative contributions of the structure

and the two structures of Exercise 13-25 that lead to the observed electric dipole moment of sulfur dioxide (charge +0.46 on S; Exercise 13-21). (Answer: 57% for the structure with two double bonds.)

13-27. Discuss the values of the enthalpy of formation of the dioxides, hexafluorides, and oxygen acids of sulfur, selenium, and tellurium in relation to position in the periodic table (see discussion of the stability of the higher oxidation states of bromine in Section 12-8).

13-28. The standard enthalpy of formation of liquid dimethylsulfone, $(CH_3)_2S=O$, is −46.9 kcal/mole, and its heat of vaporization is 12.6 kcal/mole. What is the heat of formation of $(CH_3)_2SO(g)$ from atoms? Subtract the sum of the bond energies of the single bonds in the molecule to obtain a value of the S=O bond energy. (Answer: 802.5, 85.7 kcal/mole.)

13-29. The minerals pyrite and marcasite are rather similar in structure. Each has composition FeS_2, with the sulfur atoms in pairs connected by a covalent bond. Their standard enthalpies of formation are −42.52 and −36.88 kcal/mole, respectively. One reacts more vigorously with acids and oxygen than the other. Which would you expect to be the more reactive? (Answer: Marcasite.)

13-30. Use values of enthalpy of formation to discuss the stability of compounds of selenium with oxidation number +6 relative to sulfur and tellurium (see Section 12-8).

CHAPTER 14

Nitrogen

Nitrogen is the lightest element of group V of the periodic table; the others are phosphorus, arsenic, antimony, and bismuth (Chapter 15). The chemistry of nitrogen is very interesting and important. Nitrogen is an essential element in most of the substances that make up living matter, including the proteins. Its important compounds include explosives, fertilizers, and other industrial materials.

Elementary nitrogen occurs in nature in the atmosphere, of which it constitutes 78% by volume. It is a colorless, odorless, and tasteless gas, composed of diatomic molecules, N_2. At 0°C and 1 atm pressure a liter of nitrogen weighs 1.2506 g. The gas condenses to a colorless liquid at −195.8°C, and to a white solid at −209.86°C. Nitrogen is slightly soluble in water, 1 liter of which dissolves 23.5 ml of the gas at 0°C and 1 atm.

Nitrogen is chemically unreactive; it does not burn, and at ordinary temperature does not react with other elements. At high temperatures it combines with lithium, magnesium, calcium, and boron, to form *nitrides*, with the formulas Li_3N, Mg_3N_2, Ca_3N_2, and BN, respectively. In a mixture with oxygen through which electric sparks are passed it reacts slowly to form *nitric oxide*, NO.

Nitrogen is made commercially by the fractional distillation of liquid air. In the laboratory it is conveniently made, in slightly impure form, by removing oxygen from air. It may also be made by the oxidation of ammonia by hot copper oxide:

$$2NH_3 + 3CuO \longrightarrow 3H_2O + 3Cu + N_2$$

A convenient method is by the reaction of ammonium ion and nitrite ion:

$$NH_4^+ + NO_2^- \longrightarrow 2H_2O + N_2$$

Ammonium nitrite is an unstable substance, which cannot be kept ready for use. Accordingly, in preparing nitrogen in this way sodium nitrite and ammonium chloride may be mixed in solution; decomposition occurs rapidly in the presence of a small amount of acid.

Table **14-1**

Standard Enthalpy of Formation of Some Nitrogen Compounds at 25°C (in kcal/mole)

$N_2(g)$	0.00	$NH(g)$	79.2	$NO_2^-(aq)$	−25.4
$N(g)$	113.07	$NH_3(g)$	−11.04	$NO_3^-(aq)$	−49.37
$N^+(g)$	449.98	$NH_3(aq)$	−19.32	$NH_2OH(c)$	−25.5
$NO(g)$	21.60	$NH_4^+(g)$	150	$NH_4OH(aq)$	−87.64
$NO_2(g)$	8.09	$NH_4^+(aq)$	−31.74	$H_2N_2O_2(aq)$	−13.7
$NO_3(g)$	13	$N_2H_4(l)$	12.05	$NH_4NO_3(c)$	−87.27
$N_2O(g)$	19.49	$HN_3(g)$	70.3	$NF_3(g)$	−27.2
$N_2O_3(g)$	20.18	$N_3^-(aq)$	58.6	NCl_3 (in CCl_4)	54.7
$N_2O_4(g)$	10.55	$HNO_2(aq)$	−28.4	$NH_4F(c)$	−111.6
$N_2O_5(c)$	−10.0	$HNO_3(l)$	−41.40	$NH_4Cl(c)$	−75.38

The electronic structure of the normal nitrogen atom is represented by the symbol $1s^2 2s^2 2p^3 \, {}^4S$. It involves three unpaired electrons occupying p orbitals. In molecules such as NH_3 in which the nitrogen atom forms three covalent bonds it uses the three $2p$ orbitals (with a small amount of s character; Section 9-6) as bond orbitals. In other molecules (NH_4^+, HNO_3) the nitrogen atom is quadricovalent; it then uses as bond orbitals a set of four tetrahedral bond orbitals formed by hybridization of the $2s$ orbital and the three $2p$ orbitals.

Standard enthalpy values for some nitrogen compounds are given in Table 14-1.

14-1. The Oxidation States of Nitrogen

Compounds of nitrogen are known representing all oxidation levels from −3 to +5. Some of these compounds are shown in the following chart:

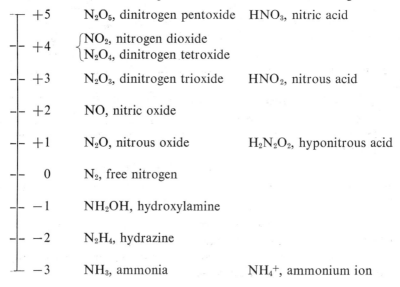

+5 N_2O_5, dinitrogen pentoxide HNO_3, nitric acid

+4 $\begin{cases} NO_2, \text{ nitrogen dioxide} \\ N_2O_4, \text{ dinitrogen tetroxide} \end{cases}$

+3 N_2O_3, dinitrogen trioxide HNO_2, nitrous acid

+2   NO, nitric oxide

+1 N_2O, nitrous oxide $H_2N_2O_2$, hyponitrous acid

0   N_2, free nitrogen

−1 NH_2OH, hydroxylamine

−2 N_2H_4, hydrazine

−3 NH_3, ammonia NH_4^+, ammonium ion

Free nitrogen is surprisingly stable, and this stability is responsible for the explosive properties of many nitrogen compounds. Usually a triple bond in a molecule causes the molecule to be less stable than molecules containing only single bonds; for example, acetylene, H—C≡C—H, is explosive, and sometimes undergoes violent detonation. The triple bond in the nitrogen molecule : N≡N :, however, seems to be especially stable. It has been estimated that the nitrogen molecule is 110 kcal/mole more stable than it would be if its bonds were normal, with the same energy as single bonds (as in a tetrahedral N_4 molecule, like the P_4 molecule described in Chapter 9).

An example of an unstable nitrogen compound is nitrogen trichloride

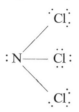

Whereas other nonmetallic chlorides (such as PCl_3, CCl_4, SCl_2, OCl_2) are stable, this substance explodes with great violence when jarred, with the evolution of a large amount of heat:

$$2NCl_3 \longrightarrow N_2 + 3Cl_2 + 110 \text{ kcal/mole}$$

The amount of heat liberated is in this case just equal to the extra stability of the nitrogen molecule.

14-2. Ammonia and Its Compounds

Ammonia, NH_3, is an easily condensable gas (b.p. $-33.4°C$; m.p. $-77.7°C$), readily soluble in water. The gas is colorless and has a pungent odor, often detected around stables and manure piles, where ammonia is produced by decomposition of organic matter. The solution of ammonia in water, called ammonium hydroxide solution (or sometimes *aqua ammonia*), contains the molecular species NH_3, NH_4OH (ammonium hydroxide), NH_4^+, and OH^-. Ammonium hydroxide is a weak base, and is only slightly ionized to ammonium ion, NH_4^+, and hydroxide ion (Figure 14-1):

$$NH_3 + H_2O \rightleftarrows NH_4OH \rightleftarrows NH_4^+ + OH^-$$

The ammonium ion has the configuration of a regular tetrahedron. The NH_4^+ ion can be described as having four electrons in four tetrahedral sp^3 orbitals (Chapter 9). In the ammonium hydroxide molecule the ammonium ion and the hydroxide ion are held together by a hydrogen bond.

The Preparation of Ammonia.   Ammonia is easily made in the laboratory by heating an ammonium salt, such as ammonium chloride, NH_4Cl, with a strong alkali, such as sodium hydroxide or calcium hydroxide:

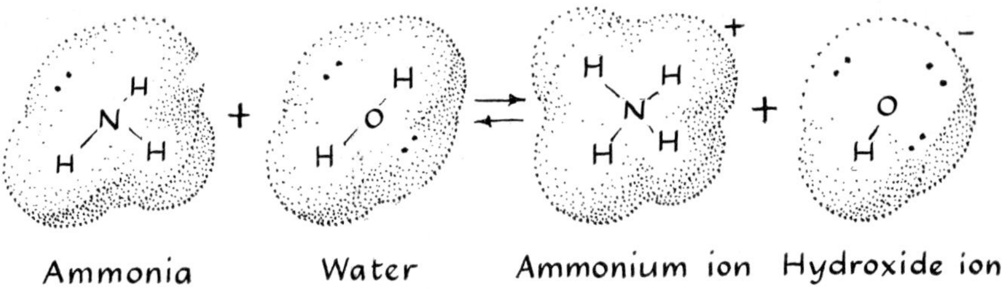

Ammonia Water Ammonium ion Hydroxide ion

Figure **14-1**

The reaction of ammonia and water to produce ammonium ion and hydroxide ion.

$$2NH_4Cl + Ca(OH)_2 \longrightarrow CaCl_2 + 2H_2O + 2NH_3$$

The gas may also be made by warming concentrated ammonium hydroxide.

The principal commercial method of production of ammonia is the *Haber process*, the direct combination of nitrogen and hydrogen under high pressure (several hundred atmospheres) in the presence of a catalyst (usually iron, containing molybdenum or other substances to increase the catalytic activity). The gases used must be specially purified, to prevent "poisoning" the catalyst. The reaction

$$N_2 + 3H_2 \longrightarrow 2NH_3$$

is exothermic, and the yield of ammonia at equilibrium is less at a high temperature than at a lower temperature. However, the gases react very slowly at low temperatures, and the reaction became practical as a commercial process only when a catalyst was found which speeded up the rate satisfactorily at 500°C. Even at this relatively low temperature the equilibrium is unfavorable if the gas mixture is under atmospheric pressure, less than 0.1% of the mixture being converted to ammonia. Increase in the total pressure favors the formation of ammonia; at 500 atmospheres pressure the equilibrium mixture is over one-third ammonia.

Smaller amounts of ammonia are obtained as a by-product in the manufacture of coke and illuminating gas by the distillation of coal, and are made by the cyanamide process. In the *cyanamide process* a mixture of lime and coke is heated in an electric furnace, forming **calcium acetylide** (*calcium carbide*), CaC_2:

$$CaO + 3C \longrightarrow CO + CaC_2$$

Nitrogen, obtained by fractionation of liquid air, is passed over the hot calcium acetylide, forming **calcium cyanamide**, $CaCN_2$:

$$CaC_2 + N_2 \longrightarrow CaCN_2 + C$$

Calcium cyanamide may be used directly as a fertilizer, or may be converted into ammonia by treatment with steam under pressure:

$$CaCN_2 + 3H_2O \longrightarrow CaCO_3 + 2NH_3$$

Ammonium Salts. The ammonium salts are similar to the potassium salts and rubidium salts in crystal form, molar volume, color, and other properties. This similarity is due to the close approximation in size of the ammonium ion (radius 1.48 Å) to these alkali ions (radius of K^+, 1.33 Å, and of Rb^+, 1.48 Å). The ammonium salts are all soluble in water, and are completely ionized in aqueous solution.

Ammonium chloride, NH_4Cl, is a white salt, with a bitter salty taste. It is used in dry batteries (Chapter 11) and as a flux in soldering and welding. Ammonium sulfate, $(NH_4)_2SO_4$, is an important fertilizer; and ammonium nitrate, NH_4NO_3, mixed with other substances, is used as an explosive, and also is used as a fertilizer.

Liquid Ammonia as a Solvent. Liquid ammonia (b.p. $-33.4°C$) has a high dielectric constant, and is a good solvent for salts, forming ionic solutions. It also has the unusual power of dissolving the alkali metals and alkaline-earth metals without chemical reaction, to form blue solutions which have an extraordinarily high electric conductivity and a metallic luster. These metallic solutions slowly decompose, with evolution of hydrogen, forming **amides,** such as sodium amide, $NaNH_2$:

$$2Na + 2NH_3 \longrightarrow 2Na^+ + 2NH_2^- + H_2$$

The amides are ionized in the solution into sodium ion and the amide ion,

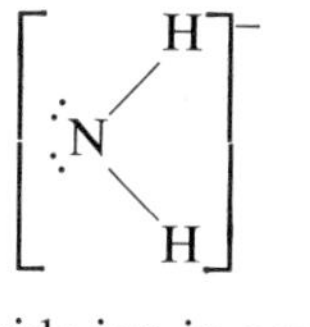

which is analogous to the hydroxide ion in aqueous systems. The ammonium ion in liquid ammonia is analogous to the hydronium ion in aqueous systems.

Ammonium Amalgam. The similarity of the ammonium ion to an alkali ion suggests that it might be possible to reduce ammonium ion to ammonium metal, NH_4. This has not been accomplished; however, a solution of ammonium metal in mercury, *ammonium amalgam*, can be made by cathodic reduction of ammonium ion.

Hydrazine, N_2H_4, has the structure

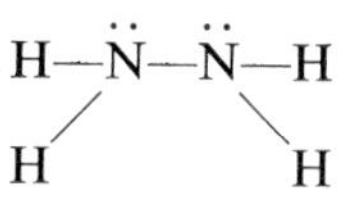

in which nitrogen has oxidation number -2. It can be made by oxidizing ammonia with sodium hypochlorite. Hydrazine is a liquid with weak basic properties, similar to those of ammonia. It has found some use as a rocket fuel. It forms salts such as $(N_2H_5)^+Cl^-$ and $(N_2H_6)^{++}Cl_2^-$.

Hydroxylamine, NH_2OH, has the structure

$$H—\overset{\cdot\cdot}{N}—\overset{\cdot\cdot}{O}:$$
$$\underset{H}{\diagup} \qquad \underset{H}{\diagdown}$$

with uninegative nitrogen. It can be made by reducing nitric oxide or nitric acid under suitable conditions. It is a weak base, forming salts such as hydroxylammonium chloride, $(NH_3OH)^+Cl^-$ (also called hydroxylamine hydrochloride).

14-3.   The Oxides of Nitrogen

Nitrous oxide, N_2O, is made by heating ammonium nitrate:

$$NH_4NO_3 \longrightarrow 2H_2O + N_2O$$

It is a colorless, odorless gas, which has the power of supporting combustion, by giving up its atom of oxygen, leaving molecular nitrogen. When breathed for a short time the gas causes hysteria; this effect, discovered in 1799 by Humphry Davy, led to the use of the name *laughing gas* for the substance. Longer inhalation causes unconsciousness, and the gas, mixed with air or oxygen, is used as a general anesthetic for minor operations. The gas also finds use in making whipped cream; under pressure it dissolves in the cream, and when the pressure is released it fills the cream with many small bubbles, simulating ordinary whipped cream.

The electronic structure of nitrous oxide is

$$\left\{ :\overset{\cdot\cdot}{N}\!\!=\!\!N\!\!=\!\!\overset{\cdot\cdot}{O}: \qquad :N\!\!\equiv\!\!N\!\!-\!\!\overset{\cdot\cdot}{\underset{\cdot\cdot}{O}}: \right\}$$

The position of the oxygen atom at the end of the linear molecule explains the ease with which nitrous oxide acts as an oxidizing agent.

Nitric oxide, NO, can be made by reduction of dilute nitric acid with copper or mercury:

$$3Cu + 8H^+ + 2NO_3^- \longrightarrow 3Cu^{++} + 4H_2O + 2NO$$

When made in this way the gas usually contains impurities such as nitrogen and nitrogen dioxide. If the gas is collected over water, in which it is only slightly soluble, the nitrogen dioxide is removed by solution in the water.

A metal or other reducing agent may reduce nitric acid to any lower stage of oxidation, producing nitrogen dioxide, nitrous acid, nitric oxide, nitrous oxide, nitrogen, hydroxylamine, hydrazine, or ammonia (ammonium ion), depending upon the conditions of the reduction. Conditions may be found that strongly favor one product, but usually appreciable amounts of other products are also formed. Nitric oxide is produced preferentially under the conditions mentioned above.

Nitric oxide is a colorless, difficultly condensable gas (b.p. −151.7°C, m.p. −163.6°C). It combines readily with oxygen to form the red gas nitrogen dioxide, NO_2.

Dinitrogen trioxide, N_2O_3, can be obtained as a blue liquid by cooling an equimolal mixture of nitric oxide and nitrogen dioxide. It is the anhydride of nitrous acid, and produces this acid on solution in water:

$$N_2O_3 + H_2O \longrightarrow 2HNO_2$$

Nitrogen dioxide, NO_2, a red gas, and its dimer **dinitrogen tetroxide,** N_2O_4, a colorless, easily condensable gas, exist in equilibrium with one another:

$$\underset{\text{Red}}{2NO_2} \rightleftarrows \underset{\text{Colorless}}{N_2O_4}$$

The mixture of these gases may be made by adding nitric oxide to oxygen, or by reducing concentrated nitric acid with copper:

$$Cu + 4H^+ + 2NO_3^- \longrightarrow Cu^{++} + 2H_2O + 2NO_2$$

It is also easily obtained by decomposing lead nitrate by heat:

$$2Pb(NO_3)_2 \longrightarrow 2PbO + 4NO_2 + O_2$$

The gas dissolves readily in water or alkali, forming a mixture of nitrate ion and nitrite ion.

Dinitrogen pentoxide, N_2O_5, the anhydride of nitric acid, can be made, as white crystals, by carefully dehydrating nitric acid with diphosphorus pentoxide or by oxidizing nitrogen dioxide with ozone. It is unstable, decomposing spontaneously at room temperature into nitrogen dioxide and oxygen.

The electronic structures of the oxides of nitrogen are shown below and at the top of the next page. Most of these molecules are resonance hybrids, and the contributing structures are not all shown; for dinitrogen pentoxide, for example, the various single and double bonds may change places.

Oxidation number +5

Dinitrogen pentoxide

Oxidation number +4

Nitrogen dioxide

Dinitrogen tetroxide

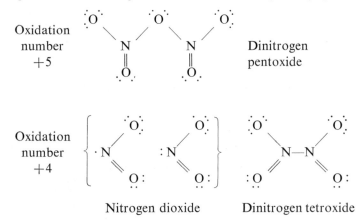

+3　　　　　　　　　　　　　　　　　　　　　　　Dinitrogen trioxide

+2　　　$\left\{ :\ddot{N}{=}\ddot{O}: \quad :\ddot{N}{=}\dot{O}: \right\}$　　Nitric oxide

+1　　　$\left\{ :\ddot{N}{=}N{=}\ddot{O}: \quad :N{\equiv}N{-}\ddot{O}: \right\}$　　Nitrous oxide

We may well ask why it is that two of the most stable of these substances, NO and NO_2, are odd molecules, representing oxidation levels for nitrogen not occurring in other compounds, and also why N_2O_3 and N_2O_5, the anhydrides of the important substances HNO_2 and HNO_3, are so unstable that they decompose at room temperature. The answer to these questions probably is that the resonance of the odd electron between the two or three atoms of the molecule stabilizes the substances NO and NO_2 enough to make them somewhat more stable than the two anhydrides.

14-4.　Nitric Acid and the Nitrates

Nitric acid, HNO_3, is a colorless liquid with melting point $-42°C$, boiling point $86°C$, and density 1.52 g/cm^3. It is a strong acid, completely ionized to hydrogen ion and nitrate ion (NO_3^-) in aqueous solution; and it is a strong oxidizing agent. It attacks the skin, and gives it a yellow color.

Nitric acid can be made in the laboratory by heating sodium nitrate with sulfuric acid in an all-glass apparatus:

$$NaNO_3 + H_2SO_4 \longrightarrow NaHSO_4 + HNO_3$$

The substance is also made commercially in this way, from natural sodium nitrate (Chile saltpeter).

Much nitric acid is made by the oxidation of ammonia. This oxidation occurs in several steps. Ammonia mixed with air burns on the surface of a platinum catalyst to form nitric oxide:

$$4NH_3 + 5O_2 \longrightarrow 4NO + 6H_2O$$

On cooling, the nitric oxide is further oxidized to nitrogen dioxide:

$$2NO + O_2 \longrightarrow 2NO_2$$

The gas is passed through a tower packed with pieces of broken quartz through which water is percolating. Nitric acid and nitrous acid are formed:

$$2NO_2 + H_2O \longrightarrow HNO_3 + HNO_2$$

As the strength of the acid solution increases, the nitrous acid decomposes:

$$3HNO_2 \rightleftarrows HNO_3 + 2NO + H_2O$$

The nitric oxide is reoxidized by the excess oxygen present and again enters the reaction.

A method (the arc process) formerly used for fixation of atmospheric nitrogen is the direct combination of nitrogen and oxygen to nitric oxide at the high temperature of the electric arc. The reaction

$$N_2 + O_2 \longrightarrow 2NO$$

is slightly endothermic, and the equilibrium yield of nitric oxide increases with increasing temperature, from 0.4% at 1500°C to 5% at 3000°C. The reaction was carried out by passing air through an electric arc in such a way that the hot gas mixture was cooled very rapidly, thus "freezing" the high-temperature equilibrium mixture. The nitric oxide was then converted into nitric acid in the way described above.

Sodium nitrate, $NaNO_3$, forms colorless crystals closely resembling crystals of calcite, $CaCO_3$ (Figure 10-4). This resemblance is not accidental. The crystals have the same structure, with Na^+ replacing Ca^{++} and NO_3^- replacing CO_3^{--}. The crystals of sodium nitrate have the same property of birefringence (double refraction) as calcite. Sodium nitrate is used as a fertilizer and for conversion into nitric acid and other nitrates. **Potassium nitrate,** KNO_3 (*saltpeter*), is used in pickling meat (ham, corned beef), in medicine, and in the manufacture of *gunpowder*, which is an intimate mixture of potassium nitrate, charcoal, and sulfur, which explodes when ignited in a closed space.

The nitrate ion has a planar structure, with each bond a hybrid of a single bond and a double bond:

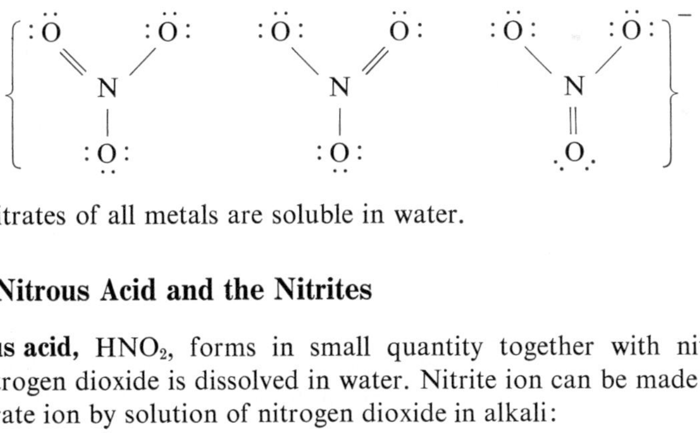

The nitrates of all metals are soluble in water.

14-5. Nitrous Acid and the Nitrites

Nitrous acid, HNO_2, forms in small quantity together with nitric acid when nitrogen dioxide is dissolved in water. Nitrite ion can be made together with nitrate ion by solution of nitrogen dioxide in alkali:

$$2NO_2 + 2OH^- \longrightarrow NO_2^- + NO_3^- + H_2O$$

Sodium nitrite, $NaNO_2$, and **potassium nitrite,** KNO_2, can be made also by decomposing the nitrates by heat:

$$2NaNO_3 \longrightarrow 2NaNO_2 + O_2$$

or by reduction with lead:

$$NaNO_3 + Pb \longrightarrow NaNO_2 + PbO$$

These nitrites are slightly yellow crystalline substances, and their solutions are yellow. They are used in the manufacture of dyes and in the chemical laboratory.

The nitrite ion is a reducing agent, being oxidized to nitrate ion by bromine, permanganate ion, chromate ion, and similar oxidizing agents. It is also itself an oxidizing agent, able to oxidize iodide ion to iodine. This property may be used, with the starch test (blue color) for iodine, to distinguish nitrite from nitrate ion, which does not oxidize iodide ion readily.

The electronic structure of the nitrite ion is

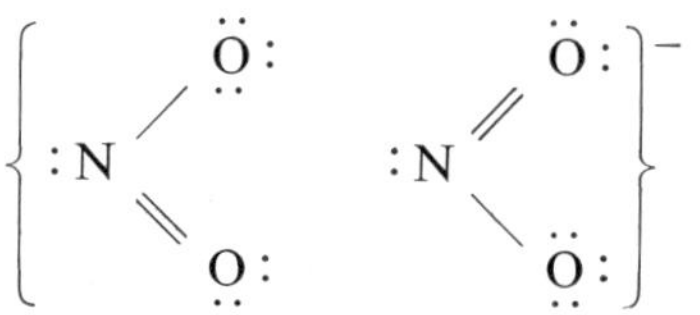

14-6.   Other Compounds of Nitrogen

Hyponitrous Acid and the Hyponitrites.   Hyponitrous acid, $H_2N_2O_2$, is formed in small quantity by reaction of nitrous acid and hydroxylamine:

$$H_2NOH + HNO_2 \longrightarrow H_2N_2O_2 + H_2O$$

It is a very weak acid, with structure

The acid decomposes to form nitrous oxide, N_2O; it is not itself formed in appreciable concentration by reaction of nitrous oxide and water. Its salts have no important uses.

Hydrogen Cyanide and Its Salts.   **Hydrogen cyanide,** HCN (structural formula H—C≡N :), is a gas which dissolves in water and acts as a very weak acid. It is made by treating a cyanide, such as **potassium cyanide,** KCN, with sulfuric acid, and is used as a fumigant and rat poison. It smells like bitter almonds and crushed fruit kernels, which in fact owe their odor to it. Hydrogen cyanide and its salts are very poisonous.

Cyanides are made by action of carbon and nitrogen on metallic oxides. For example, barium cyanide is made by heating a mixture of barium oxide and carbon to a red heat in a stream of nitrogen:

$$BaO + 3C + N_2 \longrightarrow Ba(CN)_2 + CO$$

The cyanide ion, [: C≡N :]⁻, is closely similar to a halogenide ion in its properties. By oxidation it can be converted into **cyanogen,** C_2N_2 ($: N\equiv C\!-\!C\equiv N :$), which is analogous to the halogen molecules F_2, Cl_2, etc.

The Cyanate Ion, Fulminate Ion, Azide Ion, and Thiocyanate Ion. By suitable procedures three anions can be made which are similar in structure to the carbon dioxide molecule $: \overset{..}{O}\!=\!C\!=\!\overset{..}{O} :$ and the nitrous oxide molecule $: \overset{..}{N}\!=\!N\!=\!\overset{..}{O} :$ (these structures are hybridized with other structures, such as $: O\!\equiv\!C\!-\!\overset{..}{O} :$ and its analogs). These anions are

$$\left[: \overset{..}{N}\!=\!C\!=\!\overset{..}{O} : \right]^{-} \quad \text{Cyanate ion}$$

$$\left[: \overset{..}{C}\!=\!N\!=\!\overset{..}{O} : \right]^{-} \quad \text{Fulminate ion}$$

$$\left[: \overset{..}{N}\!=\!N\!=\!\overset{..}{N} : \right]^{-} \quad \text{Azide ion}$$

A related ion is the thiocyanate ion, $\left[: \overset{..}{N}\!=\!C\!=\!\overset{..}{S} : \right]^{-}$, which forms a deep red complex with ferric ion, used as a test for iron. The azide ion also forms a deep red complex with ferric ion.

The fulminates and azides of the heavy metals are very sensitive explosives. **Mercuric fulminate,** $Hg(CNO)_2$, and **lead azide,** $Pb(N_3)_2$, are used as detonators.

14-7. The Nitrogen Cycle in Nature

Nitrogen is essential to plant and animal life. In particular, the proteins, which are important constituents of plant and animal tissues, contain about 16% nitrogen (Chapter 28).

Man obtains all of his nitrogen from the nitrogen compounds present in plant and animal food, and the combined nitrogen present in animal tissues came originally from plant food. When plant and animal tissues decay, the nitrogen is in large part returned to the atmosphere as free nitrogen. Some animal waste products containing nitrogen, such as urea, $(NH_2)_2CO$, and ammonia, are returned to the soil and utilized by plants, but there is a continual loss of nitrogen to the atmosphere as free nitrogen.

The steady state in the nitrogen cycle is achieved by the action of several different processes of converting the free nitrogen of the air into compounds that can be utilized by plants and animals. First, there are the *nitrogen-fixing bacteria*, which are associated with plants such as beans (including soy beans), peas, clover, and alfalfa. These bacteria, which exist on the root cells of these plants, have the power of converting free nitrogen from the atmosphere into nitrate ion, which is then assimilated by the plant and converted into protein. Bacteria are also involved in the process of conversion of organic matter into nitrate ion in the soil (the process of *nitrification*), and in the production of free nitrogen, which is returned to the atmosphere.

A significant amount of atmospheric nitrogen is also fixed into compounds which can be utilized by plants through the action of lightning, which causes the nitrogen and the oxygen of the air to combine. The nitrogen oxides are then carried down to the soil by falling rain, converted into nitrates, and utilized by the plants.

During recent years the natural fertilizers that provide combined nitrogen for the growth of plants have been supplemented by artificial fertilizers, made through the fixation of nitrogen by man. The processes by which atmospheric nitrogen is artificially converted into compounds have been described earlier in this chapter.

The nitrogen cycle in nature is summarized in the accompanying diagram.

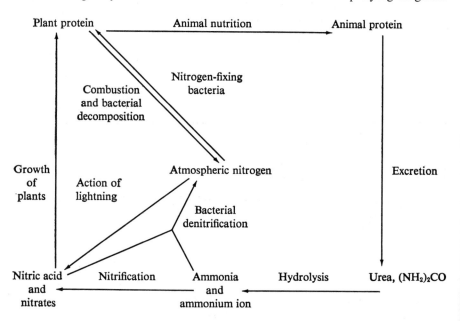

Several of the processes indicated in the diagram have been described in the preceding paragraphs. The hydrolysis of urea, a waste product of animals, occurs according to the reaction

$$(NH_2)_2CO + H_2O \longrightarrow 2NH_3 + CO_2$$

Ammonia is not easily utilized by plants. It is converted by the action of nitrifying bacteria into nitrite ion and nitrate ion. Bacterial denitrification, with loss of the utilizable nitrogen (nitrate) in the soil, sometimes occurs through conversion of nitrate ion to nitrite ion and its reaction with ammonium ion:

$$NH_4^+ + NO_2^- \longrightarrow 2H_2O + N_2$$

In order to avoid loss of nitrogen, the farmer must take care not to mix fertilizers containing nitrates and ammonium salts, and not to add nitrate fertilizer to a compost heap (which contains ammonia).

EXERCISES

14-1. What are the commercial methods of preparing (a) nitrogen, (b) ammonia, (c) nitric acid, and (d) calcium cyanamide?

14-2. Describe laboratory methods of preparing (a) ammonia, (b) nitrous oxide, (c) nitric oxide, (d) dinitrogen trioxide, (e) nitrogen dioxide, (f) nitric acid, (g) sodium nitrite, (h) hydrazine, (i) ammonium amalgam.

14-3. Write the electronic structure of the nitrate ion. Compare it with that of the carbonate ion.

14-4. Write a balanced chemical equation to represent the formation of potassium sulfate, carbon dioxide, and nitrogen from potassium nitrate, carbon, and sulfur.

14-5. What chemical reaction takes place between nitrous acid and bromine? Between nitrous acid and iodide ion?

14-6. What chemical reaction takes place between nitrogen dioxide and a solution of sodium hydroxide?

14-7. What is the electronic structure of hydrazine? Compare this molecule with hydrogen peroxide and hydroxylamine.

14-8. Balance the equation

$$N_2H_5{}^+ + Cr_2O_7{}^{--} \longrightarrow Cr^{+++} + N_2$$

14-9. What is the electronic structure of the azide ion?

14-10. How does the electronic structure of the cyanide ion compare with that of nitrogen?

14-11. What is the electronic structure of nitrous oxide?

14-12. What are possible electronic structures for dinitrogen tetroxide?

14-13. Why are ammonium salts similar in their properties to the corresponding salts of potassium and rubidium?

14-14. Write the equation for the formation of hydrazine from ammonia and sodium hypochlorite.

14-15. How much nitric acid would be produced from 20 tons of Chile saltpeter, assuming it to be pure sodium nitrate?

14-16. Under what conditions are amides, such as sodium amide, formed? To what ions in aqueous systems are the amide ion and the ammonium ion analogous?

14-17. Write the equation for the synthesis of dinitrogen pentoxide from nitrogen dioxide and ozone. Why is it necessary to be careful when synthesizing dinitrogen pentoxide in this way?

14-18. When aluminum is heated in an atmosphere of nitrogen, aluminum nitride, AlN, is formed. Aluminum nitride reacts with water to give ammonia and aluminum hydroxide. Write the equations for these reactions.

14-19. Hydrazoic acid, HN_3, is a dangerously explosive gas. Its standard enthalpy of formation (Table 14-1) is 70.3 kcal/mole. How much heat would be liberated if the products of explosion were molecular hydrogen and nitrogen?

14-20. How much heat would be produced by the explosion of hydrazoic acid if NH and N_2 were formed? If NH_3 and N_2 were formed?

14-21. The heats of sublimation of hydrogen peroxide and hydrazine are 15.5 and 12.5 kcal/mole, respectively.
(a) What do you estimate the heat of sublimation of hydroxylamine to be? (No experimental value has been reported.)
(b) From the standard enthalpy of formation of $NH_2OH(c)$ given in Table 14-1,

obtain that of $NH_2OH(g)$. (Answer: -11.5 kcal/mole.)

14-22. (a) Using the standard enthalpy of formation -11.5 kcal/mole for $NH_2OH(g)$ and the values for NH_3 and H_2O (Tables 6-1 and 14-1), compute the heat of the reaction $NH_2OH(g) + H_2(g) \longrightarrow NH_3(g) + H_2O(g)$.

(b) What bonds are broken and what are formed in the reaction? With use of the known bond-energy values (Table 10-3), evaluate the bond energy for N—O. (Answer: 42.5 kcal/mole.)

14-23. With use of the equation between bond energy and electronegativity, estimate a value for the N—O bond, and compare it with the value found in Exercise 14-22.

14-24. The heat of solution of hyponitrous acid in water can be estimated to be about 18 kcal/mole (compare 13.9 for H_2O_2, 3.8 for O_2). With this value, the standard enthalpy of formation of $H_2N_2O_2(aq)$ given in Table 14-1, and bond-energy values for the other bonds, evaluate the N=N bond energy. Compare with the values for N—N,

$N\equiv N$, C—C, C=C, and $C\equiv C$. (Answer: 138 kcal/mole.)

14-25. The engines in some large rockets are fueled with 1,1-dimethylhydrazine, $(CH_3)_2N$—NH_2, with liquid oxygen as oxidant. The products of combustion are $H_2O(g)$, $CO_2(g)$, and $N_2(g)$. Using bond-energy values, estimate a value of the heat of formation of the fuel and from this obtain the heat of combustion. On a weight basis (fuel plus oxidant), is this combination better than hydrogen and oxygen? (Ignore heats of vaporization.)

14-26. Nitrogen and chlorine have the same electronegativity, 3.0, so that one might expect the heat evolved on formation of ammonia to be three times that of hydrogen chloride. But it is just half as great (11.04 vs. 22.06 kcal/mole). Why?

14-27. Name two important ways in which atmospheric nitrogen is converted into nitrogen compounds in nature.

14-28. How do you account for the fact that although the atmosphere is mainly nitrogen, ocean salts contain almost no nitrogen compounds?

CHAPTER 15

Phosphorus, Arsenic, Antimony,

and Bismuth

The electronic structures of phosphorus, arsenic, antimony, and bismuth, as well as of nitrogen (Chapter 14), the elements of group V of the periodic table, are given in Table 15-1. Each element has three fewer electrons than

Table **15-1**

  Electronic Structures of Elements of Group V

Z	ELEMENT	K	L		M			N				O			P	
		1s	2s	2p	3s	3p	3d	4s	4p	4d	4f	5s	5p	5d	6s	6p
7	N	2	2	3												
15	P	2	2	6	2	3										
33	As	2	2	6	2	6	10	2	3							
51	Sb	2	2	6	2	6	10	2	6	10		2	3			
83	Bi	2	2	6	2	6	10	2	6	10	14	2	6	10	2	3

the following noble gas. The Russell-Saunders symbol for the atoms of these elements in the normal state is $^4S_{3/2}$. This corresponds to three unpaired electrons, occupying the three outer p orbitals, and hence to tervalence. In general, the compounds of these elements have electronic structures representing the formation of covalent bonds in sufficient number to complete the octet of electrons in the outermost shell of the group V atom.

The chemical properties of the heavier elements of group V differ significantly from those of nitrogen, the difference being smallest for phosphorus and greatest for bismuth. The differences can be attributed largely to the differences in electronegativity of the five elements: nitrogen (electronegativity 3.0) is the most electronegative, the others having electronegativities equal to or smaller than that of hydrogen (P 2.1, As 2.0, Sb 1.9, Bi 1.9). Standard enthalpy values are given in Table 15-2.

Table **15-2**

Standard Enthalpy of Formation of Some Compounds of Phosphorus, Arsenic, Antimony, and Bismuth at 25°C (kcal/mole)

	X = P	As	Sb	Bi
$X(c)^*$	0.00	0.00	0.00	0.00
$X(g)$	75.18	60.64	60.8	49.7
$X^+(g)$	329.81	304.24	261.52	219.1
$X_2(g)$	33.82	29.6	52	59.4
$X_4(g)$	13.12	35.7	48.8	
$XO(g)$	−9.7	4.79	45	16
$X_4O_6(c)$	−392	−313.94	−336.8	−275.8
$X_4O_{10}(c)$	−713.2	−437.2	−468.8	
$XH_3(g)$	2.21	41.0		
$HXO_3(c)$	−228.2			
$H_3XO_2(aq)$	−145.6			
$H_3XO_3(aq)$	−232.2	−177.3		
$H_3XO_4(aq)$	−308.1	−214.8	−215.7	
$XO_4^{---}(aq)$	−305.7	−208		
$X_2O_7^{----}(aq)$	−543.9			
$XCl_3(g)$	−66.2	−71.5	−75.2	−64.7
$XCl_5(g)$	−88.7		−93.9	
$XCl_3O(g)$	−141.5			
XBr_3	−35.9(g)	−46.61(c)	−62.1(c)	
$XBr_5(c)$	−66			
$XBr_3O(c)$	−114.6			
$XI_3(c)$	−10.9	−13.7	−23.0	
$XN(g)$	−20.2	7	74.4	

* The standard states are white phosphorus (cubic, P_4) and hexagonal arsenic, antimony, and bismuth.

15-1.   Properties of the Fifth-group Elements

The members of group V of the periodic table show the expected trend in properties with increasing atomic number (Table 15-3): nitrogen is a gas which can be condensed to a liquid only at very low temperatures; phosphorus (in the modification called *white phosphorus*) is a low-melting non-metal; and arsenic, antimony, and bismuth are metalloids with increasing metallic character.

The similarity of the elements is indicated by the formulas of their hydrides, NH_3 (ammonia), PH_3 (phosphine), AsH_3 (arsine), SbH_3, and BiH_3, and of

Table **15-3**

Properties of the Elements of Group V

	ATOMIC NUMBER	ATOMIC WEIGHT	MELTING POINT	BOILING POINT	DENSITY OF SOLID	COLOR	COVALENT RADIUS	VAN DER WAALS RADIUS
N	7	14.0067	$-209.8°C$	$-195.8°C$	1.026 g/cm^3	White	0.70 Å	1.5 Å
P	15	30.9738	44.1°	280°	1.81	White	1.10	1.9
As	33	74.9216	814°*	715°†	5.73	Gray	1.21	2.0
Sb	51	121.75	630°	1380°	6.68	Silvery white	1.41	2.2
Bi	83	208.980	271°	1470°	9.80	Reddish white	1.51	2.3

* At 36 atm.
† It sublimes.

their highest oxides, N_2O_5, P_2O_5, As_2O_5, Sb_2O_5, and Bi_2O_5. This similarity is far from complete, however; the principal acids formed by nitrogen, phosphorus, arsenic, and antimony have different formulas:

$$HNO_3 \quad \text{Nitric acid}$$
$$H_3PO_4 \quad \text{Phosphoric acid}$$
$$H_3AsO_4 \quad \text{Arsenic acid}$$
$$H_7SbO_6 \quad \text{Antimonic acid}$$

The most striking deviation from regularity in properties of these elements is the smaller stability and greater reactivity of the heavier elements than of elementary nitrogen. Whereas nitrogen can be made to combine directly with oxygen only at extremely high temperatures, as in the electric arc, and then only to a small extent, white phosphorus ignites spontaneously in air, and the heavier elements of the fifth group burn when they are heated in air.

15-2. The Oxidation States of Phosphorus

Phosphorus, like nitrogen and the other members of the fifth group, has oxidation states ranging from -3 to $+5$. The principal compounds of phosphorus are indicated in the chart on p. 420.

Phosphorus, although it is less electronegative than nitrogen, is a non-metallic element, its oxides being acid-forming and not amphoteric. The quinquepositive oxidation state of phosphorus is more stable than that of nitrogen; phosphoric acid and the phosphates are not effective oxidizing agents, whereas nitric acid is a strong oxidizing agent.

15-3. Elementary Phosphorus

Phosphorus occurs in nature mainly as the minerals *apatite*, $Ca_5(PO_4)_3F$, *hydroxy-apatite*, $Ca_5(PO_4)_3(OH)$, and tricalcium phosphate (*phosphate rock*, ranging in composition from $Ca_3(PO_4)_2$ to hydroxy-apatite). Hydroxy-apatite

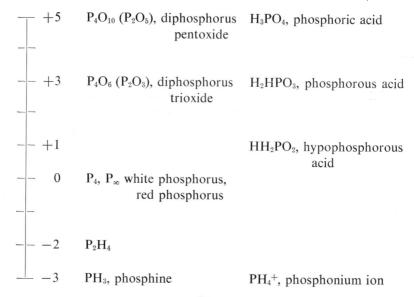

+5	P_4O_{10} (P_2O_5), diphosphorus pentoxide	H_3PO_4, phosphoric acid
+3	P_4O_6 (P_2O_3), diphosphorus trioxide	H_2HPO_3, phosphorous acid
+1		HH_2PO_2, hypophosphorous acid
0	P_4, P_∞ white phosphorus, red phosphorus	
-2	P_2H_4	
-3	PH_3, phosphine	PH_4^+, phosphonium ion

is the main mineral constituent of the bones and teeth of animals, and complex organic compounds of phosphorus are essential constituents of nerve and brain tissue and of many proteins, and are involved significantly in the metabolic reactions of living organisms.

Phosphorus was discovered in 1669 by a German alchemist, Dr. Hennig Brand, in the course of his search for the Philosopher's Stone. Brand heated the residue left on evaporation of urine, and collected the distilled phosphorus in a receiver. The name given the element (from Greek *phosphoros*, giving light) refers to its property of glowing in the dark.

Elementary phosphorus is now made by heating calcium phosphate with silica and carbon in an electric furnace (Figure 15-1). The silica forms calcium silicate, displacing diphosphorus pentoxide, P_4O_{10}, which is then reduced by the carbon. The phosphorus leaves the furnace as vapor, and is condensed under water to *white phosphorus*.

Phosphorus vapor is tetratomic: the P_4 molecule has a structure with each atom having one unshared electron pair and forming a single bond with each of its three neighbors (Figure 9-14).

At 1600°C the vapor is dissociated slightly, forming a few percent of diatomic molecules P_2, with the structure : P≡P : , analogous to that of the nitrogen molecule.

Phosphorus vapor condenses at 280.5°C to liquid white phosphorus, which freezes at 44.1°C to solid white phosphorus, a soft, waxy, colorless material, soluble in carbon disulfide, benzene, and other nonpolar solvents. Both solid and liquid white phosphorus contain the same P_4 molecules as the vapor.

White phosphorus is metastable, and it slowly changes to a stable form, *red phosphorus*, in the presence of light or on heating. White phosphorus

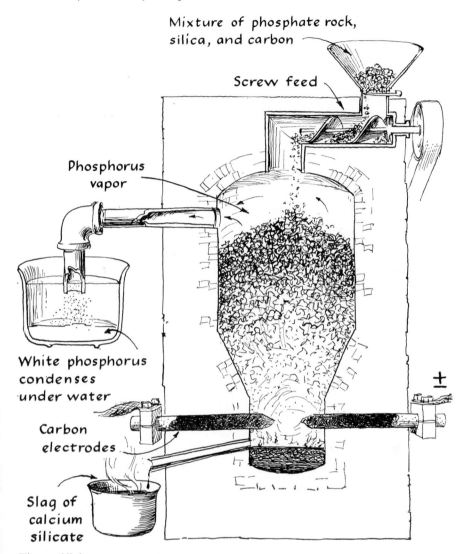

Mixture of phosphate rock, silica, and carbon

Screw feed

Phosphorus vapor

White phosphorus condenses under water

Carbon electrodes

Slag of calcium silicate

$\pm$

Figure **15-1**

Electric furnace for the manufacture of elementary phosphorus.

usually has a yellow color because of partial conversion to the red form. The reaction takes several hours even at 250°C; it can be accelerated by the addition of a small amount of iodine, which serves as a catalyst. Red phosphorus is far more stable than the white form—it does not catch fire in air at temperatures below 240°C, whereas white phosphorus ignites at about 40°C, and oxidizes slowly at room temperature, giving off a white light ("phosphorescence"). Red phosphorus is not poisonous, whereas white phosphorus is very poisonous, the lethal dose being about 0.15 g; it causes necrosis of the bones, especially those of the jaw. White phosphorus burns are painful and slow to heal. Red phosphorus cannot be converted into white phosphorus except by vaporizing it. It is not appreciably soluble in any solvent. When heated to 500° or 600°C red phosphorus slowly melts (if under pressure) or vaporizes, forming P_4 vapor.

Several other allotropic forms of the element are known. One of these, *black phosphorus*, is formed from white phosphorus under high pressure. It is still less reactive than red phosphorus.

The explanation of the properties of red and black phosphorus lies in their structure. These substances are high polymers, consisting of giant molecules extending throughout the crystal. In order for such a crystal to melt or to dissolve in a solvent, a chemical reaction must take place. This chemical reaction is the rupture of some P—P bonds and formation of new ones. Such processes are very slow.

The Uses of Phosphorus.   Large amounts of phosphorus made from phosphate rock are burned and converted into phosphoric acid. Phosphorus is also used in making matches. White phosphorus is no longer used for this purpose because of its danger to the health of the workers. Ordinary matches are now made by dipping the ends of the match sticks into paraffin, and then into a wet mixture of phosphorus sulfide, (P_4S_3), lead dioxide (or other oxidizing agent), and glue. The heads of safety matches contain antimony trisulfide and potassium chlorate or dichromate, and the box is coated with a mixture of red phosphorus, powdered glass, and glue (Figure 15-2).

Figure 15-2

The old, white phosphorus match (not used now), the ordinary match, and the safety match.

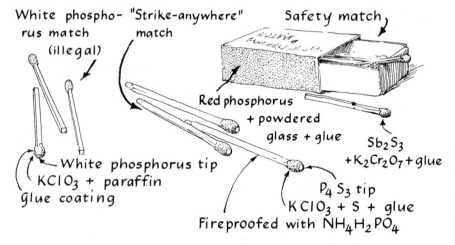

White phospho-   "Strike-anywhere"   Safety match
rus match   match
(illegal)

Red phosphorus
+ powdered
glass + glue Sb_2S_3
+$K_2Cr_2O_7$+glue

White phosphorus tip
$KClO_3$ + paraffin
Glue coating

P_4S_3 tip
$KClO_3$ + S + glue
Fireproofed with $NH_4H_2PO_4$

15-4. Phosphine

The principal hydride of phosphorus is *phosphine*, PH_3, with structure analogous to ammonia:

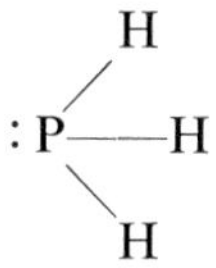

$$: P \overset{\displaystyle H}{\underset{\displaystyle H}{-\!\!\!-\!\!\!-H}}$$

Phosphine is not made by direct union of the elements. It is formed, together with the hypophosphite ion $H_2PO_2^-$, when white phosphorus is heated in a solution of alkali:

$$P_4 + 3OH^- + 3H_2O \longrightarrow 3H_2PO_2^- + PH_3$$

The gas made in this way, which contains some impurities, ignites spontaneously on contact with air and burns, forming white fumes of oxide. To avoid explosion, the air in the flask must be displaced by hydrogen or illuminating gas before the mixture in the flask is heated. Phosphine is exceedingly poisonous.

Phosphine has far less affinity for hydrogen ion than has ammonia. Its only salts are phosphonium iodide, PH_4I, phosphonium bromide, PH_4Br, and phosphonium chloride, PH_4Cl. These salts decompose on contact with water, liberating phosphine.

15-5. The Oxides of Phosphorus

Diphosphorus pentoxide (tetraphosphorus decoxide), usually assigned the formula P_2O_5, consists of molecules P_4O_{10}, with the structure shown in Figure 15-3. It is formed when phosphorus is burned with a free supply of air. It reacts with water with great violence, to form phosphoric acid, and it is used in the laboratory as a drying agent for gases.

Diphosphorus trioxide (tetraphosphorus hexoxide), P_2O_3 or P_4O_6 (Figure 15-3), is made, together with the pentoxide, by burning phosphorus with a restricted supply of air. It is much more volatile than the pentoxide (P_4O_6, m.p. 22.5°C, b.p. 173.1°C; P_4O_{10}, sublimes at 250°C), and is easily purified by distillation in an apparatus from which air is excluded.

15-6. Phosphoric Acid

Pure phosphoric acid, H_3PO_4 (also called *orthophosphoric acid*), is a deliquescent crystalline substance, with melting point 42°C. Commercial phosphoric acid is a viscous liquid. It is made by dissolving diphosphorus pentoxide in water.

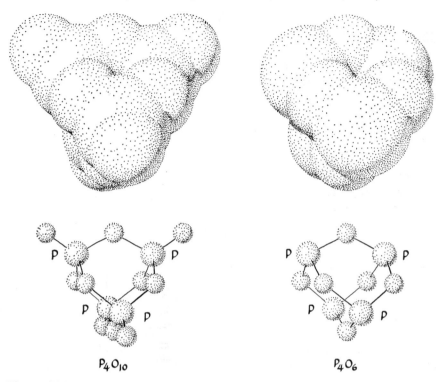

P_4O_{10} P_4O_6

Figure 15-3

Molecules of the oxides of phosphorus.

Phosphoric acid is a weak acid. It is a stable substance, without effective oxidizing power.

Orthophosphoric acid forms three series of salts, with one, two, and three of its hydrogen atoms replaced by metal. The salts are usually made by mixing phosphoric acid and the metal hydroxide or carbonate, in proper proportion. Sodium dihydrogen phosphate, NaH_2PO_4, is slightly acidic in reaction. It is used (mixed with sodium hydrogen carbonate) in baking powder, and also for treating boiler water to prevent formation of scale. Disodium hydrogen phosphate, Na_2HPO_4, is slightly basic in reaction. Trisodium phosphate, Na_3PO_4, is strongly basic. It is used as a detergent (for cleaning woodwork, etc.) and for treating boiler water.

Phosphates are valuable fertilizers. Phosphate rock itself (tricalcium phosphate, $Ca_3(PO_4)_2$, and hydroxy-apatite) is too slightly soluble to serve as an effective source of phosphorus for plants. It is accordingly converted into the more soluble substance calcium dihydrogen phosphate, $Ca(H_2PO_4)_2$. This may be done by treatment with sulfuric acid:

$$Ca_3(PO_4)_2 + 2H_2SO_4 \longrightarrow 2CaSO_4 + Ca(H_2PO_4)_2$$

Enough water is added to convert the calcium sulfate to its dihydrate, gypsum, and the mixture of gypsum and calcium dihydrogen phosphate is sold as "superphosphate of lime." Sometimes the phosphate rock is treated with phosphoric acid:

$$Ca_3(PO_4)_2 + 4H_3PO_4 \longrightarrow 3Ca(H_2PO_4)_2$$

This product is much richer in phosphorus than the "superphosphate"; it is called "triple phosphate." Over ten million tons of phosphate rock is converted into phosphate fertilizer each year.

Phosphoric acid is present in the nucleic acids, which are of fundamental importance in the biological process of reproduction of living organisms (Chapter 28).

The Condensed Phosphoric Acids. Phosphoric acid easily undergoes the process of *condensation*. Condensation is the reaction of two or more molecules to form larger molecules, either without any other products (in which case the condensation is also called *polymerization*), or with the elimination of small molecules, such as water. Condensation of two phosphoric acid molecules occurs by the reaction of two hydroxyl groups to form water and an oxygen atom held by single bonds to two phosphorus atoms.

When orthophosphoric acid is heated it loses water and condenses to **diphosphoric acid** or **pyrophosphoric acid,** $H_4P_2O_7$:

$$2H_3PO_4 \rightleftarrows H_4P_2O_7 + H_2O$$

(The name pyrophosphoric acid is the one customarily used.) This acid is a white crystalline substance, with melting point 61°C. Its salts may be made by neutralization of the acid or by strongly heating the hydrogen orthophosphates or ammonium orthophosphates of the metals. Magnesium pyrophosphate, $Mg_2P_2O_7$, is obtained in a useful method for quantitative analysis for either magnesium or orthophosphate. A solution containing orthophosphate ion may be mixed with a solution of magnesium chloride (or sulfate), ammonium chloride, and ammonium hydroxide. The very slightly soluble substance magnesium ammonium phosphate, $MgNH_4PO_4 \cdot 6H_2O$, then slowly precipitates. The precipitate is washed with dilute ammonium hydroxide, dried, and heated to a dull red heat, causing it to form magnesium pyrophosphate, which is then weighed:

$$2MgNH_4PO_4 \cdot 6H_2O \longrightarrow Mg_2P_2O_7 + 2NH_3 + 13H_2O$$

Larger condensed phosphoric acids also occur, such as **triphosphoric acid,** $H_5P_3O_{10}$. The interconversion of triphosphates, pyrophosphates, and phosphates is important in many bodily processes, including the absorption and metabolism of sugar. These reactions occur at body temperature under the influence of special enzymes (Chapter 28).

An important class of condensed phosphoric acids is that in which each phosphate tetrahedron is bonded by oxygen atoms to two other tetrahedra. These acids have the composition $(HPO_3)_x$, with $x = 3, 4, 5, 6, \cdots$. They are called the **metaphosphoric acids.** Among these acids are **tetrametaphosphoric acid** and **hexametaphosphoric acid.**

Metaphosphoric acid is made by heating orthophosphoric acid or pyrophosphoric acid or by adding water to phosphorus pentoxide. It is a viscous sticky mass, which contains, in addition to ring molecules such as $H_4P_4O_{12}$, long chains approaching $(HPO_3)_\infty$ in composition. It is the long chains, which may also be condensed together to form branched chains, that, by becoming entangled, make the acid viscous and sticky.

The process of condensation may continue further, ultimately leading to phosphorus pentoxide.

The metaphosphates are used as water softeners (Chapter 16). Sodium hexametaphosphate, $Na_6P_6O_{18}$, is especially effective for this purpose.

15-7. Phosphorous Acid

Phosphorous acid, H_2HPO_3, is a white substance, m.p. 74°C, which is made by dissolving diphosphorus trioxide in cold water:

$$P_4O_6 + 6H_2O \longrightarrow 4H_2HPO_3$$

It may also be conveniently made by the action of water on phosphorus trichloride:

$$PCl_3 + 3H_2O \longrightarrow H_2HPO_3 + 3HCl$$

Phosphorous acid is an unstable substance. When heated it undergoes auto-oxidation-reduction to phosphine and phosphoric acid:

$$4H_2HPO_3 \longrightarrow 3H_3PO_4 + PH_3$$

The acid and its salts, the *phosphites*, are powerful reducing agents. Its reaction with silver ion is used as a test for phosphite ion; a black precipitate is formed, which consists of silver phosphate, Ag_3PO_4, colored black by metallic silver formed by reduction of silver ion. Phosphite ion also reduces iodate ion to free iodine, which can be detected by the starch test (blue color) or by its coloration of a small volume of carbon tetrachloride shaken with the aqueous phase.

Phosphorous acid is a weak acid, which forms two series of salts. Ordinary sodium phosphite is $Na_2HPO_3 \cdot 5H_2O$. Sodium hydrogen phosphite, $NaHHPO_3 \cdot 5H_2O$, also exists, but the third hydrogen atom cannot be replaced by a cation. The nonacidic character of this third hydrogen atom is due to its attachment directly to the phosphorus atom, rather than to an oxygen atom:

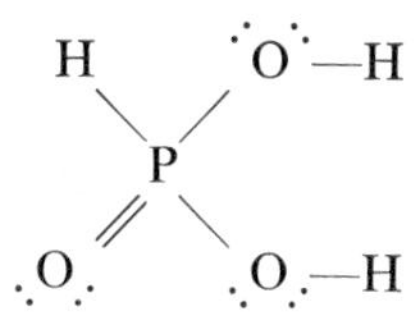

$$H \diagdown \ddot{O}'{-}H$$
$$P$$
$$.\overset{..}{O}. .\overset{..}{O}.{-}H$$

The phosphite ion is HPO_3^{--}, not PO_3^{---}.

15-8. Hypophosphorous Acid

The solution remaining from the preparation of phosphite from phosphorus and alkali contains the *hypophosphite ion*, $H_2PO_2^-$. The corresponding acid, hypophosphorous acid, HH_2PO_2, can be prepared by using barium hydroxide as the alkali, thus forming barium hypophosphite, $Ba(H_2PO_2)_2$, and then adding to the solution the calculated amount of sulfuric acid, which precipitates barium sulfate and leaves the hypophosphorous acid in solution.

Hypophosphorous acid is a weak monoprotic acid, forming only one series of salts. The two nonacidic hydrogen atoms are bonded to the phosphorus atom:

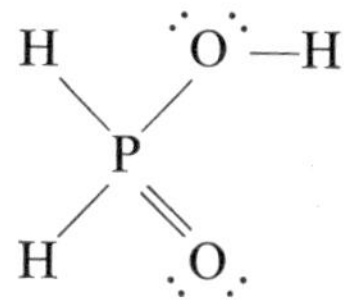

$$H \diagdown \ddot{O}'{-}H$$
$$P$$
$$H \diagup .\overset{..}{O}.$$

The acid and the hypophosphite ion are powerful reducing agents, able to reduce the cations of copper and the more noble metals.

15-9. Oxidation-reduction Properties of Phosphorus Compounds

The compounds of phosphorus differ in a striking way from the analogous compounds of chlorine in their oxidation-reduction properties (those of sulfur are intermediate). Thus the highest oxygen acid of phosphorus, H_3PO_4, is stable, and not an oxidizing agent, whereas that of chlorine, $HClO_4$, is a very strong oxidizing agent. The lower oxygen acids of phosphorus are strong reducing agents, and those of chlorine are strong oxidizing agents. The phosphide ion, P^{---}, is such a strong reducing agent that it cannot be obtained; sulfide ion, S^{--}, is a strong reducing agent; but chloride ion is stable.

These differences in properties may be accounted for in terms of the different electronegativities of the elements—3.0 for Cl, 2.5 for S, and 2.1 for P—which lead to increasing stability of the bonds with oxygen in the sequence Cl, S, P. The energies of addition of four oxygen atoms in the corresponding reactions of oxidation from the lowest to the highest oxidation states are the following:*

$$Cl^-(aq) + 4O(g) \longrightarrow ClO_4^-(aq) + 228 \text{ kcal/mole}$$
$$S^{--}(aq) + 4O(g) \longrightarrow SO_4^{--}(aq) + 464 \text{ kcal/mole}$$
$$P^{---}(aq) + 4O(g) \longrightarrow PO_4^{---}(aq) + 593 \text{ kcal/mole}$$

These values correspond to the average energy 57 kcal/mole for the $Cl\!=\!\overset{..}{\underset{..}{O}}:$

bond, 116 kcal/mole for the $S\!=\!\overset{..}{O}:$ bond, and 148 kcal/mole for the $P\!=\!\overset{..}{\underset{..}{O}}:$ bond; the increase from chlorine to phosphorus is roughly as expected from the increasing amount of ionic character of the bonds. Values for single steps usually lie within 10 kcal/mole of the average values [for example, $ClO_3^-(aq) + O(g) \longrightarrow ClO_4^-(aq) + 67 \text{ kcal/mole}$].

15-10.   The Halogenides and Sulfides of Phosphorus

By direct combination of the elements or by other methods the halogenides of terpositive phosphorus (PF_3, PCl_3, PBr_3, PI_3) and of quinquepositive phosphorus (PF_5, PCl_5) can be formed. These halogenides are gases or easily volatile liquids or solids, which hydrolyze with water, forming the corresponding oxygen acids of phosphorus. The electronic structures of the phosphorus trihalogenides and pentahalogenides have been discussed in earlier chapters. These halogenides are useful in the preparation of inorganic and organic substances.

The heats of reaction show that the bonds in PCl_5 are not as strong as those in PCl_3:

$$P(g) + 3Cl(g) \longrightarrow PCl_3(g) + 3 \times 76.1 \text{ kcal/mole}$$
$$PCl_3(g) + 2Cl(g) \longrightarrow PCl_5(g) + 2 \times 40.3 \text{ kcal/mole}$$

The decreased bond strength in PCl_5 may be attributed to the promotion energy; the phosphorus atom can be assigned the electron configuration $3s^2 3p^3$ in PCl_3 and $3s3p^3 3d$ in PCl_5.

Phosphorus oxychloride, PCl_3O, is made by partial hydrolysis of the pentachloride, by reaction of the pentachloride with the pentoxide, or in other ways. The bond energy of the $P\!=\!O$ bond in this molecule is 134 kcal/mole:

$$PCl_3(g) + O(g) \longrightarrow PCl_3O(g) + 134 \text{ kcal/mole}$$

The partial hydrolysis of phosphorus pentachloride is strongly exothermic:

$$PCl_5(g) + H_2O(g) \longrightarrow PCl_3O(g) + 2HCl(g) + 39 \text{ kcal/mole}$$

The stability of the products cannot be attributed to the ordinary effect of electronegativity (Section 9-12), because phosphorus and hydrogen, which interchange their bonds to oxygen and chlorine, have the same electroneg-

---

* The values are obtained from the standard enthalpy values given in Table 15-2 and earlier tables, with use of the value 50 kcal/mole for $P^{---}(aq)$ estimated from the values for PH_3, H_2S, S^{--}, HCl, and Cl^-.

ativity. It is, however, associated with the greater partial ionic character of the P=O bonds than of the P—Cl bonds, which has the effect of requiring smaller promotion energy (for the covalent sp^3d phases of the bonds) in PCl_3O than in PCl_5.

It is the greater effective stability of the P=O bond than of the fourth and fifth P—Cl bonds that causes phosphorus pentachloride to be a useful chemical reagent. It reacts with organic substances containing hydroxyl groups to replace these groups with chlorine atoms; for example, with ethanol to form ethyl chloride:

$$C_2H_5OH + PCl_5 \longrightarrow C_2H_5Cl + PCl_3O + HCl + 44 \text{ kcal/mole}$$

It also reacts in a similar way with inorganic oxygen acids. Thus from sulfuric acid it produces chlorosulfuric acid, HSO_3Cl:

$$SO_2(OH)_2 + PCl_5 \longrightarrow SO_2(OH)Cl + POCl_3 + HCl$$

With an excess of phosphorus pentachloride the substance sulfuryl chloride, SO_2Cl_2, is formed:

$$SO_2(OH)_2 + 2PCl_5 \longrightarrow SO_2Cl_2 + 2POCl_3 + 2HCl$$

Sulfur and phosphorus combine when heated together to form various compounds, including P_2S_5, P_4S_7, and P_4S_3. The last of these, tetraphosphorus trisulfide, is used as a constituent of match heads.

15-11. Arsenic, Antimony, and Bismuth

Arsenic, antimony, and bismuth differ from their congeners nitrogen and phosphorus in the decreasing electronegativity that accompanies increasing atomic number. The principal compounds of these elements correspond to the oxidation states +5 and +3. The state −3 also occurs; it is represented by the gaseous hydrides AsH_3, SbH_3, and BiH_3, which, however, do not form salts analogous to the ammonium and phosphonium salts.

Representative compounds of the fifth-group elements are shown in the chart on p. 430.

The oxides of arsenic are acidic; with water they form arsenic acid, H_3AsO_4, and arsenious acid, H_3AsO_3, which resemble the corresponding acids of phosphorus. Antimony pentoxide is also acidic, and its trioxide is amphoteric, behaving both as an acid and as a base (forming the antimony ion, Sb^{+++}). Bismuth trioxide is primarily a basic oxide, forming the ion Bi^{+++}; its acidic activity is slight.

Arsenic and Its Ores. Elementary arsenic exists in several forms. Ordinary *gray arsenic* is a semimetallic substance, steel-gray in color, with density 5.73 and melting point (under pressure) 814°C. It sublimes rapidly at about 450°C, forming gas molecules As_4, similar in structure to P_4. An unstable yellow crystalline allotropic form containing As_4 molecules, and soluble in carbon disulfide, also exists. The gray form has a covalent layer structure.

The chief minerals of arsenic include *orpiment*, As_2S_3 (from Latin *auripigmentum*, yellow pigment), *realgar*, AsS (a red substance), *arsenolite*, As_4O_6, and *arsenopyrite*, FeAsS. Diarsenic trioxide (arsenious oxide) is obtained by

+5	$\begin{cases} N_2O_5 \\ HNO_3 \\ \\ \end{cases}$	P_4O_{10} H_3PO_4 PCl_5	As_2O_5 H_3AsO_4	Sb_2O_5 $HSb(OH)_6$ $SbCl_5$	Bi_2O_5
+4	NO_2				
+3	$\begin{cases} N_2O_3 \\ HNO_2 \\ NCl_3 \\ \\ \end{cases}$	P_4O_6 H_2HPO_3 PCl_3	As_4O_6 H_3AsO_3 $AsCl_3$	Sb_4O_6 H_3SbO_3 $SbCl_3$ Sb^{+++}	Bi_4O_6 $BiCl_3$ Bi^{+++}
+2	NO				
+1	$\begin{cases} N_2O \\ H_2N_2O_2 \end{cases}$	HH_2PO_2			
0	N_2	P_4	As	Sb	Bi
−1	NH_2OH				
−2	N_2H_4	P_2H_4			
−3	$\begin{cases} NH_3 \\ NH_4{}^+ \end{cases}$	PH_3 $PH_4{}^+$	AsH_3	SbH_3	BiH_3

roasting ores of arsenic. The element is made by reducing the trioxide with carbon or by heating arsenopyrite:

$$4FeAsS \longrightarrow 4FeS + As_4$$

Arsenic is inert at room temperature, but ignites when heated, burning with a lavender flame to produce white clouds of the trioxide. It is oxidized to arsenic acid, H_3AsO_4, by hot nitric acid and other powerful oxidizing agents. Arsenic combines with many other elements, both metallic and nonmetallic.

Arsenic is used with lead (0.5% As) in making lead shot. It makes the metal harder than pure lead, and also improves the properties of the molten metal— the shot are made by pouring the metal through a sieve at the top of a tall tower, which permits the liquid drops to assume a spherical form and then to harden before falling into water at the base of the tower.

Arsine, AsH_3, is a colorless, very poisonous gas with a garliclike odor. It is made by reaction of a metallic arsenide, such as zinc arsenide, with acid:

$$Zn_3As_2 + 6HCl \longrightarrow 3ZnCl_2 + 2AsH_3$$

Diarsenic trioxide (*arsenious oxide*, As_4O_6) is a white solid substance which sublimes readily, and is easily purified by sublimation. Its molecules have the same structure as diphosphorus trioxide, shown in Figure 15-3. It is a violent poison, and is used as an insecticide and for preserving skins.

Diarsenic trioxide dissolves in water to form **arsenious acid,** H_3AsO_3. This acid differs from phosphorous acid in that all three of its hydrogen atoms are attached to oxygen atoms, and are replaceable by metal. It is a very weak acid. Cupric hydrogen arsenite, $CuHAsO_3$, and a cupric arsenite-acetate (called *Paris green*) are used as insecticides.

Diarsenic pentoxide, As_2O_5, is not obtained by burning arsenic, but can be made by boiling diarsenic trioxide with concentrated nitric acid. With water it forms **arsenic acid,** H_3AsO_4, which is closely similar to phosphoric acid. Sodium arsenate, Na_3AsO_4, is used as a weed killer, and other arsenates (especially of calcium and lead) are used as insecticides.

The toxicity of arsenic compounds to living organisms is utilized in chemotherapy; several organic compounds of arsenic have been discovered that are able to attack invading organisms, such as the spirochete of syphilis, when taken in amounts smaller than the amount poisonous to man.

Antimony. The principal ore of antimony is *stibnite*, Sb_2S_3, a steel-gray or black mineral that forms beautiful crystals. The metal is usually made by heating stibnite with iron:

$$Sb_2S_3 + 3Fe \longrightarrow 3FeS + 2Sb$$

Antimony is a brittle metal, silvery gray in color. It has the property of expanding on solidifying, and its main use is as a constituent of type metal (82% lead, 15% antimony, 3% tin), to which it confers this property, thus giving sharp reproductions of the mold. It is also used as a constituent of other alloys, especially for making the grids in storage batteries and for bearings.

The oxides and acids of antimony resemble those of arsenic, except that antimony in **antimonic acid** has coordination number 6, the formula of antimonic acid being $HSb(OH)_6$. A solution of potassium antimonate, $K^+[Sb(OH)_6]^-$, finds use as a test reagent for sodium ion; sodium antimonate, $NaSb(OH)_6$, one of the very few sodium salts with slight solubility in water (about 0.03 g per 100 g), is precipitated. The antimonate ion condenses to larger complexes when heated; this condensation may ultimately

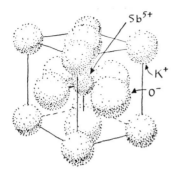

Figure 15-4 *The cubic unit of structure of the crystal of dehydrated potassium antimonate, KSbO₃.*

lead to macromolecular structures, such as that of dehydrated potassium antimonate, $KSbO_3$ (Figure 15-4).

Diantimony trioxide, Sb_4O_6, is amphoteric. In addition to reacting with bases to form *antimonites*, it reacts with acids to form antimony salts, such as antimony sulfate, $Sb_2(SO_4)_3$. The antimony ion Sb^{+++} hydrolyzes readily to form the antimonyl ion, SbO^+.

Antimony trichloride, $SbCl_3$, is a soft, colorless substance, which hydrolyzes with water, precipitating antimonyl chloride, $SbOCl$. The reaction may be reversed by adding hydrochloric acid, forming the complex anion $SbCl_4^-$. This anion can be oxidized by iodate ion to a similar complex anion of quinquevalent antimony:

$$5SbCl_4^- + 2IO_3^- + 12H^+ + 10Cl^- \longrightarrow 5SbCl_6^- + I_2 + 6H_2O$$

This reaction may be used for the quantitative determination of antimony.

Potassium antimonyl tartrate (tartar emetic, $KSbOC_4H_4O_6$) and some other compounds of antimony are used in medicine.

Bismuth. Bismuth occurs in nature as the free element, and as the sulfide Bi_2S_3 and oxide Bi_2O_3. The metal is won from its compounds by roasting and reducing the oxide with carbon. It is a brittle metal, with a silvery color showing a reddish tinge. It expands slightly on freezing. Its principal use is in making low-melting alloys.

The oxides of bismuth are basic, forming salts such as bismuth chloride, $BiCl_3 \cdot H_2O$, and bismuth nitrate, $Bi(NO_3)_3 \cdot 5H_2O$. These salts when dissolved in water hydrolyze, and precipitate the corresponding bismuthyl compounds, $BiOCl$ and $Bi(OH)_2NO_3$ (or $BiONO_3 \cdot H_2O$). The compounds of bismuth have found little use; bismuthyl nitrate and some other compounds are used to some extent in medicine.

EXERCISES

15-1. What are the formulas and structures of the oxygen acids of the +5 oxidation states of the fifth-group elements?

15-2. What are the formulas and structures of the oxygen acids of the +3 oxidation states of the fifth-group elements (include Bi(OH)₃ in this tabulation)? How do the properties of these compounds vary with atomic number?

15-3. What are apatite and hydroxy-apatite?

15-4. Write the chemical equation for the preparation of phosphorus in the electric furnace.

15-5. Write the equations for the hydrolysis

of phosphorus tribromide and for the hydrolysis of phosphorus pentachloride.

15-6. To make a soluble phosphate for use in fertilizers, $Ca_3(PO_4)_2$ is allowed to react with sulfuric acid to produce a mixture of $CaSO_4 \cdot 2H_2O$ and $Ca(H_2PO_4)_2$ or with phosphoric acid to produce $Ca(H_2PO_4)_2$ alone. Write equations for the reactions. What percentage of phosphorus is there in the first product (called "superphosphate")? In the second product ("triple phosphate")?

15-7. What are the electronic structures of phosphorous acid (H_3PO_3) and hypophosphorous acid (H_3PO_2)?

15-8. If phosphorous acid is heated to 200°C it forms phosphine and phosphoric acid. Write a balanced equation for the reaction.

15-9. Hydrogen bromide can be prepared by the reaction between phosphorus tribromide and water. Write the equation. What other phosphorus compound might be produced, if the mixture is heated?

15-10. Arsenic reacts with hot concentrated nitric acid to form arsenic acid, nitrogen dioxide, and water. Write the equation for the reaction.

15-11. What is the structure of trimetaphosphoric acid, $H_3P_3O_9$?

15-12. Write a chemical equation for the reduction of Ag^+ by a solution of sodium phosphite.

15-13. Write chemical equations illustrating the acidic and the basic properties of the +3 oxidation state of antimony.

15-14. How much phosphorus could be made from 1 ton of calcium phosphate, $Ca_3(PO_4)_2$? How much phosphorus sulfide, P_4S_3, could be made from this amount of phosphorus?

15-15. Discuss the enthalpies of formation of the trichlorides, tribromides, and triiodides of phosphorus, arsenic, and antimony in relation to electronegativity values.

15-16. Why is no value for the enthalpy of formation of $AsCl_5(g)$ given in Table 15-2? (See Section 12-8.)

15-17. The compound $P_3N_3Cl_6$ (m.p. 114°C, b.p. 257°C) has been shown by x-ray diffraction to have a six-membered ring with P and N alternating, and two chlorine atoms attached to each phosphorus atom. Assign an electronic structure to the molecule.

15-18. From the tabulated enthalpy values calculate the heats of formation of $SO(g)$ and $PO(g)$ from atoms, and compare with the values given in the text for the S=O bond energy and the P=O bond energy in the ions of the oxygen acids.

15-19. Assign electronic structures to P_4O_6 and P_4O_{10}. What bond orbitals are used by the phosphorus atom in these molecules?

15-20. The enthalpy of formation of $P_4O_{10}(c)$ is given in Table 15-2 as -713 kcal/mole, and that of $P_4O_6(c)$ as -392 kcal/mole. Using 24 and 16 kcal/mole, respectively, for heat of sublimation, evaluate the P=O bond energy. (Answer: 138 kcal/mole.)

15-21. (a) Using information in the preceding Exercise, obtain a value for the P—O bond energy.
(b) For comparison, calculate a value for the P—O bond energy from the values for P—P and O—O, with the correction for electronegativity difference.
(Answer: 86.0, 87.3 kcal/mole.)

15-22. The observed bond lengths in P_4O_{10} are 1.65 Å and 1.39 Å (the latter to oxygen atoms attached to only one phosphorus atom). The first corresponds to a single bond with a small amount of double-bond character, and the second to a triple bond. Draw a valence-bond structure involving single bonds and triple bonds. What orbitals are used as bond orbitals by the bridging oxygen atoms? By the outer oxygen atoms? How many unshared pairs do the oxygen atoms have? What orbitals are used as bond orbitals by the phosphorus atoms?

15-23. Using the structure with triple bonds to the outer oxygen atoms and assigning each bond the amount of ionic character corresponding to the electronegativity difference (Table 9-2), calculate the electric charges on the phosphorus and oxygen atoms. Does this structure give better or worse agreement with the electroneutrality principle (atomic charges 0 ± 1) than the structure with double bonds to the outer oxygen atoms?

15-24. What do you estimate the value of the electric dipole moment of the P_4O_6 molecule to be? Of the P_4O_{10} molecule?

15-25. What electronic structure would you suggest for the odd molecule ClO_2 (one unpaired electron)? Note that the chlorine-oxygen bond length is 1.49 Å in this molecule, as compared with 1.69 Å in Cl_2O. The O—Cl—O bond angle has the value 116°.

15-26. The standard enthalpy of formation of $ClO_2(g)$ is 24.7 kcal/mole, and that of $ClO(g)$ is 33 kcal/mole. What is the heat of the reaction $ClO(g) + O(g) \longrightarrow ClO_2(g)$? How does this value compare with the average value for acid anions given in Section 15-9? (Answer: 68 kcal/mole.)

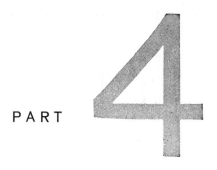

PART 4

Water, Solutions,

Chemical Equilibrium

In the study of some aspects of chemical theory in Part 2 of our book we learned how to write equations for chemical reactions and to discuss the relations between the weights of the reacting substances and their products, and also the volumes, if the substances are gases. For example, we know how to write an equation for the reaction of nitrogen and hydrogen to form ammonia. The correctly balanced equation is

$$N_2 + 3H_2 \rightleftharpoons 2NH_3$$

We can say that 28 g (2 gram-atoms) of nitrogen and 6 g (6 gram-atoms) of hydrogen might react to form 34 g (two moles) of ammonia, and that, at given temperature and pressure, one volume of nitrogen and three volumes of hydrogen might produce two volumes of ammonia.

In the preceding sentence we have to say "might produce" rather than "would produce" because we have not yet discussed the question, in any detail, as to whether a certain chemical reaction would take place or not. If we mix nitrogen and hydrogen at room temperature, will any reaction take place? If we raise the temperature, will any reaction take place? If reaction does begin to take place, will it continue until all the nitrogen or all the hydrogen has been converted into ammonia?

The questions above are examples of two general kinds of questions. First, how fast may we expect a chemical reaction to take place—what is the rate of the reaction? A chemist in the business of manufacturing ammonia is far more interested in a reaction that would produce his product in a few minutes than in a reaction that would require years.

The second question is the following: If a chemical reaction begins to take place, can it be expected to continue until all of the reacting materials are used up, or may it stop before this point? Questions of this sort relate to the subject of *chemical equilibrium.*

It has been found by experiment that if nitrogen and hydrogen are mixed at room temperature the reaction does not take place at all—the rate of the reaction is so small that it is impossible to detect any ammonia in the mixture, even after a long time. If the temperature is raised, the formation of ammonia begins to take place. If the temperature is very high, the nitrogen and hydrogen begin to react rapidly, but the reaction apparently ceases when only a small amount of the gas has been converted into ammonia. The problem of the manufacturer who wants to make ammonia by reaction of nitrogen and hydrogen is to find conditions such that the rate of the reaction is great enough to give him some ammonia in a few minutes or hours and the chemical equilibrium permits the reaction to provide a satisfactory yield of ammonia.

Many chemical reactions take place in solution, especially solution in water, and Part 4 begins with a chapter on water, Chapter 16. This chapter contains a discussion of intermolecular forces and of the hydrogen bond, an important structural feature that has a strong influence on the properties of many substances. The next chapter, Chapter 17, deals with the properties of solutions. In Chapter 18 there is a general discussion of the theory of the rate of chemical reaction and the theory of chemical equilibrium. These subjects are closely related, because in fact a system in chemical equilibrium, in which no change in composition of the system takes place with time, is not a static system; instead, chemical reactions may be taking place at a great rate. The equilibrium is a dynamic one, in which a reaction that produces a product is taking place at the same rate as the reaction that decomposes the product. For example, when a mixture of nitrogen and hydrogen is heated to high temperature, some ammonia is formed, and after a time the composition of the mixture becomes constant; under these equilibrium conditions the reaction of nitrogen and hydrogen to form ammonia continues, and the reverse reaction, the decomposition of ammonia to form nitrogen and hydrogen, also takes place, at such a rate that the amount of ammonia being decomposed is just equal to the amount being formed. In Chapter 19 there is a detailed discussion of acids and bases, with special attention to the reactions of acids and bases that involve chemical equilibria.

The aspects of chemical theory discussed in Chapters 16 to 19 are especially significant to the procedures of qualitative analysis and quantitative analysis of substances and to industrial chemistry. The systems of analysis and methods used in chemical industries provide many illustrations of the application of these principles.

Some aspects of chemical equilibrium can be treated quantitatively, with use of an equilibrium equation, which is discussed in Chapter 18 and applied in the following chapters. Mathematical equations like this one are, of course, very valuable, and they must be used if it is necessary to carry out numerical calculations. A student or a scientist who relies on equations may, however, occasionally find that he has made a very bad mistake, because of a misunderstanding as to how the equation should be used. The student (or the scientist) would be wise to refrain from using the mathematical equation unless he understands the theory that it represents, and can make a statement about the theory that does not consist just in reading the equation.

It is fortunate that there is a general qualitative principle, called *Le Chatelier's principle*, that relates to all the applications of the principles of chemical equilibrium. *When you have obtained a grasp of Le Chatelier's principle, you will be able to think about any problem of chemical equilibrium that arises, and, by use of a simple argument, to make a qualitative statement about it.* For example, with use of Le Chatelier's principle you can answer the question as to whether the conversion of nitrogen and hydrogen into ammonia would be favored by compressing the mixture of gases, and also the question as to whether it would be favored by raising the temperature. Le Chatelier's principle is discussed in the first chapter of Part 4, Chapter 16, and it is referred to in each of the following chapters.

Some years after you have finished your college work, you may (unless you become a chemist or work in some closely related field) have forgotten all the mathematical equations relating to chemical equilibrium. I hope, however, that you will not have forgotten Le Chatelier's principle.

CHAPTER 16

Water

Water is one of the most important of all chemical substances. It is a major constituent of living matter and of the environment in which we live. Its physical properties are strikingly different from those of other substances, in ways that determine the nature of the physical and biological world.

16-1. The Composition of Water

Water was thought by the ancients to be an element. Henry Cavendish in 1781 showed that water is formed when hydrogen is burned in air, and Lavoisier first recognized that water is a compound of the two elements hydrogen and oxygen.

The formula of water is H_2O. The relative weights of hydrogen and oxygen in the substance have been very carefully determined as $2.0160:16.0000$. This determination has been made both by weighing the amounts of hydrogen and oxygen liberated from water by electrolysis and by determining the weights of hydrogen and oxygen which combine to form water.

Purification of Water by Distillation. Ordinary water is impure; it usually contains dissolved salts and dissolved gases, and sometimes organic matter. For chemical work water is purified by distillation. Pure tin vessels and pipes are often used for storing and transporting distilled water. Glass vessels are not satisfactory, because the alkaline constituents of glass slowly dissolve in water. Distilling apparatus and vessels made of fused silica are used in making very pure water.

The impurity which is hardest to keep out of distilled water is carbon dioxide, which dissolves readily from the air.

Removal of Ionic Impurities from Water. Ionic impurities can be effectively and cheaply removed from water by an interesting process that involves the use of *giant molecules*—molecular structures that are so big as to constitute visible particles. A crystal of diamond is an example of such a giant molecule (Chapter 10). Some complex inorganic crystals, such as the minerals called *zeolites*, are of this nature. These minerals are used to "soften" hard water. Hard water is water containing cations of calcium, magnesium, and iron, which are undesirable because they form a precipitate with ordinary soap. The zeolite is able to remove these ions from the water, replacing them by sodium ion.

A zeolite is an aluminosilicate, with formula such as $Na_2Al_2Si_4O_{12}$ (Chapter 22). It consists of a rigid framework formed by the aluminum, silicon, and oxygen atoms, honeycombed by corridors in which sodium ions are located. These ions have some freedom of motion, and, when hard water flows over zeolite grains, some of the sodium ions run out of the corridors into the solution and are replaced by ions of calcium, magnesium, and iron. In this way the hardness of the water is removed. After most of the sodium ion has been replaced, the zeolite is regenerated by allowing it to stand in contact with a saturated brine; the reaction is then reversed, Na^+ replacing Ca^{++} and the other cations in the corridors of the zeolite.

The reactions that occur may be written with symbols. If Z^- is used to represent a small portion of the zeolite framework, carrying one negative charge, the replacement of calcium ion in the water by sodium ion may be written*

$$2\underline{Na^+Z^-} + Ca^{++} \longrightarrow \underline{Ca^{++}(Z^-)_2} + 2Na^+$$

When concentrated salt solution (brine) is run through the zeolite, the reverse reaction occurs:

$$2Na^+ + \underline{Ca^{++}(Z^-)_2} \longrightarrow 2\underline{Na^+Z^-} + Ca^{++}$$

The reason that giant molecules—the aluminosilicate framework—are important here is that these molecules, which look like large grains of sand, are not carried along in the water, but remain in the water-softening tank.

Both the positive ions and the negative ions can be removed from water by a similar method, illustrated in Figure 16-1. The first tank, A, contains grains that consist of giant organic molecules in the form of a porous framework to which acidic groups are attached. These groups are represented in the figure as *carboxyl groups*, —COOH:†

---

* A line is drawn under the formula for a substance to indicate that it is a solid.
† R represents a part of the framework, shown as a carbon atom in Figure 16-1.

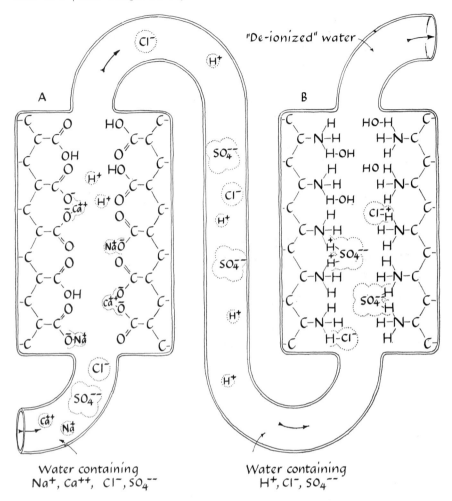

Figure 16-1

The removal of ions from water by use of giant molecules with attached acidic and basic groups.

The reactions that occur when a solution containing salts passes through tank A may be written as

$$RCOOH + Na^+ \longrightarrow (RCOO^-)Na^+ + H^+$$
$$2RCOOH + Ca^{++} \longrightarrow (RCOO^-)_2Ca^{++} + 2H^+$$

That is, sodium ions and calcium ions are removed from the solution by the acidic framework, and hydrogen ions are added to the solution. The solution is changed from a salt solution (Na^+, Cl^-, etc.) to an acid solution (H^+, Cl^-, etc.).

This acid then runs through tank B, which contains grains of giant organic molecules with basic groups attached. These groups are shown as *substituted ammonium hydroxide* groups, $(RNH_3^+)(OH^-)$:

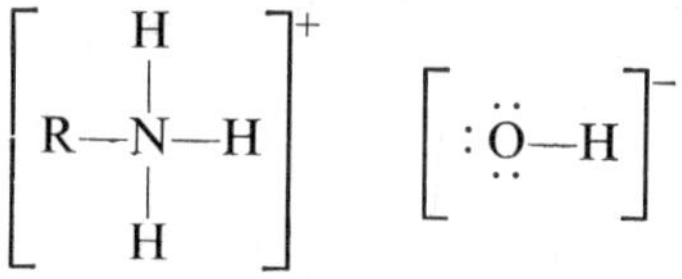

$$\left[\begin{array}{c} H \\ | \\ R-N-H \\ | \\ H \end{array}\right]^{+} \quad \left[:\ddot{O}-H\right]^{-}$$

The hydroxide ion of these groups combines with the hydrogen ion in the water:

$$OH^- + H^+ \longrightarrow H_2O$$

The negative ions then remain, held by the ammonium ions of the framework. The reactions are

$$(RNH_3^+)(OH^-) + Cl^- + H^+ \longrightarrow (RNH_3^+)Cl^- + H_2O$$
$$2(RNH_3^+)(OH^-) + SO_4^{--} + 2H^+ \longrightarrow (RNH_3^+)_2(SO_4^{--}) + 2H_2O$$

The water which passes out of the second tank contains practically no ions, and may be used in the laboratory and in industrial processes in place of distilled water.

The giant molecules in tank A may be regenerated after use by passing moderately concentrated sulfuric acid through the tank:

$$2(RCOO^-)Na^+ + H_2SO_4 \longrightarrow 2RCOOH + 2Na^+ + SO_4^{--}$$

Those in tank B may be regenerated by use of a moderately concentrated solution of sodium hydroxide:

$$(RNH_3^+)Cl^- + OH^- \longrightarrow (RNH_3^+)OH^- + Cl^-$$

16-2. The Principle of Le Chatelier

The reactions that occur in the softening of water by a zeolite and the regeneration of the zeolite provide a good example of an important general principle, **the principle of Le Chatelier.** This principle, which is named after the French chemist Henry Louis Le Chatelier (1850–1936), may be expressed in the following way: **if the conditions of a system, initially at equilibrium, are changed, the equilibrium will shift in such a direction as to tend to restore the original conditions.**

Let us recall the reaction that occurs when a hard water, containing calcium ions, is brought into contact with a sodium zeolite; this reaction is

$$2Na^+Z^- + Ca^{++} \longrightarrow Ca^{++}(Z^-)_2 + 2Na^+ \tag{1}$$

After a large amount of hard water has been run through the zeolite, no further replacement of calcium ions by sodium ions occurs; a *steady state* has been reached. The reason for the existence of the steady state is that there is also the possibility of the reverse reaction:

$$2Na^+ + \underline{Ca^{++}(Z^-)_2} \longrightarrow \underline{2Na^+Z^-} + Ca^{++} \qquad (2)$$

Even a very few sodium ions in the water might react with the calcium zeolite to cause this reaction to take place. The steady state occurs when the concentrations of calcium ion and sodium ion in the water and bound into the zeolite are such that the rate at which calcium ion is replacing sodium ion is just equal to the rate at which sodium ion is replacing calcium ion; this equilibrium of the two rates can be expressed by a single equation, with a double arrow:

$$\underline{2Na^+Z^-} + Ca^{++} \rightleftarrows \underline{Ca^{++}(Z^-)_2} + 2Na^+$$

If, now, conditions are changed by the addition of a large quantity of sodium ion, in high concentration (the addition of a concentrated salt solution), the equilibrium shifts in the way stated by Le Chatelier's principle, namely, in the direction that reduces the concentration of sodium ion in the solution. This is the direction to the left: the sodium zeolite is thus regenerated.

It is often possible to reach a useful qualitative conclusion about a chemical system by applying Le Chatelier's principle. The example that we are discussing shows that a chemical reaction may be made to proceed first in one direction and then in the opposite direction simply by changing the concentration of one or more of the reacting substances.

16-3. Other Ways of Softening Water

Hard water may also be softened by chemical treatment. In practice the use of giant organic molecules (synthetic resins) for deionizing water, described above, is restricted to industries requiring very pure water, as in making medicinal products. The zeolite method is sometimes used on a large scale, to treat the water for an entire city, but it is more often applied only for an individual house or building. Water for a city is usually treated by the addition of chemicals, followed by sedimentation when the water is allowed to stand in large reservoirs, and then by filtration through beds of sand. The settling process removes suspended matter in the water together with precipitated substances that might be produced by the added chemicals, and some living microorganisms. After filtration, the remaining living organisms may be destroyed by treatment with chlorine, bleaching powder, sodium hypochlorite or calcium hypochlorite, or ozone.

The hardness of water is due mainly to calcium ion, ferrous ion (Fe^{++}), and magnesium ion; it is these ions which form insoluble compounds with ordinary soap. Hardness is usually reported in parts per million (ppm), calculated as calcium carbonate (or sometimes in grains per gallon: 1 grain per gallon is equal to 17.1 ppm). Domestic water with hardness less than 100 ppm is good, and that with hardness between 100 and 200 ppm is fair.

Ground water in limestone regions may contain a large amount of calcium ion and hydrogen carbonate ion, HCO_3^-. Although calcium carbonate itself is insoluble, calcium hydrogen carbonate, $Ca(HCO_3)_2$, is a soluble substance. A water of this sort (which is said to have *temporary hardness*) can be softened simply by boiling, which causes the excess carbon dioxide to be driven off, and the calcium carbonate to precipitate:

$$Ca^{++} + 2HCO_3^- \longrightarrow CaCO_3(c) + H_2O + CO_2(g)$$

This method of softening water cannot be applied economically in the treatment of the water supply of a city, however, because of the large fuel cost. Instead, the water is softened by the addition of calcium hydroxide, slaked lime:

$$Ca^{++} + 2HCO_3^- + Ca(OH)_2 \longrightarrow 2CaCO_3(c) + 2H_2O$$

If sulfate ion or chloride ion is present in solution instead of hydrogen carbonate ion, the hardness of the water is not affected by boiling—the water is said to have *permanent hardness*. Permanently hard water can be softened by treatment with sodium carbonate:

$$Ca^{++} + CO_3^{--} \longrightarrow CaCO_3(c)$$

The sodium ions of the sodium carbonate are left in solution in the water, together with the sulfate or chloride ions that were already there.

In softening water by use of calcium hydroxide or sodium carbonate, enough of the substance is used to cause magnesium ion to be precipitated as magnesium hydroxide and iron as ferrous hydroxide or ferric hydroxide. Sometimes, in addition to the softening agent, a small amount of aluminum sulfate, alum, or ferric sulfate is added as a coagulant. These substances, with the alkaline reagents, form a flocculent, gelatinous precipitate of aluminum hydroxide, $Al(OH)_3$, or ferric hydroxide, $Fe(OH)_3$, which entraps the precipitate produced in the softening reaction, and helps it to settle out. The gelatinous precipitate also tends to adsorb coloring matter and other impurities in the water.*

A water that is used in a steam boiler often deposits a scale of calcium sulfate, which is left as the water is boiled away. In order to prevent this, boiler water is sometimes treated with sodium carbonate, causing the precipitation of calcium carbonate as a sludge, and preventing the formation of the calcium sulfate scale. Sometimes trisodium phosphate, Na_3PO_4, is used, leading to the precipitation of calcium as hydroxy-apatite, $Ca_5(PO_4)_3OH$, as a sludge. In either case the sludge is removed from the boiler by draining at intervals.

* *Adsorption* is the adhesion of molecules of a gas, liquid, or dissolved substance or of particles to the surface of a solid substance. *Absorption* is the assimilation of molecules into a solid or liquid substance, with the formation of a solution or a compound. Sometimes the word *sorption* is used to include both of these phenomena. We say that a heated glass vessel *adsorbs* water vapor from the air on cooling, and becomes coated with a very thin layer of water: a dehydrating agent such as concentrated sulfuric acid *absorbs* water, forming hydrates.

16-4. The Ionic Dissociation of Water

An acidic solution contains hydrogen ions, H^+ (actually hydronium ions, H_3O^+). A basic solution contains hydroxide ions, OH^-. A number of years ago chemists asked, and answered, the question, "Are these ions present in pure neutral water?" The answer is that they are present, in equal but very small concentrations.

Pure water contains hydrogen ions in concentration 1×10^{-7} moles per liter, and hydroxide ions in the same concentration. These ions are formed by the dissociation of water:

$$H_2O \rightleftarrows H^+ + OH^-$$

When a small amount of acid is added to pure water, the concentration of hydrogen ion is increased. The concentration of hydroxide ion then decreases, *but not to zero*. Acidic solutions contain hydrogen ion in large concentration and hydroxide ion in very small concentration.

16-5. Physical Properties of Water

Water is a clear, transparent liquid, colorless in thin layers. Thick layers of water have a bluish-green color.

The physical properties of water are used to define many physical constants and units. The freezing point of water (saturated with air at 1 atm pressure) is taken as 0°C, and the boiling point of water at 1 atm is taken as 100°C. The unit of volume in the metric system is chosen so that 1 ml of water at 3.98°C (the temperature of its maximum density) weighs 1.00000 gram. A similar relation holds in the English system: 1 cu ft of water weighs approximately 1000 ounces. The unit of energy, the calorie, is defined in relation to water (Section 1-6).

Most substances diminish in volume, and hence increase in density, with decrease in temperature. Water has the very unusual property of having a temperature at which its density is a maximum. This temperature is 3.98°C. With further cooling below this temperature the volume of a sample of water increases somewhat (Figure 16-2).

A related phenomenon is the increase in volume which water undergoes on freezing. These properties are discussed in detail in Section 16-7.

16-6. The Melting Points and Boiling Points of Substances

All molecules exert a weak attraction upon one another. This attraction, the *electronic van der Waals attraction*, is the result of the mutual interaction of the electrons and nuclei of the molecules; it has its origin in the electrostatic attraction of the nuclei of one molecule for the electrons of another,

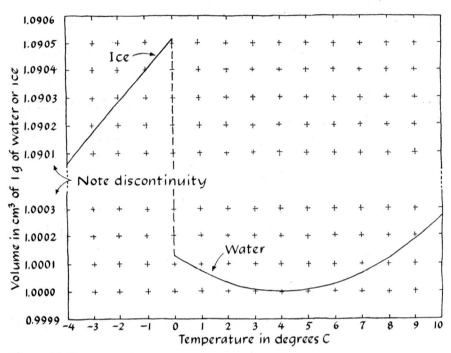

Figure 16-2

Dependence of the volume of ice and water on temperature.

which is largely but not completely compensated by the repulsion of electrons by electrons and nuclei by nuclei. The van der Waals attraction is significant only when the molecules are very close together—almost in contact with one another. At small distances (about 4 Å for argon, for example) the force of attraction is balanced by a force of repulsion due to interpenetration of the outer electron shells of the molecules (Figure 16-3).

It is these intermolecular forces of electronic van der Waals attraction that cause substances such as the noble gases, the halogens, etc., to condense to liquids and to freeze into solids at sufficiently low temperatures. The boiling point is a measure of the amount of molecular agitation necessary to overcome the forces of van der Waals attraction, and hence is an indication of the magnitude of these forces. In general, *the electronic van der Waals attraction between molecules increases with increase in the number of electrons per molecule.* Since the molecular weight is roughly proportional to the number of electrons in the molecule, usually about twice the number of electrons, the van der Waals attraction usually increases with increase in the molecular weight. **Large molecules** (containing many electrons) **attract one another more strongly than small molecules** (containing few electrons); **hence normal molecular substances with large molecular weight have high boiling points, and those with small molecular weight have low boiling points.**

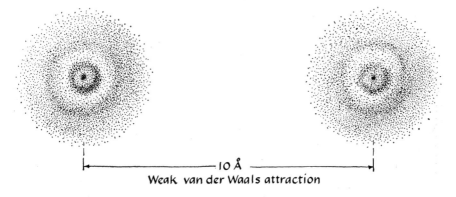

—10 Å—
Weak van der Waals attraction

Very strong van der Waals attraction
—5 Å—

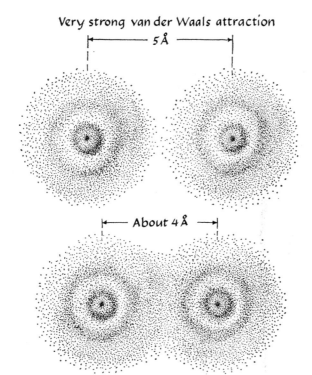

|— About 4 Å —|

Van der Waals attraction just
balanced by repulsive forces due
to interpenetration of outer electron
shells.

Figure **16-3**

Diagram illustrating van der Waals attraction and repulsion in relation to electron distribution of monatomic molecules of argon.

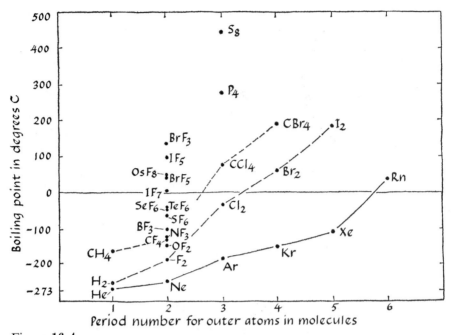

Figure 16-4

Diagram showing increase in boiling point with increase in molecular complexity.

This generalization is indicated in Figure 16-4, in which the boiling points of some molecular substances are shown. The steady increase in boiling point for sequences such as He, Ne, Ar, Kr, Xe, Rn and H_2, F_2, Cl_2, Br_2, I_2 is striking.

The similar effect of increase in the number of atoms (with nearly the same atomic number) in the molecule is shown by the following sequences:

	Ar	Cl_2	P_4	S_8
Boiling point	$-185.7°$	$-34.6°$	280°	444.6°C

	Ne	F_2	CF_4	SF_6	IF_7	OsF_8
Boiling point	$-245.9°$	$-184°$	$-161.4°$	$-62°$	4.5°	47.5°C

The theory of the van der Waals force of attraction between molecules was developed by the physicist F. London in 1929. It had been suggested that the van der Waals attraction between two HCl molecules (or other molecules with a permanent electric dipole moment; Section 9-10) was the result of the interaction of the permanent dipole moments. Careful calculations of this energy of attraction for two HCl molecules, however, gave a result only 10% of the observed interaction energy. Moreover, the interaction energy of molecules of xenon (boiling point $-107°C$) is nearly as great as that of molecules of hydrogen chloride (boiling point $-84°C$), although the molecules of xenon, which are single atoms, have no permanent electric dipole moment.

London showed that there is a van der Waals force of attraction between any two molecules that can be described as resulting from the interaction of their instantaneous electric dipole moments. For example, the 54 electrons in an atom of xenon might happen at one instant of time to be arranged in such a way that their center of charge would coincide with the nucleus, but at other instants it would lie to one side or the other of the nucleus, and the atom would have an instantaneous electric dipole moment. London found by quantum-mechanical calculation that the stable relative orientations of the instantaneous dipole moment of two atoms, such as $\rightarrowtail \rightarrowtail$, occur more often than the unstable ones, such as $\rightarrowtail \leftarrowtail$, and that the resulting effect is attraction. The London equation for the interaction energy of molecules A and B is

$$\text{Energy of attraction} = -\frac{3}{2}\frac{\alpha_A \alpha_B}{r_{AB}^6}\frac{I_A I_B}{(I_A + I_B)} \tag{3}$$

This corresponds to an inverse-seventh-power force of attraction (found by differentiating with respect to r_{AB}):

$$\text{Force of attraction} = 9\frac{\alpha_A \alpha_B}{r_{AB}^7}\frac{I_A I_B}{(I_A + I_B)}$$

In these equations r_{AB} is the distance between the centers of the molecules, I_A and I_B are excitation energies of molecules A and B (approximately the first ionization energies), and α_A and α_B are the *electronic polarizabilities* of the molecules.

The electronic polarizability of a molecule expresses the extent to which the electrons are shifted by an electric field E, to give the molecule an induced electric dipole moment, $\mu = \alpha E$. The dimensions of α are those of volume. The polarizability of xenon is 4.16 $\overset{\circ}{A}^3$ (4.16×10^{-24} cm³), which is the volume of a sphere with radius 1.00 $\overset{\circ}{A}$.

Light traversing a substance has a velocity different from light traversing a vacuum. The ratio of the velocity of light in a vacuum to that in a substance is the *index of refraction* of the substance. The interaction between the light and the substance that causes the index of refraction of the substance to differ from unity is the polarization of the atoms or molecules of the substance by the electric vector of the light. The relation between the index of refraction n and the molecular polarizability α is given by the *Lorenz-Lorentz equation*, which was derived in 1880 by the Danish physicist Ludwig Valentin Lorenz (1829–1891) and the Dutch physicist Hendrik Anton Lorentz (1853–1928). This equation, in which M is the molecular weight and d the density of the substance, is

$$\alpha = \frac{3}{4\pi N} \times \frac{n^2 - 1}{n^2 + 2} \times \frac{M}{d} \tag{4}$$

The following example shows how the molecular polarizability can be calculated from the observed value of the index of refraction.

Example 1. The value of the index of refraction n for xenon at standard conditions is 1.000703. (This is the value for the sodium D lines, wavelength 5894 Å; values of n are dependent on the wavelength of the light; for example, n for xenon varies from 1.000713 at 4800 Å to 1.000697 at 6700 Å.) What is the polarizability of the xenon atom?

Solution. The quantity M/d for a gas at standard conditions is 22,414 cm³, and n^2 for xenon is equal to 1.001406. Hence from the Lorenz-Lorentz equation we write

$$\alpha = \frac{3}{4\pi N} \times \frac{n^2 - 1}{n^2 + 2} \times \frac{M}{d}$$

$$= \frac{3}{4\pi \times 0.602 \times 10^{24}} \times \frac{1.406 \times 10^{-3}}{3.001} \times 22.414 \times 10^3$$

$$= 4.16 \times 10^{-24} \text{ cm}^3$$

Accordingly the polarizability of the xenon atom has the value $\alpha =$ **4.16 Å³**.

Example 2. The xenon crystal has the cubic closest-packed structure, with each atom surrounded by twelve others at the distance 4.41 Å. The first ionization energy of xenon is 279.7 kcal/mole. What is the value of the van der Waals energy of attraction of the atoms? Compare with the observed heat of sublimation, 3.57 kcal/mole.

Solution. We substitute $\alpha = 4.16$ Å³, $r_{AB} = 4.41$ Å, and $I = 279.7$ kcal/mole in Equation 3 to obtain the energy of attraction per pair of interacting xenon atoms:

$$\text{Energy} = -\frac{3}{2} \times \frac{4.16^2 \text{ Å}^6}{4.41^6 \text{ Å}^6} \times \frac{279.7}{2} \text{ kcal/mole} = 0.49 \text{ kcal/mole}$$

There are six nearest-neighbor interactions per xenon atom;[*] hence the calculated energy of van der Waals attraction between nearest neighbors is

$$6 \times 0.49 \text{ kcal/mole} = \textbf{2.94 kcal/mole}$$

This value is roughly equal to the observed heat of sublimation. To obtain a better calculated value we would need to take into consideration the energy of van der Waals attraction between more distant atoms and also the energy of the van der Waals repulsion.

Bond Type and Atomic Arrangement. Fifty years ago, before modern structural chemistry had been developed, it was thought that an abrupt change in melting point or boiling point in a series of related compounds could be accepted as proof of a change in type of bond. The fluorides of the elements of the second period, for example, have the following melting points and boiling points:

* Remember that each Xe—Xe interaction involves two xenon atoms.

	NaF	MgF$_2$	AlF$_3$	SiF$_4$	PF$_5$	SF$_6$
Melting point	995°	1263°	>1257°	−90°	−94°	−51°C
Boiling point	1704°	2227°	1257°*	−95°*	−85°	−64°C*

* Note that aluminum trifluoride, silicon tetrafluoride, and sulfur hexafluoride have the interesting property, described in Chapter 10 for carbon dioxide, of subliming at 1 atm pressure without melting. The temperatures given in the table as the boiling points of these two substances are in fact the subliming points, when the vapor pressure of the crystals becomes equal to 1 atm.

The great change between aluminum trifluoride and silicon tetrafluoride is, however, not due to any great change in bond type—the bonds are in all cases intermediate in character between extreme ionic bonds M$^+$F$^-$ and normal covalent bonds

M $:\overset{..}{\underset{..}{F}}:$ —but rather to a *change in atomic arrangement*. The three easily volatile substances exist as discrete molecules SiF$_4$, PF$_5$, and SF$_6$ (with no dipole moments) in the liquid and crystalline states as well as the gaseous state (Figure 16-5), and the thermal agitation necessary for fusion or vaporization is only that needed to overcome the weak intermolecular forces, and is essentially independent of the strength or nature of the interatomic bonds within a molecule. But the other three substances in the crystalline state are giant molecules, with strong bonds between neighboring ions holding the whole crystal together (NaF, sodium chloride arrangement, Figure 4-2; MgF$_2$, Figure 22-2). To melt such a crystal some of these strong bonds must be broken, and to boil the liquid more must be broken; hence the melting point and boiling point are high. A detailed discussion of these substances and their properties in terms of the relative sizes of the atoms (ionic radius ratio) is given in Section 22-2.

The extreme case is that in which the entire crystal is held together by very strong covalent bonds; this occurs for diamond, with sublimation point 4347°C at 1 atm and melting point at some higher value.

The Dependence of Melting Point on Molecular Symmetry. The foregoing discussion has in-

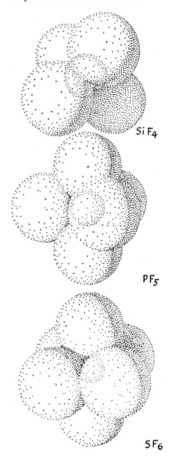

Figure **16-5** *Molecules of silicon tetrafluoride, phosphorus pentafluoride, and sulfur hexafluoride, three very volatile substances.*

Si F$_4$

PF$_5$

SF$_6$

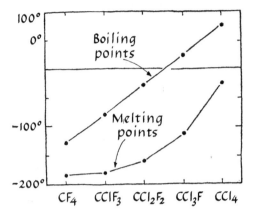

Figure **16-6**

The effect of molecular symmetry on melting point.

dicated that the melting points and the boiling points of substances are determined by several factors. One of these is the *symmetry* of the molecules, which has a pronounced effect on the melting point, but not on the boiling point: the greater the symmetry of the molecule, the higher the melting point of the substance. This effect is shown by many organic compounds, and it is strikingly evident for the series of tetrahedral molecules CF_4, CF_3Cl, CF_2Cl_2, $CFCl_3$, CCl_4 (Figure 16-6). The boiling points of these substances are very nearly a linear function of the number of chlorine atoms in the molecule, but the melting points show a pronounced deviation from linearity.

This deviation can be explained in the following way. In a liquid, which has a structure characterized by some randomness of molecular arrangement, the molecules are piled together in various ways, not determined by their symmetry. In the crystal, however, there is a striking difference: a molecule of CF_2Cl_2 can fit into its place in the crystal in only two ways (differing in rotation of the molecule through 180° around a certain axis), whereas a molecule of CF_3Cl can fit into its place in a crystal of this substance in three ways (differing by a rotation through 120° around an axis through the carbon atom and the chlorine atom), and a molecule of CF_4 can fit into its place in the crystal of the substance in twelve ways. At the melting point, where there is equilibrium between the crystal and the liquid, equal numbers of molecules must be leaving the crystal and attaching themselves to it. The chance of leaving the crystal, under the influence of thermal agitation, is the same for a molecule of high symmetry as for one of low symmetry, whereas the chance of striking the crystal in suitable orientation to stick to it is greater for the molecule of high symmetry than for that of low symmetry. Thus a molecule of CF_4 can strike the crystal and adhere to it in any one of twelve orientations, whereas the molecule of CF_2Cl_2 can strike its crystal and adhere to it in only two orientations. Accordingly, substances with molecules of high symmetry crystallize more readily than those of low symmetry; that is, they have higher melting point. Relative to CF_2Cl_2 (symmetry number 2), this effect causes an increase in melting point of about 14°C for CF_3Cl and $CFCl_3$ (symmetry number 3) and of 57°C for CF_4 and CCl_4 (symmetry number 12).

For some sequences of substances the effect of the symmetry number on the melting point is overcome by an opposite effect of the electric dipole moment. This effect can be recognized because it affects the boiling point as well as the melting point. One example of the many that might be given is methylene chloride, CH_2Cl_2, which has a large value of the electric dipole moment, 1.62 D. Its melting point, -97°C, is not about 57° lower than the average of those of the more symmetric molecules CH_4 (m.p. -182.5°C) and CCl_4 (m.p. -22.9°C), but is 6° higher. That the electric dipole is effective in this case is indicated by the boiling point of CH_2Cl_2, 40°C, which is 82° higher than the average of those of CH_4 (-161.5°C) and CCl_4 (76.7°C).

16-7. The Hydrogen Bond—the Cause of the Unusual Properties of Water

The unusual properties of water mentioned in Section 16-5 are due to the power of its molecules to attract one another especially strongly. This power is associated with a structural feature called the hydrogen bond. The melting points and boiling points of the hydrides of some nonmetallic elements are shown in Figure 16-7. The variation for a series of congeners is normal for the sequences. The curves through the points for H_2Te, H_2Se, and H_2S show the expected trend, but when extrapolated they indicate values of about -100°C and -80°C, respectively, for the melting point and boiling point of water. The observed value of the melting point is 100° greater, and that of the boiling point is 180° greater, than would be expected for water if it were a normal substance; and hydrogen fluoride and ammonia show similar, but smaller, deviations.

The values of the entropy of vaporization of water and other substances that form strong hydrogen bonds are also affected by this structural feature. This effect will be discussed in Section 16-10.

The Nature of the Hydrogen Bond. The hydrogen ion is a bare nucleus, with charge $+1$. If hydrogen fluoride, HF, had an extreme ionic structure, it could be represented as in A of Figure 16-8. The positive charge of the hydrogen ion could then strongly attract a negative ion, such as a fluoride ion, forming an $[F^-H^+F^-]^-$ or HF_2^- ion, as shown in B. This does indeed occur, and the stable ion HF_2^-, called the *hydrogen difluoride ion*, exists in considerable concentration in acidic fluoride solutions, and in salts such as KHF_2, potassium hydrogen difluoride. The bond holding this complex ion

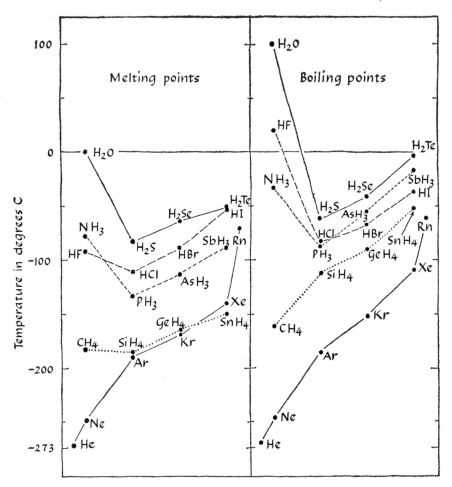

Figure **16-7**

> *Melting points and boiling points of hydrides of nonmetallic elements, showing abnormally high values for hydrogen fluoride, water, and ammonia, caused by hydrogen-bond formation.*

together, called the **hydrogen bond,** is weaker than ordinary ionic or covalent bonds, but stronger than ordinary van der Waals forces of intermolecular attraction.

Hydrogen bonds are also formed between hydrogen fluoride molecules, causing the gaseous substance to be largely polymerized into the molecular species H_2F_2, H_3F_3, H_4F_4, H_5F_5, and H_6F_6 (Figure 16-9).

In a hydrogen bond the hydrogen atom is usually attached more strongly to one of the two electronegative atoms which it holds together than to the others.* The structure of the dimer of hydrogen fluoride may be represented by the formula

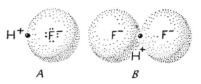

$$F^- —H^+ \cdots F^- —H^+$$

in which the dotted line represents the hydrogen bonding.

Figure **16-8** *The hydrogen fluoride molecule (A) and the hydrogen difluoride ion, containing a hydrogen bond (B).*

Because of the electrostatic origin of the hydrogen bond, only the most electronegative atoms—fluorine, oxygen, nitrogen—form these bonds. Usually an unshared electron pair of the attracted atom approaches closely to the attracting hydrogen ion. Water is an especially suitable substance for hydrogen-bond formation, because each molecule has two attached hydrogen atoms and two unshared electron pairs, and hence can form four hydrogen bonds. The tetrahedral arrangement of the shared and unshared electron pairs causes these four bonds to extend in the four tetrahedral directions in space, and leads to the characteristic crystal structure of ice (Figure 16-10). This structure, in which each molecule is surrounded by only four immediate neighbors, is a very open structure, and accordingly ice is a substance with abnormally low density. When ice melts, this tetrahedral structure is partially destroyed, and the water molecules are packed more closely together, causing water to have greater density than ice. Many of the hydrogen bonds remain, however, and aggregates of molecules with the open tetrahedral structure persist in water at the freezing point. With increase in temperature some of these aggregates break up, causing a further increase in density of the liquid; only at 4°C does the normal expansion due to increase in molecular agitation overcome this effect, and cause water to begin to show the usual decrease in density with increasing temperature.

Example 3.   The heat of sublimation of ice (to form water vapor) is 12.20 kcal/mole. The corresponding values for CH_4, H_2Se, GeH_4, H_2Te, and SnH_4 are 2.0, 5.3, 4.0, 6.6, and 5.0 kcal/mole, respectively. (a) Use the values for CH_4, H_2Se, GeH_4, H_2Te, and SnH_4 to estimate the value for a hypothetical form of ice in which the water molecules are held together by van der Waals attraction only. (b) Assuming that this value represents the energy of van der Waals attraction in ice, use it to obtain from the observed heat of sublimation of ice a value for the energy of the O—H$\cdots$O hydrogen bond in ice.

   Solution.   The molecules H_2Se and GeH_4 are isoelectronic (same number of electrons), as are also H_2Te and SnH_4. For each pair the ratio of their

---

* In KHF_2 and a few other exceptional substances the hydrogen atom is midway between the hydrogen-bonded atoms.

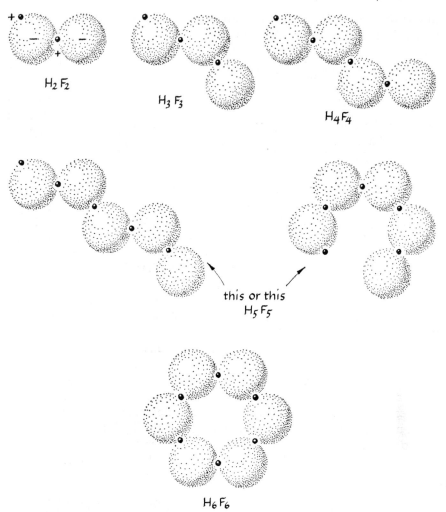

H_2F_2

H_3F_3

H_4F_4

this or this
H_5F_5

H_6F_6

Figure **16-9**

Some polymers of hydrogen fluoride.

heats of sublimation is 1.32. We assume, as a rough approximation, that the same ratio would apply also to the isoelectronic pair H_2O and CH_4 if H_2O did not form hydrogen bonds. This leads to 2.6 kcal/mole for the heat of vaporization of the hypothetical form of ice, and to the value $12.2 - 2.6 = 9.6$ kcal/mole for the energy of the hydrogen bonds in ice. There are two hydrogen bonds per H_2O molecule; hence the energy per O—H⋯O bond in ice is $9.6/2 = $ **4.8 kcal/mole.**

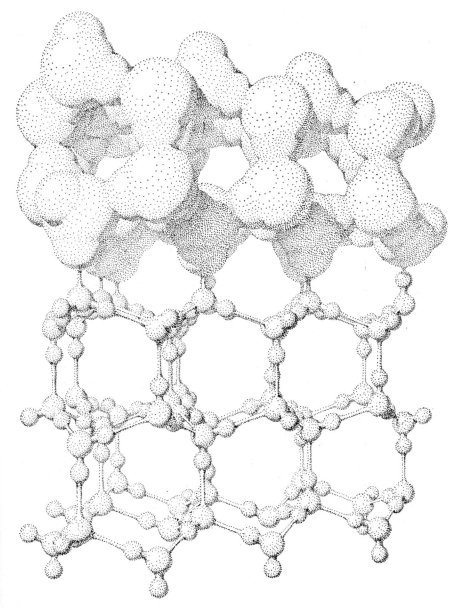

Figure **16-10**

> A small part of a crystal of ice. The molecules above are shown with approximately their correct size (relative to the interatomic distances). Note hydrogen bonds, and the open structure that gives ice its low density. The molecules below are indicated diagrammatically as small spheres for oxygen atoms and still smaller spheres for hydrogen atoms.

Illustrative
Exercises

16-1. The heat of sublimation of ammonia is 6.93 kcal/mole. Using information in Example 3, estimate the energy of the hydrogen bonds in ammonia.
(Answer: 4.6 kcal/mole per NH_3, 1.5 kcal/mole per $N—H \cdots N$.)

16-2. The heat of fusion of ice is 1.44 kcal/mole and that of methane is 0.22 kcal/mole. Using the value in Example 3 for the energy of $H—O \cdots H$ bond in ice, estimate the fraction of the hydrogen bonds in ice that are broken in the process of fusion.
(Answer: About 12%.)

16-3. The heat capacity of water at 0°C is 1.00 cal deg^{-1} g^{-1}, whereas the value estimated by Kopp's rule (Section 5-8) is 0.57 cal deg^{-1} g^{-1}. Assuming that the difference represents the heat of breaking some of the hydrogen bonds as the temperature increases, calculate the percentage left unbroken in water at the boiling point. Use the answers to the preceding exercise and Example 3 in making the calculation. (Answer: About 80%.)

16-8. The Importance of Water as an Electrolytic Solvent

Salts are insoluble in most solvents. Gasoline, benzene, carbon disulfide, carbon tetrachloride, alcohol, ether—these substances are "good solvents" for grease, rubber, organic materials generally; but they do not dissolve salts.

The reasons that water is so effective in dissolving salts are that *it has a very high dielectric constant* (about 81 at room temperature) and *its molecules tend to combine with ions, to form hydrated ions*. Both of these properties are related to the large electric dipole moment of the water molecule (Section 9-10).

The force of attraction or repulsion of electric charges is inversely proportional to the dielectric constant of the medium surrounding the charges. This means that two opposite electric charges in water attract each other with a force only $\frac{1}{81}$ as strong as in air (or a vacuum). It is clear that the ions of a crystal of sodium chloride placed in water could dissociate away from the crystal far more easily than if the crystal were in air, since the electrostatic force bringing an ion back to the surface of the crystal from the aqueous solution is only $\frac{1}{81}$ as strong as from air. It is accordingly not surprising that the thermal agitation of the ions in a salt crystal at room temperature is not great enough to cause the ions to dissociate away into the air, but that it is great enough to overcome the relatively weak attraction when the crystal is surrounded by water, thus allowing large numbers of the ions to dissociate into aqueous solution.

The Hydration of an Ion.   A related effect that stabilizes the dissolved ions is the formation of *hydrates* of the ions. Each negative ion attracts the positive ends of the adjacent water molecules, and tends to hold several water molecules attached to itself. The positive ions, which are usually smaller than the negative ions, show this effect still more strongly; each positive ion attracts the negative ends of the water molecules, and binds several molecules tightly about itself, forming a hydrate, which may have considerable stability, especially for the bipositive and terpositive cations.

The number of water molecules attached to a cation, its **ligancy,*** is determined by the size of the cation. The small cation Be^{++} forms the tetrahydrate† $Be(OH_2)_4{}^{++}$. A somewhat larger ion, such as Mg^{++} or Al^{+++}, forms a hexahydrate, $Mg(OH_2)_6{}^{++}$ or $Al(OH_2)_6{}^{+++}$ (Figure 16-11).

The forces between cations and water molecules are so strong that the ions often retain a layer of water molecules in crystals. This water is called *water of crystallization*. This effect is more pronounced for bipositive and terpositive ions than for unipositive ions. The tetrahedral complex $Be(H_2O)_4{}^{++}$ occurs in various salts, including $BeCO_3 \cdot 4H_2O$, $BeCl_2 \cdot 4H_2O$, and $BeSO_4 \cdot 4H_2O$, and is no doubt present also in solution. The following salts contain larger ions, with six water molecules in octahedral coordination:

$MgCl_2 \cdot 6H_2O$	$AlCl_3 \cdot 6H_2O$
$Mg(ClO_3)_2 \cdot 6H_2O$	$KAl(SO_4)_2 \cdot 12H_2O$
$Mg(ClO_4)_2 \cdot 6H_2O$	$Fe(NH_4)_2(SO_4)_2 \cdot 6H_2O$
$MgSiF_6 \cdot 6H_2O$	$Fe(NO_3)_2 \cdot 6H_2O$
$NiSnCl_6 \cdot 6H_2O$	$FeCl_3 \cdot 6H_2O$

In a crystal such as $FeSO_4 \cdot 7H_2O$, six of the water molecules are attached to the iron ion, in the complex $Fe(OH_2)_6{}^{++}$, and the seventh occupies another position, being packed near a sulfate ion of the crystal. In alum, $KAl(SO_4)_2 \cdot 12H_2O$, six of the twelve water molecules are coordinated about the aluminum ion and the other six about the potassium ion.

Crystals also exist in which some or all of the water molecules have been removed from the cations. For example, magnesium sulfate forms the three crystalline compounds $MgSO_4 \cdot 7H_2O$, $MgSO_4 \cdot H_2O$, and $MgSO_4$.

Clathrate Compounds. The noble gases, simple hydrocarbons, and many other substances form crystalline hydrates; for example, xenon forms the hydrate $Xe \cdot 5\frac{3}{4}H_2O$, stable at about 2°C and partial pressure of xenon 1 atm, and methane forms a similar hydrate, $CH_4 \cdot 5\frac{3}{4}H_2O$. X-ray investigation has shown that these crystals have a structure in which the water molecules form a hydrogen-bonded framework, resembling that of ice in that each water molecule is tetrahedrally surrounded by four others, at 2.76 Å, but with a more open arrangement, such as to provide cavities (pentagonal dodecahedra

---

* The ligancy of an atom is the number of atoms bonded to it or in contact with it. The ligancy was formerly called the *coordination number*.

† In these formulas water is written OH_2 instead of H_2O, to indicate that the oxygen atom of the water molecule is near the metal ion, the hydrogen atoms being on the outside. Usually the formulas are written $Be(H_2O)_4{}^{++}$, etc.

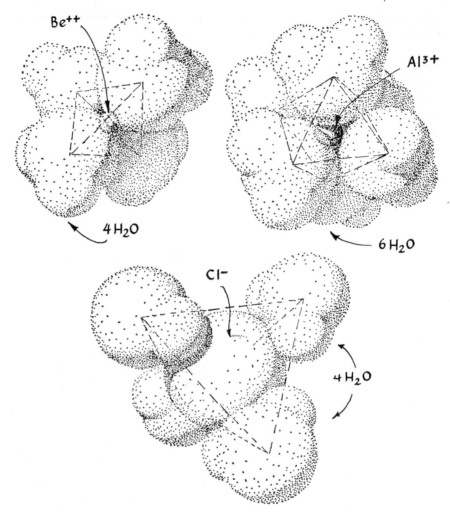

Figure **16-11**

Diagrams showing the structure of hydrated ions.

and other polygons with pentagonal or hexagonal faces) that are big enough to permit occupancy by the noble gas atoms or other molecules. Crystals of this sort are called clathrate crystals.

The structure of xenon hydrate and the hydrates of argon, krypton, methane, chlorine, bromine, hydrogen sulfide, and some other substances is shown in Figure 16-12. The cubic unit of structure has edge about 12 Å and contains 46 water molecules. Chloroform hydrate, $CHCl_3 \cdot 17H_2O$, has a somewhat more complicated structure, in which the chloroform molecule is surrounded by a 16-sided polyhedron formed by 28 water molecules.

Clathrate compounds also can be made in which the hydrogen-bonded framework is formed by organic molecules such as urea, $(H_2N)_2CO$.

Other Electrolytic Solvents. Some liquids other than water can serve as ionizing solvents, with the power of dissolving electrolytes to give electrically conducting solutions. These liquids include hydrogen peroxide, hydrogen

Figure **16-12**

> *The structure of a clathrate crystal, xenon hydrate. The xenon atoms occupy cavities (eight per unit cube) in a hydrogen-bonded three-dimensional network formed by the water molecules (46 per unit cube). The $O—H\cdots O$ distance is 2.76 Å, as in ice. Two xenon atoms, at 0, 0, 0 and $\frac{1}{2}, \frac{1}{2}, \frac{1}{2}$, are at the centers of nearly regular pentagonal dodecahedra. The other six, at $0, \frac{1}{4}, \frac{1}{2}$; $0, \frac{3}{4}, \frac{1}{2}$; $\frac{1}{2}, \frac{1}{4}, 0$; $\frac{1}{2}, \frac{3}{4}, 0$; $\frac{1}{4}, \frac{1}{2}, 0$; and $\frac{3}{4}, \frac{1}{2}, 0$, are at the centers of tetrakaidecahedra. Each tetrakaidecahedron (one is outlined, right center) has 24 corners (water molecules), two hexagonal faces, and 12 pentagonal faces.*

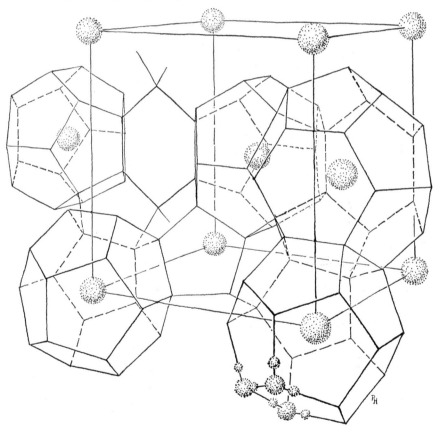

fluoride, liquid ammonia, and hydrogen cyanide. All of these liquids, like water, have large dielectric constants. Liquids with low dielectric constants, such as benzene and carbon disulfide, do not act as ionizing solvents.

Liquids with large dielectric constants are sometimes called *dipolar liquids* (or simply *polar liquids*).

The large dielectric constant of water, which is responsible for the striking power of water to dissolve ionic substances, is due in part to its power to form hydrogen bonds. The hydrogen bonds help the water molecules to line up in such a direction as to neutralize part of the electric field. Hydrogen bonds are also formed in the other liquids [hydrogen peroxide, hydrogen fluoride, ammonia (boiling point $-33.4°C$), and hydrogen cyanide] that can dissolve ionic substances.

16-9. Heavy Water

After the discovery of the heavy isotopes of oxygen, O^{17} and O^{18}, in 1929, and of deuterium, H^2, in 1932, it was recognized that ordinary water consists of molecules of several different kinds, built out of these isotopic atoms in various ways. Since these molecules have almost identical properties except for mass, the density of a sample of water is proportional to the average molecular weight of the molecules in it. If the sample of water consisted of ordinary oxygen combined only with deuterium, its molecular weight would be 20 instead of 18, and its density would accordingly be over 10% greater than that of ordinary water. The term *heavy water* is used to refer to this form of water, which may also be called *deuterium oxide*.

It may be pointed out that still heavier water might be made, by isolating the isotope O^{18}, and combining it with deuterium. This water would have density about 20% greater than ordinary water.

There is, in fact, a still heavier form of water. The isotope H^3, called tritium, is a radioactive substance with half-life 12.4 years. Ordinary tritium oxide has molecular weight 22, whereas water made from tritium and O^{18} would have molecular weight 24, and would be over 30% denser than ordinary water.

Shortly after the discovery of deuterium by H. C. Urey, Gilbert Newton Lewis prepared 1 ml of nearly pure deuterium oxide by the continued fractional electrolysis of ordinary water. Since then heavy water has been very carefully studied and new methods have been developed for its isolation which permit it to be made in large quantities. Its density at 20°C is 1.1059 g/cm³, its freezing point is 3.82°C, its boiling point 101.42°C, and its temperature of maximum density 11.6°C.

Heavy water and other compounds of deuterium are used in the study of chemical reactions, especially those taking place in living organisms. For example, an investigator might want to know whether the water that is drunk by an animal serves merely as a solvent in the animal's body, or enters into chemical reactions, converting it, with other substances, into the proteins, fats, and other constituents of the cells of the organism. He could find out by having the animal drink heavy water, and then following the course of the deuterium. The content of deuterium in water can be determined either by use of the mass spectrograph or by the accurate determination of the density of carefully distilled water made from the preparation.

In recent years heavy water has been used in the field of nuclear chemistry. Heavy water can be used instead of graphite as the moderator in a nuclear reactor. The function of the moderator is to reduce the speed of the fast neutrons emitted when nuclei undergo fission. The Canadian reactor at Chalk River is a heavy-water reactor (Chapter 30).

16-10. Entropy of Vaporization and the Structure of Liquids

In Section 5-8 it was mentioned that the entropy of vaporization (the heat of vaporization divided by the absolute temperature at the boiling point) has nearly the same value for many liquids. This fact can be used to derive some conclusions about the nature of liquids.

Values of the standard boiling point (at 1 atm pressure) and the heat of vaporization for some liquids whose gases are monatomic are given in Table 16-1 (the first 10 entries). The boiling points cover a wide range, from 27.2°K for neon to 2933°K for gold. Over the range of liquids from neon to gold the heat of vaporization also varies widely, but the ratio of heat of vaporization to temperature, which is the entropy of vaporization, ranges only from 15.8 cal deg^{-1} mole^{-1} to 25.4 cal deg^{-1} mole^{-1}. The values of the entropy of vaporization for many liquids with polyatomic molecules also lie within this range. This is the basis of Trouton's rule (Section 5-8).

Hildebrand's Rule.   An improvement on Trouton's rule was made in 1915 by the American chemist J. H. Hildebrand (born 1881). He found that the entropy of vaporization at the equilibrium temperature between the liquid and its vapor at standard molar volume (22.4 liters) is nearly the same for many substances. Values of this temperature for molar gas volume 22.4 liters are given in the third column of Table 16-1 (the method of calculating these values is discussed below). The last column of the table is the entropy of vaporization to the gas at this standard molar volume

For the 26 substances in the table these values of ΔS_{vap} are equal to 20.3 $\pm$ 0.3 cal deg^{-1} mole^{-1}. It seems likely that the various liquids, despite their different molecular structures, are similar to one another in some respect that leads to the constancy of this quantity.

Let us discuss the equilibrium between the liquid and the vapor by application of the Boltzmann distribution law. Let n_G be the number of molecules per unit volume in the gas and n_L the number per unit volume (accessible to the centers of the molecules) in the liquid. At equilibrium we write the Boltzmann distribution law for substances with monatomic molecules in the following form:

$$\frac{n_G}{n_L} = \exp\left(-\frac{\Delta H_{\text{vap}}}{RT}\right) \tag{5}$$

Here ΔH_{vap} is the heat of vaporization per mole of substance in the gas phase. The ratio V_L/V_G of the volume per molecule V_L in the liquid to that V_G in the gas is equal to n_G/n_L; hence we write

Table **16-1**

Values of Entropy of Vaporization of Some Liquids

	BOILING POINT			
SUB-STANCE	AT 1 ATM	AT STANDARD VOLUME	MOLAR HEAT OF VAPORIZATION	MOLAR ENTROPY OF VAPORIZATION (gas at standard volume)
Ne	27.2°K	21.1°K	0.431 kcal mole^{-1}	20.4 cal deg^{-1} mole^{-1}
Ar	87.3	77.5	1.56	20.4
Kr	119.9	109.9	2.16	19.6
Xe	165	153	3.02	19.8
Cu	2855	3500	72.8	20.8
Ag	2466	3000	60.7	20.2
Au	2933	3600	74.2	20.6
Zn	1180	1347	27.4	20.3
Cd	1040	1176	23.9	20.3
Hg	630	680	13.9	20.4
HCl	188.1	182	3.87	21.3
HBr	206.4	201	4.21	20.9
HI	238	235	4.72	20.1
H$_2$S	213	208	4.46	21.4
H$_2$Se	232	228	4.62	20.3
PH$_3$	185	178	3.49	19.6
AsH$_3$	211	205	4.17	20.3
CH$_4$	111.7	101	1.96	19.4
SnH$_4$	221	217	4.41	20.3
CCl$_4$	350	358	7.17	20.0
O$_2$	90.2	80.4	1.63	20.3
N$_2$	77.3	67.5	1.33	19.8
CO	81.7	72.0	1.45	20.1
F$_2$	85.2	75.4	1.51	20.0
Cl$_2$	239	236	4.88	20.7
P$_4$	553	592	11.9	20.1
			Average	20.3 ± 0.3

$$V_L = V_G \exp\left(-\frac{\Delta H_{\text{vap}}}{RT}\right) \tag{6}$$

For a gas with standard molar volume, as in Table 16-1, the volume per molecule V_G is 22.414 liters divided by Avogadro's number, 0.602×10^{24}; its value is accordingly 37,200 Å^3. The value of $\Delta H_{\text{vap}}/RT$ is 20.3 cal deg^{-1} mole^{-1}/1.987 cal deg^{-1} mole^{-1}, which is 10.21. Hence we obtain from Equation 6 the expression

$$V_L = 37{,}200 \text{ Å}^3 \times e^{-10.21} = 37{,}200 \text{ Å}^3 \times 10^{-4.435}$$
$$= 37{,}200 \text{ Å}^3/27{,}200 = 1.37 \text{ Å}^3$$

We have thus calculated for the substances in Table 16-1 that the free volume per molecule (the volume accessible to the center of the molecule) in the liquid at the boiling point is 1.37 Å^3. This volume may seem to be surprisingly small.

We know, for example (Chapter 2), that the distance between copper atoms in the copper crystal is 2.55 Å, and the volume of a sphere with this diameter is 8.6 Å³. In the liquid, which has a smaller density, the volume per atom of copper is some- what larger. However, the center of the atom cannot move throughout the entire volume. It is instead restrained by the surrounding molecules to a rather small region. The volume 1.37 Å³ accessible to the center of the atom corresponds to motion of the center within a sphere of radius 0.69 Å. Hence we conclude that in liquids such as those in Table 16-1 each molecule is free to move about 0.69 Å from its average position.

No one knows why liquids so different as the noble gases and the metals have the same free volume at their boiling points, 1.37 Å³ per molecule. The theory of liquids is still in a rather primitive state. We may hope that the explanation of this interesting fact will be provided before many years, perhaps by one of the readers of this book.

Deviations from Hildebrand's Rule. Many substances with polyatomic mole- cules have normal values of the entropy of vaporization (Table 16-1). This fact is interpreted as showing that the molecules are about as free to assume various orientations in the liquid as in the gas phase, where they are completely free. Substances whose molecules differ from a roughly spherical shape are, however, found to have values of the entropy of vaporization larger than the Hildebrand value 20.3 cal deg⁻¹ mole⁻¹. Two examples, cyanogen ($:N\equiv C-C\equiv N:$) and acetylene ($H-C\equiv C-H$), are given in Table 16-2. Acetylene has entropy of vaporization 2.5 cal deg⁻¹ mole⁻¹ greater than the normal value. If this excess is attributed to the restriction in freedom of orientation of the rodlike molecules by their neighbors in the liquid, the solid angle accessible to the axis of the average molecule is calculated to be 30% of the value 4π corresponding to complete freedom of orientation.

Substances whose molecules form hydrogen bonds have large values of the entropy of vaporization. For water, hydrogen peroxide, methanol, ethanol, ethylene glycol, and nitric acid the excess over the Hildebrand value ranges from 4.2 to 9.6 cal deg⁻¹ mole⁻¹ (Table 16-2). These values correspond to restriction in orientation by the factors 0.08 to 0.01; the accessible solid angles to which the molecules are restrained by the hydrogen bonds in the liquids are only 8% to 1% of the free-orientation values.

Helium and hydrogen are unusual in having very small values of the entropy of vaporization. This property is a quantum effect associated with their small molecular weight.

The Dependence of Vapor Pressure on Temperature. It is possible by the meth- ods of thermodynamics or statistical mechanics to derive an equation showing the relation between the value P_1 of the vapor pressure of a liquid at temperature T_1 and the value P_2 at temperature T_2. This equation is

$$\ln\left(\frac{P_2}{P_1}\right) = \frac{\Delta H_{\text{vap}}}{R}\left(\frac{1}{T_1} - \frac{1}{T_2}\right) \tag{7}$$

The equation involves the assumption that ΔH_{vap} is constant over the range of temperature T_1 to T_2.

Table 16-2

Values of Entropy of Vaporization Deviating from Hildebrand's Rule

SUB-STANCE	BOILING POINT AT 1 ATM	AT STANDARD VOLUME	MOLAR HEAT OF VAPORIZATION	MOLAR ENTROPY OF VAPORIZATION (gas at standard volume)
H_2O	373.2°K	383°K	9.72 kcal mole^{-1}	25.4 cal deg^{-1} mole^{-1}
H_2O_2	423	435	13.01	29.9
CH_3OH	338	344	8.43	24.5
C_2H_5OH	352	358	9.22	25.8
$(CH_2OH)_2$	470	489	13.6	27.8
HNO_3	353	360	9.43	26.2
NH_3	240	237	5.58	23.5
C_2N_2	252	250	5.58	22.3
C_2H_2	189	184	4.2	22.8
He	4.22	1.53	0.020	13.1
H_2	20.39	13.7	0.216	15.8

EXERCISES

16-4. Write the fundamental chemical equations for the softening of water by a zeolite and for the regeneration of the zeolite.

16-5. Write the fundamental chemical equations for the removal of most of the ionic impurities in water by the "ion-exchange" process. Why do you suppose this process is sometimes preferred to distillation for the preparation of moderately pure water for industrial use? What do you think is the simplest method of determining when the absorbers in Tanks A and B of Figure 16-1 are saturated with ions and should be regenerated?

16-6. From values of the enthalpy of formation given in Table 6-2, calculate the heat evolved on neutralization of hydrogen ion by hydroxide ion in aqueous solution. (Answer: 13.36 kcal/mole.)

16-7. Why are there no strong hydrogen bonds in liquid H_2S?

16-8. By reference to Figure 16-7, estimate the melting points and boiling points that hydrogen fluoride, water, and ammonia would be expected to have if these substances did not form hydrogen bonds. What would you expect the relative density of ice and water to be if hydrogen bonds were not formed?

16-9. In softening water, aluminum sulfate or ferric sulfate is often added as well as calcium hydroxide, with the formation of a flocculent precipitate of aluminum hydroxide or ferric hydroxide. Write equations for the formation of these two hydroxides. Why are these hydroxides useful in the process of purifying water?

16-10. What explanation can you give of the fact that calcium fluoride, CaF_2 (the mineral fluorite), is a crystalline substance with high melting point, whereas stannic chloride, $SnCl_4$, is an easily volatile liquid?

16-11. Describe the structure of ice. Explain why ice floats, and mention some ways in which this property affects our lives.

16-12. Explain why sodium chloride crystallizes from solution as unhydrated NaCl, beryllium chloride as $BeCl_2 \cdot 4H_2O$, and magnesium chloride as $MgCl_2 \cdot 6H_2O$.

16-13. What is the fraction by weight of tritium in tritium oxide? (The atomic weight of tritium is 3.0.)

16-14. Can you apply the principle of Le Chatelier to predict whether the melting point of ice becomes greater than or less than 0°C when the pressure is increased? Compare the volume of ice and that of the water obtained by melting it.

16-15. Pure water at 24°C contains $H^+(aq)$ and $OH^-(aq)$ at concentration 1.00×10^{-7} moles/liter. At a temperature 10°C different, these ions have concentration 1.40×10^{-7} moles/liter. Is this temperature 14°C or 34°C? (Consider Le Chatelier's principle and Exercise 16-6.)

16-16. The electric dipole moment of water has the value 1.84 D. The O—H bond length is 0.965 Å, and the H—O—H bond angle is 104°30′. If the dipole moment is due to charges at the positions of the nuclei, what are the values of these charges? (Answer: -0.65 on O, $+0.325$ on H, in units e.)

16-17. The only substance known to form a crystalline solution with water (that is, to be present in ice) is ammonium fluoride. Can you explain this fact? What is the structure of the crystalline solution?

16-18. Perchloric acid monohydrate forms orthorhombic crystals that are isomorphous with those of ammonium perchlorate and rubidium perchlorate. What do you conclude about the structure of the monohydrate from this fact?

16-19. The vapor of methanol, CH_3OH, contains some tetramer molecules.
(a) Can you suggest a reasonable structure for the tetramer?
(b) What would you estimate the enthalpy of formation of tetramer from monomer to be? (Answer: About 20 kcal/mole.)

16-20. When water vapor is condensed on a surface at about -120°C, it forms a modification of ice that is cubic. The oxygen atoms are in the carbon positions of diamond (Figure 10-2), and the O—H$\cdots$O distance has the same value as in hexagonal ice at this temperature (2.75 Å). What is the length of edge of the unit cube? From this information calculate the density of cubic ice at -120°C and compare with that of hexagonal ice at this temperature, which is 0.935 g/cm³. (Answer: 6.35 Å.)

16-21. From Figure 10-2 it can be seen that the diamond structure can be described in terms of cubes with edge $a/2$; each cube has four of its corners occupied by carbon atoms, and alternate cubes also have carbon atoms at their centers. The atomic positions are $0, 0, 0$; $0, \frac{1}{2}, \frac{1}{2}$; $\frac{1}{2}, 0, \frac{1}{2}$; $\frac{1}{2}, \frac{1}{2}, 0$; $\frac{1}{4}, \frac{1}{4}, \frac{1}{4}$; $\frac{1}{4}, \frac{3}{4}, \frac{3}{4}$; $\frac{3}{4}, \frac{1}{4}, \frac{3}{4}$; $\frac{3}{4}, \frac{3}{4}, \frac{1}{4}$. The largest cavities that might be occupied by a foreign molecule are at the centers of the vacant cubes ($\frac{3}{4}, \frac{1}{4}, \frac{1}{4}$; etc.). What is the largest van der Waals radius for a molecule that might fit into such a cavity in a crystal of cubic ice? Which of the noble gases might form interstitial solutions in cubic ice? (For van der Waals radii of oxygen and noble gases, see Table 9-4 and Example 11, Chapter 9.) (Answer: 1.35 Å; He and Ne.)

16-22. The unit of structure of the clathrate crystal shown in Figure 16-12 contains two small polyhedra, each with 20 water molecules at its corners, and six larger polyhedra, each with 24 water molecules at its corners. The edges are O—H$\cdots$O hydrogen bonds, with length 2.76 Å. The small polyhedron is the pentagonal dodecahedron. The distance from the center to a corner of a regular pentagonal dodecahedron is 1.40 times the length of the edge. Can you explain why xenon hydrate and methane hydrate have composition $8Xe \cdot 46H_2O$ and $8CH_4 \cdot 46H_2O$, whereas chlorine hydrate and bromine hydrate have composition $6Cl_2 \cdot 46H_2O$ and $6Br_2 \cdot 46H_2O$? What would you predict for the composition of crystals formed by water, chlorine, and xenon? (Answer: $2Xe \cdot 6Cl_2 \cdot 46H_2O$.)

CHAPTER 17

The Properties of Solutions

One of the most striking properties of water is its ability to dissolve many substances, forming *aqueous solutions*. Solutions are very important kinds of matter—important for industry and for life. The ocean is an aqueous solution which contains thousands of components: ions of the metals and nonmetals, complex inorganic ions, many different organic substances. It was in this solution that the first living organisms developed, and from it that they obtained the ions and molecules needed for their growth and life. In the course of time organisms were evolved that could leave this aqueous environment, and move out onto the land and into the air. They achieved this ability by carrying the aqueous solution with them, as tissue fluid, blood plasma, and intracellular fluids containing the necessary supply of ions and molecules.

The properties of solutions have been extensively studied, and it has been found that they can be correlated in large part by some simple laws. These laws and some descriptive information about solutions are discussed in the following sections.

17-1. Types of Solutions. Nomenclature

In Chapter 1 a solution was defined as a homogeneous material that does not have a definite composition.

The most common solutions are liquids. Carbonated water, for example, is a *liquid solution* of carbon dioxide in water. Air is a *gaseous solution* of nitrogen, oxygen, carbon dioxide, water vapor, and the noble gases. Coinage silver is a *solid solution* or *crystalline solution* of silver and copper. The structure of this crystalline solution is like that of crystalline copper, described in Chapter 2. The atoms are arranged in the same regular way, cubic closest packing, but atoms of silver and atoms of copper follow one another in a largely random sequence.

If one component of a solution is present in larger amount than the others, it may be called the **solvent**; the others are called **solutes.**

The concentration of a solute is often expressed as the number of grams per 100 g of solvent or the number of grams per liter of solution. It is often convenient to give the number of gram formula weights per liter of solution (the *formality*), the number of gram molecular weights per liter of solution (the *molarity*), or the number of gram equivalent weights per liter of solution (the *normality*). Sometimes these are referred to 1000 g of solvent; they are then called the *weight-formality, weight-molarity,** and *weight-normality*, respectively.

The **formality** (*F*) *is the number of gram formula weights of solute per liter of solution.*

The **molarity** (*M*) *is the number of moles of solute per liter of solution.*

The **normality** (*N*) *is the number of gram equivalent weights per liter of solution.*

If the formula used for a substance is its correct molecular formula, describing the molecules actually present in the solution, then the formality is the same as the molarity. For example, a 1 *F* solution of $C_{12}H_{22}O_{11}$, sucrose (ordinary sugar) is also a 1 *M* solution. But a 1 *F* solution of NaCl, sodium chloride, is not a 1 *M* solution of NaCl; it is better described as 1 *M* in Na^+ and 1 *M* in Cl^-, because the substance is completely dissociated into these ions in the solution, and no NaCl molecules are present.

Example 1. A solution is made by dissolving 64.11 g of $Mg(NO_3)_2 \cdot 6H_2O$ in water enough to bring the volume to 1 liter. Describe the system.

  Solution. The formula weight of $Mg(NO_3)_2 \cdot 6H_2O$ is 256.43; hence the solution is 0.25 *F* (0.25 formal) in this substance. The salt is, however, completely ionized in solution, to give magnesium ions, Mg^{++}, and nitrate ions, NO_3^-. Each formula of the salt produces one magnesium ion and two nitrate ions. Hence the solution is 0.25 *M* (0.25 molar) in Mg^{++} and 0.50 *M* in NO_3^-. Because magnesium is bivalent, its equivalent weight is one half its atomic weight. Hence the solution is 0.50 *N* (0.50 normal) in Mg^{++} and 0.50 *N* in NO_3^-.

For some purposes concentrations of the constituents of a solution are described by values of their *mole fractions.*

The **mole fraction** *of a molecular species is the ratio of the number of moles of that molecular species to the total number of moles.*

The sum of the mole fractions of all the molecular species is equal to unity.

Example 2. What are the mole fractions of the components of ordinary 95% ethyl alcohol?

  Solution. Each 100 g of this solution contains 95 g of ethyl alcohol

---

* Sometimes the weight-molarity is called *molality*. A few authors have used molality as the moles per liter of solution, but this usage has not been accepted.

(C_2H_5OH, MW 46.07), and 5 g of water (H_2O, MW 18). The number of moles of alcohol per 100 g of solution is $95/46.07 = 2.06$; the number of moles of water is $5/18 = 0.28$. The total number of moles is 2.34. The mole fraction of alcohol is $x_1 = 2.06/2.34 = 0.88$; that of water is $x_2 = 0.28/2.34 = 0.12$. Note that $x_1 + x_2 = 1.00$.

It is worth noting that a 1 M aqueous solution cannot be made up accurately by dissolving one mole of solute in 1 liter of water, because the volume of the solution is in general different from that of the solvent. Nor is it equal to the sum of the volumes of the components; for example, 1 liter of water and 1 liter of alcohol on mixing give 1.93 liters of solution; there occurs a volume contraction of 3.5%.

There is no way of predicting the density of a solution; tables of experimental values for important solutions are given in reference books and handbooks, such as the *International Critical Tables*, the *Handbook of Chemistry and Physics*, and *Lange's Handbook*.

Illustrative Exercises

17-1. A solution is made containing 6.3 g of nitric acid, HNO_3, in 1 liter of solution. The formula weight of HNO_3 is 63.

(a) What is the formality of the HNO_3 solution?

(b) Nitric acid is a strong acid. What is the molarity of the solution in H^+ and in NO_3^-?

17-2. A solution is made by mixing one mole (18 g) of water, one mole (32 g) of methyl alcohol, CH_3OH, and one mole (46 g) of ethyl alcohol, C_2H_5OH. What are the mole fractions of the three substances in the solution?

17-3. How many grams of $KMnO_4$ should be weighed out to make 1 liter of a 0.2000 F solution?

17-2. Solubility

A system is in **equilibrium** *when its properties remain constant with the passage of time.*

If the system in equilibrium contains a solution plus one of the components of the solution in the form of a pure substance, the concentration of that substance in the solution is called the *solubility* of the substance. The solution is called a *saturated solution*.

For example, at 0°C a solution of borax containing 1.3 g of anhydrous sodium tetraborate, $Na_2B_4O_7$, in 100 g of water is in equilibrium with the solid substance $Na_2B_4O_7 \cdot 10H_2O$, sodium tetraborate decahydrate; on standing, the system does not change, the composition of the solution remaining constant. The solubility of $Na_2B_4O_7 \cdot 10H_2O$ in water is hence 1.3 g $Na_2B_4O_7$ per 100 g, or—correcting for the water of hydration—2.5 g $Na_2B_4O_7 \cdot 10H_2O$ per 100 g.

Phases. In the discussion of solubility it is convenient to make use of the word *phase*.

A **phase** *is a homogeneous part of a system, separated from other parts by physical boundaries.*

For example, if a flask is partially full of water in which ice is floating, the system comprising the contents of the flask consists of three phases, the solid phase ice, the liquid phase water, and the gaseous phase air (Figure 17-1).

A phase in a system comprises all of the parts that have the same properties and composition. Thus if there were several pieces of ice in the system represented in Figure 17-1 they would constitute not several phases, but only one phase, the ice phase.

In the above example, a saturated solution of borax, the system consists of two phases, the solution, which is a liquid phase, and the substance $Na_2B_4O_7 \cdot 10H_2O$, a crystalline phase.

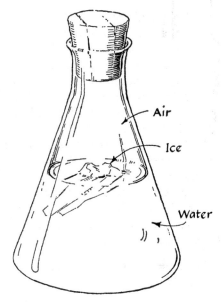

Figure **17-1**   *A system consisting of three phases.*

Change in the Solid Phase. The solubility of $Na_2B_4O_7 \cdot 10H_2O$ increases rapidly with increasing temperature; at 60°C it is 20.3 g $Na_2B_4O_7$ per 100 g (Figure 17-2). If the system is heated to a temperature somewhat above 60°C and held there for some time, a new phenomenon occurs. A third phase appears, a crystalline phase with composition $Na_2B_4O_7 \cdot 5H_2O$, and the other

Figure **17-2**

     Solubility of sodium tetraborate in water.

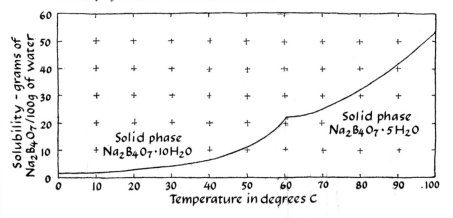

solid phase disappears. At this temperature the solubility of the decahydrate is greater than that of the pentahydrate; a solution saturated with the decahydrate is supersaturated with respect to the pentahydrate, and will deposit crystals of the pentahydrate.* The process of solution of the unstable phase and crystallization of the stable phase will then continue until none of the unstable phase remains.

In this case the decahydrate is less soluble than the pentahydrate below 61°C, and is hence the stable phase below this temperature. The solubility curves of the two hydrates cross at 61°C, the pentahydrate being stable in contact with solution above this temperature.

Change other than solvation may occur in the stable solid phase. Thus orthorhombic sulfur (Chapter 13) is less soluble in suitable solvents than is monoclinic sulfur at temperatures below 95.5°C, the transition temperature between the two forms; above this temperature the monoclinic form is the less soluble. The principles of thermodynamics require that the temperature at which the solubility curves of the two forms cross be the same for all solvents, and be also the temperature at which the vapor pressure curves intersect.

17-3.   The Dependence of Solubility on Temperature

The solubility of a substance may either increase or decrease with increasing temperature. An interesting case is provided by sodium sulfate. The solubility of $Na_2SO_4 \cdot 10H_2O$ (the stable solid phase below 32.4°C) increases very rapidly with increasing temperature, from 5 g Na_2SO_4 per 100 g of water at 0°C to 52 g at 32.4°C. Above 32.4°C the stable solid phase is Na_2SO_4; the solubility of this phase decreases rapidly with increasing temperature, from 52 g at 32.4°C to 42 g at 100°C (Figure 17-3).

Most salts show increased solubility with increase in temperature; a good number (NaCl, K_2CrO_4) change only slightly in solubility with increase in temperature; and a few, such as Na_2SO_4 and $Na_2CO_3 \cdot H_2O$, show decreased solubility (Figures 17-4 and 17-5).

The principles of thermodynamics provide a quantitative relation between the change in solubility with temperature of a substance (its *temperature coefficient of solubility*) and its *heat of solution*, the heat evolved as the substance dissolves in its nearly saturated solution. *If the heat of solution of a solid substance is positive* (that is, if heat is evolved on dissolving the substance in its nearly saturated solution) *the solubility of the solid decreases with increasing temperature, and if the heat of solution is negative the solubility increases.*

This rule may be derived from the principle of Le Chatelier, which has been discussed in the preceding chapter. If a system containing solute and solution

* The addition of "seeds" (small crystals of the substance) is sometimes necessary to cause the process of crystallization to begin.

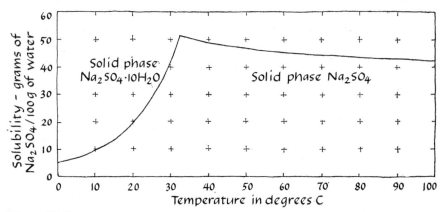

Figure **17-3**

Solubility of sodium sulfate in water.

Figure **17-4**

Solubility curves for some salts in water.

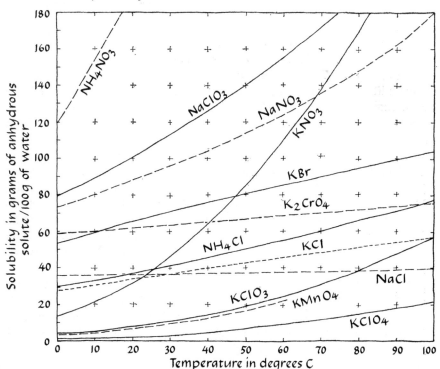

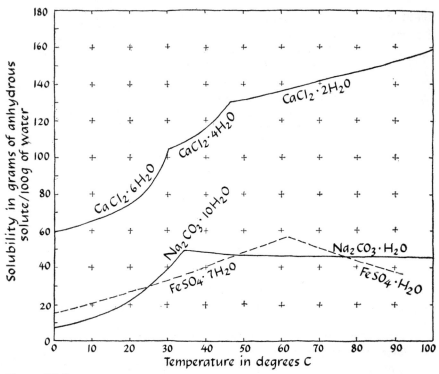

Figure 17-5

Solubility curves for salts forming two or three hydrates.

is in equilibrium at a certain temperature, and the temperature is raised, the equilibrium will shift, according to this principle, in such a way as to tend to restore the system to its original temperature, by the absorption of heat from the reaction. This shift will involve the transfer of more solute into the solution if the heat of solution is negative, or the reverse process if the heat of solution is positive. Consider a solid in equilibrium with its saturated solution at one temperature. Let the temperature be increased somewhat. If the heat of solution is negative (heat being absorbed when more of the substance is dissolved) the system would be cooled in case that some of the solid phase were to dissolve, and the temperature would then drop back toward the original temperature. Hence this process will occur, and the solubility thus increases with increase in temperature.

Most salts, corresponding to their positive temperature coefficients of solubility, have negative heats of solution in water. For example, the heat of solution of $Na_2SO_4 \cdot 10H_2O$ in water is -19 kcal per gram formula weight. The formal heat of solution of sodium chloride is -1.3 kcal and that of Na_2SO_4 is 5.5 kcal.

Illustrative Exercises

17-4. In Figure 17-3 the solubility of sodium sulfate is indicated to be 9.0 g Na_2SO_4 per 100 g of water at 10°C. If 109 g of this saturated solution were allowed to evaporate, how many grams of the crystalline phase $Na_2SO_4 \cdot 10H_2O$ would be obtained?

17-5. (a) When crystals of $FeSO_4 \cdot 7H_2O$ are dissolved in water is heat liberated or absorbed (see Figure 17-5)?

(b) When crystals of $FeSO_4 \cdot H_2O$ are dissolved in water, is heat liberated or absorbed?

(c) Can you predict whether heat is liberated or absorbed during the following reaction:

$$FeSO_4 \cdot H_2O + 6H_2O \longrightarrow FeSO_4 \cdot 7H_2O$$

[Hint: make use of the principle of conservation of energy and your answers to (a) and (b).]

17-4. The Dependence of Solubility on the Nature of Solute and Solvent

Substances vary greatly in their solubilities in various solvents. There are a few general rules about solubility, which, however, apply in the main to organic compounds.

One of these rules is that **a substance tends to dissolve in solvents that are chemically similar to it.** For example, the hydrocarbon naphthalene, $C_{10}H_8$, has a high solubility in gasoline, which is a mixture of hydrocarbons; it has a somewhat smaller solubility in ethyl alcohol, C_2H_5OH, whose molecules consist of short hydrocarbon chains with hydroxide groups attached, and a very small solubility in water, which is much different from a hydrocarbon. On the other hand, boric acid, $B(OH)_3$, a hydroxide compound, is moderately soluble in both water and alcohol, which themselves contain hydroxide groups, and is insoluble in gasoline. In fact, the three solvents themselves show the same phenomenon—both gasoline and water are miscible with (soluble in) alcohol, whereas gasoline and water dissolve in each other only in very small amounts.

The explanation of these facts is the following. Hydrocarbon groups (involving only carbon and hydrogen atoms) attract hydrocarbon groups only weakly, as is shown by the low melting and boiling points of hydrocarbons, relative to other substances with similar molecular weights. But hydroxide groups and water molecules show very strong intermolecular attraction; the melting point and boiling point of water are higher than those of any other substance with low molecular weight. This strong attraction is due to the partial ionic character of the O—H bonds, which places electric charges on the atoms. The positively charged hydrogen atoms are then attracted to the negative oxygen atoms of other molecules, forming hydrogen bonds and holding the molecules firmly together (Chapter 16). The reason that the substances such as gasoline or naphthalene do not dissolve in water is that their molecules in solution would prevent water molecules from forming as many of these strong hydrogen bonds as in pure water; on the other hand, boric acid is soluble in water because the decrease in the number of water-water bonds is compensated by the formation of strong hydrogen bonds between the water molecules and the hydroxide groups of the boric acid molecules.

17-5.   Solubility of Salts and Hydroxides

In the study of inorganic chemistry, especially qualitative analysis, it is useful to know the approximate solubility of common substances. The simple rules of solubility are given below. These rules apply to compounds of the common cations Na^+, K^+, NH_4^+, Mg^{++}, Ca^{++}, Sr^{++}, Ba^{++}, Al^{+++}, Cr^{+++}, Mn^{++}, Fe^{++}, Fe^{+++}, Co^{++}, Ni^{++}, Cu^{++}, Zn^{++}, Ag^+, Cd^{++}, Sn^{++}, Hg_2^{++}, Hg^{++}, and Pb^{++}. By "soluble" it is meant that the solubility is more than about 1 g per 100 ml (roughly 0.1 M in the cation), and by "insoluble" that the solubility is less than about 0.1 g per 100 ml (roughly 0.01 M); substances with solubilities within or close to these limits are described as *sparingly soluble*.

Class of mainly soluble substances:

All **nitrates** are soluble.

All **acetates** are soluble.

All **chlorides, bromides,** and **iodides** are soluble except those of silver, mercurous mercury (mercury with oxidation number $+1$), and lead. $PbCl_2$ and $PbBr_2$ are sparingly soluble in cold water (1 g per 100 ml at 20°C) and more soluble in hot water (3 g, 5 g, respectively, per 100 ml at 100°C).

All **sulfates** are soluble except those of barium, strontium, and lead. $CaSO_4$, Ag_2SO_4, and Hg_2SO_4 (mercurous sulfate) are sparingly soluble.

All salts of **sodium, potassium,** and **ammonium** are soluble except $NaSb(OH)_6$ (sodium antimonate), K_2PtCl_6 (potassium hexachloroplatinate), $(NH_4)_2PtCl_6$, $K_3Co(NO_2)_6$ (potassium cobaltinitrite), and $(NH_4)_3Co(NO_2)_6$.

Class of mainly insoluble substances:

All **hydroxides** are insoluble except those of the alkali metals, ammonium, and barium. $Ca(OH)_2$ and $Sr(OH)_2$ are sparingly soluble.

All normal **carbonates** and **phosphates** are insoluble except those of the alkali metals and ammonium. Many hydrogen carbonates and phosphates, such as $Ca(HCO_3)_2$, $Ca(H_2PO_4)_2$, etc., are soluble.

All **sulfides** except those of the alkali metals, ammonium, and the alkaline-earth metals are insoluble.*

---

* The sulfides of aluminum and chromium are hydrolyzed by water, precipitating $Al(OH)_3$ and $Cr(OH)_3$.

17-6. The Dependence of Solubility on Pressure

The effect of change of pressure on the solubility of crystalline or liquid substances in liquids is usually very small. For example, a pressure of 1000 atm increases the solubility of sodium chloride in water at 25°C only from 35.9 g per 100 g of water to 37.0 g per 100 g of water.

The **solubility of a gas in a liquid** (the weight of the dissolved gas) is, however, greatly increased by increase in pressure. At low pressures it is **directly proportional to the pressure of the gas** [**Henry's law,** discovered in 1803 by the British chemist William Henry (1774–1836)]. If the gas is a mixture, the solubility of each substance in the mixture is separately proportional to its partial pressure.

For example, the solubility of oxygen at 1 atm pressure in water at 18°C is 46 mg/liter, and at 10 atm pressure it is 460 mg/liter. Note that although the *weight* of oxygen dissolved by a liter of water is ten times as great at 10 atm pressure as at one atmosphere, the volume, at the applied pressure, is the same.

The solubilities of most gases in water are of the order of magnitude of that of oxygen. Exceptions are those gases which combine chemically with water or which dissociate largely into ions, including carbon dioxide, hydrogen sulfide, sulfur dioxide, and ammonia, which are extremely soluble.

Illustrative Exercise	**17-6.** It is stated above that 46 mg of oxygen can dissolve in 1 liter of water at 18°C when the pressure (partial pressure) of oxygen is 1 atm, and 460 mg when it is 10 atm.

(a) What are the volumes of these weights of oxygen at standard conditions?

(b) What are the volumes at 18°C and the respective pressures, 1 atm and 10 atm?

17-7. The Freezing Point and Boiling Point of Solutions

It is well known that the freezing point of a solution is lower than that of the pure solvent; for example, in cold climates it is customary to add a solute such as alcohol or glycerol or ethylene glycol to the radiator water of automobiles to keep it from freezing. Freezing-point lowering by the solute also underlies the use of a salt-ice mixture for cooling, as in freezing ice cream; the salt dissolves in the water, making a solution, which is in equilibrium with ice at a temperature below the freezing point of water.

It is found by experiment that the freezing-point lowering of a dilute solution is proportional to the concentration of the solute. In 1883 the French chemist François Marie Raoult (1830–1901) made the useful discovery that **the weight-molar freezing-point lowering produced by different solutes is the same for a given solvent.** Thus the following freezing points are observed for 0.1 M solutions of the following solutes in water:

Hydrogen peroxide,	H_2O_2	$-0.186°C$
Methanol,	CH_3OH	-0.181
Ethanol,	C_2H_5OH	-0.183
Dextrose,	$C_6H_{12}O_6$	-0.186
Sucrose,	$C_{12}H_{22}O_{11}$	-0.188

The *weight-molar freezing-point constant* for water has the value 1.86°C, the freezing point of a solution containing c moles of solute per 1000 g of water being $-1.86\ c$ in degrees C. For other solvents the values of this constant are the following:

SOLVENT	FREEZING POINT	WEIGHT-MOLAR* FREEZING-POINT CONSTANT
Benzene	5.6°C	4.90°
Acetic acid	17	3.90
Phenol	40	7.27
Camphor	180	40

* Moles per 1000 g of solvent.

The Determination of Molecular Weight by the Freezing-Point Method.
The freezing-point method is a very useful way of determining the molecular weights of substances in solution. Camphor, with its very large constant, is of particular value for the study of organic substances.

Example 3. The freezing point of a solution of 0.244 g of benzoic acid in 20 g of benzene was observed to be 5.232°C, and that of pure benzene to be 5.478°. What is the molecular weight of benzoic acid in this solution?

    Solution. The solution contains $0.244 \times 1000/20 = 12.2$ g of benzoic acid per 1000 g of solvent. The number of moles of solute per 1000 g of solvent is found from the observed freezing-point lowering 0.246° to be $0.246/4.90 = 0.0502$. Hence the molecular weight is $12.2/0.0502 = 243$. The explanation of this high value (the formula weight for benzoic acid, C_6H_5COOH, being 122.05) is that in this solvent the substance forms double molecules, $(C_6H_5COOH)_2$.

Evidence for Electrolytic Dissociation. One of the strongest arguments advanced by Arrhenius in support of the theory of electrolytic dissociation (Section 8-1) was the fact that the freezing-point lowering of salt solutions is much larger than that calculated for undissociated molecules, the observed lowering for a salt such as NaCl or $MgSO_4$ in very dilute solution being just twice as great and for a salt such as Na_2SO_4 or $CaCl_2$ just three times as great as expected. These results are explained by the assumption, made by Arrhenius, that NaCl and $MgSO_4$ form two ions (Na^+ and Cl^-, Mg^{++} and SO_4^{--}), whereas Na_2SO_4 and $CaCl_2$ form three ions ($2Na^+$ and SO_4^{--}, Ca^{++} and $2Cl^-$) per molecule.

Elevation of Boiling Point. *The boiling point of a solution is higher than that of the pure solvent by an amount proportional to the weight-molar concentration of the solute.* Values of the proportionality factor, the *molar boiling-point constant*, are given below for some important solvents. Boiling-point measurements for a solution can be used to obtain the molecular weight of the solute in the same way as freezing-point measurements.

SOLVENT	BOILING POINT	MOLAR* BOILING-POINT CONSTANT
Water	100°C	0.52°C
Ethyl alcohol	78.5	1.19
Ethyl ether	34.5	2.11
Benzene	79.6	2.65

* Weight-molar.

Illustrative Exercises

17-7. It was found by experiment that a solution of 12.8 g of an unknown organic compound dissolved in 1000 g of benzene has freezing point 0.49°C below that of pure benzene. What is the molecular weight of the compound?

17-8. (a) The freezing point of a 0.01 *F* aqueous solution of KCl is $-0.037°C$. How does this fact support the Arrhenius theory of ionization?

(b) What do you predict the boiling point of the solution to be?

17-8. The Vapor Pressure of Solutions. Raoult's Law

It was found experimentally by Raoult in 1887 that the partial pressure of solvent vapor in equilibrium with a dilute solution is directly proportional to the mole fraction of solvent in the solution. It can be expressed by the equation

$$P = P_0 x$$

in which P is the partial pressure of the solvent above the solution, P_0 is the vapor pressure of the pure solvent, and x is the mole fraction of solvent in the solution, as defined in the first section of this chapter. We may give a kinetic interpretation of this equation by saying that only x times as many solvent molecules can escape from the surface of a solution as from the corresponding surface of the pure solvent, and that accordingly equilibrium will be reached with the gas phase when the number of gas molecules striking the surface is x times the number striking the surface of the pure solvent at equilibrium.

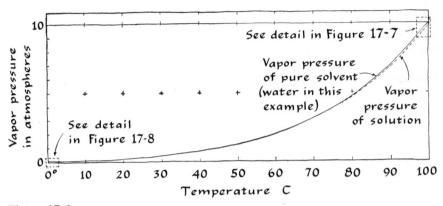

Figure 17-6

Vapor-pressure curves of water in the range 0°C to 100°C.

The Derivation of Freezing-point Lowering and Boiling-point Raising from Raoult's Law. The laws of freezing-point lowering and boiling-point raising can be derived from Raoult's law in the following way. We first consider boiling-point raising. In Figure 17-6 the upper curve represents the vapor pressure of pure solvent as a function of the temperature. The temperature at which this becomes 1 atm is the boiling point of the pure solvent. The lower curve represents the vapor pressure of a solution of a nonvolatile solute; Raoult's law requires that it lie below the curve for the pure solvent by an amount proportional to the molal concentration of solute, and that the same curve apply for all solutes, the molal concentration being the only significant quantity. This curve intersects the 1 atm line at a temperature higher than the boiling point of the solvent by an amount proportional to the molal concentration of the solute (for dilute solutions), as expressed in the boiling-point law (Figure 17-7).

Figure **17-7** *Vapor-pressure curves of water and an aqueous solution near the boiling point, showing elevation of the boiling point of the solution.*

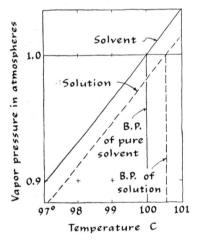

The argument for freezing-point lowering is similar. In Figure 17-8 the vapor pressure curves of the pure solvent in the crystalline state and the liquid state are shown intersecting at the freezing point of the pure solvent. At higher temperatures the crystal has higher vapor pressure than the liquid, and is hence unstable relative to it, and at lower temperatures the stability relation is reversed. The solution vapor pressure curve, lying below that of the liquid pure solvent, intersects the crystal curve at a temperature below the melting point of the pure solvent. This is the melting point of the solution.

Note that the assumption is made that the solid phase obtained on freezing the solution is pure solvent; if a crystalline solution is formed, as sometimes occurs, the freezing-point law does not hold.

17-9. The Osmotic Pressure of Solutions

If red blood corpuscles are placed in pure water they swell, become round, and finally burst. This is the result of the fact that the cell wall is permeable to water but not to some of the solutes of the cell solution (mainly *hemoglobin*, the red protein in red cells); in the effort to reach a condition of equilibrium (equality of water vapor pressure) between the two liquids, water enters the cell. If the cell wall were sufficiently strong, equilibrium would be reached when the hydrostatic pressure in the cell had reached a certain value, at which the water vapor pressure of the solution equals the vapor pressure of the pure water outside the cell. This equilibrium hydrostatic pressure is called the *osmotic pressure* of the solution.

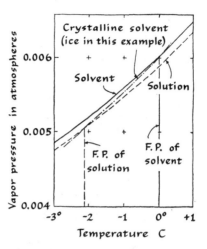

Figure **17-8** *Vapor-pressure curves of water, ice, and an aqueous solution near the freezing point, showing depression of freezing point of the solution.*

A *semipermeable membrane* is a membrane with very small holes in it, of such a size that molecules of the solvent are able to pass through but molecules of the solute are not. A useful semipermeable membrane for measurement of osmotic pressure is made by precipitating cupric ferrocyanide, $Cu_2Fe(CN)_6$, in the pores of an unglazed porcelain cup, which gives the membrane mechanical support to enable it to withstand high pressures. Accurate measurements have been made in this way to over 250 atm. Cellophane membranes may also be used, if the osmotic pressure is not large (Figure 17-9).

It is found experimentally that the osmotic pressure of a dilute solution satisfies the equation

$$\pi V = n_1 RT$$

with n_1 the number of moles of solute (to which the membrane is impermeable) in volume V, π the osmotic pressure, R the gas constant, and T the absolute temperature. This relation was discovered by van't Hoff in 1887. It is striking that the equation is identical in form with the perfect-gas equation; van't Hoff emphasized the similarity of a dissolved substance and a gas.

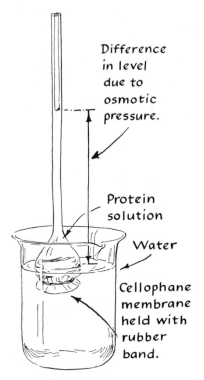

Difference
in level
due to
osmotic
pressure.

Protein
solution

Water

Cellophane
membrane
held with
rubber
band.

Figure **17-9** *The measurement of the osmotic pressure of a solution.*

For inorganic substances and simple organic substances the osmotic-pressure method of determining molecular weight offers no advantages over other methods, such as the measurement of freezing-point lowering. It has, however, been found useful for substances of very high molecular weight; the molecular weight of hemoglobin was first reliably determined in this way by Adair in 1925. The value found by Adair, 68,000, has been verified by measurements made with the ultracentrifuge, and also by the investigation of crystals of hemoglobin by the x-ray diffraction method. The same molecular weight is found for the different kinds of hemoglobin in the blood of animals of different species.

17-10. Colloids

It was found by Thomas Graham (1805–1869) in the years around 1860 that substances such as glue, gelatin, albumin, starch, etc., in solution diffuse very slowly, their diffusion rates being as small as one one-hundredth of those for ordinary solutes (salt, sugar, etc.). Graham also found that substances of these two types differ markedly in their ability to pass through a membrane such as parchment paper or collodion; if a solution of sugar and glue is put into a collodion or Cellophane bag and the bag is placed in a stream of running water the sugar soon dialyzes through the bag into the water, and the glue remains behind. This process of **dialysis** gives a useful method of separating substances of these two kinds.

We now recognize that these differences in ability to pass through the pores of a membrane and in rates of diffusion are due to differences in size of the solute molecules. Graham thought that there was a deeper difference between ordinary, easily crystallizable substances and the slowly diffusing nondialyzing substances, which he was unable to crystallize. He named the substances of the latter class *colloids* (Greek *kolla*, glue), in contradistinction to ordinary *crystalloids*. The modern usage is to define **colloids** as **substances with very large molecules or containing large aggregates of molecules.**

Some colloids consist of well-defined molecules, with constant molecular weight and definite molecular shape, permitting them to be piled in a crystalline array. Crystalline proteins include egg albumin (molecular weight 43,000) and hemoglobin (molecular weight 68,000).

Colloids may also be made by dispersing in a liquid a solid or liquid substance that is normally insoluble, such as gold, ferric oxide, arsenious sulfide, etc. A colloidal dispersion of this sort consists of very small particles of the dispersed substance, so small that their temperature motion (Brownian movement) prevents them from settling out in the gravitational field of the earth.

17-11. The Activities of Ions

During the early development of the ionic theory of electrolytic solutions it was recognized that the observed freezing-point lowering of these solutions, while greater than that corresponding to undissociated solute molecules, is not so great as expected for complete ionization. For example, the freezing point of a 0.1 F solution of KBr is $-0.345°$C. Since the freezing-point constant for water is 1.86°, this lowering requires that there be effective 0.185 moles of solute, 85% more than the number of formulas KBr present, but not 100% more. For a number of years it was thought that facts such as this showed the salts to be only partially ionized; in this case KBr was said to be 85% ionized, the solution being said to be 0.085 M in K^+, 0.085 M in Br^-, and 0.015 M in undissociated KBr.

Then, about 1904, it was noticed that many properties of solutions of salts and strong acids (such as their color) suggest that **most salts and strong acids are completely ionized in dilute solution.** This view has been generally accepted since 1923, when a quantitative theory of the interactions of ions in solution was developed by Debye and Hückel. This theory is called the *Debye-Hückel theory of electrolytes.*

The explanation of the fact that a strong electrolyte such as potassium bromide produces a smaller freezing-point lowering than calculated for complete ionization is that there are strong *electrical forces* operating between the ions, which decrease their effectiveness, so that the properties of their solutions are different from those of ideal solutions, except at extreme dilution. The interionic attraction reduces the *activity* of the ions to a value less than their concentration.

The factor by which the ion concentration is to be multiplied to obtain the ion activity is called the *activity coefficient.* For all strong electrolytes containing only univalent ions (HCl, NaCl, KNO_3, etc.) its values are approximately 0.80 at 0.1 F, 0.90 at 0.01 F, and 0.96 at 0.001 F, approaching 1 only in very dilute solutions. These activity coefficients are of significance in connection with chemical equilibrium, which is to be discussed later.

EXERCISES

17-9. Give an example of a gaseous solution, a liquid solution, and a crystalline solution.

17-10. A solution contains 10.00 g of anhydrous cupric sulfate, $CuSO_4$, in 1000 ml of solution. What is the formality of this solution in $CuSO_4$?

17-11. Saturated salt solution (20°C) contains 35.1 g NaCl per 100 g of water. What is its weight-formality? The density of the solution is 1.197 g/ml. What is its formality?

17-12. A 2 wt F solution of HCl is neutralized with 2 wt F NaOH. What is the weight formality of NaCl in the resulting solution?

17-13. Calculate the mole fraction of each component in the following solutions:
(a) 2.000 g of chloroform, $CHCl_3$, in 10.00 g of carbon tetrachloride, CCl_4.
(b) 1.000 g of acetic acid, $C_2H_4O_2$, in 20.00 g of benzene, recognizing that acetic acid actually exists in benzene solution as the dimer, $(C_2H_4O_2)_2$.

17-14. The density of constant-boiling hydrochloric acid is 1.10 g/ml. It contains 20.24% HCl. Calculate the weight molarity, the volume molarity, and the mole fraction of HCl in the solution.

17-15. Sodium perchlorate is very soluble in water. What would happen if a solution of about 70 g of $NaClO_4$ in 100 ml of water were to be mixed with a solution of about 40 g of KCl in 100 ml of water, at 20°C? (See Figure 17-4.)

17-16. Make qualitative predictions about the solubility of the following:
(a) Ethyl ether, $C_2H_5OC_2H_5$, in water, alcohol, and benzene.
(b) Hydrogen chloride in water and gasoline.
(c) Ice in liquid hydrogen fluoride and in cooled gasoline.
(d) Sodium tetraborate in water, in ether, and in carbon tetrachloride.
(e) Iodoform, HCI_3, in water and in carbon tetrachloride.

(f) Decane, $C_{10}H_{22}$, in water and in gasoline.

17-17. What can you say about the solubility in water of the substances $AgNO_3$, $PbCl_2$, PbI_2, Hg_2SO_4, $BaSO_4$, $Mg(OH)_2$, $Ba(OH)_2$, PbS, $NaSb(OH)_6$, K_2PtCl_6, KCl?

17-18. (a) The density of sodium chloride is 2.16 g/ml, and that of its saturated aqueous solution, containing 311 g NaCl per liter, is 1.197 g/ml. Would the solubility be increased or decreased by increasing the pressure? Give your calculations. (The assumption may be made that the change in volume that occurs when a small amount of salt is dissolved in a nearly saturated solution has the same sign as the volume change that occurs when a large amount of salt is dissolved in water.)
(b) Make a similar prediction for another salt, obtaining data from reference books.

17-19. By referring to Figures 17-3, 17-4, and 17-5, find three salts that on dissolving in a nearly saturated solution give out heat, and three that absorb heat.

17-20. Would heat be evolved or absorbed if some $Na_2CO_3 \cdot 10H_2O$ were dissolved in its nearly saturated aqueous solution at 30°C? If some $Na_2CO_3 \cdot H_2O$ were dissolved in this solution at 30°C?

17-21. What can you say about the heat of solution of common salt? (See Figure 17-4.)

17-22. The solubility of potassium hydrogen sulfate is 51.4 g per 100 g of water at 20°C, and 67.3 g per 100 g at 40°C. If you add some of the salt to a partially saturated solution and stir, will the system become colder or warmer?

17-23. Calculate approximately how much ethanol (C_2H_5OH) would be needed per gallon of radiator water to keep it from freezing at temperatures down to 10°F below the freezing point.

17-24. A solution containing 1 g of aluminum bromide in 100 g of benzene has a freezing point 0.099°C below that of pure benzene.

What are the apparent molecular weight and the correct formula of the solute?

17-25. The solubility of nitrogen at 1 atm partial pressure in water at 0°C is 23.54 ml/liter, and that of oxygen is 48.89. Calculate the amount by which the freezing points of air-saturated water and air-free water differ.

17-26. An aqueous solution of amygdalin (a sugarlike substance obtained from almonds) containing 96 g of solute per liter was found to have osmotic pressure 4.74 atm at 0°C. What is the molecular weight of the solute?

17-27. A 2% aqueous solution of gum arabic (simplest formula $C_{12}H_{22}O_{11}$) was found to have an osmotic pressure of 13.8 mm Hg at 25°C. What are the average molecular weight and degree of polymerization of the solute?

17-28. A solution containing 2.30 g of glycerol in 100 ml of water was found to freeze at −0.465°C. What is the approximate molecular weight of glycerol dissolved in water? The formula of glycerol is $C_3H_5(OH)_3$. What would you predict as to the miscibility of this substance with water (its solubility)?

17-29. When 0.412 g of naphthalene ($C_{10}H_8$) was dissolved in 10.0 g of camphor, the freezing point was found to be 13.0° below that of pure camphor. What is the weight molar freezing-point constant for camphor,

calculated from this observation? Can you explain why camphor is frequently used in molecular weight determinations?

17-30. A sample of a substance weighing 1.00 g was dissolved in 8.55 g of camphor, and was found to produce a depression of 9.5°C in the freezing point of the camphor. Using the value of the molar freezing-point constant found in the preceding problem, calculate the molecular weight of the substance.

17-31. Why is methyl alcohol (boiling point 65°C) a less satisfactory antifreeze than ethylene glycol (b.p. 197°C)?

17-32. The freezing point of ethylene glycol is −12°C, yet when mixed with water in a car radiator it can prevent freezing at even lower temperatures. How is this explained?

17-33. Adding alcohol to water lowers the freezing point of water, but also lowers the boiling point. Explain.

17-34. Find the osmotic pressure at 17°C of a solution containing 17.5 g of sucrose ($C_{12}H_{22}O_{11}$) in 150 ml of solution. (Answer: 8.1 atm.)

17-35. Considering that the cell wall is an osmotic membrane, explain why a lettuce salad containing salt and vinegar becomes limp in a few hours.

17-36. Why do some marine organisms burst when placed in fresh water?

CHAPTER 18

Chemical Equilibrium and the Rate

of Chemical Reaction

Two questions may be asked in the consideration of a proposed chemical process, such as the preparation of a useful substance. One of these questions is "Are the stability relations of the reactants and the expected products such that it is possible for the reaction to occur?" The second question is equally important: it is "Under what conditions will the reaction proceed sufficiently rapidly for the method of preparation to be practicable?"

18-1. Factors Influencing the Rate of Reaction

Every chemical reaction requires some time for its completion, but some reactions are fast and some are slow. Reactions between ions in solution without change in oxidation state are usually extremely fast. An example is the neutralization of a strong acid by a strong base, which proceeds as fast as the solutions can be mixed. Presumably nearly every time a hydronium ion collides with a hydroxide ion reaction occurs, and the number of collisions is very great, so that there is little delay in the reaction.

The formation of a precipitate, such as that of silver chloride when a solution containing silver ion is mixed with a solution containing chloride ion, may require a few seconds, to permit the ions to diffuse together to form the crystalline grains of the precipitate:

$$Ag^+ + Cl^- \longrightarrow AgCl(c)$$

On the other hand, ionic oxidation-reduction reactions are sometimes very slow. An example is the reduction of permanganate ion by hydrogen peroxide in sulfuric acid solution. When a drop of permanganate solution is added to a solution of hydrogen peroxide and sulfuric acid, the solution is colored pink, and this pink color may remain for several minutes, indicating that very little reaction has taken place. When, after several minutes, the solution has become colorless, another drop of permanganate is found to produce a pink color that remains for a shorter time, and a third and fourth drop are found to be decolorized still more rapidly. Finally, after a considerable amount of permanganate solution has been added and has undergone reaction, with the formation of manganous ion and the liberation of free oxygen, it is found that the permanganate solution poured in a steady stream into the container is decolorized as rapidly as it can be stirred into the hydrogen peroxide solution. The explanation of this interesting phenomenon is that a product of the reaction, manganese in a lower state of oxidation, acts as a catalyst for the reaction; the first drop of permanganate reacts slowly, in the absence of any catalyst, but the reaction undergone by subsequent drops is the catalyzed reaction.

An example of a reaction which is extremely slow at room temperature is that between hydrogen and oxygen:

$$2H_2 + O_2 \longrightarrow 2H_2O$$

A mixture of hydrogen and oxygen can be kept for years without appreciable reaction. If the gas is ignited, however, a very rapid reaction—an explosion—occurs.

Homogeneous and Heterogeneous Reactions. A reaction that takes place in a homogeneous system (consisting of a single phase) is called a **homogeneous reaction.** The most important of these reactions are those in gases (such as the formation of nitric oxide in the electric arc, $N_2 + O_2 \rightleftharpoons 2NO$) and those in liquid solutions.

A **heterogeneous reaction** is a reaction involving two or more phases. An example is the oxidation of carbon by potassium perchlorate:

$$KClO_4(c) + 2C(c) \longrightarrow KCl(c) + 2CO_2(g)$$

This is a reaction of two solid phases. This reaction and similar reactions occur when perchlorate propellants are burned. (These propellants, which are used for assisted takeoff of airplanes and for propulsion of rockets, consist of intimate mixtures of very fine grains of carbon black and potassium perchlorate held together by a plastic binder.) Another example is the solution of zinc in acid:

$$Zn(c) + 2H^+(aq) \longrightarrow Zn^{++}(aq) + H_2(g)$$

In this reaction three phases are involved: the solid zinc phase, the aqueous solution, and the gaseous phase formed by the evolved hydrogen.

The Rate of Homogeneous Reactions. Most actual chemical processes are very complicated, and the analysis of their rates is difficult. As a reaction proceeds, the reacting substances are used up and new ones are formed; the temperature of the system is changed by the heat evolved or absorbed by the reaction; and other effects may occur that influence the reaction in a complex way. In order to obtain an understanding of the rates of reaction, chemists have attempted to simplify the problem as much as possible. A good understanding has been obtained of homogeneous reactions (in a gaseous or liquid solution) that take place at constant temperature. Experimental studies are made by placing the reaction vessel in a thermostat, which is held at a fixed temperature. For example, hydrogen gas and iodine vapor might be mixed, at room temperature, and their conversion into hydrogen iodide followed by observing the change in color of the gas, the iodine vapor having a violet color and the other substances involved in the reaction being colorless. The simple quantitative theory of reaction rate in homogeneous systems has been discussed in the preceding paragraphs.

The *explosion* of a gaseous mixture, such as hydrogen and oxygen, and the *detonation* of a high explosive, such as glyceryl trinitrate (nitroglycerin), are interesting chemical reactions; but the analysis of the rates of these reactions is made difficult by the great changes in temperature and pressure that accompany them, and we shall not attempt it in this book.

The detonation of a high explosive such as glyceryl trinitrate illustrates the great rate of some chemical reactions. The rate at which a detonation wave moves along a sample of glyceryl trinitrate is about 20,000 feet per second. A specimen of high explosive weighing several grams may accordingly be completely decomposed within a millionth of a second, the time required for the detonation wave to move one quarter of an inch. Another reaction that can occur very rapidly is the fission of the nuclei of heavy atoms. The nuclear fission of several pounds of U^{235} or Pu^{239} may take place in a few millionths of a second in the explosion of an atomic bomb (Chapter 30).

The Rate of Heterogeneous Reactions.   A heterogeneous reaction takes place at the surfaces (the *interfaces*) of the reacting phases, and it can be made to go faster by *increasing the extent of the surfaces*. Thus finely divided zinc reacts more rapidly with acid than does coarse zinc, and the rate of burning of a perchlorate propellant is increased by grinding the potassium perchlorate to a finer crystalline powder.

Sometimes a *reactant is exhausted* in the neighborhood of the interface, and the reaction is slowed down. Stirring the mixture then accelerates the reaction, by bringing fresh supplies of the reactant into the reaction region.

Catalysts may accelerate heterogeneous as well as homogeneous reactions.

The rates of nearly all chemical reactions depend greatly on the *temperature*. The effect of temperature is discussed in a later section of this chapter.

Special devices may be utilized to accelerate certain chemical reactions. The formation of a zinc amalgam on the surface of the grains of zinc by treatment with a small amount of mercury increases the speed of the reduction reactions of zinc.

The solution of zinc in acid is retarded somewhat by the bubbles of liberated hydrogen, which prevent the acid from achieving contact with the zinc over its entire surface. This effect can be avoided by bringing a plate of unreactive metal, such as copper or platinum, into electric contact with the zinc (Figure 18-1). The reaction then proceeds as two separate electron reactions. Hydrogen is liberated at the surface of the copper or platinum, and zinc dissolves at the surface of the zinc plate:

$$2H^+ + 2e^- \longrightarrow H_2(g) \text{ at copper surface}$$
$$Zn \longrightarrow Zn^{++} + 2e^- \text{ at zinc surface}$$

The electrons flow from the zinc plate to the copper plate through the electric contact, and electric neutrality in the different regions of the solution is maintained by the migration of ions.

The solution of zinc in acid can be accelerated by adding a small amount of cupric ion to the acid. The probable mechanism of this effect is that zinc replaces cupric ion from the solution, depositing small particles of metallic copper on the surface of the zinc, and these small particles then act in the way described above.

Catalysis. The study of the factors that affect the rate of reaction has become more and more important with the continued great development of chemical industry. A modern method of manufacturing toluene, used for making the

Figure **18-1**

> *The interaction of an inert metal plate and a zinc plate with sulfuric acid, when the plates are not in contact (left) and when the plates are in contact (right).*

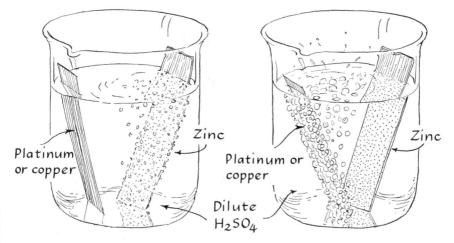

explosive trinitrotoluene (TNT) and for other purposes, may be quoted as an example. The substance methylcyclohexane, C_7H_{14}, occurs in large quantities in petroleum. At high temperature and low pressure this substance should decompose into toluene, C_7H_8, and hydrogen. The reaction is so slow, however, that the process could not be carried out commercially until the discovery was made that a certain mixture of metal oxides increases the rate of reaction enough for the process to be put into practice. A substance such as this oxide mixture, which increases the rate of the reaction without being itself changed, is called a catalyst. Other examples of catalysis have already been mentioned.

Catalysts are of very great practical significance, not only for industrial chemistry but also for life. There exist in the body many catalysts, called *enzymes*, that speed up the various physiological reactions. *Vitamins* are probably needed in part for their use as catalysts—as constituents of enzymes. A discussion of enzymes and vitamins is given in Chapter 28.

18-2.   The Rate of a First-order Reaction at Constant Temperature

If a molecule, which we represent by the general symbol A, has a tendency to decompose spontaneously

$$A \longrightarrow \text{products}$$

at a rate that is not influenced by the presence of other molecules, we expect that *the number of molecules that decompose by such a unimolecular process in unit time will be proportional to the number present*. If the volume of the system remains constant, the concentration of A will decrease at a rate proportional to this concentration. Let us use the symbol [A] for the concentration of A (in moles per liter). The rate of decrease in concentration with time is, in the language of the calculus, $-d[A]/dt$. For a unimolecular decomposition we accordingly may write the equation

$$-\frac{d[A]}{dt} = k[A] \tag{1}$$

as *the differential equation determining the rate of the reaction.** The factor k is called the *first-order rate constant*. A reaction of this kind is called a *first-order reaction*; **the order of a reaction is the sum of the powers of the concentration factors in the rate expression** (on the right side of the rate equation).

The dimensions of k for a first-order reaction are seen to be t^{-1}; with time in seconds, sec^{-1}.

For example, the rate constant k may have the value 0.001 sec^{-1}. The equation would then state that during each second 1/1,000 of the molecules present

---

* Do not be discouraged by this equation even if you have not studied the calculus and are not familiar with any equations of this sort. The expression on the left of Equation 1 is the rate of the reaction—the amount of decrease of concentration of the reacting substance in unit time. The expression on the right shows that this rate of decrease is proportional to the concentration itself.

would decompose. Suppose that at the time $t = 0$ there were 1,000,000,000 molecules per milliliter in the reaction vessel. During the first second 1,000,000 of these molecules would decompose, and there would remain at $t = 1$ sec only 999,000,000 molecules undecomposed. During the next second 999,000 molecules would decompose, and there would remain 998,001,000 molecules.* After some time (about 693 seconds) half of the molecules would have decomposed, and there would remain only 500,000,000 undecomposed molecules per milliliter. Of these about 500,000 would decompose during the next second, and so on.

The foregoing statement about the time required for half of the molecules to decompose can be verified by integrating Equation 1, to obtain the *first-order reaction-rate equation in the integrated form*. We rewrite Equation 1 as

$$\frac{d[A]}{[A]} = -k \, dt$$

We see that the expression on the left side is the differential of $\ln [A]$ (plus a constant) and that on the right side is the differential of $-kt$ (plus a constant). If we write $-\ln [A]_0$ for the first constant and kt_0 for the second constant, we obtain

$$\ln [A] - \ln [A]_0 = \ln ([A]/[A]_0) = -kt + kt_0 \tag{2}$$

On raising each side to the power e, this equation becomes

$$[A] = [A]_0 e^{-k(t-t_0)} \tag{3}$$

We see that the constant $[A]_0$ is the concentration of A at the time $t = t_0$.

It is customary to place t_0 equal to 0 (that is, to measure the time from the moment when the concentration is $[A]_0$). The equation then becomes

$$[A] = [A]_0 e^{-kt} \tag{4}$$

The ratio of the concentration of the reactant to the initial concentration decreases exponentially with time, as shown in Figure 18-2. The first-order character of a reaction may be tested by observing the rate of disappearance of the reactant at various concentrations and comparing with Equation 1, or by measuring the concentration of one system at several different times and comparing with Equation 4.

Half-life. Let $t = nt'$. The exponential expression e^{-kt} is seen to be equal to $e^{-knt'} = (e^{-kt'})^n$. Hence in each succeeding period of time t' the concentration of undecomposed molecules decreases by the same factor.

---

* These numbers are not precise. The molecules decompose at random, at the *average* rate given by Equation 1, and a small statistical fluctuation from this rate is to be expected. The error is measured by the square root of the number of molecules that have decomposed. In the theory of probability it is shown that for expectation number n of independent events the standard deviation (root mean square error) is $\sqrt{n/2} = 0.7071\sqrt{n}$, the probable error (including half the observations) is $0.4769\sqrt{n}$, and the average error is $\sqrt{n/\pi} = 0.5642\sqrt{n}$. The fractional error (ratio of error to expectation number) is seen to be proportional to $n^{-1/2}$. To halve the fractional error the number of observations must be quadrupled.

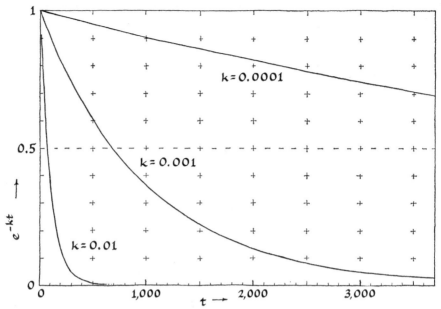

Figure 18-2

Curves showing decrease with time of the amount remaining of a sub-stance decomposing by a first-order reaction, with indicated values of the reaction-rate constant.

In the example discussed above, with $k = 0.001$ sec^{-1}, it was mentioned that at $t' = 693$ sec the value of $[A]/[A]_0$ is $\frac{1}{2}$. We see that after another 693 sec (at $t = 2t'$) it is $\frac{1}{4}$, at $t = 3t'$ it is $\frac{1}{8}$, and so on.

The time required for the concentration of a first-order reactant to decrease by one-half is called its *half-life*. We see from Equation 4 that the half-life is the value of t' at which $e^{-kt'} = \frac{1}{2}$. To evaluate t' we write

$$\ln (e^{-kt'}) = -kt' = \ln (\tfrac{1}{2})$$

$$kt' = \ln 2 = 2.30259 \log 2 = 0.69315$$

$$\text{Half-life} = t' = \frac{0.69315}{k} \tag{5}$$

From this equation, relating the half-life and the rate constant, we see that the statement that "For $k = 0.001$ sec^{-1} the half-life is 693 sec" is verified.

Radioactive Decomposition of Nuclei. The most important class of first-order reactions is the radioactive decomposition of atomic nuclei. Each nucleus of radium 226 or other radioactive nuclide has a probability of decomposition in unit time that is independent of the concentration (in general, of the presence of other particles), and in consequence the process of radioactive decay is represented by Equations 1 and 4.

Example 1. The half-life of radium ($_{88}Ra^{226}$) is 1590 years. What is the value of the decay constant? What fraction decays in one year?

Solution. From Equation 5 we write

$$k = \frac{0.693}{1590} = 0.000436 \ \text{year}^{-1}$$

Hence the decay constant has the value $\mathbf{4.36 \times 10^{-4}\ \textbf{year}^{-1}}$.

On expanding the exponential term in Equation 4 we obtain

$$e^{-kt} = 1 - kt + \tfrac{1}{2}k^2t^2 - \cdots$$

For t small the linear term above needs to be retained. We see that in unit time the fraction k decays. Hence in one year the fraction 4.36×10^{-4}, which is **0.0436%**, of the radium decays.

Example 2. In Section 30-5 it is pointed out that the age of a piece of wood can be determined by measuring its carbon-14 activity. Carbon 14 has half-life 5,760 years. The carbon 14 in fresh wood decomposes at the rate 15.3 atoms per minute per gram of carbon (this is the number of carbon-14 β-rays emitted per minute, as determined with a Geiger counter). Wood from trees that were buried by ash in the volcanic eruption of Mt. Mazama in southern Oregon has been found to give 6.90 carbon-14 beta counts per minute per gram of carbon. When did the eruption occur?

Solution. By the method used in the preceding example we find for k the value

$$k = \frac{0.693}{5760 \ \text{Y}} = 1.204 \times 10^{-4} \ \text{Y}^{-1}$$

The fraction of C^{14} undecomposed is $6.90/15.3 = 0.451$. Hence we write

$$e^{-kt} = 0.451$$
$$kt = -\ln 0.451 = -2.303 \log 0.451 = 2.303 \times 0.347 = 0.800$$
$$t = 0.800/k = 0.800/(1.204 \times 10^{-4} \ \text{year}^{-1}) = \mathbf{6640\ years}$$

Hence the eruption of Mt. Mazama occurred about 6640 years ago.

Example 3. Skeletons assigned to a form of early man called *Zinjanthropus* (East African man) have been found in the Olduvai Canyon in Tanganyika in association with volcanic ash containing potassium minerals. By use of a mass spectrograph the amount of argon 40 in the ash was measured; it was found to be 0.078% of the amount of potassium 40 present. (Potassium 40, half-life 15×10^8 years, is a radioactive isotope of potassium constituting 0.011% of natural potassium.) This argon 40 had been formed by beta decay of potassium 40, since the ash was deposited in a volcanic eruption; the older argon 40 would have been boiled out of the molten lava at the time of the eruption. How old are the skeletons?

Solution. The rate constant k for decay of K^{40} is $0.693/15.10^8$ Y $=$

4.6×10^{-10} Y^{-1}. The time t required for 0.078 % of the K^{40} to decompose is given by the equation

$$kt = 7.8 \times 10^{-4}$$
$$t = 7.8 \times 10^{-4}/k = 7.8 \times 10^{-4}/4.6 \times 10^{-10} \text{ Y}^{-1} = 1.7 \times 10^6 \text{ Y}$$

Hence the ash was laid down about **1,700,000 years** ago; this is the presumable age of the skeletons found in association with it.

Illustrative Exercises

18-1. Azomethane, CH$_3$—N=N—CH$_3$, decomposes in the gas phase by a first-order mechanism, to produce ethane and nitrogen: CH$_3$NNCH$_3 \longrightarrow$ C$_2$H$_6$ + N$_2$. At 267°C, with initial pressure 320 mm Hg (azomethane the only substance present), the pressure reached 323.2 mm Hg after 400 seconds.
(a) What fraction of the azomethane had decomposed?
(b) What is the value of the reaction-rate constant?
(c) What is the half-life of azomethane at this temperature?
(d) How long would it take for 99.22% of the substance to decompose, at this temperature?

18-2. A sample of tritium, H^3, was observed to produce beta rays at the rate of 1200 per minute. Ten months later the beta rate of the sample was 1144 counts per minute. To what value of the half-life of tritium does this measurement lead?

18-3. Carbon dioxide in the air contains some carbon 14, which is produced at a steady rate in the upper atmosphere by the reaction of cosmic-ray neutrons with nitrogen nuclei. The half-life of C^{14} is 5760 years. Atmospheric carbon dioxide gives a C^{14} beta-ray count of 184 counts per minute per mole. How many atoms of C^{12} + C^{13} are there in atmospheric CO$_2$ per atom of C^{14}?
(Answer: 0.75×10^{12}.)

18-3. Reactions of Higher Order

If reaction occurs by collision and interaction of two molecules A and B, the rate of the reaction will be proportional to the number of collisions. The number of collisions in unit volume is seen from simple kinetic considerations to be proportional to the product of the concentrations of A and B. Hence we may write as the differential rate expression for this second-order reaction

$$\text{rate of reaction} = -\frac{d[\text{A}]}{dt} = -\frac{d[\text{B}]}{dt} = k[\text{A}][\text{B}] \tag{6}$$

Here $-d[\text{A}]/dt$ is the rate of decrease in concentration of [A] and $-d[\text{B}]/dt$ is that of [B]; they are equal, the reaction being A + B $\longrightarrow$ products. The factor k is the *second-order rate constant*. Its dimensions are seen to be liter mole^{-1}, the reciprocal of concentration.

It must be emphasized that *the stoichiometric equation for a reaction does not determine its rate.* Thus the oxidation of iodide ion by persulfate ion

$$S_2O_8^{--} + 2I^- \longrightarrow 2SO_4^{--} + I_2$$

might be a third-order reaction, with rate proportional to $[S_2O_8^{--}][I^-]^2$; it is in fact second-order, with rate proportional to $[S_2O_8^{--}][I^-]$. In this case the slow, rate-determining reaction is the reaction between one persulfate ion and one iodide ion,

$$S_2O_8^{--} + I^- \longrightarrow \text{products}$$

This is followed by a rapid reaction between the products and another iodide ion.*

For gases it is convenient to use partial pressures instead of concentrations of substances. For a bimolecular gas reaction we may write

$$\text{rate of reaction} = -\frac{dP_A}{dt} = -\frac{dP_B}{dt} = kP_AP_B \tag{7}$$

The second-order reaction-rate equation can be integrated. Let us consider the case when the two reactants are present in equal concentrations (or partial pressures), or are the same substance (for example, nitrogen dioxide, for which the reaction $2NO_2 \longrightarrow N_2O_4$ occurs as a bimolecular reaction). Let

$$x = [A] = [B] \text{ (or } x = P_A = P_B)$$

Our equation in differential form is

$$-\frac{dx}{dt} = kx^2$$

We rewrite and integrate:

$$-\frac{dx}{x^2} = k \, dt$$

$$\frac{1}{x} + \text{constant of integration} = kt$$

It is convenient to take the constant of integration as $-1/c$.

$$\frac{1}{x} - \frac{1}{c} = kt$$

We rearrange the terms and solve for x:

$$\frac{1}{x} = kt + \frac{1}{c} = \frac{ckt + 1}{c}$$

$$x = \frac{c}{ckt + 1} \tag{8}$$

By placing $t = 0$, we see that c is the initial value of x.

Example 4. Hydrogen and iodine react by a bimolecular mechanism (Figure 18-3):

$$H_2(g) + I_2(g) \longrightarrow 2HI(g)$$

* The slow reaction probably produces the hypoiodite ion, IO^-.

If at a certain temperature and pressure 1% of the substance present in the smaller amount had undergone reaction in 1 minute, how long would it take for 1% to react, at the same temperature, if the volume of the sample of gas were doubled?

Solution. We see from Equation 7 that

$$-\frac{1}{P_A}\frac{dP_A}{dt} = kP_B$$

The fractional rate of removal of A is accordingly proportional to P_B. Since doubling the volume halves P_B, and hence the rate, it would take 2 minutes, twice as long, for the reaction to take place to the same extent.

Example 5.   What is the time required for half the reactants to undergo second-order reaction, when they are present in equal amounts?

Solution.   We place $x = c/2$ in Equation 8 and solve for t:

$$\frac{c}{2} = \frac{c}{ckt' + 1}$$

$$ckt' + 1 = 2$$

$$ckt' = 1$$

$$t' \text{ (for half reaction)} = \frac{1}{ck}$$

We see that the time for half reaction is not determined alone by the reaction constant k, but is inversely proportional also to the initial concentration or pressure, c.

Example 6.   Esters, such as ethyl acetate, $CH_3COOC_2H_5$, react with hydroxide ion in aqueous solution:

$$CH_3COOC_2H_5 + OH^- \longrightarrow CH_3COO^- + C_2H_5OH$$

The rate is observed to be doubled by doubling either the ester concentration or the hydroxide ion concentration. In one experiment, at 25°C, 50 ml of solution 0.200 F in NaOH and 50 ml of solution 0.010 M in $CH_3COOC_2H_5$ were poured together and stirred. After 25 seconds 50 ml of 0.200 F HCl was added; this stopped the reaction. On titrating the resultant solution to neutrality with 0.010 F NaOH, 10.0 ml was found to be needed. How much of the ester had been hydrolyzed? What is the value of the second-order reaction-rate constant for the reaction? At what time would 99.22% of the ester have reacted?

Solution.   The solution after addition of HCl would have been neutral if no reaction had taken place. The amount of NaOH required to replace that used in the reaction is equivalent to 29% of the ester; hence 20% had undergone reaction. During the reaction the value of $[OH^-]$ decreased from 0.100 M to 0.099 M; we can accordingly take it to be constant, with average value 0.0995 M. Let $x = [CH_3COOC_2H_5]$. We write

$$-\frac{dx}{dt} = k \times 0.0995x = k'x$$

This is now a first-order reaction-rate expression. In the customary way (Section 18-2) we evaluate k':

$$0.80 = e^{-k't}, \qquad t = 25 \text{ sec}$$
$$k' \times 25 \text{ sec} = -\ln 0.80 = -2.303 \log 0.80 = 2.303 \times 0.097 = 0.223$$

$$k' = \frac{0.223}{25 \text{ sec}} = 0.0089 \text{ sec}^{-1}$$

The second-order reaction-rate constant hence has the value

$$k = \frac{k'}{0.0995 \text{ mole liter}^{-1}} = \frac{0.0089 \text{ sec}^{-1}}{0.0995 \text{ mole liter}^{-1}} = \textbf{0.089 sec}^{-1}\textbf{ mole}^{-1}\textbf{ liter}$$

To determine the time required for 99.22% reaction of the ester, we note that the value of $[OH^-]$ would lie between 0.100 M and 0.095 M, and we multiply the average, 0.0975 mole liter^{-1}, by k, 0.089 sec^{-1} mole^{-1} liter, to obtain $k' = 0.0975 \times 0.089 = 0.0087$ sec^{-1} for the pseudo-first-order reaction-rate constant. The time for half reaction is 0.693/0.0087 sec^{-1} = 80 sec. For $(\frac{1}{2})^7 = 1/128 = 0.78\% = 100\% - 99.22\%$ to remain unreacted would require $7 \times 80 = \textbf{560 sec.}$

18-4. Mechanism of Reactions. Dependence of Reaction Rate on Temperature

It is everyday experience that chemical reactions are accelerated by increased temperature: the rate of many reactions at room temperature is approximately doubled for every 10°C increase in temperature.

This is a useful rule. It is only a rough rule. Reactions of large molecules, such as proteins, may have very large temperature factors; the rate of denaturation of ovalbumin (the process that occurs when an egg is boiled) increases about fiftyfold for a 10° rise in temperature.

We may obtain further insight into this question by considering the mechanism of reactions. For the reaction

$$H_2(g) + I_2(g) \longrightarrow 2HI(g)$$

at temperature T we may write the following rate equation:

$$-\frac{dP_{H_2}}{dt} = -\frac{dP_{I_2}}{dt} = kP_{H_2}P_{I_2}$$

The rate constant k is determined in part by the number of collisions at $P_{H_2} = P_{I_2} = 1$ atm (Figure 18-3). This number can be calculated by use of the kinetic theory of gases and certain assumptions about the sizes of the molecules. Only a small fraction of the collisions, however, are effective. If the molecules collide with small relative velocity, the van der Waals force of repulsion causes them to rebound elastically from one another.

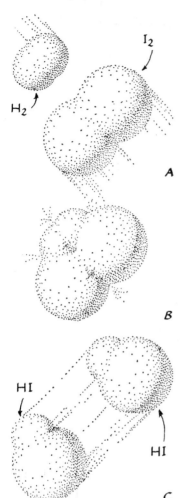

I₂

H₂

A

B

HI

HI

C

Figure 18-3 *The mechanism of the reaction of hydrogen and iodine to form hydrogen iodide.*

Activation Energy. In order to react the pair of molecules must pass through a configuration (*B* in Figure 18-3) intermediate between the initial one (*A*) and the final one (*C*). This configuration is called the *activated complex*. In general this intermediate configuration, to which we may assign the structure

$$\begin{array}{c} \text{H---I} \\ \vdots \quad \vdots \\ \text{H---I} \end{array}$$

$$\left(\text{resonance between } \begin{array}{cc} \text{H} & \text{I} \\ | & | \\ \text{H} & \text{I} \end{array} \text{ and } \begin{array}{c} \text{H---I} \\ \\ \text{H---I} \end{array}\right), \text{ has a}$$

larger energy (enthalpy) value than the reactants. Let us use E_a to represent this energy difference, which is called the *activation energy* for the reaction. From the Boltzmann distribution law we know that the fractional number of collisions with this amount of energy involves the Boltzmann exponential factor (Section 5-11). We accordingly write

$$k = A \exp\left(-\frac{E_a}{RT}\right) \tag{9}$$

and

$$\ln k = -\frac{E_a}{RT} + \ln A \tag{10}$$

Here E_a is the activation energy per mole and A is a coefficient representing the collision number, the chance that the activated complex will break up to form the reactants rather than the products, and other factors affecting the rate.

These factors depend to some extent on the temperature, but as a good approximation we may take A to be a constant. We see from Equation 10 that $\ln k$ is a linear function of $1/T$, with slope $-E_a/R$:

$$\frac{d(\ln k)}{d(1/T)} = -\frac{E_a}{R} \tag{11}$$

Experimental values of k for the reaction of H_2 and I_2 over the range $T = 550°K$ to $800°K$ are shown in Figure 18-4. By differentiating Equation

10 with respect to T, we obtain the following expression for the temperature coefficient of the reaction-rate parameter k:

$$\frac{d \ln k}{dT} = \frac{E_a}{RT^2} \qquad (12)$$

Equations 9 to 12 are called the *Arrhenius reaction-rate equations.* They were discovered in 1889 by the Swedish scientist Svante Arrhenius, who also discovered the existence of ions in electrolytic solutions (Section 8-1).

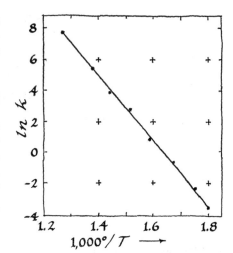

Figure 18-4   *A graph of the observed values of the logarithm of the reaction rate constant k for the reaction of hydrogen and iodine, with T^{-1} as horizontal coordinate. Units of k are liter $mole^{-1}$ sec^{-1}.*

Example 7. The observed reaction-rate curve for H_2 and I_2, Figure 18-4, has slope -21.6 in the units indicated. What is the value of the activation energy for the reaction?

    Solution. With x axis $1/T$ in place of $1000°/T$ the slope would be

$$\frac{d \ln k}{d(1/T)} = -21.6 \times 1000 = -21,600 \text{ deg}$$

From Equation 10 we see that

$$-\frac{E_a}{R} = -21,600 \text{ deg}$$

and hence

$$E_a = 21,600 \text{ deg} \times R = 21,600 \text{ deg} \times 1.987 \text{ cal deg}^{-1} \text{ mole}^{-1}$$
$$= 43,000 \text{ cal mole}^{-1}$$

The activation energy for the reaction is thus found to have the value **43,000 cal/mole.**

Activation Energy for the Reverse Reaction. In Figure 18-5 there is shown diagrammatically the change in energy accompanying a reaction. In order for the activated complex to be formed from the reactant molecules the activation energy E_a (forward) is needed. A detailed analysis shows that the activation energy E_a (reverse) differs from E_a (forward) by the difference in enthalpy of the reactants and the products. For the reactions $H_2 + I_2 \rightleftarrows 2HI$ this enthalpy difference is 2,480 cal/mole (Table 12-2); hence we can state that the value of E_a for the reaction $2HI \longrightarrow H_2 + I_2$ is $43,000 + 2,480 = 45,480$ cal/mole.

The Relation between Activation Energy and Bond Energy. Values of the activation energy can often be estimated from bond-energy values (Table 10-3).

For example, the activation energy for the combination of two atoms, such as

$$I + I \longrightarrow I_2$$

is zero. Reaction may occur whenever the two atoms collide, even at low relative velocity. (The bond energy may be converted to kinetic energy by collision with a third body.) The activation energy for the reverse reaction, the dissociation of a diatomic molecule, is just equal to the bond energy (enthalpy). For the dissociation of I_2 it is 36 kcal/mole (Table 10-3).

A rough empirical rule can be formulated for reactions in which two bonds are broken and two are formed, such as

$$H_2 + I_2 \longrightarrow 2HI$$

and its reverse reaction

$$2HI \longrightarrow H_2 + I_2$$

It is found that the activation energy for the exothermic reaction (the first one of this pair) is approximately 30% of the sum of the bond energies of the two bonds that are broken (H—H and I—I, in this case).

For an exothermic reaction in which one bond is broken and another is formed, such as

$$F + H_2 \longrightarrow HF + H$$

or

$$D + H_2 \longrightarrow HD + H$$

Figure **18-5**

Diagrammatic representation of the change in energy accompanying a chemical reaction. The top of the curve corresponds to the activated complex for the reaction.

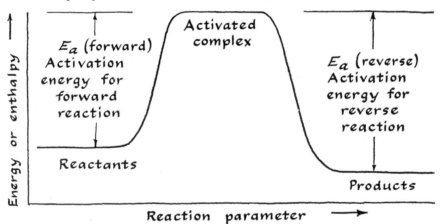

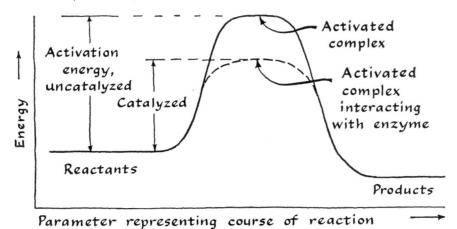

Figure 18-6

> *A diagram showing the possible effect of a catalyst in decreasing the value of the activation energy for a reaction, and thus increasing the rate of both the forward reaction and the reverse reaction.*

the activation energy is approximately 8% of the energy of the bond that is broken.

Catalysis and Activation Energy.   Little is known at the present time about the detailed mechanism of action of catalysts. There is, however, evidence that some catalysts have a structure that leads to strong interaction with the activated complex and only weak interaction with the reactants and products. The strong interaction with the activated complex leads to a decrease in the activation energy, as indicated in Figure 18-6, and hence to increase in the rate of the reaction.

18-5. Chain Reactions

When the reaction

$$H_2(g) + Br_2(g) \longrightarrow 2HBr(g)$$

was carefully investigated about 50 years ago, it was found that its rate is not proportional to the product $[H_2][Br_2]$, as expected (Equation 6). Instead, in its initial stages, with $[HBr]$ small, the rate was observed to be proportional to $[H_2][Br_2]^{1/2}$:

$$-\frac{d[H_2]}{dt} = -\frac{d[Br_2]}{dt} = k[H_2][Br_2]^{1/2}$$

This observation was accounted for by the assumption that the reaction occurs in a series of steps. The first is the dissociation of a bromine molecule into atoms:

$$Br_2 \longrightarrow 2Br$$

This is followed by a sequence of reactions, called a *chain*:

$$Br + H_2 \longrightarrow HBr + H$$
$$H + Br_2 \longrightarrow HBr + Br$$
$$Br + H_2 \longrightarrow HBr + H$$
$$H + Br_2 \longrightarrow HBr + Br$$
$$\text{etc.}$$

The chain is ultimately broken by the reaction

$$2Br \longrightarrow Br_2$$

Explosions.   A mixture of hydrogen and chlorine explodes when ignited. The over-all reaction $H_2 + Cl_2 \longrightarrow 2HCl$, which takes place by the chain mechanism analogous to that for $H_2 + Br_2$, liberates so much heat that the gas may begin to increase in temperature, instead of dissipating the heat to the environment. The reaction then proceeds more rapidly, the temperature increases more rapidly, and a very rapid reaction, called a *thermal explosion*, results.

The explosion of a mixture of hydrogen and oxygen is different in kind; it is called a *branched-chain explosion*. An initial reaction with an atom of oxygen (or of hydrogen) is followed by two reactions, that one by three, then five, and so on.*

$$O + H_2 \longrightarrow OH + H$$
$$OH + H_2 \longrightarrow H_2O + O \qquad H + O_2 \longrightarrow OH + O$$
$$O + H_2 \longrightarrow OH + H \quad OH + H_2 \longrightarrow H_2O + O \quad O + H_2 \longrightarrow OH + H$$
$$\text{etc.}$$

Important chain reactions, which under some conditions lead to explosion, are the fission and fusion of atomic nuclei (Section 30-7).

Spontaneous Combustion.   Reactions such as the combustion of fuels proceed very rapidly when combustion is begun, but fuels may remain indefinitely in contact with air without burning. The process of lighting a fire consists in increasing the temperature of part of the fuel until the reaction proceeds rapidly; the exothermic reaction then liberates enough heat to raise another portion of the fuel to the kindling temperature, and in this way the process is continued.

The oxidation of oil-soaked rags or other combustible material may occur rapidly enough at room temperature to produce sufficient heat to increase the temperature somewhat; this accelerates the oxidation, and causes further heating, until the mass bursts into flame. This process is called *spontaneous combustion*.

---

* Other reactions, involving the radical HO_2, also occur.

18-6. Chemical Equilibrium—a Dynamic Steady State

Sometimes a chemical reaction begins, continues for a while, and then appears to stop before any one of the reactants is used up: the reaction is said to have reached *equilibrium*. The reaction between nitrogen dioxide, NO_2, and dinitrogen tetroxide, N_2O_4, provides an interesting example. The gas that is obtained by heating concentrated nitric acid with copper is found to have a density at high temperatures corresponding to the formula NO_2, and a density at low temperatures and high pressures approximating the formula N_2O_4. At high temperatures the gas is deep red in color, and at low temperatures it becomes lighter in color, the crystals formed when the gas is solidified being colorless. The change in the color of the gas and in its other properties with change in temperature and change in pressure can be accounted for by assuming that the gas is a mixture of the two molecular species NO_2 and N_2O_4, in equilibrium with one another according to the equation

$$N_2O_4 \rightleftarrows 2NO_2 \qquad (13)$$
$$\text{Colorless} \qquad \text{Red}$$

It has been found by experiment that the amounts of nitrogen dioxide and dinitrogen tetroxide in the gas mixture are determined by a simple equation:

$$\frac{[NO_2]^2}{[N_2O_4]} = K \qquad (14)$$

This equation, which is called the *equilibrium equation* for the reaction, is seen to involve in the numerator the concentration of the substance on the right side of the chemical equation (Equation 13), with the exponent 2, which is the coefficient shown in the chemical equation. The denominator contains the concentration of the substance on the left side. Its exponent is 1, because in the equation as written the coefficient of N_2O_4 is 1.

The quantity K is called the *equilibrium constant* of the reaction of dissociation of dinitrogen tetroxide to nitrogen dioxide. The equilibrium constant is independent of the pressure of the system, or of the concentration of the reacting substances. It is, however, dependent on the temperature.

The Relation between the Equilib ium Equation and Rates of Reaction. The reaction $N_2O_4 \longrightarrow 2NO_2$ is a first-order reaction. Its rate equation is

$$-\frac{d[N_2O_4]}{dt} = k_1[N_2O_4]$$

The reverse reaction, $2NO_2 \longrightarrow N_2O_4$, is a second-order reaction, with rate equation (expressed as rate of formation of the product)

$$-\frac{d[N_2O_4]}{dt} = k_2[NO_2]^2$$

In a gas in which both reactions are taking place, the over-all rate of formation of N_2O_4 is given by

$$\frac{d[N_2O_4]}{dt} = k_2[NO_2]^2 - k_1[N_2O_4]$$

When the steady state with $d[N_2O_4]/dt = 0$ is reached, this equation becomes

$$k_2[NO_2]^2 = k_1[N_2O_4]$$

or

$$\frac{[NO_2]^2}{[N_2O_4]} = \frac{k_1}{k_2} = K \tag{15}$$

We see that the expression for k_1/k_2, the ratio of the two reaction rate constants, is exactly the same as the equilibrium expression of Equation 14, and hence that the equilibrium constant K is the ratio of the rate constants for the two opposing reactions.

We repeat the statement of the general principle: *chemical equilibrium is a steady state, in which opposing chemical reactions occur at equal rates.*

In some cases it has been found possible to determine the rates of the opposing reactions, and to show experimentally that the ratio of the two rate constants is indeed equal to the equilibrium constant. This has not been done for the nitrogen dioxide-dinitrogen tetroxide equilibrium, however, because the individual chemical reactions take place so rapidly that experiments have not been able to determine their rates.

Equilibria of this sort are very important in chemistry. Many industrial processes have been made practicable by the discovery of a way of shifting an equilibrium so as to produce a satisfactory amount of a desired product. In this chapter and later chapters we shall discuss quantitatively the principles of chemical equilibrium and the methods of shifting the equilibrium of a system in one direction or the other.

The Effect of Catalysts on Chemical Equilibrium.   It is a consequence of the laws of thermodynamics—the impossibility of perpetual motion—that *a system in equilibrium is not changed by the addition of a catalyst.* The catalyst may increase the rate at which the system approaches its final equilibrium state, but it cannot change the value of the equilibrium constant. Under equilibrium conditions a catalyst has the same effect on the rate of the backward reaction as on that of the corresponding forward reaction.

It is true that a system that has stood unchanged for a long period of time, apparently in equilibrium, may undergo reaction when a small amount of a catalyst is added. Thus a mixture of hydrogen and oxygen at room temperature remains apparently unchanged for a very long period of time; however, if even a minute amount of finely divided platinum (platinum black) is placed in the gas, chemical reaction begins and continues until very little of one of the reacting gases remains. In this case the system in the absence of the catalyst is not in equilibrium with respect to the reaction $2H_2 + O_2 \rightleftarrows 2H_2O$, but only in *metastable equilibrium*, the rate of formation of water being so small that true equilibrium would not be approached in a millennium.

Because of the possibility of metastable equilibrium it is necessary in practice to apply the following **equilibrium criterion**: *a system is considered to have reached equilibrium with respect to a certain reaction when the same final state is reached by approach by the reverse reaction as by the forward reaction.* This true equilibrium is called *stable equilibrium*.

The General Equation for the Equilibrium Constant. The chemical equation for a general reaction can be written in the following form:

$$aA + bB + \cdots \rightleftarrows dD + eE + \cdots \tag{16}$$

Here the capital letters A, B, D, E are used to represent different molecular species, the reactants and the products, and the small letters a, b, d, e are the numerical coefficients that tell how many molecules of the different sorts are involved in the reaction.

The equilibrium equation for this reaction is

$$\frac{[D]^d[E]^e \cdots}{[A]^a[B]^b \cdots} = K \tag{17}$$

Here K is the equilibrium constant for the reaction.

It is customary to write the concentration ratio in the way given in Equation 17 for a chemical equation such as Equation 16; that is, the *concentrations of the products (to the appropriate powers) are written in the numerator and the concentrations of the reactants in the denominator.* This is a convention that has been accepted by all chemists.

The equilibrium constant for gases is often written with partial pressure replacing concentration:

$$\frac{P_D^d P_E^e \cdots}{P_A^a P_B^b \cdots} = K_P \tag{18}$$

Unless the reaction involves no change in number of molecules, the numerical value of K_P differs from that of K.

The validity of the equilibrium equation, with K a constant at constant temperature, is a consequence of the laws of thermodynamics, if the reactants and the products are gases obeying the perfect gas laws or are solutes in dilute solution. In gases under high pressure and in concentrated solutions there occur some deviations from this equation, similar in magnitude to the deviations from the perfect gas laws. Sometimes these deviations are taken into account by introducing *activity coefficients*, as discussed for ions in solution in Chapter 17.

Examples of the use of the general equilibrium equation will be given in the following chapters of this book. This simple equation permits the chemist to answer many important questions that arise in his work.

Example 8.   Hydrogen iodide, HI, is not a very stable substance. The pure gas is colorless, but when it is made in the laboratory the gas may have a violet color, indicating the presence of free iodine. In fact, hydrogen iodide decomposes to an appreciable amount according to the equation

$$2HI \rightleftharpoons H_2 + I_2(g)$$

The equilibrium constant for this decomposition reaction has been found by experiment to have the value 0.0190 at 300°C. To what extent does hydrogen decompose at this temperature?

Solution.   In this example the value of the equilibrium constant is given without a statement as to its dimensions. Let us write the expression for the equilibrium constant:

$$K = \frac{[H_2][I_2]}{[HI]^2} = 0.0190$$

Each of the concentrations $[H_2]$, $[I_2]$, and $[HI]$ has the dimensions moles/liter. Hence we see that for this reaction the dimensions of K are those of a pure number:

$$\text{Dimensions of } K = \frac{(\text{moles/liter})(\text{moles/liter})}{(\text{moles/liter})^2} = 1$$

When hydrogen iodide decomposes, equal number of molecules of hydrogen and iodine are formed. Accordingly the concentrations of hydrogen and iodine present in the gas formed when hydrogen iodide undergoes some decomposition are equal. Let us use the symbol x to represent the concentration of hydrogen and also the concentration of iodine:

$$[H_2] = [I_2] = x$$

Then we have

$$\frac{x^2}{[HI]^2} = 0.0190$$

or

$$x^2 = 0.0190[HI]^2$$
$$x = \sqrt{0.0190} \times [HI] = 0.138[HI]$$

By solving this equation we have found that after the hydrogen iodide has decomposed enough to produce the equilibrium state at room temperature the molar concentration of hydrogen is equal to 13.8% of the molar concentration of HI. The molar concentration of iodine is also equal to 13.8% of the molar concentration of HI. The question "To what extent does hydrogen iodide decompose at room temperature?" is to be interpreted as meaning "What percentage of pure hydrogen iodide originally produced decomposes to give hydrogen and iodine?" The equation for the chemical reaction shows that two molecules of HI on reaction form only one molecule of H_2 and one of I_2. Accordingly, there must have been 27.6% more moles of HI present initially than when equilibrium is reached. Hence the extent of decomposition of the hydrogen iodide is $27.6/127.6 = 0.216$, or **21.6%.**

Relation to the Principle of Le Chatelier. It is seen that the equilibrium equation corresponds to the principle of Le Chatelier.

In Section 16-2 this principle was stated in the following words: *if the conditions of a system, initially at equilibrium, are changed, the equilibrium will shift in such a way as to tend to restore the original conditions.*

Let us consider the equilibrium state described in the above example. If the partial pressure of H_2 or I_2 in this system at equilibrium is increased by the injection of some H_2 or I_2, the reaction will proceed in such direction as to decrease this partial pressure toward the original value; that is, hydrogen and iodine will combine to HI until the partial-pressure quotient again becomes equal to the equilibrium constant.

On the other hand, if the total pressure of the system is changed there occurs no change in the H_2-I_2-HI equilibrium, because the reaction is not accompanied by any change in pressure. But change in total pressure of the system causes a shift in the ammonia equilibrium, $N_2 + 3H_2 \rightleftarrows 2NH_3$, in the direction that tends to restore the original pressure; hence increase in pressure causes formation of more ammonia. In industrial plants for the fixation of atmospheric nitrogen by the ammonia process, pressures as high as 1,000 atm are used, in order that the yield be large. But in the manufacture of toluene by the dehydrogenation of methylcyclohexane the pressure is kept low in order to obtain a large yield; here the reaction is

$$C_7H_{14}(g) \rightleftarrows C_7H_8(g) + 3H_2(g)$$

Example 9. At 500°C the equilibrium constant for the formation of ammonia by the reaction

$$N_2 + 3H_2 \rightleftarrows 2NH_3$$

has the value 1.50×10^{-5}, expressed in terms of partial pressures in atmospheres. What fraction of a stoichiometric mixture of nitrogen and hydrogen could be converted to ammonia with the total pressure kept at 1 atm? at 500 atm?

Solution. The equilibrium equation for this reaction is

$$\frac{P^2_{NH_3}}{P_{N_2}P^3_{H_2}} = 1.50 \times 10^{-5}$$

The problem states that

$$P_{H_2} = 3P_{N_2}$$

because the stoichiometric ratio N_2 to $3H_2$ is specified for these gases. The total pressure is the sum of the partial pressures of the three gases:

$$P_{N_2} + P_{H_2} + P_{NH_3} = P_{total}$$

Let

$$x = P_{NH_3}$$

Then

$$P_{N_2} + P_{H_2} = P_{total} - x$$

and

$$P_{N_2} = \tfrac{1}{4}(P_{total} - x)$$
$$P_{H_2} = \tfrac{3}{4}(P_{total} - x)$$

Therefore

$$\frac{x^2}{\tfrac{27}{256}(P_{total} - x)^4} = 1.50 \times 10^{-5}$$

$$\frac{x^2}{(P_{total} - x)^4} = 1.58 \times 10^{-6}$$

$$x = 1.26 \times 10^{-3} \times (P_{total} - x)^2$$

This quadratic equation might be solved directly. It is seen, however, that x is small compared with P_{total}. Hence as a first approximation we neglect x in comparison with P_{total} in the term on the right, where these quantities are subtracted, obtaining

$$x = 0.00126 \times P_{total}$$

For total pressure 1 atm this gives $x = P_{NH_3} = 0.00126$ atm. Remembering that two molecules of ammonia are formed from four molecules of the reactants, we see that only **0.25%** of the gas mixture is converted into ammonia.

For $P_{total} = 500$ atm this approximate method gives $x = P_{NH_3} = 0.00126 \times 500^2 = 315$ atm, which is not negligible compared with $P_{total} = 500$ atm. Direct solution of the quadratic equation gives $P_{NH_3} = 152$ atm, which leads to $P_{N_2} = 87$ atm and $P_{H_2} = 261$ atm. From these values it is calculated that at this total pressure **46.6%** of the original mixture is converted into ammonia. This calculation shows why high pressures are used in the manufacture of ammonia from the elements (Chapter 14). In practice the reaction is carried out at about 500°C and 500 atm.

Illustrative Exercises

18-4. In the contact process for making sulfuric acid, sulfur dioxide is oxidized to sulfur trioxide.

(a) Write the equation for the reaction between sulfur dioxide and oxygen, and write the equilibrium expression.

(b) At a certain temperature and concentration of oxygen the value of the equilibrium constant is such that 50% of the SO_2 is converted to SO_3 when the total pressure is 10 atm. Would the fraction converted be increased or decreased by doubling the total pressure?

18-5. In the arc process of fixing nitrogen, air is converted in part into nitric oxide, NO, by passing it through an electric arc. Why is this reaction carried out at 1 atm rather than at high pressure?

18-6. It is pointed out in Example 8 above that hydrogen iodide at 300°C decomposes to the extent of 21.6%. To what extent would 0.001 mole of HI decompose when added to 1 mole of H_2 at 300°C and 1 atm pressure?

18-7. The Effect of Change of Temperature on Chemical Equilibrium

From the principle of Le Chatelier we can predict that *increase in temperature will drive a reaction further toward completion (by increasing the equilibrium constant) if the reaction is endothermic and will drive it back (by decreasing the equilibrium constant) if the reaction is exothermic.*

For example, let us consider the NO_2-N_2O_4 equilibrium mixture at room temperature. Heat is absorbed when an N_2O_4 molecule dissociates into two NO_2 molecules:

$$N_2O_4(g) \longrightarrow 2NO_2(g) \qquad \Delta H° = 15.0 \text{ kcal/mole}$$

If the reaction mixture were to be increased in temperature by a few degrees the equilibrium would be changed, according to the principle of Le Chatelier, in such a way as to tend to restore the original temperature—that is, in such a way as to lower the temperature of the system, by using up some of the heat energy. This would be achieved by the decomposition of some additional molecules of dinitrogen tetroxide. Accordingly, in agreement with the statement above, the equilibrium constant would change in such a way as to correspond to the dissociation of more of the N_2O_4 molecules.

This principle is of great practical importance. For example, the synthesis of ammonia from nitrogen and hydrogen is exothermic (the heat evolved is 11.0 kcal per mole of ammonia formed); hence the yield of ammonia is made a maximum by keeping the temperature as low as possible. The commercial process of manufacturing ammonia from the elements became practicable when catalysts were found that caused the reaction to proceed rapidly at low temperatures.

In the preceding section it was pointed out (Equation 15) that the equilibrium constant K for a reaction is equal to k_1/k_2—that is, to the ratio of the rate constant for the forward reaction to that of the reverse reaction. We may accordingly write

$$\ln K = \ln (k_1/k_2) = \ln k_1 - \ln k_2$$

and

$$\frac{d \ln K}{dT} = \frac{d \ln k_1}{dT} - \frac{d \ln k_2}{dT} \qquad (19)$$

In Section 18-4 the Arrhenius equations were derived from the Boltzmann distribution law. One of these equations, Equation 12, gives the value of the temperature coefficient of $\ln k$:

$$\frac{d \ln k}{dT} = \frac{E_a}{RT^2}$$

We may accordingly rewrite Equation 19 as

$$\frac{d \ln K}{dT} = \frac{E_a \text{ (forward)} - E_a \text{ (reverse)}}{RT^2}$$

By an argument illustrated in Figure 18-5 we have indicated that E_a (forward) $- E_a$ (reverse) is equal to $-\Delta H^\circ$, the standard enthalpy change accompanying the reaction. Thus we are led to the important equation

$$\frac{d \ln K}{dT} = \frac{\Delta H^\circ}{RT^2} \qquad (20)$$

We see that this equation, which expresses the dependence of the equilibrium constant for a chemical reaction on the temperature, has been developed from the Boltzmann distribution law. Our development of the equation has not been a rigorous one, but the equation can be rigorously derived from fundamental principles by the methods of either statistical mechanics or chemical thermodynamics.

Over a small range of temperature, ΔH° can be considered to be a constant. When Equation 20 is integrated on this assumption, the following equation is obtained:

$$\ln \left(\frac{K(T_2)}{K(T_1)} \right) = \frac{\Delta H^\circ}{R} \left(\frac{1}{T_1} - \frac{1}{T_2} \right) \qquad (21)$$

Example 10.   The vapor pressure of water at 0°C is 4.58 mm of Hg. What is the heat of vaporization of water?

Solution.   The equilibrium constant for the reaction $H_2O(l) \longrightarrow H_2O(g)$ is

$$\frac{[H_2O(g)]}{[H_2O(l)]} = K_{\text{concentration}}$$

We may replace $[H_2O(l)]$ by a constant, and incorporate it into the equilibrium constant:

$$[H_2O(g)] = K'_{\text{concentration}}$$

or, using pressure instead of concentration,

$$P_{H_2O(g)} = K$$

We know that $P_{H_2O(g)}$ has the values $K(T_1) = 4.58$ mm of Hg at $T_1 =$

273.16°K and $K(T_2) = 760$ mm of Hg at $T_2 = 373.16°K$. From Equation 21 we obtain the equation

$$\ln \left(\frac{760}{4.58} \right) = \frac{\Delta H°}{R} \left(\frac{1}{273.16} - \frac{1}{373.16} \right)$$

Hence

$$2.303 \log 166 = \frac{\Delta H°}{R} (0.00366 - 0.00268)$$

$$2.303 \times 2.220 = \frac{\Delta H°}{R} \times 0.00098$$

$$\Delta H° = \frac{2.303 \times 2.220 \, R}{0.00098} = 10,360 \text{ cal mole}^{-1}$$

Thus we have obtained **10.36 kcal/mole** as the heat of vaporization of water over the temperature range 0°C to 100°C, with the assumption that it is constant over this range.

By use of values of the vapor pressure over smaller ranges of temperature the same procedure leads to 10.82 kcal/mole at 0°C, 10.23 kcal/mole at 50°C, and 9.72 kcal/mole at 100°C. These values are verified by calorimetric measurements.

18-8. The Driving Force of Chemical Reactions

What makes a chemical reaction go? This is a question that chemists and students have asked ever since chemical reactions began to be investigated. At the beginning of the nineteenth century the question was answered by saying that two substances react if they have a "chemical affinity" for each other. This answer, of course, had no real value until some quantitative meaning was given to "chemical affinity" and some way was found for measuring or predicting it.

It might be thought that the heat of a reaction is its driving force, and that a reaction will proceed if it evolves heat, and not proceed if it would absorb heat. We have mentioned some of these reactions in the preceding sections of this chapter; another example is that when mercuric oxide is heated it decomposes into mercury and oxygen, with absorption of heat.

Let us first ask why a liquid evaporates, even though the reaction of evaporation is endothermic. The explanation of this phenomenon is given by the examination of *probability*. Let us consider a large flask, with volume 10 liters, into which some water vapor is introduced. We might well think that it would be equally probable that a particular water molecule would be in any place in the flask—that the probability would be 1 in 10,000 that the molecule would be within any particular milliliter of volume within the flask. If enough water vapor has been introduced into the flask, however, some of it will liquefy, the rest remaining as water vapor. Let us suppose that there is 1 ml of liquid water present in a little puddle at the bottom of the flask. At room temperature most of the water-substance present in the flask will be in this puddle of liquid water, only a small fraction of the water molecules being present as water vapor. Now, although it seems very improbable that a water molecule should stay in the small volume, 1 ml, occupied by the liquid water, instead of occupying the remaining 9,999 ml of space, we know that the reason that the water vapor condenses to liquid water is that liquid water is the more stable state, and that condensation proceeds until the rate at which gas molecules strike the surface of the liquid and stick is just equal to the rate at which molecules of the liquid leave the surface and escape into the gas. This is the equilibrium condition. We see that the equilibrium condition involves a balance between the effect of *energy*, which tends to concentrate the molecules into the liquid phase, and the effect of *probability*, which tends to change the liquid into the gas. If the volume of the flask were five times as great, making the probability for the gas phase 49,999 to 1 instead of 9,999 to 1, five times as many molecules would leave the liquid phase and move to the gaseous phase. (A detailed discussion of this problem with use of the Boltzmann distribution law has been presented in Section 16-10.)

Accordingly we see that this effect of probability can be made to cause more of the liquid to evaporate, simply by increasing the volume of the system.

In the branch of science called thermodynamic chemistry a more detailed consideration is given to the relative effects of energy and probability. It has been found that the effect of probability can be described quantitatively by a new property of substances. This new property, which represents the probability of a substance in various states, is called *entropy*.

Whereas the energy change that accompanies a chemical reaction does not depend very much on the pressures of the gases or the concentrations of the solutes involved in the reaction, the entropy change does depend on these partial pressures and concentrations. In general, a system held at constant temperature will reach a steady state, called the state of equilibrium. In this state of the system the reaction has no preferential tendency to proceed either forward or backward; it has no driving force in either direction. If, however, the concentration of one of the reactants (a solute or a gas) is increased, a driving force comes into existence, which causes the reaction to go in the forward direction, until the equilibrium expression, involving the concentrations or partial pressures of reactants and products, again becomes equal to the equilibrium constant for the reaction.

It is clear from these considerations that *the driving force of a reaction depends not only on the chemical formulas of the reactants and the structure of their molecules, but also on the concentrations of the reactants and of the products.*

A great step forward was made during the second half of the last century when it was found that an energy quantity called its *free energy* can be assigned to each substance, such that a reaction in a system held at constant temperature tends to proceed if it is accompanied by a decrease in free energy; that is, if the free energy of the reactants is greater than that of the products. *The free energy of a substance is a property that expresses the resultant of the enthalpy of the substance and its inherent probability (entropy).* If the substances whose formulas are written on the left of the double arrow in a chemical equation and those whose formulas are written on the right have the same entropy (probability), the reaction will proceed in the direction that leads to the evolution of heat, that is, in the exothermic direction. If the substances on the left and those on the right have the same enthalpy, the reaction will proceed from the substances with the smaller probability (entropy) toward the substances with the greater probability (entropy). At equilibrium, when a reaction has no preferential tendency to go in either the forward or backward direction, the free energy of the substances on the left side is exactly equal to that of the substances on the right side. *At equilibrium the driving force of the enthalpy change accompanying a reaction is exactly balanced by the driving force of the probability change (entropy change).*

The relation between free energy, enthalpy, and entropy is

$$F = H - TS \tag{22}$$

For a reaction at constant temperature the change in free energy is

$$\Delta F = \Delta H - T \Delta S \tag{23}$$

It can be shown by the methods of statistical mechanics that the entropy of a system at temperature T is the Boltzmann constant k times the logarithm of the total number of quantum states for the system with each state given a weight equal to its Boltzmann exponential factor $e^{-E/kT}$:

$$S = k \ln \left[\sum_i \exp \left(-\frac{E_i}{kT} \right) \right] \tag{24}$$

The sum $\sum_i \exp(-E_i/kT)$ is called the *sum of states*. It is a measure of the probability (not normalized to unity in the usual way). Equation 24 may then be said to mean that the entropy of a system is k times the logarithm of its probability.

A substance in the form of a perfect crystal at the absolute zero is in its lowest quantum state, which may be a single state. The value of the entropy for such a substance is zero; that is, $S = k \ln 1 = 0$. This is the *third law of thermodynamics.* It was discovered by the German chemist W. Nernst (1864–1941) in 1906.

The Dependence of Thermodynamic Quantities on Temperature. If a sample of a substance at constant pressure P is heated in such a way that the only work done is the work $P \Delta V$ involved in its change in volume,* then the

---

* A change of this nature is called *change in state along a reversible path.* The nature of reversible and irreversible paths is discussed in detail in books on physical chemistry and chemical thermodynamics.

change dH in its enthalpy is equal to δq, the heat absorbed from the environment. Since $\delta q/dT$ is the heat capacity at constant pressure, C_P, we see that the temperature derivative of the enthalpy is given by the equation

$$\frac{dH}{dT} = C_P \qquad (25)$$

It can also be shown from the definition of entropy, Equation 24, that for the same process of heating the sample of substance in a reversible manner the change in entropy is $dS = \delta q/T$, and hence that the temperature derivative of the entropy is

$$\frac{dS}{dT} = \frac{C_P}{T} \qquad (26)$$

With use of these equations and a knowledge of C_P, values of H and S, and also of F, for a substance at one temperature can be calculated from the values at another temperature. For each compound an experimental value of the enthalpy of formation from the elements is needed. The entropy of every substance, in crystalline form, is known at the absolute zero ($S - 0$); it does not need to be determined by experiment.

18-9.   The Relation of the Equilibrium Constant to Standard Free-energy Change

It can be shown by the methods of statistical mechanics or chemical thermodynamics that the equilibrium constant K for a reaction is related to the change in standard free energy $\Delta F°$ accompanying the reaction by the equation

$$RT \ln K = -\Delta F° \qquad (27)$$

Values of $\Delta F°$ of formation of thousands of compounds, at $0°K$ and $298.16°K$ ($25°C$), are given in the U.S. Bureau of Standards Circular 500, "Selected Values of Chemical Thermodynamic Properties." These values may be combined to give the values of $\Delta F°$ for many other reactions, for which the equilibrium constants can then be calculated by use of Equation 27.

The study of the free energy of substances constitutes a complex subject and only a bare introduction to it can be given in a course in general chemistry. The following section deals with free-energy changes accompanying oxidation-reduction reactions; a similar treatment can also be given to other reactions.

18-10.   The Table of Standard Oxidation-reduction Potentials

In the discussion of oxidation-reduction reactions in Chapter 11, a brief table was given of oxidation-reduction couples arranged according to strength, the couple with the strongest reducing agent being at the top of the table and that with the strongest oxidizing agent at the bottom. Appendix IV is a more extensive table of this kind.

From Appendix IV we see that of the substances listed lithium metal is the strongest reducing agent, and fluoride ion is the weakest; and, conversely, fluorine is the strongest oxidizing agent and lithium ion the weakest.

There is given for each couple the value of the standard potential E°. This is the potential developed by the electric cell formed by the couple under consideration and the standard hydrogen couple $\frac{1}{2}H_2 \rightleftarrows H^+ + e^-$; this standard hydrogen couple has been selected as the reference point, with $E^\circ = 0$.

For example, a cell made with a strip of zinc as one electrode, in contact with a solution 1 M in Zn^{++}, and a piece of platinum over which bubbles of hydrogen are passing as the other electrode (Figure 11-5) would develop the potential 0.762 volt, this being the value given in the table for the couple $\frac{1}{2}Zn = \frac{1}{2}Zn^{++} + e^-$.

The potential of a cell depends on the concentrations or partial pressures of the reacting substances. The standard concentrations of the dissolved substances in Appendix IV are taken to be approximately 1 M (more accurately, unit activity, correction being made for deviation from the perfect-solution law), and the standard pressure for gases is 1 atm (corrected in very accurate work for deviation from the perfect-gas law).

18-11. Equilibrium Constants for Oxidation-reduction Couples

The zinc-hydrogen cell develops a large electrical potential, 0.762 V, because the over-all reaction

$$\tfrac{1}{2}Zn + H^+ \rightleftarrows \tfrac{1}{2}Zn^{++} + \tfrac{1}{2}H_2$$

which represents the reduction of hydrogen ion by zinc metal, has a strong tendency to go to the right, and in a cell so built that the electron reactions occur at separate electrodes this tendency results in electrons being forced into one electrode by the electrode reaction and pulled out of the other. It is clear that the equilibrium constant

$$K = \frac{[Zn^{++}]^{1/2} P_{H_2}^{1/2}}{[H^+]}$$

for the over-all reaction must have a large numerical value, corresponding to the tendency of the reaction to proceed to the right.

For a cell in which each half-cell reaction involves one electron, the product of the potential of the cell (the difference of the two standard oxidation-reduction potentials) by the value of the faraday, F, is equal to minus the standard free-energy change, ΔF°, for the reaction

$$F(E_1^\circ - E_2^\circ) = -\Delta F^\circ \tag{28}$$

From Equation 27 we see that the equilibrium constant for the reaction can be calculated from the standard potentials. Values of the equilibrium constant with the standard hydrogen couple as one half-cell are given in Appendix IV.

The meaning of the equilibrium constants of the oxidation-reduction couples can be made clear by the discussion of some examples. For the couple

$$\tfrac{1}{2}Zn \rightleftarrows \tfrac{1}{2}Zn^{++} + e^-$$

the constant is given as $K = 6.5 \times 10^{12}$. For this reaction the equilibrium expression is written according to convention as

$$K = [Zn^{++}]^{1/2}[e^-]$$

(The term [Zn] does not appear in the denominator because the activity of a crystalline substance is constant, at a given temperature, and is conventionally taken equal to unity.) It is this product that has the value 6.5×10^{12}.

This is, however, not of use until the quantity $[e^-]$, the electron concentration, has been evaluated or eliminated. It can be eliminated by combining the couple with another couple. Thus for the reaction

$$\tfrac{1}{2}H_2 \rightleftarrows H^+ + e^-$$

we have K given in the table as 1 (corresponding to $E° = 0$), which leads to

$$\frac{[H^+][e^-]}{P_{H_2}^{1/2}} = 1$$

By dividing this into the above equation we obtain

$$\frac{[Zn^{++}]^{1/2}[e^-]}{[H^+][e^-]/P_{H_2}^{1/2}} = \frac{6.5 \times 10^{12}}{1}$$

We now cancel the term $[e^-]$ and obtain the result

$$\frac{[Zn^{++}]^{1/2}P_{H_2}^{1/2}}{[H^+]} = 6.5 \times 10^{12}$$

This is the equilibrium equation corresponding to the reaction

$$\tfrac{1}{2}Zn + H^+ \rightleftarrows \tfrac{1}{2}Zn^{++} + \tfrac{1}{2}H_2$$

We may for convenience square the equilibrium expression, obtaining

$$\frac{[Zn^{++}]P_{H_2}}{[H^+]^2} = 42 \times 10^{24}$$

corresponding to the reaction

$$Zn + 2H^+ \rightleftarrows Zn^{++} + H_2$$

This tells us that the equilibrium pressure of hydrogen for the reaction of zinc with acid is extremely great; the reaction cannot be stopped by increasing the pressure of hydrogen, but will proceed until all of the zinc is dissolved.

On the other hand, for tin the equilibrium expression is

$$\frac{[Sn^{++}]P_{H_2}}{[H^+]^2} = (2 \times 10^2)^2 = 4 \times 10^4$$

Hence equilibrium would be reached, for example, by having $[Sn^{++}] = 1$, $P_{H_2} = 4$ atm, and $[H^+] = 0.01$.

The electron reactions are all written in Appendix IV so as to produce one electron. This is done for convenience; with this convention the ratio of two values of K gives the equilibrium constant for the reaction obtained by subtracting the equation for one couple from that for another. It is sometimes desirable to clear the equation of fractions by multiplying by a suitable factor; as we have seen from the examples given above, and as we know from the definition of equilibrium constant, this involves raising the equilibrium constant to the power equal to this factor.

Many questions about chemical reactions can be answered by reference to a table of standard oxidation-reduction potentials. In particular it can be determined whether or not a given oxidizing agent and a given reducing agent can possibly react to an appreciable extent, and the extent of possible reaction can be predicted. It cannot be said, however, that the reaction will necessarily proceed at a significant rate under given conditions; *the table gives information only about the state of chemical equilibrium and not about the rate at which equilibrium is approached.* For this reason the most valuable use of the table is in connection with reactions which are known to take place, to answer questions as to the extent of reaction; but the table is also valuable in telling whether or not it is worth while to try to make a reaction go by changing conditions.

The great simplification introduced by this procedure can be seen by examining the table given in Appendix IV. This table contains only 56 entries, which correspond to 56 different electron reactions. By combining any two of these electron reactions the equation for an ordinary oxidation-reduction reaction can be written. There are $56 \times 55/2$, or 1540, of these oxidation-reduction reactions that can be formed from the 56 electron reactions. The 56 numbers in the table can be combined in such a way as to give the 1540 values of their equilibrium constants; accordingly, this small table permits a prediction to be made as to whether any one of these 1540 reactions will tend to go in the forward direction or the reverse direction.

A more extensive table in the book *The Oxidation States of the Elements and Their Potentials in Aqueous Solutions*, by W. M. Latimer, occupies eight pages; the information given on these eight pages permits one to calculate values of the equilibrium constants for about 85,000 reactions, which, if written out, would occupy 1750 pages of the same size as the pages in Latimer's book; and, moreover, it is evident that if the equilibrium constants were independent of one another, and had to be determined by separate experiments, 85,000 experiments would have had to be carried out, instead of only about 400.

Some ways in which the values in Appendix IV can be used are illustrated below.

Example 11.   Is ferricyanide ion a stronger or a weaker oxidizing agent than ferric ion?

Solution.   We see from the table that the ferrocyanide-ferricyanide potential is larger than the ferrous-ferric potential; hence ferrocyanide ion is a stronger reducing agent than ferrous ion, and ferricyanide ion is a weaker oxidizing agent than ferric ion.

Example 12.   Would you expect reaction to occur on mixing solutions of ferrous sulfate and mercuric sulfate?

Solution.   The ferrous-ferric couple has potential -0.771 V and the mercurous-mercuric couple -0.910 V; hence the latter couple is the stronger oxidizing of the two, and the reaction

$$2Fe^{++} + 2Hg^{++} \longrightarrow 2Fe^{+++} + Hg_2^{++}$$

would occur, and proceed well toward completion.

Example 13.   What would you expect to occur on mixing solutions of ferrous sulfate and mercuric chloride?

Solution.   The above oxidation-reduction reaction would take place; in addition, when the solubility of the very slightly soluble salt Hg_2Cl_2 is reached this substance would precipitate, keeping the concentration $[Hg_2^{++}]$ low and causing the oxidation-reduction reaction to go further toward completion than in the previous case.

Example 14.   In the manufacture of potassium permanganate a solution containing manganate ion is oxidized by chlorine. Would bromine or iodine be as good?

Solution.   From the table we see that the values of $E°$ and K are the following:

		$E°$	K
$MnO_4^{--} \rightleftharpoons MnO_4 + e^-$		-0.54	1×10^{-9}
$Cl^- \rightleftharpoons \frac{1}{2}Cl_2 + e^-$		-1.358	2×10^{-23}
$Br^- \rightleftharpoons \frac{1}{2}Br_2(\ ) + e^-$		-1.065	1×10^{-18}
$I^- \rightleftharpoons \frac{1}{2}I_2(s) + e^-$		-0.535	1×10^{-9}

The value for iodine is so close to that for manganate-permanganate that effective oxidation by iodine (approaching completion) would not occur; hence iodine would be unsatisfactory. Bromine would produce essentially complete reaction, and in this respect would be as good as chlorine; but it costs ten times as much, and so should not be used.

EXERCISES

18-7. What value of the activation energy for a reaction corresponds to doubling the reaction rate on increase of temperature by 10°C at room temperature? At 300°C? At 600°C? (Answer: About 12,000 cal/mole; 48,000; 110,000.)

18-8. Why do foods cook faster in a pressure cooker than in an ordinary cooking pot?

18-9. Is the reaction $2NO_2 \longrightarrow N_2O_4$ speeded up more or less than the reverse reaction by an increase in temperature? For enthalpy values see Table 14-1.

18-10. If the rate of solution of zinc in hydrochloric acid is proportional to the surface area of the zinc, how much more rapidly will a thousand cubes of zinc each weighing one milligram dissolve in acid than a single cube weighing one gram?

18-11. It is found by experiment that when hydrogen iodide is heated the degree of dissociation increases. Is the dissociation of hydrogen iodide an exothermic or an endothermic reaction?

18-12. When automobile tires are stored, they age through oxidation and other reactions of the rubber. By about what factor would the safe period of storage be multiplied by lowering the storage temperature by 30°F?

18-13. If it is necessary to store oil-soaked rags, how should this be done?

18-14. Explain the change that takes place in the rate of reaction of permanganate ion and hydrogen peroxide in sulfuric acid solution as the reaction proceeds.

18-15. Does the addition of a catalyst affect the equilibrium constant of a reaction? Explain your answer.

18-16. Carbon dioxide dissolved in the seawater brought up from the depths of the ocean (more than 500 feet below the surface) gives a C^{14} beta count of 170 counts per minute per mole of carbon dioxide, whereas that in the surface water gives the same rate as atmospheric carbon dioxide, 184 counts per minute. What is the average residence time of dissolved carbon dioxide in the depths of the ocean?

18-17. Producer gas is made by the reduction of carbon dioxide to carbon monoxide by carbon. With the total pressure 1 atm, the equilibrium mixture of the two oxides at 1123°C contains 93.77% by volume of carbon monoxide, and 6.23% of carbon dioxide. What is the equilibrium constant for this reaction at this temperature? What would be the composition of the mixture in equilibrium at this temperature if the total pressure were 2 atm?

18-18. Some hydrogen iodide was introduced into a vessel and held at 350°C for some time. One mole of the gas was then allowed to flow out in such a way as to cool it rapidly enough to prevent change in its composition. The quenched equilibrium mixture was found to contain 0.117 mole of I_2. What is the equilibrium constant for the dissociation of hydrogen iodide at 350°C? (Answer: 0.0233.)

18-19. The equilibrium constant for the equilibrium $AgI(c) \rightleftarrows Ag^+(aq) + I^-(aq)$ can be written $[Ag^+][I^-] = K_{SP}$, inasmuch as the activity of $AgI(c)$ is a constant at constant temperature. K_{SP} is called the *solubility product*. The solubility of silver iodide at 25°C is 1×10^{-8} mole/liter. What is the value of the solubility product? What is the solubility of AgI in 0.0001 F KI solution? (Answer: 1×10^{-16} mole² liter⁻²; 1×10^{-12} mole/liter.)

18-20. Lead chloride is only slightly soluble in water. Would you expect its solubility in a 1 F solution of each of the following salts to be much greater than, approximately equal to, or much less than that in pure water: Na_2SO_4, KCl, $KClO_4$, $Pb(C_2H_3O_2)_2$, $NaNO_3$?

18-21. For a reaction $A + B \longrightarrow$ products

that proceeds by a second-order mechanism, the rate equation is

$$\frac{-d[A]}{dt} = k_2[A][B]$$

Show that the decrease in concentration of A can be described by the first-order equation

$$\frac{-d[A]}{dt} = k_1[A]$$

if [B] is initially very large compared with [A]. What is the relation between k_1 and k_2? (Answer: $k_1 = k_2[B]_0$.)

18-22. The reaction

$$CF_3 + H_2 \longrightarrow CF_3H + H$$

is a second-order reaction with rate constant $k_2 = 4.5 \times 10^3$ liter mole^{-1} sec^{-1} at 400°K. What is the electronic structure of the radical CF_3? If a small amount of this radical were to be introduced into hydrogen at 1 atm pressure and 400°K, how long would it take for half of it to be converted to methyl fluoride?

18-23. What value would you predict for the activation energy of the reaction of the preceding Exercise from the rough rule of Section 18-4? (The experimental value is 9.5 kcal/mole.) At what temperature would the reaction proceed twice as fast as at 400°K?

18-24. It was found by the American chemists D. P. Stevenson and D. O. Schissler— by use of a mass spectrograph to determine the composition of the reacting gas—that the reaction

$$Kr^+ + H_2 \longrightarrow KrH^+ + H$$

occurs at every collision between the reacting molecules, and that the activation energy for the reaction is zero.

(a) What electronic structure would you assign to KrH^+?
(b) Is the reaction exothermic or endothermic?
(c) What is the minimum value of the bond energy between Kr^+ and H in KrH^+? [Answer: (c) 104 kcal/mole.]

18-25. Stevenson and Schissler also observed the reaction

$$HCl^+ + HCl \longrightarrow H_2Cl^+ + Cl$$

This reaction has zero activation energy, and accordingly is exothermic. What is the electronic structure of H_2Cl^+? What value would you predict for the H—Cl—H bond angle? Can you suggest a reason for this reaction to be exothermic? (How would the electronegativity of Cl^+ compare with that of Cl?)

18-26. Ethyl chloride vapor when heated decomposes by the reaction

$$C_2H_5Cl \longrightarrow C_2H_4 + HCl$$

The reaction is observed to be of the first order, with rate constant $k = Ae^{-E^*/RT}$, $A = 1.6 \times 10^{14}$ sec^{-1}, $E^* = 59,500$ cal/mole. What is the value of k at 700°K? What fraction of the ethyl chloride would decompose in 10 minutes at this temperature? At what temperature is the reaction twice as fast? (Answer: 4.2×10^{-5} sec^{-1}; 2.5%; 712°K.)

18-27. The reaction of the preceding Exercise might have as its initial step the breaking of a carbon-chlorine bond to form the radicals C_2H_5 and Cl, followed by a chain of reactions to give the final products. The investigators concluded that the observed value of the activation energy eliminates this mechanism. What is the nature of their argument? What value would be expected for the activation energy if this were the mechanism?

18-28. What structure would you assign to the activated ethyl chloride molecule if its decomposition involves its splitting directly into ethylene and hydrogen chloride? About what value would you expect the activation energy to have (Section 18-4; Table 10-3)? (Answer: About 53 kcal/mole.)

18-29. An enzyme in the human body may increase the rate of a chemical reaction a millionfold. What energy of binding of the activated complex to the enzyme would be needed to account for this effect? (Answer: 8.5 kcal/mole.)

18-30. The density of the equilibrium mixture of N_2O_4 and NO_2 at 1 atm and 25°C is 3.18 g/liter. What is the average molecular weight of the gas? What are the partial pressures of NO_2 and N_2O_4? What is the value of the equilibrium constant for the reaction $N_2O_4 \rightleftarrows 2NO_2$? To what extent is N_2O_4 dissociated under these conditions?

18-31. Would the extent of dissociation of N_2O_4 in a flask at 1 atm pressure and 25°C change if nitrogen were introduced until the pressure reaches 2 atm? If some liquid N_2O_4 were introduced in such amount that when it had evaporated the pressure of the

N_2O_4-NO_2 equilibrium mixture had reached 2 atm? To what extent is N_2O_4 dissociated under these conditions?

18-32. Crystals of N_2O_4 are colorless, but the N_2O_4-NO_2 gas is red. Would a sealed flask containing some of this red gas become more intensely colored or less intensely colored on raising the temperature? (See Table 14-1 for enthalpy values.)

CHAPTER **19**

Acids and Bases

It is useful to give a further discussion of acids and bases after the consideration of the fundamental principles of chemical equilibrium.

In Chapter 8 an acid was defined as a hydrogen-containing substance that dissociates on solution in water to produce hydrogen ions, and a base was defined as a substance containing the hydroxide ion or the hydroxyl group that can dissociate in aqueous solution as the hydroxide ion. It was pointed out that acidic solutions have a characteristic sharp taste, due to the hydronium ion, H_3O^+, and that basic solutions have a characteristic brackish taste, due to the hydroxide ion OH^-. The alternative definitions of acids as proton donors and bases as proton acceptors were also given (Section 8-10).

In Chapter 8 it was also mentioned that the ordinary mineral acids (hydrochloric acid, nitric acid, sulfuric acid) are completely ionized (dissociated) in solution, producing one hydrogen ion for every acidic hydrogen atom in the formula of the acid, whereas other acids, such as acetic acid, produce only a smaller number of hydrogen ions. Acids such as acetic acid are called *weak acids*. A 1 F solution of acetic acid does not have nearly as sharp a taste and does not react nearly as vigorously with an active metal, such as zinc, as does a 1 F solution of hydrochloric acid, because the 1 F solution of acetic acid contains a great number of undissociated molecules $HC_2H_3O_2$, and only a relatively small number of ions H_3O^+ and $C_2H_3O_2^-$. There exists in a solution of acetic acid a steady state, corresponding to the equation

$$HC_2H_3O_2 + H_2O \rightleftarrows H_3O^+ + C_2H_3O_2^-$$

In order to understand the properties of acetic acid it is necessary to formulate the equilibrium expression for this steady state; by use of this equilibrium expression the properties of acetic acid solutions of different concentrations can be predicted.

The general principles of chemical equilibrium can be similarly used in the discussion of a weak base, such as ammonium hydroxide, and also of salts formed by weak acids and weak bases. In addition, these principles are important in providing an understanding of the behavior of *indicators*, the colored substances that were described in Chapter 8 as useful for determining whether a solution is acidic, neutral, or basic. These principles are of further importance in permitting a discussion of the relation between the concentrations of hydronium ion and hydroxide ion in the same solution.

19-1. Hydronium-ion (Hydrogen-ion) Concentration

It was mentioned in the chapter on water (Chapter 16) that pure water does not consist simply of H_2O molecules, but also contains hydronium ions in concentration about 1×10^{-7} moles per liter (at 25°C), and hydroxide ions in the same concentration. These ions are formed by the *autoprotolysis* of water (reaction of one molecule of water acting as an acid with another molecule of water acting as a base; this reaction is also called the ionization of water):

$$2H_2O \rightleftarrows H_3O^+ + OH^-$$

A molecule, such as the water molecule, that can both lose a proton and add a proton is called an *amphiprotic* molecule (Greek *amphi*, both). Only amphiprotic molecules or ions can undergo autoprotolysis.

The means by which it has been found that pure water contains hydronium ions and hydroxide ions is the measurement of the electric conductivity of water. The mechanism of the electric conductivity of a solution was discussed in Chapter 8. According to this discussion, electric charge is transferred through the body of the solution by the motion of cations from the region around the anode to the region around the cathode, and anions from the region around the cathode to the region around the anode. If pure water contained no ions its electric conductivity would be zero. When investigators made water as pure as possible, by distilling it over and over again, it was found that the electric conductivity approached a certain small value, about one ten-millionth that of a 1 *F* solution of hydrochloric acid or sodium hydroxide. This indicates that the autoprotolysis of water occurs to such an extent as to give hydronium ions and hydroxide ions in concentration about one ten-millionth mole per liter. Refined measurements have provided the value 1.00×10^{-7} *M* for $[H_3O^+]$ and $[OH^-]$ in pure water at 25°C.*

Although the hydronium ion, H_3O^+, is present in water and confers acidic

---

* The extent of autoprotolysis depends somewhat on the temperature. At 0°C $[H_3O^+]$ and $[OH^-]$ are 0.83×10^{-7} *M*, and at 100°C they are 6.9×10^{-7} *M*. When a solution of a strong acid and a solution of a strong base are mixed, a large amount of heat is given off. This shows that the reaction gives off heat, and accordingly that the reaction of dissociation of water absorbs heat. In accordance with Le Chatelier's principle, increase in the temperature would shift the equilibrium of dissociation of water in such a way as to tend to restore the original temperature; that is, the reaction would take place in the direction that absorbs heat. This direction is the dissociation of water to hydrogen ions and hydroxide ions, and accordingly the principle requires that increase in temperature cause an increased amount of dissociation of water, as is found experimentally.

properties upon aqueous solutions, it is customary to use the symbol H^+ in place of H_3O^+ and to speak of hydrogen ion in place of hydronium. In the later sections of this chapter we shall follow this custom except when the discussion is based upon the proton donor-acceptor theory (the Brønsted-Lowry theory). Accordingly, we shall use the symbol H^+ with two meanings: to represent the unhydrated proton when the Brønsted-Lowry theory is being applied, and to represent the hydronium ion, H_3O^+, when this theory is not being applied. We shall refer to H^+ in the Brønsted-Lowry applications as the proton and to H^+ (representing H_3O^+) in other discussions as the hydrogen ion (representing the hydronium ion).

The pH.   Instead of saying that the concentration of hydrogen ion in pure water is 1.00×10^{-7} M, it is customary to say that the pH of pure water is 7. This new symbol, pH, is defined in the following way: **the pH is the negative common logarithm of the hydrogen-ion concentration:**

$$pH = -\log \left[H^+\right]$$

or

$$[H^+] = 10^{-pH} = \text{antilog}\,(-pH)$$

We see from this definition of pH that a solution containing 1 mole of hydrogen ions per liter, that is, with a concentration 10^{-0} in H^+, has pH zero. A solution only one-tenth as strong in hydrogen ion, containing 0.1 mole of hydrogen ions per liter, has $[H^+] = 10^{-1}$, and hence has pH 1. The relation between the hydrogen-ion concentration and the pH is shown for simple concentrations along the left side of Figure 19-1.

Figure **19-1**

Color changes of indicators.

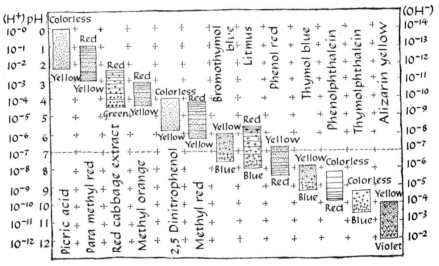

In science and medicine it is customary to describe the acidity of a solution by saying "The pH of the solution is 3," for example, instead of saying "The hydrogen-ion concentration of the solution is 10^{-3}." It is evident that the quantity pH is useful, in permitting the exponential expression to be avoided.

The chemical reactions involved in biological processes are often very sensitive to the hydrogen-ion concentration of the medium. In industries such as the fermentation industry the control of the pH of the materials being processed is very important. It is not surprising that the symbol pH was introduced by a Danish biochemist, S. P. L. Sørensen, while he was working on problems connected with the brewing of beer.

Example 1. What is the pH of a solution with $[H^+] = 0.0200$?
   Solution. The log of 0.0200 is equal to the log of 2×10^{-2}, which is $0.301 - 2 = -1.699$. The pH of the solution is the negative of the logarithm of the hydrogen-ion concentration. Hence the pH of this solution is **1.699.**

Example 2. What is the hydrogen-ion concentration of a solution with pH 4.30?
   Solution. A solution with pH 4.30 has log $[H^+] = -4.30$, or $0.70 - 5$. The antilog of 0.70 is 5.0, and the antilog of -5 is 10^{-5}. Hence the hydrogen-ion concentration in this solution is $\mathbf{5.0 \times 10^{-5}}$.

19-2. The Equilibrium between Hydrogen Ion and Hydroxide Ion in Aqueous Solution

The equation for the autoprotolysis of water is

$$2H_2O \rightleftarrows H_3O^+ + OH^-$$

The expression for the equilibrium constant, in accordance with the principle developed in the preceding chapter, is

$$\frac{[H_3O^+][OH^-]}{[H_2O]^2} = K_1$$

In this expression the symbol $[H_2O]$ represents the activity (concentration) of water in the solution (see Section 17-11 for the discussion of activity). Since the activity of water in a dilute aqueous solution is nearly the same as that for pure water, it is customary to omit the activity of water in the equilibrium expression for dilute solutions. Accordingly, the product of K_1 and $[H_2O]^2$ may be taken as another constant K_w, and we may write

$$[H_3O^+] \times [OH^-] = K_w$$

This expression states that the product of the hydronium-ion concentration and the hydroxide-ion concentration in water and in dilute aqueous solutions is a constant, at given temperature. The value of K_w is 1.00×10^{-14} moles²/liter² at 25°C. *Hence in pure water both H_3O^+ and OH^- have the concentration 1.00×10^{-7} moles per liter at 25°C, and in acidic or basic solutions the product of the concentrations of these ions equals 1.00×10^{-14}.*

Thus a neutral solution contains both hydrogen ions (hydronium ions) and hydroxide ions at the same concentration, 1.00×10^{-7}. A slightly acidic solution, containing 10 times as many hydrogen ions (concentration 10^{-6}, pH 6), also contains some hydroxide ions, one-tenth as many as a neutral solution. A solution containing 100 times as much hydrogen ion as a neutral solution (concentration 10^{-5}, pH 5) contains a smaller amount of hydroxide ion, one one-hundredth as much as a neutral solution; and so on. A solution containing 1 mole of strong acid per liter has hydrogen-ion concentration 1, and pH 0; such a strongly acidic solution also contains some hydroxide ion, the concentration of hydroxide ion being 1×10^{-14}. Although this is a very small number, it still represents a large number of actual ions in unit volume. Avogadro's number is 0.602×10^{24}, and accordingly a concentration of 10^{-14} moles per liter corresponds to 0.602×10^{10} ions per liter, or 0.602×10^7 ions per milliliter; that is, about 6,000,000 hydroxide ions per milliliter.

Illustrative Exercises

19-1. What is the pH of 0.1 F HCl solution? Of 0.1 F NaOH solution? Of the solution obtained by mixing equal volumes of these two solutions?

19-2. What is the hydrogen-ion concentration of each of the three solutions of the preceding Exercise? The hydroxide-ion concentration?

19-3. A sample of blood is found by experiment to have pH 6.8. What is its $[H^+]$? What is its $[OH^-]$? How many hydrogen ions and how many hydroxide ions (not moles) are there per milliliter?

19-3. Indicators

It was mentioned in Chapter 8 that indicators such as litmus may be used to tell whether a solution is acidic, neutral, or basic. The change in color of an indicator as the pH of the solution changes is not sharp, but extends over a range of one or two pH units. This is the result of the existence of chemical equilibrium between the two differently colored forms of the indicator, and the dependence of the color on the hydrogen-ion concentration is due to the participation of hydrogen ion in the equilibrium.

Thus the red form of litmus may be represented by the formula HIn and the blue form by In⁻, resulting from the dissociation reaction

$$HIn \rightleftharpoons H^+ + In^-$$

Red   Blue
acidic form   basic form

In alkaline solutions, with $[H^+]$ very small, the equilibrium is shifted to the right, and the indicator is converted almost entirely into the basic form (blue for litmus). In acidic solutions, with $[H^+]$ large, the equilibrium is shifted to the left, and the indicator assumes the acidic form.

Let us calculate the relative amount of the two forms as a function of $[H^+]$. The equilibrium expression for the indicator reaction written above is

$$\frac{[H^+][In^-]}{[HIn]} = K_{In}$$

in which K_{In} is the *equilibrium constant for the indicator*. We rewrite this as

$$\frac{[HIn]}{[In^-]} = \frac{[H^+]}{K_{In}}$$

This equation shows how the ratio of the two forms of the indicator depends on $[H^+]$. When the two forms are present in equal amounts, the ratio of acidic form to alkaline form, $[HIn]/[In^-]$, has the value 1, and hence $[H^+] = K_{In}$. **The indicator constant K_{In} is thus the value of the hydrogen-ion concentration at which the change in color of the indicator is half completed.** The corresponding pH value is called the pK of the indicator.

When the pH is decreased by one unit the value of $[H^+]$ becomes ten times K_{In} and the ratio $[HIn]/[In^-]$ then equals 10. Thus at a pH value 1 less than the pK of the indicator (its midpoint) the acidic form of the indicator predominates over the basic form in the ratio 10:1. In this solution 91 % of the indicator is in the acidic form, and 9% in the basic form. Over a range of 2 pH units the indicator accordingly changes from 91 % acidic form to 91 % basic form. For most indicators the color change detectable by the eye occurs over a range of about 1.2 to 1.8 units.

Indicators differ in their pK values; pure water, with pH 7, is neutral to litmus (which has pK equal to 6.8), acidic to phenolphthalein (pK 8.8), and basic to methyl orange (pK 3.7).

A chart showing the color changes and effective pH ranges of several indicators is given in Figure 19-1. The approximate pH of a solution can be determined by finding by test the indicator toward which the solution shows a neutral reaction. Test paper, made with a mixture of indicators and showing several color changes, is now available with which the pH of a solution can be estimated to within about 1 unit over the pH range 1 to 13.

In titrating a weak acid or a weak base the indicator must be chosen with care. The way of choosing the proper indicator is described in the following section.

It is seen that an indicator behaves as a weak organic acid; the equilibrium expression for an indicator is the same as that for an ordinary weak acid, as discussed in the following section.

By the use of color standards for the indicator, the pH of a solution may be estimated to about 0.1 unit by the indicator method. A more satisfactory general method of determining the pH of a solution is by use of an instrument

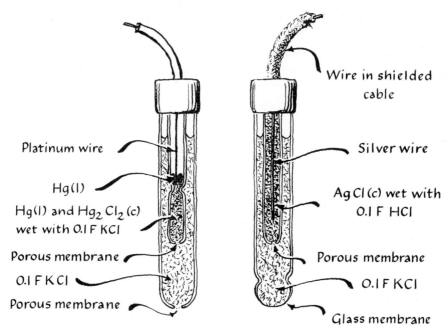

Platinum wire

Hg(l)

Hg(l) and $Hg_2 Cl_2$ (c)
wet with 0.I F KCl

Porous membrane

0.I F KCl

Porous membrane

Wire in shielded
cable

Silver wire

Ag Cl (c) wet with
0.I F HCl

Porous membrane

0.I F KCl

Glass membrane

Calomel electrode   Glass electrode

Figure 19-2

*A representation of the two electrodes of a glass-electrode pH meter.
The glass membrane is made of a special glass that has an effective
permeability to hydrogen ions. The potential of this electrode is determined by the concentration of hydrogen ions in the medium surrounding
the glass membrane.*

that measures the hydrogen-ion concentration by measuring the electric
potential of a cell with cell reaction involving hydrogen ions. Modern glass-
electrode *p*H meters are now available that cover the *p*H range 0 to 14 with
an accuracy approaching 0.01 (Figure 19-2).

The glass electrode has the structure shown at the right in Figure 19-2. The
Ag-AgCl electrode provides a reversible electric connection between the ter-
minal wire and the HCl solution. The glass bulb at the bottom is made of a
special glass that conducts the electric current by accepting protons, passing
them from one oxygen atom to another, and liberating protons on the other
side—this glass is not permeable to other ions. The mercury-calomel electrode
shown at the left permits a second reversible electric contact, not dependent
on the hydrogen-ion concentration, to be made with the solution. In measuring
the *p*H of a solution the ends of the two electrodes are placed in the solution
and the electromotive force that is developed is measured with a vacuum-tube
voltmeter. Since the conduction of current through the cell involves the trans-

fer of hydrogen ions from a solution with one hydrogen-ion activity to a solution with another hydrogen-ion activity (the solutions on the two sides of the glass membrane) and the hydrogen-ion activities are not significantly involved in the other conduction steps, the electromotive force depends upon the *p*H of the solution being tested. It is linear in the *p*H, changing by 0.059 volt per *p*H unit at 25°C.

19-4. Equivalent Weights of Acids and Bases

A solution containing one gram formula weight of hydrochloric acid, HCl, per liter is 1 *F* in hydrogen ion. Similarly a solution containing 0.5 gram formula weight of sulfuric acid, H_2SO_4, per liter is 1 *F* in replaceable hydrogen. Each of these solutions is neutralized* by an equal volume of a solution containing one gram formula weight of sodium hydroxide, NaOH, per liter, and the weights of the acids are hence equivalent to one gram formula weight of the alkali.

The quotient of the gram formula weight of an acid by the number of hydrogen atoms which are replaceable for the reaction under consideration is called the **equivalent weight of the acid.** Likewise, *the quotient of the gram formula weight of a base by the number of hydroxyl groups which are replaceable for the reaction under consideration is called the* **equivalent weight of the base.**

One equivalent weight of an acid neutralizes one equivalent weight of a base. It is important to note that the equivalent weight of a polyprotic acid is not invariant; for H_3PO_4 it may be the gram formula weight, one half this, or one third, depending on whether one, two, or three hydrogens are effective in the reaction under consideration.

The *normality* of a solution of an acid or base is the number of equivalents of acid or base per liter; a 1 *N* solution contains 1 equivalent per liter of solution. By determining, with use of an indicator such as litmus, the relative volumes of acidic and alkaline solutions that are equivalent, the normality of one solution can be calculated from the known value of the other. This process of **acid-base titration** (the determination of the *titer* or strength of an unknown solution) with use of special apparatus such as graduated burets and pipets, is an important method of volumetric quantitative analysis.

Example 3. It is found by experiment that 25.0 ml of a solution of sodium hydroxide is neutralized by 20.0 ml of a 0.100 *N* acid solution. What are the normality of the alkaline solution and the weight of NaOH per liter?

   Solution. The unknown normality *x* of the alkaline solution is found by solving the equation that expresses the equivalence of the portions of the two solutions:

* The meaning of "neutralizes" in the case of weak acids or bases is discussed in a later section of this chapter.

$$25.0x = 20.0 \times 0.100$$

$$x = \frac{20.0 \times 0.100}{25.0} = \textbf{0.080}$$

The weight of NaOH per liter is 0.080 times the equivalent weight, 40.0, or **3.20 g.**

You may find it useful to fix in your mind the following equation:

$$V_1 N_1 = V_2 N_2$$

Here V_1 is the volume of a solution with normality N_1, and V_2 is the equivalent volume (containing the same number of replaceable hydrogens or hydroxyls) of a solution with normality N_2. In solving the above exercise we began by writing this equation; $25.0x$ is $V_1 N_1$, and 20.0×0.100 is $V_2 N_2$, in this case.

Illustrative Exercises

19-4. A 1.00 N solution of hydrochloric acid is diluted with water to five times its original volume. What is its new normality?

19-5. How many grams of each of the following substances would be needed to make 1.00 liter of 0.100 N solution? The number after each formula is its formula weight. Acids: HBr (81), HNO_3 (63), H_2SO_4 (98), H_3PO_4 (98), $H_2C_2O_4 \cdot 2H_2O$ (oxalic acid dihydrate, 126). Bases: NaOH (40), NH_3 (17), $Ca(OH)_2$ (74).

19-6. A standard acid solution can be made by dissolving a weighed amount of pure benzoic acid ($HC_7H_5O_2$, one replaceable hydrogen) and making a definite volume of solution with it. How much benzoic acid should be weighed out to make 1000 ml of 0.200 N solution?

19-7. The volume 40 ml of sodium hydroxide solution is made neutral to litmus by the addition of 60 ml of 0.100 N benzoic acid. What is the normality of the sodium hydroxide solution?

19-8. In titrating vinegar (a solution of acetic acid, $HC_2H_3O_2$) with 0.120 N sodium hydroxide solution, 10.0 ml of vinegar required 55.0 ml of the alkaline solution to neutralize it. What is the strength of the vinegar, in grams of acetic acid per 100 ml of vinegar?

19-5. Weak Acids and Bases

Ionization of a Weak Acid. A 0.1 N solution of a strong acid such as hydrochloric acid is 0.1 N in hydrogen ion, since this acid is very nearly completely dissociated into ions except in very concentrated solutions. But a 0.1 N solution of acetic acid contains hydrogen ions in much smaller concentration, as is seen by testing with indicators, observing the rate of attack of metals, or simply by tasting. Acetic acid is a weak acid; the acetic acid molecules hold their protons so firmly that not all of them are transferred to water molecules to form hydronium ions. Instead, there is an equilibrium reaction,

$$HC_2H_3O_2 + H_2O \rightleftarrows H_3O^+ + C_2H_3O_2^-$$

or, ignoring the hydration of the proton,

$$HC_2H_3O_2 \rightleftharpoons H^+ + C_2H_3O_2^-$$

The equilibrium expression for this reaction is

$$\frac{[H^+][C_2H_3O_2^-]}{[HC_2H_3O_2]} = K$$

In general, for an acid HA in equilibrium with ions H^+ and A^- the equilibrium expression is

$$\frac{[H^+][A^-]}{[HA]} = K_a$$

The constant K_a, characteristic of the acid, is called its **acid constant** or **ionization constant.**

Values of acid constants are found experimentally by measuring the pH of solutions of the acids. A table of values is given later in this chapter.

Example 4. The pH of a 0.100 N solution of acetic acid is found by experiment to be 2.874. What is the acid constant, K_a, of this acid?

Solution. To calculate the acid constant we note that acetic acid added to pure water ionizes to produce hydrogen ions and acetate ions in equal quantities. Moreover, since the amount of hydrogen ion resulting from the dissociation of water is negligible compared with the total amount present, we have

$$[H^+] = [C_2H_3O_2^-] = \text{antilog}\,(-2.874) = 1.34 \times 10^{-3}$$

The concentration $[HC_2H_3O_2]$ is hence $0.100 - 0.001 = 0.099$, and the acid constant has the value

$$K_a = (1.34 \times 10^{-3})^2/0.099 = \mathbf{1.80 \times 10^{-5}}$$

The hydrogen-ion concentration of a weak acid (containing no other electrolytes which react with it or its ions) in 1 N concentration is approximately equal to the square root of its acid constant, as is seen from the following example.

Example 5. What is $[H^+]$ of a 1 N solution of HCN, hydrocyanic acid, which has $K_a = 4 \times 10^{-10}$?

Solution. Let $x = [H^+]$. Then we can write $[CN^-] = x$ (neglecting the amount of hydrogen ion due to ionization of the water), and $[HCN] = 1 - x$. The equilibrium equation is

$$\frac{x^2}{1 - x} = K_a = 4 \times 10^{-10}$$

We know that x is going to be much smaller than 1, since this weak acid is only very slightly ionized. Hence we replace $1 - x$ by 1 (neglecting the small difference between unionized hydrocyanic acid and the total cyanide concentration), obtaining

$$x^2 = 4 \times 10^{-10}$$
$$x = 2 \times 10^{-5} = [H^+]$$

The neglect of the ionization of water is also seen to be justified, since even in this very slightly acidic solution the value of $[H^+]$ is 200 times the value for pure water.

Successive Ionizations of a Polyprotic Acid. A polyprotic acid has several acid constants, corresponding to dissociation of successive hydrogen ions. For phosphoric acid, H_3PO_4, there are three equilibrium expressions:

$$H_3PO_4 \rightleftharpoons H^+ + H_2PO_4^-$$

$$K_1 = \frac{[H^+][H_2PO_4^-]}{[H_3PO_4]} = 7.5 \times 10^{-3} = K_{H_3PO_4}$$

$$H_2PO_4^- \rightleftharpoons H^+ + HPO_4^{--}$$

$$K_2 = \frac{[H^+][HPO_4^{--}]}{[H_2PO_4^-]} = 6.2 \times 10^{-8} = K_{H_2PO_4^-}$$

$$HPO_4^{--} \rightleftharpoons H^+ + PO_4^{---}$$

$$K_3 = \frac{[H^+][PO_4^{---}]}{[HPO_4^{--}]} = 10^{-12} = K_{HPO_4^{--}}$$

Note that these constants have the dimensions of concentration, mole/liter.

The ratio of successive ionization constants for a polybasic acid is usually about 10^{-5}, as in this case. We see that with respect to its first hydrogen phosphoric acid is a moderately strong acid—considerably stronger than acetic acid. With respect to its second hydrogen it is weak, and to its third very weak.

Ionization of a Weak Base. A weak base dissociates in part to produce hydroxide ions:

$$MOH \rightleftharpoons M^+ + OH^-$$

The corresponding equilibrium expression is

$$\frac{[M^+][OH^-]}{[MOH]} = K_b$$

The constant K_b is called the *basic constant* of the base.

Ammonium hydroxide is the only common weak base. Its basic constant has the value 1.81×10^{-5} at 25°C. The hydroxides of the alkali metals and the alkaline-earth metals are strong bases.

Example 6. What is the pH of a 0.1 F solution of ammonium hydroxide?
   Solution. Our fundamental equation is

$$\frac{[NH_4^+][OH^-]}{[NH_4OH]} = K_b = 1.81 \times 10^{-5}$$

Since the ions NH_4^+ and OH^- are produced in equal amounts by the dissociation of the base and the amount of OH^- from dissociation of water is negligible, we put

$$[NH_4^+] = [OH^-] = x$$

The concentration of NH_4OH is accordingly $0.1 - x$, and we obtain the equation

$$\frac{x^2}{0.1 - x} = 1.81 \times 10^{-5}$$

(Here we have made the calculation as though all the undissociated solute were NH_4OH. Actually there is some dissolved NH_3 present; however, since the equilibrium $NH_3 + H_2O \rightleftarrows NH_4OH$ is of such a nature that the ratio $[NH_4OH]/[NH_3]$ is constant, we are at liberty to write the equilibrium expression for the base as shown above, with the symbol $[NH_4OH]$ representing the total concentration of the undissociated solute, including the molecular species NH_3 as well as NH_4OH.)

Solving this equation, we obtain the result

$$x = [OH^-] = [NH_4^+] = 1.34 \times 10^{-3}$$

The solution is hence only slightly alkaline—its hydroxide-ion concentration is the same as that of a $0.00134\ N$ solution of sodium hydroxide. This value of $[OH^-]$ corresponds to $[H^+] = (1.00 \times 10^{-14})/(1.34 \times 10^{-3}) = 7.46 \times 10^{-12}$, as calculated from the water equilibrium equation

$$[H^+][OH^-] = 1.00 \times 10^{-14}$$

The corresponding pH is **11.13**, which is the answer to the problem.

Very many problems in solution chemistry are solved with use of the acid and base equilibrium equations. The uses of these equations in discussing the titration of weak acids and bases, the hydrolysis of salts, and the properties of buffered solutions are illustrated in the following sections of this chapter.

The student while working a problem should not substitute numbers in the equations in a routine way, but should think carefully about the chemical reactions and equilibria involved and the magnitudes of the concentrations of the different molecular species. Every problem solved should add to his understanding of solution chemistry. *The ultimate goal is such an understanding of the subject that the student can estimate the orders of magnitude of concentrations of the various ionic and molecular species in a solution without having to solve the equilibrium equations.*

Illustrative Exercises

19-9. What is the approximate pH of a $0.1\ F$ solution of H_3PO_4, which has first acid constant 0.75×10^{-2}? (The ionization of the second and third hydrogens can be neglected in solving this exercise.)

19-10. What is the concentration of SO_4^{--} in a $0.1\ F$ solution of H_2SO_4? The first ionization is complete, and the ionization constant for the second ionization has the value 1.2×10^{-2}.

19-11. (a) A 0.1 N solution of HCl is diluted tenfold. By how much does the acidity (concentration of hydrogen ion) change?

(b) A 0.1 N solution of acetic acid ($K_a = 1.8 \times 10^{-5}$) is diluted tenfold. By how much does the acidity change?

19-6. The Titration of Weak Acids and Bases

A liter of solution containing 0.2 mole of a strong acid such as hydrochloric acid has $[H^+] = 0.2$ and $pH = 0.7$. The addition of a strong base, such as 0.2 N NaOH, causes the hydrogen-ion concentration to diminish through neutralization by the added hydroxide ion. When 990 ml of strong base has been added, the excess of acid over base is $0.2 \times 10/1000 = 0.002$ mole, and since the total volume is very close to 2 liters the value of $[H^+]$ is 0.001, and the pH is 3. When 999 ml has been added, and the neutralization reaction is within 0.1 % of completion, the values are $[H^+] = 0.0001$ and $pH = 4$. At $pH = 5$ the reaction is within 0.01 % of completion, and at pH 6 within 0.001 %. Finally pH 7, neutrality, is reached when an amount of strong base has been added exactly equivalent to the amount of strong acid present. A very small excess of strong base causes the pH to increase beyond 7.

We see that to obtain the most accurate results in titrating a strong acid and a strong base an indicator with indicator constant about 10^{-7} ($pK = 7$)

Figure **19-3**

Acid-base titration curves.

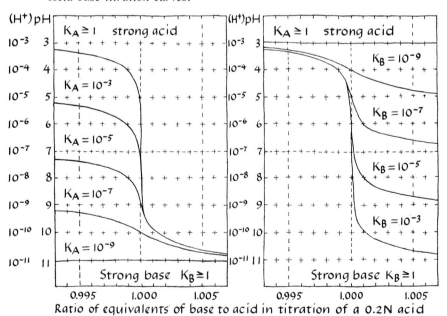

Ratio of equivalents of base to acid in titration of a 0.2N acid with a 0.2N base, either acid or base being strong.

should be chosen, such as litmus or bromthymol blue. The titration curve calculated above, and given in Figure 19-3, shows, however, that the choice of an indicator is in this case not crucial; any indicator with pK between 4 (methyl orange) and 10 (thymolphthalein) could be used with error less than 0.2%.

In titrating a weak acid (with a strong base) or a weak base (with a strong acid) greater care is needed in the selection of an indicator. Let us consider the titration of 0.2 N acetic acid, a moderately weak acid with $K_a = 1.80 \times 10^{-5}$, with 0.2 N sodium hydroxide. When an amount of the alkali equivalent to that of the acid has been added, the resultant solution is the same as would be obtained by dissolving 0.1 mole of the salt $NaC_2H_3O_2$ in a liter of water. The solution of this salt is not neutral, with pH 7, however, but is alkaline, as can be seen from the following argument, based on the Brønsted-Lowry theory.

The salt $NaC_2H_3O_2$ is completely dissociated into ions, Na^+ and $C_2H_3O_2^-$, when it is dissolved in water. The ion Na^+ has no protons, and hence is not an acid. The acetate anion, $C_2H_3O_2^-$, is, however, a base—it is the base conjugate to the acid $HC_2H_3O_2$, and it can accept a proton from an acid, such as H_2O:

$$H_2O + C_2H_3O_2^- \rightleftarrows HC_2H_3O_2 + OH^-$$

This reaction takes place to the extent determined by the value of its equilibrium constant:

$$\frac{[HC_2H_3O_2][OH^-]}{[H_2O][C_2H_3O_2^-]} = K_b$$

We may say that an aqueous solution of the neutral salt sodium acetate is alkaline, with pH greater than 7, because it contains the base (proton acceptor) acetate ion.

The value of K_b for a base is closely related to the value of the acid constant K_a of the homologous acid. Let us consider these constants for an acid HA and its homologous base A$^-$:

$$K_a = \frac{[H_3O^+][A^-]}{[HA][H_2O]}$$

$$K_b = \frac{[HA][OH^-]}{[H_2O][A^-]}$$

On multiplying the left sides and the right sides of these equations, we obtain

$$K_aK_b = \frac{[H_3O^+][A^-]}{[HA][H_2O]} \frac{[HA][OH^-]}{[H_2O][A^-]} = \frac{[H_3O^+][OH^-]}{[H_2O]^2}$$

The expression on the right side is seen to be the autoprotolysis constant for water, with value 1.00×10^{-14} (for $[H_2O]$ taken as 1; see Section 19-2); hence we have obtained the relation

$$K_b = \frac{K_w}{K_a} = \frac{1.00 \times 10^{-14}}{K_a}$$

between the acid constant and the base constant of a conjugate pair.

The acid constant of acetic acid is 1.80×10^{-5} (Section 19-5); the base constant of acetate ion accordingly has the value $1.00 \times 10^{-14}/1.80 \times 10^{-5} = 5.56 \times 10^{-10}$.

Let x be the number of acetate ions (mole/liter) that have undergone reaction with water to produce $HC_2H_3O_2$ and OH^-. The concentrations of solutes are seen to be

$$[HC_2H_3O_2] = [OH^-] = x$$
$$[C_2H_3O_2^-] = 0.1 - x$$

and the equilibrium equation is

$$\frac{x^2}{0.1 - x} = K_b = 5.56 \times 10^{-10}$$

Solution of this equation gives

$$x = 0.75 \times 10^{-5} \text{ mole/liter}$$

Hence $[OH^-] = 0.75 \times 10^{-5}$ and $[H^+] = 1.34 \times 10^{-9}$.

The pH of the solution of sodium acetate is hence 8.87. By reference to Figure 19-1 we see that *phenolphthalein, with $pK = 9$, is the best indicator to use for titrating a moderately weak acid such as acetic acid.*

The complete titration curve, showing the pH of the solution as a function of the amount of strong base added, can be calculated in essentially this way. Its course is shown in Figure 19-3 ($K_a = 10^{-5}$). We see that the solution has pH 7 when there is about 1% excess of acid; hence if litmus were used as the indicator an error of about 1% would be made in the titration.

The basic constant of ammonium hydroxide has about the same value as the acid constant of acetic acid. Hence to *titrate a weak base such as ammonium hydroxide with a strong acid methyl orange* (pK 3.8) *may be used as the indicator.*

It is possible by suitable selection of indicators to titrate separately a strong acid and a weak acid or a strong base and a weak base in a mixture of the two. Let us consider, for example, a solution of sodium hydroxide and ammonium hydroxide (ammonia). If strong acid is added until the pH is 11.1, which is that of 0.1 N ammonium hydroxide solution, the strong base will be within 1% of neutralization (Figure 19-3). Hence by using alizarine yellow (pK 11) as indicator the concentration of the strong base can be determined, and then by a second titration with methyl orange the concentration of ammonium hydroxide can be determined.

The Acidic Properties of Hydrated Ions of Metals other than the Alkalis and Alkaline Earths. Metal salts of strong acids, such as $FeCl_3$, $CuSO_4$,

$KAl(SO_4)_2 \cdot 12H_2O$ (alum), etc., produce acidic solutions; the sour taste of these salts is characteristic.

It will be recalled from the discussion in Chapter 16 that the aluminum ion in aqueous solution is hydrated, having the formula $Al(H_2O)_6^{+++}$, with the six water molecules arranged octahedrally about the aluminum ion. The hydrolysis of aluminum salts may be represented by the equations

$$Al(H_2O)_6^{+++} + H_2O \rightleftarrows H_3O^+ + Al(H_2O)_5OH^{++}$$
$$Al(H_2O)_5OH^{++} + H_2O \rightleftarrows H_3O^+ + Al(H_2O)_4(OH)_2^+$$
$$Al(H_2O)_4(OH)_2^+ + H_2O \rightleftarrows H_3O^+ + Al(H_2O)_3(OH)_3 \rightleftarrows$$
$$Al(OH)_3(c) + 3H_2O + H_3O^+$$

In these reactions the hydrated ions of aluminum lose protons, forming successive hydroxide complexes; the final neutral complex then loses water to form the insoluble hydroxide $Al(OH)_3$.

The complex ions $Al(H_2O)_5(OH)^{++}$ and $Al(H_2O)_4(OH)_2^+$ remain in solution, whereas the hydroxide $Al(OH)_3$ is very slightly soluble and precipitates if more than a very small amount is formed; precipitation occurs when the pH is greater than 3.

The protolysis of hydrated ferric ion occurs to such an extent that the color of ferric ion itself, $Fe(H_2O)_6^{+++}$, is usually masked by that of the hydroxide complexes. Ferric ion is nearly colorless; it seems to have a very pale violet color, seen in crystals of ferric alum, $KFe(SO_4)_2 \cdot 12H_2O$, and ferric nitrate, $Fe(NO_3)_3 \cdot 9H_2O$, and in ferric solutions strongly acidified with nitric or perchloric acid. Solutions of ferric salts ordinarily have the characteristic yellow to brown color of the hydroxide complexes $Fe(H_2O)_5OH^{++}$ and $Fe(H_2O)_4(OH)_2^+$, or even the red-brown color of colloidal particles of hydrated ferric hydroxide.

19-7. Buffered Solutions

Very small amounts of strong acid or base suffice to change the hydrogen-ion concentration of water in the slightly acidic to slightly basic region; one drop of strong concentrated acid added to a liter of water makes it appreciably acidic, increasing the hydrogen-ion concentration by a factor of 5000, and two drops of strong alkali would then make it basic, decreasing the hydrogen-ion concentration by a factor of over a million. Yet there are solutions to which large amounts of strong acid or base can be added with only very small resultant change in hydrogen-ion concentration. Such solutions are called **buffered solutions.**

Blood and other physiological solutions are buffered; the pH of blood changes only slowly from its normal value (about 7.4) on addition of acid or base. Important among the buffering substances in blood are the serum proteins (Chapter 28), which contain basic and acidic groups that can combine with the added acid or base.

A drop of concentrated acid, which when added to a liter of pure water increases $[H^+]$ 5000-fold (from 10^{-7} to 5×10^{-4}), produces an increase of $[H^+]$ of less than 1% (from 1.00×10^{-7} to 1.01×10^{-7}, for example) when added to a liter of buffered solution such as the phosphate buffer made by dissolving 0.2 gram formula weight of phosphoric acid in a liter of water and adding 0.3 gram formula weight of sodium hydroxide.

This is a half-neutralized phosphoric acid solution; its principal ionic constituents and their concentrations are Na^+, 0.3 M; HPO_4^{--}, 0.1 M; $H_2PO_4^-$, 0.1 M; H^+, about 10^{-7} M. From the titration curve of Figure 19-4 we see that this solution is a good buffer; to change its pH from 7 to 6.5 or 7.5 (tripling the hydrogen ion or hydroxide ion concentration) about one-twentieth of an equivalent of strong acid or base is needed per liter, whereas this amount of acid or base in water would cause a change of 5.7 pH units (an increase or decrease of $[H^+]$ by the factor 500,000). Such a solution, usually made by dissolving the two well-crystallized salts KH_2PO_4 and $Na_2HPO_4 \cdot 2H_2O$ in water, is widely

Figure **19-4**

Titration curve for phosphoric acid and a strong base.

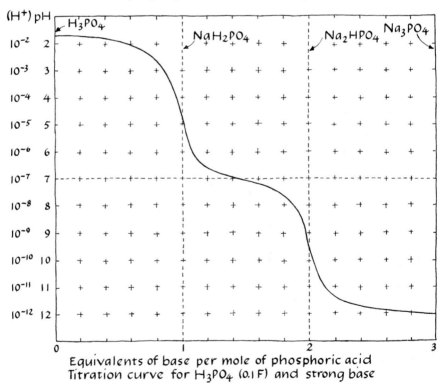

Equivalents of base per mole of phosphoric acid
Titration curve for H_3PO_4 (0.1 F) and strong base

used for buffering in the neutral region (*p*H 5.3 to 8.0).* Other useful buffers are sodium citrate-hydrochloric acid (*p*H 1 to 3.5), acetic acid-sodium acetate (*p*H 3.6 to 5.6), boric acid-sodium hydroxide (*p*H 7.8 to 10.0), and glycine-sodium hydroxide (*p*H 8.5 to 13).

The behavior of a buffer can be understood from the equilibrium equation for the acid dissociation. Let us consider the case of acetic acid-sodium acetate. The solution contains $HC_2H_3O_2$ and $C_2H_3O_2^-$ in equal or comparable concentrations. The equilibrium expression

$$\frac{[H^+][C_2H_3O_2^-]}{[HC_2H_3O_2]} = K_a$$

may be written as

$$[H^+] = \frac{[HC_2H_3O_2]}{[C_2H_3O_2^-]} K_a$$

This shows that when $[C_2H_3O_2^-]$ and $[HC_2H_3O_2]$ are equal, as in an equimolal mixed solution of $HC_2H_3O_2$ and $NaC_2H_3O_2$, the value of $[H^+]$ is just that of K_a, 1.80×10^{-5}, and hence the *p*H is 4.7. A 1:5 mixture of $HC_2H_3O_2$ and $NaC_2H_3O_2$ has $[H^+] = \frac{1}{5}K_a$ and *p*H 5.4, and a 5:1 mixture has $[H^+] = 5K_a$ and *p*H 4.0. By choosing a suitable ratio of $HC_2H_3O_2$ to $NaC_2H_3O_2$, any desired hydrogen-ion concentration in this neighborhood can be obtained.

It is seen from the equilibrium expressions that *the effectiveness of a buffer depends on the concentrations of the buffering substances;* a tenfold dilution of the buffer decreases by the factor 10 the amount of acid or base per liter that can be added without causing the *p*H to change more than the desired amount.

For the phosphate buffer in the *p*H 7 region the equilibrium constant of interest is that for the reaction

$$H_2PO_4^- \rightleftharpoons HPO_4^{--} + H^+$$

The value of $K_{H_2PO_4^{--}}$ is 6.2×10^{-8}; this is accordingly the value of $[H^+]$ expected for a solution with $[H_2PO_4^-] = [HPO_4^{--}]$.

If the buffered solution is dilute, this is its hydrogen-ion concentration. Because the activities of ions are affected by other ions, however, there is appreciable deviation from the calculated values in salt solutions as concentrated as 0.1 *M*. This fact accounts for the small discrepancies between the *p*H values calculated from equilibrium constants and those given in the buffer tables.

19-8. The Strengths of the Oxygen Acids

The oxygen acids, which consist of oxygen atoms O and hydroxide groups OH attached to a central atom ($HClO_4 = ClO_3(OH)$, $H_2SO_4 = SO_2(OH)_2$,

---

* A concentrated neutral buffer solution containing one-half gram formula weight of each salt per liter may be kept in the laboratory to neutralize either acid or base spilled on the body

etc.), vary widely in strength, from very strong acids such as perchloric acid, $HClO_4$, to very weak ones such as boric acid, H_3BO_3. It is often useful to know the approximate strengths of these acids. Fortunately there have been formulated some simple and easily remembered rules regarding these acid strengths.

The Rules Expressing the Strengths of the Oxygen Acids.   The strengths of the oxygen acids are expressed approximately by the following two rules:
  Rule 1. The successive acid constants K_1, K_2, K_3, $\cdots$ are in the ratios $1:10^{-5}$: $10^{-10}: \cdots .$

We have already noted the examples of phosphoric acid

$$K_{H_3PO_4} = 7.5 \times 10^{-3} \qquad K_{H_2PO_4^-} = 6.2 \times 10^{-8} \qquad K_{HPO_4^{--}} = 1 \times 10^{-12}$$

and sulfurous acid

$$K_{H_2SO_3} = 1.2 \times 10^{-2} \qquad K_{HSO_2^-} = 1 \times 10^{-7}$$

The rule holds well for all the acids of the class under consideration.
  Rule 2. The value of the first ionization constant is determined by the value of m in the formula $XO_m(OH)_n$: if m is zero (no excess of oxygen atoms over hydrogen atoms, as in $B(OH)_3$) the acid is very weak, with $K_1 \leqq 10^{-7}$; for m = 1 the acid is weak, with $K_1 \cong 10^{-2}$; for m = 2 ($K_1 \cong 10^3$) or m = 3 ($K_1 \cong 10^8$) the acid is strong.
  Note the occurrence of the factor 10^{-5} in both this rule and the first one. The applicability of this rule is shown by the tables at the end of this section.
  The second rule can be understood in the following way. The force attracting H^+ to ClO^- to form $ClOH$ (hypochlorous acid) is that of an O—H valence bond. But the force between H^+ and either one of the two oxygen atoms of the ion ClO_2^- to form $ClOOH$ (chlorous acid) may be smaller than that for an O—H valence bond because the total attraction for the proton is divided between the two oxygen atoms, and hence this acid (of the second class) may well be expected to be more highly dissociated than hypochlorous acid. An acid of the third class would be still more highly dissociated, since the total attraction for the proton would be divided among three oxygen atoms.
  With use of these rules we can answer questions about the choice of indicators for titration without referring to tables of acid constants.

Example 7.   What reaction to litmus would be expected of solutions of the following salts: $NaClO$, $NaClO_2$, $NaClO_3$, $NaClO_4$?
  Solution.   The corresponding acids are shown by the rule to be very weak, weak, strong, and very strong, respectively. Hence $NaClO$ and $NaClO_2$ would through hydrolysis give basic solutions, and the other two salts would give neutral solutions.

Example 8. What indicator could be used for titrating periodic acid, H_5IO_6?
Solution. This acid has one extra oxygen atom, and is hence of the second class, as is phosphoric acid. We accordingly refer to Figures 19-4 and 19-1, and see that methyl orange should be satisfactory for titrating the first hydrogen, or phenolphthalein for titrating the first two hydrogens.

Experimental Values of Acid Constants. Some values of acid constants that have been determined by experiment are given in the following tabulation.

First class; Very weak acids $X(OH)_n$ or H_nXO_n
First acid constant about 10^{-7} or less

	K_1
Hypochlorous acid, HClO	3.2×10^{-8}
Hypobromous acid, HBrO	2×10^{-9}
Hypoiodous acid, HIO	1×10^{-11}
Silicic acid, H_4SiO_4	1×10^{-10}
Germanic acid, H_4GeO_4	3×10^{-9}
Boric acid, H_3BO_3	5.8×10^{-10}
Arsenious acid, H_3AsO_3	6×10^{-10}
Antimonous acid, H_3SbO_3	1×10^{-11}

Second class; Weak acids $XO(OH)_n$ or H_nXO_{n+1}
First acid constant about 10^{-2}

	K_1
Chlorous acid, $HClO_2$	1.1×10^{-2}
Sulfurous acid, H_2SO_3	1.2×10^{-2}
Selenious acid, H_2SeO_3	0.3×10^{-2}
Phosphoric acid, H_3PO_4	0.75×10^{-2}
Phosphorous acid,* H_2HPO_3	1.6×10^{-2}
Hypophosphorous acid,* HH_2PO_2	1×10^{-2}
Arsenic acid, H_3AsO_4	0.5×10^{-2}
Periodic acid, H_5IO_6	1×10^{-3}
Nitrous acid, HNO_2	0.45×10^{-3}
Acetic acid, $HC_2H_3O_2$	1.80×10^{-5}
Carbonic acid,† H_2CO_3	0.45×10^{-6}

$$
\begin{array}{c} O \\ \| \end{array}
$$

* It is known that phosphorous acid has the structure H—P—OH and hypophosphorous
$$
\begin{array}{c} | \\ OH \end{array}
$$

$$
\begin{array}{c} O \\ \| \end{array}
$$
acid the structure H—P—OH; the hydrogen atoms that are bonded to the phosphorus atom
$$
\begin{array}{c} | \\ H \end{array}
$$
are not counted in applying the rule.

† The low value for carbonic acid is due in part to the existence of some of the un-ionized acid in the form of dissolved CO_2 molecules rather than H_2CO_3. The proton dissociation constant for the molecular species H_2CO_3 is about 2×10^{-4}. The value of K_2 is 5×10^{-11}.

Third class; Strong acids $XO_2(OH)_n$ or H_nXO_{n+2}

First acid constant about 10^3

Second acid constant about 10^{-2}

	K_1	K_2
Chloric acid, $HClO_3$	Large	
Sulfuric acid, H_2SO_4	Large	1.2×10^{-2}
Selenic acid, H_2SeO_4	Large	1×10^{-2}

Fourth class; Very strong acids $XO_3(OH)_n$ or H_nXO_{n+3}

First acid constant about 10^8

Perchloric acid, $HClO_4$	Very strong
Permanganic acid, $HMnO_4$	Very strong

Other Acids. There is no simple way of remembering the strengths of acids other than those discussed above. HCl, HBr, and HI are strong, but HF is weak, with $K_a = 7.2 \times 10^{-4}$. The homologues of water are weak acids, with the following reported acid constants:

	K_1	K_2
Hydrosulfuric acid, H_2S	1.1×10^{-7}	1.0×10^{-14}
Hydroselenic acid, H_2Se	1.7×10^{-4}	1×10^{-12}
Hydrotelluric acid, H_2Te	2.3×10^{-3}	1×10^{-11}

The hydrides NH_3, PH_3, etc., function as bases by adding protons rather than as acids by losing them.

Oxygen acids which do not contain a single central atom have strengths corresponding to reasonable extensions of our rules, as shown by the following examples.

Very weak acids: $K_1 = 10^{-7}$ or less

	K_1	K_2
Hydrogen peroxide, HO—OH	2.4×10^{-12}	
Hyponitrous acid, HON—NOH	9×10^{-8}	1×10^{-11}

Weak acids: $K_1 = 10^{-2}$

	K_1	K_2
Oxalic acid, HOOC—COOH	5.9×10^{-2}	6.4×10^{-5}

The following acids are not easily classified:

	K_1
Hydrocyanic acid, HCN	4×10^{-10}
Cyanic acid, HOCN	Strong
Thiocyanic acid, HSCN	Strong
Hydrazoic acid, HN_3	1.8×10^{-5}

Acid Strength and Condensation. It is observed that the tendency of oxygen acids to condense to larger molecules is correlated with their acid strengths.

Very strong acids, such as $HClO_4$ and $HMnO_4$, condense only with difficulty, and the substances formed, Cl_2O_7 and Mn_2O_7, are very unstable. Less strong acids, such as H_2SO_4, form condensation products such as $H_2S_2O_7$, pyrosulfuric acid, on strong heating, but these products are not stable in aqueous solution. Phosphoric acid forms pyrophosphate ion and other condensed ions in aqueous solution, but these ions easily hydrolyze to the orthophosphate ion; other weak acids behave similarly. The very weak oxygen acids, including silicic acid (Chapter 22) and boric acid, condense very readily, and their condensation products are very stable substances.

This correlation is reasonable. The unionized acids contain oxygen atoms bonded to hydrogen atoms, and the condensed acids contain oxygen atoms bonded to two central atoms:

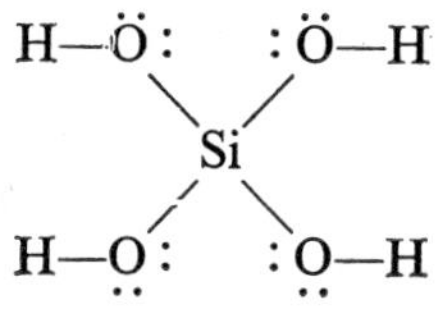

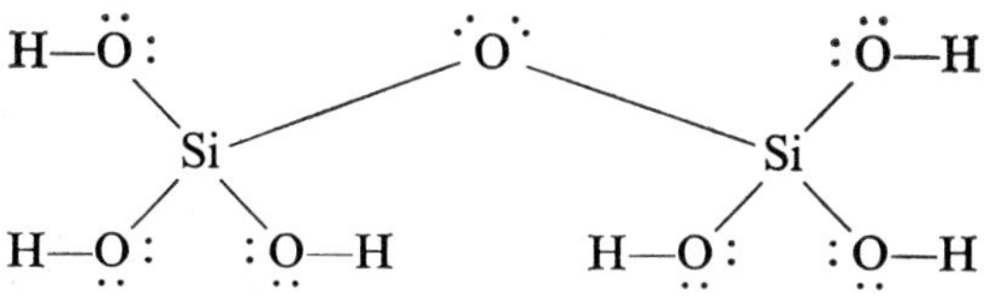

It is hence not surprising that stability of the unionized acid (low acid strength) should be correlated with stability of the condensed molecules.

19-9. Nonaqueous Amphiprotic Solvents

In Section 19-1 the autoprotolysis of the amphiprotic substance water was discussed. Every solvent whose molecules contain one or more protons and one or more unshared electron pairs in outer shells can act as an amphiprotic solvent. One of its molecules can donate a proton to a sufficiently strong base or accept a proton from a sufficiently strong acid. For example, perchloric acid dissolved in pure sulfuric acid undergoes the following reaction, in which H_2SO_4 acts as a base:

$$HClO_4 + H_2SO_4 \rightleftarrows H_3SO_4^+ + ClO_4^-$$

A prediction of the probable behavior of a solute in an amphiprotic solvent can be made by comparing the acid constant of the solute when dissolved in water with the acid constant of the solvent when dissolved in water. For example, in water perchloric acid is about 10^5 times as strong as sulfuric acid. Its greater proton-donating power probably applies also when sulfuric acid is the solvent.

Phosphoric acid, on the other hand, is in aqueous solution a weaker acid than sulfuric acid; it reacts as a base when dissolved in pure sulfuric acid:

$$H_2SO_4 + H_3PO_4 \rightleftarrows H_4PO_4^+ + HSO_4^-$$

Sulfuric acid also undergoes autoprotolysis:

$$2H_2SO_4 \rightleftarrows H_3SO_4^+ + HSO_4^-$$

Values of the autoprotolysis constant of sulfuric acid and some other amphiprotic solvents, as determined by measuring the electric conductivity of the solvent and some of its solutions, are given in Table 19-1.

The Lewis Theory of Acids and Bases. A still more general theory of acids and bases than the proton donor-acceptor theory was introduced by G. N. Lewis. He called a base anything that has available an unshared pair of elec-

Table **19-1**

Values of the Autoprotolysis Constant

SOLVENT	AUTOPROTOLYSIS CONSTANT*
H_2O	$[H_3O^+][OH^-] = 1.0 \times 10^{-14}$ (mole/liter)^2
NH_3	$[NH_4^+][NH_2^-] = 1 \times 10^{-33}$
H_2SO_4	$[H_3SO_4^+][HSO_4^-] = 2 \times 10^{-4}$
HCOOH (formic acid)	$[HC(OH)_2^+][HCOO^-] = 6 \times 10^{-7}$
CH_3COOH (acetic acid)	$[CH_3C(OH)_2^+][CH_3COO^-] = 1 \times 10^{-13}$
CH_3OH (methyl alcohol)	$[CH_3OH_2^+][CH_3O^-] = 2 \times 10^{-17}$
C_2H_5OH (ethyl alcohol)	$[C_2H_5OH_2^+][C_2H_5O^-] = 3 \times 10^{-20}$

* All values are for 25°C except that for ammonia, which is for −33°C. The value for water at 100°C is 0.5×10^{-14}.

trons, such as NH_3, $:N\!\!-\!\!H$ with H above and H below, and an acid anything that might attach itself to such a pair of electrons, such as H^+, to form NH_4^+, or BF_3, to form $F_3B\!\!-\!\!NH_3$.

This concept explains many phenomena. An example is the effect of certain substances other than hydrogen ion in changing the color of indicators. Another interesting application of the concept is its explanation of salt formation by reaction of acidic oxides and basic oxides.

EXERCISES

19-12. Define indicator, and explain why most indicators undergo their color change within a range of about 2 pH units.

19-13. Which of these oxides are acid anhydrides and which are basic anhydrides in the water system? Write an equation for each, representing its reaction with water.

P_2O_3	Fe_2O_3	Na_2O	Mn_2O_7	RaO
Cl_2O	B_2O_3	Al_2O_3	MnO	SO_2
Cl_2O_7	CO_2	I_2O_5	TeO_3	SO_3
N_2O_5	Cu_2O	MgO	SiO_2	As_2O_3

19-14. Write the equation for the autoprotolysis of water. Write the expression for the equilibrium represented by this equation and explain why for aqueous solutions it is customary to replace this equation by $[H_3O^+][OH^-] = 1.00 \times 10^{-14}$.

19-15. How many grams of each of the following substances would be needed to make up 1 liter of 0.2 N acid or base?

$$KOH \quad CaO$$
$$H_2SO_4 \quad KHSO_4$$

19-16. What is the pH to 1 pH unit of 1 N HCl? of 0.1 N HCl? of 10 N HCl? of 0.1 N NaOH? of 10 N NaOH?

19-17. What is the normality of a solution of a strong acid 25.00 ml of which is rendered neutral by 33.35 ml of 0.1111 N NaOH solution?

19-18. A patent medicine for stomach ulcers contains 2.3 g of $Al(OH)_3$ per 100 ml. How far wrong is the statement on the label that the preparation is "capable of combining with 18 times its volume of N/10 HCl"?

19-19. In 0.1 M H_3BO_3, $[H^+] = 0.78 \times 10^{-5}$. From this value calculate the ionization constant for boric acid.

19-20. What indicators should be used in titrating the following acids:

	K_a
HNO_2	4.5×10^{-4}
H_2S (first hydrogen)	1.1×10^{-7}
HCN	4×10^{-10}

19-21. With what indicators could you titrate separately for HCl and $HC_2H_3O_2$ in a solution containing both acids?

19-22. Calculate the pH of a solution that is 0.1 F in HNO_2 and 0.1 F in HCl.

19-23. What ionic and molecular species would be present in a solution prepared by mixing equal volumes of 1 N NaOH and 0.5 N NH_4OH? Estimate their concentrations.

19-24. Which of these substances form acidic aqueous solutions, which neutral, and which basic? Write equations for the reactions that give excess H^+ or OH^-.

NaCl	$(NH_4)_2SO_4$	$CuSO_4$
NaCN	$NaHSO_4$	$FeCl_2$
Na_3PO_4	NaH_2PO_4	$KAl(SO_4)_2$
NH_4Cl	Na_2HPO_4	$Zn(ClO_4)_2$
NH_4CN	$KClO_4$	BaO

19-25. Approximately how much acetic acid must be added to a 0.1 N solution of sodium acetate to make the solution neutral?

19-26. What relative weights of KH_2PO_4 and $Na_2HPO_4 \cdot 2H_2O$ should be taken to make a buffered solution with pH 6.0?

19-27. Calculate the pH of a solution that is prepared from
(a) 10 ml 0.2 F HCN, 10 ml 0.2 F NaOH
(b) 10 ml 0.2 F NH_4OH, 10 ml 0.2 F HCl
(c) 10 ml 0.2 F NH_4OH, 10 ml 0.2 F NH_4Cl

19-28. Calculate the pH of a solution that is
(a) 0.1 F in NH_4Cl, 0.1 F in NH_4OH
(b) 0.05 F in NH_4Cl, 0.15 F in NH_4OH
(c) 1.0 F in $HC_2H_3O_2$, 0.3 F in $NaC_2H_3O_2$
(d) prepared by mixing 10 ml of 1 F $HC_2H_3O_2$ with 90 ml 0.05 F NaOH
Which of these would be good buffers?

19-29. Would water act as an acid or a base when dissolved in liquid H_2S? Would H_2Se act as an acid or a base?

19-30. Hydrogen cyanide, $H—C\equiv N:$, is amphiprotic. What is its conjugate acid? Its conjugate base?

19-31. What reaction would you expect to take place when HCN is dissolved in pure sulfuric acid?

19-32. What is the concentration of the cation $H_3SO_4^+$ in pure sulfuric acid? Of the anion HSO_4^-? (See Table 19-1.) (Answer: 0.014 mole/liter, 0.014 mole/liter.)

19-33. What is the concentration of the cation $H_2C_2H_3O_2^+$ in pure acetic acid? Of the anion $C_2H_3O_2^-$?

19-34. Arrange liquid ammonia, pure acetic acid, and pure sulfuric acid in order of increasing electric conductivity, and explain your answer.

19-35. A 0.0001 F solution of sodium acetate in acetic acid has electric conductivity about 300 times that of pure acetic acid. From this fact, calculate a rough value of the autoprotolysis constant of acetic acid. Why is this value only approximate?

19-36. An exact value of the autoprotolysis constant can be obtained by use of the measured values of the electric conductivities of pure acetic acid and three acetic acid solutions: 0.0001 F $NaC_2H_3O_2$, 0.0001 F $HClO_4$, and 0.0001 F $NaClO_4$. Can you explain how the calculation is made?

19-37. Discuss the reaction $CaO + SO_3 \longrightarrow CaSO_4$ in terms of the Lewis theory of acids and bases.

19-38. Explain why a metal hydroxide such as ferric hydroxide, $Fe(OH)_3$, is much more soluble in an acidic solution than it is in a basic solution.

19-39. The mineral gypsum has the formula $CaSO_4 \cdot 2H_2O$, its solubility product being 2.4×10^{-5} mole^2/liter^2. Calculate the solubility of calcium sulfate in grams of anhydrous $CaSO_4$ per liter. Would you expect ground water with pH 7 that has filtered through a deposit of gypsum to be hard?

19-40. Would you predict acidic ground water that has filtered through a deposit of gypsum to have greater hardness, the same hardness, or smaller hardness than basic ground water that has filtered through a deposit of gypsum? Explain your answer.

19-41. Discuss the hardness of ground water in a limestone region, in terms of the pH of the water. Describe and explain the method of softening hard water with temporary hardness by the use of calcium hydroxide.

19-42. Using the solubility product of silver acetate, $[Ag^+][C_2H_3O_2^-] = 3.6 \times 10^{-3}$, and the ionization constant of acetic acid, calculate the solubility of silver acetate in a basic solution, a solution with pH 5.0, and a solution with pH 3.5.

19-43. What is the formula of the xenic acid formed by hydrolysis of xenon tetrafluoride? Write the equation for the reaction. It has been reported that this acid is weak. What value do you predict the acid constant to have? (Answer: Less than 10^{-7}.)

19-44. It was suggested long ago that xenon with oxidation number $+8$ should form the xenic acid H_4XeO_6, but this acid was first made in 1963, and its acid constants have not yet been reported. Would you predict it to be a strong acid or a weak acid? Estimate values of the four successive acid constants for this acid.

19-45. The value of the solubility product for barium carbonate is $[Ba^{++}][CO_3^{--}] = 5 \times 10^{-9}$. What is the solubility of this salt in solutions buffered at pH 12, 8, 7, and 6? How would you describe ground water that has been filtered through a deposit of barite, $BaCO_3$, and had these pH values?

19-46. Calculate the hydrogen ion concentration in the following solutions:
(a) 0.1 M $HC_2H_3O_2$, $K = 1.8 \times 10^{-5}$
(b) 0.10 M HNO_2, $K = 0.45 \times 10^{-3}$
(c) 0.006 M NH_4OH, $K_b = 1.8 \times 10^{-5}$
(d) 0.1 M HF, $K = 7.2 \times 10^{-4}$
What are the pH values of the solutions?

19-47. Carbon dioxide, produced by oxidation of substances in the tissues. is carried by the blood to the lungs. Part of it is in solution as carbonic acid, and part as hydrogen carbonate ion, HCO_3^-. If the pH of the blood is 7.4, what fraction is carried as the ion?

19-48. Estimate the acid constants of H_2SeO_4, H_3AsO_4, H_5IO_6, $HOCl$, and H_3AsO_3, without reference to the text, by using the simple rule given in this chapter.

19-49. Calculate the concentration of the various ionic and molecular species in a solution that is
(a) 0.2 F in HCl, and 0.1 F in H_2S
(b) buffered to a pH of 4, and 0.1 F in H_2S
(c) 0.2 F in KHS
(d) 0.2 F in K_2S

19-50. The poisonous *botulinus* organism does not grow in canned vegetables if the pH is less than 4.5. Some investigators (*Journal of Chemical Education* **22**, 409 [1945]) have recommended that in home canning of nonacid foods, such as beans, without a pressure canner a quantity of hydrochloric acid be added. The amount of hydrochloric acid recommended is 25 ml of 0.5 N hydrochloric acid per pint jar.

Calculate the pH that this solution would have, assuming it originally to be neutral, and neglecting the buffering action of the organic material. Also calculate the amount of baking soda ($NaHCO_3$), measured in teaspoonfuls, that would be required to neutralize the acid after the jar is open. One teaspoonful equals 4 g of baking soda.

19-51. Because of the hydronium and hydroxide ions formed by its autoprotolysis, pure water has a small electric conductivity (about 5×10^{-5} reciprocal ohm for a cube 1 cm on edge). Does pure liquid ammonia have a larger or smaller conductivity than water?

19-52. Assuming that the ions that are present have the same mobility in pure sulfuric acid as the hydronium and hydroxide ions in water, calculate a rough value for the electric conductivity of pure sulfuric acid. (Answer: 0.7 reciprocal ohm for a cube 1 cm on edge.)

REFERENCES

J. Waser, *Quantitative Chemistry*, W. A. Benjamin, Inc., New York, 1961.

L. P. Hammett, *Physical Organic Chemistry*, McGraw-Hill Book Co., Inc., New York, 1940.

R. P. Bell, *The Proton in Chemistry*, Cornell University Press, Ithaca, N.Y., 1959.

PART **5**

Metals and Alloys

and the Compounds of Metals

The seven chapters that constitute Part 5 of our book, Chapters 20 to 26, deal with the properties of many substances.

Chapter 20 deals with the nature of metals and alloys. This part of chemistry has great practical importance. The development of automobiles, airplanes, jet motors, skyscrapers, and other objects characteristic of our civilization has been determined by the properties of the known alloys, and general progress in technology has often resulted from progress in the science of metals. The rate of progress has been limited by the fact that the chemistry of metals and alloys has lagged behind other branches of chemistry. The general theory of valence, in its modern electronic form, can be used with great power in the discussion of the compounds of metals with nonmetals and of nonmetals with nonmetals, but the compounds of metals with metals, which are present in many alloys, have not yet been satisfactorily encompassed by this theory. The discussion of the nature of metals and alloys in Chapter 20 is accordingly incomplete; nevertheless, despite its incompleteness the science of metals in its present state is of great value in the fields of engineering and technology that depend upon metallic materials.

Ores are the source of metals in nature. The winning of metals from their ores, their refining, and the relation between the structure and properties of metals and alloys constitute the field of metallurgy. The chemical aspects of metallurgy are presented in the first seven sections of Chapter 21, and a brief discussion of physical metallurgy is given in the concluding section.

The subject of Chapter 22 is the chemistry of the elements of groups I, II, III, and IV. It is interesting that the central group of the periodic system, group IV, is uniquely important to both the organic world and the inorganic world. Carbon, the first element of this group, is present in practically all of the many thousands of substances that are characteristic of living organisms, and silicon, the second element in this group, is present in most of the substances that make up the earth's crust. Most of the rocks and minerals are silicates, compounds of silicon that also contain oxygen and one or more metallic elements. The nature of silicates and of other compounds of silicon is discussed in this chapter, in relation to the sizes and other properties of atoms, and similar discussions are given of the compounds of the other elements in the first four groups of the periodic table.

In Chapter 23 some general aspects of the chemistry of the transition metals, especially the formation of inorganic complexes, are discussed. The transition metals and their compounds are treated in some detail in the following chapters: iron, cobalt, nickel, and the platinum metals in Chapter 24, copper, zinc, and gallium and their congeners in Chapter 25, and the other transition metals in Chapter 26.

CHAPTER 20

The Nature of Metals and Alloys

About eighty of the more than one hundred elementary substances are metals. A metal may be defined as a substance that has large conductivity of electricity and of heat, has a characteristic luster, called metallic luster, and can be hammered into sheets (is malleable) and drawn into wire (is ductile); in addition, the electric conductivity increases with decrease in temperature.*

20-1. The Metallic Elements

The metallic elements may be taken to include lithium and beryllium in the first short period of the periodic table, sodium, magnesium, and aluminum in the second short period, the thirteen elements from potassium to gallium in the first long period, the fourteen from rubidium to tin in the second long period, the twenty-nine from cesium to bismuth in the first very long period (including the fourteen rare-earth metals), and the seventeen from francium to lawrencium.

The metals themselves and their alloys are of great usefulness to man, because of the properties characteristic of metals. Our modern civilization is based upon iron and steel, and valuable alloy steels are made that involve the incorporation with iron of vanadium, chromium, manganese, cobalt, nickel, molybdenum, tungsten, and other metals. The importance of these alloys is due primarily to their hardness and strength. These properties are a consequence of the presence in the metals of very strong bonds between the

---

* Sometimes there is difficulty in classifying an element as a metal, a metalloid, or a nonmetal. For example, the element tin can exist in two forms, one of which, the common form, called white tin, is metallic, whereas the other, gray tin, has the properties of a metalloid. The next element in the periodic table, antimony, exists in only one crystalline form, with metallic luster but with the electric properties of a metalloid, and it is brittle, rather than malleable and ductile. We shall consider tin to be a metal and antimony a metalloid.

atoms. For this reason it is of especial interest to us to understand the nature of the forces that hold the metal atoms together in metals and alloys.

20-2. The Structure of Metals

In a nonmetal or metalloid the number of atoms that each atom has as its nearest neighbors is determined by its covalence. For example, the iodine atom, which is univalent, has only one other iodine atom close to it in a crystal of iodine: the crystal, like liquid iodine and iodine vapor, is composed of diatomic molecules. In a crystal of sulfur there are S_8 molecules, in which each sulfur atom has two nearest neighbors, to each of which it is attached by one of its two covalent bonds. In diamond the quadrivalent carbon atom has four nearest neighbors. On the other hand, the potassium atom in potassium metal, the calcium atom in calcium metal, and the titanium atom in titanium metal, which have one, two, and four outer electrons, respectively, do not have only one, two, and four nearest neighbors, but have, instead, eight or twelve nearest neighbors. We may state that one of the characteristic features of a metal is that each atom has a large number of neighbors; the number of small interatomic distances is greater than the number of valence electrons.

Figure 20-1

The hexagonal close-packed arrangement of spheres. Many metals crystallize with this structure.

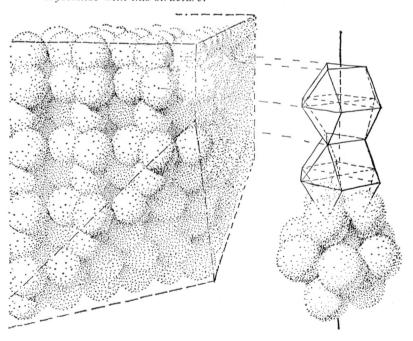

Most metals crystallize with an atomic arrangement in which each atom has surrounded itself with the maximum number of atoms that is geometrically possible. There are two common metallic structures that correspond to the closest possible packing of spheres of constant size. One of these structures, called the cubic closest-packed structure, has been described in Chapter 2. The other structure, called hexagonal closest packing, is represented in Figure 20-1. It is closely similar to the cubic closest-packed structure; each atom is surrounded by twelve equidistant neighbors, with, however, the arrangement of these neighbors slightly different

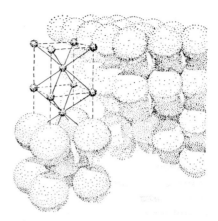

Figure **20-2** *The atomic arrangement in α-iron (body-centered arrangement).*

from that in cubic closest packing. About fifty metals have the cubic closest-packed structure or the hexagonal closest-packed structure, or both.

Another common structure, assumed by about twenty metals, is the body-centered cubic structure. In this structure, shown as Figure 20-2, each atom has eight nearest neighbors, and six next-nearest neighbors. These six next-nearest neighbors are 15% more distant than the eight nearest neighbors; in discussing the structure it is difficult to decide whether to describe each atom as having ligancy 8 or ligancy 14.

Figure **20-3**

The atomic radii of metals, plotted against atomic number.

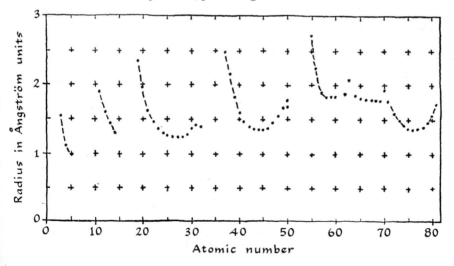

The periodicity of properties of the elements, as functions of the atomic number, is illustrated by the observed values of the interatomic distances in the metals, as shown in Figure 20-3. These values are half of the directly determined interatomic distances for the metals with a cubic closest-packed or hexagonal closest-packed structure. For other metals a small correction has been made; it has been observed, for example, that a metal such as iron, which crystallizes in a modification with a closest-packed structure and also a modification with the body-centered cubic structure, has contact interatomic distances about 3 % less in the latter structure than in the former, and accordingly a correction of 3 % can be made for body-centered cubic structures, to convert the interatomic distances to ligancy 12.

We may well expect that the strongest bonds would have the shortest interatomic distances, and it is accordingly not surprising that the large interatomic distances shown in Figure 20-3 are those for soft metals, such as potassium; the smallest ones, for chromium, iron, nickel, etc., refer to the hard, strong metals.

20-3. The Nature of the Transition Metals

The long periods of the periodic system can be described as short periods with ten additional elements inserted. The first three elements of the long period between argon and krypton, which are the metals potassium, calcium, and scandium, resemble their congeners of the preceding short period, sodium, magnesium, and aluminum, respectively. Similarly the last four elements in the sequence, germanium, arsenic, selenium, and bromine, resemble their preceding congeners, silicon, phosphorus, sulfur, and chlorine, respectively. The remaining elements of the long period, titanium, vanadium, chromium, manganese, iron, cobalt, nickel, copper, zinc, and gallium, have no lighter congeners; they are not closely similar in their properties to any lighter elements.

The properties of these elements accordingly suggest that the long period can be described as involving the introduction of ten elements in the center of the series. The introduction of these elements is correlated with the insertion of ten additional electrons into the five $3d$ orbitals of the M shell, converting it from a shell of 8 electrons, as in the argon atom, to a shell of 18 electrons. It is convenient to describe the long period as involving ten *transition metals*, corresponding to the ten electrons. We shall consider the ten elements from titanium, group IVa, to gallium, group IIIb, as constituting the ten transition elements in the first long period, and shall take the heavier congeners of these elements as the transition elements in the later series.*

* Some chemists take the ten elements scandium to zinc as the transition elements of the first long period. However, scandium and its congener yttrium rather closely resemble aluminum in their physical and chemical properties, whereas gallium and indium are quite dissimilar to aluminum; for this reason it seems wise to classify scandium and yttrium with aluminum, and gallium and indium among the transition elements.

The chemical properties of the transition elements do not change so strikingly with change in atomic number as do those of the other elements. In the series potassium, calcium, scandium, the normal salts of the elements correspond to the maximum oxidation numbers given by the positions of the elements in the periodic system, 1 for potassium, 2 for calcium, and 3 for scandium; the sulfates, for example, of these elements are K_2SO_4, $CaSO_4$, and $Sc_2(SO_4)_3$. The fourth element, titanium, tends to form salts representing a lower oxidation number than its maximum, 4; although compounds such as titanium dioxide, TiO_2, and titanium tetrachloride, $TiCl_4$, can be prepared, most of the compounds of titanium represent lower oxidation states, +2 or +3. The same tendency is shown by the succeeding elements. The compounds of vanadium, chromium, and manganese, representing the maximum oxidation numbers +5, +6, and +7, respectively, are strong oxidizing agents, and are easily reduced to compounds in which these elements have oxidation numbers +2 or +3. The oxidation numbers +2 and +3 continue to be the important ones for the succeeding elements, iron, cobalt, nickel, copper, and zinc.

A striking characteristic of most of the compounds of the transition metals is their *color*. Nearly every compound formed by vanadium, chromium, manganese, iron, cobalt, nickel, and copper is strongly colored, the color depending not only on the atomic number of the metallic element but also on its state of oxidation, and, to some extent, on the nature of the nonmetallic element or anion with which the metal is combined. It seems clear that the color of these compounds is associated with the presence of an incomplete *M* shell of electrons; that is, with an *M* shell containing less than its maximum number of electrons, 18. When the *M* shell is completed, as in the compounds of bipositive zinc ($ZnSO_4$, etc.) and of unipositive copper (CuCl, etc.), the substances are in general colorless. Another property characteristic of incompleted inner shells is *paramagnetism*, the property of a substance of being attracted into a strong magnetic field. Nearly all the compounds of the transition elements in oxidation states corresponding to the presence of incompleted inner shells are strongly paramagnetic.

The electronic structure of compounds of the transition elements will be discussed in Chapters 23 to 26.

20-4. The Metallic State

The characteristic properties of hardness and strength of the transition metals and their alloys are a consequence of the presence in the metals of very strong bonds between the atoms. For this reason it is of especial interest to us to understand the nature of the forces that hold the metal atoms together in these metals and alloys.

Let us consider the first six metals of the first long period, potassium, calcium, scandium, titanium, vanadium, and chromium. The first of these

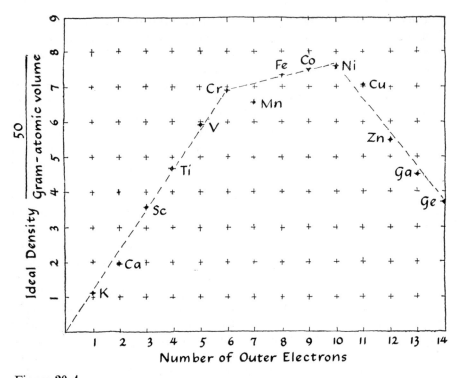

Figure 20-4

A graph of the ideal density of the metals of the first long period. The ideal density is defined here as the density that these metals would have if their atomic weights were all equal to 50.

metals, potassium, is a soft, light metal, with low melting point. The second metal, calcium, is much harder and denser, and has a much higher melting point. Similarly, the third metal, scandium, is still harder, still denser, and melts at a still higher temperature, and this change in properties continues through titanium, vanadium, and chromium. It is well illustrated in Figure 20-4, which shows a quantity called the ideal density, equal to 50/gram-atomic volume. This ideal density, which is inversely proportional to the gram-atomic volume of the metal, is the density that these metals would have if they all had the same atomic weight, 50. It is an inverse measure of the cube of the interatomic distances in the metals. We see that the ideal density increases steadily from its minimum value of about 1 for potassium to a value of about 7 for chromium, and many other properties of the metals, including hardness and tensile strength, show a similar steady increase through this series of six metals.

There is a simple explanation of this change in properties in terms of the electronic structure of the metals. The potassium atom has only one electron outside of its completed argon shell. It could use this electron to form a single covalent bond with another potassium atom, as in the diatomic molecules K_2 that are present, together with monatomic molecules K, in potassium vapor. In the crystal of metallic potassium each potassium atom has a number of neighboring atoms, at the same distance. It is held to these neighbors by its single covalent bond, which resonates among the neighbors. In metallic calcium there are *two* valence electrons per calcium atom, permitting each atom to form two bonds with its neighbors. These two bonds resonate among the calcium-calcium positions, giving a total bonding power in the metal twice as great as that in potassium. Similarly in scandium, with *three* valence electrons, the bonding is three times as great as in potassium, and so on to chromium, where, with *six* valence electrons, the bonding is six times as great.

This increase does not continue in the same way beyond chromium. Instead, the strength, hardness, and other properties of the transition metals remain essentially constant for the five elements chromium, manganese, iron, cobalt, and nickel, as is indicated by the small change in ideal density in Figure 20-4. (The low value for manganese is due to the existence of this metal with an unusual crystal structure, shown by no other element.) We can conclude that the metallic valence does not continue to increase, but remains at the value six for these elements. Then, after nickel, the metallic valence again decreases, through the series copper, zinc, gallium, and germanium, as is indicated by the rapid decrease in ideal density in Figure 20-4, and by a corresponding decrease in hardness, melting point, and other properties.

It is interesting to note that in the metallic state chromium has metallic valence 6, corresponding to the oxidation number +6 characteristic of the chromates and dichromates, rather than to the lower oxidation number +3 shown in the chromium salts, and that the metals manganese, iron, cobalt, and nickel also have metallic valence 6, although nearly all of their compounds represent the oxidation state +2 or +3. *The valuable physical properties of the transition metals are the result of the high metallic valence of the elements.*

Unsynchronized Resonance of Bonds in Metals. It is mentioned above that in potassium metal each atom, with one valence electron, can form one covalent bond, but that this bond is not between the atom and a single neighboring atom, but instead resonates among several positions. For four potassium atoms in a square, we might write two valence-bond structures:

$$
\begin{array}{cc}
\begin{array}{cc} K & K \\ | & | \\ K & K \end{array} & \begin{array}{c} K—K \\ \\ K—K \end{array} \\
\text{I} & \text{II}
\end{array}
$$

These structures are analogous to the two Kekulé structures for the benzene molecule. Resonance between the two structures would stabilize the metal relative to a crystal composed of K_2 molecules, each with a fixed covalent bond.

There are other structures, involving a transfer of an electron from one atom to another, that might be considered:

$$
\begin{array}{cccc}
\text{K}^+ \ \ \text{K} & \text{K} \ \ \text{K}^+ & \text{K}^-\!\!-\!\!\text{K} & \text{K}\!\!-\!\!\text{K}^- \\
\ \ \ | & \ \ | & \ \ \ | & \ \ \ | \\
\text{K}\!\!-\!\!\text{K}^- & \text{K}^-\!\!-\!\!\text{K} & \text{K} \ \ \text{K}^+ & \text{K}^+ \ \ \text{K} \\
\text{III} & \text{IV} & \text{V} & \text{VI}
\end{array}
$$

Resonance among all six structures would lead to greater stabilization than resonance between only I and II above. Moreover, this unsynchronized resonance gives a simple explanation of the characteristic properties of metals—the large electric conductivity and the negative temperature coefficient of electric conductivity.

Let us consider a row of potassium atoms:

$$
\text{K}\!\!-\!\!\text{K} \quad \text{K}\!\!-\!\!\text{K} \quad \text{K}^+ \quad \text{K}\!\!-\!\!\text{K}^-\!\!-\!\!\text{K} \quad \text{K}\!\!-\!\!\text{K} \quad \text{K}\!\!-\!\!\text{K}
$$

In the presence of an electric field, produced by a cathode at the left and an anode at the right, the bonds would tend to shift in such a way as to move the positive charge toward the cathode and the negative charge toward the anode:

$$
\begin{array}{llllll}
\text{K}\!\!-\!\!\text{K} \ \ \text{K}^+ & \text{K}\!\!-\!\!\text{K} & \text{K}\!\!-\!\!\text{K} & \text{K}\!\!-\!\!\text{K}^-\!\!-\!\!\text{K} & \text{K}\!\!-\!\!\text{K} \\
\text{K}^+ \ \ \text{K}\!\!-\!\!\text{K} & \text{K}\!\!-\!\!\text{K} & \text{K}\!\!-\!\!\text{K} & \text{K}\!\!-\!\!\text{K} & \text{K}\!\!-\!\!\text{K}^-\!\!-\!\!\text{K} \\
& & \text{etc.} & &
\end{array}
$$

The unsynchronized resonance of the bonds corresponds to the transfer of electric charge (electrons) that leads to high electric conductivity. This conductivity is characteristic of the structure of the metal, and hence takes place most readily at very low temperatures, when the atoms are quite regularly arranged in the crystal. At higher temperatures the thermal oscillation of the atoms introduces some disorder in their arrangement, which interferes with the resonance of the bonds, and hence causes a decrease in conductivity (negative temperature coefficient).

The Metallic Orbital.   In the valence-bond structure

$$
\begin{array}{c}
\text{K}^+ \ \ \text{K} \\
\ \ \ | \\
\text{K}\!\!-\!\!\text{K}^-
\end{array}
$$

one atom, K^-, has assumed a second valence electron, permitting it to form two covalent bonds, rather than just one. Two bond orbitals are accordingly being utilized by this atom, one more than by the neutral (unicovalent) atoms. This extra orbital, called the *metallic orbital*, is needed to permit the unsynchronized valence-bond resonance characteristic of metals: *the metallic orbital, an extra orbital not occupied by an electron or electron pair in the neutral atom, is the characteristic structural feature of metals.*

Potassium has nine reasonably stable orbitals in its outer shell: one $4s$ orbital, three $4p$ orbitals, and five $3d$ orbitals. Only one (an *spd* hybrid) is used as a bond orbital by the unicovalent atom, and others are available to serve as the metallic orbital; hence potassium is a metal. In diamond, on the other hand, the four stable orbitals of the valence shell (the tetrahedral orbitals formed by hybridization of the $2s$ orbital and the three $2p$ orbitals, Chapter 9) are all occupied by bond electrons; there is no metallic orbital, and hence diamond is not a metal.

20-5. Metallic Valence

It is mentioned in the preceding section that for the elements potassium, calcium, scandium, titanium, vanadium, and chromium the physical properties indicate that all of the electrons outside of the argon shell are used in forming bonds, and that the metallic valences for these elements are 1, 2, 3, 4, 5, and 6, respectively.

There are nine stable orbitals available for the transition elements (one $4s$, three $4p$, five $3d$), and, with one required as the metallic orbital, the metallic valence might be expected to continue to increase, and have the value 7 for manganese and 8 for iron. However, as mentioned above, the physical properties show that the metallic valence remains at the maximum of 6 for manganese, iron, cobalt, and nickel, and then begins to decrease at copper. The maximum value of 6 corresponds to the number of good bond orbitals that can be formed by hybridization of the s, p, and d orbitals. The decrease in metallic valence beginning at copper is caused by the limited number or orbitals, as shown by the example of tin.

Tin, element 50, has 14 electrons outside of the krypton shell, and nine stable orbitals ($4d$, $5s$, $5p$). The five $4d$ orbitals, which are more stable than the $5s$ and $5p$ orbitals, are occupied by five unshared electron pairs. The remaining four electrons may separately occupy the four tetrahedral $5s5p^3$ orbitals, and be used in forming four bonds, tetrahedrally directed. In fact, gray tin, one of the two allotropic forms of the element, has the diamond structure. The tin atoms in gray tin are quadrivalent, as are the carbon atoms in diamond. They have no metallic orbital, and gray tin is not a metal, but is a metalloid.

If the tin atom were to retain one of its orbitals for use as a metallic orbital, it would be bivalent rather than quadrivalent:

Gray tin:	$5s$	$5p$	$5p$	$5p$	No metallic orbital
	↑	↑	↑	↑	Quadrivalent
White tin:	$5s$	$5p$	$5p$	$5p$	One metallic orbital
	↑↓	↑	↑	Metallic orbital	Bivalent

The ordinary allotropic form of tin, white tin, has metallic properties. The observed bond lengths indicate that the valence of tin in this form is about 2.5.

The value 2.5 can be accounted for in the following way. The magnetic properties of the iron-group elements and their alloys indicate that the number of metallic orbitals in a metal is 0.72, rather than 1 (see the discussion of magnetic properties in the next section). This fractional value can be explained by the reasonable assumption that the metal contains 28% M^+, 44% M, and 28% M^-. The ions M^- do not need a metallic orbital, because they cannot accept another electron (M^{--} would be unstable, according to the electroneutrality principle, Section 9-13). The structure of white tin can accordingly be represented in the following way:

					Contribution to valence
	5s	5p	5p	5p	
28% Sn^+	↑	↑	↑	Metallic	$3 \times 0.28 = 0.84$
44% Sn	↑↓	↑	↑	Metallic	$2 \times 0.44 = 0.88$
28% Sn^-	↑↓	↑	↑	↑	$3 \times 0.28 = 0.84$
		Metallic valence of tin			**2.56**

The same argument leads to the following values for the metallic valence of the elements from copper to germanium:

Cu	Zn	Ga	Ge
5.56	4.56	3.56	2.56

Copper, zinc, and gallium are metals, with properties compatible with these values of the valence. Germanium under ordinary pressure is a metalloid, with the diamond structure and valence 4. At high pressure it is converted into another form, with greatly increased electric conductivity and density corresponding to the white tin structure and valence 2.56.

Ferromagnetism and Metallic Valence.   Iron, cobalt, and nickel are ferromagnetic metals. The ferromagnetism of iron corresponds to 2.2 electrons with unpaired spins per atom. The alloys of iron with a small amount of cobalt are more strongly ferromagnetic than pure iron. The ferromagnetism increases to a maximum value at about 28% cobalt, and then decreases, reaching the value corresponding to 1.7 unpaired electrons per atom for pure cobalt.

The maximum ferromagnetism for the alloy of 72% iron and 28% cobalt can be interpreted in the following way. The atoms in this alloy have the average atomic number 26.28, and hence have 8.28 electrons outside of the argon shell. These electrons may occupy nine orbitals: the five 3d orbitals, the 4s orbital, and the three 3p orbitals. But if all nine orbitals were available for occupancy by the electrons (6 for bond formation and the others contributing to the ferromagnetism), the number of unpaired electrons would be expected to continue to increase beyond 28 % cobalt and to reach its maximum at pure cobalt, which has nine electrons outside the argon shell. The fact that the maximum ferromagnetism is reached at 28 % cobalt (8.28 electrons outside of the argon shell) indicates that only 8.28 of the nine orbitals are available for occupancy. The remaining 0.72 orbital per atom is interpreted as the metallic orbital of 72 % of the atoms, as discussed above.

Example 1. The ferromagnetism of alloys of nickel and copper decreases from the value corresponding to 0.6 unpaired electron per atom for pure nickel to 0 for the alloy with 56 % copper. How is this fact interpreted?

    Solution. In these alloys 8.28 orbitals are available for occupancy by the electrons outside of the argon shell. The alloy of 44 % nickel and 56 % copper has an average of 10.56 such electrons per atom. Of these, 6 are bonding electrons, which occupy 6 of the 8.28 orbitals. The remaining 4.56 electrons occupy the remaining 2.28 orbitals; since the electron/orbital ratio is 2, these electrons are all paired. Hence there are no unpaired electrons in this alloy, and it is not ferromagnetic.

Example 2. What is the metallic valence of zinc?

    Solution. Zinc has 12 electrons outside the argon shell, and 8.28 orbitals for them to occupy. We place 8.28 electrons with positive spin in these orbitals, and the remaining $12 - 8.28 = 3.72$ electrons with negative spin in 3.72 of the orbitals. Hence 3.72 orbitals per atom are occupied by electron pairs, and the remaining $8.28 - 3.72 = 4.56$ orbitals per atom are occupied by single electrons. These 4.56 electrons can be used in forming bonds. Hence the metallic valence of zinc is **4.56,** as stated above.

20-6. The Nature of Alloys. The Phase Rule

    An *alloy* is a metallic material containing two or more elements. It may be homogeneous, consisting of a single phase, or heterogeneous, consisting of a mixture of phases. An example of a homogeneous alloy is coinage gold. An ordinary sample of coinage gold consists of small crystal grains, each of which is a solid solution of copper and gold, with structure of the sort represented in Figure 20-5. Another example of a homogeneous alloy is the very hard metallic substance tantalum carbide, TaC. It is a compound, with the same structure as sodium chloride (Figure 4-5). Each tantalum atom has twelve tantalum atoms as neighbors. In addition, carbon atoms, which are relatively small, are present in the interstices between the tantalum atoms and serve to bind them together. Each carbon atom is bonded to the six tantalum atoms that surround it. The bonds are $\frac{2}{3}$ bonds—the four covalent bonds resonate among the six positions about the carbon atom. Each tantalum atom is bonded not only to the adjacent carbon atoms but also to the twelve

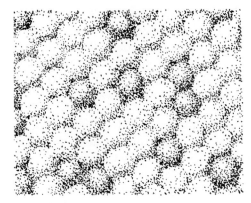

Figure 20-5

An alloy of gold and copper. The alloy consists of small crystals, each crystal being made of gold atoms and copper atoms in an orderly array, but with the atoms of the two different kinds distributed essentially at random among the atomic positions.

tantalum atoms surrounding it. The large number of bonds (nine valence electrons per TaC, as compared with five per Ta, occupying, in metallic tantalum, nearly the same volume) explains the greater hardness of the compound than of tantalum itself.

A discussion of the structure of some alloys will be given in later sections of this chapter and in the following chapters. Before entering upon this discussion we shall consider a general principle that has been found to have great value, not only in this field but also in many other fields of chemistry.

The Phase Rule—a Method of Classifying All Systems in Equilibrium. We have so far discussed a number of examples of systems in equilibrium. These examples include, among others, a crystal or a liquid in equilibrium with its vapor (Chapter 2), a crystal and its liquid in equilibrium with its vapor at its melting point (Chapter 2), a solution in equilibrium with the vapor of the solvent and with the frozen solvent (Chapter 17), and a precipitate in equilibrium with ions in solution (Chapter 18).

These systems appear to be quite different from one another. However, it was discovered by a great American theoretical physicist, Professor J. Willard Gibbs of Yale University (1839–1903), that a simple, unifying principle holds for all systems in equilibrium. This principle is called the *phase rule*.

The phase rule is a relation among the number of independent *components*, the number of *phases*, and the *variance* of a system in equilibrium. The independent components (or, briefly, the components) of a system are the substances that must be added to realize the system. The word phase has been defined earlier (p. 471). Thus a system containing ice, water, and water vapor consists of three phases but only one component (water-substance), since any two of the phases can be formed from the third. The variance of the system is the number of independent ways in which the system can be varied; these ways may include varying the temperature and the pressure, and also varying the composition of any solutions (gaseous, liquid, or crystalline) that exist as phases in the system.

The nature of the phase rule can be induced from some simple examples. Consider the system represented in Figure 20-6. It is made of water-substance (water in its various forms), in a cylinder with movable piston (to permit the pressure to be changed), placed in a thermostat with changeable temperature. If only one phase is present, both the pressure and the temperature can be arbitrarily varied over wide ranges: the variance is 2. For example, liquid water can be held at any temperature from its freezing point to its boiling point under any applied pressure. But if two phases are present the pressure is automatically determined by the temperature, and hence the variance is reduced to 1. For example, pure water vapor in equilibrium with water at a given temperature has a definite pressure, the vapor pressure of water at that temperature. And if three phases are present in equilibrium—ice, water, and water vapor—both the temperature and the pressure are exactly fixed; the

Figure 20-6

A simple system illustrating the phase rule.

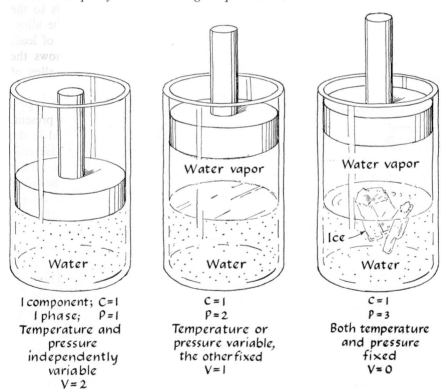

I component; C=I	C=I	C=I
I phase; P=I	P=2	P=3
Temperature and pressure independently variable	Temperature or pressure variable, the other fixed	Both temperature and pressure fixed
V=2	V=I	V=0

variance is then 0. This condition is called the *triple point* of ice, water, and water vapor. It occurs at temperature $+0.0099°C$ and pressure 4.58 mm of mercury.

We see that for this simple system, with one component, the sum of the number of phases and the variance is equal to 3. It was discovered by Gibbs that for every system in equilibrium the sum of the number of phases and the variance is 2 greater than the number of components:

Number of phases + Variance = Number of components + 2

or, using the abbreviations P, V, and C,

$$P + V = C + 2$$

This is the **phase rule**.

Examples of application of the phase rule are given in the following discussion of some alloy systems.

The Binary System Arsenic-Lead.   The phase diagram for the binary system arsenic-lead is shown as Figure 20-7. In this diagram the vertical coordinate is the temperature, in degrees centigrade. The diagram corresponds to the pressure 1 atm. The horizontal coordinate is the composition of the alloy, represented along the bottom of the diagram in atomic percentage of lead, and along the top in weight percentage of lead. The diagram shows the temperature and composition corresponding to the presence in the alloy of different phases.

The range of temperatures and compositions represented by the region above the lines AB and BC is a region in which a single phase is present, the liquid phase, consisting of the molten alloy. The region included in the triangle ADB represents two phases, a liquid phase and a solid phase consisting of crystals of arsenic. The triangle BEC similarly represents a two-phase region, the two phases being the liquid and crystalline lead. The range below the horizontal line DBE consists of the two phases crystalline arsenic and crystalline lead, the alloy being a mixture of small grains of the two elements.

Let us apply the phase rule to an alloy in the one-phase region above the line ABC. Here we have a system of two components, and, in this region, one phase; the phase rule states that the variance should be three. The three quantities describing the system which may be varied in this region are the pressure (taken arbitrarily in this diagram as 1 atm, but capable of variation), the temperature, which may be varied through the range permitted by the boundaries of the region, and the composition of the molten alloy, which may similarly be varied through the range of compositions permitted by the boundaries of the region.

An alloy in the region ADB, such as that represented by the point P, at

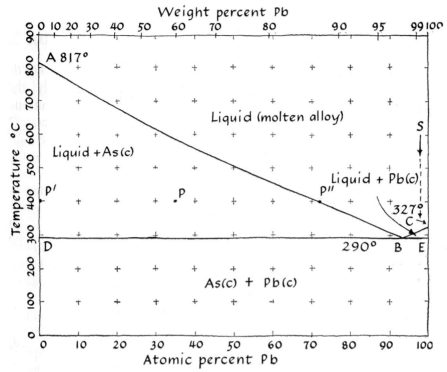

Figure 20-7

Phase diagram for the binary system arsenic-lead.

35 atomic percent lead and 400°C, lies in a two-phase region, and the variance is accordingly stated by the phase rule to be two. The pressure and the temperature are the two variables; the phase rule hence states that it is not possible to vary the composition of the phases present in the alloy. The phases are crystalline arsenic, represented by the point P' directly to the left of P, and the molten alloy, with the composition P'' directly to the right of P. The composition of the molten alloy in equilibrium with crystalline arsenic at 400°C and 1 atm pressure is definitely fixed at P''; it cannot be varied.

The only conditions under which three phases can be in equilibrium with one another at the arbitrary pressure 1 atm are represented by the point B. With three phases in equilibrium with one another for this two-component system, the phase rule requires that there be only one arbitrary variable, which we have used in fixing the pressure arbitrarily at 1 atm. Correspondingly we see that the composition of the liquid is fixed at that represented by the point B, 93 atomic percent lead, and the composition of the two solid phases is fixed, these phases being pure arsenic and pure lead. The temperature is also fixed, at the value 290°C, corresponding to the point B. This point is called the *eutectic point*, and the corresponding alloy is called the *eutectic alloy*, or simply the *eutectic*. The word eutectic means melting easily; the eutectic has a sharp melting point. When a liquid alloy with the eutectic composition is cooled, it crystallizes completely on reaching the temperature 290°C, forming a mixture of very small grains of pure arsenic and pure lead, with a fine texture. When this alloy is slowly heated, it melts sharply at the temperature 290°C.

The lines in the phase diagram are the boundaries separating a region in which one group of phases are present from a region in which another group of phases are present. A line such as *AB* is called the *freezing-point curve, liquidus curve*, or *liquidus*, and a line such as *DB* is called the *melting-point curve, solidus curve*, or *solidus*. These boundary lines can be located by various experimental methods, including the method of thermal analysis, discussed in Section 20-7.

If a molten alloy of arsenic and lead with the eutectic composition is cooled, the temperature drops at a regular rate until the eutectic temperature, 290°C, is reached; the liquid then crystallizes into the solid eutectic alloy, the temperature remaining constant until crystallization is complete. The eutectic has a constant melting point, just as has either one of the pure elementary substances.

The effect of the phenomenon of depression of the freezing point in causing the eutectic melting point to be lower than the melting point of the pure metals can be intensified by the use of additional components. Thus an alloy with eutectic melting point 70°C can be made by melting together 50 weight percent bismuth (m.p. 271°C), 27% lead (m.p. 327.5°C), 13% tin (m.p. 232°C), and 10% cadmium (m.p. 321°C), and the melting point can be reduced still further, to 47°C, by the incorporation in this alloy of 18% of its weight of indium (m.p. 155°C).

It is now possible, in terms of this phase diagram, to discuss a phenomenon mentioned in Chapter 15. It was stated there that a small amount, about $\frac{1}{2}$% by weight, of arsenic is added to lead used to make lead shot, in order to increase the hardness of the shot and also to improve the properties of the molten material. Lead shot is made by dripping the molten alloy through a sieve. The fine droplets freeze during their passage through the air, and are caught in a tank of water after they have solidified. If pure lead were used the falling drops would solidify rather suddenly on reaching the temperature 327°C. A falling drop tends not to be perfectly spherical, but to oscillate between prolate and oblate ellipsoidal shapes, as you may have noticed by observing drops of water dripping from a faucet; and hence the shot made of pure lead might be expected not to be perfectly spherical in shape. But the alloy containing $\frac{1}{2}$% arsenic by weight, represented by the arrow *S* (Figure 20-7), would begin to freeze on reaching the temperature 320°C, and would continue to freeze, forming small crystals of pure lead, until the eutectic temperature 290°C is reached. During this stage of its history the drop would consist of a sludge of lead crystals in the molten alloy, and this sluggish sludge would be expected to be drawn into good spherical shape by the action of the surface-tension forces of the liquid.

The Binary System Lead-Tin. The phase diagram for the lead-tin system of alloys is shown as Figure 20-8. This system rather closely resembles the system arsenic-lead, except that there is an appreciable solubility of tin in crystalline lead and a small solubility of lead in crystalline tin. The phase designated α (alpha) is a solid solution of tin in lead, the solubility being 19.5 weight percent at the eutectic temperature and dropping to 2% at room temperature. The phase β (beta) is a solid solution of lead in tin, the solubility being about 2% at the eutectic temperature and extremely small at room temperature. The eutectic composition is about 62 weight percent tin, 38 weight percent lead.

The composition of *solder* is indicated by the two arrows, corresponding to ordinary plumbers' solder and to half-and-half solder. The properties of solder are explained by the phase diagram. The useful property of solder is that it permits a wiped-joint to be made. As the solder cools it forms a sludge of crystals of the α phase in the liquid alloy, and the mechanical properties of

Figure **20-8**

  Phase diagram for the binary system lead-tin.

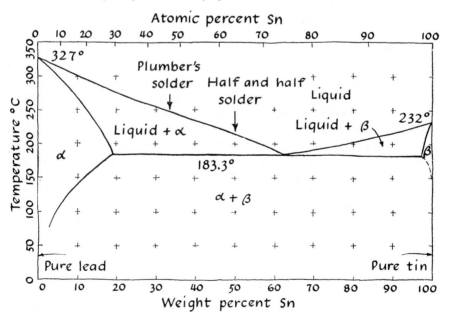

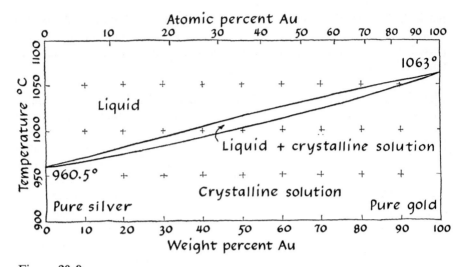

Figure **20-9**

Phase diagram for the binary system silver-gold, showing the formation of a complete series of crystalline solutions.

this sludge are such as to permit it to be handled by the plumber in an effective way. The sludge corresponds to transition through the region of the phase diagram in which liquid and the α phase are present together. For plumbers' solder the temperature range involved is about 70°, from 250°C to 183°C, the eutectic temperature.

The Binary System Silver-Gold.   The metals silver and gold are completely miscible with one another not only in the liquid state but also in the crystalline state. A solid alloy of silver and gold consists of a single phase, homogeneous crystals with the cubic closest-packed structure, described for copper in Chapter 2, with gold and silver atoms occupying the positions in this lattice essentially at random (Figure 20-5). The phase diagram shown as Figure 20-9 represents this situation. It is seen that the addition of a small amount of gold to pure silver does not depress the freezing point, in the normal way, but instead causes an increase in the temperature of crystallization.

The alloys of silver and gold, usually containing some copper, are used in jewelry, in dentistry, and as a gold solder.

The Binary System Silver-Strontium.   A somewhat more complicated binary system—that formed by silver and strontium—is represented in Figure 20-10. It is seen that four intermetallic compounds are formed, their formulas being Ag_5Sr, Ag_5Sr_3, $AgSr$, and Ag_2Sr_3. These compounds and the pure elements form a series of eutectics; for example, the alloy containing 25 weight percent strontium is the eutectic mixture of Ag_5Sr and Ag_5Sr_3.

Some other binary systems are far more complicated than this one. As many as a dozen different phases may be present, and these phases may involve variation in composition, resulting from the formation of solid solutions. Ternary alloys (formed from three components) and alloys involving four or more components are of course still more complex.

It is seen that the formulas of intermetallic compounds, such as Ag_5Sr, do not correspond in any simple way to the usually accepted valences of the element. Compounds such as Ag_5Sr can be described by saying that the strontium atom uses its two valence electrons in forming bonds with the silver atoms that surround it, and that the silver atoms then use their remaining electrons in forming bonds with other silver atoms. Some progress has been made in developing a valence theory of the structure and properties of intermetallic compounds and of alloys in general, but this field of chemistry is still far from its final form.

The silver-strontium system provides an interesting example of the way in which our knowledge of the world increases. In the first and second editions

Figure **20-10**

Phase diagram for the binary system silver-strontium, showing the formation of four intermetallic compounds.

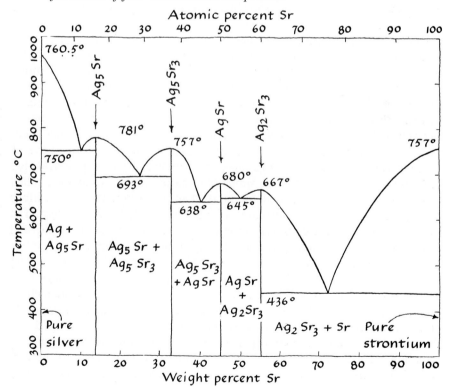

of this book the system was described as involving the intermetallic compound Ag_4Sr. This is the composition that was indicated by the reported position of the maximum of the freezing-point curve (temperature 781°C) in the diagram. However, recent x-ray investigations of the compound have shown that it has the formula Ag_5Sr. The error in determining the position of the maximum in the freezing-point curve was caused by errors of about ±10° in the measurements.

20-7. Experimental Methods of Studying Alloys

About 100 years ago a metallurgical technique called *metallography* was developed as a way of investigating the phases present in alloys. This technique consists of grinding and polishing the surface of a metallic specimen, sometimes etching it with reagents (nitric acid, picric acid, etc.) to emphasize grain boundaries and to help to distinguish between different phases, and then examining the surface with use of an optical microscope, with a method of illumination from above. In this way the sizes and shapes of crystal grains can be studied, and the presence of grains of two or more phases can be determined in alloys that to the unaided eye appear to be homogeneous. The polished and etched surface of a piece of copper is shown in Figure 2-3, and other photomicrographs of alloys, showing different phases, can be found in Chapter 24.

During recent years much use has been made of the electron microscope in the study of metals and alloys. Very thin foils of the metal are made, sometimes by dissolving the surface of the specimen with acid until holes develop; the region adjacent to a hole may be thin enough to permit penetration by the electron beam. The structure of individual crystal grains can also be determined by observing the electron diffraction pattern from a beam of electrons transmitted through a single grain. Changes in structure that occur with time, perhaps at elevated temperature, may be followed in this way.

These techniques for studying phase transitions, although powerful, are time-consuming and difficult. A simple and easily applied technique, called *thermal analysis*, has been used for more than a century. Phase transitions are characterized by the absorption or emission of a heat of transition. The way in which the heat of transition is involved in the technique of thermal analysis can be illustrated by discussion of a simple experiment.

Samples of arsenic-lead alloys (Figure 20-7) may be made, corresponding to different compositions, from pure arsenic to pure lead. A sample of pure arsenic is placed in a crucible in a furnace and heated to above the melting point. One of the junctions of a thermocouple is inserted in the sample, to permit measurement of the temperature. When the furnace is turned off, the temperature of the sample begins to decrease, because of conduction and radiation from the sample to the furnace and from the furnace to the surrounding environment. The temperature decreases with time, as indicated by

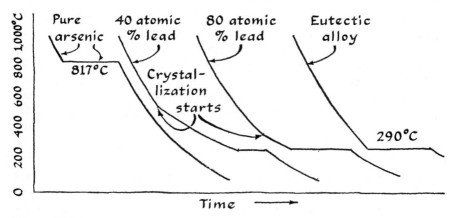

Figure **20-11**

Cooling curves for samples of arsenic-lead alloys.

the first curve in Figure 20-11. (These curves are called *cooling curves*.) At the freezing point of arsenic, 817°C, there occurs a discontinuity in the slope of the temperature-time curve, which begins to follow a horizontal course, with slope zero. During a period of time the heat of crystallization serves to balance the heat loss to the surrounding furnace. The temperature of the horizontal section of the cooling curve is the melting point of the substance. After completion of crystallization the temperature begins to drop.

The second cooling curve in Figure 20-11, corresponding to 40 atomic per-cent lead, shows a decrease in temperature and then a change in slope, which represents the beginning of crystallization of arsenic from the molten alloy. The temperature continues to drop, even though arsenic is crystallizing, be-cause the composition of the liquid alloy changes as arsenic is removed from it. The curve continues with changed slope until the temperature 290°C is reached, and then its slope becomes zero. The horizontal section represents the simul-taneous crystallization of arsenic and lead, as separate phases, at the eutectic temperature.

The next curve, for the alloy with 80 atomic percent lead, shows a lower temperature at which crystallization of arsenic begins (that is, a lower liquidus temperature) and then a longer horizontal section, representing crystallization of a larger amount of the eutectic mixture of the two crystalline phases.

The next curve corresponds to the eutectic composition, with 93 atomic percent lead (point B on Figure 20-7). This curve is qualitatively similar to the curve for a pure substance.

The alloys in the region between the eutectic composition and pure lead give cooling curves that are like those for the alloys in the other half of the phase diagram.

The method of thermal analysis can be improved and refined by the use of two samples of metal or alloy and measurement of the temperature difference between the two samples; this is called *differential thermal analysis*. For example, suppose that an alloy of iron and cobalt has been made and that it is thought that the transition* between the α phase (ferromagnetic) and the β phase (paramagnetic, with the same body-centered crystal structure as the α phase) probably lies between 700°C and 900°C. A sample of the alloy is prepared and also a sample of a similar metal, such as copper, that does not have a phase transition in this temperature range. The samples are adjusted in weight so as to have approximately equal average values of their total heat capacity. A thermocouple is placed in each sample, and they are connected with a recording apparatus in such a way that the difference in temperature between the two samples can be continuously recorded as a function of the temperature of the first sample. The two samples are placed in a furnace and heated to 1000°C, the furnace is then turned off, and the temperature recordings are made as the samples cool. A change in slope of the differential temperature indicates the transition temperature, which can in this way be determined with considerable accuracy (0.1° to 1°).

Another important and useful method of investigating alloys is by preparing samples of different compositions and making x-ray photographs of them (especially powder photographs, which are the diffraction patterns given by a large number of small crystals in random orientation). By the analysis of the diffraction patterns the number of phases present can be determined. For example, the samples of silver-strontium alloys, with phase diagram represented in Figure 20-10, are found to give characteristic diffraction patterns at six compositions: pure silver, pure strontium, and the four compositions indicated by the arrows in Figure 20-10. For an alloy with intermediate composition the diffraction pattern shows the lines characteristic of two phases, with relative intensities proportional to the relative amounts of the two phases. Moreover, it is often possible by the analysis of the diffraction pattern to determine the structure of the crystal, and thus to verify the composition. It is in this way that the compound Ag_5Sr was identified.

20-8. Interstitial Solid Solutions and Substitutional Solid Solutions

Two clearly distinct types of solid solutions (crystalline solutions) have been recognized. In solid solutions of one type, called *interstitial solid solutions*, atoms of one element are inserted into some of the interstices in the crystal lattice formed by the atoms of a second element. Usually this results in a small increase in the lattice constant of the crystal; but usually the increase in lattice constant is not large enough to compensate for the mass of the inserted atom, and the density of the interstitial solid solution may become

---

* This transition, which does not involve a change in crystal structure but only a change in relative orientations of the magnetic moments of the atoms, occurs over a range of temperature, roughly 1°. It is called a *second-order transition*.

larger than that of the substance with-out the interstitial atoms. The second sort of solid solutions, called *substitutional solid solutions*, involves the re-placement of atoms of one kind in the crystal lattice by atoms of a second kind.

An example of an interstitial solid solution is provided by martensite, a solid solution of carbon in iron. The structure shown in Figure 20-12 is an ideal structure, corresponding to one carbon atom for every two iron atoms. It is seen from the figure that the iron atoms are arranged approximately as in α-iron—that is, in the body-centered arrangement. The carbon atoms are inserted in the centers of the horizon-tal faces of the unit of structure. The presence of carbon atoms in these faces, and not in the lateral faces, causes the crystal to be tetragonal in symmetry, rather than cubic. The ver-tical edge of the unit of structure shown

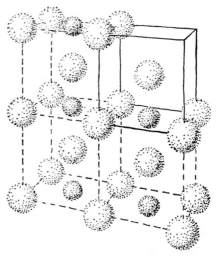

Figure **20-12** *The structure of martensite, a carbide of iron that is present in steel. The atoms of carbon (small spheres) are in the centers of the horizontal squares formed by the iron atoms, which are in a body-centered arrangement.*

in the figure is about 3% larger than the two horizontal edges. If there are not so many carbon atoms present in the phase, some of the interstitial posi-tions in the horizontal faces are unoccupied. When the number of carbon atoms becomes smaller, the horizontal faces and the lateral faces are occupied at random by carbon atoms, and the interstitial solution becomes cubic, rather than tetragonal, in symmetry.

Interstitial solid solutions are usually formed when a substance with small atoms is dissolved in a substance with large atoms—the covalent radius of carbon is 0.77 Å, and the metallic radius of iron is 1.26 Å. Solid solutions composed of atoms of nearly the same size usually are substitutional solid solutions. For example, iron and nickel form substitutional solid solutions, having atoms of iron and nickel distributed at random over the positions of the body-centered structure (for compositions between 0 and about 25 atomic percent nickel) or over the face-centered positions (for compositions between 25 and 100 atomic percent nickel). The irregularity in the lattice produced by the presence of atoms of different sizes makes itself evident in an increased electric resistance; solid solutions are not such good conductors of electricity as the pure metals.

EXERCISES

20-1. Aluminum crystallizes in cubic closest packing. How many nearest neighbors does each atom have? Predict its metallic valence from its position in the periodic table. Would you predict it to have greater or less tensile strength than magnesium? Why?

20-2. Discuss the metallic valence of the elements rubidium, strontium, and yttrium. What would you predict about change in hardness, density, strength, and melting point in this series of elementary metals?

20-3. How many nearest neighbors does an atom have in a cubic closest-packed structure (example, copper)? In a hexagonal closest-packed structure (example, magnesium)? In a body-centered structure (example, iron)?

20-4. Compare the metallic valences of sodium, magnesium, and aluminum with their oxidation numbers in their principal compounds.

20-5. Describe the structure of tantalum carbide, TaC. Can you explain why it has much greater strength and hardness than tantalum itself?

20-6. Define alloy, intermetallic compound, phase, variance, eutectic, triple point.

20-7. State the phase rule, and given an application of it.

20-8. Cadmium (m.p. 321°C) and bismuth (m.p. 271°C) do not form solid solutions nor compounds with one another. Their eutectic point lies at 61 weight percent bismuth and 146°C. Sketch their phase diagram, and label each region to show what phases are present.

20-9. What is plumber's solder? Would the alloy with 60 weight percent tin and 40 weight percent lead be satisfactory as solder?

20-10. Describe the alloy that would be obtained by cooling a melt of silver containing 8 atomic percent strontium. (See Figure 20-10.)

20-11. Describe the alloy that would be obtained by cooling a melt of silver and strontium containing 50 atomic percent Ag. Would it be homogeneous or heterogeneous? Would it melt sharply, at one temperature, or over a range of temperatures?

20-12. What is the lowest temperature at which an alloy of silver and strontium can remain liquid? What is the composition of this alloy? Is the solid alloy homogeneous or heterogeneous? Does it have a sharp melting point?

20-13. Why does the Ag-Sr alloy with 75 atomic percent Sr have a lower melting point than pure strontium?

20-14. From Figure 20-10 it is seen that the silver-strontium alloy containing 1 atomic percent Sr begins to freeze at a temperature 11° less than the freezing point of pure silver. What is the weight-molar freezing-point constant of silver? (See Section 17-7.) Silver and silicon have a phase diagram resembling that shown in Figure 20-7; neither element is soluble in the other in the crystalline state. At what temperature would the Ag-Si alloy containing 1 atomic percent Si begin to freeze? (Answer: 11° below the freezing point of silver.)

20-15. The x-ray examination of the crystalline compound of silver and strontium containing about 15% Sr is hexagonal. The unit of structure has two edges with length 5.67 Å at the angle 120° with one another and a third edge with length 4.62 Å at right angles to the other two.
(a) What is the volume of the unit? (Answer: 128.7 Å³.)
(b) What is the volume of a mole of unit cells? (Answer: 76.85 cm³.)
(c) The density of the substance has been determined to be 8.16 g/cm³. What is the mass of a mole of unit cells? (Answer: 627 g.)
(d) What are the possible formula weights of the compound?
(e) How many atoms of strontium are there in one formula?
(f) How many atoms of silver?

CHAPTER $\boxed{21}$

Metallurgy

Metals are obtained from ores. *An* **ore** *is a mineral or other natural material that may be profitably treated for the extraction of one or more metals.*

The process of extracting a metal from the ore is called *winning* the metal. *Refining* is the purification of the metal that has been extracted from the ore. *Metallurgy* is the science and art of winning and refining metals, and preparing them for use.

Processes of many different kinds are used for winning metals. The simplest processes are those used to obtain the metals that occur in nature in the elementary state. Thus nuggets of gold and of the platinum metals may be picked up by hand, in some deposits, or may be separated by a hydraulic process (use of a stream of water) when the nuggets occur mixed with lighter materials in a placer deposit.* A quartz vein containing native gold may be treated by mining it, pulverizing the quartz in a stamp mill, and then mixing the rock powder with mercury. The gold dissolves in the mercury, which is easily separated from the rock powder because of its great density, and the gold can be recovered from the amalgam (its alloy with mercury) by distilling off the mercury.

The chemical processes involved in the winning of metals are mainly the reduction of a compound of the metal (usually oxide or sulfide). The principal reducing agent that is used is carbon, often in the form of coke. An example is the reduction of tin dioxide, SnO_2, with carbon, as described in Section 21-4. Another example is the reduction of iron oxide with coke in a blast furnace (Chapter 24). Occasionally reducing agents other than carbon are used; thus antimony is won from stibnite, Sb_2S_3, by heating it with iron:

$$Sb_2S_3 + 3Fe \longrightarrow 3FeS + 2Sb$$

Whether or not a reaction may be used for winning a metal depends upon

---

* A placer deposit is a glacial deposit or alluvial deposit (made by a river, lake, or arm of the sea), as of sand or gravel, containing gold or other valuable material.

the free energies of the reactants and the products (Section 18-10, on the driving force of chemical reactions). Values of the free energy of many substances have been determined by experiment. For some reactions, especially those in which the products are similar to the reactants, the change in free energy for the reaction is nearly equal to the enthalpy change (the heat of reaction). An example is the reaction of stibnite and iron given above. Whether such a reaction is exothermic or endothermic can be predicted with reasonable confidence by use of electronegativity values (Section 9-12). In the above reaction six Sb—S bonds are broken and six Fe—S bonds are formed. The electronegativity values (Table 9-1) are 1.9 for Sb, 2.5 for S, and 1.8 for Fe. The heat of formation per metal-sulfur bond is $23(x_A - x_B)^2$ kcal/mole (Equation 1 of Chapter 9); its values are $23(2.5 - 1.9)^2 = 8.3$ kcal/mole for Sb—S and $23(2.5 - 1.8)^2 = 11.3$ kcal/mole for Fe—S. We conclude that the reaction as written is exothermic and probably also exergonic (accompanied by the evolution of free energy).

From the foregoing argument we would conclude that any element more electropositive than antimony could be used to prepare antimony from stibnite. Reference to Table 9-1 shows that many metals are in this class. Iron is used in practice rather than some other metal because it is the cheapest metal.

The most electropositive metals are won by electrolysis (Sections 8-8 and 21-6).

Carbon can be used to reduce oxide ores, even though the corresponding reactions are endothermic, because the large entropy of the gaseous product, carbon monoxide, has a large effect on the free energy change at high temperatures (Le Chatelier's principle, Section 18-8).

The principal methods of winning metals are discussed in the following sections of this chapter. The metallurgy of iron and its congeners is taken up in Chapter 24.

Impure metals are purified in various ways. Distillation is used for mercury, and sublimation for zinc, cadmium, tin, and antimony. Copper and some other metals are refined electrolytically (Section 21-7). An unusual method of refining a metal is the Mond process for nickel (Section 24-6).

21-1. The Metallurgy of Copper

Copper occurs in nature as *native copper;* that is, in the free state. Other ores of copper include *cuprite*, Cu_2O; *chalcocite*, Cu_2S; *chalcopyrite*, $CuFeS_2$; *malachite*, $Cu_2CO_3(OH)_2$; and *azurite*, $Cu_3(CO_3)_2(OH)_2$. Malachite, a beautiful green mineral, is sometimes polished and used in jewelry.

An ore containing native copper may be treated by grinding it and then washing away the gangue (the associated rock or earthy material), and melting and casting the copper. Oxide or carbonate ores may be leached with dilute sulfuric acid, to produce a cupric solution from which the copper can be deposited by electrolysis. High-grade oxide and carbonate ores may be reduced by heating with coke mixed with a suitable flux. (A flux is a material, such as limestone, that combines with the silicate minerals of the gangue to form a slag that is liquid at the temperature of the furnace, and can be easily separated from the metal.)

Sulfide ores are smelted by a complex process. Low-grade ores are first concentrated, by a process such as *flotation*. The finely ground ore is treated with a mixture of water and a suitable oil. The oil wets the sulfide minerals, and the water wets the silicate minerals of the gangue. Air is then blown through to produce a froth, which contains the oil and the sulfide minerals; the silicate minerals sink to the bottom.

The concentrate or the rich sulfide ore is then roasted in a furnace through which air is passing. This removes some of the sulfur as sulfur dioxide, and leaves a mixture of Cu_2S, FeO, SiO_2, and other substances. This roasted ore is then mixed with limestone to serve as a flux, and is heated in a furnace. The iron oxide and silica combine with the limestone to form a slag, and the cuprous sulfide melts and can be drawn off. This impure cuprous sulfide is called *matte*. It is then reduced by blowing air through the molten material:

$$Cu_2S + O_2 \longrightarrow SO_2 + 2Cu$$

Some copper oxide is also formed by the blast of air, and this is reduced by stirring the molten metal with poles of green wood. The copper obtained in this way has a characteristic appearance, and is called *blister copper*. It contains about 1% of iron, gold, silver, and other impurities, and is usually refined electrolytically, as described in Section 21-7.

21-2. The Metallurgy of Silver and Gold

The principal ores of silver are *native silver*, Ag; *argentite*, Ag_2S; and *cerargyrite* or horn-silver, AgCl. The **cyanide process** of winning the metal from these ores is widely used. This process involves treating the crushed ore with a solution of sodium cyanide, NaCN, for about two weeks, with thorough aeration to oxidize the native silver. The reactions producing the soluble complex ion $Ag(CN)_2^-$ may be written in the following way:

$$4Ag + 8CN^- + O_2 + 2H_2O \longrightarrow 4Ag(CN)_2^- + 4OH^-$$
$$AgCl + 2CN^- \longrightarrow Ag(CN)_2^- + Cl^-$$
$$Ag_2S + 4CN^- \longrightarrow 2Ag(CN)_2^- + S^{--}$$

The silver is then obtained from the solution by reduction with metallic zinc:

$$Zn + 2Ag(CN)_2^- \longrightarrow 2Ag + Zn(CN)_4^{--}$$

The **amalgamation process** is used for native silver. The ore is treated with mercury, which dissolves the silver. The liquid amalgam is then separated from the gangue and distilled, the mercury collecting in the receiver and the silver remaining in the retort.

Silver is obtained as a by-product in the refining of copper and lead. The sludge from the electrolytic refining of copper may be treated by simple chemical methods to obtain its content of silver and gold. The small amount of silver in lead is obtained by an ingenious method, the *Parkes process.* This involves stirring a small amount (about 1%) of zinc into the molten lead. Liquid zinc is insoluble in liquid lead, and the solubility of silver in liquid zinc is about 3000 times as great as in liquid lead. Hence most of the silver dissolves in the zinc. The zinc-silver phase comes to the top, solidifies as the crucible cools, and is lifted off. The zinc can then be distilled away, leaving the silver. Gold present in the lead is also obtained by this process.

Gold is obtained from its ores, such as gold-bearing quartz, by pulverizing the ore and washing it over plates of copper coated with a layer of amalgam. The gold dissolves in the amalgam, which is then scraped off and separated by distillation. The tailings may then be treated with cyanide solution, and the gold be won from the cyanide solution by electrolysis or treatment with zinc:

$$4Au + 8CN^- + O_2 + 2H_2O \longrightarrow 4Au(CN)_2^- + 4OH^-$$
$$2Au(CN)_2^- + Zn \longrightarrow 2Au + Zn(CN)_4^{--}$$

21-3. The Metallurgy of Zinc, Cadmium, and Mercury

The principal ore of zinc is *sphalerite* or *zinc blende*, ZnS. Less important ores include *zincite*, ZnO; *smithsonite*, $ZnCO_3$; *willemite*, Zn_2SiO_4; *calamine*, $Zn_2SiO_3(OH)_2$; and *franklinite*, Fe_2ZnO_4.

Many ores of zinc are concentrated by flotation before smelting. Sulfide ores and carbonate ores are then converted to oxide by roasting:

$$2ZnS + 3O_2 \longrightarrow 2ZnO + 2SO_2$$
$$ZnCO_3 \longrightarrow ZnO + CO_2$$

The zinc oxide is mixed with carbon and heated in a fire-clay retort to a temperature high enough to vaporize the zinc:

$$ZnO + C \longrightarrow Zn(g) + CO(g)$$

The zinc vapor is condensed in fire-clay receivers. At first the zinc is condensed in the cool condenser as a fine powder, called *zinc dust*, which contains some zinc oxide. After the receiver becomes hot the vapor condenses to a liquid, which is cast in ingots called *spelter*. Spelter contains small amounts of cadmium, iron, lead, and arsenic. It can be purified by careful redistillation.

The zinc oxide can also be reduced by electrolysis. It is dissolved in sulfuric acid, and electrolyzed with aluminum sheets as cathodes. The deposited zinc, which is about 99.95% pure, is stripped off the cathodes, melted, and cast into ingots, for use where pure zinc is needed, as in the production of brass. The sulfuric acid is regenerated in the process, as is seen from the reactions:

Solution of zinc oxide: $ZnO + 2H^+ \longrightarrow Zn^{++} + H_2O$
Cathode reaction: $Zn^{++} + 2e^- \longrightarrow Zn$
Anode reaction: $H_2O \longrightarrow \frac{1}{2}O_2 + 2H^+ + 2e^-$
Over-all reaction: $ZnO \longrightarrow Zn + \frac{1}{2}O_2$

Cadmium is obtained mainly as a by-product in the smelting and refining of zinc; it occurs to the amount of about one percent in many zinc ores. The sulfide of cadmium, CdS, is called *greenockite*. Cadmium is more volatile than zinc, and in the reduction of zinc oxide containing cadmium oxide it is concentrated in the first portions of dust collected in the receivers.

Mercury occurs as the native metal, in small globules of pure mercury, and as crystalline silver amalgam. Its most important ore is the red mineral *cinnabar*, HgS. Cinnabar is smelted simply by heating it in a retort in a stream of air, and condensing the mercury vapor in a receiver:

$$HgS + O_2 \longrightarrow Hg(g) + SO_2(g)$$

21-4. The Metallurgy of Tin and Lead

The principal ore of tin is *cassiterite*, SnO_2, the main deposits of which are in Bolivia and Malaya. The crude ore is ground and washed in a stream of water, which separates the lighter gangue from the heavy cassiterite. The ore is then roasted, to oxidize the sulfides of iron and copper to products that are removed by leaching with water. The purified ore is then mixed with carbon and reduced in a reverberatory furnace. The crude tin produced in this way is resmelted at a gentle heat, and the pure metal flows away from the higher-melting impurities, chiefly compounds of iron and arsenic. Some tin is purified by electrolysis.

The principal ore of lead is *galena*, PbS, which occurs, often in beautiful cubic crystals, in large deposits in the United States, Spain, and Mexico. The ore is first roasted until part of it has been converted into lead oxide, PbO, and lead sulfate, $PbSO_4$. The supply of air to the furnace is then cut off, and the temperature is raised. Metallic lead is then produced by the reactions

$$PbS + 2PbO \longrightarrow 3Pb + SO_2$$

and

$$PbS + PbSO_4 \longrightarrow 2Pb + 2SO_2$$

Some lead is also made by heating galena with scrap iron:

$$PbS + Fe \longrightarrow Pb + FeS$$

Silver is often removed from lead by the Parkes process, described in Section 21-2. Some pure lead is made by electrolytic refining.

21-5. Reduction of Metal Oxides or Halogenides by Strongly Electropositive Metals

Some metals, including titanium, zirconium, hafnium, lanthanum, and the lanthanons, are most conveniently obtained by reaction of their oxides or halogenides with a more electropositive metal. Sodium, potassium, calcium, and aluminum are often used for this purpose. Thus titanium may be made by reduction of titanium tetrachloride by calcium:

$$TiCl_4 + 2Ca \longrightarrow Ti + 2CaCl_2$$

Titanium, zirconium, and hafnium are purified by the decomposition of their tetraiodides on a hot wire. The impure metal is heated with iodine in an evacuated flask, to produce the tetraiodide as a gas:

$$Zr + 2I_2 \longrightarrow ZrI_4$$

The gas comes into contact with a hot filament, where it is decomposed, forming a wire of the purified metal:

$$ZrI_4 \longrightarrow Zr + 2I_2$$

The process of preparing a metal by reduction of its oxide by aluminum is called the *aluminothermic process*. For example, chromium can be prepared by igniting a mixture of powdered chromium(III) oxide and powdered aluminum:

$$Cr_2O_3 + 2Al \longrightarrow Al_2O_3 + 2Cr$$

The heat liberated by this reaction is so great as to produce molten chromium. The aluminothermic process is a convenient way of obtaining a small amount of liquid metal, such as iron for welding.

21-6. The Electrolytic Production of Aluminum

All commerical aluminum is made electrolytically, by a process discovered in 1886 by a young American, Charles M. Hall (1863–1914), and independently, in the same year, by a young Frenchman, P. L. T. Héroult (1863–1914). A carbon-lined iron box, which serves as cathode, contains the electrolyte, which is the molten mineral cryolite, Na_3AlF_6 (or a mixture of AlF_3, NaF, and sometimes CaF_2, to lower the melting point), in which aluminum oxide, Al_2O_3, is dissolved (Figure 21-1). The aluminum oxide is obtained from the ore *bauxite* by a process of purification, which is described below. The anodes in the cell are made of carbon. The passage of the current provides heat enough to keep the electrolyte molten, at about 100°C. The aluminum metal that is produced by the process of electrolysis sinks to the bottom of the cell, and is tapped off. The cathode reaction is

$$Al^{+++} + 3e^- \longrightarrow Al$$

The anode reaction involves the carbon of the electrodes, which is converted into carbon dioxide:

$$C + 2O^{--} \longrightarrow CO_2 + 4e^-$$

The cells operate at about 5 volts potential difference between the electrodes. Bauxite is a mixture of aluminum minerals ($AlHO_2$, $Al(OH)_3$), which

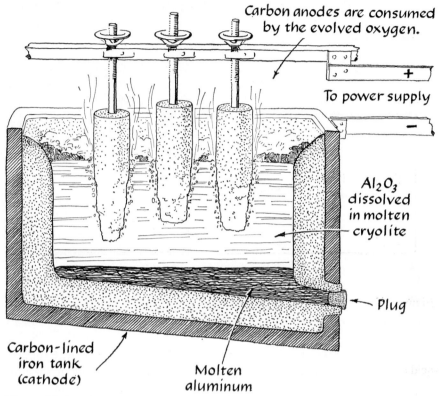

Carbon anodes are consumed by the evolved oxygen.

+

To power supply

−

Al_2O_3 dissolved in molten cryolite

Plug

Carbon-lined iron tank (cathode)

Molten aluminum

Figure **21-1**

The electrolytic production of aluminum.

contains some iron oxide. It is purified by treatment with sodium hydroxide solution, which dissolves hydrated aluminum oxide, as the aluminate ion, $Al(OH)_4{}^-$, but does not dissolve iron oxide:

$$Al(OH)_3 + OH^- \longrightarrow Al(OH)_4{}^-$$

The solution is filtered, and is then acidified with carbon dioxide, which reverses the above reaction, by forming hydrogen carbonate ion, $HCO_3{}^-$:

$$Al(OH)_4{}^- + CO_2 \longrightarrow HCO_3{}^- + Al(OH)_3$$

The precipitated aluminum hydroxide is then dehydrated by ignition (heating to a high temperature), and the purified aluminum oxide is ready for addition to the electrolyte.

21-7. The Electrolytic Refining of Metals

Several metals, won from their ores by either chemical or electrochemical processes, are further refined by electrolytic methods

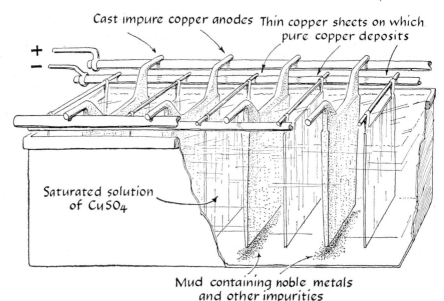

Figure 21-2

The electrolytic refining of copper.

Metallic copper is sometimes obtained by leaching a copper ore with sulfuric acid and then depositing the metal by electrolysis of the copper sulfate solution obtained in this way. Most copper ores, however, are converted into crude copper by chemical reduction, with carbon as the reducing agent. This crude copper is cast into anode plates about $\frac{3}{4}$ inch thick, and is then refined electrolytically.

The process of electrolytic refining of copper is a simple one (Figure 21-2). The anodes of crude copper alternate with cathodes of thin sheets of pure copper coated with graphite, which makes it possible to strip off the deposit. The electrolyte is copper sulfate. As the current passes through, crude copper dissolves from the anodes and a purer copper deposits on the cathodes. Metals below copper in the electromotive-force series, such as gold, silver, and platinum, remain undissolved, and fall to the bottom of the tank as a sludge, from which they can be recovered. More active metals, such as iron, remain in the solution.

21-8. Physical Metallurgy

The foregoing sections have been concerned with that branch of metallurgy usually termed *extractive* or *chemical metallurgy*. It is the oldest systematized branch of metallurgy. One of the earliest comprehensive works on the subject is *De Re Metallica*, written by the German metallurgist Georgius Agricola

(1494–1555) and published in 1556. In recent years increased emphasis has been placed on the study of another branch of metallurgy called *physical metallurgy*. In this branch of metallurgy an attempt is made to explain the physical properties, such as tensile strength, hardness, ductility, electrical and thermal conductivity, and heat capacity, of pure metals and alloys in terms of their atomic and electronic structure. One of the ultimate aims of the physical metallurgist is to be able to design alloys with any desired set of properties.

Mechanical Properties of Metals. Most metals are malleable and ductile. Instead of being smashed into splinters when struck by a hammer, a piece of metal is flattened into a sheet or foil. A crystal of a metal must hence be able to deform itself without breaking.

If a crystal of sodium chloride is deformed in such a way that the ions are moved about one ionic diameter relative to one another, then sodium ions become adjacent to sodium ions and chloride ions to chloride ions, and the repulsion of the ions of like sign causes the crystal to break into pieces. In a metal, however, the atoms are all of the same kind, and any atom can form bonds with any other atom. Moreover, the valence bonds, which resonate easily from one position to another in the crystal, can still form between neighboring atoms even if the crystal is deformed, and accordingly a crystal of a metal remains strong during deformation.

The way in which a crystal of a metal changes its shape is by *slip along glide planes*. For example, the metal zinc has the hexagonal closest packed structure indicated in Figure 20-1. The distance between the hexagonal layers of atoms is somewhat larger than for ideal closest packing—the distance between neighboring zinc atoms in the same hexagonal layer is 2.66 Å, whereas that between atoms in adjacent layers is 2.91 Å. Accordingly, we might expect it to be easy for a hexagonal layer to slip over another hexagonal layer. If a single crystal of zinc is made in the form

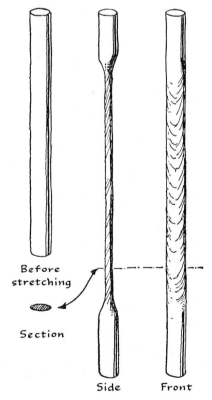

Figure **21-3** *The deformation of a rod of zinc into a ribbon, through slip along glide planes.*

Before
stretching

Section

Side   Front

of a round wire, with the hexagonal layers at an angle, as shown in the upper part of Figure 21-3, and the ends of the wire are pulled, the wire stretches out into a ribbon, through slip along the hexagonal planes, as illustrated on the right side of Figure 21-3. Photomicrographs of a metal that has been subjected to strain often show traces of these glide planes.

The slip along a glide plane does not occur by the simultaneous motion of a whole layer of atoms relative to an adjacent layer. Instead, the atoms move one at a time. There is a flaw in the structure, where an atom is missing. The atom to one side of this flaw (which is called a *dislocation*) moves to occupy the space, and leaves a space where it was; that is, the dislocation moves in the opposite direction to the atom. When the dislocation has moved all the way across the crystal grain, the whole row of atoms has moved, and the lower part of the crystal has slipped one atomic diameter in the direction of the strain. A description of some kinds of dislocations is given below.

Lattice Vacancies. One type of imperfection found in crystals is the *lattice vacancy* or *point* imperfection: an atom is missing at the place in the crystal lattice that is normally occupied by an atom, and the surrounding atoms have moved slightly toward this position. Lattice vacancies are formed by thermal agitation to an extent given by the Boltzmann distribution function (with the number of vacancies per unit volume in the metal about equal to the number of atoms per unit volume in the vapor in equilibrium with the metal). They may also be produced in larger numbers by bombardment of the metal with high-energy particles or x-rays.

Interstitial Atoms. Another type of point defect consists of an extra atom of a metal occupying a position that in the perfect crystal would be vacant. This extra atom may be a foreign atom, usually smaller than the atoms of the metal itself, such as hydrogen, carbon, nitrogen, or oxygen in iron. Larger foreign atoms may substitute for the atoms of the metal itself (see Section 20-8). It is found by experiment that a small amount of impurity in a metal may make it brittle. For example, copper containing sulfur or arsenic is brittle, rather than malleable and ductile. One way in which the foreign atoms may produce brittleness is by interfering with the motion of dislocations through the crystal; when the dislocation reaches a sulfur atom or other foreign atom in the copper crystal, it may be stopped, and the slip may thus be prevented from continuing.

Dislocations. The most important imperfections, so far as the mechanical properties of crystals are concerned, are the various imperfections called dislocations. The ease with which dislocations move through a crystal determine to a large extent its ranges of elastic and plastic deformation under an applied stress and its ultimate yield point—that is, the stress under which the crystal fractures. One kind of dislocation, called an *edge dislocation*, is shown in Figure 21-4. An edge dislocation can be described as involving removal of one-half of a plane of atoms from the crystal.

The *screw dislocation*, shown in Figure 21-5, has an axis that is either right-handed or left-handed. A crystal containing one screw dislocation is not made up of layers of atoms parallel to one another; instead it consists of a single layer of atoms, distorted about the screw axis into a helicoid or spiral ramp.

A dislocation can move through a crystal by a succession of processes, each of which involves the motion of a single atom from one position in the crystal to an adjacent position. The activation energy for this process may be small enough to permit it to occur at a rapid rate, and in consequence plastic deformation of metals under stress can take place.

Many of the mechanical properties can be understood in terms of the motion of dislocations. If a stress is applied in the right way to a metal, the metal bends. When the stress is removed, the metal either returns to its original shape or is permanently deformed. In the first case the dislocations have not moved or have moved in a reversible way; that is, the applied stress has not carried them over any foreign inclusion in the lattice or caused too many of them to collide. In the second case some dislocations have moved irreversibly, so that they do not return to their original positions upon removal of the applied stress. If the applied stress is very large, dislocations will move until many of them become piled up against some barrier, such as a foreign inclusion or the boundary between adjacent crystalline grains. In the region of a dislocation pile-up the applied stress strains the bonds in such a way as to cause failure of the material to begin.

A boundary between crystal grains can serve as a barrier to the motion of dislocations, and

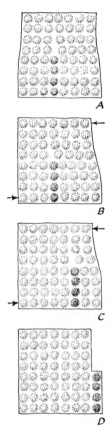

Figure **21-4** (*a*) *An edge dislocation in a metal. The shaded atoms indicate the extra part-layer of atoms.* (*b*) *The crystal grain under stress.* (*c*) *Motion of the dislocation to the right; different atoms (shaded) now constitute the dislocation.* (*d*) *The dislocation has reached the edge of the grain, forming a step; by motion of the dislocation the upper part of the crystal has moved to the left relative to the lower part.*

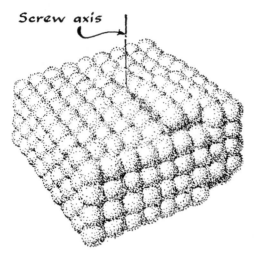

Screw axis

Figure **21-5**
A screw dislocation in a metal.

in this way can decrease the plasticity and increase the hardness of a metal. If a piece of copper is hammered until the large crystal grains are broken up into small crystal grains, the crystal boundaries may interfere with slip by stopping the motion of the dislocations. This is the mechanism of the hardening of copper and other metals by *cold work* (by hammering them or otherwise working them in the cold). Heating the work-hardened metal to the temperature at which recrystallization occurs (growth of the strained small crystals to large unstrained crystals) restores plasticity; this process is called *annealing*. The recrystallization temperature is usually about one-third to one-half of the melting point of the metal (both on the absolute temperature scale).

Pure aluminum is a soft, malleable, and ductile metal. For some purposes an alloy of aluminum that is stronger, tougher, and less ductile is needed. Aluminum alloys of this sort can be made by incorporating small amounts of other metals, such as copper and magnesium. An alloy containing about 4% copper and 0.5% magnesium may strengthen the aluminum through the formation of hard, brittle crystals of the intermetallic compound $MgCu_2$. These minute crystals, interspersed through the crystals of aluminum, can serve to key the glide planes of aluminum so effectively as to improve the mechanical properties of the alloy significantly over those of the pure metal.

EXERCISES

21-1. What is a mineral? What is an ore?

21-2. Describe the amalgamation process of winning gold and silver.

21-3. Write the equations for reaction of the mineral bromyrite, AgBr, with sodium cyanide solution, and the deposition of metallic silver.

21-4. Describe the process of obtaining refined copper from an impure copper sulfide ore, mentioning flotation, matte, and blister copper.

21-5. How are the silver and gold obtained that are present in small amounts in lead ore?

21-6. Give the name and formula of one ore of each of the following metals: zinc, cadmium, mercury, tin, lead, copper, silver, gold.

21-7. What current would need to flow through an electrolytic cell to deposit cadmium at the rate of 10 kg per hour from a $CdSO_4$ solution?

21-8. How much aluminum should be mixed with 1 kg of manganese(IV) oxide, MnO_2, to produce manganese metal?

21-9. Write the equation for the preparation of lanthanum from lanthanum(III) chloride by reduction with potassium. What relative weights of the reactants should be taken?

21-10. Would you think it likely that aluminum could be used instead of potassium in preparing lanthanum? Could calcium be used? (See the electromotive-force series and the electronegativity values, Table 9-1.)

21-11. Uranium has electronegativity 1.7 (Table 9-1). Would you expect, by comparison with iron, zinc, and other metals that are obtained from their oxides by reduction with carbon, that uranium could also be obtained from its oxide, U_3O_8, in this way?

21-12. What weight of carbon would be needed to reduce 100 kg of U_3O_8 to uranium metal?

21-13. Why does the metal lead (m.p. 327°C) remain soft, even when it is hammered— that is, why is lead not hardened by cold work in the way that copper is?

21-14. At 650°C the ratio of the number of vacancies in a crystal of copper to the number of atoms is found by experiment to be about 1×10^{-5}. A study of the statistical theory of vacancies shows that this number is approximately equal to the Boltzmann exponential factor (Section 6-12), with the energy in the exponent equal to the enthalpy of formation of a vacancy. Calculate the value of this enthalpy of formation from the vacancy/atom ratio and compare it with the enthalpy of sublimation of copper, 76 kcal/mole. (Answer: 21 kcal/mole.)

21-15. The observed recrystallization temperatures of cold-worked zinc, aluminum, silver, iron, and tantalum are 15°, 150°, 200°, 450°, and 1020°C, respectively. What is the average value of the ratio of recrystallization temperature to melting point on the absolute temperature scale? What value do you predict for the recrystallization temperature of titanium?

CHAPTER 22

Lithium, Beryllium, Boron, and Silicon,

and Their Congeners

In this chapter we shall discuss the metals and metalloids of groups I, II, III, and IV of the periodic table, and their compounds.

The alkali metals, group I, are the most strongly electropositive elements—the most strikingly metallic. Many of their compounds have been mentioned in earlier chapters. The alkaline-earth metals are also strongly electropositive.

Boron, silicon, and germanium are metalloids, with properties intermediate between those of metals and those of nonmetals. The electric conductivity* of boron, for example, is 1×10^{-6} mho/cm; this value is intermediate between the values for metals (4×10^5 mho/cm for aluminum, for example), and those for nonmetals (2×10^{-13} for diamond, for example). They have a corresponding tendency to form oxygen acids, rather than to serve as cations in salts.

Silicon (from Latin *silex*, flint) is the second element in group IV, and is hence a congener of carbon. Silicon plays an important part in the inorganic world, similar to that played by carbon in the organic world. Most of the rocks that constitute the earth's crust are composed of the silicate minerals, of which silicon is the most important elementary constituent.

The importance of carbon in organic chemistry results from its ability to form carbon-carbon bonds, permitting complex molecules, with the most varied properties, to exist. The importance of silicon in the inorganic world results from a different property of the element—a few compounds are known

---

* The electric conductivity, in mho/cm, is the current in amperes flowing through a rod with cross-section 1 cm² when there is an electric potential difference between the ends of the rod of 1 volt per cm length of the rod.

in which silicon atoms are connected to one another by covalent bonds, but these compounds are relatively unimportant. The characteristic feature of the silicate minerals is the existence of chains and more complex structures (layers, three-dimensional frameworks) in which the silicon atoms are not bonded directly to one another but are connected by oxygen atoms. The nature of these structures is described briefly in later sections of this chapter.

22-1. The Electronic Structures of Lithium, Beryllium, Boron, and Silicon and Their Congeners

The electronic structures of the elements of groups I, II, III, and IV are given in Table 22-1. The distribution of the electrons among the orbitals is

Table **22-1**

The Electronic Structures of the Elements of Groups I, II, III, and IV

Z	ELEMENT	K	L		M			N				O			P	
		$1s$	$2s$	$2p$	$3s$	$3p$	$3d$	$4s$	$4p$	$4d$	$4f$	$5s$	$5p$	$5d$	$6s$	$6p$
3	Li	2	1													
4	Be	2	2													
5	B	2	2	1												
6	C	2	2	2												
11	Na	2	2	6	1											
12	Mg	2	2	6	2											
13	Al	2	2	6	2	1										
14	Si	2	2	6	2	2										
19	K	2	2	6	2	6		1								
20	Ca	2	2	6	2	6		2								
21	Sc	2	2	6	2	6	1	2								
32	Ge	2	2	6	2	6	10	2	2							
37	Rb	2	2	6	2	6	10	2	6			1				
38	Sr	2	2	6	2	6	10	2	6			2				
39	Y	2	2	6	2	6	10	2	6	1		2				
50	Sn	2	2	6	2	6	10	2	6	10		2	2			
55	Cs	2	2	6	2	6	10	2	6	10		2	6		1	
56	Ba	2	2	6	2	6	10	2	6	10		2	6		2	
57	La	2	2	6	2	6	10	2	6	10		2	6	1	2	
82	Pb	2	2	6	2	6	10	2	6	10	14	2	6	10	2	2

the same in this table as in the energy-level chart, Figure 7-4, with one exception: the normal state of the lanthanum atom has been found by the study of the spectrum of lanthanum to correspond to the presence of one electron in the $5d$ orbital, rather than in the $4f$ orbital, as indicated in the energy-level chart.

The Russell-Saunders symbol for lithium and its congeners in the normal state is $^2S_{1/2}$, that of beryllium and its congeners is $^1S_0$, that of boron and its congeners is $^2P_{1/2}$, and that of carbon and its congeners is $^3P_0$.

The elements of group I have one more electron than the preceding noble gas, those of group II have two more, and those of group III have three more. The outermost shell of each of these noble-gas atoms is an octet of electrons, two electrons in the s orbital and six in the three p orbitals of the shell. The one, two, or three outermost electrons of the metallic elements are easily removed with formation of the cations Li^+, Na^+, K^+, Rb^+, Cs^+, Be^{++}, Mg^{++}, Ca^{++}, Sr^{++}, Ba^{++}, Al^{+++}, Sc^{+++}, Y^{+++}, and La^{+++}. Each of these elements forms only one principal series of compounds, in which it has oxidation number $+1$ for group I, $+2$ for group II, or $+3$ for group III. The metalloid boron also forms compounds in which its oxidation number is $+3$, but the cation B^{+++} is not stable.

Whereas carbon is adjacent to boron in the sequence of the elements, and also silicon to aluminum, the succeeding elements of group IV of the periodic table, germanium, tin, and lead, are widely separated from the corresponding elements of group III, scandium, yttrium, and lanthanum. Germanium is separated from scandium by the ten elements of the iron transition series, tin from yttrium by the ten elements of the palladium transition series, and lead from lanthanum by the ten elements of the platinum transition series, and also the fourteen lanthanons.*

Each of the elements of group IV has four valence electrons, which occupy s and p orbitals of the outermost shell. The maximum oxidation number of these elements is $+4$. All of the compounds of silicon correspond to this oxidation number. Germanium, tin, and lead form two series of compounds, representing oxidation number $+4$ and oxidation number $+2$, the latter being more important than the former for lead.

22-2. Radius Ratio, Ligancy, and the Properties of Substances

Some of the properties of substances can be discussed in a useful way in terms of the sizes of ions or atoms. Many of the substances mentioned in the later sections of this chapter and in the following chapters are compounds of metals, with small electronegativity, and nonmetals, with large electronegativity. The bonds between these atoms may have a sufficiently large amount of ionic character (Section 9-11) to justify the discussion of the substance as composed of cations and anions. Such a discussion may be helpful even for substances in which the bonds have a large amount of covalent character.

* There is some disagreement among chemists about nomenclature of the groups of the periodic system. We have described the transition elements as coming between groups III and IV in the long periods of the periodic table. An alternative that has found about as wide acceptance is to place them between groups II and III. See footnote, Section 20-3.

For example, let us consider again the fluorides of the elements of the second short period of the periodic table (see Section 16-6). Their formulas, melting points, boiling points, heats of fusion, and heats of vaporization (or sublimation) are the following:

	NaF	MgF₂	AlF₃	SiF₄	PF₅	SF₆
m.p.	995°	1263°	>1257°	−90°	−94°	−51°C
b.p.	1704°	2227°	1257°*	−95°*	−85°	−64°*
Heat of fusion	7.8	13.9	—	1.69	2.8	1.20 kcal/mole
Heat of vaporization	50	65	77†	4.46‡	4.1	4.08 kcal/mole

* Temperature of sublimation of crystal at 1 atm pressure.
† Heat of sublimation of crystal.
‡ Heat of vaporization at 1.74 atm.

The first three substances are crystalline solids at room temperature, with high melting and boiling points and large heats of fusion and vaporization, and the other three are gases at room temperature, with low melting and boiling points and small heats of fusion and vaporization. The pronounced change in properties between AlF_3 and SiF_4 cannot be attributed in an obvious way to the change in oxidation number, composition (number of fluorine atoms per second-row atom), or electronegativity of the second-row atom. It can, however, be accounted for by consideration of the relative sizes of the atoms.

In Figure 22-1 there are shown several ways of arranging two or more large anions, such as the fluoride ion, around a cation. For each arrangement there is given the ratio of radius of cation to radius of anion (the *radius ratio*)

Figure **22-1**

Triangular, tetrahedral, octahedral, and cubic arrangements of anions around a certain cation.

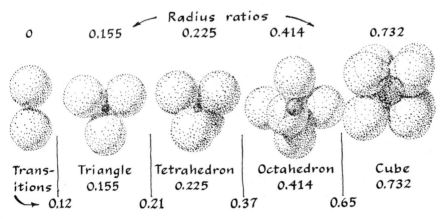

corresponding to closest packing; that is, contact of anions with one another as well as with the cation, both anions and cation being considered to be spheres.

Thus for the planar triangular structure MX_3 the distances $r_M + r_X$ and $2r_X$ have the relative values $1:\sqrt{3}$, from which we calculate $r_M/r_X = 2/\sqrt{3} - 1 = 0.155$. In a similar way the values 0.225 for ligancy 4 (a tetrahedron of anions about the cation), 0.414 for ligancy 6 (octahedron), and 0.645 for ligancy 8 (cube) are obtained.

Of substances MX_2, carbon dioxide (radius ratio 0.11, Table 8-3) forms crystals containing CO_2 molecules, silicon dioxide (radius ratio 0.29) forms crystals with tetrahedral coordination of four oxygen ions about each silicon ion (Figure 22-8), magnesium fluoride (radius ratio 0.48) and stannic oxide (radius ratio 0.51) form crystals with octahedral coordination of six anions around each cation (the rutile structure, Figure 22-2), and calcium fluoride (radius ratio 0.73) forms crystals with cubic coordination of eight anions around each cation (the fluorite structure, Figure 22-3). The ligancy (coordination number) increases with increase in the radius ratio, as indicated in Figure 22-1.

Figure **22-2** *The structure of magnesium fluoride; this substance has high melting point and boiling point. (This structure is usually called the rutile structure; it is the structure of the mineral rutile, TiO₂.)*

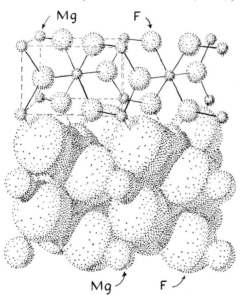

Mg   F

Mg   F

The increase in stability (decrease in energy) with increase in ligancy is easy to understand. Let us consider two ionic molecules, M^+X^-, with M^+—X^- distance r. The electrostatic interaction energy of the electric charge $+e$ and that $-e$ in one molecule is $-e^2/r$, and for two molecules it is $-2e^2/r$. Now if the ligancy changes from 1 to 2, through the formation of a square,

$$
\begin{array}{ccc}
M^+ & \!\!\!—\!\!\! & X^- \\
| & & | \\
X^- & \!\!\!—\!\!\! & M^+
\end{array}
$$

and if the M^+—X^- distance retains the value r, each of the four M^+—X^- interactions contributes $-e^2/r$ and each of the two repulsions across the diagonals contributes $e^2/(\sqrt{2}\ r)$. The total electrostatic energy for the square is then $(-4 + \sqrt{2})e^2/r = -2.59e^2/r$. The square arrangement is thus 29% more stable than two separate molecules, with respect to the electrostatic interactions.

Similar calculations show that, for constant cation-anion distance, the rutile structure (ligancy 6) is 8% more stable than the quartz structure (ligancy 4), and the fluorite structure (ligancy 8) is 5% more stable than the rutile structure.

If, however, the radius ratio is less than the value given in Figure 22-1, the anions come into contact with one another, the cation-anion distance becomes larger than the contact distance, and the structure becomes unstable relative to the structure with smaller ligancy. The approximate values of the radius ratio at which the transitions occur are shown in Figure 22-1.

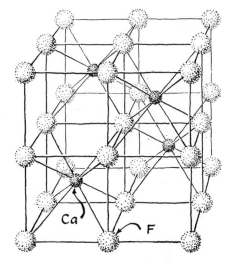

Figure **22-3** *The structure of the fluorite crystal, CaF₂.*

Germanium dioxide is an interesting example. Its radius ratio (Table 8-3) is $0.53 \text{ Å}/1.40 \text{ Å} = 0.38$. This value is very near the transition value, 0.37, from tetrahedral to octahedral coordination, and GeO_2 is in fact dimorphous, with one crystalline form having the quartz structure (ligancy 4) and the other having the rutile structure (ligancy 6).

We can now discuss the melting points and boiling points of the second-row fluorides. The ionic radii of the cations (the radius of F^- is 1.36 Å) and the radius ratios are the following:

	NaF	MgF₂	AlF₃	SiF₄	PF₅	SF₆
Radius of cation	0.95 Å	0.65 Å	0.50 Å	0.41 Å	0.34 Å	0.29 Å
Radius ratio	0.70	0.48	0.37	0.30	0.25	0.21
Expected ligancy of cation	6 or 8	6	4 or 6	4	4	4 or 3

We see that for silicon tetrafluoride the expected ligancy of silicon, 4, corresponds exactly to the formula of the molecule, SiF_4. Hence we conclude that in the crystal and liquid as well as the gas the substance consists of SiF_4 molecules (Figure 16-5). The structure of the crystal as determined by x-ray diffraction is shown in Figure 22-4. The crystal is an arrangement of tetrahedral SiF_4 molecules held together only by the van der Waals forces discussed in Section 16-6. The heat of fusion and heat of vaporization are correspondingly small, and the substance accordingly melts and boils (in fact, sublimes at 1 atm pressure) at a low temperature. For PF_5 and SF_6 the expected ligancy

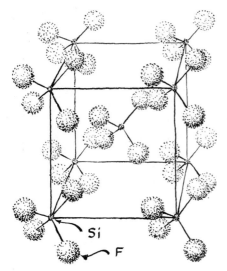

Figure **22-4** *The structure of a molecular crystal, silicon tetrafluoride. The tetrahedral SiF₄ molecules are arranged in a body-centered cubic arrangement.*

is less than the number of fluorine atoms. There is accordingly some strain in the molecules—the fluorine atoms in contact with one another are under compression and the P—F and S—F bonds are stretched; but the crystals, like those of SiF_4, consist of molecules held together only by van der Waals forces, and the melting and boiling points and heats of fusion and vaporization are close to those of silicon tetrafluoride.

In AlF_3, on the other hand, the expected ligancy of aluminum is 4 or 6, and the x-ray diffraction study of the crystals has shown the ligancy to be 6. Each aluminum atom is surrounded octahedrally by six fluorine atoms, and each fluorine atom is ligated to two aluminum atoms.* The crystal MgF_2 has the rutile structure (Figure 22-2) corresponding to the expected ligancy 6 for magnesium and with each fluorine atom ligated to three magnesium atoms, and NaF has the sodium chloride structure (Figure 4-2), in which both sodium and fluorine have ligancy 6.

Fusion and vaporization of these three substances involves not just overcoming the van der Waals attractive forces, as for SiF_4, but rather the breaking of some Al—F, Mg—F, or Na—F bonds. For this reason the heats of fusion and vaporization are large and the melting points and boiling points are high.

The foregoing discussion has been based on the relative sizes of cations and anions. A closely parallel discussion could be presented based on covalent bond radii and van der Waals radii of atoms (Section 9-15). The van der Waals radius of the fluorine atom, 1.35 Å (Table 9-4) is nearly equal to the ionic radius of the fluoride ion, 1.36 Å, and the sums of covalent radii are approximately equal to the corresponding sums of ionic radii.

The Electrostatic Valence Rule. The description of a crystal or molecule in terms of cations and anions permits us to describe the bonds in a simple and

---

* The ligancy 6 rather than 4 for aluminum in the crystal is seen to be reasonable from the following argument. With ligancy 4 for aluminum, the composition AlF_3 would require an average $\frac{4}{3}$ aluminum atoms about each fluorine atom; that is, some fluorine atoms ligated to one aluminum atom and some to two. Such a structure would be less stable than the one with ligancy 6 for aluminum.

useful way. The strength of each of the bonds formed by a cation can be defined as the electric charge of the cation divided by its ligancy. Thus in the crystal AlF_3, in which Al^{3+} has ligancy 6 (has six F^- ions coordinated about it), each of the six bonds formed by the aluminum ion has strength $\frac{3}{6} = \frac{1}{2}$. In the molecule SiF_4 each of the four bonds formed by SiF_4 has strength $\frac{4}{4} = 1$.

The electrostatic valence rule states that *the most stable structures of crystals and molecules are those in which the sum of the strengths of the bonds reaching each anion is just equal to its negative charge.*

For example, in the AlF_3 crystal each F^- is held to Al^{3+} by two bonds with strength $\frac{1}{2}$, and in the SiF_4 molecule it is held to Si^{4+} by one bond with strength 1; in each case the sum of the bond strengths equals the negative charge of the fluoride ion.*

Many of the properties of substances can be explained by the consideration of the relative sizes of ions or atoms, as illustrated above and in the following examples. Structural inorganic chemistry is, however, a new subject, and as yet far from precise. You may find it worth while to attempt to explain in terms of structure some of the properties of substances mentioned in later sections of this chapter and in the following chapters, but you must not become discouraged if you are unsuccessful. The fault may lie not with you but with the chemists of the present generation and earlier generations, who have not yet succeeded in the task of developing a really powerful theory of structural inorganic chemistry. If you become a chemist, you yourself may make a major contribution to the solution of this problem.

Example 1. Magnesium oxide and sodium fluoride have the same crystal structure, that of sodium chloride (ligancy 6). But their melting points are very different: 2800°C for MgO and 995°C for NaF. Explain.

Solution. In NaF the Na^+—F^- bonds have strength $\frac{1}{6}$, and in MgO the Mg^{++}—O^{--} bonds have strength $\frac{1}{3}$, twice as great. Because of the similarity in structure of the two substances, we may assume that the process of melting involves breaking the same fraction of the bonds. A higher temperature would be needed to break the stronger bonds in MgO than to break the weaker bonds in NaF; hence the melting point of MgO is higher than that of NaF.

Example 2. The mineral periclase, MgO, has hardness 5.8 on the Mohs scale (Section 10-2), whereas villaumite, NaF, has much smaller hardness, 3.5. Explain.

Solution. As discussed in the answer to Example 1, the bonds in MgO are stronger than those in NaF. In scratching a crystal to determine its hardness on the Mohs scale some of the bonds are broken, and for two crystals with the same structure the process of scratching can be expected

---

* These arguments can also be presented in terms of covalent bonds with partial ionic character.

to involve breaking the same number of bonds; hence for these two crystals the one with the stronger bonds should have the greater hardness.

Example 3.   The crystals NaF, NaCl, and KCl, with the same structure and the same ionic valences, have Mohs hardness 3.5, 2.5, and 2.0, respectively. Explain.

Solution.   The bond strengths (ratio of cation charge to ligancy) have the same value, $\frac{1}{6}$, for the three crystals, but the electrostatic forces become weaker in the sequence NaF, NaCl, KCl because the interionic distances (cation-anion bond lengths) increase: 2.31 Å, 2.76 Å, 3.14 Å (sum of radii, Table 8-3). Hence the crystals decrease in hardness in this sequence.

The Mohs hardness values are reliable only to about ±0.3. Note that the expression $19/(r_+ + r_-)^2$ gives the values 3.56, 2.50, and 1.93, respectively, for the three substances. The use of the inverse square might be supported by an argument based on Coulomb's law.

Example 4.   The boiling (subliming) point of AlF_3, 1257°C, is much lower than those of NaF, 1704°C, and MgF_2, 2227°C. Both the increase in charge of the cation and the decrease in interionic distance (bond length) should lead to an increase in boiling point. What is the explanation?

Solution.   It was pointed out above in the text that the value of the radius ratio for Al^{+++} and F^-, 0.37, is near to the transition value between ligancy 6 and ligancy 4, and that ligancy 6 is preferred for the AlF_3 crystal because it permits all the fluoride ions to be bonded in the same way. Aluminum chloride exists in the gas phase as molecules Al_2Cl_6, with the structure of two tetrahedra sharing an edge:

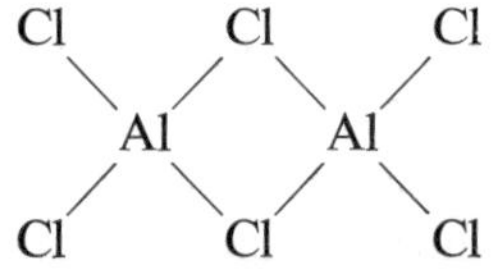

We may assume that aluminum fluoride also forms dimers Al_2F_6 with this structure, and that the stability of these molecules in the gas phase leads to the low boiling point, relative to MgF_2 and NaF.

22-3.   The Alkali Metals and Their Compounds

The elements of the first group—lithium, sodium, potassium, rubidium, and cesium*—are soft, silvery-white metals with great chemical reactivity.

---

* The sixth alkali metal, francium (Fr), element 87, has been obtained only in minute quantities, and no information has been published about its properties.

These metals are excellent conductors of electricity. Some of their physical properties are given in Table 22-2. It can be seen from the table that they melt at low temperatures—four of the five metals melt below the boiling point of water. Lithium, sodium, and potassium are lighter than water. The vapors of the alkali metals are mainly monatomic, with a small concentration of diatomic molecules (Li_2, etc.), in which the two atoms are held together by a covalent bond.

Table **22-2**

Some Properties of the Alkali Metals

	Z	MELTING POINT	BOILING POINT	DENSITY (g/cm^3)	METALLIC RADIUS*	IONIC RADIUS†	BOND ENERGY‡
Li	3	186°C	1336°C	0.530	1.55 Å	0.60 Å	27.5
Na	11	97.5°	880°	.963	1.90	.95	18.0
K	19	62.3°	760°	.857	2.35	1.33	12.2
Rb	37	38.5°	700°	1.594	2.48	1.48	11.4
Cs	55	28.5°	670°	1.992	2.67	1.69	10.7

  * For ligancy 12.
  † For singly charged cation (Na^+, for example), with ligancy 6, as in the sodium chloride crystal.
  ‡ Bond energy of $M_2(g)$, in kcal/mole.

The alkali metals are made by electrolysis of the molten hydroxides or chlorides (Chapter 8). Because of their reactivity, the metals must be kept in an inert atmosphere or under oil. The metals are useful chemical reagents in the laboratory, and they find industrial use (especially sodium) in the manufacture of organic chemicals, dyestuffs, and lead tetraethyl (a constituent of "ethyl gasoline"). Sodium is used in sodium-vapor lamps, and, because of its large heat conductivity, in the stems of valves of airplane engines, to conduct heat away from the valve heads. Cesium is used in vacuum tubes, to increase electron emission from cathodes.

Compounds of sodium are readily identified by the yellow color that they give to a flame. Lithium causes a carmine coloration of the flame, and potassium, rubidium, and cesium cause a violet coloration. These elements may be tested for in the presence of sodium by use of a blue filter of cobalt glass.

The Discovery of the Alkali Metals. The alchemists had recognized many compounds of sodium and potassium. The metals themselves were isolated by Sir Humphry Davy in 1807 by electrolyzing their hydroxides. Compounds of lithium were recognized as containing a new element by the Swedish chemist Johan August Arfwedson, in 1817. The metal itself was first isolated in 1855.

Rubidium and cesium were discovered in 1860 by the German chemist Robert Wilhelm Bunsen (1811–1899), by use of the spectroscope. Bunsen and the physicist Kirchhoff had invented the spectroscope just the year before, and cesium was the first element to be discovered by the use of this instrument. The spectrum of cesium contains two bright lines in the blue region and the spectrum of rubidium contains two bright lines in the extreme red (Section 25-5).

Compounds of Lithium. Lithium occurs in the minerals* *spodumene*, $LiAlSi_2O_6$, *amblygonite*, $LiAlPO_4F$, and *lepidolite*, $K_2Li_3Al_5Si_6O_{20}F_4$. Lithium chloride, $LiCl$, is made by fusing (melting) a mineral containing lithium with barium chloride, $BaCl_2$, and extracting the fusion with water. It is used in the preparation of other compounds of lithium.

Compounds of lithium have found use in the manufacture of glass and of glazes for dishes and porcelain objects.

Compounds of Sodium. The most important compound of sodium is sodium chloride (common salt), $NaCl$. It crystallizes as colorless cubes, with melting point 801°C, and it has a characteristic salty taste. It occurs in seawater to the extent of 3%, and in solid deposits and concentrated brines (salt solutions) that are pumped from wells. Many million tons of the substance are obtained from these sources every year. It is used mainly for the preparation of other compounds of sodium and of chlorine, as well as of sodium metal and chlorine gas. Blood plasma and other body fluids contain about 0.9 g of sodium chloride per 100 ml.

Sodium hydroxide (caustic soda), $NaOH$, is a white hygroscopic (water-attracting) solid, which dissolves readily in water. Its solutions have a smooth, soapy feeling, and are very corrosive to the skin (this is the meaning of "caustic" in the name caustic soda). Sodium hydroxide is made either by the electrolysis of sodium chloride solution or by the action of calcium hydroxide, $Ca(OH)_2$, on sodium carbonate, Na_2CO_3:

$$Na_2CO_3 + Ca(OH)_2 \longrightarrow CaCO_3 + 2NaOH$$

Calcium carbonate is insoluble, and precipitates out during this reaction, leaving the sodium hydroxide in solution. Sodium hydroxide is a useful laboratory reagent and a very important industrial chemical. It is used in industry in the manufacture of soap, the refining of petroleum, and the manufacture of paper, textiles, rayon and cellulose film, and many other products. The sodium carbonates have been discussed in Chapter 10, and many other sodium salts have been mentioned in other chapters.

Compounds of Potassium. Potassium chloride, KCl, forms colorless cubic crystals, resembling those of sodium chloride. There are very large deposits

---

* Only specialists try to remember complicated formulas, such as that of lepidolite.

of potassium chloride, together with other salts, at Stassfurt, Germany, and near Carlsbad, New Mexico. Potassium chloride is also obtained from Searles Lake in the Mojave Desert in California.

Potassium hydroxide, KOH, is a strongly alkaline substance, with properties similar to those of sodium hydroxide. Other important salts of potassium, which resemble the corresponding salts of sodium, are potassium sulfate, K_2SO_4, potassium carbonate, K_2CO_3, and potassium hydrogen carbonate, $KHCO_3$.

Potassium hydrogen tartrate (*cream of tartar*), $KHC_4H_4O_6$, is a constituent of grape juice; sometimes crystals of the substance form in grape jelly. It is used in making baking powder.

The principal use of potassium compounds is in *fertilizers*. Plant fluids contain large amounts of potassium ion, concentrated from the soil, and potassium salts must be present in the soil in order for plants to grow. A fertilizer containing potassium sulfate or some other salt of potassium must be used if the soil becomes depleted in this element.

The compounds of rubidium and cesium resemble those of potassium closely. They do not have any important uses.

Enthalpy of Formation of Compounds of the Alkali Metals. Values of the enthalpy of formation of some compounds of the alkali metals are given in Table 22-3. These values with their signs changed are the heats evolved on formation of the compounds from the elementary substances in their standard states.

Table **22-3**

Standard Enthalpy of Formation of Compounds of Alkali Metals at 25°C (kcal/mole)

	M = Li	Na	K	Rb	Cs
$M(g)$	37.07	25.98	21.51	20.51	18.83
$M^+(g)$	162.86	146.02	123.07	118.30	110.08
$M^+(aq)$*	−66.55	−57.28	−60.04	−58.9	−59.2
$M_2(g)$	47.6	33.97	30.8	29.6	27.0
$M_2O(c)$	−142.4	−99.4	−86.4	−78.9	−75.9
$MH(g)$	30.7	29.88	30.0	33	29.0
$MH(c)$	−21.61	−13.7	−13.6		
$MF(c)$	−146.3	−136.0	−134.46	−131.28	−126.9
$MCl(c)$	−97.70	−98.23	−104.18	−102.91	−103.5
$MBr(c)$	−83.72	−86.03	−93.73	−93.03	−94.3
$MI(c)$	−64.79	−68.84	−78.31	−78.5	−80.5
$M_2S(c)$		−89.2	−100	−83.2	−81.1
$M_2Se(c)$	−91.1	−63.0	−79.3		
$M_2Te(c)$		−84.0			

* Relative to assumed value 0 for $H^+(aq)$.

The small values of the electronegativity of the alkali metals (0.7 to 1.0, Table 9-1) are reflected in the large values of the heats of formation of their compounds with the nonmetallic elements. These values (127 to 146 kcal/mole for fluorides, 98 to 104 kcal/mole for chlorides, etc.) are in rough agreement with the values calculated with use of the electronegativity expression, Equation 1 of Chapter 9.

The difference in enthalpy of formation of $MH(g)$ and $MH(c)$ is the heat of sublimation of the crystal. For the alkali hydrides it is a large quantity of energy—for LiH its value is $30.7 - (-21.61) = 52.3$ kcal/mole. This value is far larger than the van der Waals energy of attraction of molecules LiH, and we are required to conclude that the crystal is not a molecular crystal, but is instead an ionic crystal, with structure similar to that of the alkali halogenides. The alkali hydrides have been shown by x-ray diffraction to contain the hydride ion, H^-; they have the sodium chloride crystal structure, with ligancy 6 for M^+ and H^-. On electrolysis of the molten hydrides molecular hydrogen is liberated at the anode.

22-4. The Alkaline-earth Metals and Their Compounds

The metals of group II of the periodic table—beryllium, magnesium, calcium, strontium, barium, and radium—are called the alkaline-earth metals. Some of their properties are listed in Table 22-4. These metals are much

Table **22-4**

Some Properties of the Alkaline-earth Metals

SYMBOL	ATOMIC NUMBER	ATOMIC WEIGHT	MELTING POINT*	DENSITY (g/cm^3)	METALLIC RADIUS	IONIC RADIUS†
Be	4	9.0122	1350°C	1.86	1.12 Å	0.31 Å
Mg	12	24.312	651°	1.75	1.60	.65
Ca	20	40.08	810°	1.55	1.97	.99
Sr	38	87.62	800°	2.60	2.15	1.13
Ba	56	137.34	850°	3.61	2.22	1.35
Ra	88	226.04	960°	(4.45)‡	(2.46)‡	

* The boiling points of these metals are uncertain; they are about 600° higher than the melting points.

† For doubly charged cation with ligancy 6; Section 8-4.

‡ Estimated.

harder and less reactive than the alkali metals. The compounds of all the alkaline-earth metals are similar in composition; they all form oxides MO, hydroxides $M(OH)_2$, carbonates MCO_3, sulfates MSO_4, etc. (M = Be, Mg, Ca, Sr, Ba, or Ra).

A Note on the Alkaline-earth Family. The early chemists gave the name "earth" to many nonmetallic substances. Magnesium oxide and calcium oxide were found to have an alkaline reaction, and hence were called the *alkaline earths*. The metals themselves (magnesium, calcium, strontium, and barium) were isolated in 1808 by Humphry Davy. Beryllium was discovered in the mineral beryl ($Be_3Al_2Si_6O_{18}$) in 1798 and was isolated in 1828.

Beryllium. Beryllium is a light, silvery white metal, which can be made by electrolysis of a fused mixture of beryllium chloride, $BeCl_2$, and sodium chloride. The metal is used for making windows for x-ray tubes (x-rays readily penetrate elements with low atomic number, and beryllium metal has the best mechanical properties of the very light elements). It is also used as a constituent of special alloys. About 2% of beryllium in copper produces a hard alloy especially suited for use in springs.

The principal ore of beryllium is *beryl*, $Be_3Al_2Si_6O_{18}$. *Emeralds* are beryl crystals containing traces of chromium, which give them a green color. *Aquamarine* is a bluish-green variety of beryl.

The compounds of beryllium have little special value, except that beryllium oxide, BeO, is used in the uranium reactors in which plutonium is made from uranium (Chapter 30).

Compounds of beryllium are very poisonous. Even the dust of the powdered metal or its oxides may cause very serious illness.

Magnesium. Magnesium metal is made by electrolysis of fused magnesium chloride, and also by the reduction of magnesium oxide by carbon or by ferrosilicon (an alloy of iron and silicon). Except for calcium and the alkali metals, magnesium is the lightest metal known; and it finds use in lightweight alloys, such as *magnalium* (10% magnesium, 90% aluminum).

Magnesium reacts with boiling water, to form magnesium hydroxide, $Mg(OH)_2$, an alkaline substance:

$$Mg + 2H_2O \longrightarrow Mg(OH)_2 + H_2$$

The metal burns in air with a bright white light, to form magnesium oxide, MgO, the old name of which is *magnesia:*

$$2Mg + O_2 \longrightarrow 2MgO$$

Flashlight powder is a mixture of magnesium powder and an oxidizing agent.

Magnesium oxide suspended in water is used in medicine (as "milk of magnesia"), for neutralizing excess acid in the stomach and as a laxative. Magnesium sulfate, "Epsom salt," $MgSO_4 \cdot 7H_2O$, is used as a cathartic.

Magnesium carbonate, $MgCO_3$, occurs in nature as the mineral *magnesite*. It is used as a basic lining for copper converters and open-hearth steel furnaces (Chapter 24).

Calcium.   Metallic calcium is made by the electrolysis of fused calcium chloride, $CaCl_2$. The metal is silvery white in color, and is somewhat harder than lead. It reacts with water, and burns in air when ignited, forming a mixture of calcium oxide, CaO, and calcium nitride, Ca_3N_2.

Calcium has a number of practical uses—as a deoxidizer (substance removing oxygen) for iron and steel and for copper and copper alloys, as a constituent of lead alloys (metal for bearings, or the sheath for electric cables) and of aluminum alloys, and as a reducing agent for making other metals from their oxides.

Calcium reacts with cold water to form calcium hydroxide, $Ca(OH)_2$, and burns readily in air, when ignited, to produce calcium oxide, CaO.

Calcium sulfate occurs in nature as the mineral *gypsum*, $CaSO_4 \cdot 2H_2O$. Gypsum is a white substance, which is used commerically for fabrication into wallboard, and conversion into *plaster of Paris*. When gypsum is heated a

Table **22-5**

  Standard Enthalpy of Formation of Compounds of
  Alkaline-earth Metals at 25°C (kcal/mole)

	M = Be	Mg	Ca	Sr	Ba
M(g)	76.63	35.9	46.04	39.2	41.96
M$^+$(g)	293.05	213.66	188.46	171.96	163.58
M^{++}(g)	714.39	561.79	463.64	427.75	395.71
M^{++}(aq)*	−93	−110.41	−129.77	−130.38	−128.67
MO(c)	−146.0	−143.84	−151.9	−141.1	−133.4
MF$_2$(c)		−263.5	−290.3	−290.3	−286.9
MCl$_2$(c)	−122.3	−153.40	−190.0	−198.0	−205.56
MBr$_2$(c)	−88.4	−123.7	−161.3	−171.1	−180.4
MI$_2$(c)	−50.6	−86.0	−127.8	−135.5	−144.0
MS(c)	−55.9	−83.0	−115.3	−113	−116
MSe(c)			−74.7	−78.7	−74.2
MTe(c)		−50			

  * Relative to assumed value 0 for H$^+$(aq).

little above 100°C it loses three-quarters of its water of crystallization, forming the powdered substance $CaSO_4 \cdot \frac{1}{2}H_2O$, which is called plaster of Paris. (Heating to a higher temperature produces anhydrous $CaSO_4$, which reacts more slowly with water.) When mixed with water the small crystals of plaster of Paris dissolve and then crystallize as long needles of $CaSO_4 \cdot 2H_2O$. These needles grow together, and form a solid mass, with the shape into which the wet powder was molded.

Strontium.   The principal minerals of strontium are strontium sulfate, *celesite*, $SrSO_4$, and strontium carbonate, *strontianite*, $SrCO_3$.

Strontium nitrate, $Sr(NO_3)_2$, is made by dissolving strontium carbonate in nitric acid. It is mixed with carbon and sulfur to make red fire for use in fireworks, signal shells, and railroad flares. Strontium chlorate, $Sr(ClO_3)_2$, is used for the same purpose. The other compounds of strontium are similar to the corresponding compounds of calcium. Strontium metal has no practical uses.

Barium. The metal barium has no significant use. Its principal compounds are barium sulfate, $BaSO_4$, which is only very slightly soluble in water and dilute acids, and barium chloride, $BaCl_2 \cdot 2H_2O$, which is soluble in water. Barium sulfate occurs in nature as the mineral *barite*.

Barium, like all elements with large atomic number, absorbs x-rays strongly, and a thin paste of barium sulfate and water is swallowed as a "barium meal" to obtain contrasting x-ray photographs and fluoroscopic views of the alimentary tract. The solubility of the substance is so small that the poisonous action of most barium compounds is avoided.

Barium nitrate, $Ba(NO_3)_2$, and barium chlorate, $Ba(ClO_3)_2$, are used for producing green fire in fireworks.

Radium. Compounds of radium are closely similar to those of barium. The only important property of radium and its compounds is its radioactivity, which has been mentioned in Chapter 3 and will be discussed further in Chapter 30.

22-5. Boron

Boron can be made by heating potassium tetrafluoroborate, KBF_4, with sodium in a crucible lined with magnesium oxide:

$$KBF_4 + 3Na \longrightarrow KF + 3NaF + B$$

The element can also be made by heating boric oxide, B_2O_3, with powdered magnesium:

$$B_2O_3 + 3Mg \longrightarrow 3MgO + 2B$$

Boron forms brilliant transparent crystals, nearly as hard as diamond. Some of its properties are given in Table 22-6.

Boron forms a compound with carbon, B_4C. This substance, **boron carbide,** is the hardest substance known next to diamond, and it has found extensive use as an abrasive and for the manufacture of small mortars and pestles for grinding very hard substances. The cubic form of boron nitride, BN, with a tetrahedral structure like that of diamond, has about the same hardness.

Boric acid, H_3BO_3, occurs in the volcanic steam jets of central Italy. The substance is a white crystalline solid, which is sufficiently volatile to be carried

Table **22-6**

Some Physical Properties of Elements of Groups III and IV

	ATOMIC NUMBER	ATOMIC WEIGHT	DENSITY (g/cm³)	MELTING POINT	ATOMIC RADIUS*	IONIC RADIUS†
B	5	10.811	2.54	2,300°C	0.80 Å	0.20 Å
Al	13	26.9815	2.71	660°	1.43	.50
Sc	21	44.956	3.18	1,200°	1.62	.81
Y	39	88.905	4.51	1,490°	1.80	.93
La	57	138.91	6.17	826°	1.87	1.15
C‡	6	12.01115	3.52	3,500°	0.77	—
Si	14	28.086	2.36	1,440°	1.17	0.41
Ge	32	72.59	5.35	959°	1.22	.53
Sn	50	118.69	7.30	232°	1.62	.71
Pb	82	207.19	11.40	327°	1.75	.84

* Single-bond covalent radius for B, C, Si, and Ge; metallic radius (ligancy 12) for the others.

† Sec. 8-4.

‡ Diamond.

along with a stream of steam. Boric acid can be made by treating borax with an acid.

The principal source of compounds of boron is the complex borate minerals, including *borax*, sodium tetraborate decahydrate, $Na_2B_4O_7 \cdot 10H_2O$; *kernite*, sodium tetraborate tetrahydrate, $Na_2B_4O_7 \cdot 4H_2O$ (which gives borax when water is added); and *colemanite*, calcium hexaborate pentahydrate, $Ca_2B_6O_{11} \cdot 5H_2O$. The main deposits of these minerals are in California.

Borax is used in making certain types of enamels and glass (such as Pyrex glass, which contains about 12% of B_2O_3), for softening water, as a household cleanser, and as a flux in welding metals. The last of these uses depends upon the power of molten borax to dissolve metallic oxides, forming borates.

The Boranes. The reaction of magnesium boride, Mg_3B_2, with water would be expected from simple valence theory to result in the production of molecules BH_3. Instead, the substance diborane, B_2H_6, is produced:

$$Mg_3B_2 + 6H_2O \longrightarrow 3Mg(OH)_2 + B_2H_6(g)$$

Diborane is a gas under ordinary conditions (m.p. $-165.5°C$, b.p. $-92.5°C$).

Many other boranes are known; those that have been the most thoroughly investigated have formulas B_4H_{10}, B_5H_9, B_5H_{11}, B_6H_{10}, and $B_{10}H_{14}$. They have found some use as rocket fuels.

The B_2H_6 molecule has the following structure:

Each boron atom has ligancy 5, and two of the hydrogen atoms have ligancy 2. The bond lengths $B—B = 1.77$ Å, $B—H = 1.33$ Å (for bridging hydrogen atoms) and 1.19 Å (for outer hydrogen atoms) indicate that the bonds are fractional bonds, each involving less than one electron pair. There are six pairs of valence electrons in the molecule, and nine bonds; hence on the average each bond is two-thirds of a single bond. The bond lengths indicate that the six electron pairs resonate among the nine positions in such a way that the five central bonds involve about five valence electrons and the four outer bonds involve seven.

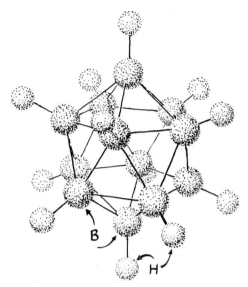

Figure **22-5** *The structure of the icosahedral dodecaborane ion,* $B_{12}H_{12}^{--}$.

Some borane ions are also known, such as $B_4H_{10}^{--}$ in $Na_2B_4H_{10}$ and $B_{12}H_{12}^{--}$ in $K_2B_{12}H_{12}$. The $B_{12}H_{12}^{--}$ ion has an interesting structure: the twelve boron atoms lie at the corners of a regular icosahedron, as shown in Figure 22-5, and each boron atom forms six bonds, five to the adjacent boron atoms in the icosahedron and one, directed outward radially, to a hydrogen atom. The bond lengths indicate bond numbers about 0.5 for the thirty B—B bonds and 0.83 for the twelve B—H bonds.

$B_{10}H_{14}$ and some other borane molecules have also been found to have structures based on the icosahedron, with some of the corners not occupied by boron atoms, and with some bridging hydrogen atoms, as in diborane. The B_{12} icosahedron is also present in elementary boron and in the hard substance B_4C. The electronic structure of these substances is as yet not encompassed satisfactorily by the theory of valence.

Values of Enthalpy of Formation of Boron Compounds. In Table 22-7 there are given values of the enthalpy of formation of some compounds of boron, aluminum, scandium, yttrium, and lanthanum. It is seen that for a series of corresponding compounds the heats of formation increase in the sequence B, Al, Sc, Y, La, corresponding to the decrease in electronegativity in this sequence.

22-6. Aluminum

Some of the physical properties of aluminum and its congeners are given in Table 22-6. Aluminum is only about one-third as dense as iron, and some of its alloys, such as duralumin (described below), are as strong as mild steel;

Table **22-7**

Standard Enthalpy of Formation of Compounds of Boron, Aluminum, and Their Congeners at 25°C (kcal/mole)

	M = B	Al	Sc	Y	La
$M(g)$	97.2	75.0	93	103	88
$M^+(g)$	290.00	214.49	245.75	255.04	218.95
$M^{++}(g)$	871.46	650.06	544.51	542.37	484.10
$M^{+++}(g)$	1747.45	1307.44	1116.81	1016.33	927.59
$M^{+++}(aq)$*		−125.4	−148.8	−168.0	−176.2
$M_2O_3(c)$	−302.0	−399.09			−458
MF_3	−265.4(g)	−311(c)			
MCl_3	−100(l)	−166.2(c)	−220.8(c)	−234.8(c)	−263.6(c)
MBr_3	−52.8(l)	−125.8(c)	−179.4(c)		
$MI_3(c)$		−75.2		−143.2	−167.4
$M_2S_3(c)$	−57.0	−121.6			−306.8

* Relative to assumed value 0 for $H^+(aq)$.

it is this combination of lightness and strength, together with low cost, that has led to the extensive use of aluminum alloys in airplane construction. Aluminum is also used, in place of copper, as a conductor of electricity; its electric conductivity is about 80% that of copper.* Its metallurgy has been discussed in Chapter 21.

The metal is reactive (note its position in the electromotive-force series, Section 11-5), and when strongly heated it burns rapidly in air or oxygen. Aluminum dust forms an explosive mixture with air. Under ordinary conditions, however, aluminum rapidly becomes coated with a thin, tough layer of aluminum oxide, which protects it against further corrosion.

Some of the **alloys of aluminum** are very useful. *Duralumin* or *dural* is an alloy (containing about 94.3% aluminum, 4% copper, 0.5% manganese, 0.5% magnesium, and 0.7% silicon) which is stronger and tougher than pure aluminum. It is less resistant to corrosion, however, and often is protected by a coating of pure aluminum. Plate made by rolling a billet of dural sandwiched between and welded to two pieces of pure aluminum is called alclad plate.

Aluminum oxide (*alumina*), Al_2O_3, occurs in nature as the mineral *corundum*. Corundum and impure corundum (*emery*) are used as abrasives. Pure corundum is colorless. The precious stones *ruby* (red) and *sapphire* (blue or other colors) are transparent crystalline corundum containing small amounts of

* The conductivity refers to the conductance of electricity by a wire of unit cross-sectional area. The density of aluminum is only 30% of that of copper; accordingly, an aluminum wire with the same weight as a copper wire with the same length conducts 2.7 times as much electricity as the copper wire.

other metallic oxides (chromic oxide, titanium oxide). Artificial rubies and sapphires can be made by melting aluminum oxide (m.p. 2,050°C) with small admixtures of other oxides, and cooling the melt in such a way as to produce large crystals. These stones are indistinguishable from natural stones, except for the presence of characteristic rounded microscopic air bubbles. They are used as gems, as bearings ("jewels") in watches and other instruments, and as dies through which wires are drawn.

Aluminum sulfate, $Al_2(SO_4)_3 \cdot 18H_2O$, may be made by dissolving aluminum hydroxide in sulfuric acid:

$$2Al(OH)_3 + 3H_2SO_4 + 12H_2O \longrightarrow Al_2(SO_4)_3 \cdot 18H_2O$$

It is used in water purification and as a mordant in dyeing and printing cloth (a *mordant* is a substance that fixes the dye to the cloth, rendering it insoluble). Both of these uses depend upon its property of producing a gelatinous precipitate of aluminum hydroxide, $Al(OH)_3$, when it is dissolved in a large amount of neutral or slightly alkaline water. The reaction that occurs is the reverse of the above reaction. In dyeing and printing cloth the gelatinous precipitate aids in holding the dye onto the cloth. In water purification it adsorbs dissolved and suspended impurities, which are removed as it settles to the bottom of the reservoir.

A solution containing aluminum sulfate and potassium sulfate, K_2SO_4, forms, on evaporation, beautiful colorless cubic (octahedral) crystals of **alum,** $KAl(SO_4)_2 \cdot 12H_2O$. Similar crystals of ammonium alum, $NH_4Al(SO_4)_2 \cdot 12H_2O$, are formed with ammonium sulfate. The alums also are used as mordants in dyeing cloth, in water purification, and in weighting and sizing paper (by precipitating aluminum hydroxide in the meshes of the cellulose fibers).

Aluminum chloride, $AlCl_3$, is made by passing dry chlorine or hydrogen chloride over heated aluminum:

$$2Al + 3Cl_2 \longrightarrow 2AlCl_3$$
$$2Al + 6HCl \longrightarrow 2AlCl_3 + 3H_2$$

The anhydrous salt is used in many chemical processes, including a cracking process for making gasoline.

22-7.   Scandium, Yttrium, Lanthanum, and the Lanthanons

Scandium, yttrium, and lanthanum,* the congeners of boron and aluminum, form colorless compounds similar to those of aluminum, their oxides having the formulas Sc_2O_3, Y_2O_3, and La_2O_3. These elements and their compounds have not yet found any important use.

---

* Actinium, the heaviest member of group III, is a radioactive element which occurs in minute quantities in uranium ores (Chapter 30).

Scandium, yttrium, and lanthanum usually occur in nature with the fourteen lanthanons, cerium (atomic number 58) to lutetium (atomic number 71).* All of these elements except promethium (which is made artificially) occur in nature in very small quantities, the principal source being the mineral *monazite*, a mixture of phosphates containing also some thorium phosphate.

The metals themselves are very electropositive, and are accordingly difficult to prepare. Electrolytic reduction of a fused oxide-fluoride mixture may be used. An alloy containing about 70% cerium and smaller amounts of other lanthanons and iron gives sparks when scratched. This alloy is widely used for cigarette lighters and gas lighters.

These elements are usually terpositive, forming salts such as $La(NO_3)_3 \cdot 6H_2O$. Cerium forms also a well-defined series of salts in which it is quadripositive. This oxidation state corresponds to its atomic number, 4 greater than that of xenon. Praseodymium, neodymium, and terbium form dioxides, but not the corresponding salts.

The bipositive europium(II) ion is stable, and europium forms a series of europium(II) salts as well as of europium(III) salts. Ytterbium and samarium have a somewhat smaller tendency to form salts representing the $+2$ state of oxidation.

The ions of several of the lanthanons have characteristic colors. A special glass containing lanthanon ions is used in glassblowers' goggles and in optical instruments.

Many of the lanthanon compounds are strongly paramagnetic. Crystalline compounds of gadolinium, especially gadolinium sulfate octahydrate, $Gd_2(SO_4)_3 \cdot 8H_2O$, are used in the magnetic method of obtaining extremely low temperatures.

The sulfides cerium monosulfide, CeS, and thorium monosulfide, ThS, and related sulfides have been found valuable as refractory substances. The melting point of cerium monosulfide is 2,450°C.

22-8.   Silicon and Its Simpler Compounds

Elementary Silicon and Silicon Alloys.   Silicon is a brittle steel-gray metalloid. Some of its physical properties are given in Table 22-6. It can be made by the reduction of silicon tetrachloride by sodium:

$$SiCl_4 + 4Na \longrightarrow Si + 4NaCl$$

The element has the same crystal structure as diamond, each silicon atom forming single covalent bonds with four adjacent silicon atoms, which

---

* Lanthanum is often considered as one of the rare-earth elements (lanthanons). For convenience, the convention is adopted here of including lanthanum as a member of group III, leaving fourteen elements in the lanthanon group.

surround it tetrahedrally. It is used in transistors, especially for service at elevated temperatures (Section 22-15).

Silicon contaminated with carbon can be obtained by reduction of silica, SiO_2, with carbon in an electric furnace. An alloy of iron and silicon, called *ferrosilicon*, is obtained by reducing a mixture of iron oxide and silica with carbon.

Ferrosilicon, which has composition approximately FeSi, is used in the manufacture of acid-resisting alloys, such as *duriron*, which contains about 15% silicon. Duriron is used in chemical laboratories and manufacturing plants. A mild steel containing a few percent of silicon may be made which has a high magnetic permeability, and is used for the cores of electric transformers.

Silicides. Many metals form compounds with silicon, called silicides. These compounds include Mg_2Si, Fe_2Si, FeSi, CoSi, NiSi, $CaSi_2$, $Cu_{15}Si_4$, and $CoSi_2$. Ferrosilicon consists largely of the compound FeSi. Calcium silicide, $CaSi_2$, is made by heating a mixture of lime, silica, and carbon in an electric furnace. It is a powerful reducing agent, and is used for removing oxygen from molten steel in the process of manufacture of steel.

Silicon Carbide. Silicon carbide, SiC, is made by heating a mixture of carbon and sand in a special electric furnace:

$$SiO_2 + 3C \longrightarrow SiC + 2CO$$

The structure of this substance is similar to that of diamond (Figure 10-2), with carbon and silicon atoms alternating; each carbon atom is surrounded by a tetrahedron of silicon atoms, and each silicon atom by a tetrahedron of carbon atoms. The covalent bonds connecting all of the atoms in this structure make silicon carbide very hard. The substance is used as an abrasive.

22-9. Silicon Dioxide

Silicon dioxide (*silica*), SiO_2, occurs in nature in three different crystal forms: as the minerals *quartz* (hexagonal), *cristobalite* (cubic), and *tridymite* (hexagonal). Quartz is the most widespread of these minerals; it occurs in many deposits as well-formed crystals, and also as a crystalline constituent of many rocks, such as granite. It is a hard, colorless substance. Its crystals may be identified as right-handed or left-handed by their face development and also by the direction in which they rotate the plane of polarization of polarized light (Figure 9-4).

The structure of quartz is closely related to that of silicic acid, H_4SiO_4. In this acid silicon has ligancy 4, the silicon atom being surrounded by a tetrahedron of four oxygen atoms, with one hydrogen atom attached to each oxygen atom. Silicic acid, which is a very weak acid, has the property of undergoing condensation very readily, with elimination of water (Section 19-9). If each of the four hydroxyl groups of a silicic acid molecule condenses with a similar hydroxyl group of an adjacent molecule, eliminating water, a structure is obtained in which the silicon atom is bonded to four surrounding silicon atoms by silicon-oxygen-silicon bonds. This process leads to a condensation product

Figure **22-6**

> *The crystal structure of quartz. Each silicon atom is bonded to four oxygen atoms, which are arranged about it at the corners of a tetrahedron, and each oxygen atom serves as a corner of two silicon tetrahedra. In this diagram most of these SiO₄ groups are represented by tetrahedra; only one group is represented by showing the spherical atoms.*

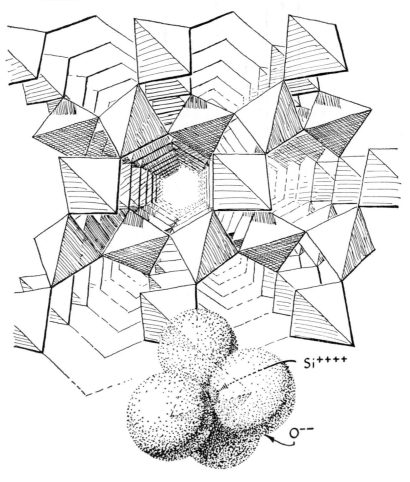

with formula SiO_2, since each silicon atom is surrounded by four oxygen atoms, and each oxygen atom serves as a neighbor to two silicon atoms (Figure 22-6). The structure of quartz and of the other forms of silica may be described as consisting of SiO_4 tetrahedra, with each oxygen atom serving as the corner of two of these tetrahedra. In order to break a crystal of quartz it is necessary to break some silicon-oxygen bonds. In this way the structure of quartz accounts for the hardness of the mineral.

Table **22-8**

Standard Enthalpy of Formation of Compounds of Silicon, Germanium, Tin, and Lead at 25°C (kcal/mole)

	M = Si	Ge	Sn*	Pb
M(g)	88.04	78.44	72	46.34
MO	−27(g)	−22.8(g)	−68.4(c)	−52.4(c)
MO₂(c)	−205.4	−128.3	−138.8	−66.12
MH₄(g)	−14.8			
MF₂(c)				−158.5
MF₄	−370(g)			−222.3(c)
MCl₂(c)			−83.6	−85.85
MCl₄	−153.0(l)	−130(l)	−130.3(l)	
MBr₂(c)			−63.6	−66.21
MBr₄	−95.1(l)		−97.1(c)	
MI₂(c)			−34.4	−41.85
MI₄(c)	−31.6			
MS(c)			−18.6	−22.54

* White tin is the standard state; the value for gray tin is 0.6 kcal/mole.

Cristobalite and tridymite are similarly made from SiO_4 tetrahedra fused together by sharing oxygen atoms, with, however, different arrangements of the tetrahedra in space from that of quartz. Three other crystalline modifications of silica have been discovered since 1956—keatite, coesite, and stishovite. Keatite and coesite contain SiO_4 tetrahedra somewhat distorted from the regular configuration (bond angles different from 109°28′). Coesite was discovered in the laboratory by subjecting silica to high pressure (about 30,000 atm), and was later found at Meteor Crater, Arizona, and other places where large meteorites have struck the earth. Stishovite was first made in 1961 by use of pressures of about 120,000 atm. It has a structure (like that of rutile, TiO_2; Figure 22-2) in which each silicon atom is octahedrally surrounded by six oxygen atoms. The presence of coesite and stishovite in rocks near a crater is evidence that the crater was formed by impact of a meteorite.

Silica Glass. If any form of silica is melted (m.p. about 1,600°C) and the molten material is then cooled, it usually does not crystallize at the original melting point, but the liquid becomes more viscous as the temperature is lowered, until, at about 1,500°C, it is so stiff that it cannot flow. The material obtained in this way is not crystalline, but is a supercooled liquid, or glass. It is called *silica glass* (or sometimes *quartz glass* or *fused quartz*). Silica glass does not have the properties of a crystal—it does not cleave, nor form crystal faces, nor show other differences in properties in different directions. The reason for this is that the atoms that constitute it are not arranged in a completely regular manner in space, but show a randomness in arrangement similar to that of the liquid.

The structure of silica glass is very similar in its general nature to that of quartz and the other crystalline forms of silica. Nearly every silicon atom is surrounded by a tetrahedron of four oxygen atoms, and nearly every oxygen atom serves as the common corner of two of these tetrahedra. However, the arrangement of the framework of tetrahedra in the glass is not regular, as it is in the crystalline forms of silica, but is irregular, so that a very small region may resemble quartz, and an adjacent region may resemble cristobalite or tridymite, in the same way that liquid silica, above the melting point of the crystalline forms, would show some resemblance to the structures of the crystals.

Silica glass is used for making chemical apparatus and scientific instruments. The coefficient of thermal expansion of silica glass is very small, so that vessels made of the material do not break readily on sudden heating or cooling. Silica is transparent to ultraviolet light, and because of this property it is used in making mercury-vapor ultraviolet lamps and optical instruments for use with ultraviolet light.

22-10. Sodium Silicate and Other Silicates

Silicic acid (orthosilicic acid), H_4SiO_4, cannot be made by the hydration of silica. The sodium and potassium salts of silicic acid are soluble in water, however, and can be made by boiling silica with a solution of sodium hydroxide or potassium hydroxide, in which it slowly dissolves. A concentrated solution of **sodium silicate,** called *water glass*, is available commercially and is used for fireproofing wood and cloth, as an adhesive, and for preserving eggs. This solution is not sodium orthosilicate, Na_4SiO_4, but is a mixture of the sodium salts of various condensed silicic acids, such as $H_6Si_2O_7$, $H_4Si_3O_8$, and $(H_2SiO_3)_\infty$.

A gelatinous precipitate of condensed silicic acids $(SiO_2 \cdot xH_2O)$ is obtained when an ordinary acid, such as hydrochloric acid, is added to a solution of sodium silicate. When this precipitate is partially dehydrated it forms a porous product called *silica gel*. This material has great powers of adsorption for water and other molecules and is used as a drying agent and decolorizing agent.

Except for the alkali silicates, most silicates are insoluble in water. Many occur in nature, as ores and minerals.

22-11. The Silicate Minerals

Most of the minerals that constitute rocks and soil are silicates, which usually also contain aluminum. Many of these minerals have complex formulas, corresponding to the complex condensed silicic acids from which they are derived. These minerals can be divided into three principal classes: the *framework minerals* (hard minerals similar in their properties to quartz), the *layer minerals* (such as mica), and the *fibrous minerals* (such as asbestos).

The Framework Minerals. Many silicate minerals have tetrahedral framework structures in which some of the tetrahedra are AlO_4 tetrahedra instead of SiO_4 tetrahedra. These minerals have structures somewhat resembling that of quartz, with additional ions, usually alkali or alkaline-earth ions, introduced in the larger openings in the framework structure. Ordinary *feldspar* (*orthoclase*), $KAlSi_3O_8$, is an example of a tetrahedral aluminosilicate mineral. The aluminosilicate tetrahedral framework, $(AlSi_3O_8^-)_\infty$, extends throughout the entire crystal, giving it hardness nearly as great as that of quartz. Some other aluminosilicate minerals with tetrahedral framework structures are the following:

Kaliophilite	$KAlSiO_4$	Analcite	$NaAlSi_2O_6 \cdot H_2O$
Leucite	$KAlSi_2O_6$	Natrolite	$Na_2Al_2Si_3O_{10} \cdot 2H_2O$
Albite	$NaAlSi_3O_8$	Chabazite	$CaAl_2Si_4O_{12} \cdot 6H_2O$
Anorthite	$CaAl_2Si_2O_8$	Sodalite	$Na_4Al_3Si_3O_{12}Cl$

A characteristic feature of these tetrahedral framework minerals is that the number of oxygen atoms is just twice the sum of the number of aluminum and silicon atoms. In some of these minerals the framework is an open one, through which corridors run that are sufficiently large to permit ions to move in and out. The *zeolite minerals*, used for softening water, are of this nature. As the hard water, containing Ca^{++} and Fe^{+++} ions, passes around the grains of the mineral, these cations enter the mineral, replacing an equivalent number of sodium ions (Section 16-1).

Some of the zeolite minerals contain water molecules in the corridors and chambers within the aluminosilicate framework, as well as alkali and alkaline-earth ions. When a crystal of one of these minerals, such as chabazite, $CaAl_2Si_4O_{12} \cdot 6H_2O$, is heated, the water molecules are driven out of the structure. The crystal does not collapse, however, but retains essentially its original size and shape, the spaces within the framework formerly occupied by water molecules remaining unoccupied. This dehydrated chabazite has a strong attraction for water molecules and for molecules of other vapors, and

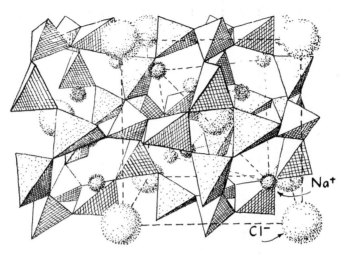

Figure **22-7**

The structure of the mineral sodalite, $Na_4Al_3Si_3O_{12}Cl$. The framework consists of AlO_4 tetrahedra and SiO_4 tetrahedra, which share corners with one another. In the spaces formed by this framework there are large chloride ions and the smaller sodium ions, represented in the drawing by spheres. The mineral lazurite has the same structure, except that the chloride ions are replaced by polysulfide groups.

can be used as a drying agent or absorbing agent for them. The structure of silica gel, mentioned above as a drying agent, is similar.

Some of the important minerals in soil are aluminosilicate minerals that have the property of base exchange, and that, because of this property, serve a useful function in the nutrition of the plant.

An interesting framework mineral is *lazurite*, or *lapis lazuli*, a mineral with a beautiful blue color. When ground into a powder, this mineral constitutes the pigment called *ultramarine*. Lazurite has the formula $Na_8Al_6Si_6O_{24}(S_x)$. It consists of an aluminosilicate framework in which there are sodium ions (some of which neutralize the charge of the framework) and anions S_x^{--}, such as S_2^{--} and S_3^{--} (Figure 22-7). These polysulfide ions are responsible for the color of the pigment. It was discovered at the beginning of the eighteenth century that a synthetic ultramarine can be made by melting together a suitable sodium aluminosilicate mixture with sulfur. Similar stable pigments with different colors can also be made by replacing the sulfur by selenium and the sodium ion by other cations.

Minerals with Layer Structures. By a condensation reaction involving three of the four hydroxyl groups of each silicic acid molecule, a condensed silicic acid can be made, with composition $(H_2Si_2O_5)_\infty$, which has the form of an infinite layer, as shown in Figure 22-8. The mineral *hydrargillite*, $Al(OH)_3$, has a similar layer structure, which involves AlO_6 octahedra (Figure 22-9). More complex layers, involving both tetrahedra and octahedra, are present in other layer minerals, such as *talc*, *kaolinite* (clay), and *mica*.

In talc and kaolinite, with formulas $Mg_3Si_4O_{10}(OH)_2$ and $Al_2Si_2O_5(OH)_4$, respectively, the layers are electrically neutral, and they are loosely superimposed on one another to form the crystalline material. These layers slide over one another very readily, which gives to these minerals their characteristic properties (softness, easy cleavage, soapy feel). In mica, $KAl_3Si_3O_{10}(OH)_2$, the aluminosilicate layers are negatively charged, and positive ions, usually potassium ions, must be present between the layers in order to give the mineral electric neutrality. The electrostatic forces between these positive ions and the negatively charged layers make mica considerably harder than kaolinite and talc, but its layer structure is still evident in its perfect basic cleavage, which permits the mineral to be split into very thin sheets. These sheets of mica are used for windows in stoves and furnaces, and for electric insulation in machines and instruments.

Other layer minerals, such as *montmorillonite*, with formula approximately $AlSi_2O_5(OH)\cdot xH_2O$, are important constituents of soils, and have also found

Figure **22-8**

A portion of an infinite layer of silicate tetrahedra, as present in talc and other minerals with layer structures.

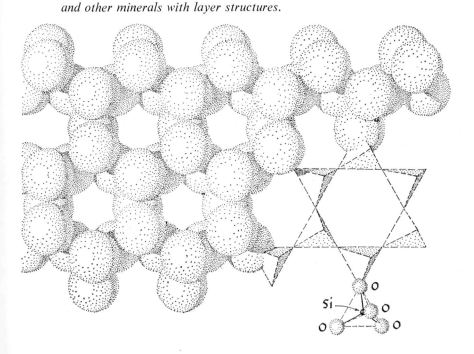

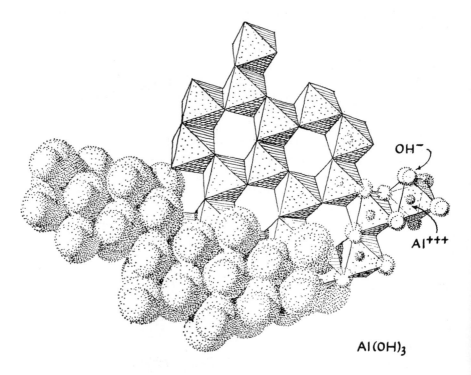

OH⁻

Al⁺⁺⁺

Al(OH)₃

Figure 22-9

The crystal structure of aluminum hydroxide, Al(OH)₃. This substance crystallizes in layers, consisting of octahedra of oxygen atoms (hydroxide ions) about the aluminum atom. Each oxygen atom serves as a corner for two aluminum octahedra.

industrial uses, as catalysts in the conversion of long-chain hydrocarbons into branched-chain hydrocarbons (to make high-octane gasoline), and for other special purposes.

The Fibrous Minerals.   The fibrous minerals contain very long silicate ions in the form of tetrahedra condensed into a chain. These crystals can be cleaved readily in directions parallel to the silicate chains, but not in the directions which cut the chains. Accordingly crystals of these minerals show the extraordinary property of being easily unraveled into fibers. The principal minerals of this sort, *tremolite*, $Ca_2Mg_5Si_8O_{22}(OH)_2$, and *chrysotile*, $Mg_6Si_4O_{11}(OH)_6 \cdot H_2O$, are called *asbestos*. Deposits of these minerals are found, especially in South Africa, in layers several inches thick. These minerals are shredded into fibers, which are then spun or felted into asbestos yarn, fabric, and board for use for thermal insulation and as a heat-resistant structural material.

22-12. Glass

Silicate materials with important uses include glass, porcelain, glazes and enamels, and cement. Ordinary glass is a mixture of silicates in the form of a supercooled liquid. It is made by melting a mixture of sodium carbonate (or sodium sulfate), limestone, and sand, usually with some scrap glass of the same grade to serve as a flux. After the bubbles of gas have been expelled, the clear melt is poured into molds or stamped with dies, to produce pressed glassware, or a lump of the semifluid material on the end of a hallow tube is blown, sometimes in a mold, to produce hollow ware, such as bottles and flasks. *Plate glass* is made by pouring liquid glass onto a flat table and rolling it into a sheet. The sheet is then ground flat and polished on both sides. *Safety glass* consists of a sheet of tough plastic sandwiched between two sheets of glass.

Ordinary glass (soda-lime glass, soft glass) contains about 10% sodium, 5% calcium, and 1% aluminum, the remainder being silicon and oxygen. It consists of an aluminosilicate tetrahedral framework, within which are embedded sodium ions and calcium ions and some smaller complex anions. Soda-lime glass softens over a range of temperatures beginning at a dull-red heat, and can be conveniently worked in this temperature range.

Boric acid easily forms highly condensed acids, similar to those of silicic acid, and borate glasses are similar to silicate glasses in their properties. *Pyrex glass*, used for chemical glassware and baking dishes, is a boro-aluminosilicate glass containing only about 4% of alkali and alkaline-earth metal ions. This glass is not as soluble in water as is soft glass, and it also has a smaller coefficient of thermal expansion than soft glass, so that it does not break readily when it is suddenly heated or cooled.

Glazes on chinaware and pottery and *enamels* on iron kitchen utensils and bathtubs consist of easily fusible glass containing pigments or white fillers such as titanium dioxide and tin dioxide.

22-13. Cement

Portland cement is an aluminosilicate powder that sets to a solid mass on treatment with water. It is usually manufactured by grinding limestone and clay to a fine powder, mixing with water to form a slurry, and burning the mixture, with a flame of gas, oil, or coal dust, in a long rotary kiln. At the hot end of the kiln, where the temperature is about 1,500°C, the aluminosilicate mixture is sintered together into small round marbles, called "clinker." The clinker is ground to a fine powder in a ball mill (a rotating cylindrical mill filled with steel balls), to produce the final product.

Portland cement before treatment with water consists of a mixture of calcium silicates, mainly Ca_2SiO_4 and Ca_3SiO_5, and calcium aluminate, $Ca_3Al_2O_6$. When treated with water the calcium aluminate hydrolyzes, forming calcium hydroxide and aluminum hydroxide, and these substances react further with the calcium silicates to produce calcium aluminosilicates, in the form of intermeshed crystals.

Ordinary *mortar* for laying bricks is made by mixing sand with slaked lime. This mortar slowly becomes hard through reaction with carbon dioxide of the air, forming calcium carbonate. A stronger mortar is made by mixing sand with Portland cement. The amount of cement needed for a construction job is greatly reduced by mixing sand and crushed stone or gravel with the cement, forming the material called *concrete*. Concrete is a very valuable building material. It does not require carbon dioxide from the air in order to harden, and it will set under water and in very large masses.

22-14.   The Silicones

When we consider the variety of structures represented by the silicate minerals, and their resultant characteristic and useful properties, we might well expect chemists to synthesize many new and valuable silicon compounds. In recent years this has been done; many silicon compounds, especially those of the class called *silicones*, have been found to have valuable properties.

The simplest silicones are the methyl silicones. These substances exist as oils, resins, and elastomers (rubberlike substances). Methyl silicone oil consists of long molecules, each of which is a silicon-oxygen chain with methyl groups attached to the silicon atoms. A short silicone molecule would have the following structure:

$$H_3C \diagdown \quad O \quad \diagup O \diagdown \quad \diagup O \diagdown \quad \diagup CH_3$$
$$Si \qquad Si \qquad Si \qquad Si$$
$$H_3C \diagup \quad \diagdown CH_3 \quad H_3C \diagup \quad \diagdown CH_3 \quad H_3C \diagup \quad \diagdown CH_3 \quad H_3C \diagup \quad \diagdown CH_3$$

A *silicone oil* for use as a lubricating oil or in hydraulic systems contains molecules with an average of about 10 silicon atoms per molecule.

The valuable properties of the silicone oils are their very low coefficient of viscosity with temperature, ability to withstand high temperature without decomposition, and chemical inertness to metals and most reagents. A typical silicone oil increases only about sevenfold in viscosity on cooling from 100°F to −35°F, whereas a hydrocarbon oil with the same viscosity at 100°F increases in viscosity about 1,800-fold at −35°F.

Resinous silicones can be made by polymerizing silicones into cross-linked molecules. These resinous materials are used for electric insulation. They have excellent dielectric properties and are stable at operating temperatures at which the usual organic insulating materials decompose rapidly. The use of these materials permits electric machines to be operated with increased loads.

Silicones may be polymerized to molecules containing 2,000 or more $(CH_3)_2SiO$ units, and then milled with inorganic fillers (such as zinc oxide or carbon black, used also for ordinary rubber), and vulcanized, by heating to cause cross-links to form between the molecules, bonding them into an insoluble, infusible three-dimensional framework.

Similar silicones with ethyl groups or other organic groups in place of the methyl groups are also used.

The coating of materials with a water-repellent film has been achieved by use of the *methylchlorosilanes*. A piece of cotton cloth exposed for a second or two to the vapor of trimethylchlorosilane, $(CH_3)_3SiCl$, becomes coated with a layer of trimethylsilicyl groups, through reaction with hydroxyl groups of the cellulose:

$$(CH_3)_3SiCl + HOR \longrightarrow (CH_3)_3SiOR + HCl$$

The exposed methyl groups repel water in the way that a hydrocarbon film such as lubricating oil would. Paper, wool, silk, glass, procelain, and other materials can be treated in this way. The treatment has been found especially useful for ceramic insulators.

22-15. Germanium

The chemistry of germanium, a moderately rare element, is similar to that of silicon. Most of the compounds of germanium correspond to oxidation number $+4$; examples are germanium tetrachloride, $GeCl_4$, a colorless liquid with boiling point $83°C$, and germanium dioxide, GeO_2, a colorless crystalline substance melting at $1,086°C$.

The compounds of germanium have found little use. The element itself, a gray metalloid, is a poor conductor of electricity. A crystal of germanium alloyed with very small amounts of other elements in contact with a fine metal wire (such as copper) forms a *rectifying junction;* that is, it permits electrons to pass through the surface between the crystal and the wire in only one direction. This rectifying power has caused germanium to find much use in recent years in special pieces of apparatus, such as radar. It is also the basis of the *transistor*, a simple apparatus for amplifying minute currents of electricity, which can replace the ordinary vacuum tube for such purposes.

The electrical conductivity of pure germanium at very low temperatures is close to zero. The crystal, like that of diamond, contains atoms with ligancy 4 and a pair of electrons for every bond. We may use a two-dimensional representation:

$$
\begin{array}{cccc}
| & | & | & | \\
-Ge- & -Ge- & -Ge- & -Ge- \\
| & | & | & | \\
-Ge- & -Ge- & -Ge- & -Ge- \\
| & | & | & | \\
-Ge- & -Ge- & -Ge- & -Ge- \\
| & | & | & |
\end{array}
$$

The electrons are restricted to the bond regions, and are not free to move when an electric field is applied. At higher temperatures an electron may be promoted to an excited orbit (5s, for example), leaving one electron in a bond where there should be two:

$$
\begin{array}{cccc}
| & | & | & | \\
-\text{Ge}- & \text{Ge}- & \text{Ge}- & \text{Ge}- \\
| & | & | & | \\
-\text{Ge}^+ \cdot^- & \text{Ge}^+- & \text{Ge}\cdot^-- & \text{Ge}- \\
| & | & | & | \\
-\text{Ge}- & \text{Ge}- & \text{Ge}- & \text{Ge}- \\
| & | & | & |
\end{array}
$$

The electron left alone in the bond between two germanium atoms each with a positive charge, $Ge^+ \cdot^- Ge^+$, is called a *hole*. The hole can contribute to the electric conductance by the motion to it of an electron from an adjacent bond, as in the following sequence:

$$
\begin{array}{ccccc}
-\text{Ge}^+ \cdot^- & \text{Ge}^+- & \text{Ge}- & \text{Ge}- & \text{Ge}-- \\
-\text{Ge}- & \text{Ge}^+ \cdot^- & \text{Ge}^+- & \text{Ge}- & \text{Ge}- \\
-\text{Ge}- & \text{Ge}- & \text{Ge}^+ \cdot^- & \text{Ge}^+- & \text{Ge}- \\
-\text{Ge}- & \text{Ge}- & \text{Ge}- & \text{Ge}^+ \cdot^- & \text{Ge}^+-
\end{array}
$$

The promoted electron also contributes to the conductance; it moves in the opposite direction to the hole.

A crystal of germanium containing some atoms of arsenic (germanium doped with arsenic) has extra electrons in the excited orbitals, because each arsenic atom contributes not only the four electrons needed for the tetrahedral bonds but also a fifth electron. Such a crystal has greater conductivity than pure germanium, and the conductivity is of the *n* type (carried by the negative electrons).

A crystal containing some atoms of aluminum, each contributing only three valence electrons, has for every aluminum atom a hole in the set of bonding electron pairs, and has conductivity of the *p* type (carried by the positive holes, which, of course, move in one direction as electrons jump in the opposite direction into them from adjacent bonding pairs).

A *p-n* junction rectifier is made by placing a *p* crystal and an *n* crystal in contact with one another, as shown in Figure 22-10. Each crystal is attached at the other end to a metal plate carrying the terminals. Both holes and electrons transfer readily to the metal plates and across the junction, and a steady current is carried when a potential is applied in such a direction as to cause both holes and electrons to move toward the junction. When the potential is reversed, however, the holes and electrons move away from the junction (bottom of Figure 22-10). There is no mechanism for rapidly producing new holes and promoted electrons at the junction—this process requires the energy to raise an electron from a bond orbital (for germanium the $4s4p^3$ tetrahedral hybrid orbitals) to an excited orbital, $5s$, and its rate is determined by the temperature (the Arrhenius exponential rate factor, Chapter 18). In consequence, the region near the junction becomes depleted of carriers and the current ceases to flow.

An *n-p-n* transistor can be made by sandwiching a *p* crystal between two *n* crystals and attaching terminals in such a way that one applied potential depletes or augments the supply of carriers for another. In this way a current in one circuit can be caused to produce a proportional current in another circuit at a higher power level.

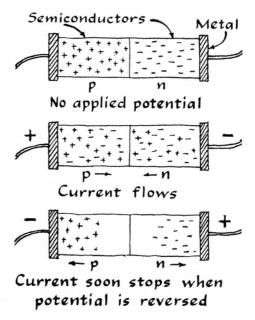

Figure **22-10** *A diagram representing a p-n junction rectifier.*

22-16. Tin

Tin is a silvery white metal, with great malleability, permitting it to be hammered into thin sheets, called tin foil. Ordinary *white tin*, which has metallic properties, slowly changes at temperatures below 18°C to a non-metallic allotropic modification, *gray tin*, which has the diamond structure. (The physical properties given in Table 22-6 pertain to white tin.) At very low temperatures, around −40°C, the speed of this conversion is sufficiently great that metallic tin objects sometimes fall into a powder of gray tin. This phenomenon has been called the "tin pest."

Tin finds extensive use as a protective layer for mild steel. Tin plating is done by dipping clean sheets of mild steel into molten tin, or by electrolytic deposition. Copper and other metals are sometimes also coated with tin.

The principal alloys of tin are *bronze* (tin and copper), *soft solder* (50% tin and 50% lead), *pewter* (75% tin and 25% lead), and *britannia metal* (tin with small amounts of antimony and copper).

Bearing metals, used as the bearing surfaces of sliding-contact bearings, are usually alloys of tin, lead, antimony, and copper. They contain small, hard crystals of a compound such as SnSb embedded in a soft matrix of tin or lead. The good bearing properties result from orientation of the hard crystals to present flat faces at the bearing surface.

Tin is reactive enough to displace hydrogen from dilute acids, but it does not tarnish in moist air. It reacts with warm hydrochloric acid to produce stannous chloride, $SnCl_2$, and hydrogen, and with hot concentrated sulfuric acid to produce stannous sulfate, $SnSO_4$, and sulfur dioxide, the equations for these reactions being

$$Sn + 2HCl \longrightarrow SnCl_2 + H_2$$

and

$$Sn + 2H_2SO_4 \longrightarrow SnSO_4 + SO_2 + 2H_2O$$

With cold dilute nitric acid it forms stannous nitrate, and with concentrated nitric acid it is oxidized to a hydrated stannic acid, H_2SnO_3.

Compounds of Tin.   Stannous chloride, made by solution of tin in hydrochloric acid, forms colorless crystals, $SnCl_2 \cdot H_2O$, on evaporation of the solution. In neutral solution the substance hydrolyzes, forming a precipitate of stannous hydroxychloride, $Sn(OH)Cl$. The hydrolysis in solution may be prevented by the presence of an excess of acid. Stannous chloride solution is used as a mordant in dyeing cloth.

The stannous ion is an active reducing agent, which is easily oxidized to stannic chloride, $SnCl_4$, or, in the presence of excess chloride ion, to the complex chlorostannate ion, $SnCl_6^{--}$.

Stannic chloride, $SnCl_4$, is a colorless liquid (boiling point 114°C), which fumes very strongly in moist air, producing hydrochloric acid and stannic acid, $H_2Sn(OH)_6$. Sodium stannate, $Na_2Sn(OH)_6$, contains the octahedral hexahydroxystannate ion (stannate ion). This complex ion is similar in structure to the chlorostannate ion. Sodium stannate is used as a mordant, and in preparing fireproof cotton cloth and weighting silk. The cloth is soaked in the sodium stannate solution, dried, and treated with ammonium sulfate solution. This treatment causes hydrated stannic oxide to be deposited in the fibers.

Stannous hydroxide, $Sn(OH)_2$, is formed by adding dilute sodium hydroxide solution to stannous chloride. It is readily soluble in excess alkali, producing the stannite ion, $Sn(OH)_3^{-}$.

Stannous sulfide, SnS, is obtained as a dark brown precipitate by addition of hydrogen sulfide or sulfide ion to a solution of a stannous salt. Stannic sulfide, SnS_2, is formed in the same way from stannic solution; it is yellow in color. Stannic sulfide is soluble in solutions of ammonium sulfide or sodium sulfide, producing the sulfostannate ion, SnS_4^{----}. Stannous sulfide is not soluble in sulfide solution, but is easily oxidized in the presence of polysulfide solutions to the sulfostannate ion. These properties are used in some schemes of qualitative analysis.

22-17. Lead

Lead is a soft, heavy, dull gray metal with low tensile strength. It is used in making type, for covering electric cables, and in many alloys. The organic lead compound lead tetraethyl, $Pb(C_2H_5)_4$, is added to gasoline to prevent knock in automobile engines.

Lead forms a thin surface layer of oxide in air. This oxide slowly changes to a basic carbonate. Hard water forms a similar coating on lead, which protects the water from contamination with soluble lead compounds. Soft water dissolves appreciable amounts of lead, which is poisonous; for this reason lead pipes should not be used to carry drinking water.

There are several oxides of lead, of which the most important are lead monoxide (*litharge*), PbO, minium or red lead, Pb_3O_4, and lead dioxide, PbO_2.

Litharge is made by heating lead in air. It is a yellow powder or yellowish-red crystalline material, used in making lead glass and for preparing compounds of lead. Red lead, Pb_3O_4, can be made by heating lead in oxygen. It is used in glass making, and for making a red paint for protecting iron and steel structures. Lead dioxide, PbO_2, is a brown substance made by oxidizing a solution of sodium plumbite, $Na_2Pb(OH)_4$, with hypochlorite ion, or by anodic oxidation of lead sulfate. It is soluble in sodium hydroxide and potassium hydroxide, forming the hexahydroxyplumbate ion, $Pb(OH)_6^{--}$. The principal use of lead dioxide is in the lead storage battery (Chapter 11).

Lead nitrate, $Pb(NO_3)_2$, is a white crystalline substance made by dissolving lead, lead monoxide, or lead carbonate in nitric acid. Lead carbonate, $PbCO_3$ occurs in nature as the mineral *cerussite*. It appears as a precipitate when a solution containing the hydrogen carbonate ion, HCO_3^-, is added to lead nitrate solution. With a more basic carbonate solution a basic carbonate of lead, $Pb_3(OH)_2(CO_3)_2$, is deposited. This basic salt, called *white lead*, is used as a white pigment in paint. For this use it is manufactured by methods involving the oxidation of lead by air, the formation of a basic acetate by interaction with vinegar or acetic acid, and the decomposition of this salt by carbon dioxide. Lead chromate, $PbCrO_4$, is also used as a pigment, under the name *chrome yellow*.

Lead sulfate, $PbSO_4$, is a white, nearly insoluble substance. Its precipitation is used as a test for either lead ion or sulfate ion in analytical chemistry.

EXERCISES

22-1. Would you predict that the alkali metals could be prepared by the aluminothermic method (reduction of the oxide with metallic aluminum)? Why?

22-2. Outline the process of manufacture of sodium hydroxide from sodium chloride by way of sodium carbonate, prepared by the ammonia-soda process. Write equations for all reactions.

22-3. Compare the properties of elements of

groups I, II, III, and IV with their electronegativities (Table 9-1). What electronegativity value separates the metals from the metalloids?

22-4. Beryllium hydroxide is essentially insoluble in water, but is soluble both in acids and in alkalis. What do you think the products of its reaction with sodium hydroxide solution are? Discuss these properties of the substance in relation to the position of beryllium in the periodic table and in the electronegativity scale.

22-5. Discuss the electronic structure of potassium fluoroborate, KBF_4. Its solution in water contains the ion BF_4^-.

22-6. What is the electronic structure of the aluminum atom? How does it explain the fact that all compounds of aluminum correspond to oxidation number $+3$?

22-7. What is the crystal structure of elementary silicon? Of silicon carbide? In what way are these structures related to the electronic structures of the atoms?

22-8. Divide the following elements into the two classes
(a) those for which you expect the electric conductivity to increase with increase in temperature, and
(b) those for which you expect it to decrease: Li, Be, diamond, Na, Mg, Al, Si, Ge, Ba. Explain your classification.

22-9. The compound AlP has a tetrahedral structure resembling that of SiC (Section 22-8). Would you expect it to be a possible substitute for germanium in a p-n junction rectifier? How could AlP be doped to give a p-crystal and an n-crystal?

22-10. The trichloride of boron has m.p. $-107°C$ and boiling point $12.5°C$, whereas that of its congener lanthanum has m.p. $870°C$ and very high b.p. What is the explanation of these greatly different physical properties?

22-11. Of the two crystal structures that might be expected for BaF_2, the MgF_2 structure and the CaF_2 structure, which would you assign to it on the basis of values of the ionic radii?

22-12. Lithium vapor is an equilibrium mixture of molecules Li and Li_2. What is the electronic structure of Li_2? Calculate the Li—Li bond energy from the values of enthalpy of formation given in Table 22-3.

22-13. What is the value of the Li—H bond energy in LiH(g)? (See Table 22-3.)

22-14. When liquid NaH is electrolyzed, hydrogen is evolved at the anode. Explain in terms of the electronic structure of the substance. What volume of H_2 (standard conditions) would be produced per faraday?

22-15. Do you think that lanthanum metal could be made from lanthanum oxide by reaction with aluminum powder (see Table 22-7)?

22-16. Why is the presence of coesite or stishovite near a crater taken as evidence that the crater was formed by impact of a meteorite? In what way is the principle of Le Chatelier involved in your answer?

22-17. Using the relation of Exercise 12-48, evaluate the electronegativities of the five alkali metals. Values of the enthalpy of ionization can be obtained from Table 22-3, and the electron affinity of the alkali-metal atoms (for which there are no experimental values) can be taken as zero. (Answer: 0.99, 0.95, 0.80, 0.77, 0.72.)

22-18. From values given in Table 22-5, calculate the enthalpy of removal of the first electron and that of the second electron from each of the alkaline-earth metals.

22-19. Using the method of Exercises 12-48 and 22-17, find the divisor of the first ionization enthalpy (previous Exercise) for the five alkaline-earth elements that gives for the sum of their electronegativities the same value as in Table 9-1, and calculate the electronegativities. (Answer: 141 kcal/mole; 1.53, 1.26, 1.01, 0.94, 0.86.)

22-20. The amount of covalent character of their bonds is such that in the compounds of the alkaline-earth metals the metal atoms have electric charge approximately $+1$. The Mulliken method of evaluating the electronegativity might accordingly be applied by assuming proportionality to the sum of the first and second ionization energies. Using the results of Exercise 22-18, calculate the appropriate divisor and the corresponding electronegativity values. (Answer: 415 kcal/mole; 1.54, 1.27, 1.01, 0.94, 0.85.)

22-21. On the assumptions that Equation 9-1 gives the heat of formation of a compound in its standard state from the elements in their standard states and that the electronegativity of chlorine is 3.00, use the values of enthalpy of formation of dichlorides in Table 22-5 to evaluate the electronegativities of the alkaline-earth metals. (Answer: 1.37, 1.18, 0.97, 0.93, 0.89.)

22-22. Apply the method of Exercise 22-20 to obtain electronegativity values for B, Al, Sc, Y, and La (Table 22-7). Note that a different divisor (377 kcal/mole) is to be used; the need for a different divisor results from the difference in electronic interactions for atoms with different numbers of valence electrons and different Russell-Saunders states. (Answer: 2.06, 1.53, 1.20, 1.17, 1.15.)

22-23. Apply the method of Exercise 22-21 to the trichlorides of Table 22-7 to obtain electronegativity values. (Answer: 1.84, 1.45, 1.21, 1.16, 1.05.)

22-24. Discuss the properties of a series of compounds discussed in this chapter in relation to electronic structure, electronegativity, and atomic sizes.

CHAPTER 23

Inorganic Complexes and the

Chemistry of the Transition Metals

23-1. The Nature of Inorganic Complexes

An inorganic molecule that contains several atoms, including one or more metal atoms, is called an *inorganic complex*. An example is nickel tetracarbonyl, $Ni(CO)_4$. An inorganic complex with an electric charge is called a *complex ion*. Familiar examples of complex ions are the ferrocyanide ion, $Fe(CN)_6^{----}$, the ferricyanide ion, $Fe(CN)_6^{---}$, the hydrated aluminum ion, $Al(H_2O)_6^{+++}$, and the deep blue cupric ammonia complex ion, $Cu(NH_3)_4^{++}$, which is formed by adding ammonium hydroxide to a solution of cupric salt. Complex ions are important in the methods of separation used in qualitative and quantitative chemical analysis and in various industrial processes.

The formation of complexes constitutes an especially important part of the chemistry of the transition metals. The special feature of the electronic structure of the transition metals that leads to their formation of stable complexes is the availability of d orbitals, as well as s and p orbitals, for bond formation, as discussed in the following section.

23-2. Tetrahedral, Octahedral, and Square Bond Orbitals

The transition metals have in their outer shells electrons occupying d, s, and p orbitals. Thus for the elements from potassium to krypton the outer-shell electrons may occupy the five $3d$ orbitals, the $4s$ orbital, and the three $4p$ orbitals, and in the succeeding sequences of transition metals the available orbitals are similar, but with increase of the total quantum number by 1 or 2.

The different transition metals have different numbers of d orbitals available for hybridization with the s orbital and the three p orbitals of the valence shell, to form bond orbitals, and the nature of the bonds formed by the metal atom depends upon the number of d orbitals available. With no d orbitals available, tetrahedral sp^3 bond orbitals of the type described in Chapter 9 may be formed. An example is provided by the zinc ion, Zn^{++}. The zinc ion has ten electrons outside of the argon shell. These ten electrons can occupy the five $3d$ orbitals in pairs, leaving the $4s$ orbital and the three $4p$ orbitals available for hybridization to form four tetrahedral bond orbitals. It is in fact found by experiment that bipositive zinc has ligancy four, forming complexes in which four atoms or groups of atoms are tetrahedrally bonded to it. Among the complexes of this sort that are discussed in following sections of the chapter and later chapters are $Zn(NH_3)_4^{++}$, $Zn(OH)_4^{--}$, and $Zn(CN)_4^{--}$.

Octahedral Orbitals.   The doubly charged iron cation, Fe^{++}, has six electrons outside of the argon shell. These six electrons can be placed in three of the five $3d$ orbitals, in pairs. The ion would then have two $3d$ orbitals available to hybridize with the $4s$ orbital and the three $4p$ orbitals, to form six bond orbitals. These d^2sp^3 hybrid bond orbitals have been found to constitute a set of six orbitals with their maxima directed in the six tetrahedral directions (along the $+x$, $-x$, $+y$, $-y$, $+z$, and $-z$ directions in a set of Cartesian coordinates); that is, toward the corners of a regular octahedron. Bipositive iron might accordingly be expected to use these orbitals in forming an octahedral complex, and in fact the complex ion $Fe(CN)_6^{----}$ has been shown by x-ray diffraction of ferrocyanide crystals to have the octahedral structure. Other examples of octahedral complexes are described in later sections of this chapter.

The electronic structure that would be expected for an isolated Fe^{++} ion is the one in which four of the $3d$ orbitals are occupied by single electrons, with parallel spin, and one is occupied by a pair of electrons. The ion with this structure would have a magnetic moment corresponding to four unpaired electron spins in parallel orientation. It is found by experiment that the hydrated ferrous ion, $Fe(H_2O)_6^{++}$, has a magnetic moment with this value, whereas the ferrocyanide ion has no magnetic moment. The conclusion can be drawn that the bonds in these two complex ions are different in character: in the hydrated ferrous ion the bonds, which have a large amount of ionic character, are formed with use of the $4s$ orbital and the three $4p$ orbitals, whereas in the ferrocyanide ion the orbitals are d^2sp^3 covalent bonds. Investigation of the magnetic properties of a complex can in many cases permit a decision to be made as to the nature of the bond orbitals used by the metal atom. It has been found by use of this magnetic criterion that complexes of metals with strongly electronegative atoms or groups are usually essentially ionic in character (without the $3d$ orbitals used in bonding), whereas those with less electronegative atoms or groups are covalent in character (with use of $3d$ orbitals in the hybrid bond orbitals).

Square Bond Orbitals.   The bipositive nickel ion, Ni^{++}, has eight electrons outside of the argon shell. These eight electrons may be introduced in the five $3d$ orbitals in two ways: either by placing three electron pairs in three of the $3d$ orbitals and an odd electron in each of the other two, with their spins parallel, or by placing four electron pairs in four of the $3d$ orbitals, leaving one $3d$ orbital available for bond formation. Complexes in which bipositive nickel has the first electronic structure would have a magnetic moment, leading to paramagnetism, whereas those in which bipositive nickel has the second structure would have zero magnetic moment.

It has been found by study of the magnetic properties of different compounds of bipositive nickel that some of them, such as the hydrated nickel ion, are paramagnetic, and accordingly form bonds in which the $3d$ orbitals do not participate. Others, such as the nickel tetracyanide ion, $Ni(CN)_4^{--}$, have no magnetic moment, and the bonds may be considered to be formed by bond orbitals involving one $3d$ orbital.

The hybrid bond orbitals that can be formed by one $3d$ orbital, one $4s$ orbital, and the set of $3p$ orbitals are four bond orbitals that lie in a plane and are directed toward the corners of a square. (The third p orbital is not involved in this set of bond orbitals.) X-ray examination of crystals has shown that bipositive nickel, palladium, and platinum form complexes of this square planar type.

The Discovery of Octahedral and Square Complexes.   The concept of the coordination of ions or groups of atoms in a definite geometric arrangement about a central metal atom was developed shortly after the beginning of the present century by the Swiss chemist A. Werner (1866–1919) to account for the existence and properties of compounds such as K_2SnCl_6, $Co(NH_3)_6I_3$, etc. Before Werner's work was carried out these compounds had been assigned formulas such as $SnCl_4 \cdot 2KCl$ and $CoI_3 \cdot 6NH_3$, and had been classed as "molecular compounds," of unknown nature. Werner showed that the properties of many complexes formed by various transition metals could be explained by the postulate that the metal atoms have ligancy 6, with the six attached groups arranged about the central atom at the corners of a circumscribed regular octahedron.

One important property that Werner explained in this way is the existence of *isomers of inorganic complexes*. For example, there are two complexes with the formula $Co(NH_3)_4Cl_2^+$, one of which is violet in color and one green. Werner identified these two complexes with the cis and trans structures shown in Figure 23-1. In the cis form the chloride ions are in adjacent positions, and

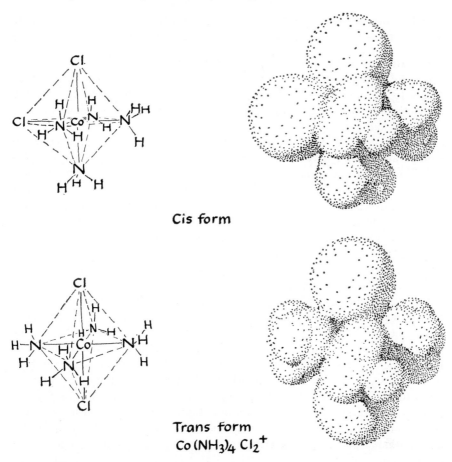

Cis form

Trans form
Co (NH₃)₄ Cl₂⁺

Figure **23-1**

The cis and trans isomers of the cobaltic tetrammine dichloride ions, $Co(NH_3)_4Cl_2^+$. In the cis form the two chlorine atoms occupy adjacent corners of the coordination octahedron about the cobalt atom, and in the trans form the two chlorine atoms occupy opposite corners.

in the trans form in opposite positions. Werner identified the violet complex with the cis configuration through the observation that it could be made easily from the carbonate-ammonia complex $Co(NH_3)_4CO_3^+$, for which only the cis form is possible. Werner also discovered square coordination and identified the square cis and trans isomers.

   In recent years a great amount of information about the structure of inorganic complexes has been gathered by the methods of x-ray diffraction, measurement of magnetic susceptibility, magnetic resonance spectroscopy, Mössbauer spectroscopy, and other techniques. This information about the structure of complexes has been correlated with their chemical properties in such a way as to bring reasonable order into this field of chemistry.

Configurations about Atoms with Unshared Electron Pairs. It has been found by experiment that in most molecules an unshared pair of electrons seems to occupy one of the corners of a coordination polyhedron, with approximately the same configuration as for a molecule with a bond in place of the unshared pair.

For example, molecules such as NH_3 and PCl_3 have trigonal pyramidal configurations that may be described as involving bonds directed approximately toward three corners of a tetrahedron, with the fourth corner occupied by the unshared electron pair. A similar description can be given to the water molecule, in which two bonds are directed approximately toward two corners of a tetrahedron and the two unshared electron pairs of the oxygen atom can be described as occupying the other two corners.

The bond angles are, however, a few degrees different from the tetrahedral angle, because of the larger amount of p character for the bond orbitals than for tetrahedral bond orbitals.

For a molecule in which the central atom forms five bonds and has one unshared pair an octahedral arrangement is to be expected, with the bonds directed toward the five corners of a square pyramid and the unshared pair occupying the sixth octahedral corner. The molecule BrF_5 has been shown to have this configuration. The bromine atom lies about 0.15 Å below the base of the pyramid, so that the F—Br—F bond angles (from the apical fluorine atom to the basal atoms) are about 86°. Accordingly the unshared electron pair occupies a somewhat larger volume about the bromine atom than the shared pairs occupy. Similarly, in ammonia, water, and related molecules each unshared pair can be described as occupying a larger solid angle than a shared pair.

The molecule PCl_5, with five shared pairs in the outer shell of the phosphorus atom, has the configuration of a trigonal bipyramid. The molecule $TeCl_4$ is similar to PCl_5, except that one unshared electron pair replaces one of the bonds. The unshared pair lies in the basal plane, rather than in one of the apical positions. Bromine trifluoride, BrF_3, can also be described as being based upon the trigonal bipyramid. The three fluorine atoms lie in the same plane as the bromine atom, the bond angles having the value 86°. The molecule can be described as forming bonds toward the two apical positions of the trigonal bipyramid and toward one of the three equatorial positions, with unshared electron pairs occupying the two other equatorial positions.

23-3. Ammonia Complexes

A solution of a cupric salt is blue in color. This blue color is due to the absorption of yellow and red light, and consequent preferential transmission of blue light. The molecular species that absorbs the light is the *hydrated* *copper ion*, probably $Cu(H_2O)_4^{++}$. Crystalline hydrated cupric salts such as $CuSO_4 \cdot 5H_2O$ are blue, like the aqueous solution, whereas anhydrous $CuSO_4$ is white.*

When a few drops of sodium hydroxide solution are added to a cupric solution a blue precipitate is formed. This is cupric hydroxide, $Cu(OH)_2$, which precipitates when the ion concentration product $[Cu^{++}][OH^-]^2$ reaches the value corresponding to a saturated solution of the hydroxide. (Here the symbol Cu^{++} is used, as is conventional, for the ion species $Cu(H_2O)_4^{++}$.) Addition of more sodium hydroxide solution leads to no further change.

If ammonium hydroxide is added in place of sodium hydroxide the same precipitate of $Cu(OH)_2$ is formed. On addition of more ammonium hydroxide, however, the precipitate dissolves, giving a clear solution with a deeper and more intense blue color than the original cupric solution.†

The solution of the precipitate cannot be attributed to increase in hydroxide-ion concentration, because sodium hydroxide does not cause it, nor to ammonium ion, because ammonium salts do not cause it. There remains undissociated NH_4OH or NH_3, which might combine with the cupric ion. It has in fact been found that the new deep blue ion species formed by addition of an excess of ammonium hydroxide is the **cupric ammonia complex** $Cu(NH_3)_4^{++}$, similar to the hydrated cupric ion except that the four water molecules have been replaced by ammonia molecules. This complex is sometimes called the *cupric tetrammine complex*, the word *ammine* meaning an attached ammonia molecule.

Salts of this complex ion can be crystallized from ammonia solution. The best known one is **cupric tetrammine sulfate monohydrate,** $Cu(NH_3)_4SO_4 \cdot H_2O$, which has the same deep blue color as the solution.

The reason that the precipitate of cupric hydroxide dissolves in an excess of ammonium hydroxide can be given in the following way. A precipitate of cupric hydroxide is formed because the concentration of cupric ion and the concentration of hydroxide ion are greater than the values corresponding to the solubility product of cupric hydroxide. If there were some way for copper to be present in the solution without exceeding the solubility product of cupric hydroxide, then precipitation would not occur. In the presence of ammonia, copper exists in the solution not as the cupric ion (that is, the hydrated cupric ion), but principally as the cupric ammonia complex, $Cu(NH_3)_4^{++}$. This complex is far more stable than the hydrated cupric ion. The reaction of formation of the cupric ammonia complex is

$$Cu^{++} + 4NH_3 \rightleftharpoons Cu(NH_3)_4^{++}$$

We see from the equation for the reaction that the addition of ammonia to the solution causes the equilibrium to shift to the right, more of the cupric

* The crystal structure of $CuSO_4 \cdot 5H_2O$ shows that in the crystal four water molecules are attached closely to the cupric ion, and the fifth is more distant.

† In describing color the adjective deep refers not to intensity but to shade; deep blue tends toward indigo.

ion being converted into cupric ammonia complex as more and more ammonia is added to the solution. When sufficient ammonia is present a large amount of copper may exist in the solution as cupric ammonia complex, at the same time that the cupric ion concentration is less than that required to cause precipitation of cupric hydroxide. When ammonia is added to a solution in contact with the precipitate of cupric hydroxide, the cupric ion in the solution is converted to cupric ammonia complex, causing the solution to be unsaturated with respect to cupric hydroxide. The cupric hydroxide precipitate then dissolves, and if enough ammonia is present the process continues until the precipitate has dissolved completely.

This process of **solution of a slightly soluble substance through formation of a complex by one of its ions** is the basis of some of the most important practical applications of complex formation. Several examples are mentioned later in this chapter.

The nickel ion forms two rather stable ammonia complexes. When a small amount of ammonium hydroxide solution is added to a solution of a nickel salt (green in color) a pale green precipitate of nickel hydroxide, $Ni(OH)_2$, is formed. On addition of more ammonium hydroxide solution this dissolves to give a blue solution, which with still more ammonium hydroxide changes color to light blue-violet.

The light blue-violet complex is shown to be the **nickel hexammine ion,** $Ni(NH_3)_6^{++}$, by the facts that the same color is shown by crystalline $Ni(NH_3)_6Cl_2$ and other crystals containing six ammonia molecules per nickel ion, and that x-ray studies have revealed the presence in these crystals of octahedral complexes in which the six ammonia molecules are situated about the nickel ion at the corners of a regular octahedron. The structure of crystalline $Ni(NH_3)_6Cl_2$ is shown in Figure 23-2.

The blue complex is probably the **nickel tetramminedihydrate ion,** $Ni(NH_3)_4(H_2O)_2^{++}$. Careful studies of the change in color with increasing ammonia concentration indicate that the ammonia molecules are added one by one and that all the complexes $Ni(H_2O)_6^{++}$, $Ni(H_2O)_5NH_3^{++}$, $Ni(H_2O)_4(NH_3)_2^{++}$, $Ni(H_2O)_3(NH_3)_3^{++}$, $Ni(H_2O)_2(NH_3)_4^{++}$, $Ni(H_2O)(NH_3)_5^{++}$, and $Ni(NH_3)_6^{++}$ exist.

Several metal ions form ammonia complexes with sufficient stability to put the hydroxides into solution. Others, such as aluminum and iron, do not. The formulas of the stable complexes are given below. There is no great apparent order about the stability or composition of the complexes, except that often the unipositive ions add two, the bipositive ions four, and the terpositive ions six ammonia molecules.

The **silver ammonia complex,** $Ag(NH_3)_2^+$, is sufficiently stable for ammonium hydroxide to dissolve precipitated silver chloride by reducing the concentration of silver ion, $[Ag^+]$, below the value required for precipitation by the solubility product of AgCl. A satisfactory test for silver ion is the formation with chloride ion of a precipitate that is soluble in ammonium

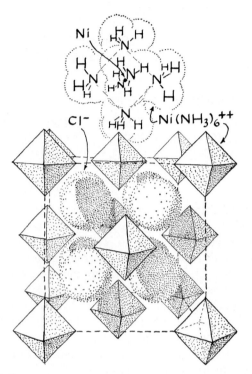

Figure **23-2**

The structure of crystalline nickel hexammine chloride, $Ni(NH_3)_6Cl_2$. The crystal contains octahedral nickel hexammine ions and chloride ions.

hydroxide. Ammonia complexes in general are decomposed by acid, because of formation of ammonium ion; for example, as in the reaction

$$Ag(NH_3)_2^+ + Cl^- + 2H^+ \longrightarrow AgCl + 2NH_4^+$$

Stable Ammonia Complexes

$Cu(NH_3)_2^+$	$Cu(NH_3)_4^{++}$	$Co(NH_3)_6^{+++}$
$Ag(NH_3)_2^+$	$Zn(NH_3)_4^{++}$	$Cr(NH_3)_6^{+++}$
$Au(NH_3)_2^+$	$Cd(NH_3)_4^{++}$	
	$Hg(NH_3)_2^{++}$	
	$Hg(NH_3)_4^{++}$	
	$Ni(NH_3)_4^{++}$	
	$Ni(NH_3)_6^{++}$	
	$Co(NH_3)_6^{++}$	

Notes: 1. Cobaltous ammonia ion is easily oxidized by air to cobaltic ammonia ion.
2. Chromic ammonia ion forms only slowly, and is decomposed by boiling, to give chromium hydroxide precipitate.

23-4. Cyanide Complexes

Another important class of complex ions includes those formed by the metal ions with cyanide ion. The common cyanide complexes are given in the following table.

Cyanide Complexes

$Cu(CN)_2^-$	$Zn(CN)_4^{--}$	$Fe(CN)_6^{---}$	$Au(CN)_4^-$
$Ag(CN)_2^-$	$Cd(CN)_4^{--}$	$Co(CN)_6^{---}$	
$Au(CN)_2^-$	$Hg(CN)_4^{--}$	$Mn(CN)_6^{----}$	
		$Fe(CN)_6^{----}$	
		$Co(CN)_6^{----}$	

Some of these complexes are very stable—the stability of the **argento-cyanide ion,** $Ag(CN)_2^-$, for example, is so great that addition of iodide ion does not cause silver iodide to precipitate, even though the solubility product of silver iodide is very small. The **ferrocyanide ion,** $Fe(CN)_6^{----}$, **ferricyanide ion,** $Fe(CN)_6^{---}$, and **cobalticyanide ion,** $Co(CN)_6^{---}$, are so stable that they are not appreciably decomposed by strong acid. The others are decomposed by strong acid, with the formation of hydrocyanic acid, HCN.

An illustration of the stability of the ferrocyanide complex is provided by the old method of making potassium ferrocyanide, $K_4Fe(CN)_6$, by strongly heating nitrogenous organic material (such as dried blood and hides) with potassium hydroxide and iron filings.

The **cobaltocyanide ion,** $Co(CN)_6^{----}$, is, like the cobaltous ammonia complex, a very strong reducing agent; it is able to decompose water, liberating hydrogen, as it changes into cobalticyanide ion.

Cyanide solutions are used in the **electroplating** of gold, silver, zinc, cadmium, and other metals. In these solutions the concentrations of uncomplexed metal ions are very small, and this favors the production of a uniform fine-grained deposit. Other complex-forming anions (tartrate, citrate, chloride, hydroxide) are also used in plating solutions.

23-5. Complex Halogenides and Other Complex Ions

Nearly all anions can enter into complex formation with metal ions. Thus stannic chloride, $SnCl_4$, forms with chloride ion the stable **hexachlorostannate ion,** $SnCl_6^{--}$, which with cations crystallizes in an extensive series of salts. Various complexes of this kind are discussed below.

Many chloride complexes are known; representative are the following:

$$CuCl_2(H_2O)_2, \ CuCl_3(H_2O)^-, \ CuCl_4^{--}$$
$$AgCl_2^-, \ AuCl_2^-$$
$$HgCl_4^{--}$$
$$CdCl_4^{--}, \ CdCl_6^{----}$$

$$SnCl_6^{--}$$
$$PtCl_6^{--}$$
$$AuCl_4^{-}$$

The cupric chloride complexes are recognizable in strong hydrochloric acid solutions by their green color. The crystal $CuCl_2 \cdot 2H_2O$ is bright green, and x-ray studies have shown that it contains the complex molecule $CuCl_2(H_2O)_2$. The ion $CuCl_3(H_2O)^-$ is usually written $CuCl_3^-$; it is highly probable that the indicated water molecule is present, and, indeed, the ion $Cu(H_2O)_3Cl^+$ very probably also exists in solution.

The stability of the **tetrachloroaurate ion,** $AuCl_4^-$, is responsible for the ability of aqua regia, a mixture of nitric and hydrochloric acids, to dissolve gold, which is not significantly soluble in the acids separately. Nitric acid serves as the oxidizing agent that oxidizes gold to the terpositive state, and the chloride ions provided by the hydrochloric acid further the reaction by combining with the auric ion to form the stable complex:

$$Au + 4HCl + 3HNO_3 \longrightarrow HAuCl_4 + 3NO_2 + 3H_2O$$

The solution of platinum in aqua regia likewise results in the stable **hexachloroplatinate ion,** $PtCl_6^{--}$.

The bromide and iodide complexes closely resemble the chloride complexes, and usually have similar formulas.

Fluoride ion is more effective than the other halogenide ions in forming complexes. Important examples are the **tetrafluoroborate ion,** BF_4^-, the **hexafluorosilicate ion,** SiF_6^{--}, the **hexafluoroaluminate ion,** AlF_6^{---}, and the **ferric hexafluoride ion,** FeF_6^{---}.

A useful complex is that formed by thiosulfate ion, $S_2O_3^{--}$, and silver ion. Its formula is $Ag(S_2O_3)_2^{---}$, and its structure is

This complex ion is sufficiently stable to cause silver chloride and bromide to be soluble in thiosulfate solutions, and this is the reason that sodium thiosulfate solution ("hypo") is used after development of a photographic film or paper to dissolve away the unreduced silver halogenide, which if allowed to remain in the emulsion would in the course of time darken through long exposure to light.

Of the nitrite complexes that with cobaltic ion, $Co(NO_2)_6^{---}$, called the **cobaltinitrite ion** or **hexanitrocobaltic ion,** is the most familiar. **Potassium cobaltinitrite,** $K_3Co(NO_2)_6$, is one of the least soluble potassium salts, and its precipitation on addition of sodium cobaltinitrite reagent is commonly used as a test for potassium ion.

Ferric ion and thiocyanate ion combine to give a product with an intense red color; this reaction is used as a test for ferric ion. The red color seems to be due to various complexes, ranging from $Fe(H_2O)_5NCS^{++}$ to $Fe(NCS)_6^{---}$. The azide ion, NNN^-, gives a similar color with ferric ion.

The Chromic and Cobaltic Complexes. Terpositive chromium and cobalt combine with cyanide ion, nitrite ion, chloride ion, sulfate ion, oxalate ion, water, ammonia, and many other ions and molecules to form a very great number of complexes, with a wide range of colors that are nearly the same for corresponding chromic and cobaltic complexes. Most of these complexes are stable, and are formed and decomposed slowly. Representative are the members of the series

$$Cr(NH_3)_6^{+++} \qquad\qquad Cr(NH_3)_5Cl^{++} \qquad\qquad Cr(NH_3)_4Cl_2^{+}$$
Yellow   Purple   Green

$$Cr(NH_3)_3Cl_3 \qquad\qquad Cr(NH_3)_2Cl_4^{-}$$
Violet   Orange-red

and

$$Co(NH_3)_6^{+++} \qquad\qquad Co(NH_3)_5H_2O^{+++} \qquad \cdots \qquad Co(H_2O)_6^{+++}$$
Yellow   Rose-red   Purple

A group such as oxalate ion, $C_2O_4^{--}$, or carbonate ion, CO_3^{--}, may occupy two of the six coordination places in an octahedral complex; examples are $Co(NH_3)_4CO_3^{+}$ and $Cr(C_2O_4)_3^{---}$.

The often puzzling color changes shown by chromic solutions are due to reactions involving these complexes. Solutions containing chromic ion, $Cr(H_2O)_6^{+++}$, are purple in color; on heating they become green, because of the formation of complexes such as $Cr(H_2O)_4Cl_2^{+}$ and $Cr(H_2O)_5SO_4^{+}$. At room temperature these green complexes slowly decompose, again forming the purple solution.

23-6. Hydroxide Complexes

If sodium hydroxide is added to a solution containing zinc ion a precipitate of zinc hydroxide is formed:

$$Zn^{++} + 2OH^- \rightleftharpoons Zn(OH)_2$$

This hydroxide precipitate is of course soluble in acid; *it is also soluble in alkali.* On addition of more sodium hydroxide the precipitate goes back into solution, this process occurring at hydroxide-ion concentrations about 0.1 M to 1 M.

To explain this phenomenon we postulate the formation of a complex ion. The complex ion that is formed is the zincate ion, $Zn(OH)_4^{--}$, by the reaction

$$Zn(OH)_2 + 2OH^- \rightleftharpoons Zn(OH)_4^{--}$$

The ion is closely similar to other complexes of zinc, such as $Zn(H_2O)_4^{++}$, $Zn(NH_3)_4^{++}$, and $Zn(CN)_4^{--}$, with hydroxide ions in place of water or ammonia molecules or cyanide ions. The ion $Zn(H_2O)(OH)_3^-$ is also formed to some extent.

The following species that exist in zinc solutions of different pH values are the following:

Acidic solution $\begin{cases} Zn(H_2O)_4{}^{++} \\ Zn(H_2O)_3(OH)^+ \end{cases}$

Neutral solution $Zn(H_2O)_2(OH)_2 \rightleftharpoons Zn(OH)_2(c)$

Basic solution $\begin{cases} Zn(H_2O)(OH)_3{}^- \\ Zn(OH)_4{}^{--} \end{cases}$

The conversion of each complex into the following one occurs by removal of a proton from one of the four water molecules of the tetrahydrated zinc ion. Each of the complexes except $Zn(H_2O)_4{}^{++}$ and $Zn(OH)_4{}^{--}$ is amphiprotic (Sections 8-10, 16-8, 19-6).

The principal common amphiprotic hydroxides and their anions* are the following:

$Zn(OH)_2$	$Zn(OH)_4{}^{--}$,	zincate ion
$Al(OH)_3$	$Al(OH_2)_2(OH)_4{}^-$,	aluminate ion
$Cr(OH)_3$	$Cr(OH_2)_2(OH_4)^-$,	chromite ion
$Pb(OH)_2$	$Pb(OH)_3{}^-$,	plumbite ion
$Sn(OH)_2$	$Sn(OH)_3{}^-$,	stannite ion

In addition, the following hydroxides evidence acidic properties by combining with hydroxide ion to form complex anions:

$Sn(OH)_4$	$Sn(OH)_6{}^{--}$,	stannate ion
$As(OH)_3$	$As(OH)_4{}^-$,	arsenite ion
$As(OH)_5$	$AsO_4{}^{---}$,	arsenate ion
$Sb(OH)_3$	$Sb(OH)_4{}^-$,	antimonite ion
$Sb(OH)_5$	$Sb(OH)_6{}^-$,	antimonate ion

Except for arsenate ion, and possibly arsenite ion, the anions are hydroxide complexes as indicated.

The hydroxides listed above form hydroxide complex anions to a sufficient extent to make them soluble in moderately strong alkali. Other common hydroxides have weaker acidic properties: $Cu(OH)_2$ and $Co(OH)_2$ are only slightly soluble in very strong alkali, and $Cd(OH)_2$, $Fe(OH)_3$, $Mn(OH)_2$, and $Ni(OH)_2$ are effectively insoluble. The common analytical method of separation of Al^{+++}, Cr^{+++}, and Zn^{++} from Fe^{+++}, Mn^{++}, Co^{++}, and Ni^{++} with use of sodium hydroxide is based on these facts.

* Because of the difficulty of determining the amount of hydration of an ion in aqueous solutions, chemists have been slow to accept these formulas; the older formulas are $ZnO_2{}^{--}$, $AlO_2{}^-$, etc.

It is possible that plumbite ion and stannite ion contain more hydroxide groups than indicated.

23-7. Sulfide Complexes

Sulfur, which is directly below oxygen in the periodic table of the elements, has many properties similar to those of oxygen. One of these is the property of combining with another atom to form complexes; there exist *sulfo acids* (thio acids) of many elements similar to the oxygen acids. An example is *sulfophosphoric acid*, H_3PS_4, which corresponds exactly in formula to phosphoric acid, H_3PO_4. This sulfo acid is not of much importance; it is unstable, and hydrolyzes in water to phosphoric acid and hydrogen sulfide:

$$H_3PS_4 + 4H_2O \longrightarrow H_3PO_4 + 4H_2S$$

But other sulfo acids, such as *sulfarsenic acid*, H_3AsS_4, are stable, and are of use in analytical chemistry and in chemical industry.

All of the following arsenic acids are known:

$$H_3AsO_4 \qquad H_3AsO_3S \qquad H_3AsO_2S_2 \qquad H_3AsOS_3 \qquad H_3AsS_4$$

The structure of the five complex anions AsO_4^{---}, AsO_3S^{---}, $AsO_2S_2^{---}$, $AsOS_3^{---}$, and AsS_4^{---} is the same: an arsenic atom surrounded tetrahedrally by four other atoms, oxygen or sulfur.

Some metal sulfides are soluble in solutions of sodium sulfide or ammonium sulfide because of formation of a complex sulfo anion. The important members of this class are HgS, As_2S_3, Sb_2S_3, As_2S_5, Sb_2S_5, and SnS_2, which react with sulfide ion in the following ways:

$$HgS + S^{--} \rightleftharpoons HgS_2^{--}$$
$$As_2S_3 + 3S^{--} \rightleftharpoons 2AsS_3^{---}$$
$$Sb_2S_3 + 3S^{--} \rightleftharpoons 2SbS_3^{---}$$
$$As_2S_5 + 3S^{--} \rightleftharpoons 2AsS_4^{---}$$
$$Sb_2S_5 + 3S^{--} \rightleftharpoons 2SbS_4^{---}$$
$$SnS_2 + S^{--} \rightleftharpoons SnS_3^{--}$$

Mercuric sulfide is soluble in a solution of sodium sulfide and sodium hydroxide (to repress hydrolysis of the sulfide, which would decrease the sulfide-ion concentration), but not in a solution of ammonium sulfide and ammonium hydroxide, in which the sulfide-ion concentration is smaller. The other sulfides listed are soluble in both solutions. CuS, Ag_2S, Bi_2S_3, CdS, PbS, ZnS, CoS, NiS, FeS, MnS, and SnS are not soluble in sulfide solutions, but most of these form complex sulfides by fusion with Na_2S or K_2S. Although SnS is not soluble in Na_2S or $(NH_4)_2S$ solutions, it dissolves in solutions containing both sulfide and disulfide, Na_2S_2 or $(NH_4)_2S_2$, or sulfide and peroxide. The disulfide ion, S_2^{--}, or peroxide oxidizes the tin to the stannic level, and the sulfostannate ion is then formed:

$$SnS + S_2^{--} \rightleftharpoons SnS_3^{--}$$

Many schemes of qualitative analysis involve separation of the copper-group sulfides (PbS, Bi_2S_3, CuS, CdS) from the tin-group sulfides (HgS, As_2S_3,

As_2S_5, Sb_2S_3, Sb_2S_5, SnS, SnS_2) by treatment with Na_2S-Na_2S_2 solution, which dissolves only the tin-group sulfides.

23-8. The Quantitative Treatment of Complex Formation

The quantitative theory of chemical equilibrium, as discussed in earlier chapters, can be applied in a straightforward manner to problems involving the formation of complexes. Some of the ways in which this can be done are exemplified in the following paragraphs.

Example 1. Ammonium hydroxide is added to a cupric solution until a precipitate is formed, and the addition is continued until part of the precipitate has dissolved to give a deep blue solution. What would be the effect of dissolving some ammonium chloride in the solution?

Solution. The weak base NH_4OH is partially ionized and is in equilibrium with dissolved ammonia:

$$NH_3 + H_2O \rightleftarrows NH_4OH \rightleftarrows NH_4^+ + OH^-$$

Addition of NH_4Cl would increase $[NH_4]^+$, which would shift the equilibrium to the left, producing more NH_3 and decreasing the hydroxide-ion concentration. The precipitate $Cu(OH)_2$ is in equilibrium with the solution according to the reaction

$$Cu(OH)_2(c) + 4NH_3 \rightleftarrows Cu(NH_3)_4^{++} + 2OH^-$$

Both the increase of $[NH_3]$ and the decrease of $[OH^-]$ caused by addition of NH_4Cl to the solution would shift this reaction to the right; hence more of the precipitate would dissolve.

Table **23-1**

Ammonia Concentrations Producing 50%
Conversion of Metal Ions to Complexes

METAL ION	COMPLEX ION	AMMONIA CONCENTRATION
Cu^+	$Cu(NH_3)_2^+$	5×10^{-6}
Ag^+	$Ag(NH_3)_2^+$	2×10^{-4}
Zn^{++}	$Zn(NH_3)_4^{++}$	5×10^{-3}
Cd^{++}	$Cd(NH_3)_4^{++}$	5×10^{-2}
	$Cd(NH_3)_6^{++}$	10
Hg^{++}	$Hg(NH_3)_2^{++}$	2×10^{-9}
	$Hg(NH_3)_4^{++}$	2×10^{-1}
Cu^{++}	$Cu(NH_3)_4^{++}$	5×10^{-4}
Ni^{++}	$Ni(NH_3)_4^{++}$	5×10^{-2}
	$Ni(NH_3)_6^{++}$	5×10^{-1}
Co^{++}	$Co(NH_3)_6^{++}$	1×10^{-1}
Co^{+++}	$Co(NH_3)_6^{+++}$	1×10^{-6}

In Tables 23-1 and 23-2 there are given values of equilibrium constants or equivalent constants for the reactions of formation of some complexes. The values of equilibrium constants must be used with some caution in making calculations. Thus for the reaction

$$Cu^{++} + 4NH_3 \rightleftarrows Cu(NH_3)_4^{++}$$

we would write

$$K = \frac{[Cu(NH_3)_4^{++}]}{[Cu^{++}][NH_3]^4}$$

as the equilibrium constant, and expect the concentration ratio

$$[Cu(NH_3)_4^{++}]/[Cu^{++}]$$

to vary with the fourth power of the ammonia concentration. This is true, however, only as an approximation, because of the fact that the reaction is more complicated than this. Actually the ammonia molecules attach themselves to the copper ion one at a time (replacing water molecules), and an accurate treatment would require that there be considered the four successive equilibria

$$Cu(H_2O)_4^{++} + NH_3 \rightleftarrows Cu(H_2O)_3NH_3^{++} + H_2O$$
$$Cu(H_2O)_3NH_3^{++} + NH_3 \rightleftarrows Cu(H_2O)_2(NH_3)_2^{++} + H_2O$$
$$Cu(H_2O)_2(NH_3)_2^{++} + NH_3 \rightleftarrows CuH_2O(NH_3)_3^{++} + H_2O$$
$$CuH_2O(NH_3)_3^{++} + NH_3 \rightleftarrows Cu(NH_3)_4^{++} + H_2O$$

The consequence of the existence of these intermediate complexes is that the formation of the final product takes place over a larger range of values of the ammonia concentration than it would otherwise. If the complex were formed

Table **23-2**

Ion Concentrations Producing 50%
Conversion of Metal Ions to Complexes

METAL ION	COMPLEX ION	ION CONCENTRATION
Cu^+	$Cu(CN)_2^-$	1×10^{-8}
	$CuCl_2^-$	4×10^{-3}
Ag^+	$Ag(CN)_2^-$	3×10^{-11}
	$AgCl_2^-$	3×10^{-3}
	$Ag(NO_2)_2^-$	4×10^{-2}
	$Ag(S_2O_3)_2^{---}$	3×10^{-7}
Zn^{++}	$Zn(CN)_4^{--}$	1×10^{-4}
Cd^{++}	$Cd(CN)_4^{--}$	6×10^{-5}
	CdI_4^{--}	3×10^{-2}
Hg^{++}	$Hg(CN)_4^{--}$	5×10^{-11}
	$HgCl_4^{--}$	9×10^{-5}
	$HgBr_4^{--}$	4×10^{-6}
	HgI_4^{--}	1×10^{-8}
	$Hg(SCN)_4^{--}$	3×10^{-6}

in one step the change from 1% to 99% conversion would require only a tenfold increase in $[NH_3]$; it is found by experiment, however, that the ammonia concentration must be increased 10,000-fold to produce this conversion, as indicated by the color change.

23-9. Polydentate Complexing Agents

In analytical chemistry and industrial chemistry extensive use is made of complexing agents with more than one atom capable of attachment to the central metal atom in a complex. Such a complexing agent is called a *polydentate ligand* or a *chelating agent* (pronounced kee'lating; from the Greek word for claw).

An example is triaminotriethylamine (tren), with the following structural formula:

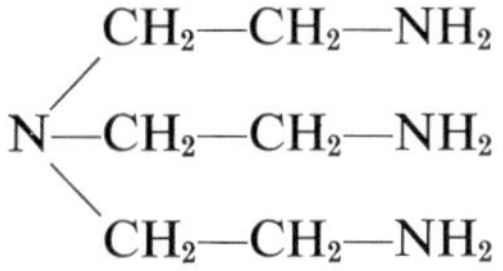

$$CH_2\!-\!CH_2\!-\!NH_2$$
$$N\!-\!CH_2\!-\!CH_2\!-\!NH_2$$
$$CH_2\!-\!CH_2\!-\!NH_2$$

All four nitrogen atoms of this molecule can coordinate with a metal atom. Thus the Zn^{++} ion forms a complex with tren in which each of the four nitrogen atoms uses its unshared pair of electrons to form a bond with the zinc atom and the nitrogen atoms are arranged approximately tetrahedrally about the central atom. The formation constant $[Zn(tren)^{++}]/[Zn^{++}][tren]$ for the complex between tren and Zn^{++}, 4.5×10^{14}, is over 400,000 times larger than that $[Zn(NH_3)_4{}^{++}]/[Zn^{++}][NH_3]^4$ of the reaction between the zinc ion and four ammonia molecules. The large value of the formation constant for the $Zn(tren)^{++}$ complex is primarily the result of the entropy factor (the fact that the four nitrogen atoms are not free to move about in the solution independently of one another, but are bonded to one another at approximately the same distance apart as in the complex).

Another polydentate complexing agent that forms complexes with many metal ions is EDTA (ethylenediaminetetra-acetic acid), with formula

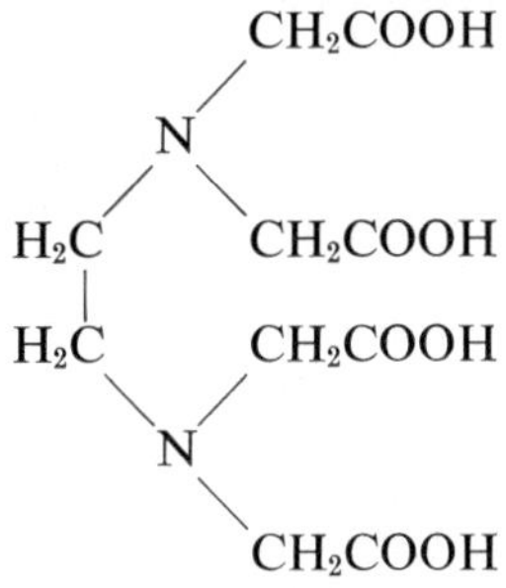

$$CH_2COOH$$
$$N$$
$$H_2C \qquad CH_2COOH$$
$$H_2C \qquad CH_2COOH$$
$$N$$
$$CH_2COOH$$

The anion of EDTA has a quadruple negative charge. The four carboxylate

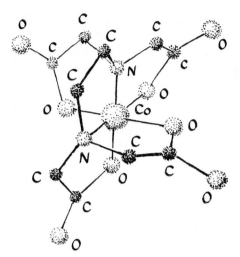

Figure 23-3 *The structure of the complex between tripositive cobalt and the anion of EDTA.*

ion groups and also the two nitrogen atoms can form bonds with a metal atom; the anion is accordingly a hexadentate complexing agent. In the stable complexes that it forms with many metal ions the two nitrogen atoms and four oxygen atoms, one of each carboxylate ion group, are approximately octahedrally arranged around the central ion. The structure of this complex with tripositive cobalt as determined by x-ray diffraction of a crystal containing the complex is shown in Figure 23-3.

EDTA (also called versene) is used in analytical chemistry and also in chemical industries. In many industrial processes, such as dyeing and the manufacture of soaps and detergents, even very small concentrations of heavy metal ions in the water interfere with the reactions. EDTA and similar agents (sequestering agents) convert the metal ions into complexes, which may not have the harmful properties of the metal ions.

EXERCISES

23-1. Discuss the effects of adding to three portions of a cupric solution (a) NH_4OH, (b) NaOH, (c) NH_4Cl. Write equations for the reactions.

23-2. To three portions of a solution containing Ni^{++} and Al^{+++} there are added (a) NaOH, (b) NH_4OH, (c) NaOH + NH_4OH. What happens in each case?

23-3. Is silver iodide more or less soluble in $1 F NH_4OH$ than in a solution $1 F$ in NH_4I and $1 F$ in NH_4OH? Why? [Note that there are two opposing effects—one resulting from the change in degree of ionization of NH_4OH and the other from the increase in concentration of iodide ion (Exercise 18-19). Which of these effects is the larger?]

23-4. Write the equation for the principal chemical reaction involved in fixing a photographic film.

23-5. Write the chemical equation for the solution of platinum in aqua regia. Explain why platinum dissolves in aqua regia but not in either hydrochloric acid or nitric acid alone.

23-6. Would sodium cyanide be an effective substitute for sodium thiosulfate as a fixer? (See Table 23-2 for data.)

23-7. Perchlorate ion is generally found to be the weakest complexing reagent of the common anions. Which solution is more acidic, $0.2 F Zn(ClO_4)_2$ or $0.2 F ZnCl_2$?

23-8. How many structural isomers of the octahedral complex $Co(NH_3)_3Cl_3$ are there?

23-9. How many isomers of the tetrahedral

complex $Zn(NH_3)_2Cl_2$ are there? Of the planar, square complex $Pt(NH_3)_2Cl_2$?

23-10. The silicon hexafluoride ion, SiF_6^{--}, is octahedral. What orbitals of the silicon atom are occupied by unshared electron pairs? By bonding electron pairs? What is the electric charge on the silicon atom and each fluorine atom, as calculated from electronegativity values?

23-11. The compounds K_2SiF_6, K_2SnF_6, and K_2SnCl_6 are known, but not K_2SiCl_6. Can you explain this fact?

23-12. The aqueous solution made by dissolving crystals of ferric nitrate, $Fe(NO_3)_3 \cdot 6H_2O$ (which has a violet color), is yellow. When an equal volume of strong nitric acid is added to the solution, it assumes a pale violet color. What reaction do you suggest to be responsible for the change in color?

23-13. How much triaminotriethylamine (Section 23-9) would need to be added to a 10,000-liter tank filled with a solution containing 1 mg of zinc ion per liter in order to decrease the concentration of Zn^{++} to one-millionth of 1 mg/liter?

23-14. In the crystal $KICl_4$ the four chlorine atoms of the ICl_4^- ion are located at the corners of a square about the iodine atom. What is the electronic structure of the complex? How many unshared pairs are there in the outer shell of the iodine atom? How would you describe the configuration of electron pairs around iodine?

23-15. The substances XeF_4 and KrF_4 were synthesized in 1962 and 1963. What is the electronic structure of their molecules? What arrangement in space of the four fluorine atoms around the central atom corresponds to the discussion in Section 23-2?

CHAPTER 24

Iron, Cobalt, Nickel, and the

Platinum Metals

In this chapter and in the two following chapters we shall discuss the chemistry of the transition metals—the elements that occur in the central region of the periodic table. These elements and their compounds have great practical importance. Their chemical properties are complex and interesting.

We shall begin the discussion of the transition metals with iron, cobalt, nickel, and the platinum metals, which lie in the center of the transition-metal region in the periodic table. The following chapter will be devoted to the elements that lie to the right of these metals; these are copper, zinc, and gallium and their congeners. Chapter 26 will deal with the chemistry of titanium, vanadium, chromium, and manganese and other elements of groups IVa, Va, VIa, and VIIa of the periodic table.

24-1. The Electronic Structures and Oxidation States of Iron, Cobalt, Nickel, and the Platinum Metals

The electronic structures of iron, cobalt, nickel, and the platinum metals are given in Table 24-1, as represented in the energy-level diagram of Figure 7-6. It is seen that each of the atoms has two outermost electrons, in the $4s$ orbital for iron, cobalt, and nickel, the $5s$ orbital for ruthenium, rhodium, and palladium, and the $6s$ orbital for osmium, iridium, and platinum. The next inner shell is incomplete, the $3d$ orbital (or $4d$, or $5d$) contains only six, seven, or eight electrons, instead of the full complement of ten.

The Russell-Saunders symbol for iron and its congeners in the normal state is $^5D_4$, that for cobalt and its congeners is $^4F_{9/2}$, and that for nickel and its congeners is $^3F_4$.

Table **24-1**

*The Electronic Structures of Iron, Cobalt, Nickel, and the
Platinum Metals*

Z	ELEMENT	K	L		M			N				O			P
		$1s$	$2s$	$2p$	$3s$	$3p$	$3d$	$4s$	$4p$	$4d$	$4f$	$5s$	$5p$	$5d$	$6s$
26	Fe	2	2	6	2	6	6	2							
27	Co	2	2	6	2	6	7	2							
28	Ni	2	2	6	2	6	8	2							
44	Ru	2	2	6	2	6	10	2	6	6		2			
45	Rh	2	2	6	2	6	10	2	6	7		2			
46	Pd	2	2	6	2	6	10	2	6	8		2			
76	Os	2	2	6	2	6	10	2	6	10	14	2	6	6	2
77	Ir	2	2	6	2	6	10	2	6	10	14	2	6	7	2
78	Pt	2	2	6	2	6	10	2	6	10	14	2	6	8	2

It might be expected that the two outermost electrons would be easily removed, to form a bipositive ion. In fact, iron, cobalt, and nickel all form important series of compounds in which the metal is bipositive. These metals also have one or more higher oxidation states. The platinum metals form covalent compounds representing various oxidation states between $+2$ and $+8$.

Iron can assume the oxidation states $+2$, $+3$, and $+6$, the last being rare, and represented by only a few compounds, such as potassium ferrate, K_2FeO_4. The oxidation states $+2$ and $+3$ correspond to the ferrous ion, Fe^{++}, and ferric ion, Fe^{+++}, respectively. The ferrous ion has six electrons in the incomplete $3d$ orbital, and the ferric ion has five electrons in this orbital. The magnetic properties of the compounds of iron and other transition elements are due to the presence of a smaller number of electrons in the $3d$ subshell than required to fill this subshell. For example, ferric ion can have all five of its $3d$ electrons with spins oriented in the same direction, because there are five $3d$ orbitals in the $3d$ subshell, and the Pauli principle permits parallel orientation of the spins of electrons so long as there is only one electron per orbital. The ferrous ion is easily oxidized to ferric ion by air or other oxidizing agents. Both bipositive and terpositive iron form complexes, such as the ferrocyanide ion, $Fe(CN)_6^{----}$, and the ferricyanide ion, $Fe(CN)_6^{---}$, but they do not form complexes with ammonia.

Cobalt(II) and cobalt(III) compounds are known; the cobalt(II) ion, Co^{++}, is more stable than the cobalt(III) ion, Co^{+++}, which is a sufficiently powerful oxidizing agent to oxidize water, liberating oxygen. But the covalent cobalt(III) complexes, such as the cobalticyanide ion, $Co(CN)_6^{---}$, are very stable, and the cobalt(II) complexes, such as the cobaltocyanide ion, $Co(CN)_6^{----}$, are unstable, being strong reducing agents.

Nickel forms only one series of salts, containing the nickel ion, Ni^{++}. A few compounds of nickel with higher oxidation number are known; of these the nickel(IV) oxide, NiO_2, is important.

Some standard enthalpy values are given in Table 24-2. They show the close similarity of the three metals. The most striking difference is that of

Table **24-2**

Standard Enthalpy of Formation of Compounds of Iron, Cobalt, and Nickel at 25°C (kcal/mole)

	M = Fe	Co	Ni
M(c)	0.00	0.00	0.00
M(g)	99.5	101.6	102.8
M$^+$(g)	280.7	283.9	280.3
M^{++}(g)	653.5	684.3	702.0
M^{++}(aq)	−21.0	−16.1	−15.3
M^{+++}(g)	1357		
M^{+++}(aq)	−11.4		
MO(c)	−63.8*	−57.1	−57.3
M$_2$O$_3$(c)	−196.8		
M$_3$O$_4$(c)	−267.8	−204	
MF$_2$(c)		−159	−159.5
MF$_2$(aq)	−177.8	−173.6	−171.5
MF$_3$	−243.1(aq)	−187(c)	
MCl$_2$(c)	−81.5	−77.8	−75.5
MCl$_3$(c)	−96.8		
MBr$_2$(c)	−60.02	−55.5	−54.2
MI$_2$(c)	−29.98	−24.4	−20.5
MS(c)	−22.72	−20.2	−17.5
M$_2$S$_3$(c)		−51	
MS$_2$(c)	−42.52 (pyrite) −36.88 (marcasite)		
MSe(c)	−16.5	−10	−10
MTe(c)	−18.6	−9	−9
M$_3$C(c)	5.0	9.5	11.0
MP(c)	−28	−35	

* For $Fe_{0.95}O$.

64 kcal/mole between the enthalpies of Fe_3O_4 and Co_3O_4. This difference can be attributed to the instability of Co(III) in forming largely ionic bonds.

As was mentioned in Chapter 20, iron, cobalt, and nickel are sexivalent in the metals and their alloys. This high metallic valence causes the bonds to be especially strong, and confers valuable properties of strength and hardness on the alloys.

24-2. Iron

Pure iron is a bright silvery-white metal, which tarnishes (rusts rapidly) in moist air or in water containing dissolved oxygen. It is soft, malleable, and ductile, and is strongly magnetic ("ferromagnetic"). Its melting point is 1535°C, and its boiling point 3000°C. Ordinary iron (alpha-iron) has the

Table 24-3

Some Physical Properties of Iron, Cobalt, and Nickel

	ATOMIC NUMBER	ATOMIC WEIGHT	DENSITY (g/cm³)	MELTING POINT	BOILING POINT	METALLIC RADIUS*	HEAT OF SUBLIMATION AT 25°C
Iron	26	55.847	7.86	1,535°C	3000°C	1.26 Å	96.7 kcal/mole
Cobalt	27	58.9332	8.93	1,480	2900	1.25	105
Nickel	28	58.71	8.89	1,452	2900	1.24	101.6

* For ligancy 12.

atomic arrangement shown in Figure 20-2 (the body-centered arrangement— each atom is in the center of a cube formed by the eight surrounding atoms). At 912°C alpha-iron undergoes a transition to another allotropic form, gamma-iron, which has the face-centered arrangement described for copper in Chapter 2 (Figures 2-4 and 2-5). At 1400°C another transition occurs, to delta-iron, which has the same body-centered structure as alpha-iron.

Pure iron, containing only about 0.01 % of impurities, can be made by electrolytic reduction of iron salts. It has little use; a small amount is used in analytical chemistry, and a small amount in the treatment of anemia.*

Metallic iron is greatly strengthened by the presence of a small amount of carbon, and its mechanical and chemical properties are also improved by moderate amounts of other elements, especially other transition metals. Wrought iron, cast iron, and steel are described in the following sections.

The Ores of Iron. The chief ores of iron are its oxides *hematite*, Fe_2O_3, and *magnetite*, Fe_3O_4, and its carbonate *siderite*, $FeCO_3$. The hydrated ferric oxides such a *limonite* are also important. The sulfide *pyrite*, FeS_2, is used as a source of sulfur dioxide, but the impure iron oxide left from its roasting is not satisfactory for smelting iron, because the remaining sulfur is a troublesome impurity.

The Metallurgy of Iron. The ores of iron are usually first roasted, in order to remove water, to decompose carbonates, and to oxidize sulfides. They are then reduced with coke, in a structure called a *blast furnace* (Figure 24-1). Ores containing limestone or magnesium carbonate are mixed with an acidic flux

* See hemoglobin, Chapter 28.

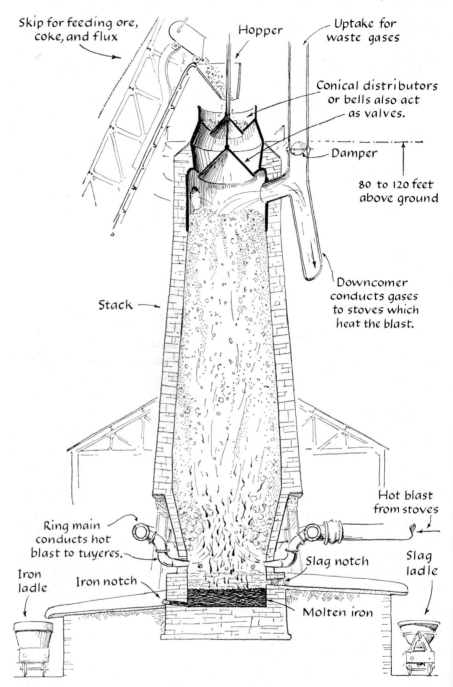

Skip for feeding ore, coke, and flux

Hopper

Uptake for waste gases

Conical distributors or bells also act as valves.

Damper

80 to 120 feet above ground

Stack

Downcomer conducts gases to stoves which heat the blast.

Hot blast from stoves

Ring main conducts hot blast to tuyeres.

Iron ladle

Iron notch

Slag notch

Molten iron

Slag ladle

Figure 24-1

A blast furnace for smelting iron ore.

(containing an excess of silica), such as sand or clay, in order to make a liquid *slag*. Limestone is used as flux for ores containing an excess of silica. The mixture of ore, flux, and coke is introduced at the top of the blast furnace, and preheated air is blown in the bottom through *tuyeres*.* As the solid materials slowly descend they are converted completely into gases, which escape at the top, and two liquids, molten iron and slag, which are tapped off at the bottom. The parts of the blast furnace where the temperature is highest are water-cooled, to keep the lining from melting.

The important reactions that occur in the blast furnace are the combustion of coke to carbon monoxide, the reduction of iron oxide by the carbon monoxide, and the combination of acidic and basic oxides (the impurities of the ore and the added flux) to form slag:

$$2C + O_2 \longrightarrow 2CO$$
$$3CO + Fe_2O_3 \longrightarrow 2Fe + 3CO_2$$
$$CaCO_3 \longrightarrow CaO + CO_2$$
$$CaO + SiO_2 \longrightarrow CaSiO_3$$

The slag is a glassy silicate mixture of complex composition, idealized as calcium metasilicate, $CaSiO_3$, in the above equation.

The hot exhaust gases, which contain some unoxidized carbon monoxide, are cleaned of dust and then are mixed with air and burned in large steel structures filled with fire brick. When one of these structures, which are called *stoves*, has thus been heated to a high temperature the burning exhaust gas is shifted to another stove and the heated stove is used to preheat the air for the blast furnace.

Cast Iron. The molten iron from the blast furnace, having been in contact with coke in the lower part of the furnace, contains several percent of dissolved carbon (usually about 3 or 4%), together with silicon, manganese, phosphorus, and sulfur in smaller amounts. These impuri-

*A tuyere is a nozzle through which an air-blast is delivered to a furnace, forge, or converter. The amount of coke required in smelting iron can be reduced by using air that has been enriched by addition of oxygen to about 23.5%. In blast furnaces using oxygen-enriched air, steam is also added to the air, in order to prevent the temperature in the blast furnace from becoming too high.

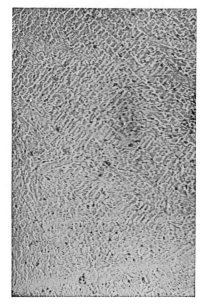

Figure **24-2** *A photomicrograph of white cast iron, which consists largely of the compound cementite, Fe_3C. Magnification $100\times$. [From Malleable Founders' Society.]*

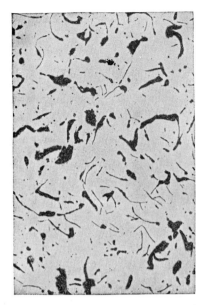

Figure 24-3   *A photomicrograph of gray cast iron, unetched. The white background is ferrite, and the black particles are flakes of graphite. Magnification 100×. [From Malleable Founders' Society.]*

ties lower its melting point from 1535°C, that of pure iron, to about 1200°C. This iron is often cast into bars called *pigs;* the cast iron itself is called *pig iron.*

When cast iron is made by sudden cooling from the liquid state it is white in color, and is called **white cast iron.** It consists largely of the compound *cementite*, Fe_3C, a hard, brittle substance (Figure 24-2).

Gray cast iron, made by slow cooling, consists of crystalline grains of pure iron (called *ferrite*) and flakes of graphite (Figure 24-3). Both white cast iron and gray cast iron are brittle, the former because its principal constituent, cementite, is brittle, and the latter because the tougher ferrite in it is weakened by the soft flakes of graphite distributed through it.

Malleable cast iron, which is tougher and less brittle than either white or ordinary gray cast iron, is made by heat treatment of gray cast iron of suitable composition. Under this treatment the flakes of graphite coalesce into globular particles, which, because of their small cross-sectional area, weaken the ferrite less than do the flakes (Figure 24-4).

Cast iron is the cheapest form of iron, but its usefulness is limited by its low strength. A great amount is converted into steel, and a smaller amount into wrought iron.

Wrought Iron.   Wrought iron is nearly pure iron, with only 0.1% or 0.2% carbon and less than 0.5% of all impurities. It is made by melting cast iron on a bed of iron oxide in a reverberatory furnace (Figure 24-5). As the molten cast iron is stirred, the iron oxide oxidizes the dissolved carbon to carbon monoxide, and the sulfur, phosphorus, and silicon are also oxidized and pass into the slag. As the impurities are removed, the melting point of the iron rises, and the mass becomes pasty. It is then taken out of the furnace and beaten under steam hammers to force out the slag.

Wrought iron is a strong, tough metal which can be readily welded and forged. In past years it was extensively used for making chains, wire, and similar objects. It has now been largely displaced by mild steel.

24-3. Steel

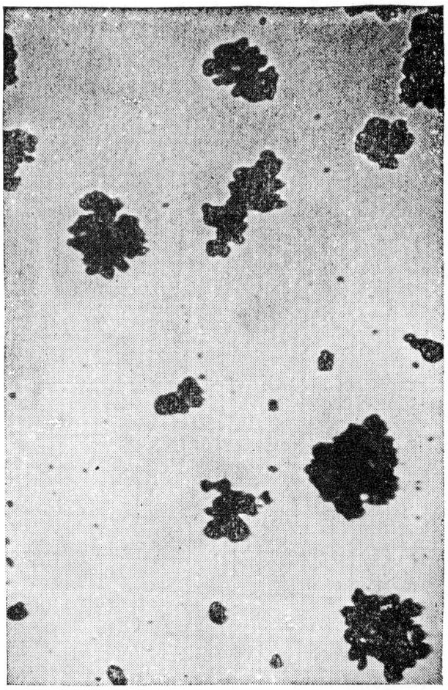

Steel is a purified alloy of iron, carbon, and other elements that is manufactured in the liquid state. Most steels are almost free from phosphorus, sulfur, and silicon, and contain between 0.1 and 1.5% of carbon. *Mild steels* are low-carbon steels (less than 0.2%). They are malleable and ductile, and are used in place of wrought iron. They are not hardened by being quenched (suddenly cooled) from a red heat. *Medium steels*, containing from 0.2 to 0.6% carbon, are used for making rails and structural elements (beams, girders, etc.). Mild steels and medium steels can be forged and welded. *High-carbon steels* (0.75 to 1.50% carbon) are used for making razors, surgical instruments, drills, and other tools. Medium steels and high-carbon steels can be hardened and tempered (see section on Properties of Steel).

At the end of World War I the United States had a steel-making capacity of nearly 50,000,000 tons of steel per year; by the end of World War II this capacity had been nearly doubled, and by 1963 tripled.

Figure **24-4** *A photomicrograph of malleable cast iron, showing ferrite (background) and globular particles of graphite. Unetched. Magnification 100×. [From Malleable Founders' Society.]*

Steel is made from pig iron chiefly by the *open-hearth process* (by which over 80% of that produced in the United States is made), the *Bessemer process*, and the *oxygen top-blowing process*. In each process either a basic or an acidic lining may be used in the furnace or converter. A basic lining (lime, magnesia, or a mixture of the two) is used if the pig iron contains elements, such as phosphorus, that form acidic oxides, and an acidic lining (silica) if the pig iron contains base-forming elements.

The Open-Hearth Process. Open-hearth steel is made in a reverberatory furnace; that is, a furnace in which the flame is reflected by the roof onto the material to be heated (Figure 24-5). Cast iron is melted with scrap steel and some hematite in a furnace heated with gas or oil fuel. The fuel and air (sometimes enriched with oxygen) are preheated by passage through a lattice of hot brick at one side of the furnace, and a similar lattice on the other side is heated by the hot outgoing gases. From time to time the direction of

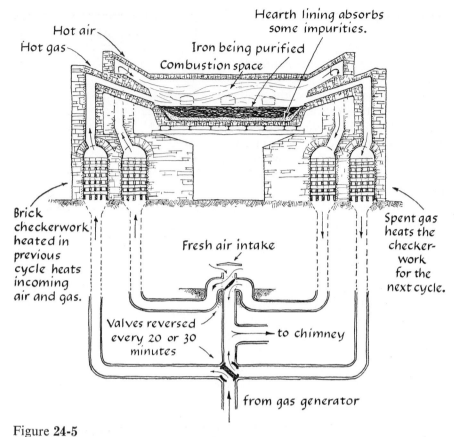

Figure 24-5

Reverberatory furnace, used for making wrought iron and steel.

flow of gas is reversed. The carbon and other impurities in the molten iron are oxidized by the hematite and by excess air in the furnace gas. Analyses are made during the run, which requires about 8 hours, and when almost all the carbon is oxidized the amount desired for the steel is added as coke or as a high-carbon alloy, usually ferromanganese or spiegeleisen. The molten steel is then cast into billets. Open-hearth steel of very uniform quality can be made, because the process can be closely checked by analyses during the several hours of the run.

The Bessemer Process.   The Bessemer process of making steel was invented by an American, William Kelly, in 1852 and independently by an Englishman, Henry Bessemer, in 1855. Molten pig iron is poured into an egg-shaped converter (Figure 24-6). Air is blown up through the liquid from tuyeres in the bottom, oxidizing silicon, manganese, and other impurities and finally the carbon. In about ten minutes the reaction is nearly complete, as is seen from the change in character of the flame of burning carbon monoxide from the mouth of the converter. High-carbon alloy is then added, and the steel is poured.

The Bessemer process is inexpensive, but the steel is not as good as open-hearth steel.

The Oxygen Top-blowing Process. Since 1955 an increasing fraction of the steel produced in the United States has been made by a new process, the oxygen top-blowing process. Iron is placed in a converter resembling the Bessemer converter (Figure 24-6), but without the tuyeres at the base. Pure oxygen (99.5%) is then blown onto the surface of the molten metal through a long water-cooled copper lance, to oxidize carbon and phosphorus. The treatment of the charge of 50 to 250 tons is completed in 40 or 50 minutes. This process gives steel of high quality.

Figure **24-6**

    Bessemer converter, used for making steel from pig iron.

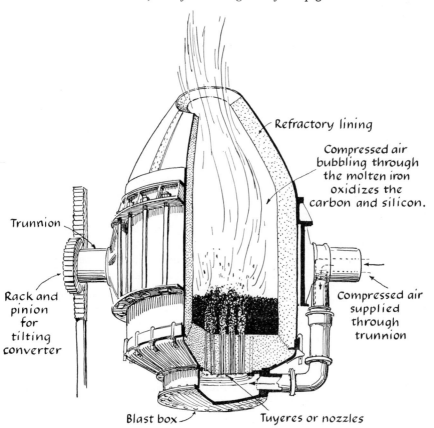

The Properties of Steel. When high-carbon steel is heated to bright redness and slowly cooled, it is comparatively soft. However, if it is rapidly cooled, by quenching in water, oil, or mercury, it becomes harder than glass, and brittle instead of tough. This hardened steel can be "tempered" by suitable reheating, to give a product with the desired combination of hardness and toughness. Often the tempering is carried out in such a way as to leave a very hard cutting edge backed up by softer, tougher metal.

The amount of tempering can be estimated roughly by the interference colors of the thin film of oxide formed on a polished surface of the steel during reheating: a straw color (230°C) corresponds to a satisfactory temper for razors, yellow (250°C) for pocket knives, brown (260°C) for scissors and chisels, purple (270°C) for butcher knives, blue (290°C) for watch springs, and blue-black (320°C) for saws.

These processes of hardening and tempering can be understood by consideration of the phases that can be formed by iron and carbon. Carbon is soluble in gamma-iron, the form stable above 912°C. If the steel is quenched from above this temperature there is obtained a solid solution of carbon in gamma-iron. This material, called *martensite*, is very hard and brittle (Figure 24-7). It confers hardness and brittleness upon hardened high-carbon steel. Martensite is not stable at room temperature, but its rate of conversion to more stable phases is so small at room temperature as to be negligible, and hardened steel containing martensite remains hard as long as it is not reheated.

Figure **24-7** *A photomicrograph of martensite, a constituent of hardened steel. Magnification 2000×. [From Dr. D. S. Clark.]*

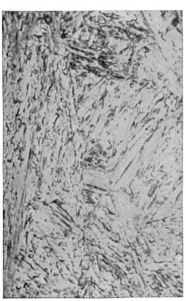

When hardened steel is tempered by mild reheating, the martensite undergoes transformation to more stable phases. The changes that it undergoes are complex, but result ultimately in a mixture of grains of alpha-iron (ferrite) and the hard carbide Fe_3C, cementite. Steel containing 0.9% carbon (*eutectoid steel*) changes on tempering into *pearlite*, which is composed of extremely thin alternating layers of ferrite and cementite (Figure 24-8). Pearlite is strong and tough. Steel containing less than 0.9% carbon (*hypo-eutectoid steel*) changes on tempering into a microcrystalline metal consisting of grains of ferrite and grains of pearlite (Figure 24-9), whereas that containing more than 0.9% carbon (*hyper-eutectoid steel*) on tempering yields grains of cementite and grains of pearlite.

Steel intended to withstand both shock and wear must be tough and strong and must also present a very hard surface. Steel objects with these properties are made by a process called *case-hardening.* Medium-carbon steel objects are heated in contact with carbon or sodium cyanide until a thin surface layer is converted into high-carbon steel, which can be hardened by suitable heat treatment. Some alloy steels are case-hardened by formation of a surface layer of metal nitrides, by heating the objects in an atmosphere of ammonia.

Alloy Steels. Many alloy steels, steel containing considerable amounts of metals other than iron, have valuable properties and extensive industrial uses. Manganese steel (12 to 14% Mn) is extraordinarily hard, and crushing and grinding machines and safes are made of it. Nickel steels have many special uses. Chromium-vanadium steel (5 to 10% Cr, 0.15% V) is tough and elastic, and is used

Figure **24-8** *A photomicrograph of pearlite, showing lamellae of ferrite and cementite. Magnification 1000×. [From Dr. D. S. Clark.]*

for automobile axles, frames, and other parts. Stainless steels usually contain chromium; a common composition is 18% Cr, 8% Ni. Molybdenum and tungsten steels are used for high-speed cutting tools.

24-4. Compounds of Iron

Iron is an active metal, which displaces hydrogen easily from dilute acids. It burns in oxygen to produce ferrous-ferric oxide, Fe_3O_4. This oxide is also made by interaction with superheated steam. One method of preventing rusting involves the production of an adherent surface layer of this oxide on iron.

Iron becomes *passive* when it is dipped in very concentrated nitric acid. It then no longer displaces hydrogen from dilute acids. However, a sharp blow on the metal produces a change that spreads over the surface from the point struck, the metal once more becoming active. This production of passivity is due to the formation of a protective layer of oxide, and the passivity is lost when the layer is broken. Passivity is also produced by other oxidizing agents, such as chromate ion; safety razor blades kept in a solution of potassium chromate remain sharp much longer than blades kept in air.

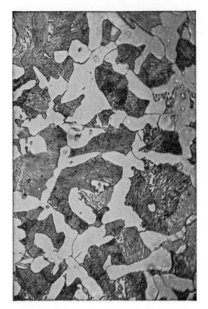

Figure **24-9**   *A photomicrograph of hypo-eutectoid steel, showing grains of pearlite. Carbon content of steel 0.38%. Magnification 500×.* [*From Dr. D. S. Clark.*]

When exposed to moist air, iron becomes oxidized, forming a loose coating of rust, which is a partially hydrated ferric oxide.

Ferrous Compounds. The ferrous compounds, containing bipositive iron, are usually green in color. Most of the ferrous salts are easily oxidized to the corresponding ferric salts through the action of atmospheric oxygen.

Ferrous sulfate, $FeSO_4 \cdot 7H_2O$, is made by dissolving iron in sulfuric acid, or by allowing pyrite to oxidize in air. The green crystals of the substance are efflorescent, and often have a brown coating of a ferric hydroxide-sulfate, produced by atmospheric oxidation. Ferrous sulfate is used in dyeing and in making ink. To make ink, a solution of tannic acid—a complex organic acid obtained by extraction of nut-galls—is mixed with ferrous sulfate, producing ferrous tannate. On oxidation by the air a fine black insoluble pigment is produced.

Ferrous chloride, $FeCl_2 \cdot 4H_2O$, is made by dissolving iron in hydrochloric acid. It is pale green in color. **Ferrous hydroxide,** $Fe(OH)_2$, is formed as a nearly white precipitate on addition of alkali to a ferrous solution. The precipitate rapidly becomes a dirty green, and finally brown, by oxidation by air. **Ferrous sulfide,** FeS, is a black compound made by heating iron filings with sulfur. It is used in making hydrogen sulfide. Ferrous sulfide is also obtained as a black precipitate by the action of sulfide ion on a ferrous salt in solution.

Ferrous carbonate, $FeCO_3$, occurs in nature as a mineral, and can be obtained as a white precipitate by the action of carbonate ion on ferrous ion in the absence of dissolved oxygen. Like calcium carbonate, ferrous carbonate is soluble in acidic waters. Hard waters often contain ferrous or ferric ion.

Ferric Compounds. The hydrated ferric ion, $Fe(H_2O)_6^{+++}$, is pale violet in color. The ion loses protons readily, however, and ferric salts in solution usually are yellow or brown, because of the formation of hydroxide complexes. **Ferric nitrate,** $Fe(NO_3)_3 \cdot 6H_2O$, exists as pale violet deliquescent crystals. Anhydrous **ferric sulfate,** $Fe_2(SO_4)_3$, is obtained as a white powder by evaporation of a ferric sulfate solution. **Iron alum,** $KFe(SO_4)_2 \cdot 12H_2O$, forms pale violet octahedral crystals.

Ferric chloride, $FeCl_3 \cdot 6H_2O$, is obtained as yellow deliquescent crystals by evaporation of a solution made by oxidation of ferrous chloride with chlorine. Solutions of ferric ion containing chloride ion are more intensely colored, yellow or brown, than nitrate or sulfate solutions because of the formation of ferric chloride complexes. Anhydrous ferric chloride, Fe_2Cl_6, can be made by passing chlorine over heated iron.

Ferric ion in solution can be reduced to ferrous ion by treatment with metallic iron or by reduction with hydrogen sulfide or stannous ion.

Ferric hydroxide, $Fe(OH)_3$, is formed as a brown precipitate when alkali is added to a solution of ferric ion. When it is strongly heated ferric hydroxide is converted into **ferric oxide,** Fe_2O_3, which, as a fine powder, is called *rouge* and, as a pigment, *Venetian red.*

Complex Cyanides of Iron. Cyanide ion added to a solution of ferrous or ferric ion forms precipitates, which dissolve in excess cyanide to produce complex ions. Yellow crystals of **potassium ferrocyanide,** $K_4Fe(CN)_6 \cdot 3H_2O$, are made by heating organic material, such as dried blood, with iron filings and potassium carbonate. The mass produced by the heating is extracted with warm water, and the crystals are made by evaporation of the solution. **Potassium ferricyanide,** $K_3Fe(CN)_6$, is made as red crystals by oxidation of ferrocyanide.

These substances contain the complexes *ferrocyanide ion*, $Fe(CN)_6^{----}$, and *ferricyanide ion*, $Fe(CN)_6^{---}$, respectively, and the ferrocyanides and ferricyanides of other metals are easily made from them.

The pigments *Turnbull's blue* and *Prussian blue* are made by addition of ferrous ion to a ferricyanide solution or ferric ion to a ferrocyanide solution. The pigments which precipitate have the approximate composition $KFeFe(CN)_6 \cdot H_2O$. They have a brilliant blue color. Ferrous ion and ferrocyanide ion produce a white precipitate of $K_2FeFe(CN)_6$, whereas ferric ion and ferricyanide ion form only a brown solution.

24-5. Cobalt

Cobalt occurs in nature in the minerals *smaltite*, $CoAs_2$, and *cobaltite*, $CoAsS$, usually associated with nickel. The metal is obtained by reducing the oxide with aluminum.

Metallic cobalt is silvery-white, with a slight reddish tinge. It is less reactive than iron, and displaces hydrogen slowly from dilute acids. It is used in special alloys, including *Alnico*, a strongly ferromagnetic alloy of aluminum, nickel, cobalt, and iron, which is used for making permanent magnets.

Cobalt ion, $Co(H_2O)_6^{++}$, in solution and in hydrated salts is red or pink in color. **Cobalt chloride,** $CoCl_2 \cdot 6H_2O$, forms red crystals, which when dehydrated change into a deep blue powder. Writing made with a dilute solution of cobalt chloride is almost invisible, but becomes blue when the paper is warmed, dehydrating the salt. **Cobalt oxide,** CoO, is a black substance which dissolves in molten glass, to give it a blue color (*cobalt glass*).

Terpositive cobalt ion is unstable, and an attempt to oxidize Co^{++} usually leads to the precipitation of **cobalt(III) hydroxide,** $Co(OH)_3$. The covalent compounds of cobalt(III) are very stable. The most important of these are **potassium cobaltinitrite,** $K_3Co(NO_2)_6$, and **potassium cobalticyanide,** $K_3Co(CN)_6$.

24-6.   Nickel

Nickel occurs, with iron, in meteorites. Its principal ores are *nickelite*, NiAs, *millerite*, NiS, and *pentlandite*, (Ni,Fe)S. The metal is produced as an alloy containing iron and other elements, by roasting the ore and reducing with carbon. In the purification of nickel by the Mond process the compound **nickel carbonyl,** $Ni(CO)_4$, is manufactured and then decomposed. The ore is reduced with hydrogen to metallic nickel under conditions such that the iron oxide is not reduced. Carbon monoxide is then passed through the reduced ore at room temperature; it combines with the nickel to form nickel carbonyl:

$$Ni + 4CO \longrightarrow Ni(CO)_4$$

Nickel carbonyl is a gas. It is passed into a decomposer heated to 150°C; the gas decomposes, depositing pure metallic nickel, and the liberated carbon monoxide is returned to be used again.

Nickel is a white metal, with a faint tinge of yellow. It is used in making alloys, including the copper-nickel alloy (75% Cu, 25% Ni) used in coinage. Iron objects are plated with nickel by electrolysis from an ammoniacal solution. The metal is still less reactive than cobalt, and displaces hydrogen only very slowly from acids.

The hydrated salts of nickel such as **nickel sulfate,** $NiSO_4 \cdot 6H_2O$, and **nickel chloride,** $NiCl_2 \cdot 6H_2O$, are green in color. **Nickel(II) hydroxide,** $Ni(OH)_2$, is formed as an apple-green precipitate by addition of alkali to a solution containing nickel ion. When heated it produces the insoluble green substance **nickel(II) oxide,** NiO. Nickel(II) hydroxide is soluble in ammonium hydroxide, forming ammonia complexes such as $Ni(NH_3)_4(H_2O)_2^{++}$ and $Ni(NH_3)_6^{++}$.

In alkaline solution nickel(II) hydroxide can be oxidized to a hydrated **nickel(IV) oxide,** $NiO_2 \cdot xH_2O$. This reaction is used in the *Edison storage cell*. The electrodes of this cell are plates coated with $NiO_2 \cdot xH_2O$ and metallic iron, which are converted on discharge of the cell into nickel(II) hydroxide and ferrous hydroxide, respectively. The electrolyte in this cell is a solution of sodium hydroxide.

24-7.   The Platinum Metals

The congeners of iron, cobalt, and nickel are the *platinum metals*—ruthenium, rhodium, palladium, osmium, iridium, and platinum. Some properties of these elements are given in Table 24-4.

Table **24-4**

Some Physical Properties of the Platinum Metals

	ATOMIC NUMBER	ATOMIC WEIGHT	DENSITY (g/cm^3)	MELTING POINT	HEAT OF SUBLIMATION AT 25°C
Ru	44	101.07	12.36	2,450°C	160 kcal/mole
Rh	45	102.905	12.48	1,985°	138
Pd	46	106.4	12.09	1,555°	93
Os	76	190.2	22.69	2,700°	175
Ir	77	192.2	22.82	2,440°	165
Pt	78	195.09	21.60	1,755°	121.6

The platinum metals are noble metals, chemically unreactive, which are found in nature as native alloys, consisting mainly of platinum.

Ruthenium and **osmium** are iron-gray metals, the other four elements being whiter in color. Ruthenium can be oxidized to RuO_2, and even to the octavalent compound RuO_4. Osmium unites with oxygen to form osmium tetroxide ("osmic acid"), OsO_4, a white crystalline substance melting at 40°C and boiling at about 100°C. Osmium tetroxide has an irritating odor similar to that of chlorine. It is a very poisonous substance. Its aqueous solution is used in histology (the study of the tissues of plants and animals); it stains tissues through its reduction by organic matter to metallic osmium, and also hardens the material without distorting it.

Ruthenium and osmium form compounds corresponding to various states of oxidation, such as the following: $RuCl_3$, K_2RuO_4, Os_2O_3, $OsCl_4$, K_2OsO_4.

Rhodium and **iridium** are very unreactive metals, not being attacked by aqua regia (a mixture of nitric acid and hydrochloric acid). Iridium is alloyed with platinum to produce a very hard alloy, which is used for the tips of gold pens, surgical tools, and scientific apparatus. Representative compounds are Rh_2O_3, K_3RhCl_6, Ir_2O_3, K_3IrCl_6, and K_2IrCl_6.

Palladium is the only one of the platinum metals that is attacked by nitric acid. Metallic palladium has an unusual ability to absorb hydrogen. At 1,000°C it absorbs enough hydrogen to correspond to the formula $PdH_{0.6}$.

The principal compounds of palladium are the salts of chloropalladous acid, H_2PdCl_4, and chloropalladic acid, H_2PdCl_6. The chloropalladite ion, $PdCl_4^{--}$, is a planar ion, consisting of the palladium atom with four coplanar chlorine atoms arranged about it at the corners of a square. The chloropalladate ion, $PdCl_6^{--}$, is an octahedral covalent complex ion.

Platinum is the most important of the palladium and platinum metals. It is grayish-white in color, and is very ductile. It can be welded at a red heat, and melted in an oxyhydrogen flame. Because of its very small chemical activity it is used in electrical apparatus and in making crucibles and other apparatus for use in the laboratory. Platinum is attacked by chlorine and dissolves in a mixture of nitric and hydrochloric acids. It also interacts with fused alkalis, such as potassium hydroxide, but not with alkali carbonates.

The principal compounds of platinum are the salts of chloroplatinous acid, H_2PtCl_4, and chloroplatinic acid, H_2PtCl_6. These salts are similar in structure to the corresponding palladium salts. Both palladium and platinum form many other covalent complexes, such as the platinum(II) ammonia complex ion, $Pt(NH_3)_4{}^{++}$.

A finely divided form of metallic platinum, called *platinum sponge*, is made by strongly heating ammonium chloroplatinate, $(NH_4)_2PtCl_6$. *Platinum black* is a fine powder of metallic platinum made by adding zinc to chloroplatinic acid. These substances have very strong catalytic activity, and are used as catalysts in commercial processes, such as the oxidation of sulfur dioxide to sulfur trioxide. Platinum black causes the ignition of a mixture of illuminating gas and air or hydrogen and air as a result of the heat developed by the rapid chemical combination of the gases in contact with the surface of the metal.

EXERCISES

24-1. Compare the stability of the free cobalt(III) ion, Co^{+++}, with that of the cobalticyanide ion, $Co(CN)_6{}^{---}$, and explain in terms of electronic structure. What are the hybrid orbitals involved in bond formation? How many electrons with unpaired spins are there in the free ion? In the complex?

24-2. What are the oxidation states of iron in hematite, magnetite, and siderite?

24-3. What are the chemical reactions for the conversion of hematite to cast iron?

24-4. Calculate the percentage of carbon in cementite.

24-5. What can you say about the equilibrium in the chemical reaction $3Fe + C \rightleftarrows Fe_3C$, as a function of the temperature, from your knowledge of the properties of steel and cast iron?

24-6. What are the chemical reactions in the open-hearth process of making steel? In the Bessemer process?

24-7. In which direction does the following chemical reaction mainly proceed?

$$Cu + Fe^{++} \rightleftarrows Fe + Cu^{++}$$

24-8. What chemical reaction do you think would take place between siderite and carbonated water?

24-9. Which do you predict would have the lower pH, an aqueous solution of ferric nitrate or an aqueous solution of ferric chloride?

24-10. What compounds of the $Fe(CN)_6{}^{---}$ ion are the most strongly colored?

24-11. Write a chemical equation for the preparation of metallic cobalt. Why is not cobalt made by the same method as is used for the commercial preparation of iron?

24-12. Name compounds of the important oxidation states of palladium and platinum.

24-13. Write an electronic structural formula for nickel carbonyl, and discuss the arrangement of the electrons around the nickel atoms in relation to the structure of krypton. Iron forms a carbonyl $Fe(CO)_5$, and chromium forms a carbonyl $Cr(CO)_6$; discuss the electronic structures of these substances.

24-14. What substances are used for making acidic linings and for making basic linings of furnaces and converters? What conditions determine the choice between acidic linings and basic linings?

24-15. In Table 9-1 iron, cobalt, and nickel are all assigned the same electronegativity, 1.8. On the assumption that Equation 9-1 gives the heat of formation of a compound in its standard state from the elements in their standard states, evaluate the electro- negativity of these three metals from the values of the enthalpy of formation of their dichlorides and of their monosulfides. (Answer: 1.69, 1.77, 1.83; 1.80, 1.84, 1.88.)

24-16. Discuss the increase in electronega- tivity in the sequence iron, cobalt, nickel in relation to enthalpy of ionization (see Exercises 22-20 and 22-22).

CHAPTER **25**

Copper, Zinc, and Gallium

and Their Congeners

In the preceding chapter we have begun the discussion of the chemistry of the transition metals through the consideration of iron, cobalt, nickel, and their congeners, the palladium and platinum metals. We shall now take up the chemistry of the elements that lie to the right of these elements in the periodic table.

The three metals copper, silver, and gold comprise group Ib of the periodic table. These metals all form compounds representing oxidation state +1, as do the alkali metals, but aside from this they show very little similarity in properties to the alkali metals. The alkali metals are very soft and light, and very reactive chemically, whereas the metals of the copper group are much harder and heavier and are rather inert, sufficiently so to occur in the free state in nature and to be easily obtainable by reducing their compounds, sometimes simply by heating. The metals zinc, cadmium, and mercury (group IIb) are also much different from the alkaline-earth metals (group II), as are gallium and its congeners (group IIIb) from the elements of group III.

In this chapter, in connection with the discussion of the compounds of silver, there is also a section on photography, including color photography (Section 25-5).

25-1. The Electronic Structures and Oxidation States of Copper, Silver, and Gold

The electronic structures of copper, silver, and gold, as well as those of zinc and gallium and their congeners, are given in Table 25-1.

Table **25-1**

Electronic Structures of Copper, Zinc, and Gallium and Their Congeners

Z	ELEMENT	K	L		M			N				O			P	
		$1s$	$2s$	$2p$	$3s$	$3p$	$3d$	$4s$	$4p$	$4d$	$4f$	$5s$	$5p$	$5d$	$6s$	$6p$
29	Cu	2	2	6	2	6	10	1								
30	Zn	2	2	6	2	6	10	2								
31	Ga	2	2	6	2	6	10	2	1							
47	Ag	2	2	6	2	6	10	2	6	10		1				
48	Cd	2	2	6	2	6	10	2	6	10		2				
49	In	2	2	6	2	6	10	2	6	10		2	1			
79	Au	2	2	6	2	6	10	2	6	10	14	2	6	10	1	
80	Hg	2	2	6	2	6	10	2	6	10	14	2	6	10	2	
81	Tl	2	2	6	2	6	10	2	6	10	14	2	6	10	2	1

It is seen that copper has one outer electron, in the $4s$ orbital of the M shell, zinc has two outer electrons, in the $4s$ orbital, and gallium has three outer electrons, two in the $4s$ orbital and one in the $4p$ orbital. The congeners of these elements also have one, two, or three electrons in the outermost shell. The shell next to the outermost shell in each case contains 18 electrons; this is the M shell for copper, zinc, and gallium, the N shell for silver, cadmium, and indium, and the O shell for gold, mercury, and thallium. This shell is called an *eighteen-electron shell.*

The Russell-Saunders symbol for copper and its congeners in the normal state is $^2S_{1/2}$, that for zinc and its congeners is $^1S_0$, and that for gallium and its congeners is $^2P_{1/2}$.

The electrons in the outermost shell are held loosely, and can be easily removed. The resulting ions, Cu^+, Zn^{++}, Ga^{+++}, etc., have an outer shell of eighteen electrons, and are called *eighteen-shell ions.* If these elements either lose their outermost electrons, forming eighteen-shell ions, or share the outermost electrons with other atoms, the resulting oxidation state is $+1$ for copper, silver, and gold, $+2$ for zinc, cadmium, and mercury, and $+3$ for gallium, indium, and thallium.

These are important oxidation states for all of these elements; there are, however, also some other important oxidation states. The cuprous ion, Cu^+, is unstable, and the cuprous compounds, except the very insoluble ones, are easily oxidized. The cupric ion, Cu^{++} (hydrated to $Cu(H_2O)_4^{++}$), occurs in many copper salts, and the cupric compounds are the principal compounds of copper. In the cupric ion the copper atom has lost two electrons, leaving it with only seventeen electrons in the M shell. In fact, the $3d$ electrons and the $4s$ electrons in copper are held by the atom with about the same energy—you may have noticed that the electronic structure given in Table 25-1 for copper differs from that given in the energy-level diagram, Figure 7-6, in that in the diagram copper is represented as having two $4s$ electrons and only nine $3d$ electrons.

The unipositive silver ion, Ag^+, is stable, and forms many salts. A very few compounds have also been made containing bipositive and terpositive silver. These compounds are very strong oxidizing agents. The stable oxidation state $+1$ shown by silver corresponds to the electronic structure of the element as given in Table 25-1. The Ag^+ ion is an eighteen-shell ion.

The gold(I) ion, Au^+, and the gold(III) ion, Au^{+++}, are unstable in aqueous solution. The stable gold(I) compounds and gold(III) compounds contain co-valent bonds, as in the complex ions $AuCl_2^-$ and $AuCl_4^-$.

The chemistry of zinc and cadmium is especially simple, in that these elements form compounds representing only the oxidation state $+2$. This oxidation state is closely correlated with the electronic structures shown in Table 25-1; it represents the loss or the sharing of the two outermost electrons. The ions Zn^{++} and Cd^{++} are eighteen-shell ions.

Mercury also forms compounds (the mercuric compounds) representing the oxidation state $+2$. The mercuric ion, Hg^{++}, is an eighteen-shell ion. In addition, mercury forms a series of compounds, the mercurous compounds, in which it has oxidation number $+1$. The electronic structure of the mercurous compounds is discussed in Section 25-10.

25-2. The Properties of Copper, Silver, and Gold

The metallurgy of copper, silver, and gold has been discussed in Chapter 21.

Copper is a red, tough metal with a moderately high melting point (Table 25-2). It is an excellent conductor of heat and of electricity when pure, and it

Table **25-2**

Some Physical Properties of Copper, Silver, and Gold

	ATOMIC NUMBER	ATOMIC WEIGHT	DENSITY (g/cm³)	MELTING POINT	BOILING POINT	METALLIC RADIUS	COLOR
Copper	29	63.54	8.97	1083°C	2,310°C	1.28 Å	Red
Silver	47	107.870	10.54	960.5°	1,950°	1.44	White
Gold	79	196.967	19.42	1063°	2,600°	1.44	Yellow

finds extensive use as an electric conductor. Pure copper that has been heated is soft, and can be drawn into wire or shaped by hammering. This "cold work" (of drawing or hammering) causes the metal to become hard, because the crystal grains are broken into much smaller grains, with grain boundaries that interfere with the process of deformation and thus strengthen the metal. The hardened metal can be made soft by heating ("annealing"), which permits the grains to coalesce into larger grains.

Silver is a soft, white metal, somewhat denser than copper, and with a lower melting point. It is used in coinage, jewelry, and tableware, and as a filling for teeth.

Gold is a soft, very dense metal, which is used for jewelry, coinage, dental work, and scientific and technical apparatus. Gold is bright yellow by reflected light; very thin sheets are blue or green. Its beautiful color and fine luster, which, because of its inertness, are not affected by exposure to the atmosphere, are responsible for its use for ornamental purposes. Gold is the most malleable and most ductile of all metals; it can be hammered into sheets only 1/100,000 cm thick, and drawn into wires 1/5,000 cm in diameter.

Alloys of Copper, Silver, and Gold.   The transition metals find their greatest use in alloys. Alloys are often far stronger, harder, and tougher than their constituent elementary metals. The alloys of copper and zinc are called *brass*, those of copper and tin are called *bronze*, and those of copper and aluminum are called *aluminum bronze*. Many of these alloys have valuable properties. Copper is a constituent also of other useful alloys, such as beryllium copper, coinage silver, and coinage gold.

Coinage silver in the United States contains 90% silver and 10% copper. This composition also constitutes *sterling silver* in the United States. British sterling silver is 92.5% silver and 7.5% copper.

Gold is often alloyed with copper, silver, palladium, or other metals. The amount of gold in these alloys is usually described in *carats*, the number of parts of gold in 24 parts of alloy—pure gold is 24 carat. American coinage gold is 21.6 carat and British coinage gold is 22 carat. *White gold*, used in jewelry, is usually a white alloy of gold and nickel.

25-3.   The Compounds of Copper

Values of the standard enthalpy of formation of some of the principal compounds of copper (and also of silver and gold) are given in Table 25-3. These values show that with the more electronegative nonmetals copper tends to form compounds of copper(II) (cupric compounds). For example, the heat of reaction of cuprous chloride with chlorine to form cupric chloride is positive:

$$CuCl(c) + \tfrac{1}{2}Cl_2(g) \longrightarrow CuCl_2(c) + 17.0 \text{ kcal/mole}$$

With sulfur and iodine, in which the bonds have little ionic character (electronegativity of copper, 1.9; of sulfur and iodine, 2.5), the cuprous compounds are the more stable.

Cupric Compounds.   The hydrated **cupric ion,** $Cu(H_2O)_4^{++}$, is an ion with light blue color that occurs in aqueous solutions of cupric salts and in some of the hydrated crystals. The most important cupric salt is **copper sulfate,** which forms blue crystals, $CuSO_4 \cdot 5H_2O$. The metal copper is not sufficiently reactive to displace hydrogen ion from dilute acids (it is below hydrogen in the electromotive-force series, Chapter 11), and copper does not dissolve in acids unless

Table **25-3**

Standard Enthalpy of Formation of Compounds of Copper, Silver, and Gold at 25°C (kcal/mole)

	M = Cu	Ag	Au
M(c)	0.00	0.00	0.00
M(g)	81.52	69.12	82.29
M+(g)	260.83	245.27	296.62
M+(aq)	12.4	25.31	
M++(g)	730.12	742.05	
M++(aq)	15.39		
M₂O(c)	−39.84	−7.31	
MO(g)	35		
MO(c)	−37.1		
M₂O₃(c)			19.3
MH(g)	71	67.7	
M₂F(c)		−50.4	
MF	44(g)	−48.5(c)	
MF₂(c)	−126.9	−88.5	
MCl(g)	32	23.2	
MCl(c)	−32.2	−30.36	−8.4
MCl₂(c)	−49.2		
MCl₃(c)			−28.3
MCl₄⁻(aq)			−77.8
MBr(g)	38		
MBr(c)	−25.1	−23.78	−4.4
MBr₂(c)	−33.2		
MBr₃(c)			−13.0
MI(g)	62		
MI(c)	−16.2	−14.91	0.2
MI₂(c)	−1.7		
M₂S(c)	−19.0	−7.60	
MS(c)	−11.6		

an oxidizing agent is present. However, hot concentrated sulfuric acid is itself an oxidizing agent, and can dissolve the metal, and dilute sulfuric acid also slowly dissolves it in the presence of air:

$$Cu + 2H_2SO_4 + 3H_2O \longrightarrow CuSO_4 \cdot 5H_2O + SO_2$$

or

$$2Cu + 2H_2SO_4 + O_2 + 8H_2O \longrightarrow 2CuSO_4 \cdot 5H_2O$$

Copper sulfate, which has the common names *blue vitriol* and *bluestone*, is used in copper plating, in printing calico, in electric cells, and in the manufacture of other compounds of copper.

Cupric chloride, $CuCl_2$, can be made as yellow crystals by direct union of the elements. The hydrated salt, $CuCl_2 \cdot 2H_2O$, is blue-green in color, and its

solution in hydrochloric acid is green. The blue-green color of the salt is due
to its existence as a complex,

$$
\begin{array}{c}
OH_2 \\
| \\
Cl-Cu-Cl \\
| \\
OH_2
\end{array}
$$

in which the chlorine atoms are bonded directly to the copper atom. The green
solution contains ions $CuCl_3(H_2O)^-$ and $CuCl_4^{--}$. All of these ions are planar,
the copper atom being at the center of a square formed by the four attached
groups. The planar configuration is shown also by other complexes of copper,
including the deep-blue ammonia complex, $Cu(NH_3)_4^{++}$.

Cupric Bromide, $CuBr_2$, is a black solid obtained by reaction of copper and
bromine or by solution of cupric oxide, CuO, in hydrobromic acid. It is interesting that cupric iodide, CuI_2, is unstable; when a solution containing cupric
ion is added to an iodide solution there occurs an oxidation-reduction reaction,
with precipitation of cuprous iodide, CuI:

$$2Cu^{++} + 4I^- \longrightarrow 2CuI(c) + I_2$$

This reaction occurs because of the extraordinary stability of cuprous iodide,
which is discussed in the following section. The reaction is used in a method
of quantitative analysis for copper, the liberated iodine being determined by
titration with sodium thiosulfate solution.

Cupric hydroxide, $Cu(OH)_2$, forms as a pale blue gelatinous precipitate
when alkali hydroxide or ammonium hydroxide is added to a cupric solution.
It dissolves very readily in excess ammonium hydroxide, forming the deep-blue
complex $Cu(NH_3)_4^{++}$ (Chapter 23). Cupric hydroxide is slightly amphoteric,
and dissolves to a small extent in a very concentrated alkali, forming
$Cu(OH)_4^{--}$.

The complex of cupric ion with tartrate ion, $C_4H_4O_6^{--}$, in alkaline solution
is used as a test reagent (*Fehling's solution*) for organic reducing agents, such
as certain sugars. This complex ion, $Cu(C_4H_4O_6)_2^{--}$, ionizes to give only a very
small concentration of Cu^{++}, not enough to cause a precipitate of $Cu(OH)_2$ to
form. The organic reducing agents reduce the copper to the unipositive state,
and it then forms a brick-red precipitate of cuprous oxide, Cu_2O. This reagent
is used in testing for sugar in the urine, in the diagnosis of diabetes.

Cuprous Compounds. Cuprous ion, Cu^+, is so unstable in aqueous solution
that it undergoes auto-oxidation-reduction into copper and cupric ion:

$$2Cu^+ \longrightarrow Cu + Cu^{++}$$

Very few cuprous salts of oxygen acids exist. The stable cuprous compounds
are either insoluble crystals containing covalent bonds or covalent complexes.

When copper is added to a solution of cupric chloride in strong hydrochloric acid a reaction occurs that results in the formation of a colorless solution containing cuprous chloride complex ions such as $CuCl_2^-$:

$$CuCl_4^{--} + Cu \longrightarrow 2CuCl_2^-$$

This complex ion involves two covalent bonds, its electronic structure being

$$\left[\; :\overset{..}{Cl}—Cu—\overset{..}{Cl}: \; \right]^-$$

Other cuprous complexes, $CuCl_3^{--}$ and $CuCl_4^{---}$, also exist.

If the solution is diluted with water a colorless precipitate of **cuprous chloride,** CuCl, forms. This precipitate also contains covalent bonds, each copper atom being bonded to four neighboring chlorine atoms and each chlorine atom to four neighboring copper atoms, with use of the outer electrons of the chloride ion. The structure is closely related to that of diamond, with alternating carbon atoms replaced by copper and chlorine (Figure 10-2).

Cuprous bromide, CuBr, and **cuprous iodide,** CuI, are also colorless insoluble substances. The covalent bonds between copper and iodine in cuprous iodide are so strong as to make cupric iodide relatively unstable, as mentioned above.

Other stable cuprous compounds are the insoluble substances cuprous oxide, Cu_2O (red), cuprous sulfide, Cu_2S (black), cuprous cyanide, CuCN (white), and cuprous thiocyanate, CuSCN (white).

25-4.   The Compounds of Silver

Silver oxide, Ag_2O, is obtained as a dark-brown precipitate on the addition of sodium hydroxide to a solution of silver nitrate. It is slightly soluble, producing a weakly alkaline solution of silver hydroxide:

$$Ag_2O + H_2O \longrightarrow 2Ag^+ + 2OH^-$$

Silver oxide is used in inorganic chemistry to convert a soluble chloride, bromide, or iodide into the hydroxide. For example, cesium chloride solution can be converted into cesium hydroxide solution in this way:

$$2Cs^+ + 2Cl^- + Ag_2O + H_2O \longrightarrow 2AgCl + 2Cs^+ + 2OH^-$$

This reaction proceeds to the right because silver chloride is much less soluble than silver oxide.

The **silver halogenides**—AgF, AgCl, AgBr, and AgI—can be made by adding silver oxide to solutions of the corresponding halogen acids. Silver fluoride is very soluble in water, and the other halogenides are nearly insoluble. Silver chloride, bromide, and iodide form as curdy precipitates when the ions are mixed. They are respectively white, pale yellow, and yellow in color, and on exposure to light they slowly turn black, through photochemical decomposition. Silver chloride and bromide dissolve in ammonium hydroxide solution, forming the **silver ammonia complex** $Ag(NH_3)_2^+$ (Chapter 23); silver iodide does not dissolve in ammonium hydroxide. These reactions are used as qualitative tests for silver ion and the halogenide ions.

Other complex ions formed by silver, such as the silver cyanide complex $Ag(CN)_2^-$ and the silver thiosulfate complex $Ag(S_2O_3)_2^{---}$, have been mentioned in Chapter 23.

Silver nitrate, $AgNO_3$, is a colorless, soluble salt made by dissolving silver in nitric acid. It is used to cauterize sores. Silver nitrate is easily reduced to metallic silver by organic matter, such as skin or cloth, and is for this reason used in making indelible ink.

Silver ion is an excellent antiseptic, and several of the compounds of silver are used in medicine because of their germicidal power.

25-5. Photochemistry and Photography

Many chemical reactions are caused to proceed by the effect of light. For example, a dyed cloth may fade when exposed to sunlight because of the destruction of molecules of the dye under the influence of the sunlight. Reactions of this sort are called *photochemical reactions*. A very important photochemical reaction is the conversion of carbon dioxide and water into carbohydrate and oxygen in the leaves of plants, where the green substance chlorophyll serves as a catalyst.

One law of photochemistry, discovered by Grotthus in 1818, is that *only light that is absorbed is photochemically effective*. Hence a colored substance must be present in a system that shows photochemical reactivity with visible light. In the process of natural photosynthesis this substance is chlorophyll.

The second law of photochemistry, formulated in 1912 by Einstein, is that *one molecule of reacting substance may be activated and caused to react by the absorption of one photon*. In some systems, such as material containing rather stable dyes, many photons are absorbed by the molecules for each molecule that is decomposed; the fading of the dye by light is a slow and inefficient process in these materials. In some simple systems the absorption of one photon results in the reaction or decomposition of one molecule.

There are also chemical systems in which a *chain of reactions* may be set off by one light quantum. An example is the photochemical reaction of hydrogen and chlorine. A mixture of hydrogen and chlorine kept in the dark does not react at room temperature. When, however, it is illuminated with blue light, reaction immediately begins. Hydrogen is transparent to all visible light; chlorine, which owes its yellow-green color to its strong absorption of blue light, is the photochemically active constituent in the mixture. The absorption of a photon of blue light by a chlorine molecule splits the molecule into two chlorine atoms:

$$Cl_2 + h\nu \longrightarrow 2Cl$$

These chlorine atoms initiate a chain of reactions, as described in Section 18-5:

$$Cl + H_2 \longrightarrow HCl + H$$
$$H + Cl_2 \longrightarrow HCl + Cl$$

It may be observed that the mixture of hydrogen and chlorine explodes when exposed to blue light. The chain of reactions may be broken through the recombination of chlorine atoms to form chlorine molecules; this reaction occurs on the collision of two chlorine atoms with the wall of the vessel containing the gas or with another atom or molecule in the gas.

A photochemical reaction of much geophysical and biological importance is the formation of ozone from oxygen. Oxygen is practically transparent to visible light and to light in the near ultraviolet region, but it strongly absorbs light in the far ultraviolet region—in the region from 1600 Å to 2400 Å. Each photon that is absorbed dissociates an oxygen molecule into two oxygen atoms:

$$O_2 + h\nu \longrightarrow 2O$$

A reaction that does not require absorption of a photon then follows:

$$O + O_2 \longrightarrow O_3$$

Accordingly there are produced two molecules of ozone, O_3, for each photon absorbed. In addition, however, the ozone molecules can be destroyed by combining with oxygen atoms, or by a photochemical reaction. The reaction of combining with oxygen atom is

$$O + O_3 \longrightarrow 2O_2$$

The reactions of photochemical production of ozone and destruction of ozone lead to a photochemical equilibrium, which maintains a small concentration of ozone in the oxygen being irradiated. The layer of the atmosphere in which the major part of the ozone is present is about 15 miles above the earth's surface; it is called the *ozone layer*.

The geophysical and biological importance of the ozone layer results from the absorption of light in the near ultraviolet region, from 2400 Å to 3600 Å, by the ozone. The photochemical reaction is

$$O_3 + h\nu \longrightarrow O + O_2$$

This reaction permits ozone to absorb ultraviolet light so strongly as to remove practically all of the ultraviolet light from the sunlight before it reaches the earth's surface. The ultraviolet light that it absorbs is photochemically destructive toward many of the organic molecules necessary in life processes, and if the ultraviolet light of sunlight were not prevented by the ozone layer from reaching the surface of the earth life in its present form could not exist.

Blueprint paper provides another interesting example of a photochemical reaction. Blueprint paper is made by treating paper with a solution of potassium ferricyanide and ferric citrate. Under action of light the citrate ion reduces the ferric ion to ferrous ion, which combines with ferricyanide to form the insoluble blue compound $KFeFe(CN)_6 \cdot H_2O$, Prussian blue. The unreacted substances are then washed out of the paper with water.

Photography. A photographic film is a sheet of cellulose acetate coated with a thin layer of gelatin in which very fine grains of silver bromide are suspended. This layer of gelatin and silver bromide is called the *photographic emulsion*. The silver halogenides are sensitive to light, and undergo photochemical decomposition. The gelatin increases this sensitivity, apparently because of the sulfur which it contains.

When the film is briefly exposed to light some of the grains of silver bromide undergo a small amount of decomposition, perhaps forming a small particle of silver sulfide on the surface of the grain. The film can then be *developed* by treatment with an alkaline solution of an organic reducing agent, such as Metol or hydroquinone, the *developer*. This causes the silver bromide grains that have been sensitized to be reduced to metallic silver, whereas the unsensitized silver bromide grains remain unchanged. By this process the developed film reproduces the pattern of the light that exposed it. This film is called the *negative*, because it is darkest (with the greatest amount of silver) in the places that were exposed to the most light.

The undeveloped grains of silver halogenide are next removed, by treatment with a fixing bath, which contains thiosulfate ion, $S_2O_3^{--}$ (from sodium thiosulfate, "hypo," $Na_2S_2O_3 \cdot 5H_2O$). The soluble silver thiosulfate complex is formed:

$$AgBr + 2S_2O_3^{--} \longrightarrow Ag(S_2O_3)_2^{---} + Br^-$$

The fixed negative is then washed. Care must be taken not to transfer the negative from a used fixing bath, containing a considerable concentration of silver complex, directly to the wash water, as insoluble silver thiosulfate might precipitate in the emulsion:

$$2Ag(S_2O_3)_2^{---} \longrightarrow Ag_2S_2O_3(c) + 3S_2O_3^{--}$$

Since there are three ions on the right, and only two on the left, dilution causes the equilibrium to shift toward the right.

A positive print can be made by exposing print paper, coated with a silver halogenide emulsion, to light that passes through the superimposed negative, and then developing and fixing the exposed paper.

Sepia tones are obtained by converting the silver to silver sulfide, and gold and platinum tones by replacing silver by these metals.

Many other very interesting chemical processes are used in photography, especially for the reproduction of color.

The Chemistry of Color Photography. The electromagnetic waves of light of different colors have different wavelengths. In the visible spectrum these wavelengths extend from a little below 4000 Å (violet in color) to nearly 8000 Å (red in color). The sequence of colors in the visible region is shown in the next to the top diagram of Figure 25-1.

The visible spectrum is only a very small part of the complete spectrum of the electromagnetic waves. At the top of Figure 25-1 other parts are indicated. Ordinary x-rays have wavelengths approximately 1 Å. Even shorter wave-lengths, 0.1, 0.01, 0.001 Å, are possessed by the gamma rays that are produced in radioactive decompositions and through the action of cosmic rays (Chapter 29). The ultraviolet region, not visible to the eye, consists of light somewhat shorter in wavelength than violet light, and the infrared consists of wave-lengths somewhat longer than red. Then there come the microwave regions, approximately 1 cm, and the longer radiowaves.

When gases are heated or are excited by the passage of an electric spark, the atoms and molecules in the gases emit light of definite wavelengths. The light that is emitted by an atom or molecule under these conditions is said to con-stitute its *emission spectrum*. The emission spectra of the alkali metals, mercury, and neon are shown in Figure 25-1. The emission spectra of elements, espe-cially of the metals, can be used for identifying them; *spectroscopic chemical analysis* is an important technique of analytical chemistry.

When white light (light containing all wavelengths in the visible region) is passed through a substance, light of certain wavelengths may be absorbed by the substance. The solar spectrum is shown in Figure 25-1. It consists of a background of white light, produced by the very hot gases in the sun, on which there are superimposed some dark lines, resulting from absorption of certain wavelengths by atoms in the cooler surface layers of the sun. It is seen that the yellow sodium lines, which occur as bright lines in the emission spectrum of sodium atoms, are shown as dark lines in the solar spectrum.

Molecules and complex ions in solution and in solid substances sometimes show sharp line spectra, but usually show rather broad absorption bands, as is indicated for the permanganate ion near the bottom of Figure 25-1. The permanganate ion has the power of absorbing light in the green region of the spectrum, permitting the blue-violet light and red light to pass through. The combination of blue-violet and red light appears magenta in color. We accordingly say that permanganate ion has a magenta color.

The human eye does not have the power of completely differentiating be-tween light of one wavelength and that of another wavelength in the visible spectrum. Instead, it responds to three different wavelength regions in different ways. All of the colors that can be recognized by the eye can be composed from three fundamental colors. These may be taken as red-green (seen by the eye as yellow), which is complementary to blue-violet; blue-red, or magenta, which is complementary to green; and blue-green, or cyan, which is comple-mentary to red. Three *primary colors*, such as these, need to be used in the development of any method of color photography.

An important modern method of color photography is the *Kodachrome*

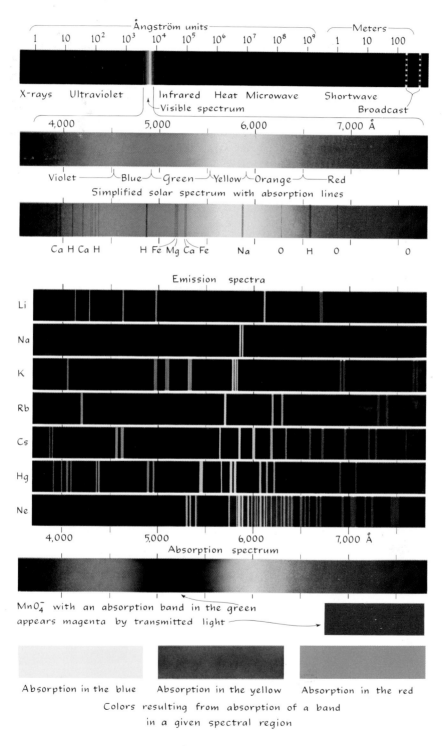

Figure **25-1** *Emission spectra and absorption spectra.*

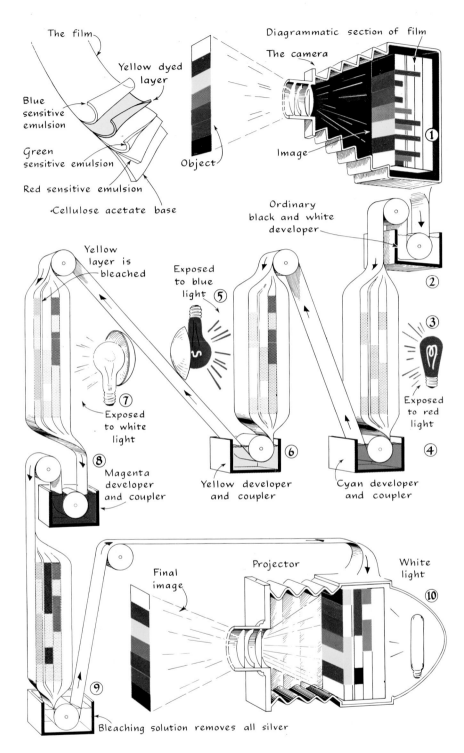

The film

Yellow dyed layer

Blue sensitive emulsion

Green sensitive emulsion

Red sensitive emulsion

Cellulose acetate base

Object

Diagrammatic section of film

The camera

Image

①

Ordinary black and white developer

②

Exposed to red light

③

④

Yellow layer is bleached

Exposed to blue light ⑤

Cyan developer and coupler

Yellow developer and coupler ⑥

Exposed to white light ⑦

⑧ Magenta developer and coupler

Final image

Projector

White light

⑩

⑨

Bleaching solution removes all silver

Figure 25-2 *The Kodachrome process of color photography.*

method, developed by the Kodak Research Laboratories. This method is illustrated in Figure 25-2. The film consists of several layers of emulsion, superimposed on a cellulose acetate base. The uppermost layer of photographic emulsion is the ordinary photographic emulsion, which is sensitive to blue and violet light. The second layer of photographic emulsion is a green-sensitive emulsion. It consists of a photographic emulsion that has been treated with a magenta-colored dye, which absorbs green light and sensitizes the silver bromide grains, thus making the emulsion sensitive to green light as well as to blue and violet light. The third photographic emulsion, red-sensitive emulsion, has been treated with a blue dye, which absorbs red light, making the emulsion sensitive to red light as well as to blue and violet (but not to green). Between the first layer and the middle layer there is a layer of yellow filter, containing a yellow dye, which during exposure prevents blue and violet light from penetrating to the lower layers. Accordingly when such a film is exposed to light the blue-sensitive emulsion is exposed by blue light, the middle emulsion is exposed by green light, and the bottom emulsion is exposed by red light.

The exposure of the different layers of photographic emulsion in the film is illustrated diagrammatically as Process 1 in Figure 25-2.

The development of Kodachrome film involves several steps, which are represented as Processes 2 to 9 in Figure 25-2. First (Process 2) the Kodachrome film after exposure is developed with an ordinary black and white developer, which develops the silver negative in all three emulsions. Then, after simple washing in water (not shown in the figure) the film is exposed through the back to red light, which makes the previously unexposed silver bromide in the red-sensitive emulsion capable of development (Process 3). The film then passes into a special developer, called cyan developer and coupler (Process 4). This mixture of chemical substances has the power of interacting with the exposed silver bromide grains in such a way as to deposit a cyan dye in the bottom layer, at the same time that the silver bromide grains are reduced to metallic silver. The cyan dye is deposited only in the regions occupied by the sensitized silver bromide grains. The next process (Process 5) consists in exposure to blue light from the front of the negative. The blue light is absorbed by the yellow dye, and so affects only the previously unexposed grains in the first emulsion, the blue-sensitive emulsion. This emulsion is then developed in a special developer (Process 6), a yellow developer and coupler, which deposits a yellow dye in the neighborhood of these recently exposed grains. The film is then exposed to white light, to sensitize the undeveloped silver bromide grains in the middle emulsion, the yellow layer is bleached, the middle emulsion is developed with a magenta developer and coupler (Process 8), and the deposited metallic silver in all three solutions is removed by a bleaching solution (Process 9), leaving only a film containing deposited cyan, yellow, and magenta dyes in the three emulsion layers, in such a way that by transmitted light the originally incident colors are reproduced (Process 10).

The development of the Kodachrome method and other methods of color photography has been a triumph of organic chemistry. It was the organic chemists who solved the problem of the synthesis of stable dyes with the special properties required for this purpose. The photographic industry, like most industries of the modern world, is a chemical industry.

25-6.   The Compounds of Gold

$KAu(CN)_2$, the potassium salt of the complex **gold (I) cyanide ion** $Au(CN)_2^-$, with electronic structure

$$[: \ddot{N} \!\!=\!\! C \!\!=\!\! Au \!\!=\!\! C \!\!=\!\! \ddot{N} :]^-$$

is an example of a gold(I) compound.* The **gold (I) chloride** complex $AuCl_2^-$ has a similar structure, and the **halogenides,** AuCl, AuBr, and AuI, resemble the corresponding halogenides of silver.

Gold dissolves in a mixture of concentrated nitric and hydrochloric acids to form **hydrogen aurichloride,** $HAuCl_4$. This acid contains the aurichloride ion, $AuCl_4^-$, a square planar complex ion:

$$\left[\begin{array}{c} : \ddot{C}l : \\ | \\ : \ddot{C}l \!-\! Au \!-\! \ddot{C}l : \\ | \\ : \ddot{C}l : \end{array} \right]^-$$

Hydrogen aurichloride can be obtained as a yellow crystalline substance, which forms salts with bases. When heated it forms **gold(III) chloride,** $AuCl_3$, and then gold(I) gold(III) chloride, Au_2Cl_4, and then gold(I) chloride, AuCl. On further heating all the chlorine is lost, and pure gold remains.

25-7.   Color and Mixed Oxidation States

The gold halogenides provide examples of an interesting phenomenon—the *deep, intense color often observed for a substance which contains an element in two different oxidation states.* Gold(I) gold(III) chloride, Au_2Cl_4, is intensely black, although both gold(I) chloride and gold(III) chloride are yellow. Cesium gold(I) gold(III) bromide, $Cs_2^+[AuBr_2]^-[AuBr_4]^-$, is deep black in color and both $CsAuBr_2$ and $CsAuBr_4$ are much lighter. Black mica (biotite) and black tourmaline contain both ferrous and ferric iron. Prussian blue is ferrous ferricyanide; ferrous ferrocyanide is white, and ferric ferricyanide is light yellow. When copper is added to a light green solution of cupric chloride, a deep brownish-black solution is formed, before complete conversion to the colorless cuprous chloride complex.

---

* The gold(I) and gold(III) compounds are often called *aurous* and *auric* compounds, respectively.

The theory of this phenomenon is not understood. The very strong absorption of light is presumably connected with the transfer of an electron from one atom to another of the element present in two valence states.

25-8. The Properties and Uses of Zinc, Cadmium, and Mercury

Zinc is a bluish-white, moderately hard metal. It is brittle at room temperature, but is malleable and ductile between 100° and 150°C, and becomes brittle again above 150°C. It is an active metal, above hydrogen in the electromotive-force series, and it displaces hydrogen even from dilute acids. In moist air zinc is oxidized and becomes coated with a tough film of basic zinc carbonate, $Zn_2CO_3(OH)_2$, which protects it from further corrosion. This behavior is responsible for its principal use, in protecting iron from rusting. Iron wire or sheet iron is *galvanized* by cleaning with sulfuric acid or a sandblast, and then dipping in molten zinc; a thin layer of zinc adheres to the iron. Galvanized iron in some shapes is made by electroplating zinc onto the iron pieces.

Zinc is also used in making alloys, the most important of which is *brass* (the alloy with copper), and as a reacting electrode in dry cells and wet cells.

Table **25-4**

Some Physical Properties of Zinc, Cadmium, and Mercury

	ATOMIC NUMBER	ATOMIC WEIGHT	DENSITY (g/cm³)	MELTING POINT	BOILING POINT	METALLIC RADIUS	COLOR	HEAT OF SUBLIMATION AT 25°C
Zinc	30	65.37	7.14	419.4°C	907°C	1.38 Å	Bluish-white	31.2 kcal/mole
Cadmium	48	112.40	8.64	320.9°	767°	1.54	Bluish-white	27.0
Mercury	80	200.59	13.55	−38.89°	356.9°	1.57	Silvery-white	14.5

Cadmium is a bluish-white metal of pleasing appearance. It has found increasing use as a protective coating for iron and steel. The cadmium plate is deposited electrolytically from a bath containing the cadmium cyanide complex ion, $Cd(CN)_4^{--}$. Cadmium is also used in some alloys, such as the low-melting alloys needed for automatic fire extinguishers. *Wood's metal*, which melts at 65.5°C, contains 50% Bi, 25% Pb, 12.5% Sn, and 12.5% Cd. Because of the toxicity of compounds of elements of this group, care must be taken not to use cadmium-plated vessels for cooking, and not to inhale fumes of zinc, cadmium, or mercury.

Mercury is the only metal that is liquid at room temperature (cesium melts at 28.5°C, and gallium at 29.8°C). It is unreactive, being below hydrogen in the electromotive-force series. Because of its unreactivity, fluidity, high density, and high electric conductivity it finds extensive use in thermometers, barometers, and many special kinds of scientific apparatus.

The alloys of mercury are called *amalgams*. Amalgams of silver, gold, and tin are used in dentistry. Mercury does not wet iron, and it is usually shipped and stored in iron bottles, called flasks, which hold 76 lbs of the metal.

The low melting points and small values of the heats of sublimation of zinc and its congeners (Table 25-4) are attributed to the fact that the gas atoms in the normal state contain only completed subshells of electrons (Russell-Saunders symbol $^1S_0$), and hence have no unpaired electrons that can be used to form chemical bonds. The first excited state of the zinc atom, ^3P, is less stable than the normal state by 92 kcal/mole. It has two unpaired electrons ($4s4p$), corresponding to bivalence.

25-9.   Compounds of Zinc and Cadmium

Values of the standard enthalpy of formation of some compounds of zinc, cadmium, and mercury are given in Table 25-5. It is seen that there is a close

Table **25-5**

Standard Enthalpy of Formation of Compounds of Zinc, Cadmium, and Mercury at 25°C (kcal/mole)

	M = Zn	Cd	Hg
M	0.00(c)	0.00(c)	0.00(l)
M(g)	31.19	26.97	14.54
M+(g)	249.25	235.80	257.13
M++(g)	664.90	627.12	689.56
M++(aq)	−36.43	−17.30	
M2O(c)			−21.8
MO(c)	−83.17	−60.86	−21.68
MH(g)	54.4	62.54	58.06
MF(g)			14
MF2(c)		−164.9	
MCl(g)	1	4.6	19
M2Cl2(c)			−63.32
MCl2(c)	−99.40	−93.00	−55.0
MBr(g)		−12	23
M2Br2(c)			−49.42
MBr2(c)	−78.17	−75.15	−40.5
MI(g)	15	19.6	33
M2I2(c)			−28.91
MI2(c)	−49.98	−48.0	−25.2
MS(g)	−14		3
MS(c)	−48.5	−34.5	−13.90
MSe(g)		1.6	16
MSe(c)	−34		−5.1
MTe(g)	30		
MTe(c)	−30	−24.30	

similarity between zinc and cadmium, and that mercury differs considerably from its two lighter congeners.

The **zinc ion,** $Zn(H_2O)_4^{++}$, is a colorless ion formed by solution of zinc in acid. It is poisonous to man and to bacteria, and is used as a disinfectant. It forms tetraligated complexes readily, such as $Zn(NH_3)_4^{++}$, $Zn(CN)_4^{--}$, and $Zn(OH)_4^{--}$. The white precipitate of **zinc hydroxide,** $Zn(OH)_2$, which forms when ammonium hydroxide is added to a solution containing zinc ion, dissolves in excess ammonium hydroxide, forming the zinc ammonia complex. The zinc hydroxide complex, $Zn(OH)_4^{--}$, which is called **zincate ion,** is similarly formed on solution of zinc hydroxide in an excess of strong base; zinc hydroxide is amphiprotic.

Zinc sulfate, $ZnSO_4 \cdot 7H_2O$, is used as a disinfectant and in dyeing calico, and in making *lithopone*, which is a mixture of barium sulfate and zinc sulfide used as a white pigment in paints:

$$Ba^{++}S^{--} + Zn^{++}SO_4^{--} \longrightarrow BaSO_4 + ZnS$$

Zinc oxide, ZnO, is a white powder (yellow when hot) made by burning zinc vapor or by roasting zinc ores. It is used as a pigment (zinc white), as a filler in automobile tires, adhesive tape, and other articles, and as an antiseptic (zinc oxide ointment).

Zinc sulfide, ZnS, is the only white sulfide among the sulfides of the common metals.

The compounds of cadmium are closely similar to those of zinc. **Cadmium ion,** Cd^{++}, is a colorless ion, which forms complexes ($Cd(NH_3)_4^{++}$, $Cd(CN)_4^{--}$) similar to those of zinc. The cadmium hydroxide ion, $Cd(OH)_4^{--}$, is not stable, and **cadmium hydroxide,** $Cd(OH)_2$, is formed as a white precipitate by addition even of concentrated sodium hydroxide to a solution containing cadmium ion. The precipitate is soluble in ammonium hydroxide or in a solution containing cyanide ion. **Cadmium oxide,** CdO, is a brown powder obtained by heating the hydroxide or burning the metal. **Cadmium sulfide,** CdS, is a bright yellow precipitate obtained by passing hydrogen sulfide through a solution containing cadmium ion; it is used as a pigment (*cadmium yellow*).

25-10. Compounds of Mercury

The mercuric compounds, in which mercury is bipositive, differ somewhat in their properties from the corresponding compounds of zinc and cadmium. The differences are due in part to the very strong tendency of the mercuric ion, Hg^{++}, to form covalent bonds. Thus the covalent crystal **mercuric sulfide,** HgS, is far less soluble than cadmium sulfide or zinc sulfide.

Mercuric nitrate, $Hg(NO_3)_2$ or $Hg(NO_3)_2 \cdot \frac{1}{2}H_2O$, is made by dissolving mercury in hot concentrated nitric acid:

$$Hg + 4HNO_3 \longrightarrow Hg(NO_3)_2 + 2NO_2 + 2H_2O$$

It hydrolyzes on dilution, unless a sufficient excess of acid is present, to form basic mercuric nitrates, such as $HgNO_3OH$, as a white precipitate.

Mercuric chloride, $HgCl_2$, is a white crystalline substance usually made by dissolving mercury in hot concentrated sulfuric acid, and then heating the dry mercuric sulfate with sodium chloride, subliming the volatile mercuric chloride:

$$Hg + 2H_2SO_4 \longrightarrow HgSO_4 + SO_2 + H_2O$$
$$HgSO_4 + 2NaCl \longrightarrow Na_2SO_4 + HgCl_2$$

A dilute solution of mercuric chloride (about 0.1%) is used as a disinfectant. Any somewhat soluble mercuric salt would serve equally well, except for the tendency of mercuric ion to hydrolyze and to precipitate basic salts. Mercuric chloride has only a small tendency to hydrolyze because its solution contains only a small concentration of mercuric ion, the mercury being present mainly as un-ionized covalent molecules:

$$: \overset{..}{\underset{..}{Cl}} - Hg - \overset{..}{\underset{..}{Cl}} :$$

Figure **25-3** *The structure of the mercuric ion, mercurous ion, mercuric chloride molecule, and mercurous chloride molecule. In the mercurous ion and the two molecules the atoms are held together by covalent bonds.*

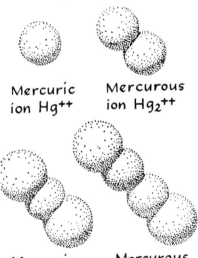

Mercuric
ion Hg^{++}

Mercurous
ion Hg_2^{++}

Mercuric
chloride
$HgCl_2$

Mercurous
chloride
Hg_2Cl_2

The electronic structure of these molecules, which have a linear configuration (Figure 25-3), is analogous to that of the gold(I) chloride complex, $AuCl_2^-$. The ease of sublimation of mercuric chloride (melting point 275°C, boiling point 301°C) results from the stability of these molecules.

Mercuric chloride, like other soluble salts of mercury, is very poisonous when taken internally. The mercuric ion combines strongly with proteins; in the human body it acts especially on the tissues of the kidney, destroying the ability of this organ to remove waste products from the blood. Egg white and milk are swallowed as antidotes; their proteins precipitate the mercury in the stomach.

With ammonium hydroxide, mercuric chloride forms a white precipitate, $HgNH_2Cl$:

$$HgCl_2 + 2NH_3 \longrightarrow$$
$$HgNH_2Cl(c) + NH_4^+ + Cl^-$$

Mercuric sulfide, HgS, is formed

as a black precipitate when hydrogen sulfide is passed through a solution of a mercuric salt. It can also be made by rubbing mercury and sulfur together in a mortar. The black sulfide (which also occurs in nature as the mineral *metacinnabarite*) is converted by heat into the red form (cinnabar). Mercuric sulfide is the most insoluble of metallic sulfides. It is not dissolved even by boiling concentrated nitric acid, but it does dissolve in aqua regia, under the combined action of the nitric acid, which oxidizes the sulfide to free sulfur, and hydrochloric acid, which provides chloride ion to form the stable complex $HgCl_4^{--}$:

$$3HgS + 12HCl + 2HNO_3 \longrightarrow 3HgCl_4^{--} + 6H^+ + \tfrac{3}{8}S_8 + 2NO + 4H_2O$$

Mercuric oxide, HgO, is formed as a yellow precipitate by adding a base to a solution of mercuric nitrate or as a red powder by heating dry mercuric nitrate or, slowly, by heating mercury in air. The yellow and red forms seem to differ only in grain size; it is a common phenomenon that red crystals (such as potassium dichromate or potassium ferricyanide) form a yellow powder when they are ground up. Mercuric oxide liberates oxygen when it is strongly heated.

Mercuric fulminate, $Hg(CNO)_2$, is made by dissolving mercury in nitric acid and adding ethyl alcohol, C_2H_5OH. It is a very unstable substance, which detonates when it is struck or heated, and it is used for making detonators and percussion caps.

Mercurous nitrate, $Hg_2(NO_3)_2$, is formed by reduction of a mercuric nitrate solution with mercury:

$$Hg^{++} + Hg \longrightarrow Hg_2^{++}$$

The solution contains the **mercurous ion,** Hg_2^{++}, a colorless ion which has a unique structure; it consists of two mercuric ions plus two electrons, which form a covalent bond between them (Figure 25-3):

$$2Hg^{++} + 2e^- \longrightarrow [Hg:Hg]^{++} \quad \text{or} \quad [Hg\!-\!Hg]^{++}$$

Mercurous chloride, Hg_2Cl_2, is an insoluble white crystalline substance obtained by adding a solution containing chloride ion to a mercurous nitrate solution:

$$Hg_2^{++} + 2Cl^- \longrightarrow Hg_2Cl_2(c)$$

It is used in medicine under the name *calomel*. The mercurous chloride molecule (Figure 25-3) has the linear covalent structure

$$: \!\overset{..}{\underset{..}{Cl}}\!-\!Hg\!-\!Hg\!-\!\overset{..}{\underset{..}{Cl}}\!:$$

The precipitation of mercurous chloride and its change in color from white to black on addition of ammonium hydroxide are used as the test for mercurous mercury in qualitative analysis. The effect of ammonium hydroxide is due to the formation of finely divided mercury (black) and mercuric amino-chloride (white) by an auto-oxidation-reduction reaction:

$$Hg_2Cl_2 + 2NH_3 \longrightarrow Hg + HgNH_2Cl + NH_4^+ + Cl^-$$

Mercurous sulfide, Hg_2S, is unstable, and when formed as a brownish-black precipitate by action of sulfide ion on mercurous ion it immediately decomposes into mercury and mercuric sulfide:

$$Hg_2^{++} + S^{--} \longrightarrow Hg_2S \longrightarrow Hg + HgS$$

25-11.   Gallium, Indium, and Thallium

The elements of group IIIb—gallium, indium, and thallium—are rare and have little practical importance. Their principal compounds represent oxidation state $+3$; thallium also forms compounds in which it has oxidation number $+1$. Gallium is liquid from 29°C, its melting point, to 1700°C, its boiling point. It has found use as the liquid in quartz-tube thermometers, which can be used to above 1200°C.

EXERCISES

25-1. What is the electronic structure of the Ag^+ ion? Of the Cu^{++} ion?

25-2. What are the constituents of brass? Of bronze?

25-3. In what form does copper exist in a cupric sulfate solution? In a strong hydrochloric acid solution? In an ammoniacal solution? Added as cupric sulfate to a solution of potassium iodide? In a solution of potassium cyanide?

25-4. Under what conditions can dilute sulfuric acid dissolve copper? Write an equation for the reaction.

25-5. Write the equation for the formation of hydrogen aurichloride by solution of gold in a mixture of nitric and hydrochloric acids, assuming that nitric oxide, NO, is also produced.

25-6. If a solution containing cupric ion and a solution containing iodide ion are mixed, a precipitate of cuprous iodide is formed, and free iodine is liberated. Write the equation for this reaction, assuming that iodide

ion is present in excess, leading to the formation of triiodide ion.

25-7. To what is the black color of biotite and black tourmaline attributed?

25-8. From information in Table 25-3 calculate the first ionization energies of atoms of copper, silver, and gold, and discuss the values in relation to the electronegativities of these elements.

25-9. Assuming that Equation 1 of Chapter 9 can be applied to the formation of compounds in their standard states from elements in their standard states, discuss the values of enthalpy of formation of the monohalogenides in Table 25-3. Should silver be assigned an electronegativity slightly larger than that of copper? How much larger?

25-10. Describe the electronic structure of the mercurous ion, the mercuric ion, the mercurous chloride molecule, and the mercuric chloride molecule. Compare the total number of electrons surrounding each mercury atom with the number in the nearest noble gas. What hybrid orbitals are used in bond formation?

25-11. Write the equation for the reaction of zinc with hydrochloric acid. Would you expect zinc to dissolve in a concentrated solution of sodium hydroxide? If so, write the equation for this reaction.

25-12. The electroneutrality principle indicates that the bonds between gold and carbon in the ion $Au(CN)_2^-$ are double bonds. What is the electronic structure of the gold atom in this complex? What orbitals are occupied by unshared electron pairs? By shared electron pairs?

25-13. What is the electronic structure of the zincate ion, $Zn(OH)_4^{--}$?

25-14. Discuss some of the enthalpy values in Table 25-3 in relation to the electronegativities of the elements.

25-15. Can you advance a likely explanation of the low melting points and boiling points of zinc, cadmium, and mercury, based on their electronic structure?

25-16. The energy of dissociation of the oxygen molecule is 118 kcal/mole. Calculate the wavelength of the photon of longest wavelength with enough energy to dissociate the molecule, and compare with the statement in Section 25-5 that ultraviolet light with wavelength less than 2400 Å is able to effect this dissociation.

25-17. From values of the enthalpy of formation of ozone and atomic oxygen given in Table 6-1, calculate the maximum wavelength of a photon with enough energy to dissociate an ozone molecule into an oxygen molecule and an oxygen atom. (Answer: 11,800 Å.)

25-18. The enthalpy of formation of mercuric fulminate is 64 kcal/mole. Write the reaction that occurs when the substance detonates. How much heat is evolved?

25-19. In December 1962 it was announced by scientists at the Argonne National Laboratory that xenon difluoride, XeF_2, had been made by a photochemical reaction. The first step in this reaction is presumably the dissociation of the fluorine molecule into two fluorine atoms through the absorption of a photon with sufficient energy to effect the dissociation. It has been found by experiment that the bond energy in the F_2 molecule is about 38 kcal/mole. What is the longest wavelength of light that would be predicted to produce this photochemical reaction?

CHAPTER 26

Titanium, Vanadium, Chromium, and

Manganese and their Congeners

In the present chapter we shall conclude the discussion of the chemistry of the transition metals. This chapter deals with the chemistry of chromium and manganese and their congeners, of groups VIa and VIIa of the periodic table, and also the preceding elements titanium and vanadium and their congeners, of groups IVa and Va. These elements are not so well known nor so important as some other transition elements, especially iron and nickel, but their chemistry is interesting, and serves well to illustrate the general principles discussed in preceding chapters.

26-1. The Electronic Structures of Titanium, Vanadium, Chromium, and Manganese and Their Congeners

The electronic structures of the elements of groups IIIa, IVa, Va, and VIa, as represented in the energy-level diagram (Figure 7-6), are given in Table 26-1. Each of the elements has either one electron or two electrons in the s orbital of the outermost shell. In addition, there are two, three, four, or five electrons in the d orbitals of the next inner shell. Reference to Figure 7-6 shows that the heaviest elements of these groups—thorium, protactinium, uranium, and neptunium—are thought to have the additional two to five electrons, respectively, in the $5f$ subshell, rather than the $6d$ subshell.

The Russell-Saunders symbol for titanium and its congeners in the normal state is $^3F_2$, that for vanadium and tantalum is $^4F_{3/2}$, that for niobium is $^6D_{1/2}$, that for chromium and molybdenum is $^7S_3$, that for tungsten is $^5D_0$, and that for manganese and its congeners is $^6S_{5/2}$.

Table **26-1**

Electronic Structures of Titanium, Vanadium, Chromium, and Manganese and Their Congeners

Z	ELEMENT	K	L		M			N				O			P
		$1s$	$2s$	$2p$	$3s$	$3p$	$3d$	$4s$	$4p$	$4d$	$4f$	$5s$	$5p$	$5d$	$6s$
22	Ti	2	2	6	2	6	2	2							
23	V	2	2	6	2	6	3	2							
24	Cr	2	2	6	2	6	5	1							
25	Mn	2	2	6	2	6	5	2							
40	Zr	2	2	6	2	6	10	2	6	2		2			
41	Nb	2	2	6	2	6	10	2	6	4		1			
42	Mo	2	2	6	2	6	10	2	6	5		1			
43	Tc	2	2	6	2	6	10	2	6	5		2			
72	Hf	2	2	6	2	6	10	2	6	10	14	2	6	2	2
73	Ta	2	2	6	2	6	10	2	6	10	14	2	6	3	2
74	W	2	2	6	2	6	10	2	6	10	14	2	6	4	2
75	Re	2	2	6	2	6	10	2	6	10	14	2	6	5	2

The oxidation state $+2$, corresponding to the loss of two electrons, is an important one for all of these elements. In particular, the elements in the first long period form the ions Ti^{++}, V^{++}, Cr^{++}, and Mn^{++}. Several other oxidation states, involving the loss or sharing of additional electrons, are also represented by compounds of these elements. The maximum oxidation state is that corresponding to the loss or sharing of all of the elements in the d orbitals of the next inner shell, as well as the two electrons in the outermost shell. Accordingly, the maximum oxidation numbers of titanium, vanadium, chromium, and manganese are $+4$, $+5$, $+6$, and $+7$, respectively.

Values of the standard enthalpy of formation of compounds of titanium and its congeners are given in Table 26-3, of vanadium and its congeners in Table 26-4, of chromium and its congeners in Table 26-5, and of manganese and rhenium in Table 26-6. For each set of congeners there is seen to be an increase in stability of compounds representing higher oxidation states with increase in atomic number. Many of the enthalpy values correspond satisfactorily to the electronegativity values of the elements, but there are some as yet unexplained deviations, such as the very large heats of formation of some compounds of uranium.

26-2. Titanium, Zirconium, Hafnium, and Thorium

The elements of group IVa of the periodic system are titanium, zirconium, hafnium, and thorium. Some of the properties of the elementary substances are given in Table 26-2.

Table 26-2

Some Properties of Titanium, Vanadium, Chromium,
and Manganese and Their Congeners

	ATOMIC NUMBER	ATOMIC WEIGHT	DENSITY (g/cm³)	MELTING POINT	BOILING POINT	METALLIC RADIUS*
Titanium	22	47.90	4.44	1,800°C	3,000°C	1.47 Å
Vanadium	23	50.942	6.06	1,700°	3,000°	1.34
Chromium	24	51.996	7.22	1,920°	2,330°	1.27
Manganese	25	54.9380	7.26	1,260°	2,150°	1.26
Zirconium	40	91.22	6.53	1,860°		1.60
Niobium	41	92.906	8.21	2,500°		1.46
Molybdenum	42	95.94	10.27	2,620°	4,700°	1.39
Hafnium	72	178.49	13.17	2,200°		1.36
Tantalum	73	180.948	16.76	2,850°		1.46
Tungsten	74	183.85	19.36	3,382°	6,000°	1.39
Rhenium	75	186.2	21.10	3,167°		1.37
Thorium	90	232.038	11.75	1,850°	3,500°	1.80
Uranium	92	238.03	18.97	1,690°		1.52

* For ligancy 12.

Titanium occurs in the minerals *rutile*, TiO_2, and *ilmenite*, $FeTiO_3$. It forms compounds representing oxidation states $+2$, $+3$, and $+4$. Pure **titanium dioxide,** TiO_2, is a white substance. As a powder it has great power of scattering light, which makes it an important pigment. It is used in special paints and in face powders. Crystals of titanium dioxide (rutile) colored with small amounts of other metal oxides have been made recently for use as gems. **Titanium tetrachloride,** $TiCl_4$, is a molecular liquid at room temperature. On being sprayed into air it hydrolyzes, forming hydrogen chloride and fine particles of titanium dioxide; for this reason it is sometimes used in making smoke screens:

$$TiCl_4 + 2H_2O \longrightarrow TiO_2 + 4HCl$$

Titanium metal is very strong, light (density 4.44 g/cm³), refractory (melting point 1,800°C), and resistant to corrosion. Since 1950 it has been produced in quantity, and has found many uses for which a light, strong metal with high melting point is needed; for example, it is used in airplane wings where the metal is in contact with exhaust flame.

Zirconium occurs in nature principally as the mineral *zircon*, $ZrSiO_4$. Zircon crystals are found in a variety of colors—white, blue, green, and red—and because of its beauty and hardness (7.5) the mineral is used as a semiprecious stone. The principal oxidation state of zirconium is $+4$; the states $+2$ and $+3$ are represented by only a few compounds.

Hafnium is closely similar to zirconium, and natural zirconium minerals usually contain a few percent of hafnium. The element was not discovered until 1923, and it has found little use.

Thorium is found in nature as the mineral *thorite*, ThO_2, and in *monazite sand*, which consists of thorium phosphate mixed with the phosphates of the lanthanons (Section 22-7). The principal use of thorium is in the manufacture of gas mantles, which are made by saturating cloth fabric with thorium nitrate, $Th(NO_3)_4$, and cerium nitrate, $Ce(NO_3)_4$. When the treated cloth is burned, there remains a residue of thorium dioxide and cerium dioxide, ThO_2 and CeO_2, which has the property of exhibiting a brilliant white luminescence when it is heated to a high temperature. Thorium dioxide is also used in the manufacture of laboratory crucibles, for use at temperatures as high as 2300°C. Thorium can be made to undergo nuclear fission, and it may become an important nuclear fuel (Chapter 30).

Table **26-3**

Standard Enthalpy of Formation of Compounds of Titanium, Zirconium, Hafnium, and Thorium at 25°C (kcal/mole)

	M = Ti	Zr	Hf	Th
$M(c)$	0.00	0.00	0.00	0.00
$M(g)$	112.7	146	168	136.6
$MO(c)$	−124.15			
$M_2O_3(c)$	−363.4			
$MO_2(c)$	−225.75	−261.5	−266.05	−292
$MF_2(c)$	−198	−230		
$MF_3(c)$	−315	−350		
$MF_4(c)$	−370	−445		−477
$MCl(g)$	122			
$MCl_2(c)$	−114	−145		
$MCl_3(c)$	−165	−208		
MCl_4	−182.0(g)	−233(g)		−285(c)
$MBr_2(c)$	−95	−120		
$MBr_3(c)$	−132	−174		
MBr_4	−131.1(g)	−192(c)		−227.1(c)
$MI_2(c)$	−61	−90		
$MI_3(c)$	−80	−128		
MI_4	−70.2(g)	−130(c)		−131(c)
$M_2S_3(c)$				−262.0
$MN(c)$	−80.7	−87.3		
$MC(c)$	−44.1	−45		

26-3. Vanadium, Niobium, Tantalum, and Protactinium

Vanadium is the most important element of group Va. It finds extensive use in the manufacture of special steels. Vanadium steel is tough and strong, and is used in automobile crank shafts and for similar purposes. The principal ores of vanadium are *vanadinite*, $Pb_5(VO_4)_3Cl$, and *carnotite*, $K(UO_2)VO_4 \cdot \frac{3}{2}H_2O$. The latter mineral is also important as an ore of uranium.

The chemistry of vanadium is very complex. The element forms compounds representing the oxidation states $+2$, $+3$, $+4$, and $+5$. The hydroxides of bipositive and terpositive vanadium are basic, and those of the higher oxidation states are amphiprotic. The compounds of vanadium are striking for their varied colors. The bipositive ion, V^{++}, has a deep violet color; the terpositive compounds, such as **potassium vanadium alum,** $KV(SO_4)_2 \cdot 12H_2O$, are green; the dark-green substance **vanadium dioxide,** VO_2, dissolves in acid to form the blue *vanadyl ion,* VO^{++}. **Vanadium(V) oxide,** V_2O_5, an orange substance, is used as a catalyst in the contact process for making sulfuric acid. **Ammonium metavanadate,** NH_4VO_3, which forms yellow crystals from solution, is used for making preparations of vanadium(V) oxide for the contact process.

Niobium (columbium) and **tantalum** usually occur together, as the minerals *columbite,* $FeCb_2O_6$, and *tantalite,* $FeTa_2O_6$. Niobium finds some use as a constituent of alloy steels. **Tantalum carbide,** TaC, a very hard substance, is used in making high-speed cutting tools.

Protactinium is a radioactive element (Chapter 30) that occurs in minute amounts in all uranium ores.

26-4. Chromium

The principal oxidation states of chromium are represented in the diagram on the following page.

The maximum oxidation number, $+6$, corresponds to the position of the element in the periodic table.

The most important ore of chromium is *chromite,* $FeCr_2O_4$. The element was

Table **26-4**

Standard Enthalpy of Formation of Compounds of Vanadium, Niobium, and Tantalum at 25°C (kcal/mole)

	M = V	Nb	Ta
M(c)	0.00	0.00	0.00
M(g)	123	184.5	186.8
MO(g)	55		
MO(c)	−100		
M$_2$O$_3$(c)	−296		
MO$_2$(c)	−171	−194	
M$_2$O$_5$(c)	−373	−463	−500
MCl$_2$(c)	−102		
MCl$_3$(c)	−143		
MCl$_4$(l)	−138		
MOCl$_3$(c)	−172	−212	
MBr$_5$(c)		−133	−143
MN(c)	−41		−58

not known to the ancients, but was discovered in 1798 in lead chromate, $PbCrO_4$, which occurs in nature as the mineral *crocoite*.

The metal can be prepared by reducing chromic oxide with metallic aluminum (Chapter 21). Metallic chromium is also made by electrolytic reduction of compounds, usually chromic acid in aqueous solution.

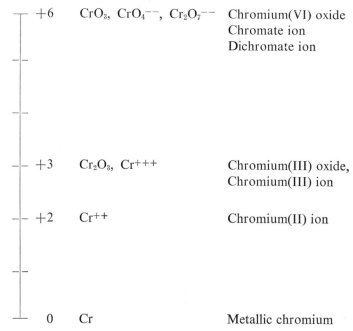

+6	CrO_3, CrO_4^{--}, $Cr_2O_7^{--}$	Chromium(VI) oxide
		Chromate ion
		Dichromate ion
+3	Cr_2O_3, Cr^{+++}	Chromium(III) oxide, Chromium(III) ion
+2	Cr^{++}	Chromium(II) ion
0	Cr	Metallic chromium

Chromium is a silvery-white metal, with a bluish tinge. It is a very strong metal, with a high melting point, 1830°C. Because of its high melting point it resists erosion by the hot powder gases in big guns, the linings of which are accordingly sometimes plated with chromium.

Although the metal is more electropositive than iron, it easily assumes a passive (unreactive) state, by becoming coated with a thin layer of oxide, which protects it against further chemical attack. This property and its pleasing color are the reasons for its use for plating iron and brass objects, such as plumbing fixtures.

Ferrochrome, a high-chromium alloy with iron, is made by reducing chromite with carbon in the electric furnace. It is used for making alloy steels. The alloys of chromium are very important, especially the *alloy steels*. The chromium steels are very hard, tough, and strong. Their properties can be attributed to the high metallic valence (6) of chromium and to an interaction between unlike atoms that in general makes alloys harder and tougher than elementary metals. They are used for armor plate, projectiles, safes, etc. Ordinary *stainless steel* contains 14 to 18% chromium, and usually 8% nickel.

Chromium in its highest oxidation state (+6) does not form a hydroxide.

The corresponding oxide, CrO_3, a red substance called **chromium(VI) oxide,** has acid properties. It dissolves in water to form a red solution of **dichromic acid,** $H_2Cr_2O_7$:

$$2CrO_3 + H_2O \longrightarrow H_2Cr_2O_7 \rightleftharpoons 2H^+ + Cr_2O_7^{--}$$

The salts of dichromic acid are called **dichromates;** they contain the dichromate ion, $Cr_2O_7^{--}$. Sexivalent chromium also forms another important series of salts, the **chromates,** which contain the ion CrO_4^{--}.

The chromates and dichromates are made by a method that has general usefulness for preparing salts of an acidic oxide—the method of *fusion with an alkali hydroxide or carbonate.* The carbonate functions as a basic oxide by

Table **26-5**

Standard Enthalpy of Formation of Compounds of Chromium, Molybdenum, Tungsten, and Uranium at 25°C (kcal/mole)

	M = Cr	Mo	W	U
M(c)	0.00	0.00	0.00	0.00
M(g)	95.0	157.5	200.0	125
M^{++}(aq)	−33.2			
M^{+++}(aq)	−61.1			−123.0
M$_2$O$_3$(c)	−272.7			
MO$_2$(c)		−130	−136.3	−259.2
MO$_3$(c)	−138.4	−178.1	−200.84	−291.0
MO$_4^{--}$(aq)	−206.3	−254.3	−266.6	
MF$_2$(c)	−181.0			
MF$_3$(c)	−265.2			−357
MF$_4$(c)				−443
MF$_5$(c)				−488
MF$_6$(g)			−416	−505
MCl$_2$(c)	−94.56	−44	−38	
MCl$_3$(c)	−134.6	−65		−213.0
MCl$_4$(c)	−104(g)	−79	−71	−251.2
MCl$_5$(c)		−90.8	−84	−262.1
MCl$_6$(c)		−90	−98.7	−272.4
MBr$_2$(c)		−29	−19	
MBr$_3$(c)		−41		−170.1
MBr$_4$(c)		−45	−35	−196.6
MBr$_5$(c)		−51	−42	
MBr$_6$(c)			−44	
MI$_2$(c)	−54.2	−12	−1	
MI$_3$(c)		−15		−114.7
MI$_4$(c)		−18	0	−127.0
MI$_5$(c)		−18	27	
MS$_2$(c)		−55.5	−46.3	
MS$_3$(c)		−61.2		
MN(c)	−29.8			−80
MC(c)			−9.09	

losing carbon dioxide when heated strongly. Potassium carbonate is preferred to sodium carbonate because potassium chromate and potassium dichromate crystallize well from aqueous solution, and can be easily purified by recrystallization, whereas the corresponding sodium salts are deliquescent and are difficult to purify.

A mixture of powdered chromite ore and potassium carbonate slowly forms **potassium chromate,** K_2CrO_4, when strongly heated in air. The oxygen of the air oxidizes chromium to the sexipositive state, and also oxidizes the iron to ferric oxide:

$$4FeCr_2O_4 + 8K_2CO_3 + 7O_2 \longrightarrow 2Fe_2O_3 + 8K_2CrO_4 + 8CO_2$$

Sometimes the oxidation reaction is aided by the addition of an oxidizing agent, such as potassium nitrate, KNO_3, or potassium chlorate, $KClO_3$. The potassium chromate, a yellow substance, can be dissolved in water and recrystallized.

On addition of an acid, such as sulfuric acid, to a solution containing chromate ion, CrO_4^{--}, the solution changes from yellow to orange-red in color, because of the formation of dichromate ion, $Cr_2O_7^{--}$:

$$2CrO_4^{--} + 2H^+ \rightleftharpoons Cr_2O_7^{--} + H_2O$$
$$\text{Yellow} \qquad\qquad \text{Orange-red}$$

The reaction can be reversed by the addition of a base:

$$Cr_2O_7^{--} + 2OH^- \rightleftharpoons 2CrO_4^{--} + H_2O$$
$$\text{Orange-red} \qquad\qquad \text{Yellow}$$

At an intermediate stage* both chromate ion and dichromate ion are present in the solution, in chemical equilibrium.

The chromate ion has a tetrahedral structure. The formation of dichromate ion involves the removal of one oxygen ion O^{--} (as water), by combination with two hydrogen ions, and its replacement by an oxygen atom of another chromate ion (see Figure 26-1).

Both chromates and dichromates are strong oxidizing agents, the chromium being easily reduced from $+6$ to $+3$ in acid solution. **Potassium dichromate,** $K_2Cr_2O_7$, is a beautifully crystallizable bright-red substance used considerably in chemistry and industry. A solution of this substance or of chromium(VI) oxide, CrO_3, in concentrated sulfuric acid is a very strong oxidizing agent, which serves as a cleaning solution for laboratory glassware.

Large amounts of **sodium dichromate,** $Na_2Cr_2O_7 \cdot 2H_2O$, are used in the tanning of hides, to produce "chrome-tanned" leather. The chromium forms an insoluble compound with the leather protein.

Lead chromate, $PbCrO_4$, is a bright yellow, practically insoluble substance that is used as a pigment (*chrome yellow*).

* There is also present in the solution some hydrogen chromate ion, $HCrO_4^-$·

$$H^+ + Cr_4O^{--} \rightleftharpoons HCrO_4^-$$

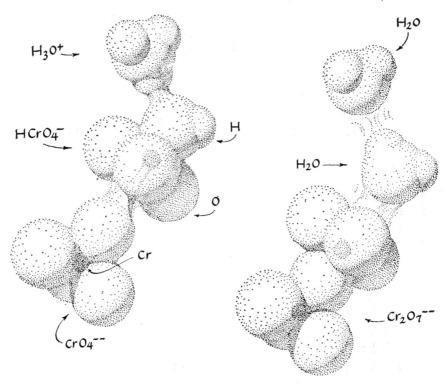

Figure **26-1**

The reaction of a hydrogen chromate ion, a chromate ion, and a hydronium ion to form a dichromate ion and water.

Compounds of Terpositive Chromium. When ammonium dichromate, $(NH_4)_2Cr_2O_7$, a red salt resembling potassium dichromate, is ignited, it decomposes to form a green powder, **chromium(III) oxide,** Cr_2O_3:

$$(NH_4)_2Cr_2O_7 \longrightarrow N_2 + 4H_2O + Cr_2O_3$$

This reaction involves the reduction of the dichromate ion by ammonium ion. Chromium(III) oxide is also made by heating sodium dichromate with sulfur, and leaching out the sodium sulfate with water:

$$Na_2Cr_2O_7 + S \longrightarrow Na_2SO_4 + Cr_2O_3$$

It is a very stable substance, which is resistant to acids and has a very high melting point. It is used as a pigment (*chrome green,* used in the green ink for paper money).

Reduction of a dichromate in aqueous solution produces **chromium(III) ion,** Cr^{+++} (really the hexahydrated ion, $[Cr(H_2O)_6]^{+++}$), which has a violet color. The salts of this ion are similar in formula to those of aluminum. *Chrome alum,* $KCr(SO_4)_2 \cdot 12H_2O$, forms large violet octahedral crystals.

Chromium(III) chloride, $CrCl_3 \cdot 6H_2O$, forms several kinds of crystals, vary-in color from violet to green, the solutions of which have similar colors. These different colors are due to the formation of stable complex ions (Figure 26-2):

$$[Cr(H_2O)_6]^{+++} \qquad \text{Violet}$$
$$[Cr(H_2O)_5Cl]^{++} \qquad \text{Green}$$
$$[Cr(H_2O)_4Cl_2]^{+} \qquad \text{Green}$$

In each of these complex ions there are six groups (water molecules and chloride ions) attached to the chromium ion. Chromium ion can be oxidized to chromate ion or dichromate ion by strong oxidizing agents, such as sodium peroxide in alkaline solution.

Chromium(III) hydroxide, $Cr(OH)_3$, is obtained as a pale grayish-green flocculent precipitate when ammonium hydroxide or sodium hydroxide is added to a chromium(III) solution. The precipitate dissolves in an excess of sodium hydroxide, forming the *chromite anion*, $Cr(OH)_4^{-}$:

$$Cr(OH)_3 + OH^- \longrightarrow Cr(OH)_4^-$$

Chromium(III) solutions are reduced by zinc in acid solution or by other

Figure 26-2

Octahedral chromic complex ions.

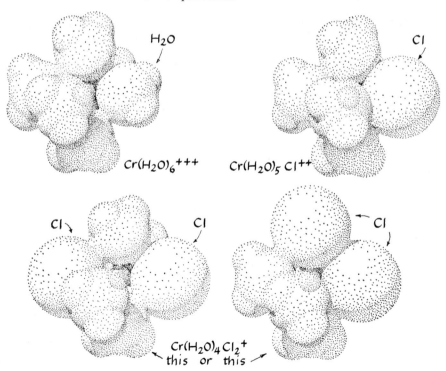

$Cr(H_2O)_6{}^{+++}$ $Cr(H_2O)_5\,Cl^{++}$

$Cr(H_2O)_4\,Cl_2{}^{+}$
this or this

strong reducing agents to *chromium(II) ion*, Cr^{++} or $[Cr(H_2O)_6]^{++}$, which is blue in color. This solution and solid chromium(II) salts are very strong reducing agents, and must be protected from the air.

26-5. The Congeners of Chromium

The three heavier elements in group VIa—molybdenum, tungsten, and uranium—have all found important special uses.

Molybdenum.   The principal ore of molybdenum is *molybdenite*, MoS_2, which occurs especially in a great deposit near Climax, Colorado. This mineral forms shiny black plates, closely similar in appearance to graphite.

Molybdenum metal is used to make filament supports in radio tubes and for other special uses. It is an important constituent of alloy steels.

The chemistry of molybdenum is complicated. It forms compounds corresponding to oxidation numbers $+6$, $+5$, $+4$, $+3$, and $+2$.

Molybdenum(VI) oxide, MoO_3, is a yellow-white substance made by roasting molybdenite. It dissolves in alkalis to produce molybdates, such as **ammonium molybdate,** $(NH_4)_6Mo_7O_{24} \cdot 4H_2O$. This reagent is used to precipitate orthophosphates, as the substance $(NH_4)_3PMo_{12}O_{40} \cdot 18H_2O$.

Tungsten.   Tungsten (also called *wolfram*) is a strong, heavy metal, with very high melting point ($3370°C$). It has important uses, as filaments in electric light bulbs, for electric contact points in spark plugs, as electron targets in x-ray tubes, and, in tungsten steel (which retains its hardness even when very hot), as cutting tools for high-speed machining.

The principal ores of tungsten are *scheelite*, $CaWO_4$, and *wolframite*, $(Fe,Mn)WO_4$.*

Tungsten forms compounds in which it has oxidation number $+6$ (tungstates, including the minerals mentioned above), $+5$, $+4$, $+3$, and $+2$. **Tungsten carbide,** WC, is a very hard compound that is used for the cutting edge of high-speed tools.

Uranium.   Uranium is the rarest metal of the chromium group. Its principal ores are *pitchblende*, U_3O_8, and *carnotite*, $K_2U_2V_2O_{12} \cdot 3H_2O$. Its most important oxidation state is $+6$ (**sodium diuranate,** $Na_2U_2O(OH)_{12}$; **uranyl nitrate,** $UO_2(NO_3)_2 \cdot 6H_2O$; etc.).

Before 1942 uranium was said to have no important uses—it was used mainly to give a greenish-yellow color to glass and glazes. In 1942, however, exactly one hundred years after the metal was first isolated, uranium became one of the most important of all elements. It was discovered in that year that

---

* The formula $(Fe,Mn)WO_4$ means a solid solution of $FeWO_4$ and $MnWO_4$, in indefinite ratio.

uranium could be made a source of nuclear energy, liberated in tremendous quantity at the will of man.

Nuclear Fission. Ordinary uranium contains two isotopes,* U^{238} (99.3%) and U^{235} (0.7%). When a neutron collides with a U^{235} nucleus it combines with it, forming a U^{236} nucleus. This nucleus is unstable, and it immediately decomposes spontaneously by splitting into two large fragments, plus several neutrons. *Each of the two fragments is itself an atomic nucleus*, the sum of their atomic numbers being 92, the atomic number of uranium.

This nuclear fission is accompanied by the emission of a very large amount of energy—about 5×10^{12} calories† per gram-atom of uranium decomposed (235 g of uranium). This is about 2,500,000 times the amount of heat evolved by burning the same weight of coal, and about 12,000,000 times that evolved by exploding the same weight of nitroglycerine. The large numbers indicate the very great importance of uranium as a source of energy; one ton of uranium (prewar price about $5000) could produce the same amount of energy as 2,500,000 tons of coal; and the use of uranium and other fissionable elements in place of coal may ultimately eliminate the disagreeable, but at present necessary, coal-mining industry.

The heavier uranium isotope, U^{238}, also can be made to undergo fission, but by an indirect route—through the transuranium elements. These elements are discussed in Chapter 30.

26-6. Manganese

The principal oxidation states of manganese are represented in the diagram on p. 694.

The maximum oxidation number, $+7$, corresponds to the position of the element in the periodic table (group VIIa).

The principal ore of manganese is *pyrolusite*, MnO_2. Pyrolusite occurs as a black massive mineral and also as a very fine black powder. Less important ores are *braunite*, Mn_2O_3 (containing some silicate); *manganite*, $MnO(OH)$; and *rhodochrosite*, $MnCO_3$.

Impure manganese can be made by reducing manganese dioxide with carbon:

$$MnO_2 + 2C \longrightarrow Mn + 2CO$$

Manganese is also made by the aluminothermic process:

$$3MnO_2 + 4Al \longrightarrow 2Al_2O_3 + 3Mn$$

Manganese alloy steels are usually made from special high-manganese alloys

---

* A minute amount, 0.006%, of a third isotope, U^{234}, is also present.

† This amount of energy weighs about 0.25 g, by the Einstein equation $E = mc^2$ (E = energy, m = mass, c = velocity of light). The material products of the fission are 0.25 g lighter than the gram-atom of U^{235}.

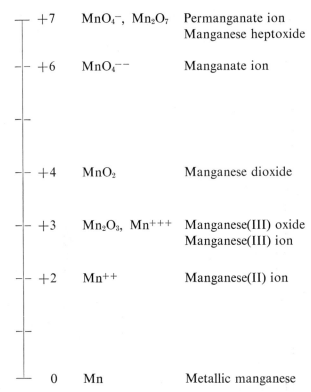

+7	MnO_4^-, Mn_2O_7	Permanganate ion Manganese heptoxide
+6	MnO_4^{--}	Manganate ion
+4	MnO_2	Manganese dioxide
+3	Mn_2O_3, Mn^{+++}	Manganese(III) oxide Manganese(III) ion
+2	Mn^{++}	Manganese(II) ion
0	Mn	Metallic manganese

prepared by reducing mixed oxides of iron and manganese with coke in a blast furnace (see Chapter 24). The high-manganese alloys (70 to 80% Mn, 20 to 30% Fe) are called *ferromanganese*, and the low-manganese alloys (10 to 30% Mn) are called *spiegeleisen*.

Manganese is a silvery-gray metal, with a pinkish tinge. It is reactive, and displaces hydrogen even from cold water. Its principal use is in the manufacture of alloy steel.

Manganese dioxide (pyrolusite) is the only important compound of quadripositive manganese. This substance has many uses, most of which depend upon its action as an oxidizing agent (with change from Mn^{+4} to Mn^{+2}) or as a reducing agent (with change from Mn^{+4} to Mn^{+6} or Mn^{+7}).

Manganese dioxide oxidizes hydrochloric acid to free chlorine, and is used for this purpose:

$$MnO_2 + 2Cl^- + 4H^+ \longrightarrow Cl_2 + Mn^{++} + 2H_2O$$

Its oxidizing power also underlies its use in the ordinary dry cell (Chapter 8).

When manganese dioxide is heated with potassium hydroxide in the presence of air it is oxidized to **potassium manganate,** K_2MnO_4:

$$2MnO_2 + 4KOH + O_2 \longrightarrow 2K_2MnO_4 + 2H_2O$$

Potassium manganate is a green salt that can be dissolved in a small amount of water to give a green solution, containing potassium ion and the *manganate ion*, MnO_4^{--}. The manganates are the only compounds of Mn^{+6}. They are powerful oxidizing agents, and are used to a small extent as disinfectants.

The manganate ion can be oxidized to *permanganate ion*, MnO_4^-, which contains Mn^{+7}. The electron reaction for this process is

$$MnO_4^{--} \longrightarrow MnO_4^- + e^-$$

In practice this oxidation is carried out electrolytically (by anodic oxidation) or by use of chlorine:

$$2MnO_4^{--} + Cl_2 \longrightarrow 2MnO_4^- + 2Cl^-$$

The process of auto-oxidation-reduction is also used; manganate ion is stable in alkaline solution, but not in neutral or acidic solution. The addition of any acid, even carbon dioxide (carbonic acid), to a manganate solution causes the production of permanganate ion and the precipitation of manganese dioxide:

$$3MnO_4^{--} + 4H^+ \longrightarrow 2MnO_4^- + MnO_2 + 2H_2O$$
$$\text{Green} \qquad\qquad\qquad \text{Magenta}$$

When hydroxide is added to the mixture of the purple solution and the brown or black precipitate, a clear green solution is again formed, showing that the reaction is reversible.

This reaction serves as another example of Le Chatelier's principle: the addition of hydrogen ion, which occurs on the left side of the equation, causes the reaction to shift to the right.

Potassium permanganate, $KMnO_4$, is the most important chemical com-

Table **26-6**

Standard Enthalpy of Formation of Compounds of Manganese and Rhenium at 25°C (kcal/mole)*

$Mn(c)$	0.00	$MnO_2(c)$	−124.45	$Re(c)$	0.00
$Mn(g)$	67.2	$MnF_2(c)$	−190	$Re(g)$	189
$Mn^{++}(aq)$	−52.3	$MnCl_2(c)$	−115.19	$ReO_3(c)$	−83
$Mn^{+++}(aq)$	−24	$MnBr_2(c)$	−90.7	$Re_2O_7(c)$	−297.5
$MnO(g)$	33.5	$MnI_2(c)$	−59.3	$ReF_6(g)$	−273
$MnO(c)$	−92.05	$MnS(c)$	−48.8	$ReS_2(c)$	−44.3
$Mn_2O_3(c)$	−228.4	$MnSe(c)$	−28.0	$ReAs_2(c)$	1
$KMnO_4(c)$	−194.4				

* No values have been reported for technetium.

pound of manganese. It forms deep purple-red prisms, which dissolve readily in water to give a solution intensely colored with the magenta color characteristic of permanganate ion. The substance is a powerful oxidizing agent, which is used as a disinfectant. It is an important chemical reagent, especially in analytical chemistry.

On reduction in acidic solution the permanganate ion accepts five electrons, to form the manganese(II) ion:

$$MnO_4^- + 8H^+ + 5e^- \longrightarrow Mn^{++} + 4H_2O$$

In neutral or basic solution it accepts three electrons, to form a precipitate of manganese dioxide:

$$MnO_4^- + 2H_2O + 3e^- \longrightarrow MnO_2 + 4OH^-$$

A one-electron reduction to manganate ion can be made to take place in strongly basic solution:

$$MnO_4^- + e^- \longrightarrow MnO_4^{--}$$

Permanganic acid, $HMnO_4$, is a strong acid that is very unstable. Its anhydride, **manganese(VII) oxide,** can be made by the reaction of potassium permanganate and concentrated sulfuric acid:

$$2KMnO_4 + H_2SO_4 \longrightarrow K_2SO_4 + Mn_2O_7 + H_2O$$

It is an unstable, dark-brown oily liquid.

The manganese(III) ion, Mn^{+++}, is a strong oxidizing agent, and its salts are unimportant. The insoluble oxide, Mn_2O_3, and its hydrate, $MnO(OH)$, are stable. When manganese(II) ion is precipitated as hydroxide, $Mn(OH)_2$, in the presence of air, the white precipitate is rapidly oxidized to the brown compound $MnO(OH)$:

$$Mn^{++} + 2OH^- \longrightarrow Mn(OH)_2$$
$$\text{White}$$

$$4Mn(OH)_2 + O_2 \longrightarrow 4MnO(OH) + 2H_2O$$
$$\text{Brown}$$

Manganese(II) ion, Mn^{++} or $[Mn(H_2O)_6]^{++}$, is the stable cationic form of manganese. The hydrated ion is pale rose-pink in color. Representative salts are $Mn(NO_3)_2 \cdot 6H_2O$, $MnSO_4 \cdot 7H_2O$, and $MnCl_2 \cdot 4H_2O$. These salts and the mineral *rhodochrosite*, $MnCO_3$, are all rose-pink or rose-red. Crystals of rhodochrosite are isomorphous with calcite.

With hydrogen sulfide manganese(II) ion forms a light pink precipitate of **manganese sulfide,** MnS:

$$Mn^{++} + H_2S \longrightarrow MnS + 2H^+$$

26-7. Acid-forming and Base-forming Oxides and Hydroxides

Chromium and manganese illustrate the general rules about the acidic and basic properties of metallic oxides and hydroxides:

1. *The oxides of an element in its higher oxidation states tend to form acids.*
2. *The lower oxides of an element tend to form bases.*
3. *The intermediate oxides may be amphoteric; that is, they may serve either as acid-forming or as base-forming oxides.*

The highest oxide of chromium, chromium(VI) oxide, is acidic, and forms chromates and dichromates. The lowest oxide, CrO, is basic, forming the chromium(II) ion Cr^{++} and its salts. Chromium(III) hydroxide, $Cr(OH)_3$, representing the intermediate oxidation state, is amphoteric. With acids it forms the salts of chromium(III) ion, such as chromium(III) sulfate, $Cr_2(SO_4)_3$, and with strong bases it dissolves to form the chromite ion, $Cr(OH)_4^-$.

Similarly, the two highest oxidation states of manganese, $+7$ and $+6$, are represented by the anions MnO_4^-, and MnO_4^{--}, and the two lowest states are represented by the cations Mn^{++} and Mn^{+++}. The intermediate state $+4$ is unstable (except for the compound MnO_2), and is feebly amphoteric.

You may want to check the rules given above by considering the properties of oxides of other elements.

26-8. The Congeners of Manganese

Technetium. No stable isotopes of element 43 exist. Minute amounts of radioactive isotopes have been made, by Segré and his collaborators, who have named the element technetium, symbol Tc.

Rhenium. The element rhenium, atomic number 75, was discovered by the German chemists Walter Noddack and Ida Tacke in 1925. The principal compound of rhenium is potassium perrhenate, $KReO_4$, a colorless substance. In other compounds all oxidation numbers from $+7$ to -1 are represented: examples are Re_2O_7, ReO_3, $ReCl_5$, ReO_2, Re_2O_3, $Re(OH)_2$.

Neptunium. Neptunium, element 93, was first made in 1940, by E. M. McMillan and P. H. Abelson, at the University of California, by the reaction of a neutron with U^{238}, to form U^{239}, and the subsequent emission of an electron from this nucleus, increasing the atomic number by 1:

$$_{92}U^{238} + _0n^1 \longrightarrow _{92}U^{239}$$
$$_{92}U^{239} \longrightarrow e^- + _{93}Np^{239}$$

Neptunium is important as an intermediate in the manufacture of plutonium (Chapter 30).

EXERCISES

26-1. Discuss the oxidation states of titanium, vanadium, chromium, and manganese in relation to their electronic structures. What electrons are removed in forming the bipositive ions? What electrons determine the highest oxidation states?

26-2. Explain why $TiCl_4$ is more effective in making smoke screens over the ocean than over dry land.

26-3. Make a diagram listing compounds representative of the various important oxidation levels of chromium and manganese.

26-4. What reduction product is formed when dichromate ion is reduced in acidic solution? When permanganate ion is reduced in acidic solution? When permanganate ion is reduced in basic solution? Write the electron reactions for these three cases.

26-5. Write equations for the reduction of dichromate ion by (a) sulfur dioxide; (b) ethyl alcohol, C_2H_5OH, which is oxidized to acetaldehyde, H_3CCHO; (c) iodide ion, which is oxidized to iodine.

26-6. Write an equation for the chemical reaction that occurs on fusion of a mixture of chromite ($FeCr_2O_4$), potassium carbonate, and potassium chlorate (which forms potassium chloride).

26-7. Write the chemical equations for the preparation of potassium manganate and potassium permanganate from manganese dioxide, using potassium hydroxide, air, and carbon dioxide.

26-8. What property of tungsten makes it suitable for use as the filament material in electric light bulbs?

26-9. What chemical reactions are taking place when a violet solution of chrome alum on treatment with hydrochloric acid turns green in color?

26-10. The two most important oxidation levels of uranium are $+4$ and $+6$. Which of these levels would you expect to have the more acidic properties?

26-11. Assign an electronic structure to the hexahydrated chromium(III) ion. What orbitals of the chromium atom are used in bond formation? How many $3d$ orbitals are occupied by unpaired electrons? What are the electric charges on the various atoms, as indicated by the electronegativity differences?

6

Organic Chemistry, Biochemistry, the Chemistry of the Fundamental Particles, and Nuclear Chemistry

The concluding section of our book consists of two chapters on each of two essentially unrelated branches of chemistry.

Chapter 27 is entitled Organic Chemistry and Chapter 28 is entitled Biochemistry. Organic chemistry is defined as the chemistry of compounds of carbon, usually excluding the metal carbides, carbonates, and a few other compounds. A discussion of some of the compounds of carbon was given in Chapter 10. In addition, many organic compounds have been taken up in connection with the theoretical discussions in the book—as, for example, in Chapter 9, dealing with covalence and electronic structure. The discussion of compounds of carbon is now continued in Chapters 27 and 28, with special attention to compounds that occur in living organisms or are important in twentieth-century civilization.

The science of organic chemistry is a very extensive one, and the selection of a small number of facts to be presented in these two chapters has necessarily been arbitrary. You can, of course, learn additional facts about organic chemistry later on in life, especially if you have mastered some basic principles. Perhaps the most important one is that the molecules of organic compounds in general involve a chain or framework of carbon atoms (together with other atoms, especially hydrogen, nitrogen, and oxygen), and that organic chemists, as well as plants and animals, are able to convert molecules of one organic substance into molecules of a related one by the use of certain reagents.

Some details about the chemical substances that make up the human body and other living organisms are given in Chapter 28. This chapter also contains a discussion of chemical reactions that take place in living organisms, the food requirements of man, and the structure and action of drugs.

Chapter 29 deals with the fundamental particles—their mass, electric charge, spin, and other properties, including the reactions by which they are converted into one another. This subject is usually considered to be a branch of physics, but the analogy between the structure (as yet largely unknown) and reactions of fundamental particles and the structure and reactions of molecules may well justify our claiming it as a branch of chemistry.

Our book ends with a chapter on the structure and reactions of the nuclei of atoms (Chapter 30). The subject of nuclear chemistry has developed greatly during the last thirty-five years. This development has led to the manufacture of new elements, some of which are valuable in medicine and in technology as well as in science. The possibilities of the use of nuclear reactions as a source of energy are so great that it is difficult to overestimate the importance of nuclear science.

CHAPTER 27

Organic Chemistry

27-1. The Nature and Extent of Organic Chemistry

Organic chemistry is the chemistry of the compounds of carbon. It is a very great subject—half a million different organic compounds have already been reported and described in the chemical literature. Many of these substances have been isolated from living matter, and many more have been synthesized (manufactured) by chemists in the laboratory.

The occurrence in nature, methods of preparation, composition, structure, properties, and uses of some organic compounds (hydrocarbons, alcohols, chlorine derivatives of hydrocarbons, and organic acids) were discussed in Chapter 10. This discussion is continued in the following sections, with emphasis on natural products, especially the valuable substances obtained from plants, and on synthetic substances useful to man. Several large parts of organic chemistry will not be discussed at all; these include the methods of isolation and purification of naturally occurring compounds, the methods of analysis and determination of structure, and the methods of synthesis used in organic chemistry, except to the extent that they have been described in Chapter 10.

There are two principal ways in which organic chemists work. One of these ways is to begin the investigation of some natural material, such as a plant, that is known to have special properties. This plant might, for example, have been found by the natives of a tropical region to be beneficial in the treatment of malaria. The chemist then proceeds to make an extract from the plant, with use of a solvent such as alcohol or ether, and, by various methods of separation, to divide the extract into fractions. After each fractionation a study is made to see which fraction still contains the active substance. Finally this process may be carried so far that a pure crystalline active substance is obtained. The chemist then analyzes the substance, and determines its molecular weight, in order to find out what atoms are contained in the molecule of the

substance. He next investigates the chemical properties of the substance, splitting its molecules into smaller molecules of known substances, in order to
determine its molecular structure. When the structure has been determined,
he attempts to synthesize the substance; if he is successful, the active material
may be made available in large quantity and at low cost.

The other way in which organic chemists work involves the synthesis and
study of a large number of organic compounds, and the continued effort to
correlate the empirical facts by means of theoretical principles. Often a knowledge of the structure and properties of natural substances is valuable in indicating the general nature of the compounds that are worth investigation. The
ultimate goal of this branch of organic chemistry is the complete understanding of the physical and chemical properties, and also the physiological properties, of substances in terms of their molecular structure. At the present time
chemists have obtained a remarkable insight into the dependence of the
physical and chemical properties of substances on the structure of their molecules. So far, however, only a small beginning has been made in attacking the
great problem of the relation between structure and physiological activity.
*This problem remains one of the greatest and most important problems of science,
challenging the new generation of scientists.*

27-2. Petroleum and the Hydrocarbons

One of the most important sources of organic compounds is petroleum
(crude oil). Petroleum, which is obtained from underground deposits that
have been tapped by drilling oil wells, is a dark-colored, viscous liquid that is
in the main a mixture of hydrocarbons (compounds of hydrogen and carbon;
see Section 10-5). A very great amount of it, approximately one billion tons,
is produced and used each year. Much of it is burned, for direct use as a fuel,
but much is separated or converted into other materials.

The Refining of Petroleum.   Petroleum may be separated into especially useful materials by a process of distillation, called *refining*. It was mentioned in
Section 10-5 that petroleum ether, obtained in this way, is an easily volatile
pentane-hexane-heptane (C_5H_{12} to C_7H_{16}) mixture that is used as a solvent and
in the dry cleaning of clothes, gasoline is the heptane-to-nonane (C_7H_{16} to
C_9H_{20}) mixture used in internal-combustion engines, kerosene is the decane-
to-hexadecane ($C_{10}H_{22}$ to $C_{16}H_{34}$) mixture used as a fuel, and heavy fuel oil is
a mixture of still larger hydrocarbon molecules.

The residue from distillation is a black, tarry material called *petroleum asphalt*. It is used in making roads, for asphalt composition roofing materials,
for stabilizing loose soil, and as a binder for coal dust in the manufacture of
briquets for use as a fuel. A similar material, *bitumen* or *rock asphalt*, is found
in Trinidad, Texas, Oklahoma, and other parts of the world, where it presumably has been formed as the residue from the slow distillation of pools of oil.

It is thought that petroleum, like coal, is the result of the decomposition of the remains of plants that grew on the earth long ago (about 250 million years ago).

Cracking and Polymerizing Processes.   As the demand for gasoline became greater, methods were devised for increasing the yield of gasoline from petroleum. The simple "cracking" process consists in the use of high temperature to break the larger molecules into smaller ones; for example, a molecule of $C_{12}H_{26}$ might be broken into a molecule of C_6H_{14} (hexane) and a molecule of C_6H_{12} (hexene, containing one double bond). There are now several rather complicated cracking processes in use. Some involve heating liquid petroleum, under pressure of about 50 atm, to about 500°C, perhaps with a catalyst such as aluminum chloride, $AlCl_3$. Others involve heating petroleum vapor with a catalyst such as clay containing some zirconium dioxide.

Polymerization is also used to make gasoline from the lighter hydrocarbons containing double bonds. For example, two molecules of ethylene, C_2H_4, can react to form one molecule of butylene, C_4H_8 (structural formula $CH_3-CH=CH-CH_3$).

Some gasoline is also made by the hydrogenation (reaction with hydrogen) of petroleum and coal. Many organic chemicals are prepared in great quantities from these important raw materials.

Hydrocarbons Containing Several Double Bonds.   The structure and properties of ethylene, a substance whose molecules contain a double bond, were discussed in Section 10-8. Some important natural products are hydrocarbons containing several double bonds. For example, the red coloring matter of tomatoes, called *lycopene*, is an unsaturated hydrocarbon, $C_{40}H_{56}$, with the structure shown in Figure 27-1.

The molecule of this substance contains thirteen double bonds. It is seen that eleven of these double bonds are related to one another in a special way— they alternate regularly with single bonds. A regular alteration of double bonds and single bonds in a hydrocarbon chain is called a *conjugated system of double bonds*. The existence of this structural feature in a molecule confers upon the molecule special properties, such as the power of absorbing visible light, causing the substance to be colored.

Other yellow and red substances, isomers of lycopene, with the same formula $C_{40}H_{56}$, are called α-**carotene,** β-**carotene,** and similar names. These substances occur in butter, milk, green leafy vegetables, eggs, cod liver oil, halibut liver oil, carrots, tomatoes, and other vegetables and fruits. They are important substances because they serve in the human body as a source of Vitamin A (see Chapter 28).

Polycyclic Substances.   Many important substances exist whose molecules contain two or more rings of atoms: these substances are called *polycyclic*

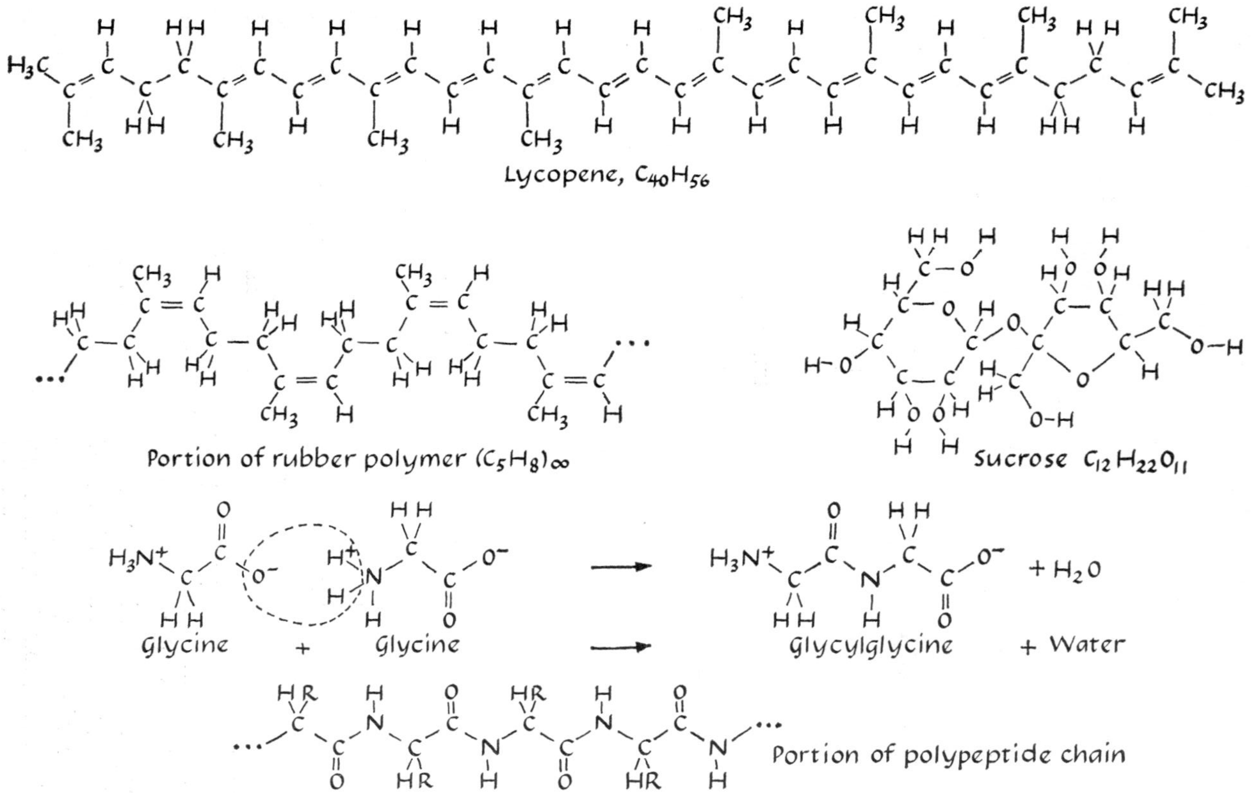

Figure 27-1 Structural formulas of some organic molecules.

substances; naphthalene, anthracene, and phenanthrene are examples of poly-cyclic aromatic hydrocarbons (Section 10-9). An example of a polycyclic aliphatic hydrocarbon is **pinene**, $C_{10}H_{16}$, which is the principal constituent of *turpentine*. Turpentine is an oil obtained by distilling a semifluid resinous material that exudes from pine trees. The pinene molecule has the following structure:

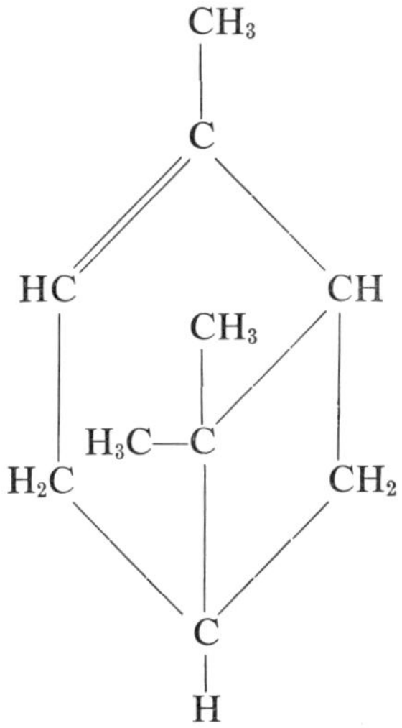

Another interesting polycyclic substance is **camphor,** obtained by steam dis-tillation of the wood of the camphor tree, or, in recent years, by a synthetic process starting with pinene. The molecule of camphor is roughly spherical in shape—it is a sort of "cage" molecule. Its structure is shown in Figure 27-2. It is to be noted that camphor is not a hydrocarbon, but contains one oxygen atom, its formula being $C_{10}H_{16}O$. A hydrocarbon is obtained by replacing the oxygen atom by two hydrogen atoms, producing the substance called *cam-phane*. Camphor is used in medicine and in the manufacture of plastics. Ordinary *celluloid* consists of nitrocellulose plasticized with camphor.

Rubber. Rubber is an organic substance, obtained mainly from the sap of the rubber tree, *Hevea brasiliensis*. Rubber consists of very long molecules, which are polymers of *isoprene*, C_5H_8. The structure of isoprene is

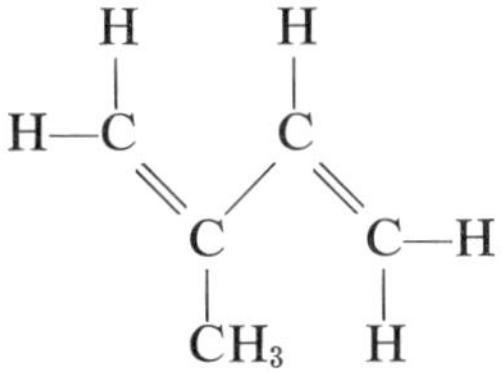

and that of the rubber polymer, as produced in the plant, is shown in Fig-ure 27-1.

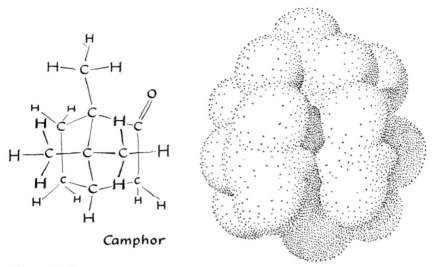

Camphor

Figure 27-2

The structure of the camphor molecule.

The characteristic properties of rubber are due to the fact that it is an aggregate of very long molecules, intertwined with one another in a rather random way. The structure of the molecules is such that they do not tend to align themselves side by side in a regular way—that is, to crystallize—but instead tend to retain an irregular arrangement.

It is interesting to note that the rubber molecule contains a large number of double bonds, one for each C_5H_8 residue. In natural rubber the configuration about the double bonds is the *cis* configuration, as shown in the structural formula in Figure 27-1. **Gutta percha,** a similar plant product that does not have the elasticity of rubber, contains the same molecules, with, however, the *trans* configuration around the double bonds. This difference in configuration permits the molecules of gutta percha to crystallize more readily than those of rubber.

Ordinary unvulcanized rubber is sticky, as a result of a tendency for the molecules to pull away from one another, a portion of the rubber thus adhering to any material with which it comes in contact. The stickiness is eliminated by the process of *vulcanization*, which consists in heating rubber with sulfur. During this process sulfur molecules, S_8, open up and combine with the double bonds of rubber molecules, forming bridges of sulfur chains from one rubber molecule to another rubber molecule. These sulfur bridges bind the aggregate of rubber molecules together into a large molecular framework, extending through the whole sample of rubber. Vulcanization with a small amount of sulfur leads to a soft product, such as that in rubber bands or (with a filler of carbon black or zinc oxide) in automobile tires. A much harder material, called vulcanite, is obtained by using a larger amount of sulfur.

The modern materials called **"synthetic rubber"** are not really synthetic rubber, since they are not identical with the natural product. They are, rather, substitutes for rubber—materials with properties and structure similar to but not identical with those of natural rubber. For example, the substance **chloroprene,** C_4H_5Cl, with the structure

$$
\begin{array}{c}
\underset{|}{\overset{H}{H-C}} \qquad \underset{|}{\overset{H}{C}} \\
\underset{|}{\overset{}{}}\diagup\diagdown \qquad \diagdown \\
C \qquad\qquad C-H \\
\underset{Cl}{|} \qquad \underset{H}{|}
\end{array}
$$

is similar to isoprene except for the replacement of a methyl group by a chlorine atom. Chloroprene polymerizes to a rubber called *chloroprene rubber.* It and other synthetic rubbers have found extensive uses, and are superior to natural rubber for some purposes.

27-3. Alcohols and Phenols

The aliphatic alcohols have a hydroxyl group, —OH, attached to a carbon atom in place of one of the hydrogen atoms of an aliphatic hydrocarbon. The two simplest alcohols, methyl alcohol (methanol) and ethyl alcohol (ethanol), have been discussed in Section 10-10. The melting points, boiling points, and densities of some alcohols are given in Table 27-1.

Some of the heavier alcohols are made from the olefines that are obtained as by-products in the refining of petroleum. For example, propylene, $CH_2\!\!=\!\!CH—CH_3$, can be hydrated by addition of water vapor at high temperature and pressure in the presence of a catalyst:

$$CH_2\!\!=\!\!CH—CH_3 + H_2O \longrightarrow CH_3—\underset{\underset{OH}{|}}{CH}—CH_3$$

The product is called *isopropyl alcohol* or *2-propanol* (the number 2 means that the substituent is on the second carbon atom in the chain, and the suffix *ol* means that the substituent is the hydroxyl group). An alcohol of this kind, with formula

$$
\begin{array}{c}
\overset{R}{\diagdown}\qquad\overset{OH}{\diagup}\\
C\\
\diagup\qquad\diagdown\\
R\qquad H
\end{array}
$$

(R being a radical with a carbon atom forming the bond) is called a secondary alcohol. Isopropyl alcohol may be called *sec*-propanol.

Table 27-1

Physical Properties of Some Alcohols and Phenols

	MELTING POINT	BOILING POINT	DENSITY OF LIQUID
Methyl alcohol, CH_3OH	−97.8°C	64.7°C	0.796 g/ml
Ethyl alcohol, CH_3CH_2OH	−117.3°	78.5°	.789
Propyl alcohol, $CH_3(CH_2)_2OH$	−127°	97.2°	.804
Isopropyl alcohol, $CH_3CHOHCH_3$	−89°	82.3°	.785
Butyl alcohol, $CH_3(CH_2)_3OH$	−89°	117.7°	.810
sec-Butyl alcohol, $CH_3CHOHCH_2CH_3$	−89°	100°	.808
tert-Butyl alcohol, $(CH_3)_3COH$	25°	83°	.789
1-Pentanol, $CH_3(CH_2)_4OH$	−78°	138°	.814
Glycol, CH_2OHCH_2OH	−17°	197°	1.116
1,2-Propanediol, $CH_2OHCHOHCH_3$		189°	1.040
1,3-Propanediol, $CH_2OHCH_2CH_2OH$		214°	1.053
Glycerol, $CH_2OHCHOHCH_2OH$	17.9°	290°	1.260
Benzyl alcohol, $C_6H_5CH_2OH$	−15.3°	205°	1.050
Phenol, C_6H_5OH	41°	182°	1.072*
o-Cresol, $CH_3C_6H_4OH$	30°	192°	1.047*
m-Cresol, $CH_3C_6H_4OH$	11°	203°	1.034
p-Cresol, $CH_3C_6H_4OH$	36°	203°	1.035*

* Density of crystalline substance.

An alcohol

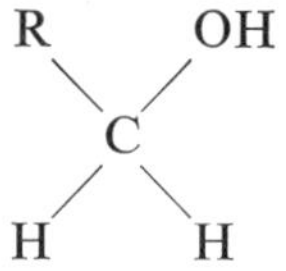

$$\begin{array}{ccc} R & & OH \\ & \diagdown \; \diagup & \\ & C & \\ & \diagup \; \diagdown & \\ H & & H \end{array}$$

is called a *primary alcohol;* examples are ethanol and 1-propanol, $CH_3CH_2CH_2OH$. *Tertiary alcohols* have the formula

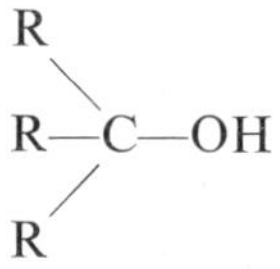

$$\begin{array}{c} R \\ \diagdown \\ R - C - OH \\ \diagup \\ R \end{array}$$

The simplest example is *tert*-butyl alcohol $(CH_3)_3COH$. The propyl and butyl alcohols are used as solvents for lacquers and other materials.

The formation of hydrogen bonds by the hydroxyl groups causes the alcohols to have higher melting and boiling points and larger solubility in water than other organic compounds with corresponding molecular weight. The lower alcohols, including *tert*-butanol, are soluble in water in all proportions. The other butanols have limited solubility in water, presumably because their less compact —C_4H_9 groups fit less readily than the *tert*-butyl group into the water structure (see the discussion of crystalline hydrates in Chapter 16).

The Polyhydroxy Alcohols. Alcohols containing two or more hydroxyl groups attached to different carbon atoms can be made. They are called the *polyhydroxy alcohols* or *polyhydric* alcohols. **Glycol,**

$$CH_2OH$$
$$|$$
$$CH_2OH$$

is used as a solvent and as an antifreeze material for automobile radiators. **Glycerol** (glycerine), $C_3H_5(OH)_3$, is a trihydroxypropane, with the structure

$$
\begin{array}{c}
H \\
| \\
H-C-OH \\
| \\
H-C-OH \\
| \\
H-C-OH \\
| \\
H
\end{array}
$$

Glycerol is a viscous liquid that is used as an antifreeze material, as a humectant (moistening agent) for tobacco, and especially for use in manufacturing explosives. It reacts with a mixture of nitric acid and sulfuric acid to form the viscous liquid **glyceryl trinitrate** (common name, **nitroglycerine**):

$$
\begin{array}{ccc}
CH_2OH & & CH_2ONO_2 \\
| & & | \\
CHOH & + 3HONO_2 \xrightarrow[H_2SO_4]{} & CHONO_2 + 3H_2O \\
| & & | \\
CH_2OH & & CH_2ONO_2
\end{array}
$$

Glyceryl trinitrate is a powerful and treacherous explosive. It was used extensively for blasting and mining in the decades about 1860, despite numerous fatal accidents. Then in 1867 the Swedish industrial chemist Alfred Nobel (1833–1896) discovered that the hazards of handling it would be greatly reduced by mixing it with an absorbent material such as diatomaceous earth, to form the product called *dynamite*. In the year 1876 Nobel also discovered the powerful detonating explosive blasting gelatin, which consists of cellulose nitrate (guncotton) that has soaked up glyceryl trinitrate, and in 1889 he developed the propellant ballistite, a plasticized mixture of cellulose nitrate and glyceryl trinitrate with composition such that it burns smoothly and rapidly and does not detonate.

The Aromatic Alcohols. An example of an aromatic alcohol is *benzyl alcohol,* C_6H_5—CH_2OH. In this substance the hydroxyl group is attached to the carbon atom of the alkyl group (methyl group) that is itself attached to the benzene ring. The properties of benzyl alcohol and other aromatic alcohols resemble those of the aliphatic alcohols.

The Phenols.   A compound in which a hydroxyl group is attached directly to the carbon atom of a benzene ring (or the naphthalene or other aromatic ring system) is called a *phenol*. The simplest phenol is **phenol** (hydroxybenzene), C_6H_5OH. The three **cresols** (ortho, meta, and para) are 1-hydroxy-2-methyl-benzene, 1-hydroxy-3-methylbenzene, and 1-hydroxy-4-methylbenzene, respectively:

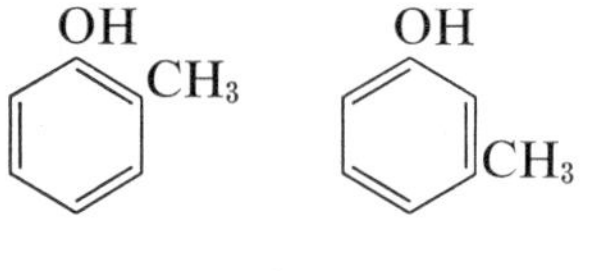

o-Cresol   m-Cresol   p-Cresol

They are obtained in the refining of coal tar, and are used as disinfectants and in the manufacture of plastics.

The properties of phenols differ considerably from those of the aliphatic and aromatic alcohols in ways that can be accounted for by the theory of resonance. The main difference is in acid strength: the alcohols (in aqueous solution) have acid constants about 1×10^{-16}, whereas the phenols are about a million times stronger, with acid constants about 1×10^{-10}.

The acid dissociation corresponds to the equilibrium reaction

$$ROH \rightleftarrows RO^- + H^+$$

For an alcohol, such as methanol, the anion RO^- has the electronic structure $H_3C{-}\overset{..}{\underset{..}{O}}:^-$. For phenol, however, the phenolate ion can be assigned a structure that is the hybrid of several valence-bond structures:

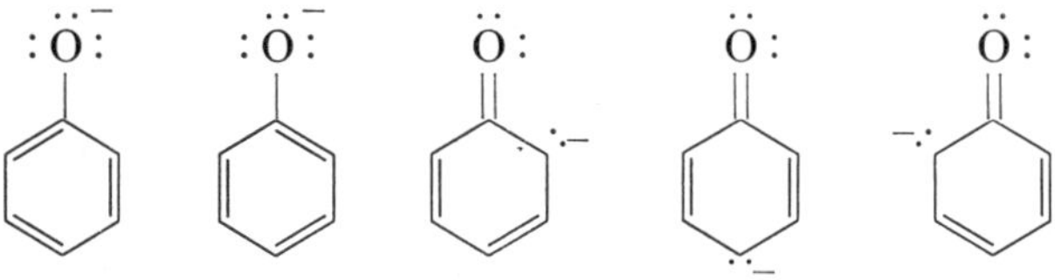

I   II   III   IV   V

The resonance energy for these five structures stabilizes the phenolate ion more than the amount by which the undissociated phenol molecule is stabilized by resonance between the two Kekulé structures (with only small contributions by the other three, which involve a separation of charges). The extra stabilization of the anion increases the acid constant; the observed factor 10^6 corresponds to the reasonable value 8 kcal/mole for the extra resonance energy of the phenolate ion.

27-4. Aldehydes and Ketones

The alcohols and ethers represent the first stage of oxidation of hydro-carbons. Further oxidation leads to substances called *aldehydes* and *ketones*. The aldehydes have the formula

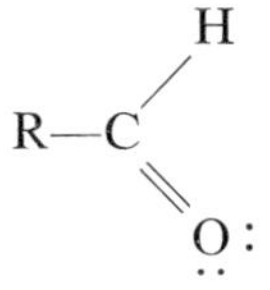

$$R-C \overset{\displaystyle H}{\underset{\displaystyle \ddot{O}\!:}{\Big\backslash\!\!\!\big/}}$$

and the ketones the formula

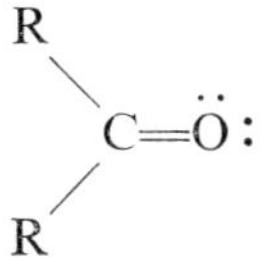

$$\overset{\displaystyle R}{\underset{\displaystyle R}{}}\!\!\!\diagdown\!\!\!\diagup C\!=\!\ddot{O}:$$

The group

$$\diagdown C\!=\!O \diagup$$

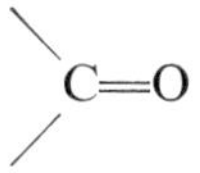

is called the *carbonyl group*. The substance **formaldehyde,**

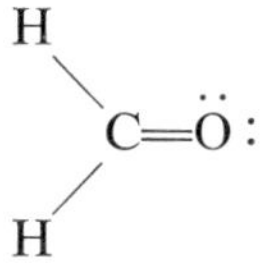

$$\overset{\displaystyle H}{\underset{\displaystyle H}{}}\!\!\!\diagdown\!\!\!\diagup C\!=\!\ddot{O}:$$

is also classed as an aldehyde. It can be made by passing methyl alcohol vapor and air over a heated metal catalyst:

$$2CH_3OH + O_2 \longrightarrow 2HCHO + 2H_2O$$

Formaldehyde is a gas with a sharp irritating odor. It is used as a disinfectant and antiseptic, and in the manufacture of plastics and of leather and artificial silk.

Acetaldehyde, CH_3CHO, is a similar substance made from ethyl alcohol.

The ketones are effective solvents for organic compounds, and are extensively used in chemical industry for this purpose. **Acetone,** $(CH_3)_2CO$, which is dimethyl ketone, is the simplest and most important of these substances. It is a good solvent for nitrocellulose.

Acrolein, $CH_2\!=\!CHCHO$, is the simplest unsaturated aldehyde. It is a liquid with the characteristic pungent odor of burning fat. It is produced when fats or oils are heated above 300°C, and it can be made by heating glycerol with a dehydrating agent:

$$C_3H_5(OH)_3 \xrightarrow[KHSO_4]{} CH_2CHCHO + 2H_2O$$

Many of the higher aldehydes and ketones have pleasant odors, and some of the aromatic aldehydes are used as flavors. An example is *vanillin*, the fragrant principle of the vanilla bean; its structural formula is

Vanillin is seen to be a phenol and an aromatic ether as well as an aldehyde. An example of a strongly fragrant ketone is *muscone*, which is obtained from the scent glands of the male musk deer and is used in perfumes. Its formula is

$$H_3C—CH—CH_2—C=O$$
$$\qquad |\underline{\qquad(CH_2)_{12}\qquad}|$$

It contains an unusually large ring (15 carbon atoms).

Physical properties of some aldehydes and ketones are given in Table 27-2.

Table 27-2

Physical Properties of Some Aldehydes and Ketones

	MELTING POINT	BOILING POINT	DENSITY OF LIQUID
Formaldehyde, HCHO	−92°C	−21°C	0.82 g/ml
Acetaldehyde, CH_3CHO	−124°	21°	.782
Propionaldehyde, CH_3CH_2CHO	−81°	49°	.807
n-Butyraldehyde, $CH_3(CH_2)_2CHO$	−98°	76°	.817
Isobutyraldehyde, $(CH_3)_2CHCHO$	−66°	62°	.794
Glyoxal, OHCCHO	15°	50°	1.14
Acrolein, $CH_2=CHCHO$	−88°	53°	0.841
Benzaldehyde, C_6H_5CHO	−26°	180°	1.050
Acetone, CH_3COCH_3	−95°	57°	0.792
Methyl ethyl ketone, $CH_3COCH_2CH_3$	−86°	80°	.805
Methyl n-propyl ketone, $CH_3CO(CH_3)_2CH_3$	−79°	102°	.812
Diethyl ketone, $CH_3CH_2COCH_2CH_3$	−42°	103°	.815
Biacetyl, $CH_3COCOCH_3$		88°	.978
Acetylacetone, $CH_3COCH_2COCH_3$	−23°	137°	.976
Acetophenone, $CH_3COC_6H_5$	20°	202°	1.026
Benzophenone, $C_6H_5COC_6H_5$	49°	306°	1.098*

* Density of crystalline substance.

27-5. The Organic Acids and Their Esters

Acetic acid, CH_3COOH, was mentioned in Section 10-10 as an example of an organic acid. The simplest organic acid is **formic acid,** HCOOH. It can be made by distilling ants, and its name is from the Latin word for ants.

Properties of some of the organic acids are given in Table 27-3. It is seen that the acid constants for the monocarboxylic acids lie in the range 2×10^{-4}

Table **27-3**

Properties of Some Carboxylic Acids

	MELTING POINT	BOILING POINT	DENSITY OF LIQUID	pK_A
Formic, HCOOH	8°C	101°C	1.226	3.77
Acetic, CH_3COOH	17°	118°	1.049	4.76
Propionic, CH_3CH_2COOH	−22°	141°	0.992	4.88
Butyric, $CH_3(CH_2)_2COOH$	−6°	164°	.959	4.82
Isobutyric, $(CH_3)_2CHCOOH$	−47°	154°	.949	4.85
Valeric, $CH_3(CH_2)_3COOH$	−35°	187°	.942	4.81
Caproic, $CH_3(CH_2)_4COOH$	−1°	205°	.945	4.81
Palmitic, $CH_3(CH_2)_{14}COOH$	64°	380°	.853	
Stearic, $CH_3(CH_2)_{16}COOH$	69°	383°	.847	
Acrylic, $CH_2{=}CHCOOH$	12°	142°	1.062	4.26
Oleic, $CH_3(CH_2)_7CH{=}CH(CH_2)_7COOH$	14°	300°	0.895	
Lactic, $CH_3CHOHCOOH$	18°		1.248	3.87
Oxalic, HOOCCOOH	189°			1.46*
Malonic, $HOOCCH_2COOH$	136°		1.631†	2.80*
Succinic, $HOOC(CH_2)_2COOH$	185°		1.564†	4.17*
Benzoic, C_6H_5COOH	122°	249°	1.266†	4.17
Salicylic, $o\text{-}HOC_6H_4COOH$	159°		1.443†	3.00

* For first dissociation.
† Density of crystalline substance.

to 1×10^{-5} (pK 3.7 to 5). The explanation of the greater acid strength of the —OH group in the carboxylic acids than in the alcohols is given by the theory of resonance; it is similar to that already given (Section 27-3) of the acid strength of the phenols. The dissociation of a carboxylic acid is represented by the equation

$$RCOOH \rightleftarrows RCOO^- + H^+$$

The anion $RCOO^-$ can be assigned two electronic structures:

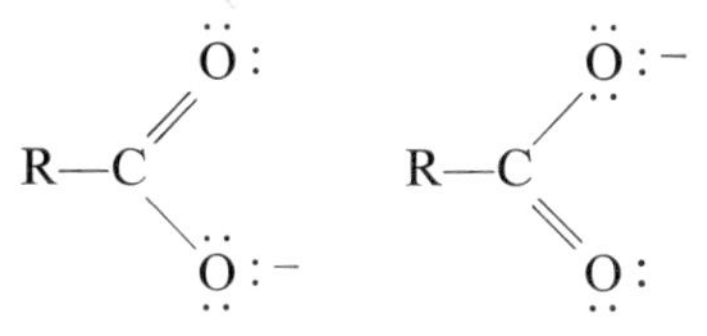

A   B

These two structures are equivalent, and the normal state of the anion can be described as a hybrid structure to which the two valence-bond structures A and B contribute equally. The anion is stabilized by the maximum amount of resonance energy, corresponding to complete resonance between the two valence-bond structures. For the undissociated acid the two valence-bond structures are A′ and B′:

$$
\begin{array}{cc}
\ddot{\text{O}}: & \ddot{\text{O}}:^{-} \\
\diagup\!\!\!\diagup & \diagup \\
\text{R--C} & \text{R--C} \\
\diagdown & \diagdown\!\!\!\diagdown \\
:\text{O--H} & \text{O}^{+}\text{--H} \\
& \ddot{} \\
\text{A}' & \text{B}'
\end{array}
$$

Structure B′ is less stable than structure A′ because it involves the separation of electric charge, and accordingly the normal state of the acid is a hybrid involving mainly A′, with only a small contribution of B′, and only a small amount of resonance stabilization. The anion is accordingly stabilized by resonance relative to the undissociated acid; this stabilization energy shifts the equilibrium to favor the ion, and thus increases the acid strength. The change in acid constant from about 1×10^{-16} (for alcohols) to 1×10^{-4} corresponds to about 16 kcal/mole greater resonance energy in the carboxylate anion than in the undissociated acid.

Formic acid and acetic acid are the first two members of a series of carboxylic acids, the *fatty acids*. The next two acids in the series are **propionic acid,** CH_3CH_2COOH, and **butyric acid,** $CH_3CH_2CH_2COOH$. Butyric acid is the principal odorous substance in rancid butter.

Some of the important organic acids occurring in nature are those in which there is a carboxyl group at the end of a long hydrocarbon chain. **Palmitic acid,** $CH_3(CH_2)_{14}COOH$, and **stearic acid,** $CH_3(CH_2)_{16}COOH$, have structures of this sort. **Oleic acid,** $CH_3(CH_2)_7CH{=}CH(CH_3)_7COOH$, is similar to stearic acid except that it contains a double bond between two of the carbon atoms in the chain.

Oxalic acid, $(COOH)_2$, is a poisonous substance that occurs in some plants. Its molecule consists of two carboxyl groups bonded together:

$$
\begin{array}{cc}
\text{HO} & \text{OH} \\
\diagdown & \diagup \\
\text{C--C} & \\
\diagup\!\!\!\diagup \quad \diagdown\!\!\!\diagdown & \\
\text{O} \qquad \text{O} &
\end{array}
$$

Lactic acid, having the structural formula

$$
\begin{array}{c}
\text{OH} \\
| \\
\text{H}_3\text{C--C--COOH} \\
| \\
\text{H}
\end{array}
$$

contains a hydroxyl group as well as a carboxyl group; it is a hydroxypropionic acid. It is formed when milk sours and when cabbage ferments, and it gives the sour taste to sour milk and sauerkraut. Tartaric acid, which occurs in grapes, is a dihydroxydicarboxylic acid, with the structural formula

$$
\begin{array}{c}
H \\
| \\
HO-C-COOH \\
| \\
HO-C-COOH \\
| \\
H
\end{array}
$$

Citric acid, which occurs in the citrus fruits, is a hydroxytricarboxylic acid, with the formula

$$
\begin{array}{c}
H \\
HC-COOH \\
| \\
HO-C-COOH \\
| \\
HC-COOH \\
H
\end{array}
$$

Benzoic acid, C_6H_5COOH, is the simplest aromatic acid. It is used in medicine as an antiseptic (in benzoated lard). **Salicylic acid,** which is *o*-hydroxybenzoic acid, *o*-HOC_6H_4COOH, is also used in medicine.

Esters are the products of reaction of acids and alcohols or phenols. For example, ethyl alcohol and acetic acid react with the elimination of water to produce **ethyl acetate:**

$$C_2H_5OH + CH_3COOH \longrightarrow H_2O + CH_3COOC_2H$$

Ethyl acetate is a volatile liquid with a pleasing, fruity odor. It is used as a solvent, especially in lacquers.

Many of the esters have pleasant odors, and are used in perfumes and flavorings. The esters are the principal flavorful and odorous constituents of fruits and flowers. Butyl acetate, $CH_3COO(CH_2)_3CH_3$, and amyl acetate, $CH_3COO(CH_2)_4CH_3$, have the odor characteristic of bananas, methyl butyrate, $CH_3(CH_2)_2COOCH_3$, has the odor characteristic of pineapples, and amyl butyrate, $CH_3(CH_2)_2COO(CH_2)_4CH_3$, has that of apricots. Methyl salicylate, *o*-$OHC_6H_4COOCH_3$, is oil of wintergreen.

Aspirin, a valuable and widely used analgesic and antipyretic drug, is the acetate of salicylic acid. Its structural formula is

Its common chemical name is acetylsalicylic acid.

The natural *fats* and *oils* are also esters, principally of the trihydroxy alcohol glycerol. Animal fats consist mainly of the glyceryl esters of palmitic acid and stearic acid. **Glyceryl oleate,** the glyceryl ester of oleic acid, is found in olive oil, whale oil, and the fats of cold-blooded animals; these fats tend to remain liquid at ordinary temperatures, whereas **glyceryl palmitate** and **glyceryl stearate** form the solid fats.

Esters can be decomposed by boiling with strong alkali, such as sodium hydroxide. This treatment forms the alcohol and the sodium salt of the carboxylic acid. When fat is boiled with sodium hydroxide, glycerine and sodium salts of the fatty acids (sodium palmitate, sodium stearate, and sodium oleate) are formed. These sodium salts of the fatty acids are called *soap.*

27-6. Amines and Other Organic Compounds of Nitrogen

The amines are derivatives of ammonia, NH_3, obtained by replacing one or more of the hydrogen atoms by organic radicals. The lighter amines, such as **methylamine,** CH_3NH_2, **dimethylamine,** $(CH_3)_2NH$, and **trimethylamine,** $(CH_3)_3N$, are gases. Trimethylamine has a pronounced fishy odor, and many other amines also have disagreeable odors.

Aniline is aminobenzene, $C_6H_5NH_2$. It is a colorless oily liquid, which on standing becomes dark in color because of oxidation to highly colored derivatives. It is used in the manufacture of dyes and other chemicals.

Many substances that occur in plant and animal tissues are compounds of nitrogen. Especially important are the proteins and nucleic acids, which are discussed in the following chapter. The principal product of the metabolism of proteins in the human body is **urea,** $(NH_2)_2CO$. It is the main nitrogenous constituent of urine.

Heterocyclic Nitrogen Compounds. Purines and Pyrimidines. Heterocyclic compounds are cyclic compounds in which one or more atoms other than carbon (usually nitrogen, oxygen, or sulfur) are present in the ring. An example is **pyridine,** C_5H_5N, a colorless liquid with an unpleasant odor, which is among the products of distilling coal. The electronic structure of pyridine can be described as a hybrid of several valence-bond structures:

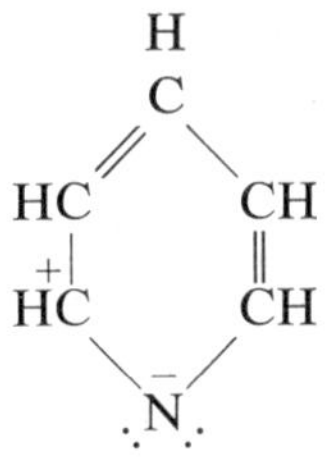

$$
\begin{array}{c}
\text{H} \\
\text{C} \\
\text{HC} \qquad \text{CH} \\
\overset{+}{\text{HC}} \qquad \text{CH} \\
\ddot{\text{N}} \text{:}
\end{array}
$$

The resonance energy of pyridine, relative to one of the Kekulé-like structures, is 43 kcal/mole. Pyridine is a base; in acidic solution it adds a proton to the unshared electron pair of the nitrogen atom, forming the pyridonium ion, $C_5H_5NH^+$.

Six-membered rings containing two or more nitrogen atoms also exist. **Pyrimidine**, $C_4H_4N_2$, is an important example. It is a colorless substance with melting point 22°C and boiling point 124°C. The two nitrogen atoms are in the meta position in the ring. Its electronic structure is a hybrid of

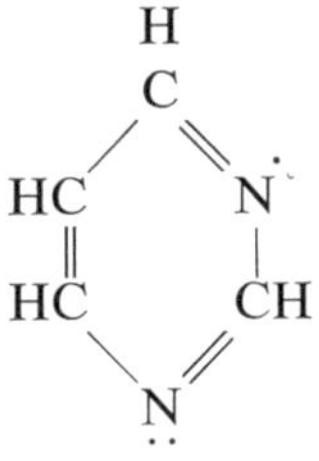

$$
\begin{array}{c}
\text{H} \\
\text{C} \\
\text{HC} \qquad \dot{\text{N}} \\
\text{HC} \qquad \text{CH} \\
\ddot{\text{N}}
\end{array}
$$

and other valence-bond structures similar to those shown above for pyridine. The partial double-bond character of all of the bonds in the ring requires that the molecules of pyridine and pyrimidine be planar.

The derivatives of pyrimidine, called the *pyrimidines*, include two substances, thymine and cytosine, that are of great importance in the chemistry of heredity. They will be discussed in the following chapter.

The *barbiturates*, which include several important drugs used as sedatives (tranquilizers) and hypnotics (sleep-producers), are closely related to the pyrimidines. The structural formulas of barbituric acid and two of its derivatives are given below; in these formulas the distribution of the hydrogen atoms between oxygen and nitrogen is uncertain, and only one of several pertinent valence-bond structures is indicated. The mechanism of the physiological action of the drugs is not known.

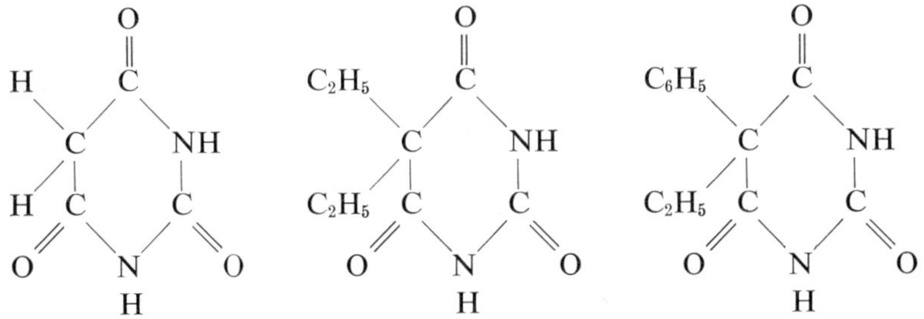

$$
\begin{array}{ccc}
\text{Barbituric acid} & \text{Barbital} & \text{Phenobarbital}
\end{array}
$$

The *purines* constitute another important class of nitrogen heterocycles. They are the derivatives of the substance **purine**, $C_5H_4N_4$, a colorless crystalline substance with melting point 217°C. The purine molecule is planar; its electronic structure is a hybrid of

and several other valence-bond structures.

Two of the purines, adenine and guanine, are important in the chemistry of heredity, and will be discussed in the following chapter.

Caffeine, a stimulant found in coffee and tea, is a purine. It is a colorless, odorless substance with melting point 236°C. Its structural formula (showing only one of the several valence-bond distributions) is

The stimulating effect of caffeine presumably results from the formation by the two oxygen atoms and the lower nitrogen atom in the five-membered ring of hydrogen bonds with some molecule that makes up a part of the nervous system; but the detailed nature of the mechanism has not yet been discovered.

Alkaloids. Alkaloids are basic (that is, alkali-like) substances of plant origin that contain at least one nitrogen atom, usually in a heterocyclic ring. Most of the alkaloids are physiologically active, and many are useful in medicine. An example is *cocaine*, a powerful local anesthetic and stimulant obtained from coca leaves. Its formula is

Nicotine, $C_{10}H_{14}N_2$, is the principal alkaloid in the tobacco plant. Its formula is

It is highly toxic and is used as an insecticide. In small quantities it acts as a stimulant and raises the blood pressure. The decreased life expectancy of cigarette smokers is thought to be due in some part to the effect of the inhaled nicotine, which is absorbed into the blood stream, but for the most part to carcinogenic hydrocarbons and other harmful substances in the smoke.

27-7. Carbohydrates, Sugars, Polysaccharides

The *carbohydrates* are substances with the general formula $C_x(H_2O)_y$. They occur widely in nature. The simpler carbohydrates are called *sugars*, and the complex ones, consisting of very large molecules, are called *polysaccharides*.

A common simple sugar is **D-glucose** (also called *dextrose* and *grape sugar*), $C_6H_{12}O_6$. It occurs in many fruits, and is present in the blood of animals. Its structural formula (not showing the spatial configuration of bonds around the four central carbon atoms) is

$$H_2C\text{---}CH\text{---}CH\text{---}CH\text{---}CH\text{---}CH$$

The molecule thus contains five hydroxyl groups and one aldehyde group.

Ordinary sugar, obtained from sugar cane and sugar beets, is **sucrose,** $C_{12}H_{22}O_{11}$. The molecules of sucrose have a complex structure, consisting of two rings (each containing one oxygen atom), held together by bonds to an oxygen atom as shown in Figure 27-1.

Many other simple carbohydrates occur in nature. These include *fructose* (fruit sugar), *maltose* (malt sugar), and *lactose* (milk sugar).

Important polysaccharides include *starch, glycogen,* and *cellulose.* Starch, $(C_6H_{10}O_5)_x$, occurs in plants, mainly in their seeds or tubers. It is an important constituent of foods. Glycogen, $(C_6H_{10}O_5)_x$, is a substance similar to starch which occurs in the blood and the internal organs, especially the liver, of animals. Glycogen serves as a reservoir of readily available food for the body; whenever the concentration of glucose in the blood becomes low, glycogen is rapidly hydrolyzed into glucose.

Cellulose, which also has the formula $(C_6H_{10}O_5)_x$, is a stable polysaccharide that serves as a structural element for plants, forming the walls of cells. Like starch and glycogen, cellulose consists of long molecules that contain rings of atoms held together by oxygen atoms, in the way shown in Figure 27-1 for the two rings of sucrose.

The sugars have the properties of dissolving readily in water and of crystallizing in rather hard crystals. These properties are attributed to the presence of a number of hydroxyl groups in these molecules, which form hydrogen bonds with water molecules and (in the crystals) with each other.

27-8. Fibers and Plastics

Silk and wool are protein fibers, consisting of long polypeptide chains (see Chapter 28). Cotton and linen are polysaccharides (carbohydrates), with composition $(C_6H_{10}O_5)_x$. These fibers consist of long chains made from carbon, hydrogen, and oxygen atoms, with no nitrogen atoms present.

In recent years synthetic fibers have been made, by synthesizing long molecules in the laboratory. One of these, which has valuable properties, is **nylon.** It is the product of condensation of adipic acid and diaminohexane. These two substances have the following structures:

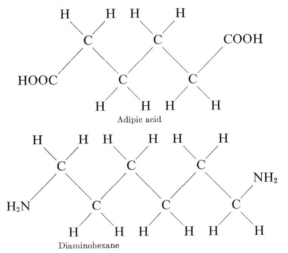

Adipic acid

Diaminohexane

Adipic acid is a chain of four methylene groups with a carboxyl group at each end, and diaminohexane is a similar chain of six methylene groups with an amino group at each end. A molecule of adipic acid can react with a molecule of diaminohexane in the following way:

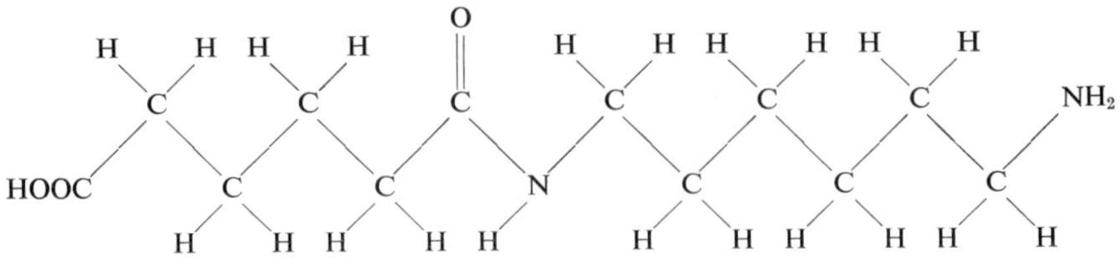

If this process is continued, a very long molecule can be made, in which the adipic acid residues alternate with the diaminohexane residues. Nylon is a fibrous material which consists of these long molecules in approximately parallel orientation.

Other artificial fibers and plastics are made by similar condensation reactions. A *thermolabile plastic* usually is an aggregate of long molecules of this sort that softens upon heating, and can be molded into shape. A *thermosetting plastic* is an aggregate of long molecules containing some reactive groups, capable of further condensation. When this material is molded and heated, these groups react in such a way as to tie the molecules together into a three-dimensional framework, producing a plastic material that cannot be further molded.

With a great number of substances available for use as his starting materials, the chemist has succeeded in making fibers and plastics that are for many purposes superior to natural materials. This field of chemistry, that of synthetic giant molecules, is still a new field, and we may look forward to further great progress in it in the coming years.

CHAPTER **28**

Biochemistry

Biochemistry is the study of the chemical composition and structure of the human body and other living organisms, of the chemical reactions that take place within these organisms, and of the drugs and other substances that interact with them.

During the past century biochemistry has developed into an important branch of science. We shall not be able in the limited space of the present chapter to give a general survey of this interesting subject, but shall instead have to content ourselves with a simple introductory discussion of a few of its aspects.

28-1. The Nature of Life

All of our ideas about life involve chemical reactions. What is it that distinguishes a living organism,* such as a man or some other animal or a plant, from an inanimate object, such as a piece of granite? We recognize that the plant or animal may have several attributes that are not possessed by the rock. The plant or animal has, in general, the power of **reproduction**—the power of having progeny, which are sufficiently similar to itself to be recognized as belonging to the same species of living organisms. The process of reproduction involves chemical reactions, the reactions that take place during the growth of the progeny. The growth of the new organism may occur only during a small fraction of the total lifetime of the animal, or may continue throughout its lifetime.

A plant or animal in general has the ability of ingesting certain materials, foods, subjecting them to chemical reactions, involving the release of energy, and secreting some of the products of the reactions. This process, by which

* The word *organism* is used to refer to anything that lives or has ever been living—we speak of dead organisms, as well as of living organisms.

the organism makes use of the food that it ingests by subjecting it to chemical reaction, is called **metabolism.**

Most plants and animals have the ability to respond to their environment. A plant may grow toward the direction from which a beam of light is coming, in response to the stimulus of the beam of light, and an animal may walk or run in a direction indicated by increasing intensity of the odor of a palatable food.

In order to illustrate the difficulty of defining a living organism, let us consider the simplest kinds of matter that have been thought to be alive. These are the *plant viruses*, such as the tomato bushy stunt virus, of which an electron micrograph has been shown as Figure 2-16. These viruses have the power of reproducing themselves when in the appropriate environment. A single molecule (individual organism) of tomato bushy stunt virus, when placed on the leaf of a tomato plant, can cause the material in the cells of the leaf to be in large part converted into replicas of itself. This power of reproduction seems, however, to be the only characteristic of living organisms possessed by the virus. After the particles are formed, they do not grow. They do not ingest food nor carry on any metabolic processes. So far as can be told by use of the electron microscope and by other methods of investigation, the individual particles of the virus are identical with one another, and show no change with time—there is no phenomenon of aging, of growing old. The virus particles seem to have no means of locomotion, and seem not to respond to external stimuli in the way that large living organisms do. But they do have the power of reproducing themselves.

Considering these facts, should we say that a virus is a living organism, or that it is not? At the present time scientists do not agree about the answer to this question—indeed, the question may not be a scientific one at all, but simply a matter of the definition of words. If we were to define a living organism as a material structure with the power of reproducing itself, then we would include the plant viruses among the living organisms. If, however, we require that living organisms also have the property of carrying on some metabolic reactions, then the plant viruses would be described simply as molecules (with molecular weight of the order of magnitude of 10,000,000) that have such a molecular structure as to permit them to catalyze a chemical reaction, in a proper medium, leading to the synthesis of molecules identical with themselves.

28-2. The Structure of Living Organisms

Chemical investigation of the plant viruses has shown that they consist of the materials called **proteins** and **nucleic acids** the nature of which is discussed in the following two sections. The giant virus particles or molecules, with molecular weight of the order of magnitude of 10,000,000, may be described as aggregates of smaller molecules, tied together in a definite way.

Many microorganisms, such as molds and bacteria, consist of single cells. These cells may be just big enough to be seen with an ordinary microscope, having diameter around 10,000 Å (10^{-4} cm), or they may be much bigger, as large as a millimeter or more in diameter. The cells have a well-organized structure, consisting of a *cell wall*, a few hundred Ångströms in thickness, within which is enclosed a semifluid material called *cytoplasm*, and often other structures that can be seen with the microscope. Other plants and animals consist largely of aggregates of cells, which may be of many different kinds in one organism. The muscles, blood vessel and lymph vessel walls, tendons, connective tissues, nerves, skin, and other parts of the body of a man consist of cells attached to one another to constitute a well-defined structure. In addition there are many cells that are not attached to this structure, but float around in the body fluids. Most numerous among these cells are the *red corpuscles* of the blood. The red corpuscles in man are flattened disks, about 70,000 Å in diameter and 10,000 Å thick. The number of red cells in a human adult is very large. There are about 5 million red cells per cubic millimeter of blood, and a man contains about 5 liters of blood, that is, 5 million cubic millimeters of blood. Accordingly there are 25×10^{12} red cells in his body. In addition, there are many other cells, some of them small, like the red cells, and some somewhat larger—a single nerve cell may be about 10,000 Å in diameter and 100 cm long, extending from the toe to the spinal cord. The total number of cells in the human body is about 10^{14}. The amount of *organization* in the human organism is accordingly very great.

The human body does not consist of cells alone. In addition there are the *bones*, which have been laid down as excretions of bone-making cells. The bones consist of inorganic constituents, calcium hydroxyphosphate, $Ca_5(PO_4)_3OH$, and calcium carbonate, and an organic constituent, *collagen*, which is a protein. The body also contains the body fluids blood and lymph, as well as fluids that are secreted by special organs, such as saliva and the digestive juices. Very many different chemical substances are present in these fluids.

The structure of cells is determined by their framework materials, which constitute the cell walls and, in some cases, reinforcing frameworks within the cells. In plants the carbohydrate cellulose, described in the preceding chapter, is the most important constituent of the cell walls. In animals the framework materials are proteins. Moreover, the cell contents consist largely of proteins. For example, a red cell is a thin membrane enclosing a medium that consists of 60% water, 5% miscellaneous materials, and 35% **hemoglobin,** an iron-containing protein, which has molecular weight 68,000, and has the power of combining reversibly with oxygen. It is this power that permits the blood to combine with a large amount of oxygen in the lungs, and to carry it to the tissues, making it available there for oxidation of foodstuffs and body constituents. It has been mentioned earlier in this section that the simplest forms of matter with the power of reproducing themselves, the viruses, consist largely of proteins, as do also the most complex living organisms.

28-3. Amino Acids and Proteins

Proteins may well be considered the most important of all the substances present in plants and animals. Proteins occur either as separate molecules, usually with very large molecular weight, ranging from about 10,000 to many millions, or as reticular constituents of cells, constituting their structural framework (Figure 28-1). The human body contains many thousands of different proteins, which have special structures that permit them to carry out specific tasks.

All proteins are nitrogenous substances, containing approximately 16% of nitrogen, together with carbon, hydrogen, oxygen, and often other elements such as sulfur, phosphorus, iron (four atoms of iron are present in each molecule of hemoglobin), and copper.

Amino Acids. When proteins are heated in acidic or basic solution they undergo hydrolysis, producing substances called amino acids. Amino acids are carboxylic acids in which one hydrogen atom has been replaced by an amino group, —NH$_2$. The amino acids that are obtained from proteins are *alpha* amino acids, with the amino group attached to the carbon atom next

Figure **28-1**

Electron micrograph of an edestin crystal showing individual molecules in the octahedral face (magnification 200,000×). Within the circumscribed area, and in other places where the surface has not been disturbed during preparation, the molecules form a hexagonal pattern. The molecules are about 80 Å in diameter and the molecular weight is 300,000. Note the molecular layers growing out over the supporting film 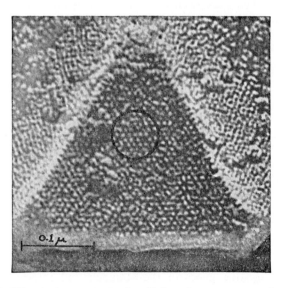 from the edges of the crystal. Edestin is a protein found in wheat, corn, and other seeds. [Reference: C. E. Hall, J. Am. Chem. Soc., **71**, 2915 (1949).]

to the carboxyl group (this carbon atom is called the alpha carbon atom). The simplest of these amino acids is **glycine, CH$_2$(NH$_2$)COOH**. The other natural amino acids contain another group, usually called R, in place of one of the hydrogen atoms on the alpha carbon atom, their general formula thus being CHR(NH$_2$)COOH.

The amino group is sufficiently basic and the carboxyl group is sufficiently acidic that in solution in water the proton is transferred from the carboxyl group to the amino group. The carboxyl group is thus converted into a carboxyl ion, and the amino group into a substituted ammonium ion. The structure of glycine and of the other amino acids in aqueous solution is accordingly the following:

$$
\begin{array}{ccc}
H & H & O \\
& \diagdown | & \| \\
H-N^+ & & C-O^- \\
& \diagup & \diagup \\
& C & \\
& \diagup \diagdown & \\
H & & R
\end{array}
$$

The amino groups and carboxyl groups of most substances dissolved in animal or plant liquids, which usually have pH about 7, are internally ionized in this way, to form an ammonium ion group and a carboxyl ion group within the same molecule.

There are twenty-four amino acids that have been recognized as important constituents of proteins. Their names are given in Table 28-1, together with the formulas of the characteristic group R. Some of the amino acids have an extra carboxyl group or an extra amino group. There is one double amino acid, *cystine*, which is closely related to a simple amino acid, *cysteine*. Four of the amino acids contain heterocyclic rings—rings of carbon atoms and one or more other atoms, in this case nitrogen atoms. Two of the amino acids given in the table, *asparagine* and *glutamine*, are closely related to two others, *aspartic acid* and *glutamic acid*, differing from them only in having the extra carboxyl group changed into an amide group,

$$
-C \diagup^{\displaystyle O} _{\diagdown NH_2}
$$

Proteins are important constituents of food. They are digested by the digestive juices in the stomach and intestines, being split in the process of digestion into small molecules, probably mainly the amino acids themselves. These small molecules are able to pass through the walls of the stomach and intestines into the blood stream, by which they are carried around into the tissues, where they may then serve as building stones for the manufacture of the body proteins. Sometimes people who are ill and cannot digest foods satisfactorily are fed by the injection of a solution of amino acids directly into the blood stream. A solution of amino acids for this purpose is usually obtained by hydrolyzing proteins.

Although all the amino acids listed in Table 28-1 are present in the proteins of the human body, not all of them need to be in the food. Experiments have been carried out which show that nine of the amino acids are essential to man. These nine **essential amino acids** are *histidine, lysine, tryptophan, phenylalanine, leucine, isoleucine, threonine, methionine,* and *valine.* The human body seems to be able to manufacture the others, which are called the nonessential amino acids. Some organisms that we usually consider to be simpler than man have greater powers than the human organisms in that they are able to manufacture all of the amino acids from inorganic constituents. The red bread mold, *Neurospora,* has this power.

Protein foods for man may be classed as *good protein foods,* those that contain all of the essential amino acids, and *poor protein foods,* those that are lacking in one or more of the essential amino acids. *Casein,* the principal protein in milk, is a good protein, from this point of view, whereas *gelatin,* a protein obtained by boiling bones and tendons (partial hydrolysis of the insoluble protein collagen produces gelatin) is a poor protein. Gelatin contains no tryptophan, no valine, and little or no threonine.

Right-handed and Left-handed Amino-acid Molecules. It was pointed out in Section 9-6 that some substances exist in two isomeric forms, called L (levo) and D (dextro) forms, with molecules that are mirror images of one another. These two forms exist for every amino acid except glycine; they differ from one another in the arrangement in space of the four groups attached to the α-carbon atom. Figure 28-2 shows the two isomers of the amino acid alanine, in which R is the methyl group, CH_3.

A most extraordinary fact is that only one of the two isomers of each of the twenty-three amino acids has been found to occur in plant and animal proteins, and that this isomer has the same configuration for all of these amino acids; that is, the hydrogen atom, carboxyl ion group, and ammonium ion group occupy the same position relative to the group R around the alpha carbon atom. This configuration is called the L configuration—*proteins are built entirely of L-amino acids.*

This is a very puzzling fact. Nobody knows why it is that we are built of L-amino acid molecules, rather than of D-amino acid molecules. All the proteins that have been investigated, obtained from animals and from plants, from higher organisms and from very simple organisms—bacteria, molds, even viruses—are found to have been made of L-amino acids.

Table **28-1**

The Principal Amino Acids Occurring in Proteins

MONOAMINOMONOCARBOXYLIC ACIDS

Glycine, aminoacetic acid   —R = —H

Alanine, α-aminopropionic acid   —CH_3

Serine, α-amino-β-hydroxypropionic acid   —CH_2OH

Threonine, α-amino-β-hydroxybutyric acid

$$—CH \bigg\langle {}^{CH_3}_{OH}$$

Methionine, α-amino-γ-methylmercaptobutyric acid   —CH_2—CH_2—S—CH_3

Valine, α-amino-isovaleric acid

$$—CH \bigg\langle {}^{CH_3}_{CH_3}$$

Norvaline, α-aminovaleric acid   —CH_2—CH_2—CH_3

Leucine, α-amino-isocaproic acid

$$—CH_2—CH \bigg\langle {}^{CH_3}_{CH_3}$$

Isoleucine, α-amino-β-methylvaleric acid

$$—CH \bigg\langle {}^{CH_2—CH_3}_{CH_3}$$

Phenylalanine, α-amino-β-phenylpropionic acid

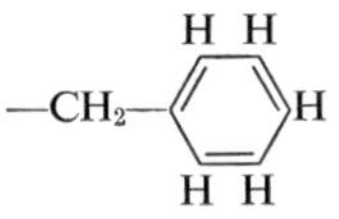

—CH_2—(phenyl ring)

Tyrosine, α-amino-β-(para-hydroxyphenyl)propionic acid

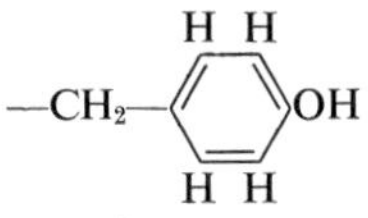

—CH_2—(para-hydroxyphenyl ring)—OH

Cysteine, α-amino-β-sulfhydrylpropionic acid   —CH_2—SH

MONOAMINODICARBOXYLIC ACIDS

Aspartic acid, aminosuccinic acid   —CH_2—COOH

Glutamic acid, α-aminoglutaric acid   —CH_2—CH_2—COOH

Hydroxyglutamic acid, α-amino-β-hydroxyglutaric acid

$$—CH \bigg\langle {}^{CH_2—COOH}_{OH}$$

Table **28-1**

(*continued*)

DIAMINOMONOCARBOXYLIC ACIDS

Arginine, α-amino-δ-guanidinovaleric acid

$$-CH_2-CH_2-CH_2-NH-C\overset{\displaystyle NH}{\underset{\displaystyle NH_2}{}}$$

Lysine, α,ϵ-diaminocaproic acid

$$-CH_2-CH_2-CH_2-CH_2-NH_2$$

DIAMINODICARBOXYLIC ACIDS

Cystine, di-β-thio-α-aminopropionic acid

$$-CH_2-S-S-CH_2-$$

AMINO ACIDS CONTAINING HETEROCYCLIC RINGS

Histidine, α-amino-β-imidazolepropionic acid

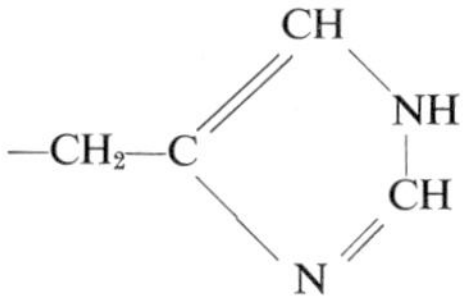

$$-CH_2-C\begin{array}{c} CH \\ \\ N \end{array}\begin{array}{c} NH \\ \\ CH \end{array}$$

Proline, 2-pyrrolidinecarboxylic acid*

$$\begin{array}{c} H \quad\quad H \\ N^+ \quad H \quad O \\ H_2C \quad\quad C-C \\ H_2C-\!\!-\!\!-CH_2 \quad O^- \end{array}$$

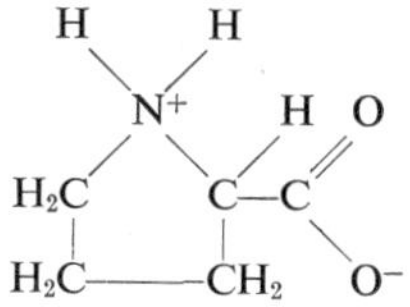

Hydroxyproline, 4-hydroxy-2-pyrrolidinecarboxylic acid*

$$\begin{array}{c} H \quad\quad H \\ N^+ \quad H \quad O \\ H_2C \quad\quad C-C \\ HC-\!\!-\!\!-CH_2 \quad O^- \\ OH \end{array}$$

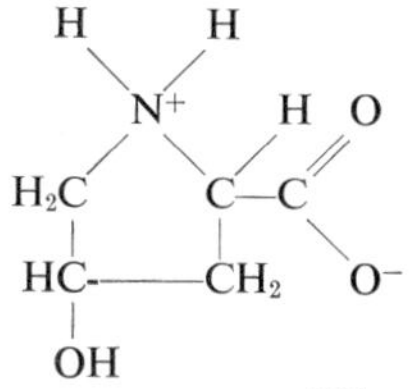

Tryptophan, α-amino-β-indolepropionic acid†

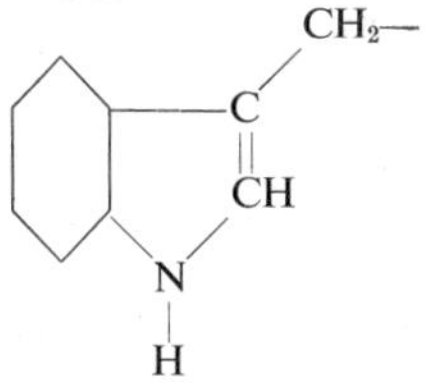

$$\begin{array}{c} CH_2- \\ C \\ CH \\ N \\ H \end{array}$$

AMINO ACIDS CONTAINING AN AMIDE GROUP

Asparagine, aminosuccinic acid monoamide

$$-CH_2-C\overset{\displaystyle O}{\underset{\displaystyle NH_2}{}}$$

Glutamine, α-aminoglutaric acid monoamide

$$-CH_2-CH_2-C\overset{\displaystyle O}{\underset{\displaystyle NH_2}{}}$$

---

* The formulas given for proline and hydroxyproline are those of the complete molecules, and not just of the groups R.

† The hexagon represents a benzene ring.

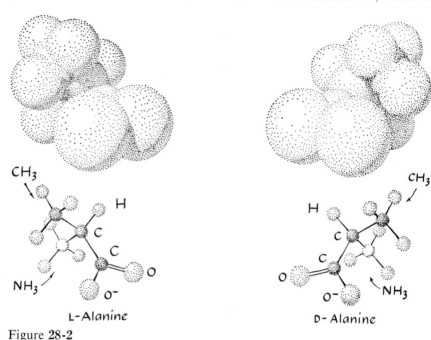

L-Alanine   D- Alanine

Figure 28-2

The two stereoisomers of the amino acid alanine.

Right-handed molecules and left-handed molecules have exactly the same properties, so far as their interaction with ordinary substances is concerned— they differ in their properties only when they interact with other right-handed or left-handed molecules. The earth might just as well be populated with living organisms made of D-amino acids as with those made of L-amino acids. A man who was suddenly converted into an exact mirror image of himself would not at first know that anything had changed about him, except that he would write with his left hand, instead of his right, his hair would be parted on the right side instead of the left, his heartbeat would show his heart to be on the right side, and so on; he could drink water, inhale air and use the oxygen in it for combustion, exhale carbon dioxide, and carry on other bodily functions just as well as ever—so long as he did not eat any ordinary food. If he were to eat ordinary plant or animal food, he would find that he could not digest it.* He could be kept alive only on a diet containing synthetic D-amino acids, made in the chemical laboratory. He could not have any children, unless he could find a wife who had been subjected to the same process of reflection into a mirror image of her original self. We see that there is the possibility that the earth might have been populated with two completely

---

* Alice: "Perhaps Looking-glass milk isn't good to drink." In *Through the Looking-Glass,* by Lewis Carroll (Charles Lutwidge Dodgson), 1872.

independent kinds of life—plants, animals, human beings of two kinds, who could not use one another's food, could not produce hybrid progeny.

No one knows why living organisms are constructed of L-amino acids. We have no strong reason to believe that molecules resembling proteins could not be built up of equal numbers of right-handed and left-handed amino-acid molecules. Perhaps the protein molecules that are made of amino-acid molecules of one sort only are especially suited to the construction of a living organism—but if this is so, we do not know why.

Nor do we know why it is that living organisms have evolved in the L-system rather than in the D-system. The suggestion has been made that the first living organism happened by chance to make use of a few molecules with the L configuration, which were present with D molecules in equal number; and that all succeeding forms of life that have evolved have continued to use L-amino acid molecules through inheritance of the character from the original form of life. Perhaps a better explanation than this can be found—but I do not know what it is.

The Primary Structure of Proteins. During the past century much effort has been devoted by scientists to the problem of the structure of proteins. This is a very important problem; if it were to be solved, we should have a much better understanding than at present of the nature of physiological reactions, and the knowledge of the structure of protein molecules would probably help in the attack on important medical problems, such as the problems of the control of heart disease and cancer.

In the period between 1900 and 1910 strong evidence was obtained by the German chemist Emil Fischer (1852–1919) to indicate that the amino acids in proteins are combined into long chains, called *polypeptide chains*. For example, two molecules of glycine can be condensed together, with elimination of water, to form the double molecule glycylglycine, shown in Figure 27-1. The bond formed in this way is called a *peptide bond*. The process of forming these bonds can be continued, resulting in the production of a long chain containing many amino-acid residues, as shown in Figure 27-1.

Chemical methods have been developed to determine how many polypeptide chains there are in a protein molecule. These methods involve the use of a reagent (fluorodinitrobenzene) that combines with the free amino group of the amino-acid residue at the end of the polypeptide chain to form a colored complex, which can be isolated and identified after the protein has been hydrolyzed into its constituent amino acids (and the end amino acid with the colored group attached). For example, the kind of hemoglobin molecule that is found in the red corpuscles of most adult human beings (called normal adult human hemoglobin or hemoglobin A) has been shown to contain four polypeptide chains. There are two chains of one kind, called the alpha chain, and two of the other, called the beta chain. The alpha chain begins with the sequence val-leu-···· (the abbreviations commonly used are the first three letters of the name of the amino acid), and the beta chain with the sequence val-his-leu-····. The hemoglobin molecule has been shown by use of the ultracentrifuge, x-ray diffraction, and other methods of investigation to be approximately spherical in shape, with diameter about 40 Å. Hence the polypeptide chains cannot be stretched out, but must be folded back and forth, to produce the globular molecule.

The order of amino-acid residues in the polypeptide chains (called the *primary structure*) was first determined for the protein insulin. The insulin molecule has molecular weight about 12,000. It consists of four polypeptide chains, of which two contain 21 amino-acid residues apiece, and the other two contain 30. The sequence of amino acids in the short chains and in the long chains was determined in the years between 1945 and 1952 by the English biochemist F. Sanger (born 1918) and his collaborators. The four chains in the molecule are attached to one another by sulfur-sulfur bonds, between the halves of cystine residues (see Table 28-1). Sequence determinations have now been made by Sanger's method for the alpha and beta chains of normal adult human hemoglobin and several other proteins. The sequence for the beta chain of human hemoglobin A (146 amino-acid residues) is the following: (Amino end or N-terminus) val-his-leu-thr-pro-glu-glu-lys-ser-ala-val-thr-ala-leu-try-gly-lys-val-aspNH$_2$-val-asp-glu-val-gly-gly-glu-ala-leu-gly-arg-leu-leu-val-val-tyr-pro-try-thr-gluNH$_2$-arg-phe-phe-glu-ser-phe-gly-asp-leu-ser-thr-pro-asp-ala-val-met-gly-aspNH$_2$-pro-lys-val-lys-ala-his-gly-lys-lys-val-leu-gly-ala-phe-ser-asp-gly-leu-ala-his-leu-asp-asp-leu-lys-gly-thr-phe-ala-thr-leu-ser-glu-leu-his-cys-asp-lys-leu-his-val-asp-pro-glu-aspNH$_2$-phe-arg-leu-leu-gly-aspNH$_2$-val-leu-val-cys-val-leu-ala-his-his-phe-gly-lys-glu-phe-thr-pro-pro-val-gluNH$_2$-ala-ala-tyr-gluNH$_2$-lys-val-val-ala-gly-val-ala-aspNH$_2$-ala-leu-ala-his-lys-tyr-his (carboxyl end or C-terminus). The sequence for the alpha chain (141 residues) has some similarity to that for the beta chain: about 75 amino-acid residues occur in essentially the same places in the chains. The alpha chain of gorilla hemoglobin differs from that of human hemoglobin in two substitutions of one amino-acid residue for another, and the gorilla and human beta chains differ by only one substitution. The difference between horse hemoglobin and human hemoglobin is about 18 substitutions per chain.

The Denaturation of Proteins.   Proteins such as insulin and hemoglobin have certain special properties that make them valuable to the organism. Insulin is a hormone that assists in the process of oxidation of sugar in the body. Hemoglobin has the power of combining reversibly with oxygen, permitting it to attach oxygen molecules to itself in the lungs, and to liberate them in the tissues. These well-defined properties show that the protein molecules have very definite structures.

A protein that retains its characteristic properties is called a *native protein:*

hemoglobin as it exists in the red cell or in a carefully prepared hemoglobin solution, in which it still has the power of combining reversibly with oxygen, is called native hemoglobin. Many proteins lose their characteristic properties very easily. They are then said to have been *denatured*. Hemoglobin can be denatured simply by heating its solution to 65°C. It then coagulates, to form a brick-red insoluble coagulum of denatured hemoglobin. Most other proteins are also denatured by heating to approximately this temperature. Egg white, for example, is a solution consisting mainly of the protein *ovalbumin*, with molecular weight 43,000. Ovalbumin is a soluble protein. When its solution is heated for a little while at about 65°C the ovalbumin is denatured, forming an insoluble white coagulum of denatured ovalbumin. This phenomenon is observed when an egg is cooked.

It is believed that the process of denaturation involves uncoiling the polypeptide chains from the characteristic structure of the native protein. In the coagulum of denatured hemoglobin or denatured ovalbumin the uncoiled polypeptide chains of different molecules of the protein have become tangled up with one another in such a way that they cannot be separated; hence the denatured protein is insoluble. Some chemical agents, including strong acid, strong alkali, and alcohol, are good denaturing agents.

The Secondary Structure of Proteins. The way in which the polypeptide chains of a protein molecule are arranged in space is called the *secondary structure* of the protein. During recent years much progress has been made in this field, especially by use of the x-ray diffraction method.

The principal type of secondary structure is shown in Figure 28-3. The polypeptide chain is folded into a helix. There are about 3.6 amino-acid residues per turn of the helix—about 18 residues in 5 turns. Each residue is linked to residues in the preceding and following turns by hydrogen bonds between the N—H groups and the oxygen atom of the C=O group. The side chains R of the different residues project radially from the helix; there is plenty of room for them, so that the sequence of residues can be an arbitrary one. This configuration is called the alpha helix.

Many fibrous proteins, including hair, fingernails, horn, and muscle, consist of polypeptide chains with the configuration of the alpha helix, arranged approximately parallel to one another, with the axis of the helix in the direction of the fiber. In some of these proteins the polypeptide chains, with the configuration of the alpha helix, are twisted about one another, to form cables or ropes (Figure 28-4). Hair and horn can be stretched out to over twice their normal length; this process involves breaking the hydrogen bonds of the alpha helix, and forcing the polypeptide chains into a stretched configuration. Silk fibers consist of polypeptide chains with the stretched configuration, attached to one another by hydrogen bonds that extend laterally, as shown in Figure 28-5.

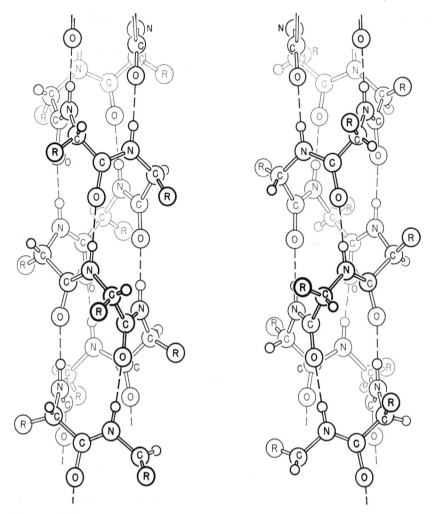

Figure 28-3

A drawing showing two possible forms of the α helix; the one on the left is a left-handed helix, and the one on the right is a right-handed helix. The right-handed helix of polypeptide chains is found in many proteins. The amino-acid residues have the L configuration in each case. The circles labeled R represent the side chains of the various residues.

During the last few years a nearly complete determination of the structure of a globular protein, *myoglobin*, has been carried out by the English scientist J. C. Kendrew and his collaborators. Myoglobin, which is found in muscle, is a protein rather similar to hemoglobin, but with only one polypeptide chain

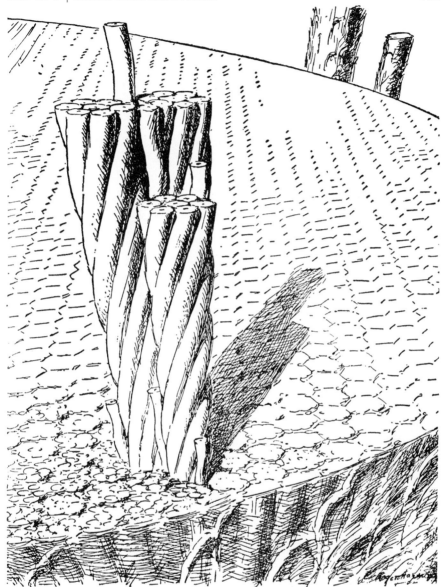

Figure 28-4

A drawing representing the molecular structure of hair, fingernail, muscle, and related fibrous proteins. The protein molecules have the configuration of the α helix (Figure 28-3); each molecule is represented in this drawing as a rod with circular cross section. These fibrous proteins contain seven-stranded cables, consisting of a central α helix and six others that are twisted about it. The spaces between these cables are filled with additional α helixes.

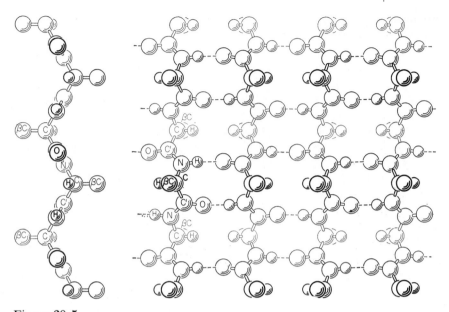

Figure **28-5**

A drawing of the antiparallel-chain pleated sheet, a protein structure found for silk fibers.

in the molecule (molecular weight about 17,000). The myoglobin molecule has been shown by x-ray diffraction of myoglobin crystals to contain a polypeptide chain that does not form a single helix, but instead coils into seven short segments with the configuration of the alpha helix, which are connected by nonhelical sections. The x-ray investigation of hemoglobin, carried out by the English scientist Max Perutz and his collaborators, has shown that its molecule closely resembles an aggregate of four groups with the myoglobin structure.

28-4. Nucleic Acids. The Chemistry of Heredity

One of the most amazing and interesting aspects of the world is the existence of human beings and other living organisms who are able to have progeny, to whom they transmit many of their own characters. The mechanism by means of which a child develops in such a way as to resemble his parents has been under intensive study for a century, and the progress in understanding this phenomenon has been especially rapid during the last few years.

In 1866 the Abbot Gregor Johann Mendel (1822–1884) developed a simple theory of inheritance on the basis of experiments that he had carried out with peas in the garden of the Augustinian monastery at Brno, in Moravia (now Czechoslovakia). He found that his experimental results could be accounted for by assuming that each of the plants of the second generation receives from each of the two parent plants a determiner or factor (now called a *gene*) for each inherited character. The genes are now described as being arranged linearly in a larger structure, one of the chromosomes, which can be seen in the nuclei of cells.

Different genes that may occur at the same locus in a chromosome are called *alleles* or *allelomorphic genes*. For example, Mendel hybridized two strains of peas that differed from one another in that the seeds were round in one strain and wrinkled in the other. The first-generation hybrid progeny had round seeds. However, when they were allowed to become self-fertilized he found that about three-quarters of the second-generation progeny had round seeds and about one-quarter had wrinkled seeds. His explanation of this observation, and of many others like it, is that the peas of the first strain carry two alleles for roundness, and those of the second strain two alleles for wrinkledness. The hybrids of these two strains inherit one of each of these two alleles (one from each parent), and Mendel assumed that the allele for roundness is the *dominant* gene and that for wrinkledness is *recessive*, so that the possession of one each of the two allelomorphic genes leads to roundness (as does the possession of two genes for roundness). In the next generation, obtained by self-fertilization of the first-generation progeny, the allele for roundness or the allele for wrinkledness is inherited at random from the one parent, and also at random from the other parent. About one-quarter of the progeny would then be expected to have the genic composition RR (with R representing the dominant allele), one-half to have the genic constitution Rr or rR, and one-quarter to have the genic constitution rr. The progeny RR would have round seeds, the heterozygotes Rr and rR would also have round seeds, because of the assumed dominance of R, and the recessive homozygotes rr would have wrinkled seeds.

The theory of the gene was greatly developed in the years following 1910 as the result of work on the fruit fly, *Drosophila*, carried out by Thomas Hunt Morgan and his collaborators (especially A. H. Sturtevant, Calvin Bridges, and H. J. Muller), who were able to determine the order in which many genes are located in the chromosomes of this organism. Further progress was made by other investigators (G. W. Beadle and E. L. Tatum, in particular) with use of the red bread mold, *Neurospora*, and by J. Lederberg and others who have studied the genetics of bacteria.

An example of the relation between genes and protein molecules is provided by the different kinds of hemoglobin that have been found in the red cells of human beings. In 1949 it was discovered that some human beings, patients with the disease sickle-cell anemia, have in their red cells a form of hemoglobin (hemoglobin S) that is different from that in the red cells of most people (hemoglobin A). The difference is not great: the two alpha chains of the hemoglobin-S molecule are identical with those of the hemoglobin-A molecule, and each beta chain has one amino-acid residue that is different. The beta chain of hemoglobin A has a residue of glutamic acid in the sixth position from the free amino end (see the sequence on p. 732), whereas the beta chain of hemoglobin S has in this position a residue of valine; all of the other amino-acid residues are the same.

The abnormal hemoglobin in the red cells of the sickle-cell-anemia patients causes a very serious disease. Each of the two parents of a patient with this disease is found by experiment to have in his red cells a fifty-fifty mixture of hemoglobin A and hemoglobin S, and one-quarter of the children of such marriages are found, on the average, to be sickle-cell homozygotes, with the genic constitution SS and the disease sickle-cell anemia. It is evident that the two genes A and S carry out their functions essentially independently of one another; in a heterozygote, with genic constitution AS, each of the genes manufactures its own kind of hemoglobin, and each red cell contains a mixture of hemoglobin A and hemoglobin S.

About 25 years ago evidence was obtained showing that a gene is a molecule of **deoxyribonucleic acid** (usually abbreviated as **DNA**). The chemical nature of DNA has now been determined, and its molecular structure is known. The nature of this structure is such as to permit considerable insight to be obtained about the mechanism by means of which these molecules duplicate themselves, in order that the duplicates may be passed on to the progeny, or in order that the living organism may grow, through cell division, with each cell having its complement of genes.

DNA consists of units, called nucleotides, that are held together by chemical bonds in a linear array, called a polynucleotide chain or a nucleic acid molecule. Each nucleotide consists of three parts: a molecule of phosphoric acid, a molecule of a sugar, **deoxyribose,** and a molecule of a nitrogen compound, called a nitrogen base. The molecules of sugar and molecules of phosphoric acid are condensed together to form long chains:

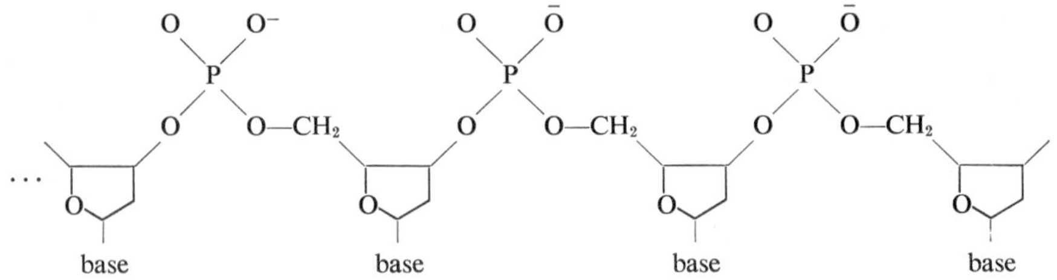

At the present time it is estimated that each DNA chain contains about 5,000 nucleotide residues.

In the above diagram the residue of the sugar deoxyribose is represented by the symbol

$$-CH_2$$

Deoxyribose is a pentose (sugar with formula $C_5H_{10}O_5$) that has lost one oxygen atom, giving it the formula $C_5H_{10}O_4$; its structural formula is

In DNA the two hydroxyl groups marked with an asterisk condense with hydroxyl groups of separate molecules of phosphoric acid, $OP(OH)_3$, to form the DNA chain. The nitrogen atom of the nitrogen base replaces the hydroxyl group marked with two asterisks.

The nitrogen bases found in DNA comprise the two purines **adenine** and **guanine** and the two pyrimidines **thymine** and **cytosine**; in the formulas shown in Figure 28-6 the asterisk indicates the hydrogen atom that is replaced by the carbon atom of the sugar ring in DNA, and the double bonds correspond to only one of the several valence-bond structures for each molecule. The molecules are planar, because each of the bonds in the purine and pyrimidine rings has some double-bond character.

Chemical analysis of DNA from the nuclei of cells showed that, although the relative number of molecules of the two purines adenine and guanine varies from species to species, the molecular ratio adenine/thymine is unity and the ratio guanine/cytosine is unity. For example, the percentages in human sperm are 31% adenine, 19% guanine, 31% thymine, and 19% cytosine.

This experimental result was interpreted only when a theory of the structure of DNA had been developed. In 1954 the American biologist J. D. Watson and the British biophysicist F. H. Crick proposed that molecules of DNA consist of two chains wrapped about one another in a helical configuration, in such a way that at every level, 3.3 Å apart along the axis of the double helix, there occurs a residue of either adenine or guanine and one of either thymine or cytosine, and that these residues occur in complementary pairs: either as an adenine-thymine pair or as a guanine-cytosine pair. The explanation of this complementary pairing is shown in Figure 28-6. It is seen that adenine and thymine can form two hydrogen bonds with one another, whereas cytosine and guanine can form three. The Watson-Crick double helix is shown in Figure 28-7.

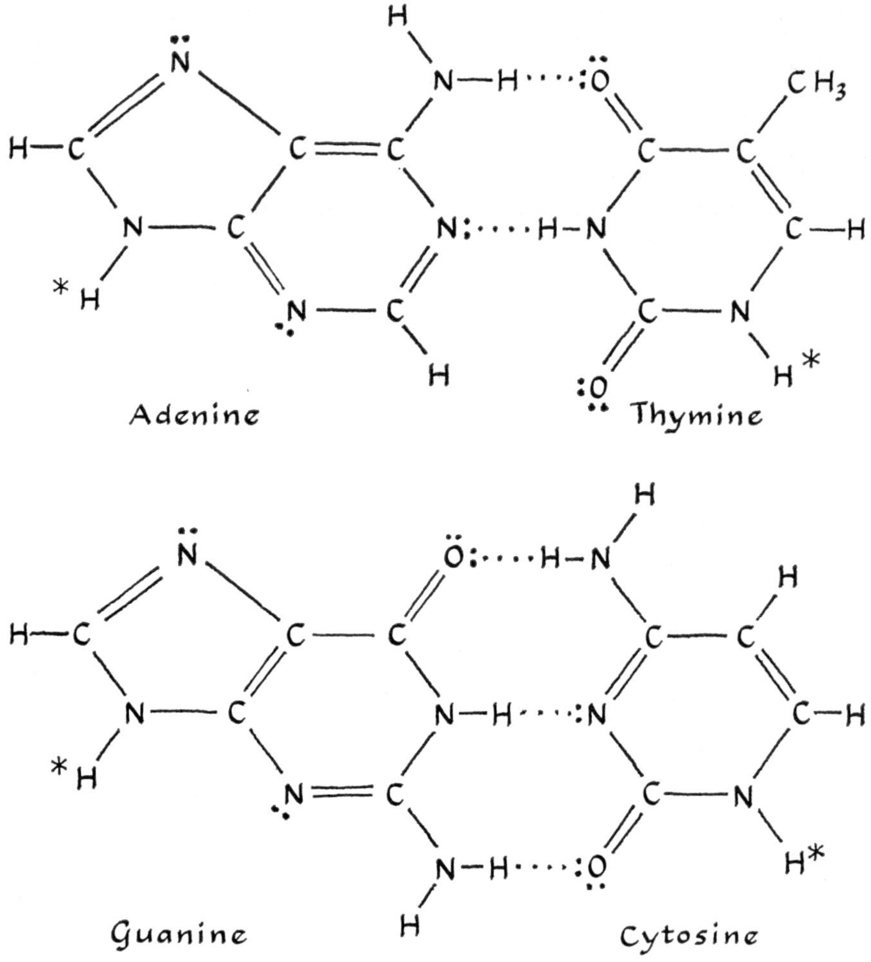

Figure 28-6

Specific hydrogen bonding between adenine and thymine and between cytosine and guanine.

According to the Watson-Crick proposal, the four bases adenine, thymine, guanine, and cytosine, which may be represented by the letters A, T, G, and C, occur in a characteristic sequence in one of the two polynucleotide chains of a gene and in the complementary sequence in the other polynucleotide chain. At each level there is one of the following four pairs of nitrogen bases: —A⫶⫶T—, —T⫶⫶A—, —G⫶⫶⫶C—, —C⫶⫶⫶G—. The dashes indicate either two or three hydrogen bonds, as shown in Figure 28-6.

The sequence of bases in a gene constitutes a code that determines the nature of the character that is conferred upon the organism that has inherited

the gene. It is believed that the sequence of bases in a gene usually determines
the sequence of amino-acid residues in a polypeptide chain (a protein) that
is synthesized in the cell under the influence of the gene. At the present time
it is thought that the synthesis of a polypeptide chain, such as the beta chain

Figure **28-7**

> *The double helix proposed by Watson and Crick as the structure of
> the gene (two complementary molecules of deoxyribonucleic acid).*

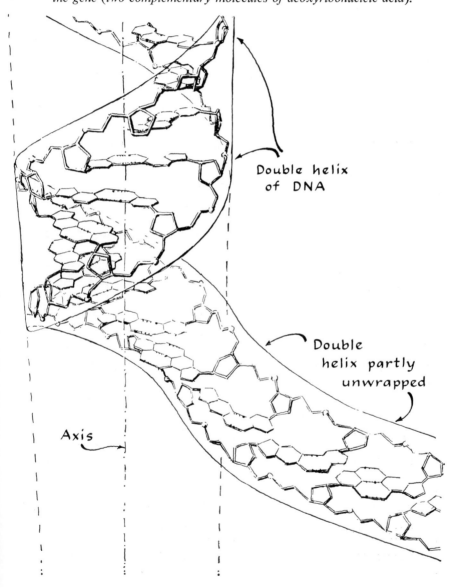

Double helix
of DNA

Double
helix partly
unwrapped

Axis

of the hemoglobin molecule, by the corresponding gene takes place in two steps: the beta-chain gene, in the nucleus of the cell, serves as a template for the synthesis of some thousands of molecules of **RNA (ribonucleic acid,** which is similar to DNA but has a sugar residue, ribose, with a hydroxyl group in place of one of the hydrogen atoms of deoxyribose), to which it transfers the beta-chain code. The RNA molecules then combine molecules of the various amino acids together in the proper sequence to produce the hemoglobin beta chains. Each RNA molecule probably manufactures some tens of thousands of beta chains—there are about 100 million hemoglobin molecules in the mature red cell.

Figure 28-8

> *A diagram showing the postulated method of reduplication of the gene through formation of a polynucleotide chain complementary to each of the two mutually complementary chains of the original gene. The helical arrangement of the two chains is not indicated in this diagram.*

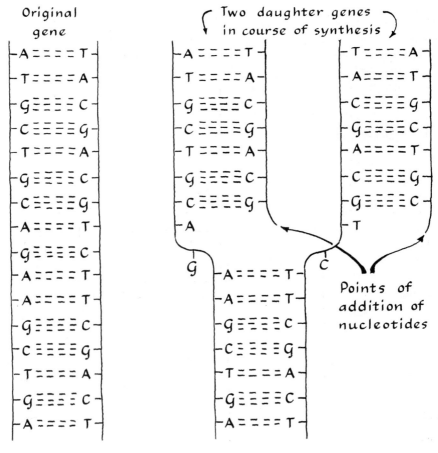

In addition to controlling the manufacture of other molecules, the DNA reduplicates itself. The Watson-Crick mechanism of *reduplication* of DNA molecules in the course of cell division is postulated to be the following: a double helix of complementary polynucleotides begins to uncoil into the separate chains; new polynucleotide chains begin to be synthesized, with the old ones as the templates, and the new chain that is being synthesized in approximation to each of the old chains is identical with the other old chain, in order to preserve the complementariness. Thus when the process is completed there are two identical double helixes, each consisting of one old chain and one newly synthesized chain (Figure 28-8). The half-old half-new character of first-generation daughter molecules of DNA in bacterial cultures has been verified by experiments with isotopes (nitrogen 15).

Rapid progress is being made in determining by experiment the relation between the sequence of nitrogen bases in the DNA chains and the sequence of amino-acid residues in the polypeptide chains of proteins that are synthesized under the control of these genes. There is no doubt that this work will in the course of time lead to a penetrating understanding of the nature of life. The significance of chemistry to life is shown in an especially striking way by the features of molecular structure that are involved in the complementariness of adenine and thymine and of guanine and cytosine, especially the presence of atoms in positions in the planar molecules that permit the formation of two hydrogen bonds by the first pair and of three by the second.

28-5. Metabolic Processes. Enzymes and Their Action

The chemical reactions that take place in a living organism are called *metabolic processes* (Greek *metabole*, change). These reactions are of very many kinds. Let us consider what happens to food that is ingested. The food may contain complex carbohydrates, especially starch, that are split up into simple sugars in the process of digestion, and then pass through the walls of the digestive tract into the blood stream. The sugars may then be converted, in the liver, into glycogen (animal starch), which has the same formula as starch, $(C_6H_{10}O_5)_x$, where x is a large number. Glycogen and other polysaccharides constitute one of the important sources of energy for animals. They combine with oxygen to form carbon dioxide and water, with liberation of energy, part of which can be used for doing work, and part to keep the body warm.

We have mentioned before that proteins in foodstuffs are split in the stomach and intestines into amino acids or simple peptides, which pass through the walls into the blood stream, and then may be built up into the special proteins needed by the organism. A process of tearing down the proteins of the body also takes place. For example, red cells have a lifetime of a few weeks, at the end of which they are destroyed, being replaced by newly formed red cells. The nitrogen of the protein molecules that are torn down is eliminated in the urine, as urea, $CO(NH_2)_2$.

Fats that are ingested are also decomposed in the process of digestion into simpler substances, which then are used by the body for fuel and as structural material.

Some of the chemical reactions that take place in the body can also be made to take place in beakers or flasks in the laboratory. For example, a protein can be decomposed into amino acids in the laboratory by adding strong acids to it and boiling for a long time. Similarly, sugar can be oxidized to carbon dioxide and water; if a little cigarette ash or other solid material is rubbed onto a cube of sugar, the sugar can be lighted by a match, and it will then burn in air, producing carbon dioxide and water:

$$C_{12}H_{22}O_{11} + 12O_2 \longrightarrow 12CO_2 + 11H_2O$$

However, it has not been found possible to cause these chemical reactions to take place in the laboratory at the temperature of the human body, except in the presence of special substances obtained from plants or animals. These substances, enzymes, are proteins that have a catalytic power for certain reactions. Thus the saliva contains a special protein, an enzyme called *salivary amylase* or *ptyalin*, which has the power of catalyzing the decomposition of starch into a sugar, maltose, $C_{12}H_{22}O_{11}$. The reaction that is catalyzed by salivary amylase is

$$(C_6H_{10}O_5)_x + \frac{x}{2}H_2O \longrightarrow \frac{x}{2}C_{12}H_{22}O_{11}$$

Saliva is mixed with a food, such as potato, while the food is being chewed, and during the first few minutes that the food is in the stomach the salivary amylase causes the conversion of the starch into maltose to take place.

Similarly, there is an enzyme in the stomach, *pepsin*, that has the power of serving as a very effective catalyst for the reaction of hydrolysis of proteins into amino acids—that is, for splitting the peptide bond by reaction with water, to form an amino group and a carboxyl group. Pepsin does its work most effectively in a somewhat acidic solution. Gastric juice is in fact rather strongly acidic, its pH being about 0.8—it is hence somewhat more strongly acidic than 0.1 F hydrochloric acid.

The stomach also contains an enzyme, *rennin*, that assists in the digestion of milk, and another enzyme, *lipase*, that catalyzes the decomposition of fats into simpler substances. Additional enzymes involved in the digestion of polysaccharides, proteins, and fats take part in the continuation of the digestion in the intestines; these enzymes are contained in the intestinal juice, pancreatic juice, and bile.

The chemical reactions that take place in the blood and in the cells of the body are also in general catalyzed by enzymes. For example, the process of oxidation of sugar is a complicated one, involving a number of steps, and it is believed that a special enzyme is present to catalyze each of these steps. It has been estimated that there may be twenty thousand or thirty thousand different enzymes in the human body, each constructed in such a way as to permit it to serve as an effective catalyst for a particular chemical reaction useful to the organism.

In recent years many enzymes have been isolated and purified. Many, indeed, have been crystallized. A great deal of work has been done in an effort to discover the mechanism of the catalytic activity of enzymes. So far, however, no one has succeeded in determining the structure of any enzyme, nor in finding out how the enzyme does its job. This general problem is one of the most important of all of the problems of biochemistry.

Heat Values of Foods. One important use of foods is to serve as a source of energy, permitting work to be done, and of heat, keeping the body warm. Foods serve in this way through their oxidation within the body by oxygen that is extracted from the air in the lungs and is carried to the tissues by the hemoglobin of the blood. The ultimate products of oxidation of most of the hydrogen and carbon in foods are water and carbon dioxide. The nitrogen is for the most part converted into urea, $CO(NH_2)_2$, which is eliminated in the urine.

Heats of combustion of foods and their relation to dietary requirements have been thoroughly studied. The food ingested daily by a healthy man of average size doing a moderate amount of muscular work should have a total heat of combustion of about 3,000 kcal. About 90% of this is made available as work and heat by digestion and metabolism of the food.

Fats and carbohydrates are the principal sources of energy in foods. Pure fat has a caloric value (heat of combustion) of 4,080 kcal per pound, and pure carbohydrate (sugar) a caloric value of about 1,860 kcal per pound. The caloric values of foods are obtained by use of a bomb calorimeter, just as was described for fuels. The third main constituent of food, protein, is needed primarily for growth and for the repair of tissues. About 50 g of protein is the daily requirement for an adult of average size. Usually about twice this amount of protein is ingested. This amount, 100 g, has a caloric value of only about 400 kcal, the heat of combustion of protein being about 2,000 kcal per pound. Accordingly, fat and carbohydrate must provide about 2,600 kcal of the 3,000 kcal required daily.

28-6. Vitamins

Man requires nine amino acids in his diet, in order to keep in good health. It is not enough, however, that the diet contain proteins that provide these nine amino acids, and a sufficient supply of carbohydrates and fats to provide energy. Other substances, both inorganic and organic, are also essential to health.

Among the inorganic constituents that must be present in foods in order that a human being be kept in good health we may mention sodium ion, chloride ion, potassium ion, calcium ion, magnesium ion, iodide ion, phosphorus (which may be ingested as phosphate), and several of the transition metals. Iron is necessary for the synthesis of hemoglobin and of some other protein molecules in the body that serve as enzymes; in the absence of sufficient iron in the diet, anemia will develop. Copper is also required; it seems to be involved in the process of manufacture of hemoglobin and the other iron-containing compounds in the body.

The organic compounds other than the essential amino acids that are required for health are called *vitamins*. Man is known to require at least thirteen vitamins: vitamins A, B_1 (thiamine), B_2 (riboflavin), B_6 (pyridoxin), B_{12}, C (ascorbic acid), D, K, niacin, pantothenic acid, inositol, para-aminobenzoic acid, and biotin.

Although it has been recognized for over a century that certain diseases occur when the diet is restricted, and can be prevented by additions to the diet (such as lime juice for the prevention of scurvy), the identification of the essential food factors as chemical substances was not made until a few years ago. Progress in the isolation of these substances and in the determination of their structure has been rapid in recent years, and many of the vitamins are now being made synthetically, for use as dietary supplements. It is usually possible for a diet to be obtained that provides all of the essential food substances in satisfactory amounts, but in some cases it is wise to have the diet supplemented by vitamin preparations.

Vitamin A has the formula $C_{20}H_{29}OH$, and the structure

It is yellow, oily substance, which occurs in nature in butterfat and fish oils. Lack of vitamin A in the diet causes a scaly condition of the eyes, and similar abnormality of the skin in general, together with a decreased resistance to infection of the eyes and skin. In addition there occurs a decreased ability to see at night, called *night blindness*. There are two mechanisms for vision, one situated in the cones of the retina of the eye, which are especially concentrated in the neighborhood of the fovea (the center of vision), and the other situated in the rods of the retina. Color vision, which is the ordinary vision, used when the intensity of light is normal, involves the retinal cones. Night vision, which operates when the intensity of light is very small, involves the rods; it is not associated with a recognition of color. It has been found that a certain protein, *visual purple*, which occurs in the rods, takes part in the process of night vision. Vitamin A is the prosthetic group of the visual purple molecule, and a deficiency in this vitamin leads for this reason to a decrease in the ability to see at night.

A protein, such as visual purple, that has a characteristic chemical group other than the amino acid residues as part of its structure is called a *conjugated protein*. Such a characteristic group in a conjugated protein is called a *prosthetic group* (Greek *prosthesis*, an addition). Hemoglobin is another example of a conjugated protein. Each hemoglobin molecule consists of a simple protein called globin to which there are attached four prosthetic groups called *heme groups*. The formula of the heme group is $C_{34}H_{32}O_4N_4Fe$.

It is not essential that vitamin A itself be present in food in order to prevent the vitamin A deficiency symptoms. Certain hydrocarbons, the *carotenes*, with formula $C_{40}H_{56}$ (similar in structure to lycopene, Figure 27-1) can be converted into vitamin A in the body. These substances, which are designated by the name *provitamin A*, are red and yellow substances that are found in carrots, tomatoes, and other vegetables and fruits, as well as in butter, milk, green leafy vegetables, and eggs.

Thiamine, Vitamin B₁, has the following formula (that shown is for thiamine chloride):

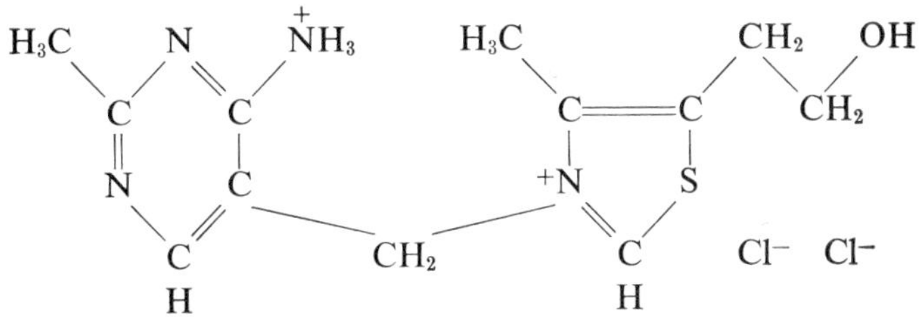

A lack of thiamine in the diet causes the disease beri-beri, a nerve disease that in past years was common in the Orient. Just before 1900 it was found by Eijkman in Java that beri-beri occurred as a consequence of a diet consisting largely of polished rice, and that it could be cured by adding the rice polishings to the diet. In 1911 Casimir Funk assumed that beri-beri and similar diseases were due to lack of a substance present in a satisfactory diet and missing from a deficient diet, and he attempted to isolate the substance whose lack was responsible for beri-beri. He coined the name vitamin for substances of this sort (he spelled it vitamine because he thought that the substances were amines). The structure of vitamin B₁, thiamine, was determined by R. R. Williams, E. R. Buchman, and their collaborators in 1936.

Thiamine seems to be important for metabolic processes in the cells of the body, but the exact way in which it operates is not known. There is some evidence that it is the prosthetic group for an enzyme involved in the oxidation of carbohydrates. The vitamin is present in potatoes, whole cereals, milk, pork, eggs, and other vegetables and meats.

Riboflavin, Vitamin B$_2$, has the following structure:

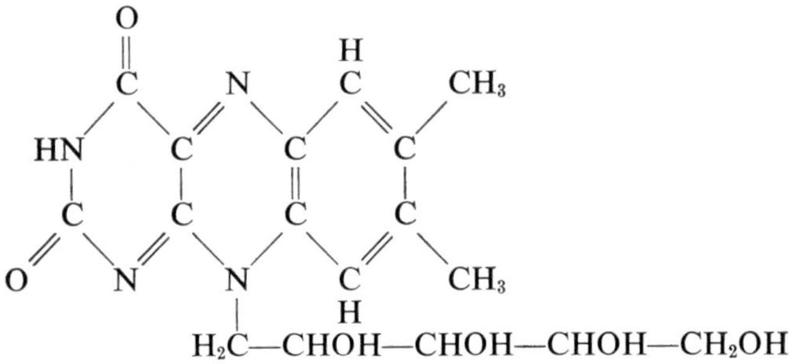

$$H_2C—CHOH—CHOH—CHOH—CH_2OH$$

It seems to be essential for growth and for a healthy condition of the skin. Riboflavin is known to be the prosthetic group of an enzyme, called *yellow enzyme*, that catalyzes the oxidation of glucose and certain other substances in the animal body.

Vitamin B$_6$ (pyridoxin) has the formula

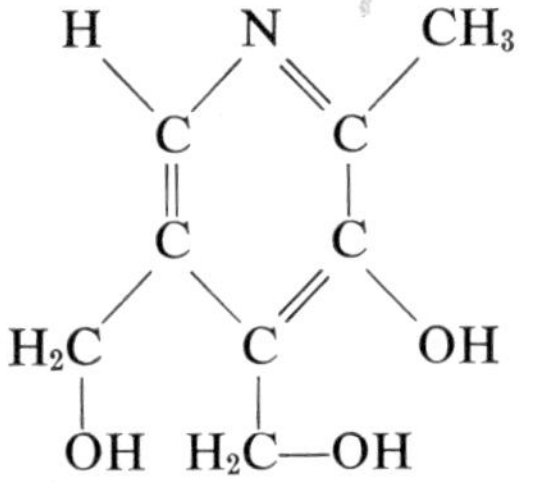

It is present in yeast, liver, rice polishings, and other plant and animal foods, and is also produced synthetically. It has the power of stimulating growth, and of preventing skin eruptions (dermatitis).

Vitamin B$_{12}$ is involved in the manufacture of the red corpuscles of the blood. It can be used for the treatment of pernicious anemia, and it is perhaps the most potent substance known in its physiological activity: 1 microgram per day (1×10^{-6} g) of vitamin B$_{12}$ is effective in the control of the disease. The vitamin can be isolated from liver tissue, and is also produced by molds and other microorganisms. Each molecule of vitamin B$_{12}$ contains one cobalt atom. This is the only compound of cobalt that is known to be present in the human body.

Ascorbic acid, Vitamin C, is a water-soluble vitamin of great importance. A deficiency of vitamin C in the diet leads to scurvy, a disease characterized by loss of weight, general weakness, hemorrhagic condition of the gums and skin, loosening of the teeth, and other symptoms. Sound tooth development seems to depend upon a satisfactory supply of this vitamin, and a deficiency is thought to cause a tendency to incidence of a number of diseases.

The formula of ascorbic acid is the following:

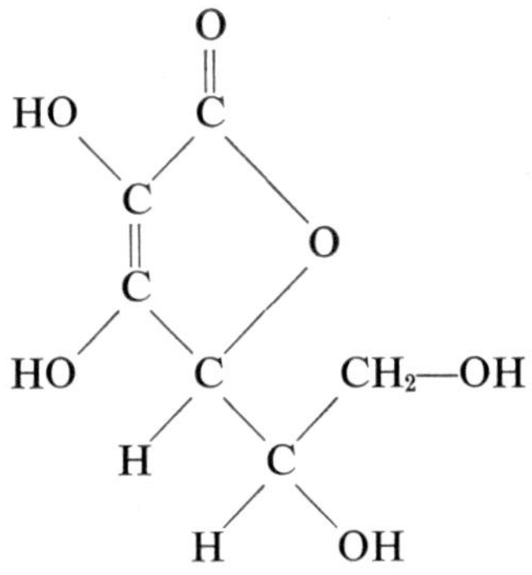

$$
\begin{array}{c}
& & O \\
& & \parallel \\
HO & & C \\
\diagdown & & \diagup \diagdown \\
& C & & O \\
& \parallel & & \diagup \\
& C & & \\
\diagup & \diagdown & & \\
HO & & C & CH_2\!-\!OH \\
& \diagup \diagdown & \diagup \\
& H & C \\
& & \diagup \diagdown \\
& & H & OH
\end{array}
$$

The vitamin is present in many foods, especially fresh green peppers, turnip greens, parsnip greens, spinach, orange juice, and tomato juice. The daily requirement of vitamin C is about 60 mg.

Vitamin D is necessary in the diet for the prevention of rickets, a disease involving malformation of the bones and unsatisfactory development of the teeth. There are several substances with antirachitic activity. The form that occurs in oils from fish livers is called vitamin D_3; it has the following chemical structure:

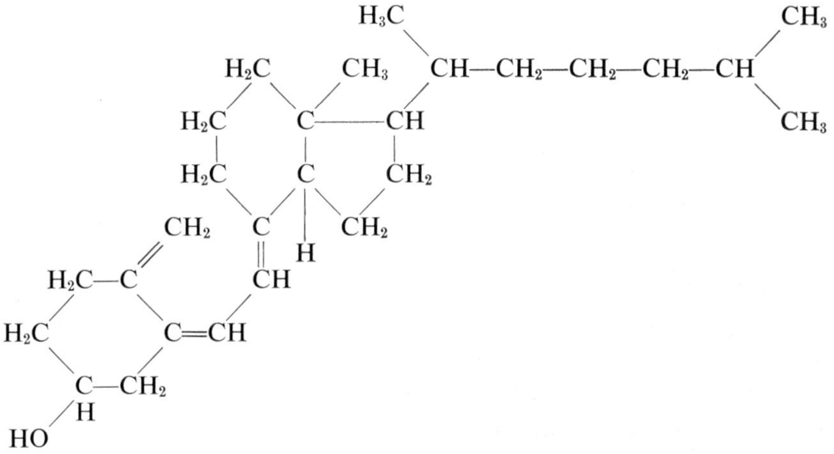

$$
\begin{array}{c}
& & & H_3C & & & & & & CH_3 \\
& & & \diagdown & & & & & & \diagup \\
& H_2C & & CH_3 & CH\!-\!CH_2\!-\!CH_2\!-\!CH_2\!-\!CH \\
& \diagup & \diagup & \diagup & & & & & & \diagdown \\
H_2C & & C\text{------}CH & & & & & & & CH_3 \\
| & & | & | \\
H_2C & & C & CH_2 \\
\diagdown & & | & \diagdown \\
CH_2 & C & | & CH_2 \\
& \diagup\!\diagup & \parallel & H & \diagup \\
H_2C\!-\!C & CH \\
\diagup & & \diagdown \\
H_2C & & C\!=\!CH \\
\diagdown & & \diagup \\
& C\!-\!CH_2 \\
& \diagup H \\
HO
\end{array}
$$

Only a very small amount of vitamin D is necessary for health—approximately 0.01 mg per day. The vitamin is a fat-soluble vitamin, occurring in cod-liver oil, egg yolks, milk, and in very small amounts in other foods. Cereals, yeast, and milk acquire an added vitamin D potency when irradiated with ultraviolet light. The radiation converts a fatty substance (a *lipid*) that is present in the food, a substance called *ergosterol*, into another substance, *calciferol* (vitamin D_2), that has vitamin D activity. The structure of calciferol is closely related to that of vitamin D_3.

Whereas most vitamins are harmless even when large quantities are ingested, vitamin D is harmful when taken in large amounts.

Vitamin E, while not necessary for health, seems to be required for the reproduction and lactation of animals. Niacin, a member of the B group of vitamins, is necessary for the prevention of the deficiency disease pellagra. Pantothenic acid, inositol, p-aminobenzoic acid, and biotin are substances involved in the process of normal growth. Vitamin K is a vitamin that prevents bleeding, by assisting in the process of clotting of the blood.

It is interesting that many "simpler organisms" do not require so many substances for growth as does man. It was mentioned above that the red bread mold, *Neurospora*, can synthesize all the amino acids present in proteins, whereas man is unable to synthesize nine of them, but must obtain them in his diet. The red bread mold is also able to manufacture other substances that man requires as vitamins. The only organic growth substance required by this organism is biotin. Similarly, the food requirements of the rat, while greater than those of *Neurospora*, are not so great as those of man. The rat, for example, does not require ascorbic acid (vitamin C) in its diet, but is able to synthesize this substance, which is present as an important constituent in the tissues of the animal.

28-7. Hormones

Another class of substances of importance in the activity of the human body consists of the *hormones*, which are substances that serve as messengers from one part of the body to another, moving by way of the blood stream. The hormones control various physiological processes. For example, when a man is suddenly frightened, a substance called *epinephrine* (also called adrenalin) is secreted by the suprarenal glands, small glands that lie just above the kidneys. The formula of epinephrine is

When epinephrine is introduced into the blood stream it speeds up the action of the heart, causes the blood vessels to contract, thus increasing the blood pressure, and causes glucose to be released from the liver, thus providing an immediate source of extra energy.

Thyroxin is a secretion of the thyroid gland that controls metabolism. *Insulin* is a secretion of the pancreas that controls the combustion of carbohydrates. Both of these hormones are proteins, thyroxin having a prosthetic group that contains iodine. Many other hormones are known, some of which are proteins and some simpler chemical substances.

It has been recognized that diseases (such as goiter) affecting the thyroid gland may arise from a deficient production of thyroxin, which can be remedied by the introduction of added iodide ion into the diet. The disease *diabetes mellitus,* characterized by the appearance of sugar in the urine and perhaps due to a deficient production of the hormone insulin, has in recent decades been treated by the injection of insulin, obtained from the pancreatic glands of animals. The hormones *cortisone* and *ACTH* (adrenocorticotropic hormone) have been shown recently to have strong therapeutic activity toward rheumatoid arthritis and some other diseases.

28-8. Chemistry and Medicine

From the earliest times chemicals have been used in the treatment of disease. The substances that were first used as drugs are natural products such as in the leaves, branches, and roots of plants. As the alchemists discovered or made new chemical substances, these substances were tried out to see if they had physiological activity, and many of them were introduced into early medical practice. For example, both mercuric chloride, $HgCl_2$, and mercurous chloride, Hg_2Cl_2, were used in medicine, mercuric chloride as an antiseptic, and mercurous chloride, taken internally, as a cathartic and general medicament.

The modern period of *chemotherapy,* the treatment of disease by use of chemical substances, began with the work of Paul Ehrlich (1854–1915). It was known at the beginning of the present century that certain organic compounds of arsenic would kill protozoa, parasitic microorganisms responsible for certain diseases, and Ehrlich set himself the task of synthesizing a large number of arsenic compounds, in an effort to find one that would be at the same time toxic (poisonous) to protozoa in the human body and nontoxic to the human host of the microorganism. After preparing many compounds he synthesized *arsphenamine,* which has the structure of a linear high polymer:

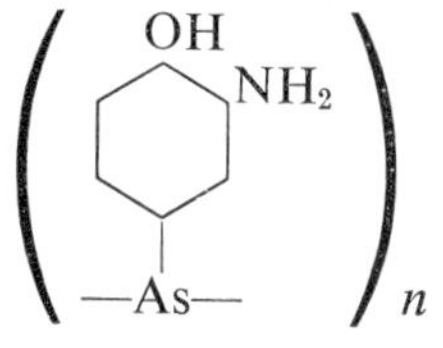

This compound used to be called 606; the name is said to have resulted from the fact that it was the 606th compound of arsenic synthesized by Ehrlich in his investigation.

Arsphenamine has been found to be extremely valuable. Its greatest use is in the treatment of syphilis; the drug attacks the microorganism responsible for this disease, *Spirocheta pallida*. It has also been useful in the treatment of some other diseases. Now it is being superseded by penicillin (which we shall discuss below) in the treatment of syphilis.

Since Ehrlich's time there has been continual progress in the development of new chemotherapeutic agents. Thirty years ago the infectious diseases constituted the principal cause of death; now most of these diseases are under effective control by chemotherapeutic agents, some of which have been synthesized in the laboratory and some of which have been isolated from microorganisms. At the present time only a few of the infectious diseases constitute major hazards to the health of man, and we may confidently anticipate that the control of these diseases by chemotherapeutic agents will be achieved in a few years.

The recent period of rapid progress began with the discovery of the **sulfa drugs** by G. Domagk. In 1935 Domagk discovered that the compound prontosil, a derivative of *sulfanilamide*, was effective in the control of streptococcus infections. It was soon found by other workers that sulfanilamide itself is just as effective in the treatment of these diseases, and that it could be administered by mouth. The formula of sulfanilamide is given in Table 28-2. Sulfanilamide is effective against hemolytic streptococcic infections and meningococcic infections. As soon as the value of sulfanilamide was recognized chemists synthesized hundreds of related substances, and investigations were made of their usefulness as bacteriostatic agents (agents with the power of controlling the spread of bacterial infections). It was found that many of these related substances are valuable, and their use is now an important part of medical practice. *Sulfapyridine* has been found valuable for the control of pneumococcic pneumonia (pneumonia due to the *Pneumococcus* microorganisms), as well as of other pneumococcic infections and gonorrhea. *Sulfathiazole* is used for these infections and also for the control of staphylococcic infections, which occur especially in carbuncles and eruptions of the skin. These and other sulfa drugs are all derivatives of sulfanilamide itself, obtained by replacing one of the hydrogen atoms of the amide group (the NH_2 bonded to the sulfur atom) by some other group (Table 28-2).

The introduction of **penicillin** into medical treatment was the next great step forward. In 1929 Professor Alexander Fleming, a bacteriologist working in the University of London, noticed that bacteria that he was growing in a dish in his laboratory were not able to grow in the region immediately surrounding a bit of mold that had accidentally begun to develop. He surmised that the mold was able to produce a chemical substance that had *bacteriostatic action*, the power of preventing the bacteria from growing, and he made a preliminary investigation of the nature of this substance. Ten years later, perhaps spurred on by the successful use of the sulfa drugs in medicine, Professor Howard Florey and Dr. E. B. Chain of the University of Oxford decided to make a careful study of the antibacterial substances that had been reported in order to see whether they would be similarly useful in the treatment of disease. When

Table **28-2**

Structural Formulas of Sulfa Drugs and Penicillin

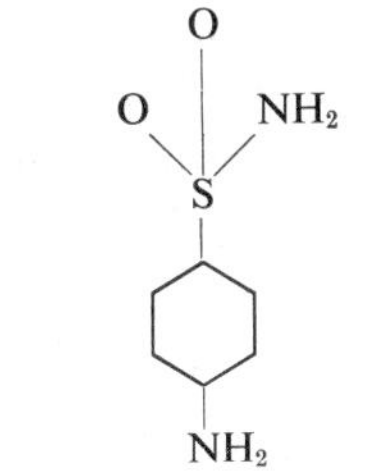

Sulfanilamide

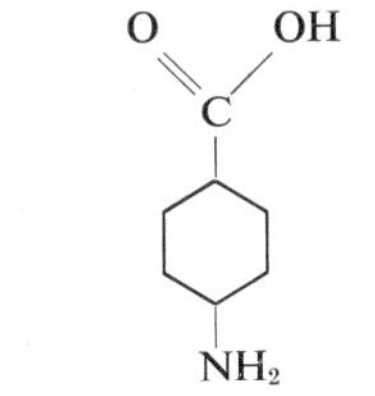

Para-aminobenzoic acid

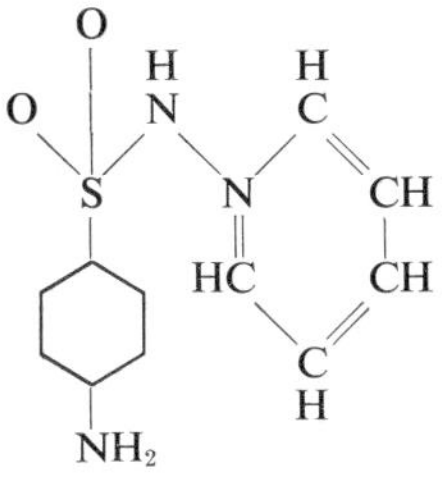

Sulfapyridine

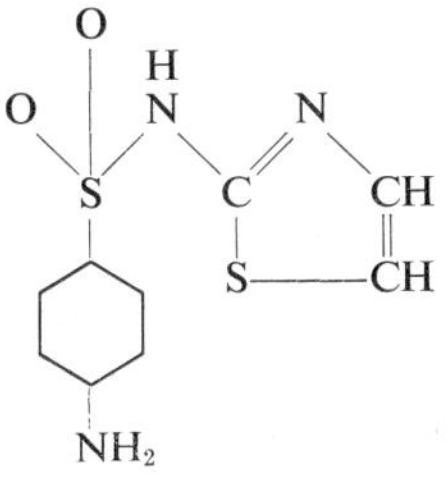

Sulfathiazole

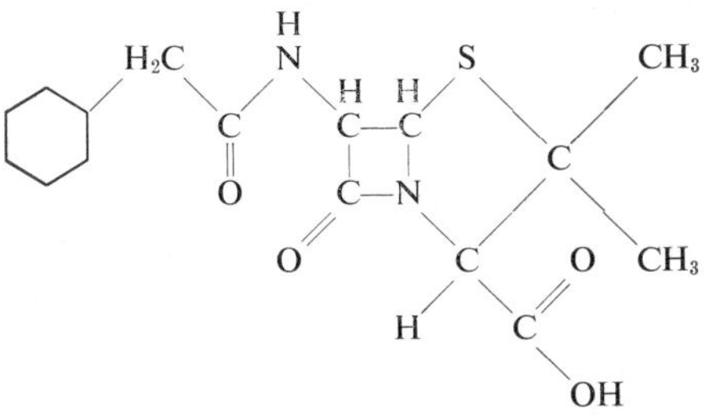

Penicillin G

they tested the bacteriostatic power of the liquid in which the mold *Penicillium notatum* that had been observed by Fleming was growing, they found it to be very great, and within a few months the new antibiotic substance penicillin was being used in the treatment of patients. Through the cooperative effort of many investigators in the United States and England rapid progress was made during the next two or three years in the determination of the structure of penicillin, the development of methods of manufacturing it in large quantities, and the investigation of the diseases that could be effectively treated by use of it. Within less than a decade this new antibiotic agent has become the most valuable of all drugs. It provides an effective therapeutic treatment of many diseases.

The structure of penicillin is shown in Table 28-2. The substance has been synthesized, but no cheap method of synthesizing it has been developed, and the large amount of penicillin that is being manufactured and used in the treatment of disease is made by growing the mold penicillium in a suitable medium and then extracting the penicillin from the medium. Important forward steps in the introduction of penicillin into medical treatment were the development of strains of the mold that produced the desired penicillin in large quantities, and the discovery of the best medium on which to grow the mold.

It is interesting that a number of slightly different penicillins are formed in nature by different strains of the mold. The formula in Table 28-2 represents benzyl penicillin (penicillin G), which is the product that is now manufactured and used. Other naturally occurring penicillins differ from benzyl penicillin only with respect to the part of the molecule that is shown on the left side of the structure. In benzyl penicillin there is indicated a benzyl group, C_6H_5—CH_2—, in this position. Penicillin K contains the normal heptyl group in this position, the hydrocarbon chain $CH_3CH_2CH_2CH_2CH_2CH_2$—. It is not as effective as penicillin G in the treatment of infections. Scores of other penicillins have been made and investigated.

The spectacular success of penicillin as a chemotherapeutic agent has led to the search for other antibiotic products of living organisms. *Streptomycin*, which is produced by the mold *Actinomyces griseus*, has been found to be valuable in the treatment of diseases that are not effectively controlled by penicillin, and some other bacteriostatic agents also have been found to have significant value.

Another very great step forward has been made since 1955 by the discovery of substances that can control the development of viral infections. Penicillin, streptomycin, and the sulfa drugs are effective against bacteria but not against viruses. It has recently been found, however, that *chloramphenicol* (Chloromycetin) and *aureomycin*, both of which are substances manufactured by molds (the molds *Streptomyces venezuele* and *Streptomyces aureofaciens* respectively), have the power of controlling certain viral infections.

The Relation between the Molecular Structure of Substances and Their Physiological Activity. No one knows what the relation between the molecular structure of substances and their physiological activity is. We know the structural formulas of many drugs, vitamins, and hormones—some of these formulas have been given in the preceding sections. It is probable, however, that most of these substances produce their physiological action by interacting with or combining with proteins in the human body or in the bacterium or virus that they counteract; and we do not yet know the structure of any of these proteins.

A suggestion has been made about the way in which the sulfa drugs exercise their bacteriostatic action. It seems probable that this suggestion is essentially correct. It has been found that a concentration of sulfanilamide or other sulfa drug that would prevent bacterial cultures from growing under ordinary circumstances loses this power when some para-aminobenzoic acid is added. The amount of para-aminobenzoic acid required to permit the bacteria to increase in number is approximately proportional to the excess of the amount of the sulfa drug over the minimum that would produce bacteriostatic action. This *competition* between the sulfa drug and para-aminobenzoic acid can be given a reasonable explanation. Let us assume that the bacteria need to have some para-aminobenzoic acid in order to grow; that is, that para-aminobenzoic acid is a vitamin for the bacteria. Probably it serves as a vitamin by combining with a protein to form an essential enzyme; presumably it serves as the prosthetic group of this enzyme. It is likely that the bacterium synthesizes a protein molecule that has a small region, a cavity, on one side of itself into which the para-aminobenzoic acid molecule just fits.

The sulfanilamide molecule is closely similar in structure to the para-aminobenzoic molecule (see Table 28-2). Each of the molecules contains a benzene ring, an amino group ($-NH_2$) attached to one of the carbon atoms of the benzene ring, and another group attached to the opposite carbon atom. It seems not unlikely that the sulfanilamide molecule can fit into the cavity on the protein, thus preventing the para-aminobenzoic molecule from getting into this place. If it is further assumed that the sulfanilamide molecule is not able to function in such a way as to make the complex with the protein able to act as an enzyme, then the explanation of the action of sulfanilamide is complete. It is thought that the protein fits tightly around the benzene ring and the amino group, but not around the other end of the molecule. The evidence for this is that derivatives of sulfanilamide in which various other groups are attached to the sulfur atom are effective as bacteriostatic agents, whereas compounds in which other groups are attached to the benzene ring or the amino group are not effective.

Nobody knows why penicillin is able to control many bacterial infections, nor why chloramphenicol and aureomycin attack viruses; but we may hope that further studies will lead to the solution of this great problem of the molecular basis of the action of drugs, and we may then expect great further progress to occur in medical research. When the mechanism of the action of drugs has been understood, it will be possible for investigators to attack the problem presented by a new disease in a logical and systematic way; new chemotherapeutic agents can then be developed by logical, scientific procedures, rather than by chance.

REFERENCES

Scientific American offprints (see Appendix VI):

5. The Structure of the Hereditary Material

31. The Structure of Protein Molecules
47. The Origin of Life
54. Nucleic Acids
121. The Three-Dimensional Structure of a Protein Molecule
123. The Genetic Code

CHAPTER 29

The Chemistry of the Fundamental

Particles

During recent years there has been a great increase in our knowledge of the world. Atoms have been found to consist of electrons and nuclei, and the atomic nuclei have been found to consist of protons and neutrons. Moreover, in addition to the electron, the proton, and the neutron, many other particles classed as fundamental have been discovered.

The field of science dealing with the nature and the reactions of the fundamental particles is developing very rapidly at the present time. Work in this field of science has been carried out largely by physicists, but the reactions by means of which the fundamental particles are created, converted into others, and destroyed are in a general way similar to chemical reactions, and we may be justified in considering the study of these reactions and the properties of the fundamental particles themselves as constituting the field of the chemistry of the fundamental particles.

At the present time about 34 fundamental particles are known. This number includes 6 (the photon, the graviton, two neutrinos, and two antineutrinos) that move only with the speed of light, and 28 that move only at speeds less than the speed of light. In accordance with the theory of relativity, the particles that move only at the speed of light have zero rest-mass, whereas the others have finite rest-mass.

Much of the knowledge about the fundamental particles has been obtained during the last decade. The scientists who have been working in this field have made many completely unexpected discoveries, which are changing our ways of thinking about the world. Just as the discoveries in the field of atomic and molecular science, discussed in earlier chapters, and the field of nuclear science, to be discussed in the following chapter, have had profound effects upon our daily lives, changing the nature of our civilization and especially the methods of waging war, so may we expect that the new knowledge about fundamental particles will in the course of time have equally profound effects upon our lives. If Benjamin Franklin were alive today, he might well say "It is impossible to imagine the height to which may be carried during the next *twenty* years the power of man over matter."

29-1. The Classification of the Fundamental Particles

At the present time it is convenient to classify the thirty-four fundamental particles in the following way:

8 baryons (the proton, the neutron, and six heavier particles)
8 antibaryons
8 mesons and antimesons
8 leptons and antileptons
The photon
The graviton

Most of the fundamental particles can be described as constituting either *matter* or *antimatter*. The existence of these two kinds of matter was predicted, on the basis of relativistic quantum mechanics, by P. A. M. Dirac (born 1902), the English theoretical physicist who first developed a theory of quantum mechanics compatible with the theory of relativity. His prediction has been thoroughly confirmed by experiment. Every electrically charged particle has a counterpart that is identical with it in some properties and opposite to it in others: the masses and spins are identical, but the electric charges are opposite. For example, the electron, which constitutes a part of ordinary matter, and the positron, which is the antielectron, have opposite electric charges, $-e$ and $+e$, respectively; their masses are the same; and each has a spin represented by the spin quantum number $\frac{1}{2}$, which permits two ways of orienting the spinning particle in a magnetic field. Some neutral particles have antiparticles and some are their own antiparticles. Whenever a particle and the corresponding antiparticle come together they annihilate each other. Their masses are totally converted into high-energy light waves or, in some cases, into lighter particles moving with great speeds. The Einstein equation $E = mc^2$ gives the amount of energy that is released when a particle and its antiparticle annihilate one another with formation of radiant energy. The neutral particles that are their own antiparticles decay very rapidly.

Antimatter does not exist except fleetingly on earth. Particles of antimatter are created by collisions, as described in the following section, and the antiparticles are then rapidly destroyed as they react with particles of ordinary matter with which they collide.

There is the possibility that some regions of the universe, perhaps some nebulae, are composed of antimatter. The hydrogen atom in such a region consists of a positron moving about an antiproton. The collision between an antimatter nebula and a nebula composed of ordinary matter would result in the liberation of a tremendous amount of radiant energy, and might be recognized by astronomers.

Fermions and Bosons. The elementary particles may be divided into two classes on the basis of the magnitude of their spin. The electron was described in Chapter 7 as having spin $\frac{1}{2}$. It has an angular momentum determined by the spin quantum number $\frac{1}{2}$, and in a magnetic field it can orient its angular momentum with component either $+\frac{1}{2}$ or $-\frac{1}{2}$ in the direction of the field (the unit of angular momentum is the Bohr unit $h/2\pi$). It was also mentioned in Chapter 7 that two electrons cannot occupy the same orbital in an atom unless they have opposite orientations of their spin; that is, they cannot be in exactly the same quantum state, as they would be if they occupied the same orbital and both had positive orientation of the spin. This is the expression of the Pauli exclusion principle. (They are also said to obey Fermi statistics, but we shall not be able to discuss the meaning of this expression; Fermi statistics is closely related to the Pauli exclusion principle.)

Particles that have spin $\frac{1}{2}$ are called *fermions*, named after the physicist Enrico Fermi. In accordance with the Pauli exclusion principle, no two identical fermions can be in exactly the same quantum state.

The baryons, antibaryons, leptons, and antileptons are all fermions with spin $\frac{1}{2}$. According to theory, particles with spins $\frac{3}{2}, \frac{5}{2}, \cdots$ would also be fermions.

Particles with integral spin $(0, 1, 2, \cdots)$ are called *bosons*, named after the Indian physicist S. N. Bose. They interact with one another in a way that permits two or more particles to be in exactly the same quantum state. The photon, the graviton, and the mesons are bosons. The mesons all have spin 0. The photon has spin 1. The graviton, which is the quantum of the gravitational field, is expected to have spin 2.

The **photon** or light quantum is now accepted as one of the fundamental particles. Newton discussed both a corpuscular theory and a wave theory of light. During the nineteenth century a great emphasis was given to the wave theory of light in connection with experiments on the diffraction of light. Then in 1905 Einstein pointed out that a number of puzzling experimental results could be interpreted in a simple way if it were assumed that light (visible light, ultraviolet light, radio waves, gamma rays, etc.) have some of the properties of particles (Section 3-10). He called these "particles" of light "light quanta," and the name photons has since come into use. The amount of energy constituting a light quantum is determined by the frequency of the light; it is $E = h\nu$.

The properties of light cannot be described completely by analogy with either ordinary waves or ordinary particles. In the discussion of some phenomena the description of light as wave motion is found to be the more useful, and in the discussion of other phenomena the description of light in terms of photons is preferred (Sections 3-11, 3-12). This wave-particle duality applies also to matter. Electrons, protons, neutrons, and other material particles have been found to have some properties that we usually correlate with wave motion. For example, a beam of electrons or a beam of neutrons can be diffracted in the same way as a beam of x-rays. Electron diffraction and neutron diffraction have turned out to be valuable techniques for investigating the structure of crystals and gas molecules. The wavelength associated with an electron, a neutron, or other particle depends on its rest-mass and the speed with which it is traveling. It is given by the de Broglie equation, $\lambda = h/mv$, in which λ is the wavelength of the particle, h is Planck's constant, m is the mass, and v is the speed (Section 3-11).

The main distinction between photons and material particles with finite rest-mass is that in a vacuum photons travel always at constant speed, the speed of light, whereas particles with finite rest-mass are able to travel at various speeds relative to the observer, up to a maximum of the speed of light, which for these particles would correspond to infinite energy.

The symbol used for the photon is γ (the Greek letter gamma). This symbol was originally used for γ-rays, which are photons of high energy liberated in the course of the radioactive decomposition of nuclei (Chapter 30).

The value 1 for the spin of the photon is connected with the polarization of light, discussed in Chapter 9. Right-handed circularly polarized light corresponds to a component $+1$ of the spin in the direction of motion of light, and left-handed circularly polarized light to the component -1.

Photons may be emitted or absorbed by an oscillating electric dipole, such as a negatively charged electron rotating around a positively charged proton. It might be thought that a system of two masses, such as the earth and the moon, rotating about their common center would emit gravitational quanta. These gravitational quanta are called gravitons. No one has yet thought of a good way of studying the properties of gravitational waves, and the existence of the graviton, a quantized gravitational wave, has not yet been verified by any experiment.

29-2. The Discovery of the Fundamental Particles

The **electron** has been discussed throughout this book. It was the first of the fundamental particles to be recognized, having been discovered by J. J. Thomson in 1897. It is present in ordinary matter, and is easily separated from the atomic nuclei to which it is ordinarily attached.

The **proton** was observed as positively charged rays in a discharge tube in 1886 by the German physicist E. Goldstein. The nature of the rays was not at first understood. In 1898 the German physicist W. Wien made a rough determination of their ratio of charge to mass, and accurate measurements of this sort, which verified the existence of protons as independent particles in a discharge tube containing ionized hydrogen at low pressure, were made by J. J. Thomson in 1906.

The next particle to be discovered (aside from the photon) was the **positron** (the antielectron), found in 1932 by the American physicist Carl D. Anderson (born 1905). The positrons were found among the particles produced by the interaction of cosmic rays with matter. They are identical with electrons except that their electric charge is $+e$ instead of $-e$.

The mass of the electron corresponds, according to the Einstein equation $E = mc^2$, to the energy 510,976 electron volts (0.510976 MeV; 1 MeV is 1 million electron volts). Hence the annihilation of an electron and a positron liberates 1.022 MeV of energy, which might be in the form of two photons, each with the energy 0.511 MeV and corresponding wavelength 0.02426 Å.

A rapidly moving electron that strikes the anode in an x-ray tube (Figure 2-25) is suddenly slowed down, and much of its energy is converted into a photon of x-radiation. If its kinetic energy is greater than 1.022 MeV, this amount of energy may be converted into an electron-positron pair. Electron-positron pair production can be carried out in this way in the laboratory with use of particles that have been given large amounts of kinetic energy in a particle accelerator, as described later in this section. The positrons that were first observed by Anderson were produced, together with electrons, by the impingement of cosmic-ray particles against particles of ordinary matter. Cosmic rays are described later in this section.

The **neutron** was discovered in 1932 by the English physicist James Chadwick (born 1891). It had been observed in 1930 by two German investigators, Bothe and Becker, that a very penetrating radiation is produced when beryllium metal is bombarded with alpha particles from radium. Bothe and Becker considered the radiation to consist of γ-rays. Frédéric Joliot and his wife Irène Joliot-Curie then discovered that this radiation from beryllium, when passed through a block of paraffin or other substance containing hydrogen, produces large number of protons. Because of the difficulty of understanding how protons could be produced by γ-rays, Chadwick carried out a series of experiments that led to the discovery that the rays from beryllium are in fact composed of particles with no electric charge and with mass approximately equal to that of the proton. Because they have no electric charge, neutrons interact with other forms of matter very weakly, except at very small distances, less than 10^{-12} cm.

The existence of the **antiproton** was verified in 1955 by Segré, Chamberlain, Wiegand, and Ypsilantis, by use of a particle accelerator (the Berkeley synchrotron) that could generate particles with energy 6 GeV (the GeV, giga-electron volt, is 1,000 MeV). The mass of the proton-antiproton pair is 1836 times that of the electron-positron pair, and accordingly 1836 × 1.022 MeV =

1,876 MeV of energy is needed to produce this pair of heavier particles.* The antiproton has negative electric charge, mass equal to the charge of the proton, and spin $\frac{1}{2}$.

The discovery of some of the other fundamental particles will be described in later sections.

Cosmic Rays. Cosmic rays are particles of very high energy that reach the earth from interstellar space or other parts of the cosmos or that are produced in the earth's atmosphere by the rays from outer space. The discovery that ionizing radiation on the earth's surface comes from outer space was made by the Austrian physicist Victor Hess, who made measurements of the amount of ionization in the earth's atmosphere during balloon ascents to a height of 15,000 feet in 1911 and 1912. Many of the fundamental particles in addition to the positron were discovered in the course of studies of cosmic rays.

Cosmic rays that impinge on the outer part of the atmosphere consist of protons and the nuclei of heavier atoms moving with great speed. The cosmic rays that reach the earth's surface consist in large part of mesons, positrons, electrons, and protons produced by reaction of the fast protons and other atomic nuclei with atomic nuclei in the atmosphere.

Some of the phenomena produced by cosmic rays can be explained only if it is assumed that particles are present with energy in the range from 10^{15} to 10^{20} eV. The great accelerators that have been or are being built (following section) produce or will produce particles with energies in the range 10^6 to 10^{12} eV. There is no way known at present to accelerate particles to energies as great as those of the fastest particles in cosmic rays, and accordingly the study of cosmic rays will probably continue to yield information about the universe that cannot be obtained in any other way.

Particle Accelerators. In recent years great progress has been made in the laboratory production of high-speed particles. The first efforts to accomplish this involved the use of transformers. Different investigators built transformers and vacuum tubes operating to voltages as high as three million volts, in which protons, deuterons, and helium nuclei could be accelerated. In 1931 an electrostatic generator was developed by R. J. Van de Graaff, an American physicist, involving the carrying of electric charges to the high-potential electrode on a moving insulated belt. Van de Graaff generators have been built and operated to produce potential differences up to fifteen million volts.

The **cyclotron** was invented by the American physicist Ernest Orlando Lawrence (1901–1958) in 1929. In the cyclotron positive ions (protons, deuterons, or other light nuclei) are given successive accelerations by repeatedly

---

* This is the amount of energy needed for proton-antiproton pair production by collision of two similar particles moving with equal speeds in opposite directions in the coordinate system of the laboratory. A much larger amount of energy—nearly 6 GeV—must be imparted to a particle in order that a pair may be produced when it collides with a stationary particle. It is for this reason that plans are being made to construct a double accelerator, such that two beams of particles might be directed against one another.

falling through a potential difference of a few thousand volts. The charged particles are caused to move in circular paths by a magnetic field, produced by a large magnet between whose pole pieces the apparatus is placed (Figure 29-1). Cyclotrons can be used to accelerate particles to about 100 MeV, but the relativistic change in mass of the particle then causes it to get out of phase with the alternating electric field, so that higher energies cannot be obtained.

A new accelerator, the **synchrotron,** in which a number of the particles are injected and the frequency of the alternating field is adjusted to compensate for the relativistic change in mass, was proposed by the Russian physicist V. Veksler and independently by the American physicist E. M. McMillan in 1945. By use of the synchrotron principle particles have now been accelerated to about 30 GeV, and plans are at present being made for intercontinental

Figure **29-1**

Diagram showing how the cyclotron works.

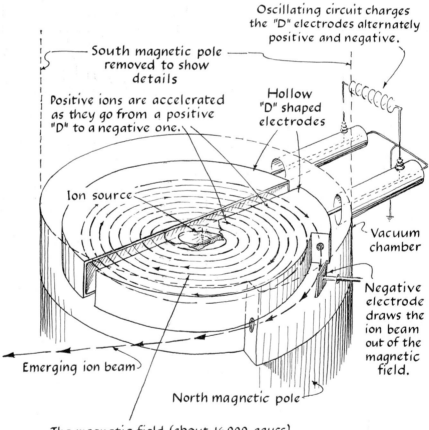

Oscillating circuit charges the "D" electrodes alternately positive and negative.

South magnetic pole removed to show details

Positive ions are accelerated as they go from a positive "D" to a negative one.

Hollow "D" shaped electrodes

Ion source

Vacuum chamber

Negative electrode draws the ion beam out of the magnetic field.

Emerging ion beam

North magnetic pole

The magnetic field (about 16,000 gauss) curves the ion beam, the radius increasing with velocity of the ions.

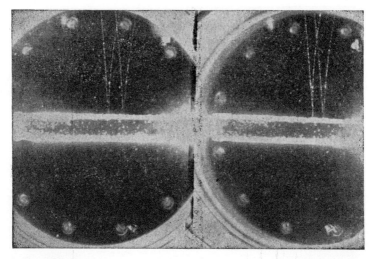

Figure **29-2**

A direct view and a mirror view of two electron-positron pairs produced by a cosmic-ray photon near the nucleus of a lead atom in a lead plate 1 cm thick in a cloud chamber. This photograph was made about 1934 by Carl D. Anderson, the discoverer of the positron. There is a magnetic field present, which causes the paths of the electron and the positron to curve in opposite directions.

cooperation in the construction of a giant accelerator to produce particles in the range 300 GeV to 1000 GeV.

The reactions of particles can be observed by the study of the tracks of the particles in a cloud chamber or a bubble chamber. The **cloud chamber,** which was invented by the English physicist C. T. R. Wilson (1869–1959) in 1911, is a chamber containing air saturated with water vapor. When the air is suddenly expanded by increasing the volume of the chamber by moving a piston, the air is cooled and becomes supersaturated, so that droplets of water form. These droplets tend to form around the ions that are produced as high-energy electrically charged particles traverse the gas, and thus the droplets define the paths of the particles. Neutral particles do not form paths, but their presence can sometimes be detected by the presence of paths radiating from a point where the neutral particle underwent a reaction that produced high-energy charged particles. The **bubble chamber,** invented by the American physicist D. A. Glaser (born 1926) in 1952, has found extensive use in recent years. It is a chamber containing a liquid held at a temperature slightly above its boiling point. The ions formed by high-energy particles traversing the liquid serve as centers of formation of small vapor bubbles, which define the tracks of the particles.

A cloud-chamber photograph is shown as Figure 29-2 and a bubble-chamber photograph as Figure 29-3.

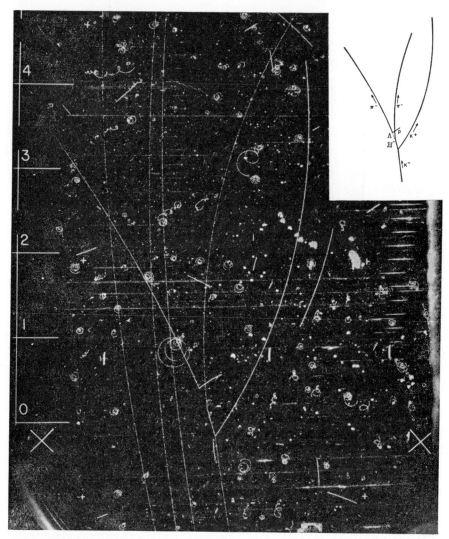

Figure 29-3

An event recorded in the 72-inch liquid-hydrogen bubble chamber of the University of California (L. W. Alvarez and coworkers). The incident particle is a negative kaon, in a beam of these particles. By collision with a proton it forms a positive kaon and a negative xion. The negative xion then decomposes to form a lambda particle and a negative pion. The lambda particle, which is neutral, produces no track. It is shown as decomposing to form a proton and a negative pion.

Another instrument for defining the tracks of high-energy particles is the **spark chamber.** This instrument contains a gas, and a series of metal plates that can be electrically charged to such a potential between alternate plates as nearly to cause a spark to pass from one plate to an adjacent one. If a track of ions is formed by a high-energy particle the spark follows the track, and can be photographed. In the 1962 neutrino experiment (Section 29-5) a spark chamber 10 feet by 6 feet by 4 feet was used, containing 90 aluminum plates 4 feet square and 1 inch thick, $\frac{1}{2}$ inch apart, with neon as the gas.

29-3.   The Forces between Nucleons. Strong Interactions

In 1932, when the neutron was discovered, it was recognized that the heavier atomic nuclei can be described as being built of protons and neutrons, with the electric charge equal to the number of protons and the mass number equal to the sum of the number of protons and the number of neutrons; that is, equal to the number of nucleons, with a nucleon either a proton or a neutron. The question immediately arose as to the nature of the forces holding the neutrons and protons together. If electrostatic forces were the only forces operating between nucleons the heavier nuclei would break up, because of the electrostatic repulsion between the protons.

It was evident that the force of attraction between nucleons must be a strong force at small distances, stronger than the repulsion due to the positive electric charges on the protons, and a weak force at large distances, weaker than the electrostatic repulsion. Careful studies of the size of the heavier nuclei and the scattering of nucleons from one another led to the discovery that two nucleons attract one another with approximately a constant force when they are less than 1.4×10^{-13} cm apart, and that the internucleonic force, other than electrostatic repulsion of protons, drops rapidly to zero at distances greater than 1.4×10^{-13} cm.

The idea of action at a distance is not a satisfying one; instead, physicists have developed a **quantum theory of force fields,** in which the field at some distance from its source is thought of as carried to that point by a messenger or quantum of the field. For electrostatic attraction and repulsion these messengers are the photons, and for gravitational attraction they are described as being gravitons. In 1935 the Japanese physicist Hideki Yukawa (born 1907) proposed an answer to the question of the mechanism of the force of attraction between nucleons. He pointed out that, whereas messengers that have zero rest-mass, such as photons and gravitons, can extend their influence to infinity, a messenger with finite rest-mass could reach only a limited distance from the particle. He suggested that messengers of this sort are involved in the interaction of nucleons, and from the known range of internucleonic force, 1.4×10^{-13} cm, he calculated that the rest-mass of these particles should be about 274 times the electronic mass. These particles, which are intermediate

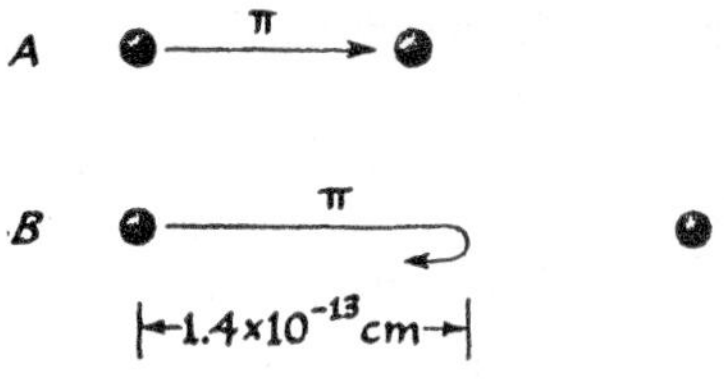

A

B

$\vdash\!1.4\times10^{-13}cm\!\rightarrow\!\vdash$

(Nucleons and pion messenger)

Figure 29-4 *A diagram illustrating the range of internucleonic forces.*

in mass between electrons and nucleons, are called **mesons** (Greek *mesos*, middle).

Let us consider two nucleons a small distance apart, less than 1.4×10^{-13} cm, as shown in A in Figure 29-4. One of the nucleons produces or emits a messenger particle, a meson, which travels with a speed close to that of light and is destroyed in the neighborhood of the second par ticle. This process of production and destruction of the messenger particle gives rise to the force of attraction.

If, however, the two particles are farther apart than 1.4×10^{-13} cm, as in B, the emitted messenger particle is not able to traverse the distance between the particles, but instead turns back and disappears. There is accordingly no interaction between the nucleons at the larger distance. The reason that the range of the messenger particles is restricted can be understood by consideration of the uncertainty principle.

Let us consider the reaction

$$p^+ \rightleftarrows p^+ + \pi^0$$

Here we use π^0 to represent a messenger particle; the mesons responsible in the main for internuclear forces are called **pions.** This reaction, the reaction of a proton to form a proton plus a pion, violates the principle of conservation of mass-energy. Until the uncertainty principle was discovered no reaction of this sort would ever have been considered.

However, because of the uncertainty relation between energy and time we may consider a reaction such as this, which violates the principle of conservation of mass-energy, provided that the length of time during which we consider the reaction to be taking place is less than the time Δt given by the uncertainty principle. We make use of the equation $\Delta E \cdot \Delta t = h/2\pi$ given in Section 7-8. The length of time in which we are interested is the time required for a particle moving with a speed close to that of light to move the distance 1.4×10^{-13} cm. The corresponding value of ΔE, the uncertainty for mass-energy, is $h/2\pi$ divided by this time Δt, $1.4 \times 10^{-13}/3 \times 10^{10}$ (the speed of light), which is $\Delta t = 0.47 \times 10^{-23}$ sec. The value of ΔE is accordingly $1.05 \times 10^{-27}/0.47 \times 10^{-23} = 2.24 \times 10^{-4}$ erg, and the corresponding value in mass units, obtained by dividing by c^2 (since $E = mc^2$), is 2.49×10^{-25} g, which is 274 times the mass of the electron. Yukawa accordingly stated that the short range of internucleonic forces could be explained by assuming that the interactions are carried out by particles with mass about 274 times the mass of the electron. No such particles were known at that time.

In 1936 particles with mass 207 times the mass of the electron and with either a positive or a negative charge were discovered by Anderson and Neddermeyer and independently by Street and Stevenson in the course of cosmic-ray experiments. These particles, which are now called **muons,** were at first thought to be the Yukawa particles. However, if they were responsible for the internucleonic forces they would interact strongly with nucleons. This strong interaction should cause them to react within a period of time about 10^{-23} sec when in the neighborhood of a nucleon. Muons were found to decompose in free space, their half-life being about 10^{-6} sec, and their rate of decomposition was found not to be greatly changed when a beam of muons was passed through solid substances and the muons were thus subjected to the influence of nucleons; hence they could not be the Yukawa particles.

When this last experiment was carried out, in 1945, the physicists were again at a loss to account for internucleonic forces, but not for long, because the strongly interacting mesons, which were named pions, were soon discovered. Cosmic-ray experiments with use of stacks of photographic emulsions to detect the tracks of the charged particles, carried out in 1947 by the British physicist C. F. Powell (born 1903) and his coworkers, led to the discovery of three particles, the positive pion, neutral pion, and negative pion, with masses 273.3 for π^+ and π^- and 264.3 for π^0 and with the properties of strong interaction with nucleons that had been predicted by Yukawa. There is now no doubt that the internucleonic forces that operate in atomic nuclei involve pions. It has been shown by experiment that charged pions as well as neutral pions are involved in the internucleonic forces. The equations for the charged-pion forces are

$$p^+ \rightleftarrows n + \pi^+$$
$$n \rightleftarrows p^+ + \pi^-$$

Other particles, especially the rho and omega particles (Section 29-10), are probably also involved in the internucleonic forces.

29-4. The Structure of Nucleons

The proton and the neutron are closely similar in properties except that the proton has positive charge and the neutron is electrically neutral. The mass of the neutron is only about 0.1 % greater than that of the proton. Both particles have spin $\frac{1}{2}$. The proton-proton, proton-neutron, and neutron-neutron internucleonic forces at small distances are essentially the same. Because of these facts, the idea arose some years ago that the proton and the neutron are simply two states of one particle, the nucleon.

In Chapter 7 we have pointed out that an electron in an atom may have two orientations of its spin relative to the direction of a magnetic field or of the angular momentum vector produced by its orbital motion. These two directions, represented by $+\frac{1}{2}$ and $-\frac{1}{2}$, respectively, are said to give rise to a doublet. The doublet is associated with the spin quantum number $\frac{1}{2}$. This suggested that the proton and the neutron may constitute an *electric-charge doublet*. It has been suggested that the nucleon has an intrinsic electric charge with magnitude $+\frac{1}{2}$ (in units e) and an electric-charge vector with magnitude $\frac{1}{2}$ which can assume two orientations (not in ordinary, three-dimensional space, but in some undefined space) such as to contribute either $+\frac{1}{2}$ to the resultant charge, to produce the proton, or to contribute $-\frac{1}{2}$, to produce the neutron. The proton and the neutron, according to this picture, constitute the two states of the electric-charge doublet of a nucleon with intrinsic charge $+\frac{1}{2}$ and electric-charge vector $\frac{1}{2}$. Similarly, the antiproton and the antineutron constitute the two states of the corresponding type of antimatter, the anti-nucleon, with intrinsic charge $-\frac{1}{2}$ and electric-charge vector $\frac{1}{2}$.

In 1961 some experimental results providing support for this picture of the proton and the neutron were reported by Robert Hofstadter and his coworkers at Stanford University and by a group of investigators at Cornell University. These physicists studied the scattering of high-speed electrons by protons and neutrons, and were able to interpret their experiments to determine the distribution of electric charge within the proton and the neutron.

They reported that both the proton and the neutron can be described as involving a central ball of positive charge, somewhat less than $0.5e$, extending to the radius about 0.3×10^{-13} cm. Surrounding the ball is a shell, extending to about 1×10^{-13} cm, and with positive charge $+\frac{1}{2}e$ for the proton and negative charge $-\frac{1}{2}e$ for the neutron. In addition, there is a fringe of positive electricity in both the proton and the neutron, amounting to about $0.15e$ and extending to about 1.5×10^{-13} cm.

It is possible that the fringe represents ephemeral mesons that constitute the mechanism of production of the strong internucleonic interactions. Except for the cloud of mesons surrounding it, the nucleon can be described, in its two states, the proton and the neutron, as consisting of a central ball of positive charge, $+\frac{1}{2}e$, which may be identified with the intrinsic charge of the neutron, and a shell, $+\frac{1}{2}e$ for the proton and $-\frac{1}{2}e$ for the neutron, representing the component of the electric-charge vector.

These results about the structure of the nucleon give exciting promise of great future developments in the understanding of the fundamental nature of the universe.

Several other charge doublets, corresponding to the two aspects of an electric-charge vector $\frac{1}{2}$ (also called *isotopic spin*), are known. In addition, as will be seen in the tables given in the following sections, there are several charge triplets that are known, groups of three particles with closely similar properties except for their electric charge, $+1$, 0, and -1. These charge triplets can be described as the three states of a single particle with electric-charge vector 1, which can have the component $+1$, 0, or -1. The three pions, π^+, π^0, π^-, constitute such a charge triplet (Section 29-9).

29-5. Leptons and Antileptons

We begin the tabulation of the fundamental particles by discussing the leptons and antileptons. There are eight of these particles known. Some of their properties are given in Table 29-1. Except for the muon and antimuon, they are stable particles. The word lepton is from the Greek *leptos*, small.

Table **29-1**

Leptons and Antileptons*

NAME	ELECTRIC CHARGE			MASS	XENICITY (strangeness)	SPIN
	+1	0	−1			
Electron			e^-	0.511 MeV	0	$\frac{1}{2}$
Muon			μ^-	105.66	0	$\frac{1}{2}$
Electron neutrino		ν		0	0	$\frac{1}{2}$R†
Muon neutrino		ν'		0	0	$\frac{1}{2}$R†
Positron	$\bar{e}^+$			0.511	0	$\frac{1}{2}$
Antimuon	$\bar{\mu}^+$			105.66	0	$\frac{1}{2}$
Electron antineutrino		$\bar{\nu}$		0	0	$\frac{1}{2}$L†
Muon antineutrino		$\bar{\nu}'$		0	0	$\frac{1}{2}$L†

* The electron, muon, and neutrino have lepton number +1; the positron, antimuon, and antineutrino have lepton number −1; all other particles have lepton number 0.

† The spin of the neutrinos corresponds to a right-handed screw, that of the antineutrinos to a left-handed screw.

The muon, μ^-, was the first particle with mass intermediate between the electron and the proton to be discovered. It is present in cosmic rays. It is made by the following reaction:

$$\bar{\pi}^- \longrightarrow \mu^- + \bar{\nu}'$$

The positive muon, the antimuon ($\bar{\mu}^+$), is made by a similar reaction from the positive pion. Both the positive pion and the negative pion are present in cosmic rays. They decompose rapidly, with half-life about 2.56×10^{-8} sec, to form muons. The muon and the antimuon themselves decompose, to form an electron (or positron), a neutrino, and an antineutrino:

$$\mu^- \longrightarrow e^- + \nu + \bar{\nu}$$
$$\bar{\mu}^+ \longrightarrow \bar{e}^+ + \nu + \bar{\nu}$$

The muon and the antimuon have no significance with respect to inter-nucleonic forces. Their nature is uncertain. It is possible that they represent an excited state of the electron and positron. A striking indication that they are closely related to the electron and positron is provided by the observed value of the magnetic moment of the muon. The electron has been found by magnetic resonance experiments to have values ± 1.00116 Bohr magnetons for the component of its magnetic moment in the direction of a magnetic field. (The deviation from unity is attributed to the photon field surrounding the electron.) The proton and neutron, which have a complex structure (Section 29-4), have magnetic moments that are not related in a simple way to the Bohr magneton. But the observed components of the muon in the direction of a magnetic field are $\pm (1.00115 \pm 0.00002)$ muonic Bohr magnetons. (The muonic Bohr magneton is the Bohr magneton multiplied by the ratio of electron mass to muon mass.) The identity of this value with the value for the electron shows that the muon and the electron have closely similar structures, and the close approximation of each value to unity is strong evidence that their structure is simple in comparison with that of the proton and neutron.

In 1962 P. A. M. Dirac published a theory of the muon in which it is described as an excited vibrational state of the electron. The postulated vibration is spherically symmetric; it is the rhythmic increase and decrease of size of the sphere of negative electricity constituting the particle.

Neutrinos and Antineutrinos. Weak Interactions. The neutrino is a particle with zero rest-mass and spin $\frac{1}{2}$; it differs from the photon primarily in the value of the spin (the photon has spin 1). The existence of the neutrino was proposed in 1927 by W. Pauli, in order to account for the apparent lack of conservation of energy in the process of emission of a β particle (an electron) by a radioactive nucleus, as discussed in Chapter 30. It had been observed that all radioactive nuclei of the same kind that emitted an α particle, such as radium 226 (Figure 30-1), shoot out their particles with the same energy, as expected from the law of conservation of mass-energy, but that, on the other hand, radioactive atoms that emit β particles, such as Pb 214, emit the β particles with varying energies. Pauli, and later Fermi, suggested that another particle, with small or zero rest-mass, is also emitted when the nucleus undergoes radioactive decay with emission of a β particle, and that the energy of the reaction is divided between the β particle and the other particle, which Fermi named the neutrino.

In 1934 Fermi developed his theory of β decay, in order to explain the puzzling observation that some radioactive nuclides shoot out an electron in the course of radioactive decomposition, although they were supposed to be composed only of protons and neutrons. He pointed out that atoms emit photons when they change from one quantum state to another, although it is not believed that the atoms contain the photons; instead, it is accepted that the photon is created at the time when it is emitted. Fermi suggested that the electrons, the β particles, are created when the radioactive nucleus undergoes decomposition, and that at the same time one of the neutrons inside the nucleus becomes a proton, and a neutrino (or, rather, an antineutrino) is emitted.

The fundamental reaction of the Fermi theory is

$$n \longrightarrow p^+ + e^- + \bar{\nu}$$

This is the reaction of decomposition of the free neutron (Table 29-4). The free neutron decomposes with a half-life of 1040 sec. In many nuclei the neutron is made stable by interaction with other nucleons, but in some nuclei it remains unstable, and this reaction takes place.

Neutrinos interact only very weakly with other particles, and the existence of the neutrino was not verified by experiment until 1956. In that year the American physicists Reines and Cowan showed that neutrinos from a nuclear reactor passing through a liquid-hydrogen bubble chamber cause a reaction to take place that is approximately the reverse of the decay of a neutron:

$$\bar{\nu} + p^+ \longrightarrow n + \bar{e}^+$$

The decay of a neutron into a proton, an electron, and a neutrino cannot be explained by strong interactions (Section 29-3) or by electromagnetic forces. Fermi assumed that another kind of interaction, called weak interaction, occurs among some particles. It is about 10^{-15} times as strong as the strong interactions that occur between nucleons and similar particles, and it leads to reaction times of the order of 10^{-8} sec, instead of the time 10^{-23} sec that applies to strong interactions.

Neutrinos and antineutrinos have spin $\frac{1}{2}$, but they have an extraordinary property that was discovered in 1957 as a result of the work of the Chinese physicists Tsung-Dao Lee (born 1926) and Chen Ning Yang (born 1922), working in the United States. These theoretical physicists and the experimental physicists whom they inspired found that the neutrino, which has spin $\frac{1}{2}$, always orients its spin in the direction of its motion, so that it moves through space with the speed of light as though it were a right-handed propeller. The antineutrino always orients its spin in the opposite direction, and moves as though it were a left-handed propeller.

In 1960 it was proposed by several physicists, in order to explain a number of experimental observations in a simple way, that there are two neutrinos and two antineutrinos, with somewhat different properties. It was postulated that one neutrino (ν) and one antineutrino ($\bar{\nu}$) have a close relation of some sort to the electron and positron, and the other neutrino (ν') and antineutrino ($\bar{\nu}'$) have a similar relation to the muon and antimuon. Experimental verification of this hypothesis was obtained in 1962 by a difficult experiment carried out by a group of Columbia University and Brookhaven National Laboratory scientists. As mentioned above, Reines and Cowan had shown that a neutrino produced by a reaction involving electrons reacts with a proton to produce a neutron and an electron. In the 1962 experiment it was shown that neutrinos produced by the decomposition of muons react with protons to produce only muons, and not electrons:

$$\bar{\nu}' + p^+ \longrightarrow n + \bar{\mu}^+$$

We shall call the two neutrinos the *electron neutrino*, ν, and the *muon neutrino*, ν'. At the present time nothing can be said about their nature, to explain the difference in their properties in terms of a difference in structure.

29-6. Mesons and Antimesons

The known mesons and antimesons, eight in number, are listed in Table 29-2. The kaons are the antiparticles of the antikaons, and the two charged

Table **29-2**

Mesons and Antimesons*

NAME	ELECTRIC CHARGE +1	0	−1	MASS	INTRINSIC CHARGE	CHARGE SPIN	XENICITY (strangeness)	SPIN
Eta		η^0		550 MeV	0	0	0	0
Kaons		K^0	K^-	497.8, 494	$-\frac{1}{2}$	$\frac{1}{2}$	−1	0
Antikaons	$\overline{K}^+$	$\overline{K}^0$		494, 497.8	$+\frac{1}{2}$	$\frac{1}{2}$	+1	0
Pions	π^+	π^0	π^-	139.6, 135, 139.6	0	1	0	0

* The muon was originally named the meson, and then the μ meson, but it is now placed in the lepton class. Mesons and antimesons have baryon number 0 and lepton number 0. All the particles listed in this table have spin 0 (zero angular momentum). The positive pion and the negative pion are the antiparticles of one another. The neutral pion is its own antiparticle, and the eta is its own antiparticle. The inclusion of eta in this set of particles is somewhat arbitrary; see Sections 29-10 and 29-11.

pions are antiparticles of one another. The neutral pion is its own antiparticle, and the eta particle is its own antiparticle. All of the mesons are unstable; their decay reactions will be discussed in Section 29-8.

The pions and kaons were discovered in experiments with cosmic rays, and their properties have been determined by use both of cosmic rays and of high-energy particles produced by particle accelerators. The pions were discovered by Powell and his collaborators, as mentioned in the previous section. The kaons were discovered about 1950 by many investigators.

29-7. Baryons and Antibaryons

The baryons include the nucleons and heavier particles. There are eight baryons and eight antibaryons known, as listed in Table 29-3. The word baryon is from the Greek *barys*, heavy. The word hyperon (Greek *hyper*, beyond) is also used; it refers to the baryons other than the proton and the neutron.

The baryons other than the proton and the neutron were discovered in the period between 1950 and 1960 by use of cosmic rays and particle accelerators.

Table 29-3

*Baryons and Antibaryons**

NAME	ELECTRIC CHARGE			MASS	INTRINSIC CHARGE	CHARGE SPIN	XENICITY (strangeness)	SPIN
	+1	0	−1					
Xi particles		Ξ^0	Ξ^-	1311, 1318.4 MeV	$-\frac{1}{2}$	$\frac{1}{2}$	−2	$\frac{1}{2}$
Sigma particles	Σ^+	Σ^0	Σ^-	1189.4, 1191.5, 1196	0	1	−1	$\frac{1}{2}$
Lambda particle		Λ		1115.4	0	0	−1	$\frac{1}{2}$
Nucleons (proton, neutron)	p^+	n		938.2, 939.5	$+\frac{1}{2}$	$\frac{1}{2}$	0	$\frac{1}{2}$
Xi antiparticles	$\bar{\Xi}^+$	$\bar{\Xi}^0$		1318.4, 1311	$+\frac{1}{2}$	$\frac{1}{2}$	+2	$\frac{1}{2}$
Sigma antiparticles	$\bar{\Sigma}^+$	$\bar{\Sigma}^0$	$\bar{\Sigma}^-$	1196, 1191.5, 1189.4	0	1	+1	$\frac{1}{2}$
Lambda antiparticle		$\bar{\Lambda}$		1115.4	0	0	+1	$\frac{1}{2}$
Antineutron, antiproton		$\bar{n}$	$\bar{p}^-$	939.5, 938.2	$-\frac{1}{2}$	$\frac{1}{2}$	0	$\frac{1}{2}$

* Baryons have baryon number +1. Antibaryons have baryon number −1. Both have lepton number 0.

Their masses range from 1115 to 1318 MeV. All baryons have spin $\frac{1}{2}$ and are fermions, obeying the Pauli exclusion principle.

29-8. The Decay Reactions of the Fundamental Particles

Most of the fundamental particles decompose spontaneously. The exceptions, the stable particles, comprise the proton, the antiproton, the electron, the positron, and the particles that move with the speed of light.

Even though many of the fundamental particles were discovered only a few years ago, a tremendous amount of information has been gained about their properties and the reactions by which they are produced, changed into other

Table 29-4

Reactions of Decay of Particles

	REACTION	RATIO (%)	HALF-LIFE (seconds)
Baryons:	$\Xi^0 \longrightarrow \Lambda + \pi^0$		$\sim 2 \times 10^{-10}$
	$\Xi^- \longrightarrow \Lambda + \pi^-$		2×10^{-10}
	$\Sigma^+ \longrightarrow p^+ + \pi^0$	46 ± 6	0.8×10^{-10}
	$n + \pi^+$	54 ± 6	
	$\Sigma^0 \longrightarrow \Lambda + \gamma$		$\sim 10^{-20}$
	$\Sigma^- \longrightarrow n + \pi^-$		1.6×10^{-10}
	$\Lambda \longrightarrow p^+ + \pi^-$	63 ± 3	2.4×10^{-10}
	$n + \pi^0$	37 ± 3	
	$n \longrightarrow p^+ + e^- + \bar{\nu}$		1040
Mesons:	$\eta^0 \longrightarrow \pi^+ + \pi^0 + \pi^-$		$\sim 10^{-23}$
	$K_1^0 \longrightarrow \pi^+ + \pi^-$	78 ± 6	1.0×10^{-10} *
	$\pi^0 + \pi^0$	21 ± 6	
	$K_2^0 \longrightarrow \pi^+ + \pi^-$	78 ± 6	6×10^{-8}
	$\pi^0 + \pi^0$	22 ± 6	
	$K^- \longrightarrow \mu^- + \bar{\nu}'$	59 ± 2	1.22×10^{-8}
	$\pi^0 + \pi^-$	26 ± 2	
	$\pi^+ + \pi^- + \pi^-$	5.7 ± 0.3	
	$\pi^0 + \pi^0 + \pi^-$	1.7 ± 0.3	
	$e^- + \nu + \pi^0$	4.2 ± 0.4	
	$\mu^- + \bar{\nu}' + \pi^0$	4.0 ± 0.8	
	$\pi^+ \longrightarrow \bar{\mu}^+ + \nu'$	100	2.56×10^{-8}
	$\bar{e}^+ + \nu$	0.013	
	$\pi^0 \longrightarrow \gamma + \gamma$		2×10^{-15}
Leptons:	$\mu^- \longrightarrow e^- + \nu' + \bar{\nu}$		10^{-6}

* In a beam of neutral kaons K^0 and antikaons $\overline{K}^0$ the particles decompose at two rates, to give the same products. This behavior is explained by saying that the beam contains particles K_2^0 that are in the quantum state corresponding to symmetric resonance of K^0 and $\overline{K}^0$ and also particles K_1^0 that are in the quantum state corresponding to antisymmetric resonance of K^0 and $\overline{K}^0$. The kaon-antikaon pair is the only pair known to have this property.

forms of matter, and destroyed. The reactions by which the unstable particles decay are listed in Table 29-4, which also gives the values of the half-life. All of these decay reactions are unimolecular reactions, the nature of which has been discussed in Chapter 18.

Conservation Principles. By analyzing the tracks produced by individual particles in cloud chambers, stacks of photographic emulsions, and bubble chambers, and by other methods of detecting particles, the decay of individual particles has been studied, and it has been found that in every case there is conservation of mass-energy and conservation of momentum. Other conservation principles have also been found to be adhered to rigorously, as follows:

Conservation of angular momentum
Conservation of electric charge
Conservation of baryon number
Conservation of lepton number

The principle of conservation of electric charge is illustrated by the decay reactions given in Table 29-4. For example, the lambda particle, which is a hyperon, with mass somewhat greater than that of a nucleon, can decompose either to form a proton and a negative pion or to form a neutron and a neutral pion. In the first case the lambda particle, which is neutral, forms a positively charged particle and a negatively charged particle; in the second case it forms two neutral particles.

A more complicated example, also given in Table 29-4, is the decomposition of the negative kaon. This particle has been observed to decompose in six different ways. Five of the reactions of decomposition lead to the formation of a negatively charged particle and one or two neutral particles. The sixth reaction leads to the formation of a positively charged particle, a positive pion, and two negatively charged particles, negative pions. Hence in each of the six reactions there is conservation of electric charge.

There is also conservation of the baryon number in every reaction. The baryons have baryon number $+1$ and the antibaryons have baryon number -1; all other particles have baryon number 0. In the various processes of formation of baryons and antibaryons they are always formed in pairs, one baryon and one antibaryon. Similarly, the decomposition of a baryon always leads to the formation of another baryon, plus other particles with 0 baryon number. Thus the negative xi particle is observed to decompose to form a lambda particle, which has baryon number $+1$, and a negative pion, which has baryon number 0.

Leptons, which include the electron, the neutrino, and the muon, have lepton number $+1$, and antileptons have lepton number -1; all other particles have lepton number 0. There is rigorous conservation of the lepton number in all reactions. For example, the neutron, which has lepton number 0, decomposes to form a proton, also with lepton number 0, an electron, and an antineutrino. The lepton numbers of the electron and the antineutrino add up to 0, so that in this reaction, as in all others listed in Table 29-4, there is conservation of the lepton number.

There are also some conservation principles that are observed to hold for strong interactions but not for weak interactions. This matter is discussed in the following section.

29-9. Strangeness (Xenicity)

A great contribution to the understanding of the nature of the fundamental particles was made in the period between 1953 and 1956 by the American physicist Murray Gell-Mann and the Japanese physicist K. Nishijima, working independently. The classification of the fundamental particles given in Tables 29-1, 29-2, and 29-3 is in considerable part due to their efforts. This classification is based upon the concept of charge multiplets and the concept of strangeness. Neither of these concepts can be said to be thoroughly understood at the present time, and it is likely that some additional great contributions will be made in the near future.

In Section 29-4 it was pointed out that the close similarity in properties of the neutron and the proton, except for electric charge, suggests that these two particles represent two aspects of the same particle, the nucleon. The nucleon may be said to have intrinsic electric charge $+\frac{1}{2}$ and an electric-charge vector $\frac{1}{2}$, which can have the component $+\frac{1}{2}$ or $-\frac{1}{2}$ in ordinary space, leading to the resultant electric charge $+1$ for the proton and 0 for the neutron. The proton and neutron can then be described as a charge doublet.*

The diagram in Figure 29-5 shows that the 24 particles represented in the diagram constitute three charge singlets, six doublets, and three triplets. The charge singlets have electric-charge vector equal to 0, and intrinsic charge 0. The doublets all have electric-charge vector equal to $\frac{1}{2}$; the nucleon, antinucleon, kaons, and xions have intrinsic charge $+\frac{1}{2}$ or $-\frac{1}{2}$. A charge doublet can thus have electric charges either 0 and $+1$ or 0 and -1. The triplets, with electric-charge vector 1 and intrinsic charge 0, have electric charges $+1$, 0, and -1, corresponding to the three orientations of the charge vector.

The idea of strangeness was introduced by Gell-Mann and Nishijima to explain in a rough way the rates of decay reactions. Some of the unstable particles are expected to decay by virtue of the strong interactions (Section 29-3), and this decomposition should be very rapid, with half-lives of the order of 10^{-23} sec. An example is the decay of the η^0 particle, to form three pions; its half-life is about 10^{-23} sec.

Many other particles, however, are observed to have much longer half-lives, of the order of 10^{-9} sec. These particles accordingly live 10^{14} times as long as predicted for them on the basis of the theory of strong interactions.

* The idea of charge multiplets was introduced into physics by the American physicists B. Cassen and E. U. Condon in 1936.

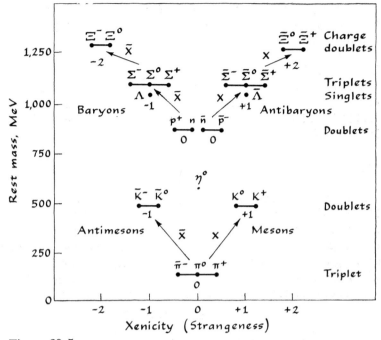

Figure **29-5**

A diagram representing the masses and xenicities of some of the elementary particles.

Because of this deviation from the expected behavior, these particles were called strange particles.

Gell-Mann and Nishijima suggested that a characteristic property, which is called strangeness, should be assigned to the particles, such that there is conservation of strangeness for reactions involving strong interactions but violation of conservation of strangeness for weak interactions. *Xenicity** may be a better name for this property than strangeness.

The values of the xenicity are shown in Figure 29-5. Pions, the eta particle, nucleons, and antinucleons have xenicity 0. The kaons, antilambda particle, and antisigma particles have xenicity +1, and the antikaons, lambda particle, and sigma particles have xenicity −1. The antixions have xenicity +2, and the xions have xenicity −2.

The conservation principle is that for strong interactions there must be conservation of xenicity; the sum of the xenicities for the reactants equals the sum of the xenicities for the products. Reactions in which the sum of the xenicities changes by one unit can occur as a result of weak interactions, but these reactions are slow. Reactions in which the sum changes by two units are very slow.

* From Greek *xenos*, stranger.

The eta particle has xenicity 0, and the pions have xenicity 0. There is, accordingly, no change in xenicity accompanying the decay of the eta particle, and the reaction is very fast.

Table 29-4 contains many examples of reactions in which there is a change in xenicity. The negative antikaon, $\bar{K}^-$, has xenicity -1. It can decay in six ways, to form pions and leptons (the muon, the electron, an antineutrino), all of which have xenicity 0. The total half-life for these various reactions is 1.22×10^{-8}, far longer than the half-life for the eta decomposition, and this long half-life is attributed to the change in xenicity.

29-10.   Resonance Particles and Complexes

In 1952 it was found by Enrico Fermi and his coworkers, who were studying the scattering of a beam of pions by protons, that the scattering is much larger when the pions have about 200 MeV of kinetic energy than for smaller or greater amounts of kinetic energy. This observation was interpreted as showing that there is a strong interaction between the pion and the proton, which can be described as corresponding to the formation of a short-lived particle or complex, to which the symbol N^* has been assigned:

$$\pi + p \rightleftarrows N^*$$

The mass of N^* is about 1237 MeV. Its half-life is about 10^{-23}; and, in accordance with the uncertainty relation between energy and time (Section 7-8), the mass (energy) of the particle is not well defined, but has an uncertainty of about ± 60 MeV. (The half-life 10^{-23} sec is in fact calculated from the observed distribution function for the mass of the N^* complex.)

Since 1952 about a score of these short-lived particles or complexes have been discovered. They are called *resonance particles* or *resonance complexes*. One of them, η^0, has been included in our listing of the mesons (Table 29-2). It is produced by reaction of a pion and a neutron (within a deuteron):

$$\pi^+ + d^+ \longrightarrow \eta^0 + p^+ + p^+$$

It is the lightest of the resonance particles, with mass 550 MeV. It decomposes, with half-life 10^{-23} sec, by the reaction

$$\eta^0 \longrightarrow \pi^+ + \pi^- + \pi^0$$

The next lightest resonance particles are the ρ particles, ρ^+, ρ^0, and ρ^-, with mass 760 MeV. They constitute a charge triplet (inherent charge 0, charge spin 1, angular momentum spin 1). They are formed by the following reactions:

$$\pi^+ + p^+ \longrightarrow \rho^+ + p^+$$
$$p^+ + \bar{p}^- \longrightarrow \rho^0 + \pi^+ + \pi^-$$
$$\pi^- + p^+ \longrightarrow \rho^- + p^+$$

They decompose, with half-life about 10^{-23} sec, as follows:

$$\rho^+ \longrightarrow \pi^+ + \pi^0$$
$$\rho^0 \longrightarrow \pi^+ + \pi^- \quad \text{or} \quad \rho^0 \longrightarrow \pi^0 + \pi^0$$
$$\rho^- \longrightarrow \pi^- + \pi^0$$

The only other known resonance particle that resembles the eta particle and the rho particles in having lepton number 0, baryon number 0, and strangeness 0 is the ω^0 particle, which has mass 790 MeV, inherent charge 0, charge spin 0, and angular momentum spin 1. It has been observed to be formed in the following ways:

$$\rho^+ + \overline{p}^- \longrightarrow \omega^0 + \pi^+ + \pi^-$$
$$\pi^+ + d^+ \longrightarrow \omega^0 + p^+ + p^+$$

It has half-life 4×10^{-23} sec, corresponding to two ways of decomposing:

$$\omega^0 \longrightarrow \pi^+ + \pi^- + \pi^0$$

or

$$\omega^0 \longrightarrow \pi^0 + \gamma$$

Other resonance particles or complexes that decompose into pions and kaons or into pions or kaons and one of the baryons are also known. Their masses lie in the range from 880 MeV to 2000 MeV.

At the present time there is no satisfactory theory of these particles. It seems likely, however, that some of them may be classed with the fundamental particles (see the following section), and that others may be described as complexes of two or more fundamental particles, possibly with resonance among several structures, roughly analogous to the resonance of molecules among several valence-bond structures.

Positronium, Muonium, Mesonic Atoms. In 1953 it was observed that a positron and an electron combine to form a pseudo-atom, somewhat similar to the hydrogen atom. In the hydrogen atom the electron can be described as moving around an essentially stationary nucleus, the proton. In the pseudo-atom formed by a positron and an electron, which has been given the name *positronium*, the two particles have the same mass, so that they carry out similar motions about their center of mass, the point midway between the two.

It was found by the American physicist Martin Deutsch that there are two kinds of positronium. The kind in which the spin of the positron is anti-parallel to that of the electron is called parapositronium, and that in which the two spins are parallel is called orthopositronium. Parapositronium decomposes with destruction of the positron and the electron and production of two photons, its half-life being 0.9×10^{-10} sec. Orthopositronium decomposes with production of three photons, and half-life 1.0×10^{-7} sec. The existence of positronium was detected by the observation of a delay between its production (by decomposition of sodium 22, which emits positrons) and its annihilation. The time of delay was found to correspond to the sum of two first-order reactions, with the values of the half-life given above.

Muonium, a pseudo-atom involving a negative muon moving about a proton, has also been observed. Other mesonic atoms, having structures similar to ordinary atoms but with a muon or other meson replacing one of the electrons, have also been observed. For example, muonic neon is a neon atom with a negative muon in place of an electron.

A muonic molecule ion, $[H^+\mu^-D^+]^+$, in which a proton and a deuteron are held together by a negative muon, has also been made. The proton and the deuteron are sufficiently close together, about 0.003 Å apart, to permit reaction between them, liberating the muon and producing a helium-3 nucleus plus an additional muon, with release of 5.4 MeV of energy. The use of a mesonic molecule of this sort might possibly permit the controlled release of energy through nuclear fusion (Section 30-7).

29-11. Classification of the Fundamental Particles

There is little doubt that in the course of time some system of description of the fundamental particles will be developed in terms of their structure. At the present time there is no way of formulating a description that is so convincingly significant as to cause scientists to accept it as superior to others. A possible description, which may have usefulness in helping the student to remember the particles, is given in the following paragraphs.

Let us assume that there are six *protogons* (Greek *protos*, first, and *gone*, that which generates): the lepton, L; the antilepton, $\overline{L}$; the nucleon, N; the antinucleon, $\overline{N}$; the xenon,* X; and the antixenon, $\overline{X}$.

We assume that the lepton has intrinsic charge $-\frac{1}{2}$, charge vector $\frac{1}{2}$, and spin $\frac{1}{2}$. In its two aspects it is the electron and the neutrino. Similarly, the antilepton, with intrinsic charge $+\frac{1}{2}$, charge vector $\frac{1}{2}$, and spin $\frac{1}{2}$, corresponds to the positron and the antineutrino.

The nucleon, with intrinsic charge $+\frac{1}{2}$, charge vector $\frac{1}{2}$, and spin $\frac{1}{2}$, corresponds to the proton and the neutron, and the antinucleon to the antiproton and the antineutron.

The xenon has never been observed as an independent particle. We assume it to have xenicity 1, whereas the other protogons have xenicity 0 (except that the antixenon has xenicity -1). The xenon is assumed to have intrinsic charge $+\frac{1}{2}$, charge vector $\frac{1}{2}$, and spin 0. Similarly, the antixenon has intrinsic charge $-\frac{1}{2}$, charge vector $\frac{1}{2}$, and spin 0.

These postulated properties are summarized in Table 29-5.

The three pions, the eta particle, the three rho particles, and the omega particle can all be described as $L\overline{L}$. $L\overline{L}$ has intrinsic charge 0, charge vector either 0 or 1, and spin either 0 or 1 (and lepton number, baryon number, and xenicity all 0, as have the eight particles that we are discussing). Thus $L\overline{L}$

---

* The name xenon for the strangeness protogon is appropriate. There is little danger of confusing the protogon xenon (symbol X) with the element xenon (symbol Xe).

Table **29-5**

A Set of Protogons

	INTRINSIC CHARGE	CHARGE VECTOR	SPIN (angular momentum)	LEPTON NUMBER	BARYON NUMBER	XENICITY
Lepton, L	$-\frac{1}{2}$	$\frac{1}{2}$	$\frac{1}{2}$	1	0	0
Antilepton, $\overline{L}$	$+\frac{1}{2}$	$\frac{1}{2}$	$\frac{1}{2}$	-1	0	0
Nucleon, N	$+\frac{1}{2}$	$\frac{1}{2}$	$\frac{1}{2}$	0	1	0
Antinucleon, $\overline{N}$	$-\frac{1}{2}$	$\frac{1}{2}$	$\frac{1}{2}$	0	-1	0
Xenon, X	$+\frac{1}{2}$	$\frac{1}{2}$	0	0	0	1
Antixenon, $\overline{X}$	$-\frac{1}{2}$	$\frac{1}{2}$	0	0	0	-1

leads to two charge singlets (one with spin 0 and one with spin 1) and two charge triplets (one with spin 0 and one with spin 1):

	Charge Vector	Spin	Particles
$L\overline{L}$	1	0	π^-, π^0, π^+
$L\overline{L}$	0	0	η^0
$L\overline{L}$	1	1	ρ^-, ρ^0, ρ^+
$L\overline{L}$	0	1	ω^0

All eight of these particles might be classed as mesons. We have, however, listed only the four with spin 0 in Table 29-2.

The two kaons, with xenicity 1, can be considered to be the pion plus a xenon; i.e., $L\overline{L}X$. The pion has intrinsic charge 0 and the xenon has intrinsic charge $\frac{1}{2}$, so that the kaon doublet would have intrinsic charge $\frac{1}{2}$. The pion has charge vector 1 and the xenon has charge vector $\frac{1}{2}$, which can be added vectorially to the pion vector to give the resultant $\frac{1}{2}$. The spin remains unchanged by the addition of the xenon. The two antikaons are similarly described as $L\overline{L}\overline{X}$.

Also, the lambda singlet and the sigma triplet can be obtained from a nucleon by the addition of an antixenon, and the xion doublet can then be obtained by the further addition of another antixenon, as indicated in Figure 29-5.

The lambda singlet results from the addition of the antixenon to the nucleon in such a way that the two electric-charge vectors, each with magnitude $\frac{1}{2}$, combine to the resultant 0, whereas the sigma triplet results from their combination with the resultant 1.

Many alternative descriptions of some of the fundamental particles as compounds of others may be formulated, but at the present time they cannot be said to have great significance. It is likely that further experimental and theoretical work will soon lead to clarification. Fifty years ago the elements, about 100 in number, had to be described as independent particles; now we describe them as consisting of electrons, protons, and neutrons, with mesons contributing to the binding forces in the atomic nuclei. When the next edition of this book is prepared it may be possible to describe the particles that are now called fundamental particles in terms of a half-dozen truly fundamental particles—though perhaps not the six protogons that are mentioned above. We may be able to explain why electric charge is rigorously conserved in all known reactions, to discuss internucleonic forces in a quantitative way, to account for the masses of electrons, mesons, baryons, and the resonance particles and complexes, and to discuss intrinsic charge, electric-charge vectors, and xenicity in a more meaningful way than is now possible.

Without becoming nuclear chemists or fundamental-particle physicists, we may all await with eagerness the increase in knowledge about the nature of the universe that will surely be obtained through the efforts of scientists all over the world during the coming years.

REFERENCES

Scientific American offprints (see Appendix VI):

202. Anti-Matter

207. Mesonic Atoms

213. Elementary Particles

226. Pions

230. The Neutrino

232. The Neutron

244. The Antiproton

251. Particle Accelerators

219. The Nuclear Reactor as a Research Instrument

214. The Bubble Chamber

239. Where Do Cosmic Rays Come From?

275. The Muon

The Ultimate Atom (Positronium), H. C. Corben and S. De Benedetti, *Scientific American*, December 1954.

The Two-neutrino Experiment, L. M. Lederman, *Scientific American*, March 1963.

CHAPTER 30

Nuclear Chemistry

The field of nuclear chemistry deals with the reactions that involve changes in atomic nuclei. This field began with the discovery of radioactivity and the work of Pierre and Marie Curie on the chemical nature of the radioactive substances. After some decades, during which natural radioactivity was rather thoroughly investigated, a great increase in knowledge resulted through the discovery of artificial radioactivity.

Nuclear chemistry has now become a large and important branch of science. About 920 radioactive nuclides (isotopes) have been made in the laboratory, whereas only about 272 stable nuclides and 55 unstable (radioactive) nuclides have been detected in nature. The use of radioactive isotopes as "tracers" has become a valuable technique in scientific and medical research. The controlled release of nuclear energy promises to lead us into a new world, in which the achievement of man is no longer severely limited by the supply of energy available to him.

30-1. Natural Radioactivity

After their discovery of polonium and radium in 1898 (Chapter 3), the Curies found that radium chloride could be separated from barium chloride by fractional precipitation of the aqueous solution by addition of alcohol, and by 1902 Madame Curie had prepared 0.1 g of nearly pure radium chloride, with radioactivity about 3,000,000 times that of uranium. Within a few years it had been found that natural radioactive materials emit three kinds of rays capable of sensitizing the photographic plate (Chapter 3). These rays—alpha rays, beta rays, and gamma rays—are affected differently by a magnetic field (Figure 3-12). Alpha rays are the nuclei of helium atoms, moving at high speeds; beta rays are electrons, also moving at high speeds; and gamma rays are photons, with very short wavelengths.

It was soon discovered that the rays from radium and other radioactive

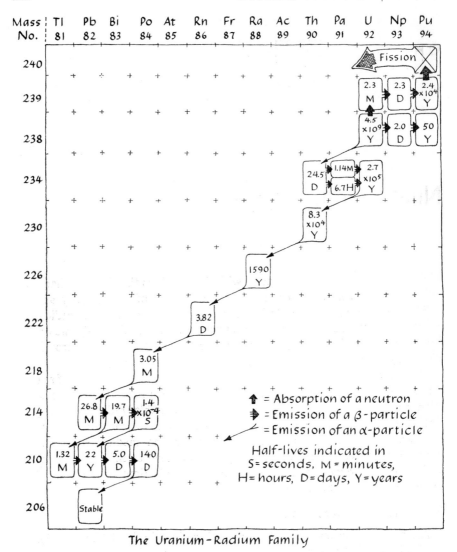

The Uranium–Radium Family

Figure 30-1

The uranium-radium series.

elements cause regression of cancerous growths. These rays also affect normal cells, "radium burns" being caused by overexposure; but often the cancerous cells are more sensitive to radiation than normal cells, and can be killed by suitable treatment without serious injury to normal tissues. The medical use in the treatment of cancer is the main use for radium. Since about 1950, considerable use has also been made of the artificial radioactive isotope cobalt 60 as a substitute for radium (Section 30-4).

Through the efforts of many investigators the chemistry of the radioactive elements of the uranium series and the thorium series was unraveled during the first two decades of the twentieth century, and that of the neptunium series during a few years from 1939 on.

The Uranium Series of Radioactive Disintegrations. When an alpha particle (He^{++}) is emitted by an atomic nucleus the nuclear charge decreases by two units; the element hence is transmuted into the element two columns to the left in the periodic table. Its mass number (atomic weight) decreases by 4, the mass of the alpha particle. When a beta particle (an electron) is emitted by a nucleus the nuclear charge is increased by one unit, with no change in mass number (only a very small decrease in atomic weight); the element is

Figure **30-2**

The uranium-actinium series.

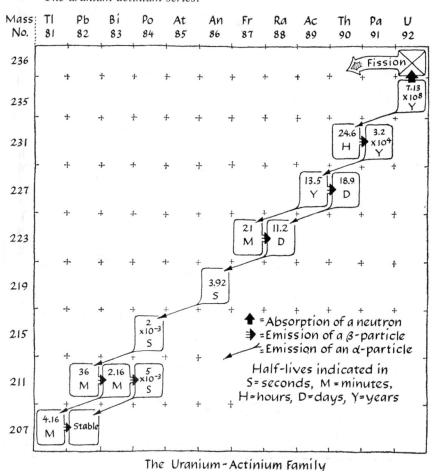

The Uranium-Actinium Family

transmuted into the element one column to its right. No change in atomic number or atomic weight is caused by emission of a gamma ray.

The nuclear reactions in the **uranium-radium series** are shown in Figure 30-1. The principal isotope of uranium, U^{238}, constitutes 99.28% of the natural element. This isotope has a half-life of 4,500,000,000 years. It decomposes by emitting an alpha particle and forming Th^{234}. This isotope of thorium under-goes decomposition with β-emission, forming Pa^{234}, which in turn forms U^{234}. Five successive α-emissions then occur, giving Pb^{214}, which ultimately changes to Pb^{206}, a stable isotope of lead.

The **uranium-actinium series,** shown in Figure 30-2, is a similar series beginning with U^{235}, which occurs to the extent of 0.71% in natural uranium. It leads, through the emission of seven alpha particles and four beta particles, to the stable isotope Pb^{207}.

The Thorium Series. The third natural radioactive series begins with the long-lived, naturally occurring isotope of thorium, Th^{232}, which has half-life

Figure **30-3**

The thorium series.

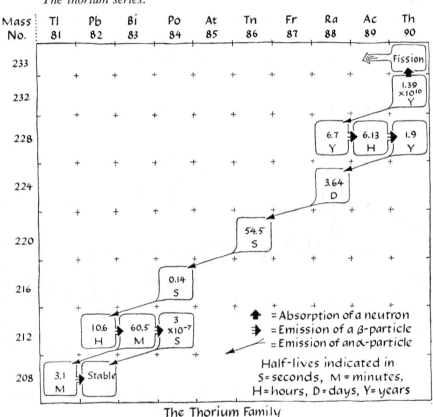

The Thorium Family

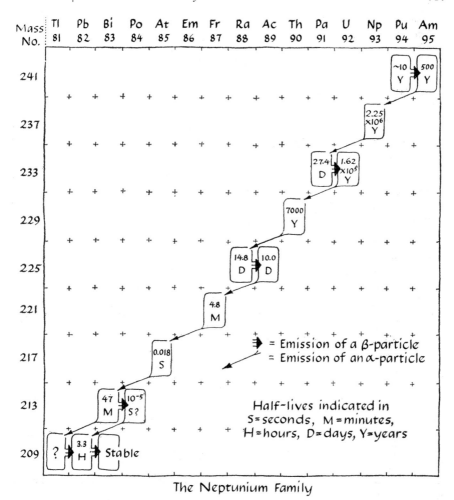

The Neptunium Family

Figure **30-4**

The neptunium series.

1.39×10^{10} years (Figure 30-3). It leads to another stable isotope of lead, Pb^{208}.

The Neptunium Series. During the last war the fourth radioactive series was discovered. This series (Figure 30-4) is named after its longest-lived member, which is Np^{237}.

The nature of radioactive disintegration within each of the four series—the emission of β-particles, with mass nearly zero, or of α-particles, with mass 4—is such that all the members of a series have mass numbers differing by a multiple of 4. The four series can hence be classified as follows (*n* being integral):

The 4n series = the thorium series
The 4n + 1 series = the neptunium series
The 4n + 2 series = the uranium-radium series
The 4n + 3 series = the uranium-actinium series

30-2. The Age of the Earth

Measurements made on rocks containing radioactive elements can be interpreted to provide values of the age of the rocks, and hence of the age of the earth; that is, the time that has elapsed since the oldest rocks were laid down. For example, one gram of U^{238} would in its half-life of 4.5×10^9 years decompose to leave 0.5000 g of U^{238} and to produce 0.0674 g of helium and 0.4326 g of Pb^{206}. (Each atom of U^{238} that decomposes forms eight atoms of helium, with total mass 32, leaving one atom of Pb^{206}.) If analyses showed that the nuclides were present in a rock in the ratios of these numbers, the rock would be assumed to be 4.5×10^9 years old. The U^{235}/Pb^{207} ratio, the Th^{232}/Pb^{208} ratio, the K^{40}/Ar^{40} ratio, and the Rb^{87}/Sr^{87} ratio are also being used for determining the ages of rocks. Ages around 3.0×10^9 years have been determined for rocks found in Finland, Canada, and Africa, and about 4.5×10^9 years for meteorites. The present estimate of the age of the earth and other planets in the solar system is 4.5×10^9 years.

30-3. Artificial Radioactivity

Stable atoms can be converted into radioactive atoms by bombardment with particles traveling at high speeds. In the early experimental work the high-speed particles used were alpha particles from Bi^{83} (called radium C). The first nuclear reaction produced in the laboratory was that between alpha particles and nitrogen, carried out by Lord Rutherford and his collaborators in the Cavendish Laboratory at Cambridge in 1919. The nuclear reaction that occurs when nitrogen is bombarded with alpha particles is the following:

$$_7N^{14} + {_2}He^4 \longrightarrow {_8}O^{17} + {_1}H^1$$

In this reaction a nitrogen nucleus reacts with a helium nucleus, which strikes it with considerable energy, to form two new nuclei, an O^{17} nucleus and a proton.

The O^{17} nucleus is stable, so that this nuclear reaction does not lead to the production of artificial radioactivity. Many other elements, however, undergo similar reactions with the production of unstable nuclei, which then undergo radioactive decomposition.

Many nuclear reactions result from the interaction of nuclei and neutrons. The early experiments with neutrons were carried out by use of a mixture of radon and beryllium metal. The alpha particles from radon react with the beryllium isotope Be^9 to produce neutrons in the following ways:

$$_4Be^9 + _2He^4 \longrightarrow _6C^{12} + _0n^1$$
$$_4Be^9 + _2He^4 \longrightarrow 3_2He^4 + _0n^1$$

Neutrons are also prepared by reactions in the cyclotron and in uranium reactors.

The Kinds of Nuclear Reactions.   Many different kinds of nuclear reactions have now been studied. Spontaneous radioactivity is a nuclear reaction in which the reactant is a single nucleus. Other known nuclear reactions involve a proton, a deuteron, an alpha particle, a neutron, or a photon (usually a gamma ray) interacting with the nucleus of an atom. The products of a nuclear reaction may be a heavy nucleus and a proton, an electron, a deuteron, an alpha particle, a neutron, two or more neutrons, or a gamma ray. In addition, there occurs the very important type of nuclear reaction in which a very heavy nucleus, made unstable by the addition of a neutron, breaks up into two parts of comparable size, plus several neutrons. This process of fission has been mentioned in Chapter 26 and is described in a later section of the present chapter.

Examples of a few of these reactions have been mentioned above. As another example, the production of radioactive phosphorus, P^{32}, by bombardment of ordinary phosphorus, P^{31}, with 10-million volt deuterons from a cyclotron may be mentioned. The reaction is

$$_{15}P^{31} + _1H^2 \longrightarrow _{15}P^{32} + _1H^1$$

The P^{32} nuclide decomposes with emission of electrons, its half-life being 14.3 days.

Artificial radionuclides decompose with emission of an alpha particle and a photon (gamma ray), or of an electron and an antineutrino, or of an antielectron (positron) and a neutrino. An example of the last is the decomposition of C^{11}, which has half-life 20.4 minutes:

$$_6C^{11} \longrightarrow _5B^{11} + \bar{e}^+ + \nu$$

Manufacture of the Transuranium Elements.   The first transuranium element to be made was a neptunium isotope, $_{93}Np^{239}$. This nuclide was made by E. M. McMillan and P. H. Abelson in 1940 by bombarding uranium with high-speed deuterons:

$$_{92}U^{238} + _1H^2 \longrightarrow _{92}U^{239} + _1H^1$$
$$_{92}U^{239} \longrightarrow _{93}Np^{239} + e^-$$

The first isotope of plutonium to be made was Pu^{238}, by the reactions

$$_{92}U^{238} + _1H^2 \longrightarrow _{93}Np^{238} + 2_0n^1$$
$$_{93}Np^{238} \longrightarrow _{94}Pu^{238} + e^-$$

The Np^{238} decomposes spontaneously, emitting electrons. Its half-life is 2.0 days.

During and since World War II some quantity, of the order of one million pounds, of the nuclide Pu^{239} has been manufactured. This nuclide is relatively stable; it has a half-life of about 24,000 years. It slowly decomposes with the emission of alpha particles. It is made by the reaction of the principal isotope of uranium, U^{238}, with a neutron, to form U^{239}, which then undergoes spontaneous radioactive decomposition with emission of an electron to form Np^{239}, which in turn emits an electron spontaneously, forming Pu^{239}:

$$_{92}U^{238} + _0n^1 \longrightarrow _{92}U^{239}$$
$$_{92}U^{239} \longrightarrow _{93}Np^{239} + e^-$$
$$_{93}Np^{239} \longrightarrow _{94}Pu^{239} + e^-$$

Plutonium and the next four transuranium elements—americium, curium, berkelium, and californium—were discovered by Professor G. T. Seaborg and his collaborators at the University of California in Berkeley. Americium has been made as Am^{241} by the following reactions:

$$_{92}U^{238} + _2He^4 \longrightarrow _{94}Pu^{241} + _0n^1$$
$$_{94}Pu^{241} \longrightarrow _{95}Am^{241} + e^-$$

This nuclide slowly undergoes radioactive decomposition, with emission of alpha particles. Its half-life is 500 years. Curium is made from plutonium 239 by bombardment with helium ions accelerated in the cyclotron:

$$_{94}Pu^{239} + _2He^4 \longrightarrow _{96}Cm^{242} + _0n^1$$

The nuclide Cm^{242} is an alpha-particle emitter, with half-life about 5 months. Other isotopes of curium have also been made. One is Cm^{240}, made by bombarding plutonium, Pu^{239}, with high-speed helium ions:

$$_{94}Pu^{239} + _2He^4 \longrightarrow _{96}Cm^{240} + 3_0n^1$$

Using only very small quantities of the substances, Seaborg and his collaborators succeeded in obtaining a considerable amount of information about the chemical properties of the transuranium elements. They have found that, whereas uranium is similar to tungsten in its properties, in that it has a pronounced tendency to assume oxidation state $+6$, the succeeding elements are not similar to rhenium, osmium, iridium, and platinum, but show an increasing tendency to form ionic compounds in which their oxidation number is $+3$. This behavior is similar to that of the rare-earth metals.

30-4.   The Use of Radioactive Elements as Tracers

A valuable technique for research that has been developed in recent years is the use of both radioactive and nonradioactive isotopes as tracers. By the use of these isotopes an element can be observed in the presence of large quantities of the same element. For example, one of the earliest uses of tracers was the experimental determination of the rate at which lead atoms move around through a crystalline sample of the metal lead. This phenomenon is called *self-diffusion*. If some radioactive lead is placed as a surface layer on a sheet of lead, and the sample is allowed to stand for a while, it can then be cut up into thin sections parallel to the original surface layer, and the radioactivity present in each section can be measured. The presence of radioactivity in layers other than the original surface layer shows that lead atoms from the surface layer have diffused through the metal.

In the discussion of chemical equilibrium in Chapter 18 it was pointed out that a system in chemical equilibrium is not static, but that instead chemical reactions may be proceeding in the forward direction and the reverse direction at equal rates, so that the amounts of different substances present remain constant. At first thought it would seem to be impossible to determine experimentally the rates at which different chemical reactions are proceeding at equilibrium. It has now been found possible to make experiments of this sort, however, with the use of isotopes as tracers.

Perhaps the greatest use for radioactive nuclides as tracers will continue to be in the field of biology and medicine. The human body contains such large amounts of the elements carbon, hydrogen, nitrogen, oxygen, sulfur, etc., that it is difficult to determine the state of organic material in the body. An organic compound containing a radioactive nuclide, however, can be traced through the body. An especially useful radioactive nuclide for these purposes is carbon 14. This isotope of carbon has a half-life of about 5000 years. It undergoes slow decomposition with emission of beta rays, and the amount of the isotope present in a sample can be followed by measuring the beta activity. Large quantities of C^{14} can be readily made in a nuclear reactor, by the action of slow neutrons on nitrogen:

$$_7N^{14} + _0n^1 \longrightarrow {}_6C^{14} + _1H^1$$

The process can be carried out by running a solution of ammonium nitrate into the nuclear reactor, where it is exposed to neutrons. The carbon that is made in this way is in the form of the hydrogen carbonate ion, HCO_3^-, and it can be precipitated as barium carbonate by adding barium hydroxide solution. The samples of radioactive carbon are very strongly radioactive, containing as much as 5% of the radioactive isotope.

The Unit of Radioactivity, the Curie. It has been found convenient to introduce a special unit in which to measure amounts of radioactive material. The unit of radioactivity is called the *curie*. One curie of any radioactive substance is an amount of the substance such that 3.70×10^{10} atoms of the substance undergo radioactive disintegration per second.

The curie is a rather large unit. One curie of radium is approximately one gram of the element. (The curie was originally defined in such a way as to make a curie of radium equal to one gram, but because of improvement in technique it has been found convenient to define it instead in the way given above.)

It is interesting to point out that in a disintegration chain of radioactive elements in a steady state all of the radioactive elements are present in the same radioactive amounts. For example, let us consider one gram of the element radium, in a steady state with the first product of its decomposition, radon (Rn^{222}), and the successive products of disintegration (see Figure 30-2). The rate at which radon is being produced is proportional to the amount of radium present, one atom of radon being produced for each atom of radium that undergoes decomposition. The number of atoms of radium that undergo decomposition in unit time is proportional to the number of atoms of radium present; the decomposition of radium is a unimolecular reaction. Now when the system has reached a steady state the number of atoms of radon present remains unchanged, so that the rate at which radon is itself undergoing radioactive decomposition must be equal to the rate at which it is being formed from radium. Hence the radon present in a steady state with one gram of radium itself amounts to one curie.

The amount of radon present in a steady state with one gram of radium can be calculated by consideration of the first-order reaction-rate equations discussed in Chapter 18. The reaction-rate constant for the decomposition of radium is inversely proportional to its half-life. Hence when a steady state exists, and the number of radium atoms undergoing decomposition is equal to the number of radon atoms undergoing decomposition, the ratio of the numbers of radon atoms and radium atoms present must be equal to the ratio of their half-lives.

30-5. Dating Objects by Use of Carbon 14

One of the most interesting recent applications of radioactivity is the determination of the age of carbonaceous materials by measurement of their radioactivity due to carbon 14. This technique of radiocarbon dating, which was developed by an American physical chemist, Willard F. Libby, permits the dating of samples containing carbon with an accuracy of around 200 years. At the present time the method can be applied to materials that are not over about 50,000 years old.

Carbon 14 is being made at a steady rate in the upper atmosphere. Cosmic-ray neutrons transmute nitrogen into carbon 14, by the reaction given in the preceding section. The radiocarbon is oxidized to carbon dioxide, which is thoroughly mixed with the nonradioactive carbon dioxide in the atmosphere, through the action of winds. The steady-state concentration of carbon 14 built up in the atmosphere by cosmic rays is about one atom of radioactive carbon to 10^{12} atoms of ordinary carbon. The carbon dioxide, radioactive and nonradioactive alike, is absorbed by plants, which fix the carbon in their tissues. Animals that eat the plants also similarly fix the carbon, containing 1×10^{-12} part radiocarbon, in their tissues. When a plant or animal dies, the amount of radioactivity of the carbon in its tissues is determined by the amount of radiocarbon present, which is the amount corresponding to the steady state in the atmosphere. After 5,760 years (the half-life of carbon 14), however, half of the carbon 14 has undergone decomposition, and the radioactivity of the material is only half as great. After 11,520 years only one-quarter of the original radioactivity is left, and so on. Accordingly, by determining the radio-activity of a sample of carbon from wood, flesh, charcoal, skin, horn, or other plant or animal remains, the number of years that have gone by since the carbon was originally extracted from the atmosphere can be determined.

In applying the method of radiocarbon dating, a sample of material containing about 30 g of carbon (about 1 ounce) is burned to carbon dioxide, which is then reduced to elementary carbon in the form of lamp black. The beta-ray activity of the elementary carbon is then determined, with the use of Geiger counters, and compared with the beta-ray activity of recent carbon, which is 15.3 ± 0.1 decompositions per minute per gram of carbon. The age of the sample is then calculated by the use of the equation for a first-order reaction (Chapter 18). The method was checked by measurement of carbon from the heartwood of a giant Sequoia tree, for which the number of tree rings showed that $2,928 \pm 50$ years had passed since the wood was laid down. This check was satisfactory, as were also similar checks with other carbonaceous materials, such as wood in 1st Dynasty Egyptian tombs 4,900 years old, whose dating was considered to be reliable.

The method of radiocarbon dating has now been applied to several hundred samples. One of the interesting conclusions that have been reached is that the last glaciation of the northern hemisphere occurred about 11,400 years ago. Specimens of wood from a buried forest in Wisconsin, in which all of the tree trunks are lying in the same direction as though pushed over by a glacier, were found to have an age of $11,400 \pm 700$ years. The age of specimens of organic materials laid down during the last period of glaciation in Europe was found to be $10,800 \pm 1,200$ years. Many samples of organic matter, charcoal, and other carbonaceous material from human camp sites in the western hemisphere have been dated as extending to 11,400 years ago; a very few older ones (30,000 years) have been found.

The eruption of Mt. Mazama in southern Oregon, which formed the crater now called Crater Lake, was determined to have occurred $6,453 \pm 250$ years ago, by the dating of charcoal from a tree killed by the eruption. Three hundred pairs of woven rope sandals found in Fort Rock Cave, Oregon, which had been covered by an earlier eruption, were found to be $9,053 \pm 350$ years old. The Lascaux Cave near Montignac, France, contains some remarkable paintings made by prehistoric man; charcoal from camp fires in this cave was found to have the age $15,516 \pm 900$ years. Linen wrappings from the Dead Sea scrolls of the Book of Isaiah, recently found in a cave in Palestine and thought to be from about the first or second century B.C., were dated $1,917 \pm 200$ years old.

Table **30-1** *Isotopes of the Lighter Elements*

Z	NAME	MASS NUMBER	MASS*	PERCENT ABUNDANCE	HALF-LIFE†	RADIATION
0	Electron	0	0.0005486			
0	Neutron	1	1.008665			
1	Proton	1	1.007276			
1	Hydrogen	1	1.007825	99.985		
		2	2.014102	0.015		
		3	3.014949		12.26 Y	e^-
2	Alpha	4	4.001507			
2	Helium	3	3.016030	0.00013		
		4	4.002604	~100		
		5	5.012296		2×10^{-21} S	
		6	6.018900		0.81 S	e^-
		7			60×10^{-6} S	e^-
3	Lithium	5	5.012541		~10^{-21} S	
		6	6.015126	7.42		
		7	7.016005	92.58		
		8	8.022488		0.85 S	
		9	9.027300		0.17 S	e^-
4	Beryllium	6	6.019780		$\geq 4 \times 10^{-21}$ S	
		7	7.016931		53 D	γ
		8	8.005308		~3×10^{-16} S	
		9	9.012186	100		
		10	10.013535		2.7×10^6 Y	e^-
		11	11.021660		13.6 S	e^-, γ
5	Boron	8	8.024612		0.78 S	e^+
		9	9.013335		$\geq 3 \times 10^{-19}$ S	
		10	10.012939	19.6		
		11	11.009305	80.4		
		12	12.014353		0.020 S	e^-, γ
		13	13.017779		0.035 S	e^-
6	Carbon	10	10.016830		19 S	e^+, γ
		11	11.011433		20.5 M	e^+
		12	12.000000	98.89		
		13	13.003354	1.11		
		14	14.003242		5760 Y	e^-
		15	15.010600		2.25 S	e^-, γ
		16	16.014702		0.74 S	e^-
7	Nitrogen	12	12.018709		0.011 S	e^+
		13	13.005739		10.0 M	e^+
		14	14.003074	99.63		
		15	15.000108	0.37		
		16	16.006089		7.35 S	e^-, γ
		17	17.008449		4.14 S	e^-
8	Oxygen	14	14.008597		71 S	e^+, γ
		15	15.003072		124 S	e^+
		16	15.994915	99.759		
		17	16.999133	0.037		
		18	17.999160	0.204		
		19	19.003577		29 S	e^-, γ
		20	20.004071		14 S	e^-, γ
9	Fluorine	16	16.011707		~10^{-19} S	
		17	17.002098		66 S	e^+
		18	18.000950		111 M	e^+
		19	18.998405	100		
		20	19.999986		11 S	e^-, γ
		21	20.999972		5 S	e^-
10	Neon	18	18.005715		1.46 S	e^+, γ
		19	19.001892		18 S	e^+
		20	19.992440	90.92		
		21	20.993849	0.257		
		22	21.991384	8.82		
		23	22.994475		38 S	e^-, γ
		24	23.993597		3.38 M	e^-, γ

* Carbon-12 scale.
† S = second, M = minute Y = year.

30-6. The Properties of Nuclides

The nuclides of the various elements show many interesting properties. Most of the known nuclides corresponding to the first ten elements are listed in Table 30-1. The masses given in column three of this table refer to the new atomic weight scale, in which $C^{12} = 12.00000$.

For most elements other than those that form part of the natural radio-active series the distribution of nuclides for an element has been found to be the same for all natural occurrences. The average natural distribution is shown in the fourth column of the table.

Some striking regularities are evident, especially for the heavier elements. The elements of odd atomic number have only one or two natural nuclides, whereas those of even atomic number are much richer in nuclides, many having eight or more. It is also found that the odd elements are much rarer in nature than the even elements. The elements with no stable isotopes (technetium, atomic number 43; astatine, atomic number 85; promethium, atomic number 61) have odd atomic numbers.

The Packing Fraction. Consideration of the masses of the nuclides shows that they are not additive. Thus the mass of the ordinary hydrogen atom is 1.007825, and that of the neutron is 1.008665. If the helium atom were made from two hydrogen atoms and two neutrons without change in mass, its mass would be 4.032980, but it is in fact less, only 4.002604. The masses of the heavier atoms are also less than they would be if they were composed of hydrogen atom and neutrons without change in mass.

The loss in mass accompanying the formation of a heavier atom from hydrogen atoms and neutrons shows that these reactions are strongly exothermic. A very large amount of energy is evolved in the formation of the heavier atoms from hydrogen atoms and neutrons, an amount given by the Einstein equation $E = mc^2$. The more stable the heavy nucleus, the larger is the decrease in mass from that of the neutrons and protons from which the nucleus may be considered to be made.

It is customary to describe the decrease in mass by means of a quantity called the *packing fraction*. This is the difference in mass, per nucleon in the nucleus, relative to O^{16} as standard. A nuclide that has atomic mass equal exactly to its mass number on the O^{16} scale is said to have zero packing fraction.

The packing fractions for the elements are shown in Figure 30-5. It is seen that the elements of the first long period of the periodic table, between chromium and zinc, lie at the minimum of the curve, and can accordingly be considered to be the most stable of all the elements. If one of these elements were to be converted into other elements, the total mass of the other elements would be somewhat greater than that of the reactants, and accordingly energy would have to be added in order to cause the reaction to occur. On the other hand, either the heavier or the lighter elements could undergo a nuclear reaction to

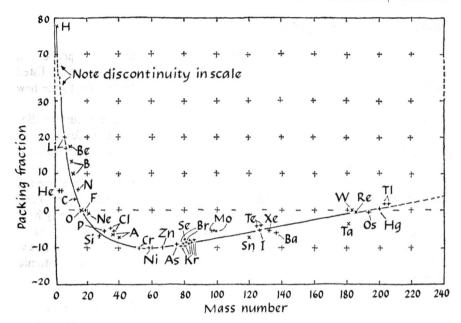

Figure 30-5

The mass packing fractions of the elements.

form the elements with mass numbers in the neighborhood of 60, and these nuclear reactions would be accompanied by the evolution of a large amount of energy.

Scientists have attempted to develop a theory of the origin of nuclear species on the basis of the extensive information now available about nuclear reactions, but this effort has been only partially successful. One idea is that the elements have been produced by synthesis from hydrogen by a succession of captures interspersed where necessary by decrease in atomic number through β decay. There is convincing astronomical evidence that the universe is expanding. The light from distant galaxies contains spectral lines that can be identified, but their frequencies are not those observed in the laboratory; instead, there is a shift in wavelength to the red (the red-shift). The same fractional shift in wavelength is observed for all of the spectral lines and for the continuum in the optical spectrum and also for all radio waves emitted by a particular galaxy. This fact is the basis for the belief that the red-shift is due to the Doppler effect (the dependence of observed frequency on the relative velocities of emitter and observer) and that the distant galaxies are receding from us. It was discovered by the American astronomers Hubble and Humason about 30 years ago that the red-shift is greatest for the most distant galaxies. The magnitude of the velocity of the galaxies as deduced from the red-shift and distances of the galaxies fixes the time of creation of the universe at about 15×10^9 years ago.

The American scientist George Gamow postulated that at that time, the beginning, the universe consisted of a huge ball of neutrons bathed in radiation, which immediately began to expand because of its great internal energy. Some of the neutrons then began to decay to form protons, electrons, and neutrinos, liberating 0.78 MeV of energy per neutron. The protons could then capture neutrons to form deuterons, and, in the neutron-capture theory of the origin of nuclides, the process of neutron capture would continue, and would build up the distribution of nuclides that is observed.

There are, however, some difficulties about this theory. One is that there are no stable nuclides with mass 5 or mass 8, and thus no synthesis of the elements beyond these masses through neutron capture alone is possible; the synthesis stops when all of the hydrogen has been turned into helium 4.

An alternative theory of nuclide synthesis is that this synthesis has taken place and is still taking place in the center of stars. This theory has been supported principally by the British astrophysicist Fred Hoyle. The problem of the instability of the nuclides with mass 5 and mass 8 is overcome by way of reactions such as the following:

$$3_2\text{He}^4 \rightleftarrows {}_6\text{C}^{12*} \longrightarrow {}_6\text{C}^{12} + \gamma$$

At a temperature of 100 million degrees and density of 10,000 g/cm^3 in the center of a star, there is an equilibrium involving three alpha particles and an excited state of the carbon-12 nucleus, with energy 7.653 MeV greater than the normal state of the nucleus. The excited C^{12} nucleus can change to the normal state by emission of a photon. Various other known nuclear reactions can then lead to the synthesis of all of the heavier nuclides.

The Structure of Nuclei. Experiments such as those involving the scattering of fast electrons by nuclei have led to the determination of the sizes of nuclei. For all nuclei, the radius R is given quite well as a function of the nuclear number A by the following equation:

$$R = A^{1/3} \times 1.4 \times 10^{-13} \text{ cm}$$

The volume of a sphere with radius R is $\frac{4}{3}\pi R^3$. With R given by the above equation, the volume is equal to 11.5 A f^3, where f, the fermi, is a unit of length equal to 1×10^{-13} cm. The effective volume per nucleon in atomic nuclei is thus about 11.5 f^3.

Since the range of internucleonic forces is about 1.4 f, as mentioned in Section 29-3, we see that nuclei do not have a closest-packed structure in which each nucleon is surrounded by several others to which it is strongly bound, but instead have a rather open structure. If the nucleons were arranged in a simple cubic lattice, with each nucleon bonded to six neighbors at the distance 1.4 f, the volume per nucleon would be only 2.7 f^3, less than one-quarter the observed volume 11.5 f^3.

The observed electric-charge distribution in the alpha particle (root-mean-square radius 1.68 f), compared with that in the proton (0.85 f), is compatible with a tetrahedral structure of four nucleons with nucleon-nucleon bond length 1.4 f.

Nucleonic Valence. There is, moreover, some evidence that nucleons might be described, in a chemical way, as having valence 3, and able to form only three valence bonds. When a neutron and a proton interact to form a deuteron the amount of the decrease in mass corresponds to the liberation of 2.2 MeV of energy. This energy quantity may be taken as the energy of the nucleon-nucleon bond in the deuteron. When two neutrons and a proton combine to form H^3 or two protons and a neutron combine to form He^3, the amounts of energy released are 8.4 MeV and 7.8 MeV, respectively. The three nucleons may be considered to form three bonds, each being bonded to the other two, and, correspondingly, the total bond energy in H^3 and He^3 is observed to be roughly three times the energy of the bond in the deuteron. The addition of a fourth nucleon, to form the alpha particle, is accompanied by the release of still more energy; the total bond energy of the alpha particle is 28 MeV, which may be taken as the energy of the six bonds along the edges of a tetrahedron with the four nucleons at the four corners. It is evident that the valency of the nucleon is not saturated in H^3 and He^3, but can increase from the value 2 to the value 3, which is expressed in the alpha particle.

A fifth nucleon, however, cannot attach itself to the alpha particle. When He^4 is bombarded with neutrons, a nucleus with mass 5, He^5, is formed, but it is unstable, and within about 10^{-21} sec it breaks up again into He^4 and a neutron. A similar reaction is observed when He^4 is bombarded with protons; the nucleus Li^5 is unstable. We accordingly conclude that the valence of the nucleons is completely satisfied in the alpha particle, and that the nucleon has the maximum valence 3.

The values of the packing fraction shown in Figure 30-5 similarly indicate that the nucleons do not have valence any greater in the heavier nuclei than that which they exercise in the alpha particle. There might be, of course, some resonance stabilization associated with resonance of three bonds among more positions, in case that a nucleon were to have ligancy greater than 3, but the amount of resonance stabilization is never more than about 10% of the bond energy represented in the alpha particle.

The Alpha-particle Nucleus. One of the theories of nuclear structure is that alpha particles are present in the nucleus. A general theory describes the nucleus as resembling a nucleon liquid, with the nucleons not having any well-defined arrangement relative to one another. It is possible, however, that they tend to form groups of four, the alpha particles, each with a tetrahedral structure (edge of tetrahedron 1.4 f), and that the alpha particles and additional nucleons move around freely within the volume of the nucleus in the way characteristic of liquids. The effective radius of the alpha particle, 2.2 f, corresponds to a reasonable van der Waals diameter.

Magic Numbers. Some of the observed properties of nuclei show that there is a special stability associated with certain numbers of protons and certain numbers of neutrons. These numbers, which are known as *magic numbers*, are 2, 8, 20, 50, 82, and 126. The numbers can be correlated with the subshell numbers that have been developed in the discussion of the electrons in atoms. The magic number 2 is, of course, the number of fermions that can occupy a 1s orbital. The magic number 8 may be described as the number of fermions occupying a 1s orbital and the three 2p orbitals; in nuclei it is to be expected that a particle in a 2p orbital would be more stable than in a 2s orbital. The magic number 20 similarly corresponds to pairs of fermions occupying the 1s orbital, the three 2p orbitals, the 2s orbital, and the five 3d orbitals. The larger magic numbers can be similarly made, but the details are too complex to justify their presentation here. The observed properties of nuclei, such as spin, correspond well with this shell model. The aggregation of nucleons into alpha particles is not incompatible with the existence of special stability at the nucleon mag c numbers.

The shell model of the nucleus was developed by the American physicists Eugene Wigner and Maria Goeppert Mayer, the German physicist J. Hans D. Jensen, and others during the period 1933 to 1950.

As further investigations are carried out by the many scientists who are working in the field of nuclear chemistry and nuclear physics, we may anticipate that much more detailed information about nuclear structure will be obtained.

30-7. Nuclear Fission and Nuclear Fusion

The instability of the heavy elements relative to those of mass number around 60, as shown by the packing fraction curve, suggests the possibility of spontaneous decomposition of the heavy elements into fragments of approximately half-size (atomic masses 70 to 160, atomic numbers 30 to 65). This fission has been accomplished.

It was reported on January 6, 1939, by the German physicists O. Hahn and F. Strassmann that barium, lanthanum, cerium, and krypton seemed to be present in substances containing uranium that had been exposed to neutrons. Within two months more than forty papers were then published on the fission of uranium. It was verified by direct calorimetric measurement that a very large amount of energy is liberated by fission—over 5×10^{12} calories per mole. Since a pound of uranium contains about 2 gram-atoms, the complete fission of one pound of this element, or a similar heavy element, produces about 10×10^{12} calories. This may be compared with the heat of combustion of 1 pound of coal, which is approximately 4×10^{6} calories. Thus uranium as a source of energy is $2\frac{1}{2}$ million times more valuable than coal.

Uranium 235 and plutonium 239, which can be made from uranium 238, are capable of undergoing fission when exposed to slow neutrons. It was also shown by the Japanese physicist Nishina in 1939 that the thorium isotope Th^{232} undergoes fission under the influence of fast neutrons.

It has been customary to use the *megaton* as a unit of energy released in nuclear fission (or fusion, discussed below). One megaton is equal to the energy of explosion of one million tons of the ordinary explosive TNT. The energy of fission of 110 pounds of uranium or plutonium is one megaton.

Uranium and thorium may well become important sources of heat and energy in the world of the future. There are large amounts of these elements available—the amount of uranium in the earth's crust has been estimated as 4 parts per million and the amount of thorium as 12 parts per million. The deposits occur distributed all over the world.

The fission reactions can be chain reactions. These reactions are initiated by neutrons. A nucleus U^{235}, for example, may combine with a neutron to form U^{236}. This isotope is unstable, and undergoes spontaneous fission, into two particles of roughly equal atomic number, the sum of the atomic numbers being 92; that is, the protons in the U^{236} nucleus are divided between the two daughter nuclei (Figure 30-6). These daughter nuclei also contain some of the

Figure 30-6

The process of nuclear fission (linear magnification about 10^{12}).

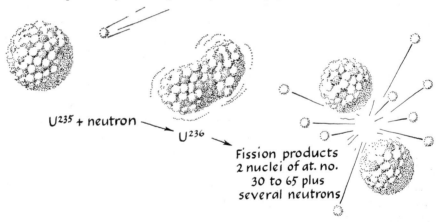

U^{235} + neutron

U^{236}

Fission products
2 nuclei of at. no.
30 to 65 plus
several neutrons

neutrons originally present in the U^{236} nucleus. Since, however, the ratio of neutrons to protons is greater in the heavier nuclei than in those of intermediate mass, the fission is also accompanied by the liberation of several free neutrons. The neutrons that are thus liberated may then combine with other U^{235} nuclei, forming additional U^{236} nuclei, which themselves undergo fission. A reaction of this sort, the products of which cause the reaction to continue, is called a chain reaction or an autocatalytic reaction.

If a mass of U^{235} or Pu^{239} weighing a few pounds and in suitable form, such as a hollow sphere, is suddenly compressed into a small volume, the auto-catalytic fission of the nuclei occurs nearly completely, and the amount of energy 0.009 megaton per pound that undergoes fission is released. An ordinary *atomic bomb* consists of a few pounds of U^{235} or Pu^{239} and a mechanism for suddenly compressing the metal. Each of the atomic bombs exploded over Hiroshima and Nagasaki in August 1945 had explosive energy of about 0.020 megatons (20 kilotons). Modern weapons involving fission alone have explosive energy 0.001 megaton to 0.1 megaton.

The process of *nuclear fusion* also may liberate energy. From the packing-fraction diagram we see that the fission of a very heavy nucleus converts about 0.1% of its mass into energy. Still larger fractions of the mass of very light nuclei are converted into energy by their fusion into heavier nuclei. The process 4H $\longrightarrow$ He, which is the principal source of the energy of the sun, involves the conversion of 0.7% of the mass into energy. The similar reaction of a deuteron and a triton to form a helium nucleus and a neutron is accompanied by the conversion of 0.4% of the mass into energy:

$$_1H^2 + {}_1H^3 \longrightarrow {}_2H^4 + {}_0n^1$$

It was found by experiment (in 1952) that these materials surrounding an ordinary atomic bomb (a few pounds of U^{235} or Pu^{239}) undergo reaction at the temperature of many millions of degrees produced by the reaction. Tritium is, however, inconvenient and expensive to use because it is radioactive and unstable (half-life 12 years). In 1953 it was shown that a fission-fusion bomb could be made by placing some of the stable solid substance *lithium deuteride*, LiD, about an ordinary fission bomb. Some of the reactions that occur are the following:

$$D^2 + D^2 \longrightarrow He^3 + n$$
$$D^2 + D^2 \longrightarrow H^3 + p$$
$$n + Li^6 \longrightarrow He^4 + H^3$$
$$H^3 + D \longrightarrow He^4 + n$$
$$p + Li^7 \longrightarrow He^4 + He^4$$

The amount of energy released in the fusion of lithium deuteride is about 60 megatons per ton of the material undergoing fusion, as compared with 20 megatons per ton of uranium undergoing fission. The largest nuclear bomb so far exploded, the Soviet bomb of November 1961, was a fission-fusion bomb with explosive energy of about 60 megatons, about 10 times that of all bombs used in the Second World War.

The standard present-day nuclear weapons are three-stage fission-fusion-fission bombs (superbombs). An ordinary 20-megaton superbomb (50:50 fission-fusion) has as its first-stage material (the detonator) a few pounds of plutonium, with some ordinary explosive to compress it suddenly. The second-stage material is about 300 pounds of lithium deuteride, which is surrounded by a shell of ordinary uranium metal (U^{238}, the third-stage material) weighing somewhat more than 1000 pounds. The U^{238} undergoes fission through reaction with fast neutrons.

The *manufacture of plutonium* is carried out by a controlled chain reaction. A piece of ordinary uranium contains 0.71% of U^{235}. An occasional neutron strikes one of these atoms, causing it to undergo fission and release a number of neutrons. The autocatalytic reaction does not build up, however, if the piece of uranium is small, because the neutrons escape, and some of them may be absorbed by impurities, such as cadmium, the nuclei of which combine very readily with neutrons.

However, if a large enough sample of uranium is taken, nearly all of the neutrons that are formed by the fission remain within the sample of uranium, and either cause other U^{235} nuclei to undergo fission, or are absorbed by U^{238}, converting it into U^{239}, which then undergoes spontaneous change to Pu^{239}. This is the process used in practice for the manufacture of plutonium. A large number of lumps of uranium are piled together, alternately with bricks of graphite, in a structure called a reactor, or pile. The first uranium pile ever constructed, built at the University of Chicago and put into operation on December 2, 1942, contained 12,400 pounds of uranium metal. Cadmium rods are held in readiness to be introduced into cavities in the pile, and to serve to arrest the reaction by absorbing neutrons, whenever there is danger of its getting out of hand.

The large reactors that were put into operation in September, 1944, at Hanford, Washington, were of such size as to permit the fission reaction to proceed at the rate corresponding to an output of energy amounting to 1,500,000 kilowatts.

The significance of the uranium reactors as a source of radioactive material can be made clear by a comparison with the supply of radium now in use. About 1000 curies (1000 grams) of radium has been separated from its ores and put into use, mainly for medical treatment. The rate of operation mentioned above for the reactors at Hanford represents the fission of about 5×10^{20} nuclei per second, forming about 10×10^{20} radioactive atoms. The concentration of these radioactive atoms will build up until they are undergoing decomposition at the rate at which they are being formed. Since 1 curie corresponds to 3.70×10^{10} disintegrating atoms per second, these reactors develop a radioactivity of approximately 3×10^{10} curies—that is, about thirty million times the radioactivity of all the radium that has been so far isolated from its ores.

The foregoing calculation illustrates the great significance of the fissionable elements as a source of radioactive material. Their significance as a source of energy has also been pointed out, by the statement that 1 pound of uranium or thorium is equivalent to $2\frac{1}{2}$ million pounds of coal. When we remember that uranium and thorium are not rare elements, but are among the more common elements—the amount of uranium and thorium in the earth's crust being about the same as that of the common element lead—we begin to understand the promise of nuclear energy for the world of the future, and the possibility of its great contributions to human welfare, if civilization is not brought to an end by war. I believe that the discovery of the controlled fission of atomic nuclei and controlled release of atomic energy is the greatest discovery that has been made since the controlled use of fire was discovered by primitive man.

REFERENCES

Scientific American offprints (see Appendix VI).

102. The Age of the Solar System

217. The Atomic Nucleus

228. The Structure of the Nucleus

235. Models of the Nucleus

253. The Age of the Elements in the Solar System

242. The Synthetic Elements I

243. The Synthetic Elements II

The Metric System of

Weights and Measures

It is customary in scientific work to express quantities in terms of the units of the metric system. This system is simpler than the system of weights and measures commonly used in the United States, in that only powers of ten are involved in the relation between different units for the same quantity.

The *mass* of an object is measured in terms of *grams* (g) or *kilograms* (kg), the kilogram being equal to 1,000 g. The kilogram is defined as the mass of a standard object made of a platinum-iridium alloy and kept in Paris. One pound is equal approximately to 454 g, and hence 1 kg is equal approximately to 2.2 lb. (Note that it has become customary in recent years for the abbreviations of units in the metric system to be written without periods.)

The metric unit of length is the meter (m), which is equal to about 39.37 inches. The meter was formerly defined as the distance between two engraved lines on a standard platinum-iridium bar kept in Paris by the International Bureau of Weights and Measures; in 1960 it was redefined, by international agreement, as 1,650,763.63 wavelengths of the orange-red spectral line of krypton 86 (wavelength $6057.8021\cdots$Å). The *centimeter* (cm), which is $1/100$ m, is about 0.4 inch. The *millimeter* (mm) is $1/10$ cm.

The *metric unit of volume* is the *liter* (l),* which is approximately 1.06 U.S. quarts. The *milliliter* (ml), equal to $1/1,000$ l, is usually used as the unit of volume in the measurement of liquids in chemical work. The milliliter is defined as the volume occupied by exactly 1 g of water at 3.98°C (the temperature at which its density is the greatest) and under a pressure of one atmosphere.

At the time that the metric system was set up, in 1799, it was intended that

* The word liter is usually used in this book, instead of its abbreviation, to avoid confusion o l and 1.

the milliliter be exactly equal to the cubic centimeter (cm³). However, it was later found that the relation between the gram, as given by the prototype kilogram, and the centimeter is such that the milliliter is not exactly equal to the cubic centimeter, but is instead equal to 1.000027 cm³. It is obvious that the distinction between ml and cm³ is ordinarily unimportant.

A table of conversion factors for some units in the metric system and the corresponding units in the English system is given below.

CONVERSION FACTORS

	ENGLISH TO METRIC	METRIC TO ENGLISH
Length	1 in = 2.540 cm	1 cm = 0.3937 in
Area	1 sq in = 6.4516 cm²	1 cm² = 0.1550 sq in
Volume and capacity	1 cu in = 16.386 cm³	1 ml = 0.061 cu in
		= 0.033814 U.S. fluid oz
	1 cu ft = 28.317 liters	1 liter = 0.26418 U.S. gal
		= 0.21998 Br. gal
	1 U.S. gal (liq) = 3.7853 l	1 l = 0.035316 cu ft
Mass	1 lb (avoir) = 453.59 g	1 g = 0.03527 oz (avoir)
	1 oz (avoir) = 28.35 g	1 kg = 2.20462 lb (avoir)
Force	1 dyne = 1.01972 mg	
	1 g = 980.665 dyne	
Pressure	1 lb/sq in = 70.307 g/cm²	1 g/cm² = 0.01422 lb/sq in
	1 lb/sq in = 0.068046 atm	1 atm = 14.696 lb/sq in
	1 atm = 1033.2 g/cm² = 760 mm of Hg	
Energy, Work, Heat	1 ft lb = 1.35582 joule (abs)	1 joule (abs) = 0.73756 ft lb
	1 cal = 4.1840 joule (abs)	
	1 joule = 10^7 erg = 0.23901 cal	
	1 kilocalorie (kcal) = 1,000 cal	

Probable Values of Some Physical and

Chemical Constants (Carbon-12 Scale)

Avogadro's number $N = 0.60229 \times 10^{24}$

Electronic charge $e = 1.6021 \times 10^{-19}$ abs.-coulombs $= 4.8029 \times 10^{-10}$ abs.-e.s.u.

Mass of electron $m = 9.1083 \times 10^{-28}$ g

Triple point of water on absolute scale $0°C = 273.16 \pm 0.01°K$

Boltzmann constant $k = 1.3805$ erg deg^{-1}

Standard molar gas volume $(RT)_{0°C} = 22.4134$ liter atm $mole^{-1}$

Gas constant $R = 0.082055$ liter atm deg^{-1} $mole^{-1} = 1.9872$ cal deg^{-1} $mole^{-1}$

Faraday $F = 96,490$ abs.-coulombs $mole^{-1}$

Velocity of light $c = 2.997930 \times 10^{10}$ cm sec^{-1}

Planck's constant $h = 6.6252 \times 10^{-27}$ erg sec

Energy in ergs of one absolute-volt-electron $= 1.60206 \times 10^{-12}$ erg

Energy in calories per mole for one absolute-volt-electron per molecule $=$ 23,053 cal $mole^{-1}$

The Vapor Pressure of Water

at Different Temperatures

TEMPERATURE (°C)	VAPOR PRESSURE (mm of mercury)	TEMPERATURE (°C)	VAPOR PRESSURE (mm of mercury)
−10 (ice)	1.0	31	33.7
−5 (ice)	3.0	32	35.7
0	4.6	33	37.7
5	6.5	34	39.9
10	9.2	35	42.2
15	12.8	36	44.6
16	13.6	37	47.1
17	14.5	38	49.7
18	15.5	39	52.4
19	16.5	40	55.3
20	17.5	45	71.9
21	18.6	50	92.5
22	19.8	60	149.4
23	21.1	70	233.7
24	22.4	80	355.1
25	23.8	90	525.8
26	25.2	100	760.0
27	26.7	110	1,074.6
28	28.3	150	3,570.5
29	30.0	200	11,659.2
30	31.8	300	64,432.8

Standard Oxidation-reduction

Potentials and Equilibrium Constants

The values apply to temperature 25°C, with standard concentration for aqueous solutions 1 M and standard pressure of gases 1 atm.

	E^0	K
$Li \rightleftarrows Li^+ + e^-$	3.05	4×10^{50}
$Cs \rightleftarrows Cs^+ + e^-$	2.92	1×10^{49}
$Rb \rightleftarrows Rb^+ + e^-$	2.92	1×10^{49}
$K \rightleftarrows K^+ + e^-$	2.92	1×10^{49}
$\frac{1}{2}Ba \rightleftarrows \frac{1}{2}Ba^{++} + e^-$	2.90	5×10^{48}
$\frac{1}{2}Sr \rightleftarrows \frac{1}{2}Sr^{++} + e^-$	2.89	4×10^{48}
$\frac{1}{2}Ca \rightleftarrows \frac{1}{2}Ca^{++} + e^-$	2.87	2×10^{48}
$Na \rightleftarrows Na^+ + e^-$	2.712	4.0×10^{45}
$\frac{1}{3}Al + \frac{4}{3}OH^- \rightleftarrows \frac{1}{3}Al(OH)_4^- + e^-$	2.35	3×10^{39}
$\frac{1}{2}Mg \rightleftarrows \frac{1}{2}Mg^{++} + e^-$	2.34	2×10^{39}
$\frac{1}{2}Be \rightleftarrows \frac{1}{2}Be^{++} + e^-$	1.85	1×10^{31}
$\frac{1}{3}Al \rightleftarrows \frac{1}{3}Al^{+++} + e^-$	1.67	1×10^{28}
$\frac{1}{2}Zn + 2OH^- \rightleftarrows \frac{1}{2}Zn(OH)_4^{--} + e^-$	1.216	2.7×10^{20}
$\frac{1}{2}Mn \rightleftarrows \frac{1}{2}Mn^{++} + e^-$	1.18	7×10^{19}
$\frac{1}{2}Zn + 2NH_3 \rightleftarrows \frac{1}{2}Zn(NH_3)_4^{++} + e^-$	1.03	2×10^{17}
$Co(CN)_6^{----} \rightleftarrows Co(CN)_6^{---} + e^-$	0.83	1×10^{14}
$\frac{1}{2}Zn \rightleftarrows \frac{1}{2}Zn^{++} + e^-$	.762	6.5×10^{12}
$\frac{1}{3}Cr \rightleftarrows \frac{1}{3}Cr^{+++} + e^-$	.74	3×10^{12}
$\frac{1}{2}H_2C_2O_4(aq) \rightleftarrows CO_2 + H^+ + e^-$	.49	2×10^{8}
$\frac{1}{2}Fe \rightleftarrows \frac{1}{2}Fe^{++} + e^-$	.440	2.5×10^{7}
$\frac{1}{2}Cd \rightleftarrows \frac{1}{2}Cd^{++} + e^-$	.402	5.7×10^{6}
$\frac{1}{2}Co \rightleftarrows \frac{1}{2}Co^{++} + e^-$	.277	4.5×10^{4}
$\frac{1}{2}Ni \rightleftarrows \frac{1}{2}Ni^{++} + e^-$	.250	1.6×10^{4}
$I^- + Cu \rightleftarrows CuI(s) + e^-$	.187	1.4×10^{3}
$\frac{1}{2}Sn \rightleftarrows \frac{1}{2}Sn^{++} + e^-$	.136	1.9×10^{2}
$\frac{1}{2}Pb \rightleftarrows \frac{1}{2}Pb^{++} + e^-$	.126	1.3×10^{2}
$\frac{1}{2}H_2 \rightleftarrows H^+ + e^-$	.000	1
$\frac{1}{2}H_2S \rightleftarrows \frac{1}{2}S + H^+ + e^-$	-0.141	4.3×10^{-3}
$Cu^+ \rightleftarrows Cu^{++} + e^-$	-0.153	2.7×10^{-3}
$\frac{1}{2}H_2O + \frac{1}{2}H_2SO_3 \rightleftarrows \frac{1}{2}SO_4^{--} + 2H^+ + e^-$	-0.17	1×10^{-3}

(continued)

Reaction	E	K
$\frac{1}{2}Cu \rightleftarrows \frac{1}{2}Cu^{++} + e^-$	-0.345	1.6×10^{-6}
$Fe(CN)_6^{----} \rightleftarrows Fe(CN)_6^{---} + e^-$	-0.36	9×10^{-7}
$I^- \rightleftarrows \frac{1}{2}I_2(s) + e^-$	-0.53	1×10^{-9}
$MnO_4^{--} \rightleftarrows MnO_4^- + e^-$	-0.54	1×10^{-9}
$\frac{4}{3}OH^- + \frac{1}{3}MnO_2 \rightleftarrows \frac{1}{3}MnO_4^- + \frac{2}{3}H_2O + e^-$	-0.57	3×10^{-10}
$\frac{1}{2}H_2O_2 \rightleftarrows \frac{1}{2}O_2 + H^+ + e^-$	-0.682	3.5×10^{-12}
$Fe^{++} \rightleftarrows Fe^{+++} + e^-$	-0.771	1.1×10^{-13}
$Hg \rightleftarrows \frac{1}{2}Hg_2^{++} + e^-$	-0.799	3.7×10^{-14}
$Ag \rightleftarrows Ag^+ + e^-$	-0.800	3.5×10^{-14}
$H_2O + NO_2 \rightleftarrows NO_3^- + 2H^+ + e^-$	-0.81	3×10^{-14}
$\frac{1}{2}Hg \rightleftarrows \frac{1}{2}Hg^{++} + e^-$	-0.854	4.5×10^{-15}
$\frac{1}{2}Hg_2^{++} \rightleftarrows Hg^{++} + e^-$	-0.910	5.0×10^{-16}
$\frac{1}{2}HNO_2 + \frac{1}{2}H_2O \rightleftarrows \frac{1}{2}NO_3^- + H^+ + e^-$	-0.94	2×10^{-16}
$NO + H_2O \rightleftarrows HNO_2 + H^+ + e^-$	-0.99	2×10^{-17}
$\frac{1}{2}ClO_3^- + \frac{1}{2}H_2O \rightleftarrows \frac{1}{2}ClO_4^- + H^+ + e^-$	-1.00	2×10^{-17}
$Br^- \rightleftarrows \frac{1}{2}Br_2(l) + e^-$	-1.065	1.3×10^{-18}
$H_2O + \frac{1}{2}Mn^{++} \rightleftarrows \frac{1}{2}MnO_2 + 2H^+ + e^-$	-1.23	2×10^{-21}
$Cl^- \rightleftarrows \frac{1}{2}Cl_2 + e^-$	-1.358	1.5×10^{-23}
$\frac{7}{6}H_2O + \frac{1}{3}Cr^{+++} \rightleftarrows \frac{1}{6}Cr_2O_7^{--} + \frac{7}{3}H^+ + e^-$	-1.36	1×10^{-23}
$\frac{1}{2}H_2O + \frac{1}{6}Cl^- \rightleftarrows \frac{1}{6}ClO_3^- + H^+ + e^-$	-1.45	4×10^{-25}
$\frac{1}{3}Au \rightleftarrows \frac{1}{3}Au^{+++} + e^-$	-1.50	6×10^{-26}
$\frac{4}{5}H_2O + \frac{1}{5}Mn^{++} \rightleftarrows \frac{1}{5}MnO_4^- + \frac{8}{5}H^+ + e^-$	-1.52	3×10^{-26}
$\frac{1}{2}Cl_2 + H_2O \rightleftarrows HClO + H^+ + e^-$	-1.63	4×10^{-28}
$H_2O \rightleftarrows \frac{1}{2}H_2O_2 + H^+ + e^-$	-1.77	2×10^{-30}
$Co^{++} \rightleftarrows Co^{+++} + e^-$	-1.84	1×10^{-31}
$F^- \rightleftarrows \frac{1}{2}F_2 + e^-$	-2.65	4×10^{-44}

The Boltzmann Distribution Law

in Classical Mechanics

In classical mechanics the state of a particle can be described by giving the values of its coordinates, x, y, and z, and of the corresponding components of its velocity, v_x, v_y, and v_z. It is convenient in classical statistical mechanics to use the components of linear momentum, $p_x = mv_x$, $p_y = mv_y$, and $p_z = mv_z$, in place of the components of the velocity; here m is the mass of the particle.

We ask: For the system consisting of a single particle in a rectangular box with volume V in thermodynamic equilibrium with its environment at absolute temperature T, what is the probability that the particle will be in the state in which its x coordinate lies between x and $x + dx$, its y coordinate between y and $y + dy$, its z coordinate between z and $z + dz$, and the three components of its momentum between p_x and $p_x + dp_x$, p_y and $p_y + dp_y$, and p_z and $p_z + dp_z$, respectively? It was shown by Maxwell and Boltzmann that the answer is the following:

$$\text{Probability} = \exp\left(-E/kT\right)dxdydzdp_xdp_ydp_z \qquad (1)$$

The expression is similar to that in the numerator or denominator of Equation 11 of Chapter 5, with $dxdydzdp_xdp_ydp_z$ in place of the quantum weight of the corresponding quantum-theory equation. In classical theory the number of states is infinite, but proportional to the six-dimensional differential volume $dxdydzdp_xdp_ydp_z$. The Boltzmann exponential factor is the same for classical theory as for quantum theory.

In classical theory the energy E is the sum of the kinetic energy and the potential energy. The kinetic energy $\frac{1}{2}mv^2$ is

$$\frac{p_x^2}{2m} + \frac{p_y^2}{2m} + \frac{p_z^2}{2m}$$

a function of the momenta only, and the potential energy is a function of the coordinates x, y, and z only. [For example, if the particle is in the gravitational field of the earth the potential energy is mgz, in which z is the vertical coordinate (height above the surface of the earth) and g is the gravitational constant; see Example 11 of Chapter 6.] With $E = E_{kin} + E_{pot}$, the exponential factor $\exp[-(E_{kin} + E_{pot})/kT]$ can be written as the product of two factors, $\exp(-E_{kin}/kT)\exp(-E_{pot}/kT)$, and the probability expression of Equation 1 becomes the product of a function of x, y, and z and a function of p_x, p_y, and p_z. This form means that the distribution of probabilities in coordinate space x, y, z, which depends upon the potential energy function $E_{pot}(x,y,z)$, and the distribution of probabilities in momentum space p_x, p_y, p_z, which depends upon the kinetic energy function $E_{kin}(p_x,p_y,p_z) = (p_x^2 + p_y^2 + p_z^2)/2m$, can be discussed independently of one another. The corresponding expressions are

$$\text{Probability in coordinate space} = \exp(-E_{pot}/kT)dxdydz \qquad (2)$$
$$\text{Probability in momentum space} = \exp(-E_{kin}/kT)dp_xdp_ydp_z \qquad (3)$$

The use of these expressions is illustrated by examples given in the text. Equation 3 leads directly to the Maxwell-Boltzmann distribution law for molecular velocities, which has been discussed in Section 6-11.

Selected Readings

The *Scientific American* Offprints listed below by number are available from your bookstore or from W. H. Freeman and Company, 660 Market Street, San Francisco 4, California, and Hyde House, West Central Street, London, W.C.1.

NUMBER	READING
5	*The Structure of the Hereditary Material*, F. H. C. Crick, October 1954.
31	*The Structure of Protein Molecules*, L. Pauling, R. B. Corey, and R. Hayward, July 1954.
47	*The Origin of Life*, G. Wald, August 1954.
54	*Nucleic Acids*, F. H. C. Crick, September 1957.
85	*Organic Chemical Reactions*, J. D. Roberts, November 1957.
102	*The Age of the Solar System*, H. Brown, April 1957.
121	*The Three-Dimensional Structure of a Protein Molecule*, J. C. Kendrew, December 1961.
122	*The Path of Carbon in Photosynthesis*, J. A. Bassham, June 1962.
123	*The Genetic Code*, F. H. C. Crick, October 1962.
202	*Anti-Matter*, G. Burbidge and F. Hoyle, April 1958.
205	*The Quantum Theory*, K. K. Darrow, March 1952.
207	*Mesonic Atoms*, S. De Benedetti, October 1956.
212	*The Principle of Uncertainty*, G. Gamow, January 1958.
213	*Elementary Particles*, M. Gell-Mann and E. P. Rosenbaum, July 1957.
214	*The Bubble Chamber*, D. A. Glaser, February 1955.
217	*The Atomic Nucleus*, R. Hofstadter, July 1956.
219	*The Nuclear Reactor as a Research Instrument*, D. J. Hughes, August 1953.
226	*Pions*, R. E. Marshak, January 1957.
228	*The Structure of the Nucleus*, M. G. Mayer, March 1951.
230	*The Neutrino*, P. Morrison, January 1956.
232	*The Neutron*, P. and E. Morrison, October 1951.
235	*Models of the Nucleus*, R. E. Peierls, January 1959.
239	*Where Do Cosmic Rays Come From?*, B. Rossi, September 1953.
242	*The Synthetic Elements I*, G. T. Seaborg and I. Perlman, April 1950.
243	*The Synthetic Elements II*, G. T. Seaborg and A. Ghiorso, December 1956.
244	*The Antiproton*, E. Segré and C. C. Wiegand, June 1956.
251	*Particle Accelerators*, R. R. Wilson, March 1958.
253	*The Age of the Elements in the Solar System*, J. H. Reynolds, November 1960.
256	*The Mass Spectrometer*, A. O. C. Nier, March 1952.
263	*Frozen Free Radicals*, C. M. Herzfeld and A. M. Bass, March 1957.
275	*The Muon*, S. Penman, July 1961.
286	*Chemical Topology*, E. Wasserman, November 1962.

Index